# 33rd EUROPEAN SYMPOSIUM ON COMPUTER AIDED PROCESS ENGINEERING

# VOLUME 4

# COMPUTER-AIDED CHEMICAL ENGINEERING, 52

# 33ʳᵈ EUROPEAN SYMPOSIUM ON COMPUTER AIDED PROCESS ENGINEERING

# VOLUME 4

*Edited by*

## Prof. Antonios C. Kokossis
*National Technical University of Athens*
*School of Chemical Engineering*
*Athens, Greece*

## Prof. Michael C. Georgiadis
*Aristotle University of Thessaloniki*
*School of Engineering*
*Department of Chemical Engineering*
*Greece*

## Prof. Efstratios Pistikopoulos
*Chemical Engineering*
*Texas A&M Energy Institute*
*TX, USA*

ELSEVIER

Amsterdam – Boston – Heidelberg – London – New York – Oxford
Paris – San Diego – San Francisco – Singapore – Sydney – Tokyo

Elsevier
Radarweg 29, PO Box 211, 1000 AE Amsterdam, Netherlands
The Boulevard, Langford Lane, Kidlington, Oxford OX5 1GB, UK
50 Hampshire Street, 5th Floor, Cambridge, MA 02139, USA

**Notices**
Knowledge and best practice in this field are constantly changing. As new research and experience
broaden our understanding, changes in research methods, professional practices, or medical treatment
may become necessary.

Practitioners and researchers must always rely on their own experience and knowledge in evaluating
and using any information, methods, compounds, or experiments described herein. In using such
information or methods they should be mindful of their own safety and the safety of others, including
parties for whom they have a professional responsibility.

To the fullest extent of the law, neither the Publisher nor the authors, contributors, or editors, assume
any liability for any injury and/or damage to persons or property as a matter of products liability,
negligence or otherwise, or from any use or operation of any methods, products, instructions, or ideas
contained in the material herein.

**British Library Cataloguing in Publication Data**
A catalogue record for this book is available from the British Library

**Library of Congress Cataloging-in-Publication Data**
A catalog record for this book is available from the Library of Congress

ISBN (Volume 4):  978-0-443-28803-6
ISBN (Set) :      978-0-443-15274-0
ISSN:             1570-7946

For information on all Elsevier publications visit our
website at https://www.elsevier.com/

  Working together
to grow libraries in
developing countries

www.elsevier.com • www.bookaid.org

*Publisher:* Candice Janco
*Acquisition Editor:* Anita Koch
*Editorial Project Manager:* Lena Sparks
*Production Project Manager:* Paul Prasad Chandramohan
*Designer:* Greg Harris

Typeset by STRAIVE

# Contents

## T6: Multi scale energy systems engineering (organized by the EFCE energy section)

## T7: Sustainable supply chains and ecosystems

# T8: Education and knowledge transfer

Antonis Kokossis, Michael C. Georgiadis, Efstratios N. Pistikopoulos (Eds.)
PROCEEDINGS OF THE 33rd European Symposium on Computer Aided Process Engineering
(ESCAPE33), June 18-21, 2023, Athens, Greece
© 2023 Elsevier B.V. All rights reserved. http://dx.doi.org/10.1016/B978-0-443-15274-0.50423-6

# Ensemble Kalman Filter for estimation of intracellular nucleotide sugars from extracellular metabolites in monoclonal antibodies

Luxi Yu [a], Ehecatl Antonio del Rio Chanona [a], Cleo Kontoravdi [a]

[a] *Sargent Centre for Process Systems Engineering, Department of Chemical Engineering, Imperial College London, London, SW7 2AZ, United Kingdom*

## Abstract

The emergence of Quality by Design (QbD) and Process Analytical Technology (PAT) paradigm supported by the FDA imposes a strong motivation for digital transformation in biopharmaceutical industry. The inherent complexity of bioprocess dynamics, batch-to-batch variability resulting from raw materials and process operations, as well as the need for accelerating product manufacturing, makes dynamic soft sensors such as Kalman Filters highly desirable for process development, monitoring, and control. In this work, we develop an Ensemble Kalman Filter framework in the context of monoclonal antibody bioprocessing, where the noise on physical sensors is mitigated for extracellular metabolite states by integrating the process' dynamic mechanistic model and sensor measurements. More importantly, the framework accurately estimates the nucleotide sugar concentrations, an intracellular state of the cell that is not routinely measured in industry due to experimental complexity. The proposed EnKF soft sensor retrieves this knowledge through state inference, providing valuable insights for monitoring and control of key quality attributes such as glycan distribution.

**Keywords**: Antibody Bioprocessing; Metabolites; Nucleotide Sugar Donors; Ensemble Kalman Filter

## 1. Introduction

Glycoproteins such as monoclonal antibodies represent the largest group of biologically derived medicines with substantial market growth in the foreseeable years. Nucleotide sugar donors (NSD) are activated forms of monosaccharides that act as direct co-substrates for synthesizing glycosylated proteins, with their intracellular levels providing insights on the cell state. Real-time NSD information in bioprocesses can support decision-making on extracellular nutrient feeding towards controlling and monitoring key product quality attributes such as glycan distribution. However, NSD measurements are challenging to obtain experimentally and are therefore not routinely performed in industry. As NSDs are synthesised metabolically, several predictive models have been built to link extracellular metabolites with intracellular NSD concentrations. Whilst these models can be highly accurate in predicting NSD concentrations (Kotidis et al., 2019, Jedrzejewski et al., 2014, Sou et al., 2017, Villiger et al., 2016) , they are usually system-specific and require extensive re-parameterization for changes in experimental conditions, cell line or product.

As an alternative to the system-specific predictive models, Kalman Filters (KF) employ a mechanistic process model to predict system transition from a previous to the current state while integrating the information from hard sensor measurements. In addition to unmeasured state inference, the idea of KF is to produce better estimations of the measured states compared to either measurements or model predictions alone (Narayanan et al., 2020). Here, a Monte-Carlo based KF for non-linear systems, Ensemble Kalman Filter (EnKF), is proposed to estimate NSD concentrations using a mechanistic model and corrected by easy-to-obtain extracellular metabolite measurements. The EnKF is able to filter noise in metabolite measurements and subsequently enables a more accurate estimation of NSD concentrations. The combination of sensor observations and first principles modeling reduces the reliance on highly specific mechanistic models and makes obtaining accurate NSD knowledge possible without directly measuring them, offering great promise for applying the QbD paradigm to ensure product quality during manufacturing.

## 2. Material and Methods

### 2.1. Experiment Description

A fed-batch CHO cell culture process producing an IgG antibody was used to evaluate the performance of the EnKF-based soft sensor, where the culture was supplemented with glucose and amnio acid nutrients on even days of the entire 12-day cell culture period. Daily measurements were taken for all of the metabolites and NSDs. The experimental set up and associated dataset can be found in full in Jędrzejewski (2015).

### 2.2. Mechanistic Model Description

The mechanistic model used in this study consists of two parts, the cell culture model and the NSD metabolic model. Briefly, the cell culture model describes the cell growth and death, extracellular metabolism, and antibody production, whereas the NSD metabolic model was formulated to account for the specific cell growth rate, intracellular metabolite reactions and the transport of NSDs into the Golgi. A detailed model description can be found in Kotidis *et al.* (2019).

### 2.3. Simulation of True Values

Here, it is assumed that the true value for each of the extracellular metabolites and intracellular NSDs can be simulated by adding a white Gaussian process noise to the mechanistic model. Although true values are not available in real-life scenarios, the simulated true states are only used to examine the effectiveness of the EnKF-based soft sensor and their values are not used in executing the algorithm.

### 2.4. Data Augmentation of Experimental Observations

Due to nonlinearities in the growth rate equation, the availability of additional, artificial measurements allows implementation of a more stable and robust EnKF estimation. For this purpose, we have augmented the experimental dataset with artificial measurements. The latter were generated by adding sensor noise, in the form of variance calculated from the experimental triplicate to the true state trajectories described in 2.3.

### 2.5. Ensemble Kalman Filter

The EnKF is a Monte-Carlo based KF, where an ensemble of state vectors is randomly sampled from a large cloud of states that represents a specific probability density function. The ensemble is then integrated forward in time through the true non-linear process model and updated when a new observation becomes available (Evensen, 1994). The update step in EnKF introduces additional approximations when non-Gaussianity or non-linearity are involved, where the ensemble 'shift' towards the new observation through linear Gaussian state-space model (Katzfuss et al., 2016). Regardless, EnKF has been successfully applied to many complex non-linear and non-

Gaussian cases, although the deviation from Gaussian behaviour becomes more important when the ensemble predictions are substantially different from the observations (Aanonsen et al., 2009).

Figure 1 presents the implementation of the EnKF in this work. The algorithm starts by sampling an ensemble of states for each metabolite and NSD, with a mean equal to the estimated initial conditions and a covariance representing the uncertainty of this first-estimate of the initial state. The number of draws for the ensemble is determined by $2L+1$ where $L$ is the number of states, a rule of thumb that is commonly used in Unscented Kalman Filter (UKF) (Hommels et al., 2009). Since UKF is an approximation of EnKF and this rule of thumb is used to propagate the approximate distribution on the UKF, we decided to apply the same heuristic to approximate the distribution via Monte Carlo by the EnKF. The selected EnKF ensemble is then propagated through the non-linear process model $f$, with a white Gaussian noise $w$ added at every time step. Here, the effect of the error propagation through correlated states must be taken into account when designing the covariance matrix of the process noise $w$. This is to ensure a reliable evolution of the ensemble variance, as a sensible estimate of the model variance is of vital importance for the success of EnKF (Evensen, 1994). In practice, the design of process noise covariance matrix is a trial-and-error procedure based on which matrix yields the most accurate state estimation for that specific filter structure (Alag and Gilyard, 1990).

The mean at time step $k$, $\hat{x}_k \in \mathbb{R}^{n_x}$, of the ensemble is then calculated following the prediction step and the state covariance, $P_k \in \mathbb{R}^{n_x \times n_x}$, can be estimated from the spread of the ensemble $X_k$. It should be noted that the state covariance $P_k$ is not an explicitly expressed matrix for implementation of EnKF, but rather an intermediate state for calculating the Kalman gain in the update step (Houtekamer and Mitchell, 2005). In this work, the EnKF algorithm has been designed to only go through the update step if the measurement is available at that time point. Following the prediction step, the Kalman gain $K$ in the update step can be interpreted as a ratio of how much the algorithm trusts the model prediction versus the measurement. The Kalman gain $K$ is then used as a weighting factor to scale the residual between sensor measurement and model prediction, which ultimately output the filtered state $x$ for the next prediction step.

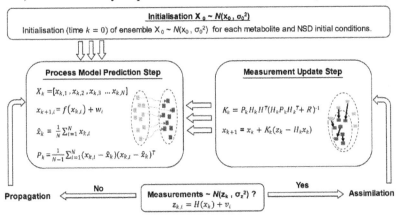

Figure 1. The Ensemble Kalman Filter algorithm, adapted from Pellenq and Boulet (2004). **Notations:** $X$, sampled ensemble; $f$, process model; $w$, white Gaussian noise of process; $x$, process states; $P$, state covariance; $K$, Kalman gain; $H$, measurement function; $R$, measurement noise covariance; $z$, measurement; $v$, white Gaussian noise of measurement

## 3. Results & Discussion

### 3.1. Metabolites correction

As shown in Figure 2, the EnKF showcases an excellent performance on predicting the viable cell density, antibody titre, extracellular metabolites glucose and ammonia concentrations when plotted against the true trajectory of the states. As the Kalman gain $K$ is involved in the update step as a scaling factor, the filtered results will lie in-between the measurements and the model prediction. The mechanistic model predicts all four states accurately from the start of the cell culture period until the lag phase, and then gradually deviates from the true value. This results in an overestimation for viable cell density and antibody production titre, underestimation of glucose levels, and slight underestimation and then overestimation of the ammonia levels in the exponential and stationary phase, respectively. In contrast, the EnKF estimation is closer to the true value for the entire cell culture period and converges with time propagation. This phenomenon is particularly obvious for glucose, for which the EnKF lies closer to the model prediction than the true value from Day 4 to Day 6, but gradually converges towards the end of the culture period and matches almost exactly to the true value trajectory.

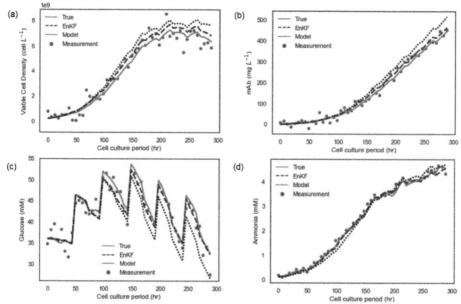

Figure 2. Comparison of true trajectory (solid line), states estimated by EnKF propagation (dashed line), mechanistic model prediction (dotted line) and noisy measurements (scatter) for (a) viable cell density $X_v$ (b) antibody titre $mAb$ (c) glucose concentration and (d) ammonia concentration

### 3.2. NSD estimator

The estimation of unmeasured NSD states, UDP-Galactose (UDPGal) and UDP-glucose (UDPGlc) concentrations, is compared with their respective true value trajectories, as illustrated in Figure 3 (a) and (b). UDPGlc is the high-energy donor form of glucose, which synthesizes glycogen and other glucose-containing molecules such as dolichol P-glucose, the key substrate for initiating the glycosylation process (Varki, 2017). On the other hand, UDPGal serves as the main precursor for galactosylation, a highly desirable characteristic for enhanced antibody-dependent cellular cytotoxicity (Kotidis et al.,

2019). Therefore, real-time estimation of UDPGal levels offers valuable knowledge on developing process engineering strategies for optimizing the product glycan distribution. For example, extracellular galactose feeding has been consistently reported to increase the UDPGal pool, which then promotes galactosylation on the recombinant product (Blondeel and Aucoin, 2018). Here, although sensor measurements for UDPGal and UDPGlc concentrations are not directly available for implementation of the EnKF, the extracellular data appear to be correlated with intracellular NSD levels. NSD concentrations are therefore implicitly corrected from the available extracellular metabolite measurements through the EnKF update step and propagated forward in time with the EnKF prediction step. Overall, the EnKF outperforms the mechanistic model, especially towards the end of the cell culture period where the EnKF converges towards the true value. The computed time-resolved mean squared error (MSE) in Figure 3 (b) and (c) shows that pure mechanistic model is more prone to system instability and model inaccuracies. The MSE for both NSD concentrations is consistently lower for EnKF. For UDPGal concentration estimation, the MSE reduces past the exponential phase, while the MSE for UDPGlc concentration remains low throughout the culture period, in contrast with that for the mechanistic model, which increase rapidly in late-stage culture.

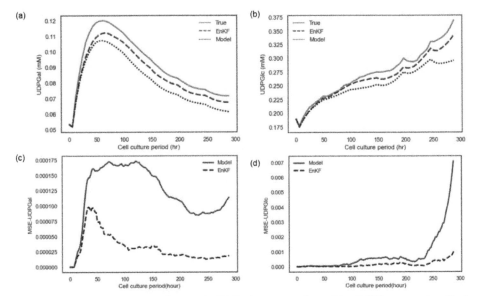

Figure 3. Comparison of true trajectory (solid line), states estimated by EnKF propagation (dashed line), mechanistic model prediction (dotted line) for (a) UDPGal concentration (b) UDPGlc concentration. Model prediction and EnKF estimation MSE computed against the true trajectory for (c) UDPGal concentration and (d) UDPGlc concentration

## 4. Conclusion & Outlook

Herein, we present the implementation of EnKF for estimation of intracellular NSD concentrations. The proposed EnKF framework performs well with respect to reducing sensor noise and estimating unmeasured NSD levels accurately, which therefore support in-process decision-making and product quality control based on easy-to-obtain extracellular measurements. Moreover, the incorporation of time-discrete sensor observations infuses a degree of data-driven characteristic to the mechanistic process model while retaining the system dynamic knowledge, thereby potentially providing greater flexibility in transferring the framework to other process conditions, cell line or product.

## References

AANONSEN, S. I., NŒVDAL, G., OLIVER, D. S., REYNOLDS, A. C. & VALLÈS, B. 2009. The Ensemble Kalman Filter in Reservoir Engineering—a Review. *SPE Journal,* 14, 393-412.

ALAG, G. S. & GILYARD, G. B. 1990. A proposed Kalman Filter Algorithm for Estimation of Unmeasured Output Variables for an F100 Turbofan Engine. *NASA Technical Memorandum 4234.*

BLONDEEL, E. J. M. & AUCOIN, M. G. 2018. Supplementing glycosylation: A review of applying nucleotide-sugar precursors to growth medium to affect therapeutic recombinant protein glycoform distributions. *Biotechnol Adv,* 36, 1505-1523.

EVENSEN, G. 1994. Sequential data assimilation with a nonlinear quasi-geostrophic model using Monte Carlo methods to forecast error statistics. *Journal of Geophysical Research: Oceans,* 99, 10143-10162.

HOMMELS, A., MURAKAMI, A. & NISHIMURA, S. 2009. Comparison of the Ensemble Kalman filter with the Unscented Kalman filter: application to the construction of a road embankment. *GEO International.*

HOUTEKAMER, P. L. & MITCHELL, H. L. 2005. Ensemble Kalman filtering. *Quarterly Journal of the Royal Meteorological Society,* 131, 3269-3289.

JEDRZEJEWSKI, P. M. 2015. A platform for the optimisation of metabolic pathways for glycosylation to achieve a narrow and targeted glycoform distribution. *PhD Thesis,* Imperial College London.

JEDRZEJEWSKI, P. M., DEL VAL, I. J., CONSTANTINOU, A., DELL, A., HASLAM, S. M., POLIZZI, K. M. & KONTORAVDI, C. 2014. Towards controlling the glycoform: a model framework linking extracellular metabolites to antibody glycosylation. *Int J Mol Sci,* 15, 4492-522.

KATZFUSS, M., STROUD, J. R. & WIKLE, C. K. 2016. Understanding the Ensemble Kalman Filter. *The American Statistician,* 70, 350-357.

KOTIDIS, P., JEDRZEJEWSKI, P., SOU, S. N., SELLICK, C., POLIZZI, K., DEL VAL, I. J. & KONTORAVDI, C. 2019. Model-based optimization of antibody galactosylation in CHO cell culture. *Biotechnol Bioeng,* 116, 1612-1626.

NARAYANAN, H., LUNA, M. F., VON STOSCH, M., CRUZ BOURNAZOU, M. N., POLOTTI, G., MORBIDELLI, M., BUTTE, A. & SOKOLOV, M. 2020. Bioprocessing in the Digital Age: The Role of Process Models. *Biotechnol J,* 15, e1900172.

PELLENQ, J. & BOULET, G. 2004. A methodology to test the pertinence of remote-sensing data assimilation into vegetation models for water and energy exchange at the land surface. Agronomie, EDP Sciences, 2004, 24 (4), pp.197-204.

SOU, S. N., JEDRZEJEWSKI, P. M., LEE, K., SELLICK, C., POLIZZI, K. M. & KONTORAVDI, C. 2017. Model-based investigation of intracellular processes determining antibody Fc-glycosylation under mild hypothermia. *Biotechnol Bioeng,* 114, 1570-1582.

VARKI, A. 2017. *Essentials of glycobiology,* Cold Spring Harbor, New York, Cold Spring Harbor Laboratory Press.

VILLIGER, T. K., SCIBONA, E., STETTLER, M., BROLY, H., MORBIDELLI, M. & SOOS, M. 2016. Controlling the time evolution of mAb N-linked glycosylation - Part II: Model-based predictions. *Biotechnology Progress,* 32, 1135-1148.

Antonis Kokossis, Michael C. Georgiadis, Efstratios N. Pistikopoulos (Eds.)
PROCEEDINGS OF THE 33rd European Symposium on Computer Aided Process Engineering
(ESCAPE33), June 18-21, 2023, Athens, Greece
© 2023 Elsevier B.V. All rights reserved. http://dx.doi.org/10.1016/B978-0-443-15274-0.50424-8

# Towards a unified multi-scale strategy for bio-manufacturing process development

Thomas Bisgaard,[a] Nima Nazemzadah,[b] Eduardo Krebs Kleingesinds,[a] Negin Yousefi,[a] Christian Beenfeldt,[b] Seyed Soheil Mansouri,[a,*]

[a]*PROSYS, Department of Chemical and Biochemial Engineering, Technical University of Denmark, Søltofts Plads, Buidling 228A, 2800 Kongens Lyngby, Denmark*
[b]*Knowledge Hub Zealand, Holbækvej 141 B, DK-4400, Kalundborg*

*seso@kt.dtu.dk*

## Abstract

Biomanufacturing has been increasingly receiving attention in the past few decades due to the need for sustainable production of various consumables, global energy crisis, and climate change. The biomanufacturing sector or the so called biosolution has found application in the production of various products such as fine and bulk chemical, pharmaceuticals, food and feed products, and biofuels. However, this industrial sector is facing a lot of challenges mainly due to scalability issues and lack of fundamental understanding from the process development point of view, which need to be addressed. Hence, a unified systematic multi-scale approach is required to address some of the current challenges by providing profound knowledge of the fundamental phenomena at various scales for a more efficient process scale-up. In this study, a conceptual systematic framework is proposed that incorporated the fundamental knowledge from various disciplines that potentially could tackle some of the aforementioned challenges within the biosolutions framework.

**Keywords**: multi-scale, modelling, scale-up, bioprocess, microalgae.

## 1. Introduction

Biosolutions is a multidisciplinary commercial area that targets the use of biological systems such as enzymes, microorganisms, bio-based chemicals, and bio-based materials. The ongoing "green transition" and the increasing demand for nutritious and sustainable foods for the growing global population are key drivers of biosolutions. Novel proteins satisfy both aspects and remain a field of high interest. Industries involved in the production of commodities or foods (such as biofuels and novel proteins) in large quantities suffer from low profit margin thereby making the economic /environmental feasibility very sensitive to for example (i) scale of production and thus the scale-up process, (ii) raw material prices, and (iii) energy prices. Therefore, a robust scale-up methodology and experimental infrastructure are of utmost importance. Biosolutions often lean towards large scales of production and low value raw materials (e.g., local raw materials, valorization of "waste" streams such as CO2 and process water) to obtain a feasible business case. Biosolutions Zealand is an international lighthouse project that aims to develop state-of-the-art biosolution technologies with commercial focus, while strengthening its sector in Denmark with a focus on Kalundborg Symbiosis. The symbiosis in Kalundborg, Denmark, known as one of the largest symbiosis self-sufficient networks, is comprised of various production facilities for water, energy, food, feed, and biopharmaceutical products and has been an originally-evolving environmental collaboration for more than five decades. The network aims to tackle sustainability challenges within economic, social, and environmental scopes by exploiting the potential within a sustainable collaboration framework. A multi-scale strategy can have a crucial role in developing a fundamental understanding of process development activities in such a complex framework. This could potentially lead to optimized process operation, less lab and pilot experiments, lower unnecessary product losses, and more importantly lower time required from process development to meeting market demands. As the energy crisis is rapidly growing as a global challenge, such a strategy will lead to optimum energy utilization, potentially lower global warming potential and harmful emission within a production facility or a production network such as Kalundborg Symbiosis.

In this work, we sketch a framework that provides a suitable chronological methodology and toolbox to bring a potential product to the market by virgin raw materials or by upgrading waste stream(s) microorganisms. The challenges and perspectives are highlighted and discussed for each step. Finally, a case study within the Biosolutions Zealand project is presented.

## 2. Framework for Biosolutions

It is well-known that bioreactors comprise a multi-scale complexity, in the sense that the links between hydrodynamic (bulk scale), local fermentation media conditions experienced by the individual cells (heterogeneities), and the cellular reactions and networks, are far from established. Therefore, experimentation is currently considered as an inevitable yet costly and time-consuming activity in production scale-up. Ideally, scale-up can be performed successfully and robustly in silico (simulation) using minimum amount of experimental work. This framework (Figure 1) summarizes the promising tools for the process of taking a target product to the market (a biosolution), and incorporates the scale-up elements presented by (Wang et al. 2014; Wang et al. 2020).

### 2.1. Step 1. System Identification

An idea for a biosolution either arises from a targeted desired product or a targeted technology with the aim of identifying valuable product(s) for a given symbiotic environment. A targeted technology could be microalgae photobioreactor (as the case study presented later). Hence, in this step, all $P$ product candidates, $S$ material side-streams must be systematically identified. Additionally, all energy sources must be identified, however, this is only used for Step 6. Due to advances in strain optimization using either genetic engineering (i.e., genetically modified organisms, GMO's) and high throughput cultivation for natural random mutations, we recommend also to list the $N$ potential candidate production host microorganisms. The biosolution identification problem now comprises a $P \times S \times N$ multidimensional search space as a single-product example.

High throughput screening (HT) has become common practice in most biobased manufacturing. It is carried out in micro-liter scale at controlled conditions, with typical commercial configurations up to 96 simultaneous cultivations (e.g., 96 well-plate). The target is to screen among the many candidates using optical or spectroscopic measurement techniques to significantly reduce the search space. Parameters such as mass transfer, strain robustness towards concentration changes, etc., are commonly not addressed in HT experiments.

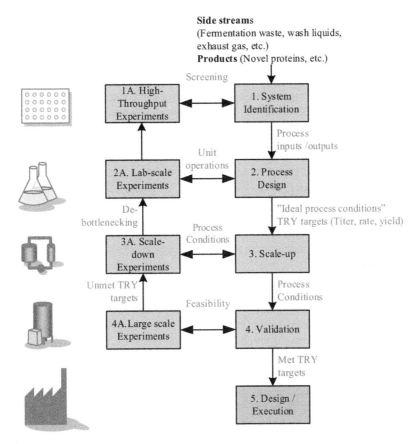

Figure 1. Biosolutions Framework.

## 2.2. Step 2. Process Design

The conceptual is a classical discipline, that aims to identify process flowsheet, mass balance, overall plant layout, techno-economic and sustainability feasibility, and a coarse price estimate. Another important aspect of the conceptual design includes assessment of performance indicators (PI's), which covers as a minimum the techno-economic feasibility and sustainability. The process design task will define targets for the process and hence the following tasks. The targets are titer (gram product per volume), rate (gram product per volume per time), yield (gram product per gram raw material), together with recovery rates at each separation step. The targets define the techno-economic feasible design space. Titer, rate, and yield are commonly known as TRY.

Laboratory experimentation may be used to identify feasible upstream and/or downstream unit operations. For upstream, the experiments could cover shake flask and bench-scale bioreactors. The aim of shake flask studies is to map the optimal ("ideal") conditions of the microorganisms. Such studies typically involve data-driven optimization such as one factor at the time or factorial design (e.g., RSM, Response surface methodology), complemented by statistical tools such as ANOVA. When the optimal conditions are identified, kinetic models must be fitted to the experimental data. Simple stoichiometric models should be developed to obtain the ideal cultivation trajectory. The conditions determined at this step will be a proper initial estimate of the trajectory that must be further refined during the scale-up procedure using model-based scale-up techniques. Integration of Step 1 and Step 1 are possible with modern facilities, e.g., Gamble et al. 2021.

### 2.3. Step 3. Scale-up

The main task in performing scale-up is to understand the metabolic–hydrodynamic coupling during fermentation and achieve your final goal. Computational Fluid Dynamics (CFD) Euler-Lagrangian particles appear to provide a useful tool for this, in which the lifeline of single cells can be analyzed quantitatively (Lapin et al. 2004; Haringa 2022), thereby facilitating targeted experimentation, e.g., down-scale studies (Lapin et al. 2004; Noorman 2011). Hence, CFD can be coupled with a segregated description of the cell population (Pigou & Morchain 2015). Wang et al. (Wang et al. 2020) highlight the four key challenges in model development for scale-up studies:

I.     Lack of metabolic data representing the variable conditions inside bioreactors.
II.    Kinetic models do not capture the nonlinear structure of cellular kinetics.
III.   Inappropriately designed experiments for parameter identification and estimation.
IV.    No minimization of uncertainty via data reconciliation.

Metabolomics is one of the promising tools to support key challenges outlined in points I, II, and IV. It has been demonstrated that metabolic activity depends on the culture media (Pigou & Morchain 2015; Noorman 2014; Xu et al. 1999).

### 2.4. Step 4. Validation

Validation is performed to address the uncertainty associated with scale-up. Access to an experimental scale-up facility comprises a huge challenge for companies (in particular small to SME's, small and medium-sized enterprises) due to high investment cost and due to the gap of knowledge that lies across various scales in process development. To avoid unnecessary capital investment, several alternatives exist and continue to emerge, such as rental facility, e.g., mobile scale-up facility (containerized) (Fahr et al. 2022). On another note, these validation scale-up strategies should be coupled with model-based scale-up solutions to support the validation phase quite efficiently. In the biosolutions project, a combinatorial strategy using model-based scale-up and mobile facilities are explored to provide a understanding in depth of the various process steps and to avoid large investment on a fixed facility. A more generalized solution can be developed to support as many production facilities as possible that are capable of mimicking the larger scale process steps. The intention is to develop a mobile facility that is easier to adapt to a variety of processes by using a modularity concept. The modularity concept in this project lies on the different process steps such as upstream and downstream, waste handling and utility management. However, on the early-step design of the mobile unit, several considerations have been made in terms of capacity and compatibility for replacing unit operations at various steps.

### 2.5. Step 5. Design /Execution

Upon completion of conceptual design (Step 4A through 4C), the following phases focus on the translation of process to physical equipment, via specifications, etc., during basic design (BD). Following BD is the detailed design (DD) in which technical drawings, equipment and pipe sizing are made to initiate the execution (construction, C&Q, and validation). Process design changes should be minimized at this step since degrees of freedom are lowered with project progression.

## 3. Case Study: Microalgae

Microalgae can be a source of high valued biomolecules such as proteins and lipids of interest of food and /or pharmaceutical production, while being relatively robust to the process conditions of side streams (Andrade et al. 2018). Hence, they are subject of bioremediation and valorization applications.

Five industrial side streams from a Danish company was investigated initially to illustrate the proposed methodology. At present *Chlorella vulgaris* was selected as the microorganism and photobioreactor was selected as the technology. The following aim is to valorize the side stream by selecting valuable compounds produced by microalgae after cultivation.

The *Chlorella vulgaris* was cultivated in the five different side streams at three different concentrations as a preliminary example of HT screening (diluted versions of the side stream) and under sterile and non-sterile conditions (Figure 2A). As a control experiment, cultivation was also carried out in a chemically defined media (CDM). The experiments were conducted under controlled environment (150 rpm, 25 C, 40 μmol intensity, 12h/12h cycle).

The results suggested that *Chlorella vulgaris* presents a favorable growth pattern using one of the side-streams rather than CDM (Figure 2B) which is supposed to be tested at larger scales that allow extended process monitoring and control with a subset of conditions from the HTS.

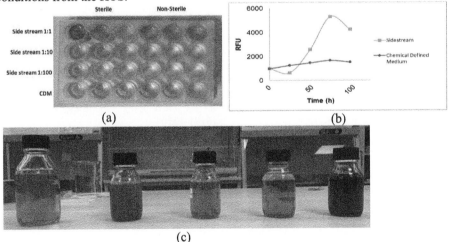

(a)                                                                                 (b)

(c)

Figure 2. Step 1A HT Screening example (a) 24 well-plate of cultivation at different side streams (b) Absorbance of 24 well-plate experiment that is used to correlate the growth rate. (c) Industrial side streams.

At the time of writing, the necessary biomass is produced in shake flasks to quantify the TRY. Furthermore, the biomass will be used in supercritical CO2 extraction lab-scale test to quantify the recovery. Ultimately, the goal of this microalgae study is to develop a process that can be validated in containerized pilot scale at the company's facility. I.e., up to Step 4.

## Acknowledgement

This work is conducted in Biosolutions Zealand project under Danmarks Erhvervs-fremmebestyrelse, funded by the European Regional fund.

## References

Andrade, L. M., Andrade, C. J., Dias, M., Nascimento, C., & Mendes, M. A. (2018). Chlorella and spirulina microalgae as sources of functional foods. Nutraceuticals, and Food Supplements,6(1), 45-58.

EM-DK, Danish Ministry of Industry, Business, and Financial Affairs, https://em.dk/ministeriet/arbejdsomraader/erhvervspolitik/biosolutions/. Accessed November 2022.

Fahr, S., Peña-Benavides, S.A., Thiel, L., Sengoba, C., Karacasulu, K., Ihling, N., Sosa-Hernández, J.E., Gilleskie, G., Woodley, J.M., Parra-Saldivar, R., Mansouri, S.S., Roh, K. (2022), Industrial and Engineering Chemistry Research, 61(35), 13191-13204.

Gamble, C., Bryant, D., Carrieri, D., Bixby, E., Dang, J., Marshall, J., Doughty, D., Colwell, L., Berndl, M., Roberts, J., Frumkin, F. From bioRxiv 28-Jan-2023, https://doi.org/10.1101/2021.08.06.453272, Machine Learning Optimization of Photosynthetic Microbe Cultivation and Recombinant Protein Production, 2021.

Haringa, C. (2022). An analysis of organism lifelines in an industrial bioreactor using Lattice-Boltzmann CFD. Engineering in Life Sciences, 1–16.

Lapin, A., Müller, D., & Reuss, M. (2004). Dynamic behavior of microbial populations in stirred bioreactors simulated with Euler-Lagrange methods: Traveling along the lifelines of single cells. Industrial and Engineering Chemistry Research, 43(16), 4647–4656.

Noorman, H. (2011). An industrial perspective on bioreactor scale-down: What we can learn from combined large-scale bioprocess and model fluid studies. Biotechnology Journal, 6(8), 934–943.

Pigou, M., & Morchain, J. (2015). Investigating the interactions between physical and biological heterogeneities in bioreactors using compartment, population balance and metabolic models. Chemical Engineering Science, 126, 267–282.

Fahr, S., Peña-Benavides, S.A., Thiel, L., Sengoba, C., Karacasulu, K., Ihling, N., Sosa-Hernández, J.E., Gilleskie, G., Woodley, J.M., Parra-Saldivar, R., Mansouri, S.S., Roh, K. Mobile On Demand COVID-19 Vaccine Production Units for Developing Countries, Industrial & Engineering Chemistry Research, 61, 35, 2022, 13191-13204.

Wang, G., Chu, J., Noorman, H., Xia, J., Tang, W., Zhuang, Y., & Zhang, S. (2014). Prelude to rational scale-up of penicillin production: A scale-down study. Applied Microbiology and Biotechnology, 98(6), 2359–2369.

Wang, G., Haringa, C., Noorman, H., Chu, J., & Zhuang, Y. (2020, August 1). Developing a Computational Framework To Advance Bioprocess Scale-Up. Trends in Biotechnology, 38(8), 846–856.

Xu, B., Jahic, M., & Enfors, S. O. (1999). Modeling of overflow metabolism in batch and fed-batch cultures of Escherichia coli. Biotechnology Progress, 15(1), 81–90.

Antonis Kokossis, Michael C. Georgiadis, Efstratios N. Pistikopoulos (Eds.)
PROCEEDINGS OF THE 33rd European Symposium on Computer Aided Process Engineering
(ESCAPE33), June 18-21, 2023, Athens, Greece

# Development of a framework for simulation of biotechnological processes

Priscila Marques da Paz[a], Caroline Satye Martins Nakama[b] and Galo Antonio Carrillo Le Roux[a]

[a]*Department of Chemical Engineering, Polytechnic School, University of São Paulo. Av. Prof. Luicano Gualberto, trav. 3, 380, São Paulo, 05508-010, Brazil*
[b]*Department of Chemical Engineering, Norwegian University of Science and Technology, Høgskoleringen 1, Trondheim, 7034, Norway*

## Abstract

The development of Process Systems Engineering tools that can integrate experimental information with models is fundamental to obtain higher yields and increase productivity of a bioprocess. This is not a simple task, and there is a need for tools that facilitate the collaboration in a multidisciplinary group. In this context, developing computational frameworks for simulation and parameter estimation of bioprocesses that could be used comprehensively by researchers with different backgrounds is the goal of this work. The structure of such frameworks is carefully designed based on an ontology to describe bioprocesses. A helpful tool is the Unified Modeling Language and its use for software generalization is demonstrated along with a case study, showing that the software could serve as a model or example of good practice of software development for guiding simulations and parameter estimations of bioprocess in a structured way.

**Keywords**: bioprocesses, object-oriented programming, prototype, systems biology, unified modelling language.

## 1. Introduction

Biotechnological processes promote microorganisms' synthetizing ability to produce complex molecules that are difficult to access by traditional chemical synthesis, besides to promoting a sustainable and eco-friendly alternative. However, to make the production of a target compound economically viable, a bioprocess needs to be designed and developed to adapt an engineered microbial producer strain (Hemmerich et al., 2021). Process Systems Engineering (PSE) tools together with an experimental effort are necessary to improve the economic potential and sustainability of a new bioprocess. Besides, the required dataset size increases steadily over the years, mainly due to the technical improvements in the data measurement techniques. Often, the extensive experimental data can only be processed and interpreted through the development of quantitative methods. Combining PSE and biotechnological abilities is not a simple task, and there is a need for tools that facilitate the work and collaboration in a multidisciplinary group, which is the mark of the systems biology area (Meyer and Saez-Rodriguez, 2021). Systems biology is the scientific field that studies how the properties of biological systems emerge from the interaction of multiple components. This approach has become essential to cope with the increase in information (Bassalo and Gill, 2016; Meyer and Saez-Rodriguez, 2021). An advanced systems biology model would ideally be based on physical laws and verified by comparing how its predictions fit experimental data. However, this is not always possible. Indeed, knowledge of the fundamental physical principles that give rise to biochemical processes is often incomplete, even for simple systems, and the available information which describes a biological system requires simplifying assumptions to allow model building. Thus, terms based first principles can be studied and incorporated into models, making them more and more complete through the years (Meyer and Saez-Rodriguez, 2021). This is the reason why systems biology is considered a multidisciplinary topic, which indicates that rarely a single person will have a deep knowledge in all fields (Zuo and Zhao, 2018).

In this context, developing computational frameworks become desirable to guide applications in bioprocess modeling. It is recommended the structure be carefully designed, since researchers with different backgrounds are able not only to use the software, but also to contribute with new models as studies in biotechnology are updated. In this way, architecture software becomes as important as developing it. Even in simple cases, it is recommended that the entire system be modeled before starting its implementation, since systems often tend to increase in size, complexity and scope. Developing the architecture is common in the computer science field, and demonstrates the software's flexibility to new editions. For the reasons given, it is interesting to bring these concepts to biotechnology to have a tool along these lines. To guarantee the (re)usability of the system, ontologies are an option to support the sharing of information structures (Guedes, 2018). Ontology is an explicit specification of a conceptualization, and typically involves classes, their relationships and axioms to describe the intended semantics (Marquardt et al., 2010). It is important that every party involved, from developers to users, reach a common understanding of the abstractions and semantics, since the software is intended to be distributed across multiple locals and researchers.

The knowledge represented by ontology allows instantiations of bioprocess components, which makes the information easy and readily shared since these components are standardized and organized. One of the tools used for the design of ontologies is the Unified Modeling Language (UML), which provides the basis for developing software architecture in an organized and generalized way and avoids inconsistencies between requirements specification documents and implementation (Arora et al., 2020; Yurin and Dorodnykh, 2020). In this work, methods and techniques which can describe bioprocesses are implemented in Julia, covering options of growth models, as well as different operation modes. The use of UML for software generalization is demonstrated with a case study, showing that the software could serve as a model or example of good practice of software development for guiding simulations and parameter estimations of bioprocess in a structured way.

## 2. Methodology

### 2.1. Software architecture: ontology for bioprocesses

Ontology has a philosophical origin, where there is interest in the conceptualization of the world of what exists and the essence of things. The basic element of the ontology is the class, which represents a collection of components that share common characteristics. It is organized by hierarchy, in which each inherited property is assigned to subclasses. Components belonging to the same class are called instances, and the characteristics or parameters of the class are the attributes. Each attribute can be identified by its name and has one or more values specific to the class it belongs to. More details can be described in the visual tool that represents ontology: UML (Marquardt et al., 2010; Zhang et al.,

2013). A flowchart that summarizes the methodology used in this paper is shown in Figure 2.1.

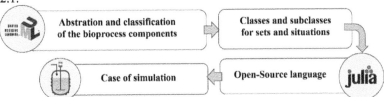

Figure 2.1. Overview of methodology for software architecture

For this work, UML diagrams were implemented using the StarUML software (version 4.5.1), and two types of diagrams were chosen: use case (Figure 3.1.b) and class diagrams (Figure 3.1.a). The first is the most general form of UML and presents an external version of the functionality that the system should offer to users, without details about how such functionality will be implemented. It presents a simple and easy-to-understand language, so that users can readily get an idea of how the system will behave. This diagram is of great help in identifying and understanding the system requirements, helping to specify, visualize and document the system features, functions and services desired by the user. It consists of two main items: actors and use cases. The actors, represented by "skinny dolls", can be the users, other systems or even some special hardware that will use the system in some way. The functionalities that the system will make available to the actors are known as use cases, which is represented by ellipses containing a succinct text describing the action. Interactions between them are represented by lines (Guedes, 2018). The second diagram (class diagram) includes classes, interfaces and relationships. Classes are the model for creating objects, providing specification of attributes and operations that an instance of the class can complete. These operations are treated as functions or procedures, i.e., how actions will happen. Each class can implement more than one interface and each interface can be implemented by several different classes. Relationships have a similar concept to that in the use case diagram, but with more details and more types of relationship (Guedes, 2018).

### 2.2. Bioprocess modelling: starting equations

Bioprocess are represented by the class diagram, abstraction and classification of its components are done based on equations in the most generic way possible, which allows additions of more complex concepts related to the component to be made, either in the class itself or through interactions with other created ones. The first class created was *OperationMode* and the abstract characteristics for it came from the general mass balance (Doran, 2013):

$$\frac{dM}{dt} = M_i - M_O + R_G - R_C \qquad (2.1)$$

where the derivative $dM/dt$ is the mass accumulated within the system and it is zero if the system is in steady-state, $M_i$ is the mass entering through system boundaries, i.e., the mass flow rate of a component entering the reactor, $M_O$ is the mass flow rate leaving the system, $R_G$ is the mass rate of generation of a component by reaction, and $R_C$ is the mass rate of its consumption. Inherited classes are created for: continuous mode, which considers the entire equation, batch and fed-batch mode with same characteristics, but differing by the first having $M_i$ and $M_O$ equal to zero, while in the second only $M_O$ is zero. Considering that, when a bioprocess is carried out by microorganisms, $R_G$ is given by:

$$R_G = \mu_X X \qquad (2.2)$$

where $\mu_X$ is the specific growth rate. A similar situation can be found for $R_C$ with a specific death constant.

$$R_C = k_d X \tag{2.3}$$

Continuing with the creation of classes, it becomes noticeable that a class for microbial growth and death should be created. Cell growth and product formation reflect general kinetics and stoichiometry of intracellular reactions. So, the new class *CellGrowth* will interact with the $R_G$ attribute of the *OperationMode* class, as *CellDeath* with $R_c$. *CellGrowth* will enable that different types of growth can be chosen for the system, since rates like $\mu_X$ can be described in several ways. One of the most commonly used method is relating $\mu_X$ to substrate $S$, taking the form of saturation kinetics. For example, when it is assumed that a single substrate $S$ is limiting for $\mu_X$, while changes in other nutrient concentrations have no effect, this can be described by the Monod equation or alternative ones, such as Blackman, Tessier, Moseer and Contois equations. On the other hand, when substrate or product concentrations are high and inhibitory substances are present in the medium, $\mu_X$ depends on the inhibitor concentration. Then, these situations can be described by others equations. A similar situation occurs with the *CellDeath* class, which must consider the mechanisms for decreasing cell mass, for example, when temperature changes, $K_d$ can vary according to the Arrhenius equation (Shuler et al., 2002).

Growth kinetics has stoichiometrically related parameters, such as cell maintenance and yield coefficients, and it is also influenced by environmental conditions. There is a set of factors to be considered and consecutively, new classes arise and interactions with other classes can be performed. For example, in aerobic processes, oxygen becomes a limiting factor for growing and therefore, the oxygen transfer (OTR) from the gas phase to the liquid phase and the oxygen consumption rate (OUR) should be considered as subclasses belonging to a new *Oxygen* class, which can describe the model's dissolved oxygen. Thus, the architecture provides situations and paths for assembling models (Shuler et al., 2002).

*2.3. Case study for bioprocess*

The intended use of the system and the mentioned classes, both projected so far in the UML diagrams, were used to guide the software programming. The language chosen for the implementation of the code was Julia by its high-performance, flexibly dynamic and open source. A case study to evaluate its operation was carried out with the properties: data simulation of biomass (X), substrate (S) and product (P) in batch, with cell growing by Monod equation. The parameters are $\mu_{max} = 0.3$ h$^{-1}$, $Ks = 0.2$ g/l, $Yxs = 0.06$ g/g, $Yps = 0.46$ g/g and initial values of $X_0 = 0.06$ g, $S_0 = 9.54$ g and $P_0 = 0.00$ g (Doran, 2013).

## 3. Results and discussion

*3.1. Software architecture: UML diagrams*

A prototype representing the system and some definitions are shown in a section of the class diagram in Figure 3.1a, and the use case diagram, which describes an overview of actions, is shown in Figure 3.1b. In Figure 3.1.a, the bioreactor mass balance is represented by the *OperationMode* class, which is divided according to the data they will receive from Equation 2.1. Each operating mode is a subclass, which inherits mass balance characteristics and are called by the *Continuous*, *BatchMode* and *FedBatchMode* subclasses.

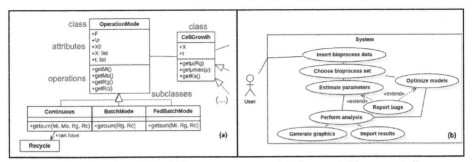

Figure 3.1. UML diagrams of bioprocess system: (a) class and (b) use case diagrams.

The equations for each of these classes depend on mass that enters or leaves the system. Within the *Continuous* subclass, recycle can be also considered. Other classes that have been generated are *CellGrowth* and *CellDeath* and may also be present in operating modes. *CellGrowth* subclasses were determined in a similar way as seen in *OperationMode* and include the different limitations that can occur for cell growth. These subclasses are represented by three dots to also indicate that the class diagram is dynamic, as the software architecture is, and can grow depending on what is added to the model.

Figure 3.1.b shows the cascade of actions, from the insertion of bioprocess data in the system to the generation and import of results. The idea is that the users indicate what they would like to do in the system according to the data they have: simulate or estimate parameters, or even optimizing them. For simulation they should indicate the operating mode and the type of growth, plus the kinetic parameters necessary; for parameter estimation, bioprocess data should be provided; and for optimization, a complete model and objective function should be defined, choosing which variables will be free and what will be optimized, according to the purpose of the model.

During the development of this structure, it was noticed that the abstraction of concepts involving bioprocess must be done with care, in order to generate several options, and it should allow for increasing complexity and flexibility of the analysis.

### 3.2. Simulation modelling

In the case study, a batch bioreactor is simulated and shown in Figure 3.2. $X$, $S$ and $P$ data were generated considering total time of 100 h.

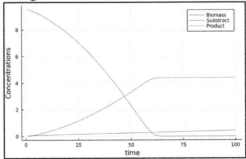

Figure 3.2. Data simulation for batch bioprocess.

The equations used to generate this simulation data can be recycled to perform, in other contexts, parameter estimation and optimization. In addition, the system can grow in number of equations to be considered in the model, which could make the differentiating of equations more laborious. To cover these issues without compromising the software's functionality, the code implemented in Julia was adapted to the JuMP language in advance. JuMP is a domain-specific algebraic modeling language embedded in Julia and has a syntax that mimics natural mathematical expressions (Dunning et al, 2017). Because it only comprises algebraic equations, the differential equations (ODE) were discretized using Implicit Euler, which is a first-order orthogonal collocation method. Higher orders of this method can be implemented to deal with stiff problems (Biegler, 2010), which is interesting to be considered in this work to cover more complex bioprocesses that may involve stiff ODE systems. Although JuMP is mainly used to perform optimization, it can be adapted for simulation, as it happened here. The premeditated use of it will positively impact the software's development to deal with more complex problems and also involving optimization cases.

## 4. Conclusions

This prototype can bring new perspectives for bioprocesses modelling, as currently the software community has given great attention to architectures as a key abstraction in design process. The use of UML for software generalization is demonstrated with a case study, showing that the software could serve as a model or example of good practice of software development for guiding simulations and parameter estimations of bioprocess in a structured way. In summary, this prototype is an alternative tool for model-based integration and analysis of data, which can be the seed of a new, robust and sophisticated tool for systems biology.

## References

V. Arora et al., 2020, Orientation-based ant colony algorithm for synthesizing the test scenarios in uml activity diagram, Information and Software Technology, v. 123, p. 1–21.

M. Bassalo and R. Gill, 2016, Directed evolution and synthetic biology applications to microbial Systems, Current Opinion in Biotechnology, v. 39, p. 126–133.

L. T. Biegler 2010, Nonlinear programming: concepts, algorithms, and applications to chemical processes. MOS-SIAM Series on Optimization.

P. Doran, 2013, Bioprocess engineering principles: Second edition, Elsevier.

I. Dunning et al., 2017, JuMP: A modeling language for mathematical optimization. SIAM Review, v. 59, p. 295-320.

G. Guedes, 2018, UML 2 - Uma abordagem prática, Novatec.

J. Hemmerich et al., 2021, pyfoomb: Python framework for object oriented modeling of bioprocesses, Engineering in Life Sciences, v. 21, p. 242-257.

W. Marquardt et al., 2010, OntoCAPE, Springer Berlin Heidelberg, ISBN 978-3-642-04654-4.

P. Meyer and J. Saez-Rodriguez, 2021, Advances in systems biology modeling: 10 years of crowdsourcing dream challenges, Cell Systems, v. 12, p. 636–653.

M. Shuler and F. Kargi, 2002, Bioprocess Engineering: Basic Concepts, Pearson, second edition.

A. Yurin and N. Dorodnykh, 2020, Personal knowledge base designer: Software for expert systems prototyping, SoftwareX, v. 11, p. 1–6.

J. Zhang et al., 2013, A logic-reasoning based system to harness bioprocess experimental data and knowledge for design, Biochemical Engineering Journal, v. 74, p. 127–135, ISSN 1369703X.

Z. Zuo and K. Zhao, 2018, The more multidisciplinary the better? - the prevalence and interdisciplinarity of research collaborations in multidisciplinary institutions, Journal of Informetrics, v. 12, p. 736–756.

## Acknowledgements

This research was financially supported by the Coordination of Superior Level Staff Improvement (CAPES) grant no. 88887.464619/2019-00, PROEX program and National Council for Scientific and Technological Development (CNPq) for Priscila M. da Paz scholarship (142147/2019-2).

Antonis Kokossis, Michael C. Georgiadis, Efstratios N. Pistikopoulos (Eds.)
PROCEEDINGS OF THE 33rd European Symposium on Computer Aided Process Engineering
(ESCAPE33), June 18-21, 2023, Athens, Greece

# Knowledge modelling framework for per-and poly-fluoroalkyl substances (PFAS) treatment solutions

Madeleine Bussemaker[a*], Nikos Trokanas[b], Ioannis Kavakiotis[b] Franjo Cecelja[a]

*aUniversity of Surrey, Guildford, UK*
*bToolboks, Athens, Greece*
*m.bussemaker@surrey.ac.uk*

## Abstract

Remediation of per-and poly-fluoroalkyl substances (PFAS) is challenged with complexities of solutions, recalcitrance of end products and stringent, evolving regulations. Grouping, characterization and classification of PFAS compounds, environmental contaminations and treatment technologies through knowledge modelling has potential to overcome these challenges. Treatment technologies are often required to work in sequences, called treatment trains to achieve complete removal of PFAS from the environment i.e. a removal/separation stage followed by a degradation stage. Here, an ontology framework is presented to classify PFAS compounds and treatment technologies. Potential applications for the knowledge model to support decision making in environmental remediation and technology research and development is discussed.

**Keywords**: Per-and poly-fluoroalkyl substances (PFAS); remediation; ontology; knowledge modelling; treatment trains

## 1. Introduction

Per- and poly-fluorinated alkyl substances (PFAS) are a class of ~10,000 persistent chemicals, used for >50 years to produce, surfactants, surface treatments, aqueous fire-fighting foams (AFFFs), and plastics such as polytetrafluoroethylene (PTFE) (Buck 2021). Complete remediation of PFAS is challenged by their recalcitrance and bioaccumulation in flora and fauna (Ahrens 2011). PFAS are released into the environment from landfill, manufacturing plants, ground contaminations and sewage treatment plants. Common PFAS are now restricted under the Stockholm Convention on Persistent Organic Pollutants. However, as PFAS are banned, replacement PFAS compounds (next-gen PFAS, e.g. GenX) are introduced with unknown, toxicity and persistence. PFAS are estimated to cost the EU €52-€84 bn per year in health-related issues (Goldenman 2019). PFAS degradation technologies are often limited by i) incomplete mineralisation leading to smaller PFAS fragments; ii) select efficacy, unable to degrade all PFAS; iii) toxic by-products; iv) high energy and/or long treatment times; v) impact of the matrix composition; and vi) integration into end-to-end treatment trains.

Ontology engineering is proposed to support implementation of treatment regimens for PFAS remediation. Approaches to treatment design (e.g. superstructure optimization in wastewater treatment plants) are challenged by the extensive, up-to-date domain-specific knowledge required. For example, variable contamination characteristics, emerging technologies, developing policies and new PFAS types. Ontologies have been used to address a wide range of knowledge-intensive tasks, from linked data (Samwald et al., 2011) to molecule modelling for drug discovery (Lin et al. 2017) and to industrial symbiosis, matching of waste streams to waste processing technologies (Trokanas 2014) with the aim to create processing paths. Ontology engineering can enable formalization of data and knowledge representation of complex data sets from chemical elements to biological and genomic data, to enable the identification of missing relationships (or steps), support classification and clustering models, as well as graph learning approaches.

However, within the domain of environmental remediation knowledge modelling is limited with some examples in management of resources (Goel et al 2013), planning (Safavi 2015), and water flow modelling (Chau 2007). The objective of this work is to present a classification framework that combines the use of knowledge modelling for representation of complex chemistries and PFAS treatment options. The framework is a first step towards a decision support tool for PFAS remediation.

## 2. Framework Development

### 2.1. PFAS Classification

PFAS are defined as any compound with a fully fluorinated carbon, i.e. $-CF_2-$ ethyl group or $-CF_3$ methyl group and can be classed as non-polymer and polymer substances. In the environment, non-polymer PFAS are more common with detailed information on nomenclature available in literature (e.g. Buck 2011). In 2018 The OECD identified 4,730 PFAS substances (OECD, 2018), however fewer than 6% are reported to be globally relevant (Buck 2021). For the development of the knowledge model, established chemical classifications are used to manually group classes and subclasses, (e.g. Table 1). PFAS compounds may belong to two or more classes, e.g., a long chain perfluoroalkyl acid (PFAA) may be a carboxylic or sulfonic acid. Chemical classifications allow integration with existing Chemical ontologies, e.g. Chemical Entities of Biological Interest (ChEBI).

Table 1. Example classes of PFAS compounds

| Perfluoroalkyl Substances | Subclass | Chemical structure |
|---|---|---|
| **Perfluoroalkyl acids (PFAAs)** $C_nF_{2n+1}-R$ *(where R is a hydrophilic functional group)* | Perfluoroalkyl carboxylic acids (PFCAs) | $C_nF_{2n+1}COOH$ |
| | Perfluoroalkyl sulfonic acids (PFSAs) | $C_nF_{2n+1}SO_3H$ |
| | Short chain (SC) PFAA | $C_nF_{2n+1}-R$     $n \leq 5$ |
| | Long chain (LC) PFAA | $C_nF_{2n+1}-R$     $n \geq 6$ |
| **Polyfluoroalkyl Substances** | | |
| **Fluorotelomer (FT) substances** *Used or made from the fluorotelomer process* | (n:2) Fluorotelomer alcohols ((n:2) FTOHs) | $C_nF_{2n+1}CH_2CH_2OH$ |
| | (n:2) Fluorotelomer sulfonic acids ((n:2) FTSAs) | $C_nF_{2n+1}CH_2CH_2SO_3H$ |
| **Perfluoroalkyl ether acids (PFEAs)** *Perfluoroalkyl moieties connected by ether bonds* | Perfluoroether carboxylic acids (PFECAs) | e.g. GenX or HFPO-DA with the same protonated form: $C_3F_7OCF(CF_3)-COOH$ |
| | Perfluoroether sulfonic acids (PFESAs) | e.g. n:2 Cl-PFESA: $Cl(CF_2)_nO(CF_2)_2SO_3H$ |

Chemical classifications also create classes that underpin treatment efficacy, manufacturing methods, persistence, and degradation products. Initial manufacturing of PFAS was based on the PFAAs perfluorooctane sulfonic acid (PFOS) and perfluorooctanoic acid (PFOA) (where n=7 and n=8, respectively) known collectively as PFOX. Now almost all bodies of water contain at least 1 ng/L of PFOX (Ahrens 2014), and most treatment and toxicology research is based on these two compounds. However, fluorotelomers (FTs) and perfluoroalkylether acids (PFEAs) have replaced PFOS and PFOA, leading to new profiles of persistent PFAS in groundwater (Backe 2013). FTs are based on shorter perfluorinated carbon chains (usually C4 or C6), linked to a hydrophilic end group via what is usually a two-carbon alkane chain. The FT compound class leads to formation of shorter chain PFAAs, or fluorotelomer sulfonates, depending on the initial structure. PFEAs are manufactured from short perfluoroalkyl moieties connected by ether bonds and have worldwide persistence (Pan 2018). PFEAs are resistance to hydroxyl radical mediated oxidation, photolysis and biodegradation, and are highly mobile, hence have similar remediation issues to their predecessor compounds.

## 2.2. Classification of treatment technologies

Treatment technologies initially focus on treatments for water contaminations. In general treatments can be classed into two types; i) separation/concentration treatment where low concentration (<ng/L) waste streams can be treated, producing a clean water that meets regulatory standards, and ii) degradation treatments where the main aim is to degrade the PFAS compounds into smaller PFAS fragments and/or to complete mineralization. The difficulty in achieving complete mineralization of PFAS comes from their extremely strong C–F bond and the shielding of carbons by fluorine components of the molecule (Kirsch 2004). Hence developing appropriate treatment trains that also mineralize PFAS are one of the key challenges for PFAS remediation. Numerous reviews exist into PFAS treatment technologies (e.g. Ross et al 2018; Horst et al, 2018; Kucharzyk et al 2017) here we aim to discuss the nuances of different regimes to underpin the ontology framework.

### 2.2.1. Separation / concentration treatments

Separation / concentration methods are grouped into granular/powder activated carbons (GAC/PAC), resins and silicas, membrane separation and foam fractionation (Table 2). Treatment properties can be attributed to each treatment class, as defined in Table 2 (Rahman 2014). Within each class, data properties will be further identified to capture the nuances of the treatment regimen and subclasses identified.

Table 2. Separation / concentration treatments, with relevant properties. NR = not reported.

| TREATMENT | Efficacy for different PFAS | | | Matrix effects | Waste/side streams |
|---|---|---|---|---|---|
| | PFEA | SC | LC | | |
| GAC / PAC | None to moderate | Moderate /ineffective | Moderate (not all precursors) | Organics compete | Contaminated solid (PAC), solid for regeneration (GAC) |
| Resins and silicas | NR | IX is less efficient | Yes | Depends on absorbent | Regenerate solutions |
| Membrane separation | NR | Yes | Yes | Impacted by organics | Membrane rejectate, spent membranes |
| Foam-fractionation | NR | Yes | Yes | Unlikely to interfere | Concentrated PFAS solution (ppm range), sedimentation |

### 2.2.2. Degradation treatment technologies

Degradation mechanisms can be thermal, oxidative, biological, physical and reductive. In each case the mode of operation / technology used varies, along with the efficacy and matrix effects. For example, advanced oxidative processes (AOPs) and biological treatments are not effective at complete PFAS mineralization (Ross et al, 2018) and leave shorter chain PFAAs. Incineration, a thermal treatment can convert ~20-45% of the fluorine to toxic hydrogen fluoride (HF) gas (Aleksandrov et al 2019; Taylor et al 2014) and can emit gaseous fluorocarbons and unconverted PFAS with insufficient incinerator temperatures or residence times (Meng et al, 2017). Electrochemical reduction can be non-selective and reduction of matrix elements must be considered (Horst et al 2018). Classifications must allow for technologies that support multiple mechanisms. For example, reductive methods include metal-mediated reduction (e.g. catalysis in supercritical water, zero valent metals) (Kucharzyk et al 2017) and methods that promote the generation of the hydrated electron (photolytic, electrolytic and plasma) (Ross et al 2018). However electrolytic and photolytic technologies can also use oxidative degradation. Similarly ultrasonic technologies (i.e. sonolysis) are considered to be oxidative at low frequency, and argued to be pyrolytic (thermal) or reductive via the aqueous electron at high frequencies (Sidnell et al 2022). The ontology structure is therefore developed to allow such classifications (Figure 1).

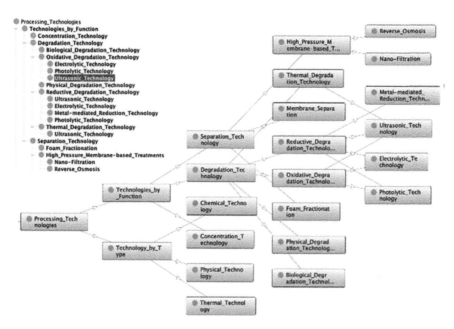

Figure 1. The PFAS Treatment technology ontology structure for a selection of treatment types.

### 2.2.3. Proposed ontology structure

Identified classes and object properties for technology classification (Table 3) are designed to capture the necessary considerations for overall remediation efficacy. The characteristics of function and type are chosen to allow for later development of knowledge graphs and inferencing around novel treatment technologies and/or new PFAS compounds, i.e. to handle missing information. Each technology may have more than one output stream, then each output stream can be classed according to environmental release laws, drinking water standards and potential further treatment options.

Within each treatment technology further object properties must be assigned to avoid sweeping generalizations around a class of technologies, often seen in literature. For example, ultrasonic degradation of PFAS can be highly dependent on frequency, additives, and reactor geometry. At low frequencies (<100 kHz) very little degradation is seen without additives, whereas at high frequency (100-1000 kHz) complete mineralization has been reported at ambient temperatures (Sidnell et al, 2022). Similarly electrolytic methods will depend on the electrolyte, electrode material and reactor configuration (Ryan et al 2021). Approaching the comparison and selection of technologies through knowledge modelling therefore highlights such nuances and enables better-informed decision making.

Table 3 Classes and object properties underpinning the PFAS treatment technology modelling

| Classes | Examples |
|---|---|
| Function | Separation, concentration, degradation |
| Type | Thermal, physical, biological, chemical |
| By mechanism | Oxidation, reduction, membrane separation, ion exchange etc |
| **Object properties** | **Examples** |
| Output stream | F⁻, $CO_2$, SC PFAS, LC PFAS, PFAAs, co-contaminants... |
| Input composition | PFAS concentration, co-contaminants |
| Efficiency | Fluoride release rate, PFAS degradation / removal rate |
| Common parameters | Temperature, volume, pressure |
| Developmental stage | Laboratory, pilot scale, industrial scale |
| Cost | Capital, operational, energy consumption |

## 3. Future applications and development of PFAS ontology

The classification framework for the PFAS ontology has potential application in supporting selection of treatment trains, provide predictions about technology efficacy, and focusing research and development of treatment technologies. Through modelling the inputs and outputs separation / concentration technologies can be matched with appropriate degradation technologies using matching algorithms (Trokanas 2014). This is especially useful since degradation technologies tend to be expensive at treating dilute solutions and more efficient at higher concentrations. For example, at concentrations in the mg/L range high frequency sonolysis tends to be zero order, but at lower concentrations is first order. Hence the zero-order regime is more energy efficient per gram of PFAS destroyed. Technology matching will show potential treatment trains given a composition profile of a PFAS contamination and desired PFAS output profile. Thus, has potential to inform economically and environmentally optimal treatment regimens.

One of the key challenges of PFAS remediation is the complete mineralization of all PFAS types. Due to the difficulty in destroying PFAS, many of the technologies applied are in various stages of development, with the majority of research on PFOS and PFOA degradation. Effective technologies often come at high energy and capital cost and more research and development is required to understand efficacies for new and emerging PFAS in a range of matrices. The nuances of each emerging technology are often only fully appreciated by subject-matter experts and there is danger in over-generalization of different treatment regimes. The ontology will inform knowledge graph development to facilitate machine learning to highlight necessary experiments and/or likely outcomes of various treatment regimes. If a known treatment has overlapping characteristics with an unknown treatment technology then the knowledge graph can be used to infer and predict the outcomes of the unknown treatment technology.

## 4. Conclusions

Here we presented a framework for developing an ontology around PFAS remediation. The ontology will be able to be integrated with existing knowledge models and is useful for creating a common language to model PFAS treatment regimes, support decision making on PFAS treatment trains and underpin research, development and learning around emerging PFAS degradation technologies.

## 5. References

L. Ahrens. 2011, Polyfluoroalkyl compounds in the aquatic environment: A review of their occurrence and fate. J Environ Monit. 13(1):20-31.

L. Ahrens, Bundschuh M., 2014 Fate and effects of poly- and perfluoroalkyl substances in the aquatic environment: A review. Environ Toxicol Chem.,33(9):1921-1929

K. Aleksandrov, Gehrmann HJ, Hauser M, Mätzing, H., Pigeon, D., Stapf, D., & Wexler, M Waste incineration of polytetrafluoroethylene (PTFE) to evaluate potential formation of per- and poly-fluorinated alkyl substances (PFAS) in flue gas. Chemosphere. 2019;226:898-906.

W. J. Backe, Day TC, Field JA., 2013, Zwitterionic, cationic, and anionic fluorinated chemicals in aqueous film forming foam formulations and groundwater from U.S. military bases by nonaqueous large-volume injection HPLC-MS/MS. Environ Sci Technol. 47(10):5226-34.

R. Buck, Korzeniowski, S. H., Laganis, E., & Adamsky, F., 2021. Identification and classification of commercially relevant per-and poly-fluoroalkyl substances (PFAS). Integrated environmental assessment and management, 17(5), 1045-1055.

K. W. Chau, 2007. An ontology-based knowledge management system for flow and water quality modeling. Advances in Engineering Software, 38(3), 172-181.

D. Goel, Chaudhury, S., & Ghosh, H. 2017. Smart water management: An ontology-driven context-aware IoT application. In International Conference on Pattern Recognition and Machine Intelligence (pp. 639-646). Springer, Cham.

J. Horst, McDonough J, Ross I, Dickson, M., Miles, J., Hurst, J., & Storch, P., 2018 Water treatment technologies for PFAS: The next generation. Groundw Monit Remediat. 38(2):13-23.

P. Kirsch, 2004, Modern Fluoroorganic Chemistry, Synthesis, Reactivity, Applications. Weinheim: Wiley-VCH;

K. H. Kucharzyk, Darlington R, Benotti M, Deeb R, Hawley E., 2017, Novel treatment technologies for PFAS compounds: A critical review. J Environ Manage. 204:757-764.

Y. Lin, S. Mehta, H. Küçük-McGinty, H., Turner, J.P., Vidovic, D., Forlin, M., Koleti, A., Nguyen, D.T., Jensen, L.J., Guha, R. and Mathias, S.L., 2017 Drug target ontology to classify and integrate drug discovery data. J Biomed Semant 8, 50

J. Meng, Lu Y, Wang T, Wang, P., Giesy, J. P., Sweetman, A. J., & Li, Q.,2017, Life cycle analysis of perfluorooctanoic acid (PFOA) and its salts in China. Environ Sci Pollut Res. 24(12):11254-64.

OECD. Toward a New Comprehensive Global Database of PAFs. Vol 2018.; 2018

Y. Pan Y, Zhang H, Cui Q, Sheng, N., Yeung, L.W., Sun, Y., Guo, Y. and Dai, J. 2018, Worldwide distribution of novel perfluoroether carboxylic and sulfonic acids in surface water. Environ Sci Technol. 52(14):7621-7629.

M. Rahman, Peldszus S, Anderson WB., 2014, Behaviour and fate of perfluoroalkyl and polyfluoroalkyl substances (PFASs) in drinking water treatment: A review. Water Res. 50:318-340.

I. Ross, McDonough J, Miles J, Storch, P., Thelakkat Kochunarayanan, P., Kalve, E., Hurst, J., S. Dasgupta, S., Burdick, J., 2018, A review of emerging technologies for remediation of PFASs. Remediation. 28(2):101-126.

D. Ryan, Mayer, B., Baldus C, McBeath S, Wang Y, & McNamara P, 2021, Electrochemical technologies for per-and polyfluoroalkyl substances mitigation in drinking water and water treatment residuals. AWWA Water Science, 3(5), e1249.

H. Safavi, Golmohammadi, M, & Sandoval-Solis S, 2015, Expert knowledge based modeling for integrated water resources planning and management in the Zayandehrud River Basin. J Hydrology, 528, 773-789.

C. Samwald, C. Jentzsch, C.S. Bouton, E. Kallesøe, J. Willighagen, M.S. Hajagos, E. Marshall, O. Prud'hommeaux, E. Hassanzadeh. Pichler and S. Stephens, 2011. Linked open drug data for pharmaceutical research and development. Journal of cheminformatics, 3(1), p.19.

T. Sidnell, Wood R, Hurst J, Lee J, & Bussemaker M, 2022. Sonolysis of Per-And Poly Fluoroalkyl Substances (PFAS): A meta-analysis. Ultrasonics sonochemistry, 105944.

P. Taylor, Yamada T, Striebich RC, Graham JL, Giraud RJ., 2014 Investigation of waste incineration of fluorotelo mer-based polymers as a potential source of PFOA in the environment. Chemosphere. 110:17-22.

N. Trokanas, Cecelja, F., & Raafat, T., 2014. Semantic input/output matching for waste processing in industrial symbiosis. Computers & Chemical Engineering, 66, 259-268.

Antonis Kokossis, Michael C. Georgiadis, Efstratios N. Pistikopoulos (Eds.)
PROCEEDINGS OF THE 33rd European Symposium on Computer Aided Process Engineering
(ESCAPE33), June 18-21, 2023, Athens, Greece

# Combined metabolic modeling and experimental data for enhanced biotechnological production

Anita L. Ziegler,[a]* Melanie Filbig,[b]* Johannes Parschau,[a,b] Till Tiso,[b] Lars M. Blank,[b] Alexander Mitsos,[a,1]

[a]*Process Systems Engineering (AVT.SVT), RWTH Aachen University, Aachen, Germany*
[b]*Institute of Applied Microbiology (iAMB), Aachen Biology and Biotechnology (ABBt), RWTH Aachen University, Aachen, Germany*
*Equally contributing authors [1]Corresponding author, email: amitsos@alum.mit.edu*

## Abstract

Biotechnological products are promising sustainable alternatives to fossil-derived fuels and plastics. A modified strain of the bacterium *Pseudomonas putida* KT2440 produces 3-(3-hydroxyalkanoyloxy)alkanoic acids (HAA) from glucose, which can serve as a precursor for bioplastic and biofuel production. We investigate the use of acetate as alternative, sustainable, and low-cost substrate. We use an expanded version of the genome-scale metabolic model *i*JN1463 to improve the understanding of the metabolism. Rates and yields calculated from experimentally obtained data were used as input for flux balance analysis (FBA) and compared to computational data. Despite substantial model-experiment mismatch, FBA provides insights into the acetate metabolization. Finally, we utilize the optimization-based gene knockout method OptKnock to propose potential targets for strain engineering with the aim of improved product yields.

**Keywords**: Metabolic modeling, Biotechnology, Acetate, HAA, *Pseudomonas putida.*

## 1. Introduction

Genome-scale metabolic models (GEMs) contain the entire set of genes of an organism and the metabolic reactions encoded by those genes. GEMs are built based on experimentally obtained data and genome annotation data and are used to predict cellular responses and metabolic fluxes under different environmental conditions, *e.g.*, different substrates, by optimization techniques such as flux balance analysis (FBA) (Varma & Palsson 1994). Thus, GEMs help to understand metabolic processes in a cell and increasingly find applications in biotechnology to support and reduce experimental approaches. FBA formulates a cellular objective and metabolic constraints as a linear optimization program to quantify the metabolic state of a cell under the assumption of a steady state (Orth 2010). Thereby, optimal metabolic flux distributions are calculated to predict growth rates, as well as maximal theoretical biomass or product yields. The experimental results can in turn be used to validate and optimize the model predictions.

Improving the performance of a biotechnological strain often requires time-consuming genetic engineering. To reduce experimental effort, the elimination of reactions that result in a beneficial metabolic configuration for improved product yields can be predicted with GEMs. The bilevel programming framework OptKnock was developed by Burgard *et al.* (2003) to propose optimal gene deletions in *Escherichia coli.*

We investigate the biosynthesis of 3-(3-hydroxyalkanoyloxy)alkanoic acids (HAA) with an engineered *Pseudomonas putida* KT2440 strain on acetate in an approach combining experimental and computational methods. HAA can be produced recombinantly using *P. putida* KT2440 KS3 (Blesken 2020). The current production, however, relies on glucose. Herein, we focus on acetate as an alternative substrate, as it is a low-cost, biotechnological substrate due to its abundance in several side streams (Kiefer 2021) and can be produced from C1-gases, such as $CO_2$ (Kiefer 2021). Thus, acetate contributes to an improved $CO_2$ balance of the overall process. Although *P. putida* KT2440 KS3 can use acetate as the sole carbon source, the growth behavior of the strain is impaired by the presence of the C2-compound and product titers lag behind titers achieved from glucose. FBA and OptKnock are used to help understand the altered metabolism on acetate when compared to metabolizing glucose and find potential targets for strain engineering toward optimized product formation. As a basis for FBA and OptKnock, several GEMs are available for *P. putida*. The most current and complete model available is *i*JN1463 (Nogales 2020). In this study, *i*JN1463 was expanded to contain the synthesis and export reactions for HAA. Experimental data including growth rate, biomass yield, product yield, substrate uptake rate, as well as $CO_2$ production rate were obtained from shake flask cultivations of *P. putida* KT2440 KS3 on glucose and acetate. While the substrate uptake rate was used as input for FBA, the other data were used to compare and evaluate computationally obtained data. Internal fluxes were calculated and displayed with special interest on $CO_2$-forming reactions. Moreover, beneficial gene deletions resulting in higher HAA yields were predicted using OptKnock in several rounds comprising one to five target reactions. This work highlights the possibilities and advantages of a combined approach of experimental and computational work.

## 2. Methods

### 2.1. Experimental methods

The bacterium *P. putida* KT2440 KS3 (Blesken 2020) was cultivated in mineral salts medium as described by (Hartmans 1989) with threefold buffer concentration when 0.17 Cmol of glucose or fourfold buffer concentration when 0.17 Cmol acetate, were used as the sole carbon source. Cultivations were performed in 500 ml shake flasks with 10 % filling volume at 250 rpm and a shaking diameter of 50 mm. Main cultures were inoculated with a defined volume of the pre-cultures to start with an optical density at 600 nm ($OD_{600}$) of 0.1. Cultivations with online monitoring of $CO_2$ resulting from bacterial metabolic activity were performed with 0.13 Cmol glucose or acetate in 1 L shaking flasks with a 50 ml filling volume. Biomass formation was monitored offline by measurement of the $OD_{600}$, which was converted into cell dry weight (CDW) using a correlation of 0.31 g $L^{-1}$.

Concentrations of glucose and acetate were determined using HPLC as described by Blesken *et al.* (2020). HAA titers in cultivation broth were determined using an Ultimate3000 HPLC system with a dual gradient pump, connected to a Corona Veo Charged Aerosol Detector (all Thermo Scientific). An analytical and an inverse gradient set up of 0.2 % formic acid in acetonitrile and 0.2 % formic acid in ultrapure water were applied for chromatographic separation with a NUCLEODUR C18 Gravity column (Macherey-Nagel) with 150 mm length and a diameter of 3 mm.

$CO_2$ production during cultivation was monitored using BSP-$CO_2$ sensors and the BlueVIS software (BlueSens gas sensor GmbH). Yields of biomass per substrate were calculated by division of the maximal reached CDW by the applied substrate concentration. Product yields were determined by dividing maximal product concentration by applied substrate concentration. Substrate uptake rates were calculated by dividing the growth rate µ by the biomass yield per substrate.

### 2.2. Flux balance analysis and visualization

To obtain insights into the metabolism, FBA was performed according to

$$\max_{v \in \mathbb{R}^n} \; c^T v$$
$$s.t. \; S v = 0$$
$$v_i^{lb} \leq v_i \leq v_i^{ub} \; \forall i \in \{1,..,n\},$$

$v$: flux vector; $n$: number of reactions
$c$: parameter vector to choose objective flux
$S$: stoichiometric matrix from GEM
$lb$: lower bound; $ub$: upper bound

where the maximization of the biomass flux or the maximization of the HAA flux was chosen as objective function. The FBA is based on the stoichiometric matrix $S$ of a GEM. The GEM applied in this work is *i*JN1463 (Nogales 2020), which contains 2,927 reactions, 2,153 metabolites and 1,462 genes. We extended the network by the gene *rhlA* and the reactions specific to the strain KS3, namely four synthesis reactions in the cytosol, one for each HAA congener, and four transport reactions from the cytosol to the extracellular space. With the extracellular HAA congeners as reactants, one exchange reaction was added that simulates the production of HAA in the congener composition that was experimentally determined. Exchange reactions represent the exchange of the cell with the environment and enable closing the mass balance. The stoichiometric factors in the exchange reactions were adjusted on each substrate to display the altered HAA composition on glucose and acetate. The software COBRApy (opencobra.github.io/cobrapy) serves to conduct the FBA and Gurobi 9.5.2 serves as solver. Substrate uptake rates determined experimentally were set as input. To visualize the fluxes through the network, the software Escher (escher.github.io) was utilized.

### 2.3. Optimal knockouts

Genes encode enzymes that catalyze reactions. When knocking out a certain gene by means of genetic engineering, the associated reaction is not catalyzed anymore, *i.e.*, cannot carry flux anymore. To suggest gene knockouts, the formulation OptKnock was applied, which suggests reactions that are advantageous to block, *e.g.*, reactions towards a byproduct. OptKnock is a bilevel optimization program, where the upper level maximizes the flux of the target chemical, and the lower level maximizes the flux of biomass as follows:

$$\max_{y \in \{0,1\}^r} \; v_{HAA}$$
$$s.t. \; \max_{v \in \mathbb{R}^n} v_{biomass}$$
$$s.t. \; S v = 0$$
$$(By)_i \, v_i^{lb} \leq v_i \leq (By)_i \, v_i^{ub} \; \forall i \in \{1,..,n\}.$$

$y$: knockout vector
$r$: number of (possibly reversible) reactions
$B$: mapping matrix ($r$ to $n$)

In this study, the HAA exchange reaction flux $v_{HAA}$ was set as objective function of the upper level and the biomass flux $v_{biomass}$ as objective in the lower level. For numerical reasons, the stoichiometric network with $r$, possibly reversible, reactions was transformed to an irreversible network with $n$ irreversible reactions. OptKnock was implemented in our in-house software libALE (Djelassi 2020) and solved using the solver Gurobi 9.5.2.

## 3. Results and discussion

### 3.1. Cultivation on acetate is possible, but achieves lower yields than on glucose

*P. putida* KT2440 KS3 was cultivated on 0.17 Cmol glucose and acetate to determine growth rate, HAA production rate, biomass, and product yield, as well as substrate uptake rate (Figure 1). While on glucose, the strain reaches a maximal cell dry weight (CDW) of 1.6 g L$^{-1}$ after 9 h with a growth rate of 0.47 h$^{-1}$, the strain reached a final biomass of 1 g L$^{-1}$ CDW after 14 h cultivation time on acetate, exhibiting a growth rate of 0.37 h$^{-1}$. Thus, the biomass yield per substrate is 35 % lower on acetate than on glucose. HAA formation is threefold higher on glucose than on acetate: while on glucose, a final HAA titer of 270 mg L$^{-1}$ was reached after 9 h, on acetate a maximal titer of 90 mg L$^{-1}$ was reached after 14 h. The pH increases during the course of the cultivation to a pH above 8 due to the consumption of acetic acid from the medium.

a)                                                                      b)

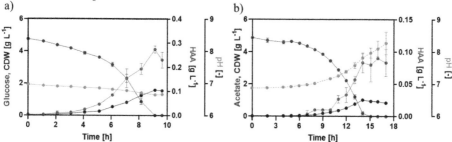

Figure 1: Biomass, HAA and substrate concentration, and pH during cultivation of *P. putida* KT2440 KS3 on a) 0.17 Cmol glucose and b) 0.17 Cmol acetate.

Measurements of the $CO_2$ produced by the microbes during cultivation revealed a slightly higher $CO_2$ production on acetate than on glucose. While on glucose *P. putida* KT2440 KS3 produced 0.35 Cmol $CO_2$ per Cmol substrate, on acetate 0.37 Cmol $CO_2$ were produced per Cmol substrate. All in all, *P. putida* KT2440 KS3 exhibits lower rates and yields on acetate than on glucose, which might result from the lower enthalpy of combustion of acetate (437 kJ Cmol$^{-1}$) compared to glucose (467 kJ Cmol$^{-1}$). However, growth as well as product formation is possible from acetate as sole carbon source. In order to elucidate acetate metabolism and calculate maximal theoretical yields, FBA was performed in a next step. For FBA, substrate uptake rates are required. These substrate uptake rates were determined on 0.17 Cmol glucose and 0.17 Cmol acetate to be 7.8 mmol g$_{CDW}$$^{-1}$ h$^{-1}$ (0.04 Cmol g$_{CDW}$$^{-1}$ h$^{-1}$) and 28.5 mmol g$_{CDW}$$^{-1}$ h$^{-1}$ (0.057 Cmol g$_{CDW}$$^{-1}$ h$^{-1}$), respectively.

### 3.2. Flux balance analysis gives insights into the altered metabolic configuration

FBA was used to calculate the theoretical yield of biomass and HAA per substrate. Those theoretical yields were then compared to wet lab results that were calculated from experimental data (Table 1).

Table 1: Yield of biomass and HAA on glucose and on acetate: wet lab results, i.e., calculated from experimental data, vs. dry lab results, i.e., from flux balance analysis (FBA). The errors represent the standard deviations of triplicate cultivations (n=3). For FBA, the uptake rates were set to equal experimentally determined uptake rates. In case (a) of the FBA, the objective function is the flux of biomass; in case (b) the flux of HAA.

| | Substrate | Wet lab | Dry lab |
|---|---|---|---|
| $Y_{Biomass/Substrate}$ [g$_{CDW}$ g$^{-1}$] | Glucose | 0.34±0.01 | 0.54 (a) |
| | Acetate | 0.22±0.01 | 0.46 (a) |
| $Y_{HAA/Substrate}$ [Cmol Cmol$^{-1}$] | Glucose | 0.097±0.005 | 0.68 (b) |
| | Acetate | 0.030±0.001 | 0.59 (b) |

When cultivating on glucose, the biomass yield reaches 63 % of the theoretical biomass yield, which is a small difference, when considering that the theoretical yield does not account for any product or byproduct formation. On acetate, 48 % of the theoretical biomass yield is reached experimentally, which is a larger difference. Overall, we conclude that FBA is a valid means to predict growth of *P. putida* KT2440 KS3, especially on glucose. One possible explanation for the greater deviation with acetate as a substrate is the toxic effect of the substrate (Kiefer 2021), which is not considered in the metabolic network. When looking at the HAA yields, FBA predicts values seven times higher or more, than determined experimentally for both substrates. Hence, the experimental yield has much potential for improvement. However, the overall trend of a lower HAA yield on acetate than on glucose is predicted in the FBA.

To find a reason for this trend, in a next step, the altered tricarboxylic acid (TCA) cycle of the cell on glucose vs. on acetate was visualized in Escher maps (Figure 2). The magnitude of the fluxes in the TCA gives insights into the energy demand of a cell.

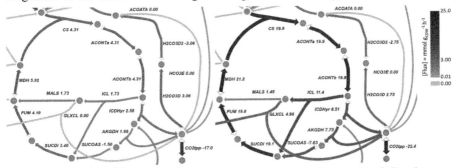

Figure 2: Visualization of the tricarboxylic acid cycle with glucose as carbon substrate (left) and acetate as carbon source (right). Biomass flux is the objective function; a substrate uptake of 0.05 Cmol $g_{CDW}^{-1}$ $h^{-1}$ and a threshold of 0.01 mmol $g_{CDW}^{-1}$ $h^{-1}$ on the HAA exchange reaction were set as constraints to the FBA. Reactions are labeled with BIGG ID (bigg.ucsd.edu) and the flux value. The figure was adapted from Parschau (2022).

The Escher maps reveal that the cell exhibits a different metabolic configuration on glucose than on acetate, meaning altered reaction fluxes inside the cell. The TCA cycle exhibits fluxes of 1.5-5.9 mmol $g_{CDW}^{-1}$ $h^{-1}$ on glucose, whereas it displays fluxes of 7.6-21.2 mmol $g_{CDW}^{-1}$ $h^{-1}$ on acetate. The higher fluxes through the TCA cycle probably result from the higher energy demand on acetate and the lower energy content of this carbon source. The $CO_2$ data derived from FBA follow the same trend as $CO_2$ data obtained experimentally: with acetate as substrate, more $CO_2$ is produced than on glucose, namely 22.4 mmol $g_{CDW}^{-1}$ $h^{-1}$ vs. 17.0 mmol $g_{CDW}^{-1}$ $h^{-1}$ on glucose. Hence, more byproduct is formed on acetate. This may cause less HAA production on acetate than on glucose.

### 3.3. Two gene deletions may lead to improved yield

The optimization formulation OptKnock was used to suggest beneficial blocking of reactions, resulting in higher HAA yields. When only one reaction was set to be blocked, no solution was found that improved HAA yield. For two reactions, the HAA yield per substrate increases to 0.53 Cmol Cmol$^{-1}$ while reducing the biomass production to the set threshold of 0.08 h$^{-1}$. The HAA yield thereby reaches 90 % of the theoretical yield (see Table 1). The suggested enzymatic reactions to be blocked are catalyzed by dihydromonapterin reductase (NADPH) and dihydromonapterin reductase (NADH). These reactions are located in the biomass synthesis pathway. Hence, by reducing the carbon flux to biomass, the carbon flux is redirected towards HAA synthesis. However, experimental experience indicates that HAA production is highly connected to biomass production. Presumably, knocking out these reactions would impede the organism. The next gene knockout suggestion addresses five reactions due to numerical problems with three and four reactions. The result for five reactions shows no improvement compared to the two knockouts. We conclude that two knockouts are sufficient to improve the HAA yield. In conclusion, the results show that there is potential for improving the yield by applying metabolic engineering. However, more advanced optimization formulations should be considered that guarantee for a minimal product yield (Tepper & Shlomi 2009) and that better represent the microorganism (Apaydin 2017) to improve the predictions.

## 4. Conclusion

In our study, we have shown that HAA can be produced on acetate as sole carbon source by an engineered *P. putida* strain, however with a lower yield than on glucose. We have explained this by the toxicity of acetate and the altered metabolic configuration of the cell. The integration of experiments and simulations has brought confidence because both methods displayed the same trend. We found that more $CO_2$ is produced during growth on acetate, which reduces the carbon atoms available for HAA yield. To reduce the model-experiment mismatch, regulatory effects should be considered in the model formulation. We have suggested gene knockouts to improve the yield of HAA on acetate, which must be elaborated deeper by more advanced formulations and proven in the laboratory as a next step. Moreover, fermentation conditions with lower acetate concentrations can mitigate the toxicity of acetate to the cell and further improve HAA yield.

**Author Contributions:** ALZ designed the computations and MF designed the laboratory experiments. JP performed the computational and experimental laboratory work under the supervision of ALZ and MF. ALZ, MF and JP visualized, analyzed, and discussed the data. ALZ and MF wrote the manuscript draft. TT, LMB and AM conceptualized the project, discussed the data, and reviewed the draft. All authors read and approved the final manuscript.

**Acknowledgements:** This project was funded by the Deutsche Forschungsgemeinschaft (DFG, German Research Foundation) under Germany´s Excellence Strategy – Cluster of Excellence 2186 „The Fuel Science Center" – ID: 390919832

## References

M. Apaydin, L. Xu, B. Zeng, X. Qian, 2017, Robust mutant strain design by pessimistic optimization, BMC Genomics, 18, 6, 677.

C. C. Blesken, I. Bator, C. Eberlein, H. J. Heipieper, T. Tiso, L. M. Blank, 2020, Genetic Cell-Surface Modification for Optimized Foam Fractionation, Front. Bioeng. Biotech., 8, 1116.

A. P. Burgard, P. Pharkya, C. D. Maranas, 2003, Optknock: A bilevel programming framework for identifying gene knockout strategies for microbial strain optimization, Biotechnol. Bioeng., 84, 6, 647-57.

H. Djelassi, O. Stein, A. Mitsos, 2020, Discretization-based algorithms for the global solution of hierarchical programs, Lehrstuhl für Systemverfahrenstechnik, RWTH Aachen University.

S. Hartmans, J. P. Smits, M. J. van der Werf, F. Volkering, J. A. de Bont, 1989, Metabolism of Styrene Oxide and 2-Phenylethanol in the Styrene-Degrading Xanthobacter Strain 124X, Appl. Environ. Microbiol., 55, 11, 2850-5.

D. Kiefer, M. Merkel, L. Lilge, M. Henkel, R. Hausmann, 2021, From acetate to bio-based products: underexploited potential for industrial biotechnology, Trends Biotechnol., 39, 4, 397-411.

J. Nogales, J. Mueller, S. Gudmundsson, F. J. Canalejo, E. Duque, J. Monk, A. M. Feist, J. L. Ramos, W. Niu, B. Ø. Palsson, 2020, High-quality genome-scale metabolic modelling of *Pseudomonas putida* highlights its broad metabolic capabilities, Environ. Microbiol., 22, 1, 255-69.

J. D. Orth, I. Thiele, B. Ø. Palsson, 2010, What is flux balance analysis?, Nature Biotechnol., 28, 3, 245-48.

J. Parschau, 2022, Numerical optimization supported by experimental data towards improved production of 3-(3-hydroxyalkanoyloxy)alkanoic acids by *Pseudomonas putida*, Bachelor Thesis, RWTH Aachen University.

N. Tepper, T. Shlomi, 2009, Predicting metabolic engineering knockout strategies for chemical production: accounting for competing pathways, Bioinformatics, 26, 4, 536-43.

A. Varma, B. Ø. Palsson, 1994, Stoichiometric flux balance models quantitatively predict growth and metabolic by-product secretion in wild-type Escherichia coli W3110, Appl. Environ. Microbiol., 60, 10, 3724-3.

Antonis Kokossis, Michael C. Georgiadis, Efstratios N. Pistikopoulos (Eds.)
PROCEEDINGS OF THE 33rd European Symposium on Computer Aided Process Engineering
(ESCAPE33), June 18-21, 2023, Athens, Greece

# Machine learning models for predicting membranolytic anticancer peptides

Fatemeh Alimirzaei,[a] Chris A. Kieslich,[a]

[a]*Chemical Engineering Department, Auburn University, Auburn, AL 36849, USA*
*cak0071@aburn.edu*

## Abstract

After heart disease, cancer is the second leading cause of death worldwide. Recently, membranolytic anticancer peptides (ACPs) have received considerable attention for their ability to target and kill cancer cells. Identification of ACPs is costly and usually time-consuming. Therefore, the development of efficient computational methods is of a great importance to aid in the identification of potential ACP candidates. In the current study, we developed multiple models using support vector machines (SVMs), gradient boosting classifiers (GB), and random forest classifiers (RF) to predict membranolytic anticancer activity given a peptide sequence. Oscillations in physiochemical properties in protein sequences have been shown to be predictive of protein structure and function, and in this work, we are taking advantage of these known periodicities to predict ACP sequences. To this end, Fourier transforms were applied to the property factor vectors to measure the amplitude of the physiochemical oscillations, which served as the features for our models. Peptides targeting breast and lung cancer cells were collected from the CancerPPD database and converted into physiochemical vectors using 10 property factors for the 20 natural amino acids. Using these datasets, cross-validation has been applied to train and tune the models based on multiple training and testing sets. Additionally, feature selection has been performed to further optimize our SVM models. To evaluate the models, performance has been quantified based on cross-validation classification accuracy. Furthermore, to try our prediction accuracy, we have also considered other sets of physiochemical features and properties of amino acids from the literature into our models.

**Keywords**: Membranolytic anticancer peptides, Computer-aided drug design, Machine learning

## 1. Introduction

Cancer is the second leading cause of death worldwide, and it is anticipated the number of deaths caused by cancer will be more than 13 million by 2030 (Liscano et al. 2020). Not only are conventional cancer therapies expensive, but poor specificity often leads to devastating side effects, such as anemia, gastrointestinal mucositis, alopecia, cardiotoxicity, or osteoporosis (Manavalan et al. 2017; Gabernet et al. 2016). Moreover, cancer cells may develop resistance to chemotherapy and receptor-targeted anticancer agents (Gabernet et al. 2019). Therefore, developing innovative anticancer drugs is essential to attenuate cancer cell proliferation (Manavalan et al. 2017).

Recently, membranolytic anticancer peptides (ACPs) have been proposed as a potential strategy in the fight against cancer by disrupting cancer cell membranes and destroying them. ACPs are typically short peptides composed of 10–60 amino acids that can inhibit tumor cell proliferation or migration or suppress the formation of tumor blood vessels and are less likely to cause drug resistance (Xie et al. 2020). They tend to be amphipathic, positively charged, and many of them change their structure from random to helical conformation upon associating with a preferred lipid bilayer (Queme-Pena et al. 2021). It has been hypothesized that the cationic nature leads to their selectivity for cancer with negatively charged lipid membranes (Grisoni et al. 2019). However, only a limited number of potent anticancer peptides are known to date. For instance, just 7% of the 2981 peptides annotated in the antimicrobial peptide database (APD3) (Wang et al. 2016), a group sharing physiochemical properties with ACPs, have been tested for anticancer activity (Grisoni et al. 2019), or only 53 peptides in the cancerPPD database possess low micromolar activity (EC50< 5μM) to be useful for cancer treatment (Grisoni et al. 2019). Furthermore, their experimental identification and development are laborious, expensive, and time-consuming (Yu et al. 2020). Last but not least, the underlying structure-activity relationship that explains the membranolytic properties of these peptides is not completely understood (Queme-Pena et al. 2021). Therefore, innovative tools like sequence-based computational methods are needed for the fast identification and design of potent ACP candidates (Manavalan et al. 2017). To identify ACPs, existing methods try to discriminate ACPs from non-ACPs and then predict their anticancer activity based on the features extracted from known ACPs which their identities are held by publicly available datasets like CancerPPD (Shoobuatong et al. 2018).

In the current study, we are developing models that predict whether a peptide will exhibit ACP activity given only an amino acid sequence of the peptide. For this purpose, we are trying to identify patterns in the physiochemical properties of ACPs by using Fourier Transform-based features that measure the oscillations of physiochemical properties along the length of peptides. Previously we have shown that oscillations in physiochemical properties in peptide sequences are predictive of antiviral peptide activity (Kieslich et al. 2021). Here we aim to take advantage of these known periodicities of amino acid properties to develop models that predict anticancer peptide activity. Furthermore, by performing feature selection, we can determine which features are the most important predicting ACP activity that have the potential of forming a design template.

## 2. Methods

In this work, Python has been used to perform all steps of our analysis, which includes the generation of physiochemical vectors for each peptide, Fourier-based feature extraction, training/validation of classification models for predicting membranolytic anticancer activity, as well as SVM-based feature selection. Below are more elaborate descriptions of how these elements were implemented in this study.

### 2.1. ACP Dataset

One of the crucial requirements for developing data-driven classification models is having access to adequately large datasets containing both amino acid sequence and function labels. Currently, there are multiple publicly available databases which hold the identities of some known anticancer peptides, including APD (Wang et al. 2004), CancerPPD (Tyagi et al. 2015), DADP (Novkovic et al. 2012), DBAASP (Pirtskhalava et al. 2021), LAMP (Zhao et al. 2013). In our study, two peptide datasets targeting breast and lung cancer were chosen owed to their relevance for human health (2.9 million cases for each cancer type in 2018) (Grisoni et al. 2019). These datasets were previously assembled and curated manually from CancerPPD (Grisoni et al. 2019), so that the final training sets contained 232 peptides targeting breast cancer cells, including 116 active and 116 nonactive ACPs, and 198 peptides targeting lung cancer cells containing 99 active and 99 nonactive ACPs.

## 2.2. Feature Extraction

One of the prerequisites for training a machine learning-based classifier is transforming the original raw training data into a set of "features". For this purpose, we first converted the amino acid sequences of each peptide in our raw dataset into physiochemical vectors using 10 physical properties factors of the 20 naturally occurring amino acids. These 10 physicochemical property factors were generated based on principle component analysis of a large set of amino acid physicochemical properties (Kidera et al. 1985). Kidera et al. describe the property factors as α-helix or bend-structure preference-related, bulk-related, structure preference-related, hydrophobicity-related, and 5 additional property factors that represent mixtures of several physicochemical properties. Each peptide is converted into 10 physiochemical vectors (numerical vectors) based on each of the physicochemical property factors. Afterwards, we used the fft function in Python to apply Fourier transforms to each of the property factor vectors. It is worth mentioning, in order to make sure that the same number of frequency (Fourier) components have been generated for each property vector, we have applied zero-padding with the assumption of a maximum sequence length of 64 amino acids. The maximum ACP sequence length across both peptide datasets is 38 amino acids. In this way, the amino acid properties corresponding to positions that are longer than a given peptide were set to zero. After using zero padding and the Fourier transform, 64 Fourier coefficients are generated for each property of each peptide. However, Fourier transform spectrums are in mirror shape, and only half of the coefficients (i.e., 32) were considered in addition to the center (0). Ultimately there were 33 features for each of the ten property factors in each peptide, which means 330 features are extracted for each peptide (feature set1). In other words, each sequence was represented by 33 Fourier coefficients measuring the oscillation of the 10 property factors.

We also generated two more feature sets for further evaluation of our prediction accuracies. For feature set 2, we added 10 additional features to feature set 1 based on amino acid composition. The additional features were based on the percentage of amino acid positions that fit categories of positively charged, negatively charged, aliphatic, aromatic, polar, hydrophobic, size (tiny, small, large), as well as the total charge of the peptide. The amino acid categories were based on those that have been previously proposed for a related task (Manavalan et al. 2017). For generating the feature set3, instead of 10 amino acids property factors used to create feature set1, we applied 8 newly reported properties of amino acids by Medina-Ortiz et al. that are related to α structure, β structure, hydrophobicity, volume, energy, hydropathy, secondary structure, and other indexes (Medina-Ortiz et al. 2022).

## 2.3. Support Vector Machines and Grid-search

In this study, all support vector machines have been trained by using the svc function in Python based on the radial kernel (Gaussian radial basis function (RBF)). In order to tune the cost and gamma hyperparameters of the SVM models, a grid search has been used with cost and gamma values based on powers of ten, $10n \ \forall \ n \in [0, \ldots, 6]$ for cost values and $10n \ \forall \ n \in [-6, \ldots, 0]$ for gamma values, where n is an integer.

## 2.4. SVM Feature Selection

Feature selection plays a critical role in data science since it leads to the identification of the fundamental set of predictive descriptors (features). Furthermore, it can increase the robustness of the model to prevent overfitting (Kiesich et al. 2021). Previously, a feature selection algorithm has been developed based on non-linear SVM, which is common in nature and has been applied to predict faults in chemical plants (Onel et al. 2018) and HIV-1 viral entry (Kieslich et al. 2016). It is a model-based algorithm requiring first training an SVM model prior to computing a criterion quantifying the contribution between each single feature to the SVM objective function to determine which features to eliminate. The criterion (Eq. 1) is derived in terms of sensitivity analysis of the dual formulation of SVM models.

$$crit_k = -\frac{1}{2}\sum_i \sum_j \alpha_i^* \alpha_j^* y_i y_j \left. \frac{\partial K(x_i \circ z, x_j \circ z)}{\partial z_k} \right|_{z=1} \tag{1}$$

This algorithm applies a greedy approach in order to rank the features, so that at the beginning it starts with training a model based on all of the features, computes the criteria for all features and then removes a fraction of the features with the largest criteria values. (In other words, the largest criteria values have the least importance for the model). In the current work, %33 of the remaining features has been removed after each iteration of the algorithm, and the hyperparameters have been retuned after each iteration of the algorithm. The feature ranking procedure was applied to each of the five training sets and a consensus ranking was generated based on the average rank of each feature across five training sets.

### 2.5. Cross Validation and SVM Models Accuracy

Five-fold cross-validation, based on two balanced training datasets, was applied to tune and validate the models based on the first sorting of the peptide sequences according to length, and then choose five training and testing sets with an equal number of samples for each peptide class in each peptide datasets, separately. For all datasets, model performance was evaluated based on classification accuracy which is reported as the fraction of classes (active or nonactive ACPs) that have been predicted accurately in the test sets.

### 2.6. Gradient Boosting and Random Forest Models

In this study, all gradient boosting and random forest models have been trained and evaluated using "sklearn.ensemble" and "sklearn.metrics" packages in Python. Also, like the SVM model, 5-fold cross-validation was performed to generate train/test sets for them. It is worth mentioning for both of these models, we used the default values of the parameters controlling the size of the tree publicly available on the "scikit_learn" website (Scikit-learn: Machine Learning in Python) (Pedregosa et al. 2011).

**Table 1.** Statistics of the performance of machine learning-based models predicting ACP activities.

| Cancer type | Feature set/Number of features | SVM model accuracy/Minimum number of features to maintain the accuracy | Gradient Boosting model accuracy | Random Forest model accuracy |
|---|---|---|---|---|
| Breast | Set1/330 | 76%/≈330 | 68% | 68% |
|  | Set2/340 | 79%/≈280 | 59% | 60% |
|  | Set3/264 | 68%/≈240 | 62% | 62% |
| Lung | Set1/330 | 83%/≈25 | 75% | 72% |
|  | Set2/340 | 82%/≈270 | 74% | 73% |
|  | Set3/264 | 75%/≈130 | 66% | 65% |

## 3. Results

Based on the proposed feature sets (3 sets in total), we developed models using SVM, Gradient Boosting, and Random Forest methods to distinguish the active and nonactive ACP peptides based on the Breast and Lung datasets. For SVM classification tasks, we performed feature selection to rank the physicochemical features. To measure the contribution of each feature to model accuracy we performed five-fold cross-validation after adding each feature one at a time, starting with the highest-ranked feature. Also, for gradient boosting and random forest models, we have done five-fold cross-validation for all datasets and calculated the average accuracy across 5 train/test sets for each predictive model, discriminating two classes of ACPs targeting breast and lung cancer cells. A summary of obtained results of all the predictive model performances is shown in Table 1. Among them, the SVM model using feature sets2 has the highest accuracy (79%) for discriminating active and nonactive anticancer peptides targeting breast cancer cells. Also, for distinguishing between active and nonactive ACPs targeting lung cancer cells, the SVM model using feature set 1 has the highest accuracy (83%) compared to the rest of the predictive models. These reported cross-validation accuracies are the average of the classification accuracies for the five training and testing sets. As it is seen in Figure 1, the minimum number of features required to maintain those accuracies is around 280 features for the model predicting anticancer activities of the peptides targeting breast cancer cells, and approximately 25 features are needed to maintain the highest accuracy of the model predicting ACP targeting lung cancer cells. It is worth mentioning features in the x-axis on the plots are ordered based on the feature selection algorithm meaning adding more and more features. For example, those 25 features are the most important ones to distinguish active and nonactive ACPs targeting lung cancer cells.

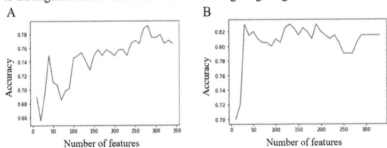

**Figure 1.** Feature contribution to model accuracy based on feature selection ranking. A) Feature selection results for classifying active vs. nonactive anticancer peptides targeting breast cancer cells; B) Feature selection results for classifying active vs. nonactive anticancer peptides targeting lung cancer cells.

## 4. Conclusion

In this study, we have developed a support vector machine, gradient boosting, and random forest models that distinguish between active and nonactive ACP sequences for two membranolytic ACP datasets targeting breast and lung cancer cells. To develop these models, we used different sets of amino acid property factors of naturally occurring amino acids from the literature to convert ACP sequences into property vectors that served as the input for the generation of Fourier-based features. Our results show that SVM models perform better in discriminating ACP activity. In addition, by ranking the importance of the developed Fourier-based features, we were able to train SVM models with improved accuracy and generalizability, while also starting to gain some insights into the importance of oscillations of physiochemical properties for ACP function. It can be concluded that our approach for feature extraction and model development, specifically including the SVM feature selection algorithm, has the potential for use in predicting peptide properties and functions as well as designing innovative anticancer peptides in the future. However, given the remaining challenges in discriminating between active and nonactive ACPs, more efforts are required that might need both further computational and even experimental investigations.

# References

G. Gabernet, A. T. Muller, J. A. Hiss, G. Schneider, 2016, Membranolytic anticancer peptides. Medchemcomm, 7(12): 2232-2245.

G. Gabernet, G. Gabernet, D. Gautschi, A.T. Müller, C.S. Neuhaus, L. Armbrecht, P.S. Dittrich, J.A. Hiss, G. Schneider, 2019, In silico design and optimization of selective membranolytic anticancer peptides. Sci Rep, 9(1), 11282.

F. Grisoni, C. S. Neuhaus, M. Hishinuma, G. Gabernet, J. A. Hiss, M. Kotera, 2019, De novo design of anticancer peptides by ensemble artificial neural networks. J Mol Model, 25(5), 112.

A. Kidera, Y. Konishi, M. Oka, T. Ooi, H.A. Scheraga, 1985, Statistical-Analysis of the Physical-Properties of the 20 Naturally-Occurring Amino-Acids. Journal of Protein Chemistry, 4(1), 23-55.

C.A. Kieslich, F. Alimirzaei, H. Song, M. DO, P. Hall, 2021, Data-driven prediction of antiviral peptides based on periodicities of amino acid properties, in Computer Aided Chemical Engineering, M. Türkay and R. Gani, Editors, Elsevier, 2019-2024.

C.A. Kieslich, P. Tamamis, Y.A. Guzman, M. Onel, C.A. Floudas, 2016, Highly accurate structure-based prediction of HIV-1 coreceptor usage suggests intermolecular interactions driving tropism. PLOS ONE, 11(2), e0148974.

Y. Liscano, Y., J. Onate-Garzon, and J.P. Delgado, 2020, Peptides with Dual Antimicrobial-Anticancer Activity: Strategies to Overcome Peptide Limitations and Rational Design of Anticancer Peptides. Molecules, 25(18), 4245.

B. Manavalan, S. Basith, T.H. Shin, M. O. Kim, G. Lee, 2017, MLACP: machine-learning-based prediction of anticancer peptides. Oncotarget, 8(44), 77121-77136.

D. Medina-Ortiz, S. Contreras, J. Amado-Hinojosa, J. Torres-Almonacid, J.A. Asenjo, M. Navarreto, A. Olivera-Nappa, 2022, Generalized Property-Based Encoders and Digital Signal Processing Facilitate Predictive Tasks in Protein Engineering. Frontiers in Molecular Biosciences, 9, 898627.

M. Novkovic, M. Novković, J. Simunić, V. Bojović, A. Tossi, D. Juretić, 2012, DADP: the database of anuran defense peptides. Bioinformatics, 28(10), 1406-7.

M. Onel, C.A. Kieslich, Y.A. Guzman, C.A. Floudas, E.N. Pistikopoulos, 2018, Big Data Approach to Batch Process Monitoring: Simultaneous Fault Detection and Identification Using Nonlinear Support Vector Machine-based Feature Selection. Comput. Chem. Eng., 115, 46-63.

M. Pirtskhalava, A. A Amstrong, M. Grigolava, M. Chubinidze, E. Alimbarashvili, B. Vishnepolsky, A. Gabrielian, A. Rosenthal, D. E Hurt, M. Tartakovsky, 2021, DBAASP v3: database of antimicrobial/cytotoxic activity and structure of peptides as a resource for development of new therapeutics. Nucleic Acids Research, 49(D1), D288-D297.

M. Queme-Pena, T. Juhasz, G. Kohut, M. Ricci, P. Singh, I. C. Szigyarto, Z. I. Papp, L. Fülöp, T. Beke-Somfai, 2021, Membrane Association Modes of Natural Anticancer Peptides: Mechanistic Details on Helicity, Orientation, and Surface Coverage. Int J Mol Sci, 22(16).

W. Shoombuatong, N. Schaduangrat, C. Nantasenamat, 2018, Unraveling the bioactivity of anticancer peptides as deduced from machine learning, 17, 734-752.

A. Tyagi, A. Tuknait, P. Anand, S. Gupta, M. Sharma, D. Mathur, A. Joshi, S. Singh, A. Gautam, G. P.S. Raghava, 2015, CancerPPD: a database of anticancer peptides and proteins. Nucleic Acids Research, 43(D1), D837-D843.

G.S. Wang, X. Li, and Z. Wang, 2016, APD3: the antimicrobial peptide database as a tool for research and education. Nucleic Acids Research, 44(D1), D1087-D1093.

Z. Wang, G. Wang, 2004, APD: the Antimicrobial Peptide Database. Nucleic Acids Res, 32(Database issue), D590-2.

M. Xie, D. Liu, Y. Yang, 2020, Anti-cancer peptides: classification, mechanism of action, reconstruction and modification. Open Biol, 10(7), 200004.

L. Yu, R. Jing, F. Liu, J. Luo, 2020, DeepACP: A Novel Computational Approach for Accurate Identification of Anticancer Peptides by Deep Learning Algorithm. Mol Ther Nucleic Acids, 22, 862-870.

X. Zhao, H. Wu, H. Lu, G. Li, Q. Huang, 2013, LAMP: A Database Linking Antimicrobial Peptides. PLoS One, 8(6), e66557.

Antonis Kokossis, Michael C. Georgiadis, Efstratios N. Pistikopoulos (Eds.)
PROCEEDINGS OF THE 33rd European Symposium on Computer Aided Process Engineering
(ESCAPE33), June 18-21, 2023, Athens, Greece

# Data-driven prediction of peptide-MHC binding using oscillations of physicochemical properties

Hyeju Song,[a] Chris A. Kieslich, [a]

[a]*Auburn University, Auburn, AL 36849, USA*
*kieslich@auburn.edu*

## Abstract

The Major Histocompatibility Complex (MHC) molecules play a major role in T-cell immunogenicity through the recognition of 'non-self' peptides derived from foreign antigens. Therefore, predicting peptides that trigger immune responses is of great interest for the general understanding of T-cell-mediated immunity and the design of peptide-based vaccines and cancer immunotherapy treatments. The presented work tests the performance of allele-specific SVM classification models in the prediction of pMHC binding. The models aim to classify MHC class II binding and non-binding peptides based on their amino acid sequences and derived features. In developing the models, we take advantage of underlying periodicities in physicochemical properties along the sequence of a peptide that has been shown to be predictive of protein structure and function. Once the physicochemical descriptors are generated, Fourier transforms are then applied to be able to encode peptide sequences of varying lengths. In training and testing the model, a comprehensive dataset of MHC class II binding peptides that includes 44 unique MHC class II alleles (molecules) with 60630 binding affinities is taken from the IEDB database. Cross-validation and hyperparameter tuning are applied across multiple train and test datasets. A feature selection algorithm is also incorporated into the model development to identify an essential set of predictive features. The blind test set prediction accuracy of the developed allele-specific models ranges from 0.58- 0.93, with an average classification accuracy of 0.73.

**Keywords**: Computational biology, data-driven, machine learning, support vector machines, Major Histocompatibility Complex, feature selection

## 1. Introduction

Understanding peptide-protein binding in T-cell immunity has potential applications in many biomedical fields, including the development of peptide-based vaccines and personalized cancer immunotherapy. Identifying T-cell epitopes first involves predicting if peptides derived from an antigen (e.g. viral protein) bind to specific Major Histocompatibility Complex (MHC) molecules since the formation of peptide-MHC (pMHC) complexes is a key determinant in the T-cell immunogenicity. Over the past years, a number of computational prediction methods have been developed to identify MHC-binding peptides as an alternative to costly and time-consuming experimental methods (Sanchez-Trincado et al. 2017). In general, the prediction of interactions between MHCs and peptides is challenging due to the highly polymorphic nature of

MHCs and also the varying length of binding peptides. Moreover, it is further compounded by non-binding residues, also known as peptide flanking regions (PFRs), which have been found to affect its binding affinity.

Current state-of-the-art binding prediction tools typically utilize artificial neural networks trained on sequence data with experimental binding affinity measurements. Although those sequence-based neural network models perform highly accurate predictions, they are hardly interpretable, limiting both biological insights and analysis of feature contributions. An alternative approach is machine learning methods such as support vector machine (SVM), which can be more interpretable and generalizable across peptide-MHC interactions.

One other limitation of previously developed models is that most do not incorporate information regarding the physicochemical properties of amino acids and, even when they do, they ignore the order of residues, which is known to be closely related to protein structure and function. Previously, it has been shown that families of protein structure and function can be categorized by underlying periodicities in protein or peptide physicochemical properties along the amino acid sequence (Eisenberg et al. 1984; Rackovsky 1998). Based on this observation, as well as numerical tricks such as fast Fourier transforms and zero-padding, these oscillations of physicochemical properties can be incorporated into prediction models, while also allowing the encoding of peptide sequences with varying lengths into the same number of features. A recent study on predicting antiviral peptides has shown the potential of using such Fourier-based coefficients as features for SVMs (Kieslich et al. 2021).

Here, we have developed allele-specific SVM models for the prediction of pMHC binding using the oscillations of physicochemical properties along the sequence of peptides. Our models were trained to classify binders and non-binders using supervised learning based on quantitative binding affinity experimental data. Furthermore, a previously developed feature selection algorithm was applied to rank the importance of the derived features to further optimize the developed models.

## 2. Methods

An overview of the model development procedure used in the presented work is shown in Figure 1. All steps of model development and analysis which include data preprocessing, feature selection, training of SVMs, and model evaluation are performed using Python programming language. Each step is described in detail in the sections that follow.

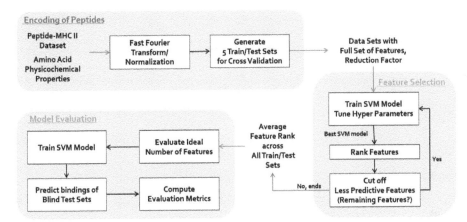

**Figure 1**. Overview of model development and evaluation procedures.

### 2.1. Peptide-MHC Class II Binding Data

The human MHC dataset was sourced from the Immune Epitope Database (IEDB) on Sep 30, 2022 (Fleri et al. 2017). Each peptide-MHC entry in the dataset consists of the peptide sequence, the MHC allele, and the measured binding affinity. For our dataset, only the quantitative type of measurements (e.g., IC50, EC50, and $K_D$) were chosen, and entries with measurement values larger than 50000 nM were excluded from the dataset. Note that a lower value indicates higher binding affinities and vice versa. We also limited the length of peptides to range from 13 to 21 amino acids. The resulting binding affinity datasets consisted of 60630 entries with 44 unique MHC alleles and 10806 unique peptides. A binding affinity cutoff was set to 1000 nM to distinguish between binders and non-binders, which has been widely used for MHC class II binding classification. The final dataset was split into a training set and a blind test set for the evaluation of model performance with a ratio of 80:20 in a stratified sampling manner. The training set was then split again to generate 5 cross-validation sets of training/testing sets using the same approach.

### 2.2. Encoding Strategy

The first step in encoding peptide sequences is to convert them into numerical values. In this work, we adopt 10 physicochemical property factors that have been shown to describe 86% of the variance of the original 188 properties from which they were derived (Kidera et al, 1985). For each physicochemical property factor, a given peptide is converted into a corresponding physicochemical property vector (Figure 2, left), resulting in 10 physicochemical property vectors per peptide. To ensure that every peptide is represented by the same number of features, the 10 physicochemical property vectors are zero-padded assuming a maximum sequence length of 32 amino acids. Then, a Fourier transform is applied to each property vector using the Fast Fourier Transform (FFT) function of the SciPy package in Python, and we took the moduli (Figure 2, right) of the complex Fourier coefficients for frequency values between 0 and 0.5 as final features for training the SVMs which consists of 170 elements.

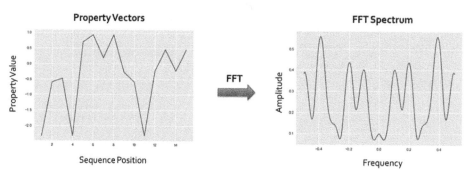

**Figure 2.** Fourier transform of property vectors into FFT Spectrum.

### 2.3. Support vector machines

We trained a total of 44 allele-specific binary classification SVM models based on the nonlinear radial basis kernel using the SVC function in the Python Scikit-learn package. For each SVM model, the hyper-parameters cost (C) and gamma (g) are tuned by grid-search, with values of $10^n \, \forall \, n \in \{-3, \cdots, 3\}$, where n is an integer. In validating the SVM models, performance was assessed with 5-fold cross-validation with each training/testing set containing equal ratios of binders to non-binders. The accuracy of the SVM models was evaluated by computing classification accuracy, which is computed as to the percentage of entries in a testing set where the predictions were correct.

### 2.4. Feature selection

Feature selection, also known as variable selection, is a process by which the number of features is reduced to a subset of predictive features by eliminating redundant or irrelevant ones when developing prediction models. The process benefits machine learning tasks by decreasing the chances of over-fitting while potentially improving its accuracy and reducing training time. In this work, we have adopted a feature selection algorithm based on non-linear SVMs, which was proposed by Kieslich et al. (Kieslich et al. 2016). The algorithm has been applied to the broad area of prediction study including HIV-1 viral entry and fault detection in chemical plants (Kieslich et al. 2016, Onel et al. 2018, Onel et al. 2019).

The algorithm uses a greedy approach and ranks the features based on the criterion (Eq. 1), which characterizes the importance of feature k. The criterion was derived from the objective function of the dual formulation of the SVM model since solving the formulation, in general, is required to employ non-linear kernels for feature selection.

$$crit_k = -\frac{1}{2}\sum_i\sum_j \alpha_i^* \alpha_j^* y_i y_j \left. \frac{\partial K\left(x_i \circ z, x_j \circ z\right)}{\partial z_k}\right|_{z=1} \tag{1}$$

The algorithm initially starts with an SVM model with all of the features and computes the criteria for each feature. Then the features are ranked based on their criteria values, and given the feature reduction factor, the algorithm iteratively removes a set of features that has the largest criteria values. The presented work used the reduction factor of 1/3, meaning 33% of the remaining features are removed after each iteration. Hyper-parameters are tuned again based on the remaining features after each iteration, and a consensus feature rank is also generated by averaging ranks across the five training sets.

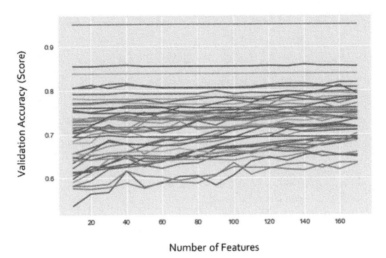

**Figure 3.** Feature contribution of 44 MHC alleles obtained from feature selection.

## 3. Results

The feature selection analysis was implemented for 44 allele-specific SVMs based on the generated physicochemical features. The feature selection algorithm provided the feature rank of each MHC allele model, and the contribution of each feature was measured by training and testing individual SVMs with five-fold cross-validation after adding 10 features at a time. The validation accuracies were computed as the mean accuracy of test set prediction over cross-validation with best hyper-parameters. As can be seen in Figure 3, overall, there was a trend that the addition of features leads to a steady increase in validation accuracy across most of the MHC alleles. Those models achieve the accuracies of 0.53-0.94 only with the first 10 features, and they improve up to 0.62-0.94 as we incorporate more features. In general, maximum accuracies were achieved when almost all features are used to train each model. Meanwhile, horizontal lines are also observed for some alleles, where we can infer that the models are biased due to the limited amount of data and, for the most part, are the result of largely imbalanced classification datasets.

For each MHC allele, the optimal number of features was selected from the above feature selection analysis (Figure 3). The final allele-specific SVM classification models were trained and optimized with those features identified as minimum features required for maximum validation accuracy and then evaluated by performing prediction on the blind dataset. As shown in Figure 4, the prediction accuracy is relatively consistent across the feature-optimized allele-specific models, ranging from 0.58- 0.93 with an average of 0.73. Overall, those models exhibit sound prediction performance, indicating the use of physicochemical property-derived features enables SVMs to capture the interactions between peptides and MHC molecules.

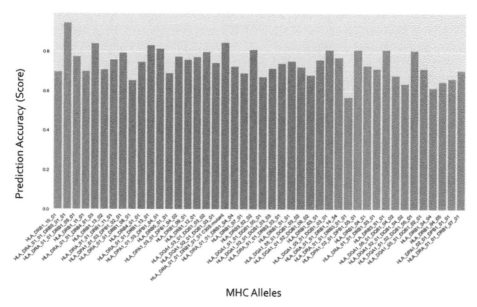

**Figure 4.** Blind set prediction accuracy of the feature-optimized allele-specific SVM models.

## 4. Conclusions

In this work, we have developed 44 allele-specific binary classification SVM models that were trained based on the binding affinity datasets to classify MHC binding and non-binding peptides. Features for the SVMs were derived from the physicochemical properties of amino acids and extracted from Fourier analysis, assuming the oscillation of properties along the sequence can be predictive for peptide-MHC binding. Nonlinear SVM-based feature selection analysis was also performed during the workflow to measure the contributions of features and identify an optimal list of features. As a result, the proposed approach has shown the potential of physicochemical properties derived features in the prediction of peptide-protein interactions or functions. Future work will need to investigate the generalizability and interpretability of the prediction models for a better understanding of pMHC interactions across MHC alleles. The developed models with further analysis could be used to provide a guideline for developing and designing peptide vaccines and immunotherapeutics.

## References

Eisenberg, D., Weiss, R. M., & Terwilliger, T. C. (1984). The hydrophobic moment detects periodicity in protein hydrophobicity. Proceedings of the National Academy of Sciences, 81(1), 140-144.

Fleri, W., Paul, S., Dhanda, S. K., Mahajan, S., Xu, X., Peters, B., & Sette, A. (2017). The immune epitope database and analysis resource in epitope discovery and synthetic vaccine design. Frontiers in immunology, 8, 278.
https://www.ncbi.nlm.nih.gov/pmc/articles/PMC5348633/pdf/fimmu-08-00278.pdf

Kidera, A., Konishi, Y., Oka, M., Ooi, T., & Scheraga, H. A. (1985). Statistical analysis of the physical properties of the 20 naturally occurring amino acids. Journal of Protein Chemistry, 4(1), 23-55.

Kieslich, C. A., Alimirzaei, F., Song, H., Do, M., & Hall, P. (2021). Data-driven prediction of antiviral peptides based on periodicities of amino acid properties. In Computer Aided Chemical Engineering (Vol. 50, pp. 2019-2024). Elsevier.

Kieslich, C. A., Tamamis, P., Guzman, Y. A., Onel, M., & Floudas, C. A. (2016). Highly accurate structure-based prediction of HIV-1 coreceptor usage suggests intermolecular interactions driving tropism. PloS one, 11(2), e0148974.
https://www.ncbi.nlm.nih.gov/pmc/articles/PMC4747591/pdf/pone.0148974.pdf

Onel, M., Kieslich, C. A., Guzman, Y. A., Floudas, C. A., & Pistikopoulos, E. N. (2018). Big data approach to batch process monitoring: Simultaneous fault detection and diagnosis using nonlinear support vector machine-based feature selection. Computers & chemical engineering, 115, 46-63.

Onel, M., Kieslich, C. A., & Pistikopoulos, E. N. (2019). A nonlinear support vector machine-based feature selection approach for fault detection and diagnosis: Application to the Tennessee Eastman process. AIChE Journal, 65(3), 992-1005.
https://www.ncbi.nlm.nih.gov/pmc/articles/PMC7202572/pdf/nihms-1010061.pdf

Rackovsky, S. (1998). "Hidden" sequence periodicities and protein architecture. Proceedings of the National Academy of Sciences, 95(15), 8580-8584.

Sanchez-Trincado, J. L., Gomez-Perosanz, M., & Reche, P. A. (2017). Fundamentals and methods for T-and B-cell epitope prediction. Journal of Immunology Research, 2017.

Antonis Kokossis, Michael C. Georgiadis, Efstratios N. Pistikopoulos (Eds.)
PROCEEDINGS OF THE 33rd European Symposium on Computer Aided Process Engineering
(ESCAPE33), June 18-21, 2023, Athens, Greece
© 2023 Elsevier B.V. All rights reserved. http://dx.doi.org/10.1016/B978-0-443-15274-0.50430-3

# A Computational Pipeline to Optimize 3D Scaffolds for Cancer Immunotherapy

Lucy Todd,[a] Matthew Chin,[a] Marc-Olivier Coppens,[a*]

[a] *Centre for Nature Inspired Engineering & Department of Chemical Engineering, University College London, Torrington Place, London WC1E 7JE, United Kingdom*
*Email of the corresponding author: m.coppens@ucl.ac.uk*

## Abstract

Cancer diagnostic and treatment research continue to expand at unprecedented rates with new and promising discoveries being published regularly. However, within the realm of exciting cancer treatment improvements often lays the overlooked need for streamlined engineering systems and efficient data analytical methods. This research looks to achieve both in the framework of improving the *ex vivo* T-cell culturing environment required for Adoptive Cell Transfer (ACT) cancer immunotherapy. A unique set of Nature Inspired Solutions (Coppens, 2021) was applied to design and analyze 9600, unique, 3D Voronoi scaffolds as potential cell culturing environments. The streamlined design process involved a complex combination of computer languages and platforms and yet, was able to design and calculate various physical parameters of the 9600 scaffolds in just a few hours. To efficiently analyze and process the scaffolds, a novel systems engineering web-based networking software (the 4D Kauffman Fitness Network) was designed. This software integrates both key geometrical characteristics of the scaffolds (such as porosity, surface area and average mean curvature) and biological aspects related to the cells (such as proliferation rate). During testing, this software efficiently processed the 9600 scaffolds in under 20 s, designing a wide variety of networks which filtered the scaffolds selected for future wet lab testing. The highly adaptable and accessible nature of this software provides multiple potential applications in a wide range of scientific, data management and business sectors.

**Keywords**: Cancer Immunotherapy, Process Management, Network Design

## 1. Introduction

### 1.1. Background

There are very few people today who have not been affected by a cancer diagnosis either personally or through a loved one. Cancer can often appear as a growing, undefeatable threat. However, the portfolio of life-saving treatments continue to expand with ever increasing success rates. One of the most promising cancer immunotherapy treatments today is the Chimeric Antigen Receptor (CAR) T-cell Adoptive Cell Transfer (ACT). During this treatment, a patient's own immune-cells (T-cells) are extracted, proliferated, and activated *ex vivo*, genetically engineered to attack the specific tumour cells and then re-infused back into the patient. One of the main challenges with this treatment is the large number of activated T-cells required to proliferate (Jin et al., 2021). Currently, *ex vivo* T-cell culturing environments are often 2D, which neglect to facilitate the 3D mechanical and physical interactions required for efficient T-cell proliferation and activation (Jensen & Teng, 2020). We posit that a holistic, systems approach is essential.

By applying the Nature Inspired Solution (NIS) methodology developed at the UCL Centre for Nature-Inspired Engineering (Coppens, 2021), over 9000 unique, lymph node inspired, small-world, 3D T-cell culturing scaffolds have been designed.

A small-world network is a graph which requires a small number of steps to progress from one node to any other node within the network. This small-world feature is mathematically demonstrated through sigma ($\sigma$), a combination of the path length between nodes and a clustering coefficient, where $\sigma > 1$ shows a small-world network (Humphries et al, 2008). Examining the network topology of the fibroblastic reticular cell network (FRCN) found in the lymph nodes, Novkovic et al. demonstrated how the FRCN had $\sigma > 1$ and a number of vertices approximated by the following equation:

$$v(6.52 * 10^{-5}) = x \qquad [1]$$

where v was the volume of the design space and x was the approximate number of vertices (Novkovic et al., 2016). Therefore, a small-world network, 3D scaffold was designed. The breadth of scaffolds examined as potential cell culturing environments was then expanded upon to efficiently streamline the design and analysis process. A Voronoi pattern was chosen as the next structural type to be examined due to the similarities in network structure to the FRCN found in the lymph node.

### 1.2. Voronoi Structure and Lloyd's Algorithm

Voronoi diagrams are designed by populating a defined space (such as a square or cube) with a certain number of points. Lines are then drawn at average distances between adjacent points resulting in a collection of Voronoi cells. For this research, twenty orientations (seeds) of each of the 3D Voronoi scaffolds generated from 5-17 points were designed. Lloyd's "relaxation" algorithm was then applied to each of those scaffolds to produce a larger set of structures with differing geometric and topological parameters.

Lloyd's algorithm is a popular classification algorithm that was first designed by Stuart P. Lloyd in 1982 (Lloyd, 1982). This algorithm has since been applied in a wide variety of fields, including astronomy (Ordovás-Pascual & Sánchez Almeida, 2014) and biology (Ralf-Herwig et al., 1999). Applied to the designed Voronoi scaffolds, Lloyd's algorithm iteratively averages the volume of each Voronoi cell within the 3D structure and repositions the Voronoi generating point to the centre of the average volume. Over the course of a number of iterations, a "relaxed" state is achieved where no further iterations will shift the Voronoi's generating points. For this research, 40 iterations were selected for each Voronoi scaffold; very little change was noticed after about 15 iterations. Therefore, the combination of 12 different selections of Voronoi generating points, each with 20 different seeds, each with 40 Lloyd iterations, resulted in the 9600 Voronoi scaffolds designed.

### 1.3. The Streamlined Design Process

The process involved in designing and calculating the various geometric and topological parameters for each of the 9600 scaffolds required a combination of code written in the Grasshopper plugin of the Rhino software (McNeel, 2010), Python and R. This highly complex, multi-step procedure was efficiently streamlined to be capable of designing and calculating around 10 different geometric and topological parameters for 9600 Voronoi scaffolds in just a few hours. This process along with the specific parameters calculated will be discussed further in Section 2.

### 1.4. The 4D Kauffman Fitness Network

The pure magnitude of scaffolds being designed required an innovative computational method to analyze and process the parameters calculated for each of the scaffolds. Therefore, a novel, web-based data analytical method, inspired by Stuart Kauffman's NK fitness landscape, was designed (Kauffman, 1993). Kauffman visually demonstrated the likely evolutionary path of a series of simple proteins by stating each protein as a node in a network where edges were drawn between proteins of similar amino acid composition (Kauffman, 1993). Fitness parameters (such as the life span of the protein) were listed for each protein, such that, for any protein selected, it was possible to track the various evolutionary paths likely to occur for a protein to achieve a higher fitness and evolutionary state. Applying this methodology, where scaffolds were treated as the nodes and the various parameters calculated as the criteria by which the edges were drawn, a 4D Kauffman Fitness Network was designed. During testing, this software efficiently and successfully processed the 9600 scaffolds, designing a wide selection of networks which filtered the scaffolds selected for wet lab testing. This software, along with how it was applied, will be discussed in more detail in Section 3.

## 2. The Scaffold Design Process Journey

### 2.1. The Map

Every successful journey requires an informative map, and such was the case for these Voronoi scaffolds. Figure 1 demonstrates the various stages of the Voronoi scaffold's design and calculation process. The following sections will provide further information into the process systems required for each of the steps visualized in Figure 1.

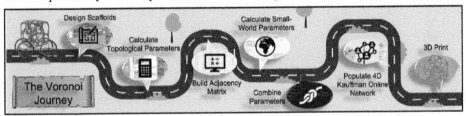

**Figure 1:** A map of the various steps taken during the design of the Voronoi scaffolds.

### 2.2 The Design

Voronoi structures, based off varying numbers of generating points, were iterated 40 times using Lloyd's algorithm to create a collection of similar and yet unique Voronoi structures. This design code was originally written in a visual programming language (VPL). However, the VPL code included over 50 separate components and, as Table 1 demonstrates, the computational process time was considerable in view of the large number of Voronoi structures to be designed. Therefore, this code was transferred into a Python plugin component within the VPL which was subsequently parallelized. Traditionally, Grasshopper executes code on a single thread, therefore, the parallelization of the code had to be completed through a Python plugin package which was capable of multi-threading the code. Parallelizing within the Python plugin of Grasshopper initially provided a considerable challenge as the Python version within Rhino is locked in at version 2.7. It was also important to distinguish at what point the code could be parallelized as the Lloyd algorithm iterations required the Voronoi pattern from the previous iteration. However, once the code was adequately parallelized over the 64 CPU cores, this resulted in a 2- to 3-fold increase in efficiency (as shown in Table 1) which ensured 9600 Voronoi scaffolds were designed and their parameters calculated, in just over an hour.

| Coding Type | Number of Structures Generated | Time (s) | Avg. Time per Structure (s) |
|---|---|---|---|
| VPL | 12 | 17.5 | 1.49 |
| Python *(code parallelized)* | 12 | 6.2 | 0.52 |
| VPL | 40 | 55.5 | 1.39 |
| Python *(code parallelized)* | 40 | 19.3 | 0.48 |
| Python *(code parallelized)* | 800 | 477.3 | 0.60 |

**Table 1:** The average time the computer required to complete the various parallelized and non-parallelized codes in seconds. Three trials of each calculation were completed with the average times appearing in the table above. Visual programming language has been abbreviated to VPL.

### 2.3 Mathematical Properties

In order to comprehensively understand and examine the scaffolds, a wide selection of the geometric and topological features of the Voronoi scaffolds were calculated. These included the porosity, surface area, average mean curvature, the number of generating points, the number of vertices, the number of edges, a topological parameter (the average number of edges connected to the vertices), Euler's characteristic and the minimum, maximum and average edge length. All of these were included in the Python code shown in Table 1 allowing any initial calculation errors to be easily changed and re-calculated for the thousands of scaffolds. This would also allow any future geometric, topological or physical parameters to be added to the code and efficiently calculated for all the scaffolds. In addition to this list of calculations, an adjacency matrix was also calculated for a selection of the scaffolds. This adjacency matrix was required to calculate the small-world parameter of sigma ($\sigma$) for each of the scaffolds. Table 2 shows an example of the parameters calculated for one of the Voronoi scaffolds.

| Points | Seed | Iteration | Min EL | Max EL | Avg. EL | SA |
|---|---|---|---|---|---|---|
| 13 | 5 | 0 | 0.0263μm | 86.7μm | 31.5μm | 60600μm² |
| **Vertices** | **Edges** | **Euler** | **Topology** | **Porosity** | **Sigma** | **AMC** |
| 65 | 126 | 14 | 3.88 | 83.5% | 2.13 | -0.0751 |

**Table 2:** The various topological and geometric parameters calculated for a Voronoi structure generated from 13 points before any Lloyd algorithm iterations. The abbreviated titles are edge length (EL), surface area (SA) and average mean curvature (AMC).

## 3. 4D Kauffman Fitness Network

### 3.1. The Design

As discussed in Section 1.4, a networking software was designed to assist in analyzing and processing the 9600 Voronoi scaffolds. Designing this networking software required satisfying a variety of user and systems parameters. Firstly, the software needed to be capable of handling 9600 unique environments with around 10 separate topological characteristics. Secondly, the platform needed to allow for user integration and adaptability so networks and graphs could be re-designed based off prioritizing different geometric parameters. Thirdly, these new iterations of the networks and graphs needed to be effectively processed and displayed for user ease and efficiency. Finally, this data needed to be easy to export in a workable format. To satisfy these various parameters, an online, web-based platform written in Python was selected. The web-based environment was chosen as this would be highly user friendly and allow the software to be easily applied in other sectors outside of computational research.

Initially the Python code, cycling through the dozen Excel files containing the 9600 scaffolds, was unable to produce an online network capable of redesigning, based off of user inputs, without crashing. It was only when each scaffold was redefined as a unique node, with its geometric and topological characteristics listed within the node's dictionary, that the software began to operate smoothly. This was likely due to each scaffold being simplified to one unit (a single node) rather than a series of 10 separate data units (1 for each of the characteristics). This node data was also highly efficient in being converted back into a data frame to produce a downloadable Excel file (something it completed in a matter of seconds).

### 3.2. The Application

Although the 4D Kauffman Fitness Network was capable of processing thousands of scaffolds, data gleaned from the graphs and networks produced, resulted in a significant filtering of the scaffolds. Of the 9600 Voronoi scaffolds designed, 952 contained $65\pm2$ vertices (Equation 1) and only 73 of those had $\sigma$ values greater than 1 (small-world networks). These 73 were further narrowed down to 36 "unique" scaffolds, as scaffolds designed from later Lloyd iterations were often indistinguishable and, therefore, the software combined them into a single node. Figure 2 demonstrates one of the generated online web-pages produced from the 4D Kauffman Fitness Network. Each node in the network on the right is a scaffold that corresponds to a point in the graph on the left. Two separate clusters can be clearly visualized in both the network and the graph demonstrating which scaffolds have similar surface area, average mean curvature and porosity. Network cluster (a) and (b) correspond to the circles (a) and (b) in the graph.

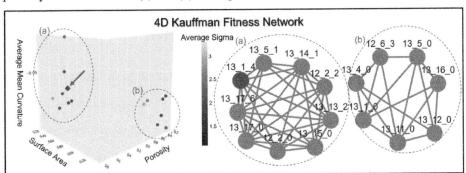

**Figure 2:** A generated 4D Kauffman Fitness Network showing 2 clusters of scaffolds in both the graph and network (indicated by the circles (a) & (b)) demonstrating the scaffolds similar in surface area, average mean curvature and porosity. The blue scaffold has been selected ("clicked-on" in the software) with its respective point highlighted as diamond, and shown with a red arrow, in the graph on the left. The labels for the nodes in the network on the right are the scaffold names (given as X_Y_Z) which denote the number of Voronoi generating points (X), the seed number with which the orientation of those points was saved (Y) and the number of Lloyd's algorithm iterations (Z).

## 4. Future Work

Future applications for both the design process and analysis software are now being explored. Firstly, the design process will be applied to other structural patterns including Lattice and Delaunay structures. Secondly, the analysis software will be utilized to select the scaffolds to be 3D printed and tested with live T-cells for cancer immunotherapy applications. Finally, the 4D Kauffman Fitness Network can be tested and applied in other scientific and business sectors where collections of similar environments or products need to be processed and graphically analyzed.

## 5. Conclusion

The nature-inspired solution methodology applied to both the 3D T-cell culturing environments (through a lymph-node inspired scaffold design) and the software designed for the analysis of the scaffolds (inspired through Kauffman's evolutionary protein mapping) provided creative insight into the unique engineering solutions described. The computational pipeline designed and calculated 10 separate topological and geometric parameters for 9600 Voronoi scaffolds in under a few hours. These scaffolds were then filtered to 36 unique, small-world scaffolds using the novel 4D Kauffman Fitness Network with new networks and graphs being generated in a few seconds. The efficient design pipeline and analysis software provided the foundational framework to test these 3D scaffolds as *ex vivo* T-cell culturing environments for CAR ACT cancer immunotherapy. The software presented here has wider applicability for systems engineering research, beyond cancer immunotherapy.

## References

M.-O. Coppens, 2021, Nature-Inspired Chemical Engineering for Process Intensification, Annu. Rev. Chem. Biomol. Eng., 12, 1, 187–215.

M. Humphries, K. Gurney, 2008, Network 'Small-World-Ness': A Quantitative Method for Determining Canonical Network Equivalence, PLoS ONE, 3, 4.

C. Jensen & Y. Teng, 2020, Is It Time to Start Transitioning From 2D to 3D Cell Culture?, Frontiers in Molecular Biosciences, 7, 33.

Z. Jin, X. Li, X. Zhang, P. DeSousa, T. Xu, & A. Wu, 2021, Engineering the fate and function of human T-Cells via 3D bioprinting, Biofabrication, 13, 3.

S. A. Kauffman, 1993, The origins of order: self-organization and selection in evolution, Oxford University Press.

S. P. Lloyd, 1982. Least Squares Quantization in PCM, IEEE Transactions on information theory, 28, 2.

M. Novkovic, L. Onder, J. Cupovic, J. Abe, D. Bomze, V. Cremasco, E. Scandella, J. v. Stein, G. Bocharov, S. J. Turley, & B. Ludewig, 2016, Topological Small-World Organization of the Fibroblastic Reticular Cell Network Determines Lymph Node Functionality, PLoS Biol., 14, 7, e1002515.

I. Ordovás-Pascual, & J. Sánchez Almeida, 2014, A fast version of the k-means classification algorithm for astronomical applications, Astronomy and Astrophysics, 565.

A. Ralf-Herwig, J. Poustka, C. Müller, C. Bull, H. Lehrach, & J. O'Brien, 1999, Large-Scale Clustering of cDNA-Fingerprinting Data, Genome Research, 9, 11, 1093.

R. McNeel, 2010, Rhinoceros 3D, Version 6.0, Robert McNeel & amp, Associates, Seattle, WA.

Antonis Kokossis, Michael C. Georgiadis, Efstratios N. Pistikopoulos (Eds.)
PROCEEDINGS OF THE 33rd European Symposium on Computer Aided Process Engineering
(ESCAPE33), June 18-21, 2023, Athens, Greece

# Developing Cole-Cole model for *Bacillus subtilis* fermentation

Kumar Rajan Gopa[a], Tom Wenzel[a], Sankalp Jena[a], Supasuda Assawajaruwan[b], Valentin Khaydarov[a], Leon Urbas[a]

*[a]Technische Universität Dresden, Dresden 01062, Germany*
*[b]Evonik Operations GmbH, Rodenbacher Chaussee 4, 63457 Hanau, Germany*
*kumar.rajan_gopa@tu-dresden.de*

## Abstract

During the fermentation of *Bacillus Subtilis* it is unperceivable to observe the formation of spores since, following the evolution of spores is time consuming due to various sampling and analytical procedures. Dielectric spectroscopy has shown promising results, where the measured permittivity is correlated with the cell concentration. Most of the existing works focus on determining cell concentration and not on the determination of spores. In this work, we develop a permittivity model for cells in the fermentation solution based on the Cole-Cole equations that can be used to detect the sporulation phase in future work. Utilizing the data from several fermentation runs of *Bacillus Subtilis*, a superposition hypothesis is proposed. In this hypothesis, the model equations from Cole and Cole (1941) are used and the theoretical permittivity response of the cells is calculated. As a first step, the Cole-Cole model is developed, and the modeled permittivity values are fitted to the measured data and the results are analyzed.

**Keywords**: Cole-Cole, Permittivity, Sporulation, Superposition

## 1. Introduction

*Bacillus Subtilis* is an industrially significant gram-positive spore-forming bacteria which is used in the large-scale production of various bioproducts (Abi *et al.*, 2010). The biological system along with the spore formation and evolution mechanism is complex and difficult to model. In addition, the drawbacks of offline measurement like longer and infrequent sampling make the online monitoring and detection of spores highly desirable. One of the most promising online monitoring techniques is the dielectric spectroscopy, especially in its scanning frequency mode. There have been several works where the permittivity measurements have been found to reveal information related to changes in morphological phases. Opel, Li and Amanullah (2010) and Randek and Mandenius (2020) found the influence of cell sizes on the permittivity data.

In general, there are several modeling approaches applied on the permittivity data obtained from dielectric spectroscopy. Among them Konakovsky *et al.* (2015) used principal component analysis to predict the viable cell concentration (VCC). Dabros *et al.* (2009) applied Cole-Cole modeling and compared the results with linear and multivariate regression models. These works establish Cole-Cole modeling as a viable method for modeling cell concentrations from permittivity data.

Since the bacterial spores are much smaller and their presence is difficult to detect, works on the application of dielectric spectroscopy and identifying the presence of spores are rarely present. Abi *et al.* (2010) focused on the *Bacillus* species and identified the physiological phases using the scanning frequency data. Studied parameters are capacitance, conductivity, and Cole-Cole parameters to monitor and predict the effect of operating conditions. In our study to determine the effect of spores on the permittivity data, we have applied a superposition hypothesis in conjunction with Cole-Cole modeling. This methodology is expected to result in a residual permittivity that can be indicative of the spore dynamics. This will enable the online monitoring of sporulation and to gain insight about the current fermentation phase in progress thereby reducing the time and effort required for sampling and other analytical procedures.

## 2. Theory

During the fermentation process of *Bacillus Subtilis*, the bacteria present in the culture consume the nutrients and undergo cell division. This is known as the vegetative cycle. In the initial period of fermentation, the culture broth has enough nutrients, resulting in exponential growth of bacteria. Once the nutrient depletion occurs, the cells cannot maintain the exponential growth rate. Normally this would result in a slowdown and the cells which are deprived of the nutrients will start dying. This phase is known as the stationary phase. In case of bacterial species like *Bacillus Subtilis*, a depletion of nutrients or any other adverse condition leads to a secondary cycle. This is called the sporulation cycle where a part of the population preserves its genetic material by forming dormant spores. In the last phase, a part of the vegetative cell population may convert itself into spores and the remaining cell population undergoes cell lysis. This phase is known as the death phase.

### 2.1. Dielectric spectroscopy

Over the years dielectric spectroscopy has been identified as a viable method for the online detection of cells (Teixeira *et al.*, 2009). It relies on the principle that under the influence of an electric field an exposed medium can act as an electric capacitor – in this case the cells and spores. This permittivity is measured by the probe. Since the amount of electric charge stored is related to the cell volume and the cell size this is a sufficient indicator on detecting the cells (Markx and Davey, 1999).

Dielectric spectroscopy could be conducted in two modes: 1. Dual frequency mode where a single frequency and a baseline frequency are used in parallel. 2. The scanning frequency mode where the permittivity is measured over a range of frequencies called the beta frequency (Dabros *et al.*, 2009). In the present case we use scanning frequency mode that consists of 25 frequencies ranging from 50 kHz to 20000 kHz that are scanned in one time step.

### 2.2. Experimental

*Bacillus subtilis* strain 168 (DSM 23778) was applied in this study. The inoculum was prepared in CASO-Bouillon as a pre-culture medium. Then it was inoculated into the minimal medium containing glucose as a carbon source. Batch cultivation was carried out in a 2-L stirred tank reactor with 1-L working volume. The 100 mL pre-culture was incubated at 30°C for 8 h and then it was inoculated into the bioreactor. The fermentation was run for 48 h at different temperature profiles. The bioreactor was equipped with dielectric sensor (Futura, Aber) to gain an insight of fermentation in real time. Temperature and glucose levels were changed for each experiment, with glucose levels in the range of 12.5-20 g/l and temperature levels in the range of 25 °C to 45°C. For some experiments multiple temperature changes were carried out during the course of the fermentation process. The following data were used:

1. Spectral data – Permittivity measurement with sampling rate of around 2 per minute and spans over 25 frequencies from 50 kHz to 20000 kHz.
2. Offline data – Cell/spore count and the substrate added. About 14 samples.

Maskow *et al.* (2008) have pointed out that other intracellular products could be detected from the dielectric spectroscopy signals. We expect spores to be such products that could be detected. We hypothesize that the residual permittivity between the measured and (cell-) modeled data can provide information about the spore concentration.

$$\varepsilon_{sensor}(\omega) = \varepsilon_{cells}(\omega, N_{cells}) + \varepsilon_{spores}(\omega, N_{spores}) + u \tag{1}$$

Where $\varepsilon$ is the total permittivity of the fermentation solution [pF/cm], $\omega$ is the angular frequency [rad/s], $N$ is the number density of either cells or spores [CFU/ml], and $u$ is an unknown factor. An Illustration of the proposed superposition hypothesis is shown in Figure 1 on the left side. We propose that the sensor data can be modeled and fitted during the growth phase ideally since there is no contribution of spores to the permittivity signal. To model the permittivity of the cells we use a spherical cell model without cell size distribution. These assumptions could lead to a model error, since the cells are not ideally spherical, and their size is distributed. In order to compensate this model error, a correction factor $\theta_0$ is introduced. We assume this linear correction factor as a first approach. The permittivity of the cells is then described as the product of the spherical cell model and the correction factor:

$$\varepsilon_{cells}(\omega) = \theta_0 \, \varepsilon_{model}(\omega, N_{cells}) \tag{2}$$

Using the approach from Maskow *et al.* (2008) the growth phase can be defined as the time span until the maximum of the permittivity is reached (see Figure 1). Following the equation system for Cole-Cole model present in Dabros *et al.* (2009), the permittivity equation (3) is used.

$$\varepsilon_{model}(\omega, N_{cells}) = \Delta\varepsilon \frac{1 + \left(\frac{\omega}{\omega_c}\right)^{1-\alpha} \sin\left(\frac{\pi}{2}\alpha\right)}{1 + \left(\frac{\omega}{\omega_c}\right)^{2-2\alpha} + 2\left(\frac{\omega}{\omega_c}\right)^{1-\alpha} \sin\left(\frac{\pi}{2}\alpha\right)} + \varepsilon_\infty \tag{3}$$

Where $\Delta\varepsilon$ is the span in which the permittivity signal varies, $\varepsilon_\infty$ is the permittivity at infinite frequency, $\omega_c$ is the critical angular frequency where half of $\Delta\varepsilon$ is reached and $\alpha$ is the empirical Cole-Cole factor. The Cole-Cole $\alpha$ for biological cells was reported to be in the range 0.1 – 0.2 (Dabros *et al.*, 2009). In the current work, a constant value throughout the batch process of 0.1 is used. The calculation of the constant $\Delta\varepsilon$ is based on the Pauly-Schwan spherical cell model.

$$\Delta\varepsilon = \frac{3 \, N_{cells} \, \pi \, r_{cells}^4 \, C_m}{\varepsilon_0} \tag{4}$$

Where $r_{cells}$ is the volume equivalent diameter of the cells, $C_m$ is the membrane permittivity, and $\varepsilon_0$ is the vacuum permittivity. $C_m$ is assumed to 0.01 F/cm$^2$ Yardley *et al.* (2000). For the rod shaped bacteria the radius of the volume equivalent idealized sphere of 0.78 μm was used (Errington and Aart, 2020). As suggested by Downey *et al.* (2014) an exponential growth is expected and validated with offline measurements.

$$N_{cells}(t) = N_{cells,t=0} e^{kt} \tag{5}$$

# 3. Results and discussion

## 3.1. Implementation of the Cole-Cole-model

In our approach we use the assumptions mentioned to determine the value of $\Delta\varepsilon$. For $\alpha$ a value of 0.1 is assumed. As shown in Figure 1 (right), the values for $\omega_c$ and $\varepsilon_\infty$ are taken from the graph. For $\varepsilon_\infty$ the permittivity value for the highest frequency is used. This procedure assumes that there is no significant change in the permittivity when the frequency is increased. To calculate $\Delta\varepsilon$ information cell size and number are required. About 13 offline measurements were obtained during a 50-hour fermentation batch. To increase the number of the data points exponential curve fitting during the growth phase is applied.

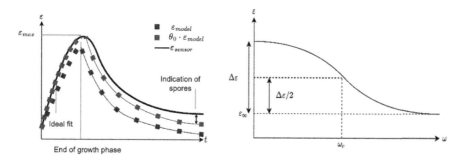

Figure 1: Illustration of the superposition hypothesis (left) and graphical representation of the Cole-Cole parameters (right).

## 3.2. Fitting part – growth phase

Three batches KW1, KW2 and KW3 were considered for analysis. For KW1, the starting conditions were 12.5 g/l glucose and 30 °C temperature. No temperature change was made during the experiment. KW2 and KW3 included multiple temperature changes, with KW2 having a starting glucose concentration of 12.5 g/l and KW3 with 20 g/l. This ensured that each of the considered batch had differing batch conditions. The data set for the cell numbers can be increased when exponential curve fitting for equation (5) is used. Figure 2 compares the measured and the modelled permittivity during the growth phase at two frequencies for the batch number KW1. In a first step the Cole-Cole model $\varepsilon_{model}$ without the fitting factor $\theta_0$ is shown.

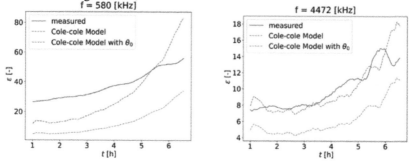

Figure 2: Permittivity data measured, model for $g_1$ and extended model for different frequencies at KW1.

As outlined in the superposition hypothesis the model can be fitted better to the data when the factor $\theta_0$ is introduced. It can be shown that there is a significant difference between the Cole-Cole model and the sensor data. We assume that the deviation is mostly down to either the inaccurate spherical model or the cell size assumptions. In Table 1 the corresponding values for $\theta_0$ and the root mean square error (RMSE) before (0) and after (1) the introduction of $\theta_0$ is shown for the fermentation batches KW1, KW2 and KW3. The proposed procedure shows that the modeled data after the introduction of $\theta_0$ have a better fit at higher frequencies. Although all three batches had different conditions, all three achieved better fit with this method. The lowest RMSE1 and $\theta_0$ closest to one were obtained for KW1 where no temperature variation was applied. No perfect fit for $\varepsilon_{cells}$ is achieved during the growth phase, but the mean error has been significantly reduced. The temperature change applied in the initial hours might have caused a higher RMSE0 values for KW2 and KW3. The reasons for deviations (RMSE1) could be due to imprecise assumptions, especially for the cell radius.

| KW | 1 | | | 2 | | | 3 | | |
|---|---|---|---|---|---|---|---|---|---|
| f [kHz] | 580 | 1120 | 4472 | 580 | 1120 | 4472 | 580 | 1120 | 4472 |
| $\theta_0$ [-] | 2.5 | 2.3 | 1.6 | 4.2 | 3.8 | 1.6 | 7.7 | -0.8 | 0.6 |
| RMSE0 [-] | 25.3 | 18.5 | 4.0 | 34.4 | 23.7 | 3.9 | 38.5 | 21.4 | 6.4 |
| RMSE1 [-] | 13.2 | 9.3 | 1.5 | 7.0 | 3.7 | 1.8 | 17.6 | 34.5 | 5.4 |

Table 1: RMSE values for the scalar factor $\theta_0$ before and after optimization

In the following work, this approach will be extended to the remaining time periods of the fermentation batch till the end of the batch. The estimated $\theta_0$ will be applied in equation 1 to obtain the residual permittivity that could be analyzed to establish the presence of spores.

## 4. Conclusion

Cole-Cole modeling was identified as a suitable method that can be used to model the permittivity during the fermentation of bacteria. Using the superposition hypothesis and Cole-Cole modeling, an alternate model to describe the fermentation process of *Bacillus subtilis* was developed and the various components that contribute towards the total permittivity of the system were outlined. The linear correction parameter $\theta_0$ has been used in this first approach to compensate for the inaccuracies in the cell model. It is observed that the modelled permittivity is in better agreement with the sensor data for higher frequencies. This work will be extended in the next stage to calculate the residual permittivity which might provide information on the development of spores, especially after the growth phase. Further work with increased number of offline measurements would provide a better fit with the current model. This model could be extended to determine the cell radius of the species more precisely. Since *Bacillus subtilis* is ellipsoidal in nature, models other than the spherical shell model could be used to improve the model fit.

## Acknowledgements:

We want to thank the BMWK (German Federal Ministry of Economic Affairs and Climate Action, Support codes 01MK20014T) for their financial support.

# References

Abi, A., Sarrafzadeh, M. H., Mehrnia, M. R., & Ghommidh, C. (2010). Application of dielectric permittivity measurements in physiological state monitoring of bacillus subtilis culture. 2010 2nd International Conference on Chemical, Biological and Environmental Engineering, 26–29. https://doi.org/10.1109/ICBEE.2010.5650641

Cole, K. S., & Cole, R. H. (1941). Dispersion and Absorption in Dielectrics I. Alternating Current Characteristics. The Journal of Chemical Physics, 9(4), 341–351. https://doi.org/10.1063/1.1750906

Dabros, M., Dennewald, D., Currie, D. J., Lee, M. H., Todd, R. W., Marison, I. W., & von Stockar, U. (2009). Cole–Cole, linear and multivariate modeling of capacitance data for on-line monitoring of biomass. Bioprocess and Biosystems Engineering, 32(2), Art. 2. https://doi.org/10.1007/s00449-008-0234-4

Downey, B. J., Graham, L. J., Breit, J. F., & Glutting, N. K. (2014). A novel approach for using dielectric spectroscopy to predict viable cell volume (VCV) in early process development. Biotechnology Progress, 30(2), 479–487. https://doi.org/10.1002/btpr.1845

Errington, J. and Aart, L.T. van der (2020) 'Microbe Profile: Bacillus subtilis: model organism for cellular development, and industrial workhorse: This article is part of the Microbe Profiles collection.', Microbiology, 166(5), pp. 425–427. Available at: https://doi.org/10.1099/mic.0.000922.

Konakovsky, V., Yagtu, A., Clemens, C., Müller, M., Berger, M., Schlatter, S., & Herwig, C. (2015). Universal Capacitance Model for Real-Time Biomass in Cell Culture. Sensors, 15(9), Art. 9. https://doi.org/10.3390/s150922128

Markx, G. H., & Davey, C. L. (1999). The dielectric properties of biological cells at radiofrequencies: Applications in biotechnology. Enzyme and Microbial Technology, 25(3), Art. 3. https://doi.org/10.1016/S0141-0229(99)00008-3

Maskow, T., Röllich, A., Fetzer, I., Ackermann, J.-U., & Harms, H. (2008). On-line monitoring of lipid storage in yeasts using impedance spectroscopy. Journal of Biotechnology, 135(1), Art. 1. https://doi.org/10.1016/j.jbiotec.2008.02.014

Opel, C. F., Li, J., & Amanullah, A. (2010). Quantitative modeling of viable cell density, cell size, intracellular conductivity, and membrane capacitance in batch and fed-batch CHO processes using dielectric spectroscopy. Biotechnology Progress, NA-NA. https://doi.org/10.1002/btpr.425

Randek, J., & Mandenius, C.-F. (2020). In situ scanning capacitance sensor with spectral analysis reveals morphological states in cultures for production of biopharmaceuticals. Sensors and Actuators B: Chemical, 313, 128052. https://doi.org/10.1016/j.snb.2020.128052

Teixeira, A. P., Oliveira, R., Alves, P. M., & Carrondo, M. J. T. (2009). Advances in on-line monitoring and control of mammalian cell cultures: Supporting the PAT initiative. Biotechnology Advances, 27(6), Art. 6. https://doi.org/10.1016/j.biotechadv.2009.05.003

Yardley, J. E., Kell, D. B., Barrett, J., & Davey, C. L. (2000). On-Line, Real-Time Measurements of Cellular Biomass using Dielectric Spectroscopy. Biotechnology and Genetic Engineering Reviews, 17(1), 3–36. https://doi.org/10.1080/02648725.2000.10647986

Antonis Kokossis, Michael C. Georgiadis, Efstratios N. Pistikopoulos (Eds.)
PROCEEDINGS OF THE 33rd European Symposium on Computer Aided Process Engineering
(ESCAPE33), June 18-21, 2023, Athens, Greece
© 2023 Elsevier B.V. All rights reserved. http://dx.doi.org/10.1016/B978-0-443-15274-0.50432-7

# Improving accuracy scores of neural network driven QSAR models of mutagenicity

Alexander D. Kalian,[a] Emilio Benfenati,[b] Olivia J. Osborne,[c] Jean-Lou C.M. Dorne,[d] David Gott,[c] Claire Potter,[c] Miao Guo,[a*] Christer Hogstrand,[a*]

[a]King's College London, Franklin-Wilkins Building, 150 Stamford St., London SE1 9NH, United Kingdom
[b]IRCCS - Istituto di Ricerche Farmacologiche Mario Negri, Via Mario Negri 2, 20156 Milano, Italy
[c]Food Standards Agency, 70 Petty France, London SW1H 9EX, United Kingdom
[d]European Food Safety Authority (EFSA), Via Carlo Magno 1A, 43126 Parma, Italy
*christer.hogstrand@kcl.ac.uk (CH); miao.guo@kcl.ac.uk (MG)

## Abstract

Multiple QSAR models of mutagenicity were created and compared, using knowledge graph approaches to train and test multi-layer perceptron classifiers, following dimensionality reduction from several thousand dimensions to hundreds of dimensions via principal component analysis. Such knowledge graphs were built in one case using molecular fingerprint based structural similarities, while in another case using molecular fragments found via application of the Girvan-Newman algorithm. A simple hybrid model was also explored. However, both competing QSAR models performed with comparable accuracies, with both sensitivity and specificity scores for each occurring within range of 70%. The predictions of both models were in agreement in an average of 71% of cases, meaning that each could offer a related yet notably different perspective of toxicological space; hence a simple hybrid model was trialed, which only output predictions agreed between both constituent models, which averaged at 78% accuracy.

**Keywords**: QSAR, deep-learning, neural-networks, classification, toxicology

## 1. Introduction

Food and drink products contain a variety of chemicals, of which some are intentionally present (e.g. preservatives) while others are unintentionally present (e.g. environmental contaminants) [1]. The possible risks posed by consumption of food and drink chemicals to human and animal health, are ideally evaluated via chemical risk assessments (CRAs) carried out by regulatory bodies [1]. Current CRA frameworks are overly reliant on *in-vivo* studies on live animals [1], which pose significant ethical, scientific relevancy, and scalability-based concerns for the future of this space. New Approach Methodologies (NAMs), such as Quantitative Structure-Activity Relationship (QSAR) modelling, may be used to address some of these limitations and contribute to future frameworks that regulatory bodies may utilise [2].

QSAR modelling is an *in-silico* approach which relies on the premise that molecular structures are correlated with corresponding biological activities [2]; hence, in a toxicological context, QSAR models quantify relationships between toxicological properties of molecules and quantitative metrics concerning molecular structures. There is no universally agreed upon metric for reliably quantifying molecular structures [2], however a variety of different approaches exist, such as structural similarity coefficients (SCs – which quantify structural similarities between pairs of molecules via techniques such as molecular fingerprinting [2] or alternatively applications of graph theory), as well as molecular fragmentation (of which numerous algorithms exist in order to split a molecular structure into smaller substructures, which may then be correlated with certain toxicological properties). QSAR models frequently use machine learning (ML) to construct models; in a toxicological context, this typically entails regression algorithms that can predict continuous metrics [3] (e.g. benchmark doses, for hazard assessments), however classification algorithms are more appropriate for certain endpoints that are thresholded and hence associated with discrete predictions [3] – e.g. mutagenicity is a thresholded endpoint where molecules may be assessed into discrete classes: A (strongly mutagenic), B (weakly mutagenic) and C (non-mutagenic) [4].

QSAR models of mutagenicity were compared as part of the 2014 Ames/QSAR International Challenge Project, involving a variety of rule-based QSAR frameworks such as SARpy and Toxtree, as well as statistical QSAR frameworks such as CEASAR and AMBIT. Sensitivity and specificity scores varied, however none were able to consistently surpass accuracy scores of 80% (considering both sensitivities and specificities), furthermore with many displaying imbalance across classes [4]. Neural networks (NNs) are a popular ML technique, using layers of artificial neurons with weights that may be optimised to form complex models. A 2021 study used feed-forward NNs to build a QSAR model of mutagenicity which was 84% accurate [5], while a separate 2021 study used graph convolutional NNs (GCNs) in order to obtain sensitivity scores that were consistently matching or below 70% and specificity scores that were consistently above 90% [6].

The aim of this study was to use NNs to construct and optimize novel QSAR models of mutagenicity, using data from *in-vitro* Ames mutagenicity studies. While *in-vitro* methods are NAMs that are frequently used in studies concerning mutagenicity, with certain advantages over *in-vivo* studies [2], they nonetheless continue to be limited in terms of efficiency and scalability, which *in-silico* techniques such as QSAR modelling may help address [2], as part of a potential future ecosystem of NAMs used in CRA. Furthermore, mutagenicity is a comparatively more thoroughly covered endpoint, in terms of data available in open source, as well as with literature concerning competing QSAR models [4], when compared to comparatively lesser covered endpoints such as neurotoxicity and cardiotoxicity; hence mutagenicity may serve as a more intuitive starting endpoint, for the construction and optimisation of novel QSAR models that may eventually be adapted and applied to more challenging endpoints in future.

## 2. Methods

### 2.1. SC-Based QSAR Model

The first QSAR model constructed used SCs (via molecular fingerprinting) to build a knowledge graph encoding similarities between constituent molecules of a dataset, which was then reduced in dimensionality via principal component analysis (PCA) and subsequently used to train and test a multi-layer perceptron (MLP) model.

Six SC algorithms that used molecular fingerprinting were separately used to create competing SC-based QSAR models; these were the Cosine, Tanimoto, Dice, Kulczynski, McConnaughey and Rogot-Goldberg SCs, each with their own unique methodology.

Each SC algorithm first required molecular fingerprints to be generated for each molecule, for which Morgan fingerprints were used. The Morgan fingerprinting algorithm was used as a function of the open-source cheminformatics Python library RDKit, with a specified radius of 3 and maximum number of 2048 bits. Following obtainment of Morgan fingerprints for all possible pairs of molecules, the six algorithms were each used to calculate SCs between all Morgan fingerprint pairs.

The dataset of molecules used was that associated with the 2014 Ames/QSAR International Challenge Project, with Ames mutagenicity data collected from a variety of different studies, for a variety of organic molecules provided in canonical SMILES (simplified molecular-input line-entry) notation. Following data curation measures (such as excluding molecules with inconsistencies in descriptors, or with incomplete mutagenicity data), the final dataset used in this study contained 11,268 molecules. The occurrences of A, B and C classes in the data were imbalanced, which was alleviated via combining classes A and B into a single "mutagenic" class, while assigning class C as a "non-mutagenic" class (an approach similar to those used in past studies [4]). The two classes nonetheless remained imbalanced, hence further balancing was carried out via assignment of training and testing data.

The 11,268 molecules were split into approximately 80% training data and 20% testing data, using random sampling via pseudorandom numbers, with each molecule treated as a sample to be used in an MLP classifier model. Knowledge graphs for training data were constructed, using individual molecules as nodes, connected via edges to every present node (including to themselves) and weighted according to SCs between corresponding molecule pairs. Feature vectors for each training sample molecule were derived from the weightings of edges in the knowledge graph connected to the corresponding node. Feature vectors for training data similarly contained calculated edge data to the existing nodes in the knowledge graph, effectively describing how each test sample molecule would be positioned in the knowledge graph, if included.

Each feature vector was naturally of several thousand dimensions, which would have proven problematic for training effective models with simple architectures. PCA was implemented via the Python-based ML package scikit-learn, to reduce dimensionality, while conserving as much information contained within the multidimensional data as possible. Final dimensionalities were varied between 2-220 (see Figure 2), for the sake of finding an optimal dimensionality.

The NNs used were MLP classifiers, also implemented via scikit-learn in Python, with two hidden layers containing 500 artificial neurons, while using the rectified linear unit (ReLU) activation function, along with the Adam optimisation algorithm (a stochastic gradient-based algorithm, which is typically suitable for larger datasets) for weight optimisation. The strength of the L2 regularization term was set to $1 \times 10^{-5}$, while the number of epochs was set to 1,000. All other parameters remained as default.

### 2.2. Fragmentation-Based QSAR Model

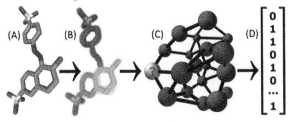

Figure 1: schematic diagram demonstrating how (A) an input molecule [7] would be (B) fragmented before (C) being placed in a graph of mutagenic/non-mutagenic molecules that shared substructures. (D) A feature vector would then be derived, based on connections.

A second QSAR model was constructed and applied to the same dataset, using knowledge graphs, PCA and MLP classifiers in an identical nature to that of the SC-based QSAR model, but instead using molecular fragmentation to construct knowledge graphs.

Fragments of molecules were obtained via consideration of canonical SMILES descriptors as molecular graphs, using graph theory (the Python library pysmiles was used to convert between canonical SMILES and Python Graph objects). Fragmentation was treated as a community detection problem, with communities of each molecular graph identified and regarded as molecular fragments via the Girvan-Newman algorithm; a widely used hierarchical community detection method available as a function of the NetworkX library of Python. The algorithm required a specified number of communities to be identified, hence a separate algorithm output ascending values for each new molecule, until all fragments found by the Girvan-Newman algorithm were within a specified size range in terms of constituent atoms (excluding hydrogen atoms). Three different size ranges were considered: 2-7, 3-12 and 3-15.

Once lists of fragments for every molecule were obtained, knowledge graphs were constructed (see Figure 1). Training and testing data assignment, as well as subsequent PCA and use of MLP classifiers, were identical to as described in Section 2.1.

### 2.3. Hybrid QSAR Model

Following training and testing of the QSAR models described in Sections 2.1 and 2.2, a simple hybrid model was explored via testing both models in parallel (with the same training data for each) and only outputting predictions that were agreed by both models. Within the hybrid model, the SC-based QSAR model used the cosine similarity, whereas the fragmentation-based QSAR model used a size range of 3-12 atoms for finding fragments. Both constituent models also used reduced dimensionalities of 100.

## 3. Results and Analysis

### 3.1. Individual QSAR Model Results

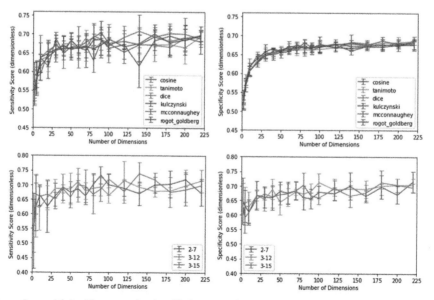

Figure 2: sensitivity (for correctly classified mutagenic molecules) and specificity (for correctly classified non-mutagenic molecules) scores, for the SC-based QSAR model (top row) and the fragmentation-based QSAR model (bottom row).

As observed from Figure 2, increased dimensionalities initially improved accuracy scores, as higher dimensionalities of data from knowledge graphs were presumably necessary for sufficiently conserving information regarding a complex toxicological space. For the SC-based model, convergence within range of 70% accuracy was apparent from approximately 100 dimensions onwards, as sufficient dimensionality was reached and inclusion of further dimensions contributed comparatively less to describing the complex toxicological space. Convergence for the fragmentation-based model appeared to have occurred less extremely and at lower dimensionalities. No consistent differences in performance were visible, concerning different SC algorithms or fragment size ranges (the latter may indicate that smaller substructures could have been responsible for causing mutagenic/non-mutagenic effects), however it should be noted that higher variances were generally present for sensitivity scores than for specificity scores; this is deemed to be due to the data equalisation measures that were performed, which successfully equalised the average sensitivity and specificity scores, but however caused greater numbers of non-mutagenic test samples to give rise to greater certainty in specificity scores than for sensitivity scores. The fragmentation-based model displayed marginally higher converged accuracy scores, than for the SC-based QSAR model, however the two models are overall deemed as closely comparable in performance.

### 3.2. Hybrid QSAR Model Results

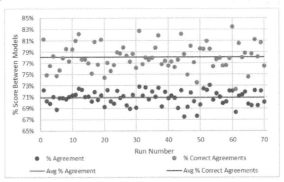

Figure 3: percentage agreements between constituent models, along with overall hybrid model performance, over 70 repeat runs.

Figure 3 demonstrates that an average of 71% ± 1% of predictions were agreed by constituent models, which gave rise to a hybrid model with an average accuracy score of 78% ± 2%. It was furthermore found that percentage agreement between the models was strongly positively correlated with percentage accuracy of the resulting hybrid model, with a Pearson correlation coefficient calculated at 0.8.

### 4. Conclusions

Our results suggested that the novel QSAR approaches explored were effective in modelling mutagenicity. Dimensionality reduction via PCA was a critical step for improving accuracy scores, via better enabling MLP classifiers to navigate a multidimensional toxicological space. Explored parameters such as individual SC algorithms, along with searched fragment sizes, were found to be less relevant for improving accuracy scores. Compared to existing QSAR models in this space, the two individual QSAR models underperformed, however the hybrid model formed by both outperformed certain studies and matched others in average accuracy score [4-6]. Accuracy scores may be further improved by developing additional constituent QSAR models for the final hybrid model, as well as exploring parameter optimization for the NNs involved, alongside novel NN architectures and potentially more advanced and specialised NNs than MLPs. Exploration of differing dimensionality reduction algorithms may also prove beneficial, especially non-linear techniques such as autoencoders and locally linear embedding, which may perform better in preserving any complex multidimensional decision boundaries between classes that may potentially exist in higher dimensional toxicological space.

## References

[1] J.C. Larsen, 2006. Risk assessment of chemicals in European traditional foods. Trends in Food Science & Technology, 17(9), pp.471-481.

[2] S.E. Escher, et al., 2019. Towards grouping concepts based on new approach methodologies in chemical hazard assessment: the read-across approach of the EU-ToxRisk project. Archives of toxicology, 93(12), pp.3643-3667.

[3] P. Gramatica, 2013. On the development and validation of QSAR models. In Computational toxicology, pp. 499-526.

[4] M. Honma et al., 2019. Improvement of quantitative structure–activity relationship (QSAR) tools for predicting Ames mutagenicity: outcomes of the Ames/QSAR International Challenge Project. Mutagenesis, 34(1), pp.3-16.

[5] R. Kumar et al., 2021. A deep neural network–based approach for prediction of mutagenicity of compounds. Environmental Science and Pollution Research, 28(34), pp.47641-47650.

[6] C. Hung et al., 2021. QSAR modeling without descriptors using graph convolutional neural networks: the case of mutagenicity prediction. Molecular diversity, 25(3), pp.1283-1299.

[7] National Center for Biotechnology Information (2022). PubChem Compound Summary for CID 17730, Sunset Yellow FCF. Retrieved December 8, 2022 from https://pubchem.ncbi.nlm.nih.gov/compound/Sunset-Yellow-FCF.

## Acknowledgements

This work was supported by grants from the Biotechnology and Biological Sciences Research Council [grant number BB/T008709/1] and the Food Standards Agency [Agency Project FS900120]

The views expressed in this article do not reflect the views of the European Food Safety Authority (EFSA) and/or are a reflection of the views of the authors only.

This paper aims to contribute to the international network on Advancing the Pace of Chemical Risk Assessment (APCRA), to contribute to the use of New Approach Methodologies (NAMs) in chemical risk assessment and ultimately reduce animal testing.

Antonis Kokossis, Michael C. Georgiadis, Efstratios N. Pistikopoulos (Eds.)
PROCEEDINGS OF THE 33rd European Symposium on Computer Aided Process Engineering
(ESCAPE33), June 18-21, 2023, Athens, Greece
© 2023 Elsevier B.V. All rights reserved.  http://dx.doi.org/10.1016/B978-0-443-15274-0.50433-9

# Investigating tunable experiment variable effects on hiPSC-CMs maturation via unsupervised learning

Shenbageshwaran Rajendiran, Mohammadjafar Hashemi, Ferdous Frinklea,
Nathan Young, Elizabeth Lipke, Selen Cremaschi*

*Department of Chemical Engineering, Auburn University, Auburn, AL 36849, USA*
*selen-cremaschi@auburn.edu*

## Abstract

Cardiomyocytes (CMs) are heart cells responsible for heart contraction and relaxation. CMs can be derived from human induced pluripotent stem cells (hiPSCs) with high yield and purity. Mature CMs can potentially replace dead and dysfunctional cardiac tissue and be used for screening cardiac drugs and toxins. However, hiPSCs-derived CMs (hiPSC-CMs) are immature, which limits their utilization. Therefore, it is crucial to understand how experimental variables, especially tunable ones, of hiPSC expansion and differentiation phases affect the hiPSC-CM maturity stage. This study applied clustering algorithms to day 30 cardiac differentiation data to investigate if any maturity-related cell features could be related to the experimental variables. The best models were obtained using k-means and Gaussian mixture model clustering algorithms based on the evaluation metrics. They grouped the cells based on eccentricity and elongation. The cosine similarity between the clustering results and the experimental parameters revealed that the Gaussian mixture model results have strong similarities of 0.88, 0.94, and 0.93 with axial ratio, diameter, and cell concentration.

**Keywords**: hiPSC encapsulation, CM differentiation, hiPSC-CM maturation, clustering techniques, K Means clustering

## 1. Introduction

Cardiovascular disease (CVD) is the leading cause of death worldwide (Ahmed et al., 2020). A heart attack can cause the loss of more than one billion heart cells, initiating blood flow overload and overstretching on viable cardiac cells, potentially leading to death. Because the human heart has limited regenerative capacity, it cannot replace damaged cells. Engineered heart tissue is a potential alternative for heart failure due to the difficulties associated with Cardiac Implantable Electronic devices (CIEDs) and heart transplants, two available therapies (Kempf et al., 2016). Human-induced pluripotent stem cells (hiPSCs) can be differentiated into CMs with the potential to produce therapeutic CMs (Tani et al., 2022). However, CMs produced by current differentiation protocols are immature. Immature CMs differ substantially from mature ones. For example, immature CMs have underdeveloped mitochondria, limited fatty acid oxidation capacity, less elongated cells, and disorganized sarcomeres and myofibrils. Research is ongoing to develop protocols that lead to mature hiPSC-CMs (Hamledari et al., 2022).

This paper applied clustering algorithms to group hiPSC-CMs based on maturity-relevant features and investigated the relationship between clustering results and tunable experimental variables of the differentiation protocol with the aim of identifying variables that produce more matured CMs. Clustering, instead of classification, was employed because the hiPSC-CMs cannot be labeled to train a classifier. The CMs were produced through hiPSC hydrogel encapsulation and direct differentiation within a 3D-engineered tissue microenvironment (Chang et al., 2020). The unbiased data were collected from 17 different batches, with each batch having different experimental variables, such as axial ratio (AR), cell concentration, PEG-fibrinogen (PF) concentration, and microspheroid size (i.e., diameter). Eight clustering algorithms from Scikit-learn (Fabian Pedregosa) were applied to day 30 cardiac differentiation data. The maturity-relevant features considered for clustering were cell area, cell circularity, eccentricity, elongation, sarcomere length, sarcomere organization score, and orientation index. The k-means and Gaussian mixture clustering algorithms yielded the best clusters based on evaluation metrics.

## 2. Experimental Procedure for hiPSC-CM Production and Data Collection

*2.1. HiPSC Culture, Encapsulation, and Cardiomyocyte Differentiation*

Un-Arc 16 Facs II (Shinnawi et al., 2015) was cultured on Geltrex (Gibco) with E8 media. The hiPSCs were resuspended in PF precursor solution at 30-60 million cells/mL and encapsulated within PF by using a novel microfluidic system as described previously (Finklea et al., 2021). Microspheroids with different sizes and ARs were produced (Seeto et al., 2019). The D-optimal experimental design was used, assuming Gaussian process model. Microspheroids were cultured for an additional 2 days in E8 media with daily media changes (days -2 and -1). To analyze the initial size and AR of the microspheroids, the autofluorescence of the photoinitiator Eosin Y in PF was captured using the FITC filter on the Nikon Eclipse Ti fluorescence microscope at low magnification. Standard plugins in ImageJ were used for quantification. To initiate cardiac differentiation on day 0, microspheroids were transferred to chemically defined cardiac differentiation media (CDM3) supplemented with CHIR99021 (5 – 7.5 μM, STEMCELL Technologies). Exactly 24 h later, the media was exchanged for CDM3 supplemented with 5 μM IWP2 (STEMCELL Technologies). Fresh CDM3 was added on days 3, 5, 7, and 10; following day 10, microspheroids were cultured in RPMI/B27 (Gibco). The differentiation outcomes were assessed using flow cytometry on day 10 using the primary antibodies, such as cTnT (Invitrogen) and MF20 (DSHB), and secondary antibody (1:300, AlexaFluor 647 goat anti-mouse IgG (ThermoFisher)).

*2.2. Microspheroid dissociation and replating*

Microspheroids on day 30 of differentiation were dissociated by incubating in a Collagenase-B (1 mg/mL, Roche) supplemented by DNase (0.05 mg/mL, Worthington) in PBS dissociation solution at 37 °C for about 8 minutes. The cells were plated on a Matrigel-coated coverslip in RPMI 20 medium (RPMI 1640 medium with 20% FBS, Atlanta Biologicals) supplemented with 5μM RI for 2 days before starting staining. After fixation, the cells were washed with PBS, permeabilized with PBS-T containing 0.2% Triton X-100 in PBS for 30 minutes, and blocked with 10% FBS in PBS blocking buffer for 45 minutes at room temperature. Cells were incubated in primary antibody (aSA) overnight at 4 °C. After washing, cells were incubated in the secondary antibody (Alexa Fluor 568, 1:200), and nuclei stained with Bisbenzimide Hoechst 3342 (MilliporeSigma) for 1 hour at room temperature. All samples were visualized with Nikon Eclipse TE2000 Inverted Microscopes equipped with a Nikon A1 plus Confocal Microscope System. To assess hiPSC-CMs cell morphology and sarcomere structure, SarcOmere Texture Analysis (Sutcliffe et al., 2018) was used for immunofluorescent confocal images.

## 3. Clustering Algorithms

### *3.1. K -means Clustering*

Given the number of clusters ($|C|$), the algorithm (Likas et al., 2003) randomly initializes $|C|$ cluster centroids ($\mu_j, j = 1,2,\ldots,|C|$) and assigns a class membership to each point ($x_i, i = 1,2,\ldots,n$) based on its closest centroid. Then, the centroids are reestimated using Eq. (1). Each point is reassigned a new class membership based on the new centroids. The steps are repeated until class memberships stop changing.

$$\sum_{i=0}^{n} \min_{\mu_j \in C} \left( \left\| x_i - \mu_j \right\|^2 \right) \tag{1}$$

### *3.2. Gaussian Mixture Model Clustering*

The Gaussian mixture model (Yang et al., 2012) assumes that all data points come from a finite number of Gaussian distributions with unknown parameters. The distribution parameters are estimated by the expectation maximization (EM) algorithm. The EM algorithm first assigns the mean and variance of the distributions either randomly or based on the centroids of k-means clustering results. The probability of a point belonging to a cluster is calculated using the distribution parameters. Cluster means and variances are improved by maximizing the likelihood of the data given those parameters, and the procedure is repeated until the mean and variance of each distribution stop changing.

### *3.3. Agglomerative Clustering*

Agglomerative clustering (Murtagh & Legendre, 2014) is a hierarchical algorithm that uses a bottom-up approach. Each data point is initially considered a "cluster." The algorithm proceeds by successively merging clusters using a selected linkage criterion. Criterion using ward, complete, average, and single linkage minimizes the sum of squared distances within all clusters, the maximum distance between observations of pairs of clusters, the average of the distances between all observations of pairs of clusters, and the distance between the closest observations of pairs of clusters, respectively.

## 4. Metrics Used for Evaluating Clustering Results

The three evaluation metrics used to assess the cluster results were Silhouette score, Calinski-Harabasz index (CH), and the Davies-Bouldin index (DB). Based on the results of these metrics, the best three cluster models were selected. Silhouette score (Shahapure & Nicholas) for a data point, $s$, is calculated using the distance between that point and all other points in the same and nearest clusters. The average silhouette score of all the data points gives the Silhouette score for the clusters. Silhouette score is between -1 and 1, with 1 indicating that the clusters are well separated. The CH (Maulik & Bandyopadhyay, 2002) is the ratio of the sum of dispersion between and within clusters for all clusters. The CH is higher for dense and separated clusters. The DB (Maulik & Bandyopadhyay, 2002) is defined as the average similarity between each cluster $C_a$ and its most similar one $C_b$. The similarity score, $R_{ab}$, given in Eq. (2), is calculated between cluster $a$ and $b$, $d_a$ is the average distance between each point in cluster $a$ and its centroid, and $D_{ab}$ is the distance between cluster centroids $a$ and $b$. The DB is calculated by Eq. (3). Values closer to zero indicate better clustering.

$$R_{ab} = \frac{d_a + d_b}{D_{ab}} \tag{2}$$

$$DB = \frac{1}{k} \sum_{i=1}^{k} \max_{i \neq j} R_{ab} \tag{3}$$

## 5. Results and Discussion

### 5.1. Clustering Results

Five hundred thirteen (513) hiPSC-CMs from 17 batches were analyzed to obtain cell morphological features, such as cell area, eccentricity, circularity, elongation, and sarcomere properties, such as sarcomere length, orientation index, and organization score. Only k-means, Gaussian mixture model, and agglomerative clustering algorithms were found to be applicable to the dataset. The agglomerative clustering algorithm grouped almost all hiPSC-CMs in one cluster. These clustering results were not further analyzed. Because this study aims to investigate the relationship between mature and immature hiPSC-CMs and experimental variables, the number of clusters was set to two.

Based on the evaluation metrics, k-means clustering yielded the best model with a Silhouette score of 0.17, CH of 107, and DB of 1.99. Gaussian mixture model clustering with spherical, full, and diagonal covariance yielded the following models in that order. The evaluation metrics for these models were similar to those for the k-means algorithm. Analyzing the two clusters yielded by the k-means and Gaussian mixture model algorithms revealed that the hiPSC-CMs were clustered based on eccentricity and elongation. Mature CMs typically have an elliptical shape with larger eccentricity and elongation values (Karbassi et al., 2020).

The k-means algorithm grouped hiPSC-CMs with eccentricity values between 0.7 and 1 and elongation between 2 and 10 in one cluster, which we named the "Mature" cluster, and the remaining cells in another, we named the "Immature" cluster. The Gaussian mixture model algorithms yielded clusters with the same cell property ranges. The overall clustering results suggest that eccentricity and elongation were significant features for separating mature hiPSC-CMs from immature cells by unsupervised learning.

### 5.2. Relationship between hiPSC-CM Maturity and Tunable Experimental Variables

To investigate the potential relationship between hiPSC-CM maturity and tunable experimental variables, we calculated the percentage of hiPSC-CMs clustered as "Mature" in each of the 17 batches. A set of tunable experimental variables, namely AR, diameter, cell concentration PEG concentration, and PF concentration, were used in each batch. Then, the Cosine similarity (Xia et al., 2015) between this percentage and each tunable experimental variable for each clustering result was calculated. Cosine similarity is a measure of similarity between two vectors. Using cosine similarity, we quantify how similar the percentage of mature CMs to the experimental variables. The resulting similarity values are plotted in Figure 1. The PEG and PF concentration results were not considered because there were only three values for these variables. Figure 1 illustrates that the strongest similarity metric values were observed for the results obtained using the Gaussian mixture model clustering, with a cosine similarity of 0.88 with AR, 0.94 with diameter, and 0.93 with the cell concentration. The cosine similarity values for the results obtained with the k-means algorithm are similar, with a cosine similarity of 0.86 with AR, 0.92 with diameter, and 0.91 with cell concentration.

Figure 2 plots the percentage of "Mature" hiPSC-CMs in each batch calculated using Gaussian mixture model clustering results versus AR (Figure 2(a)), diameter (Figure 2(b)), and cell concentration (Figure 2(c)). Figures 2(a), 2(b), and 2(c) suggest that there is a relationship between the percentage of "Mature" hiPSC-CMs and AR, diameter, and cell concentration. Three of the five batches with ARs less than two have less than 45 % of hiPSC-CMs clustered as "Mature". In contrast, batches with an AR greater than two have at least 45% hiPSC-CMs clustered as "Mature", except for one. Figure 2(c) shows that when the concentration is equal to 60 million cells/mL, the percentage of mature cells is greater than 50%. These observations suggest the existence of non-linear and potentially complex relationships between the mature hiPSC-CMs and the ARs, diameters, and cell concentration, which should be further investigated.

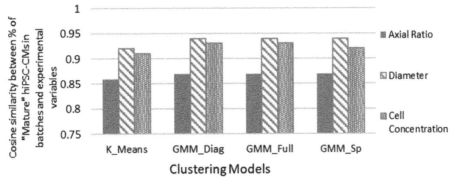

**Figure 1** – Cosine similarity between the percentage of "Mature" hiPSC-CMs in batches based on the clustering results and the experimental parameters. K_Means – k-means clustering, GMM_Diag, GMM_Full, and GMM_Sp – Gaussian mixture model with diagonal, full, and spherical covariance function.

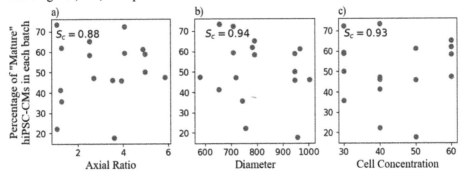

**Figure 2** - Percentage of mature hiPSC-CMs clustered by k means clustering vs. **(a)** AR **(b)** Diameter **(c)** Cell concentration. $S_c$ – Cosine similarity between the percentage of mature CMs and each experimental parameter.

## 6. Conclusions and Future Directions

Using day 30 cardiac differentiation data, we identified eccentricity and elongation as the significant features for clustering hiPSC-CMs into two groups via k-means and Gaussian mixture model clustering algorithms. The results of the Gaussian mixture and k-means models suggested that there is a concurrent relationship between ARs, diameter, and cell concentration, all experimentally tunable variables, and hiPSC-CMs with higher eccentricity and elongation, which are associated with maturity. Future work will investigate using different clustering approaches that relax the compact set assumption for determining better "Mature" cell cluster boundaries. Then, the relationships between the experimental variables and mature hiPSC-CMs will be modeled to aid in directing hiPSC differentiation towards mature CMs.

## 7. Acknowledgments

This work is funded by NSF grant number 2135059.

# References

Ahmed, R. E., Anzai, T., Chanthra, N., & Uosaki, H. (2020). A Brief Review of Current Maturation Methods for Human Induced Pluripotent Stem Cells-Derived Cardiomyocytes. *Front Cell Dev Biol, 8*, 178.

Chang, S., Finklea, F., Williams, B., Hammons, H., Hodge, A., Scott, S., & Lipke, E. (2020, Jul). Emulsion-based encapsulation of pluripotent stem cells in hydrogel microspheres for cardiac differentiation. *Biotechnol Prog, 36*(4), e2986.

Fabian Pedregosa, G. V., Alexandre Gramfort, Vincent Michel, Bertrand Thirion, Olivier Grisel, Mathieu Blondel, Peter Prettenhofer, Ron Weiss, Vincent Dubourg, Jake Vanderplas, Alexandre Passos, David Cournapeau, Matthieu Brucher, Matthieu Perrot, Édouard Duchesnay;. *Scikit-learn: Machine Learning in Python.* https://scikit-learn.org/stable/about.html#citing-scikit-learn

Finklea, F. B., Tian, Y., Kerscher, P., Seeto, W. J., Ellis, M. E., & Lipke, E. A. (2021, Jul). Engineered cardiac tissue microsphere production through direct differentiation of hydrogel-encapsulated human pluripotent stem cells. *Biomaterials, 274*, 120818.

Hamledari, H., Asghari, P., Jayousi, F., Aguirre, A., Maaref, Y., Barszczewski, T., Ser, T., Moore, E., Wasserman, W., Klein Geltink, R., Teves, S., & Tibbits, G. F. (2022). Using human induced pluripotent stem cell-derived cardiomyocytes to understand the mechanisms driving cardiomyocyte maturation. *Front Cardiovasc Med, 9*, 967659

Karbassi, E., Fenix, A., Marchiano, S., Muraoka, N., Nakamura, K., Yang, X., & Murry, C. E. (2020, Jun). Cardiomyocyte maturation: advances in knowledge and implications for regenerative medicine. *Nat Rev Cardiol, 17*(6), 341-359.

Kempf, H., Andree, B., & Zweigerdt, R. (2016, Jan 15). Large-scale production of human pluripotent stem cell derived cardiomyocytes. *Adv Drug Deliv Rev, 96*, 18-30.

Kerscher, P., Kaczmarek, J. A., Head, S. E., Ellis, M. E., Seeto, W. J., Kim, J., Bhattacharya, S., Suppiramaniam, V., & Lipke, E. A. (2017, Aug 14). Direct Production of Human Cardiac Tissues by Pluripotent Stem Cell Encapsulation in Gelatin Methacryloyl. *ACS Biomater Sci Eng, 3*(8), 1499-1509.

Likas, A., Vlassis, N., & J. Verbeek, J. (2003). The global k-means clustering algorithm. *Pattern Recognition, 36*(2), 451-461.

Maulik, U., & Bandyopadhyay, S. (2002). Performance evaluation of some clustering algorithms and validity indices. *IEEE Transactions on Pattern Analysis and Machine Intelligence, 24*(12), 1650-1654.

Murtagh, F., & Legendre, P. (2014). Ward's Hierarchical Agglomerative Clustering Method: Which Algorithms Implement Ward's Criterion? *Journal of Classification, 31*(3), 274-295.

Seeto, W. J., Tian, Y., Pradhan, S., Kerscher, P., & Lipke, E. A. (2019). Rapid Production of Cell-Laden Microspheres Using a Flexible Microfluidic Encapsulation Platform. *Small, 15*(47), 1902058.

Shahapure, K. R., & Nicholas, C. (2020). Cluster Quality Analysis Using Silhouette Score.

Shinnawi, R., Huber, I., Maizels, L., Shaheen, N., Gepstein, A., Arbel, G., Tijsen, A. J., & Gepstein, L. (2015, Oct 13). Monitoring Human-Induced Pluripotent Stem Cell-Derived Cardiomyocytes with Genetically Encoded Calcium and Voltage Fluorescent Reporters. *Stem Cell Reports, 5*(4), 582-596.

Sutcliffe, M. D., Tan, P. M., Fernandez-Perez, A., Nam, Y. J., Munshi, N. V., & Saucerman, J. J. (2018, Jan 19). High content analysis identifies unique morphological features of reprogrammed cardiomyocytes. *Sci Rep, 8*(1), 158.

Tani, H., Tohyama, S., Kishino, Y., Kanazawa, H., & Fukuda, K. (2022, Mar). Production of functional cardiomyocytes and cardiac tissue from human induced pluripotent stem cells for regenerative therapy. *J Mol Cell Cardiol, 164*, 83-91.

Xia, P., Zhang, L., & Li, F. (2015). Learning similarity with cosine similarity ensemble. *Information Sciences, 307*, 39-52.

Yang, M.-S., Lai, C.-Y., & Lin, C.-Y. (2012). A robust EM clustering algorithm for Gaussian mixture models. *Pattern Recognition, 45*(11), 3950-3961.

Antonis Kokossis, Michael C. Georgiadis, Efstratios N. Pistikopoulos (Eds.)
PROCEEDINGS OF THE 33rd European Symposium on Computer Aided Process Engineering
(ESCAPE33), June 18-21, 2023, Athens, Greece

# On the systematic development of large-scale kinetics using stability criteria and high-throughput analysis of curated dynamics from genome-scale models

Konstantinos Mexis, Stefanos Xenios, and Antonis Kokosis*

*Department of Process Engineering, NTUA, Iroon Politechniou 6 Zografou, Athens, Greece*
*Corresponding author: akokossis@mail.ntua.gr*

## Abstract

This paper is part of a general effort to integrate disjoint stages of the Design-Build-Test-Learn cycle that addresses the simultaneous design of biocatalysts with process engineering. Engineering kinetics are currently based on regression studies based on experimental data with limited reference to the underlying reaction pathways. Instead, the ORACLE framework offers an attractive environment to generate populations of large-scale (curated) dynamics and a platform for in-silico kinetic models to check for physiological relevance and stability. Stability checks have reported low rates of success and the paper explains a systematic approach that combines deterministic methods and data analytics to accelerate realizable kinetics that could be set a basis to connect the dynamics of the cell with the dynamics of the process. The work is demonstrated with the production of muconic from S. cerevisiae which is achieved by shunting the shikimic pathway. The ORACLE framework consists of two reduction stages where the first one ensures that the generated kinetic models are physiologically relevant and the second one checks the model's stability. The conventional method produced 370 physiologically relevant models out of which 70 were stable (19.2%) whereas our approach increased uptake of acceptable solutions to 97.7%.

**Keywords**: metabolic engineering; machine learning; rule extraction; S.Cerevisiae; muconic acid;

## 1.     Introduction

The typical design process towards a sustainable bio-production of chemicals follows the iterative Design-Build-Test-Learn (DBTL) cycle. The design involves the selection of the platform organism and the heterologous reactions that need to be expressed to produce the desired chemicals as well as strategies (enzyme upregulations or downregulations) to enhance product yield. The build module involves the genetic transformation and gene editing of the platform organism in accordance to the strategies of the design step. The test module we gather information on the cloning results, omics data and help comprehend cellular behavior. Small batch experiments showcase the developed strain's desired product yield as well as some key metabolites secretion rates. The learn module takes into account the generated information from the test step and incorporates it into new metabolic strategies to further optimize and increase the desired flux.

Optimization and Risk Analysis of Complex Living Entities (ORACLE) is an attractive methodology to formalize development stages and set a basis for the development of large-scale kinetics. The approach combines mathematical optimization and data analytics. The ORACLE framework is a venue to connect genome-scale models with process engineering. Thermodynamic Flux Analysis is used to predict potential fluxes at steady states; reduction methods and parameter sampling can be applied to produce candidates for observable dynamics. Pruning tests and stability checks can be applied to determine candidates for large-scale kinetic models. Such models are valuable in scale-up studies, in the design and optimization of bioreactors, also to manipulate pathways as required to increase yields and selectivity. The screening of candidates and the analysis of uncertainty are critical issues in the current methodology that currently embraces hypotheses and heuristics to

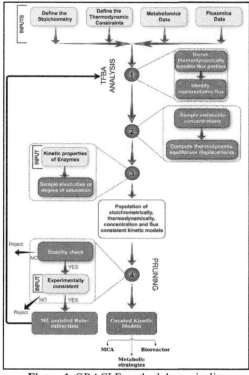

**Figure 1**. ORACLE methodology pipeline

tackle the large size and complexity of the problem. The challenges offer room for systems methods to add rigor, automate the analysis, and improve the quality and relevance of the high-throughput experiments. The paper explains the application of a systems approach to tackle stability of curated kinetics models demonstrating significant improvements in the quality of the results.

## 2.    Pilot study: Muconic acid production from S.cerevisiae

The pilot study involves a Genome-Scale model produced for the mutant strain of S. Cerevisiae that produces muconic acid via the shunting of shikimic pathways. The model is thermodynamically curated and reduced in order to generate kinetic models through the ORACLE framework. A total of 23500 kinetic models was generated; 370 of them remained within physiological bounds. Only 70 out of 370 models showed great stability to random initial metabolite concentration. Due to the small percentage of stable models, we deployed a decision tree classifier to extract rules on key

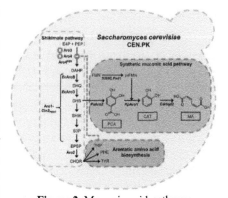

**Figure 2**. Muconic acid pathway

kinetic parameters that affect the system stability. The decision tree's input kinetic parameters were the enzyme saturation (sigma) and thermodynamic displacement (gamma) parameters. The differences in the development of decision trees motivated the remaining analysis where we explored different rule extraction approaches.

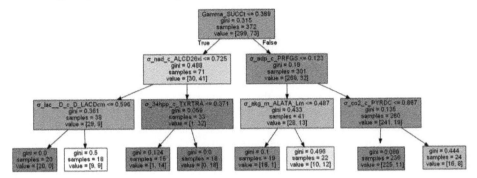

**Figure 3**. Decision tree of kinetic parameters

## 3.     **Methods and Materials**

### 3.1.    *Parameter classification problem*

The parameter classification problem is the identification of a subspace in the parameter space wherein the parameters satisfy a given property (GP). Let us consider an *n*-dimensional space of parameters $p_1, p_2, \dots, p_n$, and assume that the GP is satisfied provided a function of these parameters satisfies $f(p_1, p_2, \dots, p_n) > 0$. The task is to find ranges of $p_1, p_2, \dots, p_n$, for which the GP is satisfied without any knowledge of the exact functional form of $f(p_1, p_2, \dots, p_n)$. As applied in the population of the curated kinetic models, the parameters $p_1, p_2, \dots, p_n$ account for the saturation and thermodynamic displacement parameters of the kinetic model; GP would be satisfied if the referred kinetic model passes the stability tests.

### 3.2.    *Learning-based Rule-extraction Algorithms*

*Rule-extraction* is important to understand how the system functions. Rule extraction methods are typically used in conjunction with learning algorithms that feature an inherent explanation capability (*surrogate model*). In our case several ML methods (*black-box models*) are trained using saturation and thermodynamic displacement parameters of

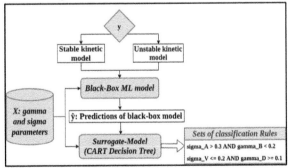

**Figure 4**. Pipeline to obtain a surrogate model

curated kinetic models to predict whether the curated kinetic model is stable or not. Then, a CART decision tree (*surrogate model*) was trained to approximate predictions of the black box models.

### 3.3.    *Skope-Rules*

*Skope-Rule* extraction is a rule-based interpretable model that allocates logical rules with high precision to fuse them. The difference from other rule-extraction methods stands in that decision rules are actual inputs. Rules are extracted from tree ensembles; similar or duplicated rules are removed based on similarity thresholds. A fitted tree defines a set of rules; rules are then tested selecting and merging rules with higher precision. In our case, the Skope-Rules algorithm is implemented on training tree ensemble models on saturation and thermodynamic displacement parameters. They algorithm is used to predict if a given kinetic model is stable or not.

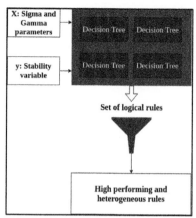

**Figure 5**. Skope-Rules pipeline

## 4.    **Methodology**

The adopted rules-extraction procedure is outlined in the following steps:

**Step 1a.** The physiologically relevant generated kinetic models are used to define a *dataset* that consists of an *input* (*X*) and an *answer set* (*y*). The *input set* contained all the *gamma* (thermodynamic displacement) and *saturation* (*sigma*) parameters for each kinetic model; the *answer set* answers if the model is stable or not.

**Step 1b.** The dataset was split into a *training set* and a *validation set* in an 80:20 ratio. The *training set* was then used to train and extract the rules from the machine learning models, while the *validation set* was used to validate the accuracy of the extracted rules. We computed the *Stability Index* (SI) as the ratio between the number of kinetic parameters sets that passed the *stability check.*

**Step 2.** Several machine learning classificators ("*black-box*" *models*) were built using this *training set*. Then, these models were used to predict the labels, i.e. the *answer set*, for the *input set* mentioned in *Step 1*. The employed machine learning algorithms used as "black-box" models were; Logistic Regression and Support Vector Machines.

**Step 3.** A decision tree (*surrogate model*) was built on the *input set* of the training data and the *predictions* of the black-box model. The rules generated from the decision tree represented the generalization behavior of the black-box model. We ranked the classification rules based on the number of training samples (kinetic parameter sets) that they enclose and we selected the rule enclosing the most samples.

**Step 4.** From the *validation set,* we selected only the kinetic models that satisfied the extracted rules and computed the SI over these sampled models. If the obtained SI is improved, the extracted rules and the general methodology as well are valid.

**Step 5.** Finally, we generated new populations of kinetic models based on the inferred rules from *Step 3* independently of the training set. We calculated the SI obtained and compared it with the one from the *training set*. If the SI and the number of feasible kinetic models are improved, the rules extracted from the black-box model are valid and the uncertainty in kinetic parameters is reduced.

## 5.    **Results and Discussion**

Different sets of rules were extracted from each black-box model and the rule enclosing the most training examples was finally selected for each model. These inferred rules constrained the saturations and the corresponding kinetic parameters of some critical enzymes, reducing the sampling space and, as a result, the uncertainty in the model analysis. The critical parameters that affect the stability of the generated kinetic models and the inferred rules according to every black-box model are presented in *Table 1*.

| Black Box Model | Rules |
|---|---|
| Logistic Regression | Gamma_GLUDC≤6.27e-09 |
| | Sigma_[chor_c]_CHORS≤0.126 |
| Decision Tree | Gamma_HCO3E>0.856 |
| | Sigma_[nad_c]≤0.524 |
| SVM | Gamma_GLUDC≤6.27e-09 |
| | Sigma_[2oxoadp_m]≤0.646 |
| | Sigma_[g6p_c]≤0.522 |
| | Sigma_[gmp_c]≤0.999 |
| Skope rules | Gamma_FBA≤0.527 |
| | Sigma_[nad_m]>0.484 |
| | Sigma_[glu__L_m]≤0.862 |

**Table 1**. Rules extracted from each machine learning algorithm

| Reaction Name | Reaction Stoichiometry |
|---|---|
| GLUDC | glu__L_c + h_c ⇌ 4abut_c + co2_c |
| CHORS | 3psme_c → chor_c + pi_c |
| H3COE | co2_c + h2o_c ⇌ h_c + hco3_c |
| GAPD | g3p_c + nad_c + pi_c ⇌ 13dpg_c + h_c + nadh_c |
| 2OXOADPTm | 2oxoadp_m + akg_c ⇌ 2oxoadp_c + akg_m |
| LMPD biomass | Biomass reaction |
| GK1 | atp_c + gmp_c ⇌ adp_c + gdp_c |
| FBA | fdp_c ⇌ dhap_c + g3p_c |
| ALCD26xi | h_c + nadh_c + id3acald_c ⇌ nad_c + ind3eth_c |
| ASPTA | akg_c + asp__L_c ⇌ glu__L_c + oaa_c |

**Table 2.** List of reactions that came up during the Machine Learning analysis

In order to quickly validate the accuracy of the extracted rules, we sampled from the *validation set* (as described in paragraph *2.4*) only the kinetic models that satisfied these rules and computed the Stability Index over them. The obtained SI for every implemented machine learning algorithm was improved over the SI computed on the training test, meaning that our method is able to determine and constrain the critical kinetic parameters that lead to more feasible kinetic models. We proceeded with the generation of new kinetic models implementing the extracted rules for the parameters that seem to affect stability. A total of 200 physiologically relevant kinetic models were produced for every different set of rules. In addition, we implemented all the rules combined and generated again 200 physiologically relevant models. The generated models underwent the ORACLE stability check where 100 random concentration perturbations were performed using a wide range $(0.5[X_{ref}] \leq [X] \leq 2[X_{ref}])$ of initial values. We deemed a kinetic model stable if 95/100 times the metabolite concentrations returned to steady state. The results obtained are presented on *Figure 6*.

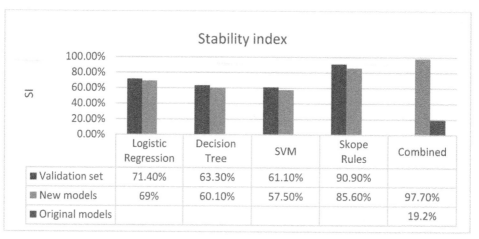

**Figure 6.** Stability Index obtained from extracted rules for every machine learning model. *Validation Set:* SI is computed on samples following extracted rules on validation set. *New Models:* SI is computed on new kinetic models, generated based on extracted rules. *Original Models:* SI is computed on kinetic models generated originally, with no inferred rules.

## 6. Conclusion

The production of large scale metabolic kinetic models is hindered by the uncertainty of predicting the kinetic parameters and producing physiologically relevant and robust kinetic models. Using the ORACLE framework, we are able to generate large populations of kinetic models but the biggest percentage of them are not stable. In this work the uncertainty in the model analysis is reduced through the use of machine learning principles. Using machine learning classification and explainability techniques we were able to raise the stability index of the generated models. We were able to reach up to 97.7% stability on our generated models implementing simultaneously all the extracted rules which leads to postulate that it is better to constrain such systems as much as possible to get more feasible results.

## Acknowledgments

The authors acknowledge support from the EPFL team of Prof. Hatzimanikatis, especially Miskovic Ljubisa, who assisted in applying the ORACLE methodology. The research project was supported by the Hellenic Foundation for Research and Innovation (H.F.R.I.) under the "2nd Call for H.F.R.I. Research Projects to support Post-Doctoral Researchers" (Project Number: 3817).

## References

Xenios, S., Weilandt, D., Vasilis, H., Miskovic, L., & Kokosis, A. (2022). On the integration of process engineering with metabolomics for the production of muconic acid: the case for Saccharomyces Cerevisiae. Computer Aided Chemical Engineering, 541–546.

Andreozzi, S., Miskovic, L., & Hatzimanikatis, V., 2016, iSCHRUNK – In Silico Approach to Characterization and Reduction of Uncertainty in the Kinetic Models of Genome-scale Metabolic Networks. *Metabolic Engineering, 33*, 158–168.

Barakat, N., & Bradley, A. P., 2010, Rule extraction from support vector machines: A review. *Neurocomputing, 74*(1–3), 178–190

Antonis Kokossis, Michael C. Georgiadis, Efstratios N. Pistikopoulos (Eds.)
PROCEEDINGS OF THE 33rd European Symposium on Computer Aided Process Engineering
(ESCAPE33), June 18-21, 2023, Athens, Greece
© 2023 Elsevier B.V. All rights reserved. http://dx.doi.org/10.1016/B978-0-443-15274-0.50435-2

# Development and assessment of intensification alternatives on the lignocellulosic bioethanol production process

Yulissa M. Espinoza-Vázquez [a], Fernando Israel Gómez-Castro [a*], Eduardo Sánchez-Ramírez [a], Araceli G. Romero-Izquierdo [b].

*aDepartamento de Ingeniería Química, División de Ciencias Naturales y Exactas, Campus Guanajuato. Universidad de Guanajuato, Noria Alta S/N, Guanajuato, Gto. 36050, México. fgomez@ugto.mx*
*bFacultad de Ingeniería, Universidad Autónoma de Querétaro, Cerro de las Campanas S/N, Querétaro, Qro. 76010, México.*

## Abstract

In this work, the design of the conventional process to produce bioethanol from lignocellulosic biomass is developed. The conventional process consists of pretreatment, hydrolysis, and fermentation of the biomass to obtain bioethanol and other bioproducts. The bioethanol is purified up to 99% through extractive distillation. Different options for intensification are proposed to improve such conventional process. The analysis of the developed production schemes is performed by simulation in the software Aspen Plus V.11. The first intensified scheme (I-1) consisted in the elimination of the glycerol purification column. The second intensified scheme (I-2) consisted in the elimination of the column that purifies the ethanol-ammonia mixture, by means of the implementation of a side stream. Scheme I-2 reduces the thermal load by 2.36%, which is associated with a lower capital cost.

**Keywords**: bioethanol, lignocellulosic biomass, process intensification, process simulation.

## 1. Introduction

Fossil fuels contributed with 79.7 % of the total energy used in the world in 2015 (Banco Mundial, 2022). In addition, the U.S. Energy Information Administration (EIA) estimated that in 2021, the consumption of gasoline in the U.S. transportation sector resulted in the emission of about 1,018 million metric tons (MMmt) of carbon dioxide ($CO_2$) (Energy Information Administration, 2022). To reduce the dependence on fossil fuels and their environmental impact, the use of biofuels has been proposed as a viable solution. Those biofuels are obtained from renewable biomass and are considered one of the most feasible options to reduce $CO_2$ emissions in the transportation sector (Alam and Tanveer, 2020). Bioethanol stands out among the fuels that can be obtained from lignocellulosic biomass. This alcohol is used in blends of 10 vol% with gasoline (Costagliola et al., 2016) and can be used to partially replace the use of gasoline.

Biomass is renewable organic feedstock that can be obtained from plants and animals. The composition of the plant biomass generally comprises cellulose, hemicellulose, and lignin; referred to as lignocellulosic biomass. By 2020, the production of agricultural residues in the world has been reported as $2.14 \times 10^9$ tons (FAO, 2022), with a high contribution of residues from corn, sorghum, wheat, and barley crops. Sorghum is important at national level since Mexico is its main producer in Central America. to be economically feasible, the conversion of biomass into biofuels must take place in a biorefinery scheme. A biorefinery is a facility that integrates biomass conversion processes and equipment to produce fuels, energy, and chemicals. In the biorefinery scheme based on lignocellulosic materials, it is necessary to break down the lignin structure on the feedstock, then obtaining fermentable sugars from cellulose and hemicellulose. The initial lignin removal requires a pretreatment stage. In the literature there are several studies related to the production of lignocellulosic bioethanol, such as the work developed by Conde-Mejía et al. (2012), in which different types of pretreatments as well as different conversion technologies were analyzed to find the best configuration of this process in economic and environmental terms. Similarly, Duque et al. (2020) analyzed the production of ethanol from barley straw combining a soda and enzyme-catalyzed extrusion pretreatment, reporting a production of 15.8 g ethanol/100 g raw barley straw. In these studies, several types of biomass and different conversion pathways were analyzed, with the major objective of obtaining feasible pathways with high yields. Nevertheless, biofuels must also be economically competitive with their fossil counterparts; this implies that the biofuels production costs must be reduced. In this context, process intensification (PI) plays a key role, since it can help to generate compact, energy-efficient, safer, and more environmentally friendly processes. Therefore, in this work, the design of the conventional process to produce bioethanol from lignocellulosic biomass is developed. Areas of opportunity are detected for the conventional process, proposing and evaluating intensification alternatives, such as thermally coupled columns and columns with side streams, aiming to the improvement of the energetic performance of the conventional process.

## 2. Case Study

The case study is based on the work of Conde-Mejía et al. (2013), considering 87,539 kg/h of sorghum residues as feedstock. Data in Table 1 show the composition of the lignocellulosic material. The carbohydrates profile of the feedstock is shown in Table 2.

**Table 1.** Composition of lignocellulosic biomass (Conde-Mejía et. al., 2013).

| Component | % wt. | Formula |
|---|---|---|
| Cellulose | 27.56 | $C_6H_{10}O_5$ |
| Hemicellulose | 15.37 | $C_5H_8O_4$ |
| Lignin | 14.11 | $C_{7.3}H_{13.9}O_{1.3}$ |
| Carbohydrates | 42.93 | |

**Table 2.** Carbohydrates profile (Conde-Mejía, *et. al.,* 2013).

| Component | % wt. | Formula |
|---|---|---|
| Galactan | 9.41 | $C_6H_{10}O_5$ |
| Manan | 3.62 | $C_6H_{10}O_5$ |
| Arabinan | 29.90 | $C_5H_8O_4$ |

The pretreatment is carried out with dilute acid, due to the low sulfuric acid prices and the high yields of the treatment. Table 3 shows the reactions occurring in the pretreatment reactor, as well as their yields. In this reactor, 0.49 wt% of $H_2SO_4$ is used at 160 °C and 1 atm. On the other hand, acid hydrolysis is carried out in a reactor at 220 °C and 1 atm. The hydrolysis reactions are presented in Table 4. As a next step, fermentation is carried out using urea ($CH_4N_2O$) in a $CH_4N_2O$/sorghum residues mass ratio of 1:32.18, at 34°C and 1 atm. Fermentation reactions are presented in Table 5.

**Table 3.** Reactions for the pretreatment process (Conde-Mejía et. al., 2013).

| Reaction | Yield | Reference reagent | Equation |
|---|---|---|---|
| $C_6H_{10}O_5 + H_2O \rightarrow C_6H_{12}O_6$ | 0.065 | Cellulose | (1) |
| $C_6H_{10}O_5 + 0.5H_2O \rightarrow 0.5C_{12}H_{22}O_{11}$ | 0.007 | Cellulose | (2) |
| $C_5H_8O_4 + H_2O \rightarrow C_5H_{10}O_5$ | 0.75 | Hemicellulose | (3) |
| $C_5H_8O_4 \rightarrow C_5H_4O_2 + 2H_2O$ | 0.15 | Hemicellulose | (4) |
| $C_6H_{10}O_5 + H_2O \rightarrow C_6H_{12}O_6$ | 0.75 | Galactan | (5) |
| $C_6H_{10}O_5 \rightarrow C_6H_6O_3 + 2H_2O$ | 0.15 | Galactan | (6) |
| $C_6H_{10}O_5 + H_2O \rightarrow C_6H_{12}O_6$ | 0.75 | Manan | (7) |
| $C_6H_{10}O_5 \rightarrow C_6H_6O_3 + 2H_2O$ | 0.15 | Manan | (8) |
| $C_5H_8O_4 + H_2O \rightarrow C_5H_{10}O_5$ | 0.75 | Arabinan | (9) |
| $C_5H_8O_4 \rightarrow C_5H_4O_2 + H_2O$ | 0.10 | Arabinan | (10) |

**Table 4.** Reactions for the hydrolysis process (Conde-Mejía et. al., 2013).

| Reaction | Yield | Reference reagent | Equation |
|---|---|---|---|
| $C_6H_{10}O_5 + 0.5H_2O \rightarrow 0.5C_{12}H_{22}O_{11}$ | 0.012 | Cellulose | (11) |
| $C_6H_{10}O_5 + H_2O \rightarrow C_6H_{12}O_6$ | 0.8 | Cellulose | (12) |
| $C_{12}H_{22}O_{11} + H_2O \rightarrow 2C_6H_{12}O_6$ | 1 | Cellobiose | (13) |
| $C_5H_8O_4 + H_2O \rightarrow C_5H_{10}O_5$ | 0.99 | Hemicellulose | (14) |
| $C_5H_{10}O_5 \rightarrow C_5H_4O_2 + H_2O$ | 0.8 | Xylose | (15) |

**Table 5.** Reaction for the fermentation process (Conde-Mejía et. al., 2013).

| Reaction | Yield | Reference reagent | Equation |
|---|---|---|---|
| $CH_4N_2O + H_2O \rightarrow 2NH_3 + CO_2$ | 0.99 | Urea | (16) |
| $C_6H_{12}O_6 \rightarrow 2C_2H_6O + 2CO_2$ | 0.92 | Glucose | (17) |
| $C_6H_{12}O_6 + 2H_2O \rightarrow 2C_3H_8O_3 + O_2$ | 0.002 | Glucose | (18) |
| $C_6H_{12}O_6 + CO_2 \rightarrow 2C_4H_6O_4 + O_2$ | 0.008 | Glucose | (19) |
| $C_6H_{12}O_6 \rightarrow 3C_2H_4O_2$ | 0.022 | Glucose | (20) |
| $C_6H_{12}O_6 \rightarrow 2C_3H_6O_3$ | 0.013 | Glucose | (21) |
| $3C_5H_{10}O_5 \rightarrow 5C_2H_6O + 5CO_2$ | 0.85 | Xylose | (22) |
| $3C_5H_{10}O_5 + 5H_2O \rightarrow 5C_3H_8O_3 + 2.5O_2$ | 0.029 | Xylose | (23) |
| $3C_5H_{10}O_5 + 5CO_2 \rightarrow 5C_4H_6O_4 + 2.5O_2$ | 0.009 | Xylose | (24) |
| $2C_5H_{10}O_5 \rightarrow 5C_2H_4O_2$ | 0.024 | Xylose | (25) |
| $3C_5H_{10}O_5 \rightarrow 5C_3H_6O_3$ | 0.014 | Xylose | (26) |
| $C_5H_{10}O_5 \rightarrow 5C_3H_6O_3$ | 1 | Arabinose | (27) |
| $C_5H_{12}O_6 \rightarrow 2C_3H_6O_3$ | 1 | Galactose | (28) |
| $C_6H_{12}O_6 \rightarrow 2C_3H_6O_3$ | 1 | Mannose | (29) |
| $C_6H_{12}O_6 \rightarrow 2C_3H_6O_3$ | 1 | Glucose | (30) |
| $3C_5H_{10}O_5 \rightarrow 5C_3H_6O_3$ | 1 | Xylose | (31) |
| $C_2H_4O_2 + NH_3 \rightarrow C_2H_7NO_2$ | 1 | Acetic Acid | (32) |
| $H_2SO_4 + 2NH_3 \rightarrow N_2H_8SO_4$ | 1 | Sulfuric Acid | (33) |

Through these conversion steps, it is possible to obtain 15,482.61 kg/h of ethanol; however, the fermentation effluent still requires a purification process. The description of the strategy used to simulate and design the whole process will be presented in the following section.

## 3. Methodology

Bibliographical research was carried out to determine the parameters required for the simulation of the solid components present in the biomass, *i.e.* cellulose, hemicellulose and lignin; these data has been obtained from the database of the National Renewable Energy Lab (1996). NRTL was used as the thermodynamic model, due to the complexity of the involved mixtures and the operating conditions (Conde-Mejía et. al., 2013). Case study was simulated in the software Aspen Plus V.11 using RYield reactors. Process flow diagram is shown in Figure 1. In the purification section, C-1 is the distillation column for the separation of $CO_2$ as top product with a purity of 95% mass, with heavy components at the bottom. The bottoms stream is fed to a rectifier (C-2) with partial condenser, for the removal of by-products. This is followed by an extractive distillation column (C-3), using glycerol as extractant agent with a mass ratio of 1:1 with relation to the amount of ethanol in the stream. A column is used for the extraction of the ammonia present (C-4) in the stream, obtaining ethanol with a purity of 0.99. Finally, a column for the purification of glycerol (C-5) is required, aiming to a 99% recovery. Operating conditions are shown in Table 6.

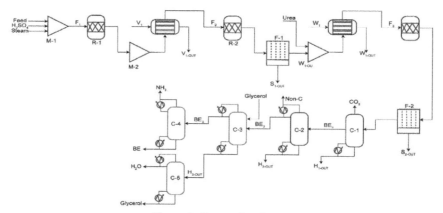

**Figure 1:** Conventional process.

**Table 6.** Feed conditions for the columns of the conventional process.

| Unit | Temperature (°C) | Pressure (bar) |
|------|------------------|----------------|
| C-1  | 34               | 1              |
| C-2  | 100.46           | 1.33           |
| C-3  | 57.51            | 1              |
| C-4  | 41.73            | 1.01           |
| C-5  | 170.76           | 1.70           |

Following the simulation of the conventional process, two schemes are proposed for the intensification of the ethanol distillation sequence, aiming to reduce the number of equipment and the thermal load. Figure 1 highlights the area to be intensified in red. Characteristics of the schemes are obtained by recursive simulation and sensitivity analysis to determine the configuration with the lowest heat duty, while maintaining the specified ethanol purity.

## 4. Results

The first scheme (I-1) consists of replacing C-5 by a side rectifier, intending to reduce the heat duty while reducing the number of units. Figure 2 shows the scheme. The ethanol-water mixture leaving the column C-2 is fed into the thermally coupled extractive column C-3. The design consists of 30 stages, where glycerol is feed at stage 2 and the BE$_2$ stream is fed at stage 10. Interconnecting flows are located at stage 29.

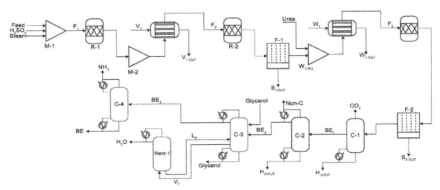

**Figure 2:** Intensified scheme 1 (I-1).

The second intensified scheme (I-2) involves replacing column C-4 by a side stream where ethanol is concentrated, as shown in Figure 3. In this scheme, the ammonia present in the mixture is obtained as top product in C-3. The column C-3 has 30 stages, where the glycerol enters in stage 10 and the stream BE$_2$ is fed at stage 25. The side stream is obtained from stage 4. Operating conditions of both schemes are shown in Table 7.

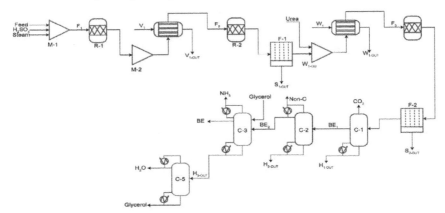

**Figure 3:** Intensified scheme 2 (I-2).

**Table 7.** Feed conditions to the columns of the intensified schemes.

| Scheme, unit | Temperature (°C) | Pressure (bar) |
|---|---|---|
| I-1, C-4 | 42.01 | 1 |
| I-2, C-5 | 192.02 | 2.18 |

Table 8 shows that I-1 consumes 2.36 % less energy than the conventional scheme. Meanwhile, I-2 has an energy reduction of 1.82 %. In both intensified schemes, 99% of the available bioethanol and 99% of the glycerol are recovered, being the heat duty in the reboilers the representative variable of these implementations.

**Table 8.** Comparison of schemes

| Scheme<br>Variable | Conventional | I-1 | I-2 |
|---|---|---|---|
| Q (kW) | 150,200.63 | 146,654.3 | 147,463.47 |
| Bioethanol Recovery (kg/h) | 14,472.67 | 14,435.15 | 14,431.04 |
| Glycerol Recovery (kg/h) | 14,540.74 | 14,542.23 | 14,536.96 |

## 5. Conclusions

The design of the conventional bioethanol production process from sorghum residues has been carried out. Two intensification alternatives have been proposed for the purification stage, with the goal of reducing the number of units and the thermal duty without compromising the recovery of the biofuel and the solvent. Scheme I-1 achieves a reduction of 3,546.33 kW as well as the incorporation of the glycerol recovery in a thermally coupled system. The recovery of bioethanol and glycerol is maintained at the target values of 99%. Finally, it is important to mention that the implementation of a rigorous optimization algorithm can achieve lower thermal duties with higher recoveries for the proposed schemes.

## References

M.S., Alam, M. S. Tanveer, 2020, Conversion of biomass into biofuel: a cutting-edge technology, In L. Singh, A. Yousuf, D. Madhab (Eds.), Bioreactors, Elsevier, p. 55–74.

Banco Mundial, 2022, Consumo de energía procedente de combustibles fósiles (% del total), https://datos.bancomundial.org/indicador/EG.USE.COMM.FO.ZS, last consulted on November 23, 2022. (Spanish).

C. Conde-Mejía, A. Jiménez-Gutiérrez, M. M. El-Halwagi, 2013, Assessment of combinations between pretreatment and conversion configurations for bioethanol production, ACS Sustainable Chemistry & Engineering, 1, 8, 956–965.

C. Conde-Mejía, A. Jiménez-Gutiérrez, M. M. El-Halwagi, 2012, A comparison of pretreatment methods for bioethanol production from lignocellulosic materials, Process Safety and Environmental Protection, 90, 189–202.

M. A. Costagliola, M. V. Prati, S. Florio, P. Scorletti, D. Terna, P. Iodice, D. Buono, A. Senatore, 2016, Performances and emissions of a 4-stroke motorcycle fuelled with ethanol/gasoline blends, Fuel, 183, 470–477.

A. Duque, P. Doménech, C. Alvarez, M. Ballesteros, P. Manzanares, 2020. Study of the bioprocess conditions to produce bioethanol from barley straw pretreated by combined soda and enzyme-catalyzed extrusion, Renewable Energy, 158, 263–270.

Energy Information Administration, 2022, How much carbon dioxide is produced from U.S. gasoline and diesel fuel consumption?, https://www.eia.gov/tools/faqs/faq.php?id=307&t=10, last consulted on November 23, 2022.

Food and Agriculture Organization of the United Nations (FAO), 2022, Crops and livestock products, https://www.fao.org/faostat/en/#data/QCL, last consulted on November 20, 2022.

National Renewable Energy Lab, 1996, Development of an aspen plus physical property database for biofuels components (no. nrel/tp-425-20685), Tech. rep., NREL, United States. https://www.nrel.gov/docs/legosti/old/20685.pdf, last consulted on November 23, 2022.

J. G. Segovia-Hernández, M. Vázquez-Ojeda, F. Gómez-Castro, C. Ramírez-Márquez, M. Errico, S. Tronci, B. G. Rong, 2014, Process control analysis for intensified bioethanol separation systems, Chemical Engineering and Processing: Process Intensification, 75, 119–125.

Antonis Kokossis, Michael C. Georgiadis, Efstratios N. Pistikopoulos (Eds.)
PROCEEDINGS OF THE 33rd European Symposium on Computer Aided Process Engineering
(ESCAPE33), June 18-21, 2023, Athens, Greece

# Optimal ship-based $CO_2$ transport chains from Mediterranean emission points to the North Sea

Federico d'Amore*, Matteo C. Romano

*Politecnico di Milano, Department of Energy, via Lambruschini 4, IT-20156 Milano (Italy).*
*federico.damore@polimi.it*

## Abstract

Carbon capture and storage is one option for reducing industrial $CO_2$ emissions. Ship $CO_2$ transport is gaining interest due to its potential competitive cost, lower risk, and higher flexibility with respect to pipelines. This work focusses on the cost of ship $CO_2$ transport chains in the European context. The objective is to develop an economic model of $CO_2$ transport via ship, including the chain stages: liquefaction, buffer storage, loading, ship, conditioning, and unloading. An optimisation model is proposed to determine the minimum transport cost from Southern European ports to permanent geological storage in the North Sea. The minimum cost is found around 26 €/t of $CO_2$ for a total transported $CO_2$ of 103 Mt/y, which may be cost-competitive with pipelines for long distance routes via large vessels (greater than 50 kt).

**Keywords**: Carbon capture and storage; $CO_2$ ship transport; chain logistics; optimisation; mixed integer linear programming.

## 1. Introduction

Energy and industry carbon dioxide ($CO_2$) sources generate more than half of the annual worldwide $CO_2$ emissions (IEA, 2022). Carbon capture and storage (CCS) consists in a range of technologies that can separate the $CO_2$ from these concentrated sources, to avoid its release to the atmosphere (Bui et al., 2018). Then, the $CO_2$ is compressed, purified, transported, and permanently stored in geological sequestration sites (IPCC, 2005).

Europe has significant potential for $CO_2$ geological sequestration, especially in the offshore area of the North Sea (Holler and Biebahn, 2011) where different CCS research projects are in an advanced phase of implementation (e.g., Northern Lights, 2022), while storage basins identified in the Mediterranean area (e.g., in the Adriatic Sea and off the coasts of Greece) currently exhibit an early-stage degree of investigation and limited capacity (Donda et al., 2011; Koukouzas et al., 2021). Ship $CO_2$ transport could foster the development of CCS projects in European regions that are far from the North Sea (e.g., the Mediterranean), and such marine alternative to pipelines may be key due to its potentially competitive cost (Weihs et al., 2014), greater flexibility (Neele et al., 2014), and lower risk (Kjarstad et al., 2016).

A ship-based $CO_2$ transport chain is constituted by multiple stages: liquefaction, intermediate storage, naval shipping, conditioning, and unloading (IEAGHG, 2020); each stage comprises several options in terms of process parameters (e.g., the transport pressure, Roussanaly et al., 2021) and chain design alternatives (e.g., the unloading strategy, Roussanaly et al., 2013; 2014). This leads to the necessity of addressing such combinatorial complexity from a systems perspective. The objective of this work is to provide a detailed economic model of $CO_2$ transport by ship; the economic model is exploited for the development of a mixed integer linear programming (MILP) optimisation framework, to minimise the total cost of a European ship-based $CO_2$ transport chain. This optimisation model is tested on a transport chain including the most significant industrial $CO_2$ emission points in southern Europe located in the vicinity of strategic $CO_2$ collection ports, and geological sequestration in the North Sea. Different unloading scenarios and carbon reduction targets are investigated. The resulting minimum unitary transport cost is 26 €/t, for transporting more than 103 Mt/y of $CO_2$, which may be competitive with pipeline transport for very long-distance routes.

## 2. Modelling framework

A ship-based $CO_2$ transport chain is constituted by several sequential stages $i$ = {$liq$, $stor$, $load$, $ship$, $cond$, $unload$, $pipe$} (Figure 1). This study assumes that the $CO_2$ arrives from the capture plant as a pressurised gas at pressure $P_{in}$. In the liquefaction plant ($liq$) the $CO_2$ is liquefied through compression at its transport pressure $P_t$. This work is based on a low $P_t$ design (7 barg, -50°C), as low $P_t$ benefits from lower costs with respect to medium $P_t$, if considering the whole transport chain (IEAGHG, 2020; Roussanaly et al., 2021). Then, the $CO_2$ is stored ($stor$) in buffer tanks to ensure continuous operation, to be subsequently loaded ($load$) onto ships ($ship$). This study considers vessel capacities $C_{ship}$ [t] form 10 kt to 100 kt per ship. The transport stages downstream ship transport depend on the unloading strategy ($unload$): (S1: port-to-port) the $CO_2$ is unloaded onshore, stored in an unloading buffer storage facility, then sent to offshore sequestration via an offshore pipeline ($pipe$); (S2: port-to-FSI) the $CO_2$ is unloaded, through equipment onboard vessels, to a floating storage and injection (FSI) platform with intermediate storage tanks; and (S3: port-to-direct injection) the $CO_2$ is directly injected to the offshore basin without any unloading buffer storage hence, lower capital investment than S1 and S2, but higher risk in operation due to batch-wise unloading. The final stage is conditioning ($cond$), which increases the $CO_2$ pressure and temperature for injection.

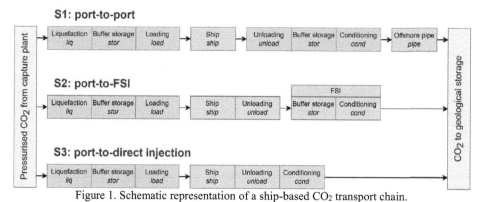

Figure 1. Schematic representation of a ship-based $CO_2$ transport chain.

## 3. Mathematical formulation

This study optimises a ship-based $CO_2$ transport chain at a European-scale. It is assumed that the $CO_2$ is captured from large-scale industrial emitters located in Southern Europe: 5 steel plants for a total emission of 26.5 Mt/y (17 % of sectorial European $CO_2$), 25 refineries for a total of 43.8 Mt/y (33 % of sectorial European $CO_2$), and 42 cement plants for a total of 33.1 Mt/y (23 % of sectorial European $CO_2$) (d'Amore et al., 2021). The spatially-explicit features are described by means of nodes $n$, comprising ports and geological sequestration in the North Sea. The $CO_2$ collection ports are chosen among large-scale harbours located in the vicinity of selected $CO_2$ emission points, and the port of Stavanger (Norway) is chosen as a $CO_2$-to-storage hub for unloading S1 (Figure 2).

Figure 2. Geographic location of $CO_2$ emission clusters and collection ports, and yearly $CO_2$ emissions available at each port for ship transport.

The objective is to minimise the total annual cost $TC$ [€/y] of the ship transport chain:

$$objective = \min(TC) \qquad (1)$$

$$TC = \sum_i TC_i = \sum_i \left( \frac{CAPEX_i}{lifetime} + OPEX_i \right) \qquad \forall i \qquad (2)$$

being $TC_i$ [€/y] given by the investment cost ($CAPEX_i$ [€/y], scaled over a 20 years' *lifetime*) and operational expenditure ($OPEX_i$ [€/y]) of the stages $i$ of the transport chain. Costs of stages $i$ are based on data from IEAGHG (2020) and the methodology is reported in d'Amore et al. (2023). The operational design input parameters are the inlet pressure $P_{in}$, the transport pressure $P_t$, the vessel capacity $C_{ship,n,n'}$, the number of ships $N_{ship,n,n'}$, the sailing distance $d_{n,n'}$ [km], and the operational transit speed $v_{ship}$ [km/h], to determine the amount of $CO_2$ transported $\dot{Q}_{ship,n,n'}$ [t/y] through vessel *ship* from $n$ to $n'$, which depends on $C_{ship,n,n'}$, $N_{ship,n,n'}$, on the number of roundtrips per year $N^{rtrip}_{ship,n,n'}$ [y⁻¹], and on the maximum vessel filling $\eta_{tank}$ (set at 95 %):

$$\dot{Q}_{ship,n,n'} = C_{ship,n,n'} \cdot N_{ship,n,n'} \cdot N^{rtrip}_{ship,n,n'} \cdot \eta_{tank} \qquad \forall ship, n, n' \qquad (3)$$

The total yearly amount of $CO_2$ transported via ships from $n$ to $n'$ is equal to:

$$\dot{Q}_{n,n'} = \sum_{ship} \dot{Q}_{ship,n,n'} \qquad \forall n, n' \qquad (4)$$

Considering the yearly amount of $CO_2$ transported $\dot{Q}^{tr}_n$ [t/y] from port $n$ and that sequestered $\dot{Q}^{seq}_n$ [t/y] in node $n$, it is possible to impose the mass balance at each port $n$:

$$\dot{Q}_n^{tr} + \sum_{n\prime} \dot{Q}_{n\prime,n} = \sum_{n\prime} \dot{Q}_{n,n\prime} + \dot{Q}_n^{seq} \qquad \forall n \qquad (5)$$

where $\dot{Q}_n^{tr}$ is bounded by the amount of $CO_2$ available $\dot{Q}_n^{capt}$ [t/y] at port $n$ (Figure 2). The final aim is to sequester a fraction $\alpha$ [%] of the total $CO_2$ from capture plants:

$$\sum_n \dot{Q}_n^{tr} = \alpha \cdot \sum_n \dot{Q}_n^{capt} \qquad (6)$$

## 4. Results

The MILP problem was optimised on a 3.0 GHz computer (32 GB RAM), by using GAMS software and CPLEX solver (optimality gap lower than 2 %). It emerges that liquefaction and ship represent about 10 % and 40 %, respectively, of the total investment, independently from the analysed unloading scenario. Other significant contributions to capital expenditures were found to be case-specific: namely offshore pipelines in S1 (up to 39 % of the total investment), FSI unit in the S2 option (comparable with the cost of ships), and conditioning in S3. Variable costs are dominated by ships operation and by liquefaction. Direct unloading (S3) emerges as the most cost-effective scenario. In fact, the results show that the unitary cost for transporting via ship 103 Mt/y of $CO_2$ is equal to: 26.1 €/t (S1), 26.4 €/t (S2), and 25.6 €/t (S3, though it could be an unfavourable design due to discontinuous injection) (Figure 3). As $\alpha$ increases the selected ports and distances increase as well, so the unitary cost rises because: (i) more ports determine the installation of more onshore infrastructure; and (ii) more ships are needed as each journey takes longer. In fact, the optimal chain design avoids as much as possible (i.e., for low values of $\alpha$) ports far from Stavanger, to minimise ship transport costs. For instance (Figure 4), the optimal chain for S3 involves the use of few but large ships from Spain and Portugal for $\alpha$=30 %, while the network expands to more ships and ports located in Mediterranean France and Italy for $\alpha$= 60%, and towards Greece and the Black Sea for $\alpha$=100 %.

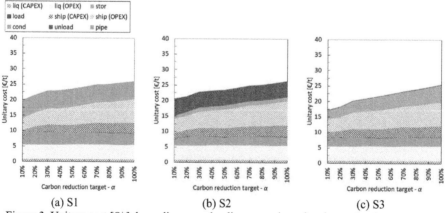

Figure 3. Unitary cost [€/t] depending on unloading scenario and carbon reduction target $\alpha$.

Ships investment cost depends on the choice in the vessel size: a decrease in the maximum size from 100 kt to 50 kt produces a +38 % increase in the investment for ships, though with limited effect on the overall cost of the transport chain (+10 %). Differently, deploying small vessels (10 kt) would double the chain cost. At the same time, optimised ship $CO_2$ transport through large-scale vessels (over 50 kt) is cost competitive with pipelines for long-distance routes, e.g., to connect Greece with the North Sea (Figure 5).

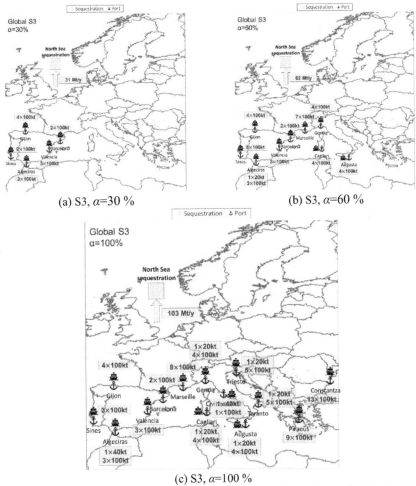

(a) S3, $\alpha$=30 %

(b) S3, $\alpha$=60 %

(c) S3, $\alpha$=100 %

Figure 4. Optimal ship transport chains for S3 under increasing carbon reduction target $\alpha$.

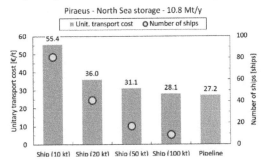

Figure 5. Ship vs. pipeline long-distance $CO_2$ transport from Greece (Piraeus) to North Sea storage. Unitary transport costs for pipelines are computed from d'Amore et al. (2021).

## 5. Conclusions

This study proposed a modelling tool for the economic and logistic optimisation of ship $CO_2$ transport chains from large-scale Southern Europe emitters to the North Sea offshore storage. Depending on the unloading strategy, we found that the minimum unitary cost for transporting via ship 103 Mt/y of $CO_2$ is equal to 26.1 €/t (port-to-port), 26.4 €/t (port-to-floating storage and injection), and 25.6 €/t (port-to-direct injection), though this latter does not comprise a buffer storage prior to injection and is designed as a batch-wise process. Importantly, it was demonstrated that an optimal design of ship transport via large-scale vessels (50-100 kt) can be cost competitive with pipeline transport for very long distance routes (e.g., from Greece to the North Sea), while the use of small ships (10 kt) results in twice the cost of pipelines.

## References

M. Bui, C.S. Adjiman, A. Bardow, E.J. Anthony, A. Boston, S. Brown, P.S. Fennell, S. Fuss, A. Galindo, L.A. Hackett, J.P. Hallett, H.J. Herzog, G. Jackson, J. Kemper, S. Krevor, G.C. Maitland, M. Matuszewski, I.S. Metcalfe, C. Petit, G. Puxty, J. Reimer, D.M. Reiner, E.S. Rubin, S.A. Scott, N. Shah, B. Smit, J.P.M. Trusler, P. Webley, J. Wilcox, N. Mac Dowell, 2018, Carbon capture and storage (CCS): The way forward, Energy Environ. Sci., 11, 1062-1176

F. d'Amore, L. Natalucci, M.C. Romano, 2023, Optimisation of ship-based $CO_2$ transport chains from Southern Europe to the North Sea, In peer review

F. d'Amore, M.C. Romano, F. Bezzo, 2021, Optimal design of European supply chains for carbon capture and storage from industrial emission sources including pipe and ship transport, Int. J. Green. Gas Control, 109, 103372

F. Donda, V. Volpi, S. Persoglia, D. Parushev, 2011, $CO_2$ storage potential of deep saline aquifers: The case of Italy, Int. J. Greenh. Gas Control, 5, 327-335

S. Holler, P. Viebahn, 2011, Assessment of $CO_2$ storage capacity in geological formations of Germany and Northern Europe, Energy Proc, 4, 4897-4904

IEA, 2022, Data and statistics, https://www.iea.org/data-and-statistics/data-browser?country=WORLD&fuel=Energyconsumption&indicator=CO2Industry

IEAGHG, 2020, The status and challenges of $CO_2$ shipping infrastructures, https://ieaghg.org/ccs-resources/blog/new-ieaghg-report-the-status-and-challenges-of-co2-shipping-infrastructures

IPCC, 2005, IPCC Special Report on Carbon Dioxide Capture and Storage. Prepared by Working Group III of the Intergovernmental Panel on Climate Change, https://www.ipcc.ch/report/carbon-dioxide-capture-and-storage/

J. Kjarstad, R. Skagestad, N.H. Eldrup, F. Johnsson, 2016, Ship transport - A low cost and low risk $CO_2$ transport option in the Nordic countries, Int. J. Greenh. Gas Control, 54, 168-184

N. Koukouzas, P. Tyrologou, D. Karapanos, J. Carneiro, P. Pereira, F. de Mesquita Lobo Veloso, P. Koutsovitis, C. Karkalis, E. Manoukian, R. Karametou, 2021, Carbon capture, utilisation and storage as a defense tool against climate change: Current developments in west Macedonia (Greece), Energies, 14, 3321

F. Neele, H.A. Haugen, R. Skagestad, 2014, Ship transport of $CO_2$ - Breaking the $CO_2$-EOR deadlock, Energy Procedia, 63, 2638-2644

Northern Lights, 2022, Website, https://norlights.com/

S. Roussanaly, J.P. Jakobsen, E.H. Hognes, A.L. Brunsvold, 2013, Benchmarking of $CO_2$ transport technologies: Part I - Onshore pipeline and shipping between two onshore areas, Int. J. Greenh. Gas Control, 19, 584-594

S. Roussanaly, A.L. Brunsvold, E.S. Hognes, 2014, Benchmarking of $CO_2$ transport technologies: Part II - Offshore pipeline and shipping to an offshore site, Int. J. Greenh. Gas Control, 28, 283-299

S. Roussanaly, H. Deng, G. Skaugen, T. Gundersen, 2021, At what pressure shall $CO_2$ be transported by ship? An in-depth cost comparison of 7 and 15 barg shipping, Energies, 14, 5635

G.A.F. Weihs, K. Kumar, D.E. Wiley, 2014, Understanding the economic feasibility of ship transport of $CO_2$ within the CCS chain, Energy Procedia, 63, 2630-2637

Antonis Kokossis, Michael C. Georgiadis, Efstratios N. Pistikopoulos (Eds.)
PROCEEDINGS OF THE 33rd European Symposium on Computer Aided Process Engineering
(ESCAPE33), June 18-21, 2023, Athens, Greece

# DynHeat: Heat Exchanger Network Design for Batch Processes via Dynamic Optimization

Dörthe Franzisca Hagedorn,[a] Sören Demandt,[a] Florian Joseph Baader,[b,c]
Christiane Reinert,[a] Niklas von der Aßen [a]

[a] *Institute of Technical Thermodynamics, RWTH Aachen University, Schinkelstr. 8, 52062 Aachen, Germany*
[b] *Energy & Process Systems Engineering - Department of Mechanical and Process Engineering, ETH Zurich, 8092 Zürich, Switzerland*
[c] *Institute of Energy and Climate Research - Energy Systems Engineering (IEK-10), Forschungszentrum Jülich GmbH, Jülich, Germany*

## Abstract

Heat integration can reduce the consumption of external utilities in batch processes. Batch processes often include process steps with dynamic temperature progression, such as heating in vessels. During heat integration between those process steps, the temperature difference decreases over time. Exploiting the thermodynamic potential for heat integration can, therefore, lead to long process durations. Hence, there is a trade-off between the total cost of heat integration and the process duration. A method is missing to map this trade-off while considering the dynamic temperature progression. We introduce the Dyn-Heat optimization method for heat exchanger network design in dynamic batch processes based on dynamic optimization. We apply the DynHeat method to a case study and perform a multi-objective optimization regarding the process duration and the total cost. We find that the DynHeat method can propose a suitable heat exchanger network design and operation mode for the regarded case study.

**Keywords**: Energy Efficiency, Heat Integration, Pinch Method, Logarithmic Mean Temperature Difference, Dynamic Processes

## 1. Introduction: Heat Integration in Batch Processes

Meeting thermal energy demands in industrial processes by external utilities is economically and environmentally expensive. Heat integration can reduce the consumption of external utilities by reusing waste heat. For heat integration, a heat exchanger network needs to be built. To obtain cost-optimal heat exchanger networks, the total cost should be considered, comprising operational costs for utility consumption and investment costs for heat-exchangers.

Common existing approaches for heat exchanger network design, based on the Pinch Method (Linnhoff and Flower, 1978) or the superstructure model by Yee and Grossmann (1990) and most of their extensions, reviewed by Klemeš and Kravanja (2013), assume stationary process streams. In practice, many industries work with instationary batch processes. In batch processes, the products are often cooled down or heated up in vessels, which leads to temperatures changing over time. When using heat integration in such processes, the transferred heat between two products decreases over time as the temperature difference between those products decreases. Thus, exploiting the full thermodynamic potential for heat integration between two products leads to long process durations. Hence, heat integration in dynamic batch processes causes a trade-off between process duration and total cost for heat integration. This trade-off needs to be considered when designing heat exchanger networks for dynamic batch processes. A suitable method for heat exchanger network design for dynamic batch processes should, thus, represent the dynamic temperature profiles accurately to determine both the amount of integrated heat and the process duration.

In practice, the Pinch Method is commonly used for estimating the thermodynamic potential for heat integration of a process. The Pinch Method can be adapted to varying thermal demands by averaging the demands over time (time-average model) or by dividing the time horizon into several time slices (time-slice model) (Kemp and Lim, 2020). However, both approaches still assume temporary stationary process streams. Vaselenak et al. (1986) propose a heuristic method to handle different types of temperature progression of batch products in tanks in heat integration problems. Dowidat et al. (2014) extend the time-slice model to dynamic temperature progression by introducing additional time slices. However, both approaches do not explicitly design a heat exchanger network. In Dowidat et al. (2016), the authors introduce a match ranking matrix for the design of economically efficient heat exchanger networks. However, the approach relies on heuristic rules instead of considering the actual costs. Furthermore, in all the approaches mentioned above, the timing of the processes needs to be known in advance, and the trade-off between process duration and total costs, is not taken into account. Castro et al. (2015) introduce an optimization model for combined heat integration and scheduling in order to optimize the makespan of the process. However, in their approach, matches between process streams can be derived but no design optimization is included.

In conclusion, no optimization method exists that can represent the trade-off between process duration and total cost for thermal energy supply in heat integrated dynamic batch processes. In this contribution, we bridge this gap by developing the DynHeat optimization method for heat exchanger network design of dynamic batch processes while taking the trade-off between total cost and the process duration into account.

## 2. The DynHeat Method

The aim of the DynHeat method is to design a heat exchanger network for dynamic batch processes while taking the trade-off between total cost, comprising operational costs and investment costs, and the process duration into account. In the corresponding DynHeat optimization model, we model products that either need to be heated or cooled in vessels. The thermal demands can be provided by external utilities or via heat integration. For heat integration, there is the option of building an external heat exchanger between every two vessels. A scheme of the DynHeat model is shown in *Figure 1*.

To address the trade-off between cost and duration, we perform a multi-objective optimization with the total cost $C^{total}$ of one process run as one objective function and the process duration $\tau^{final}$ as the other objective function. The total cost $C^{total}$ for one process run are composed of the investment cost for the heat exchangers and operational cost for external utility:

$$C^{total} = \left( \sum_{h \in H} (A_h^{cu} + A_h^{HI}) + \sum_{c \in C} (A_c^{hu} + A_c^{HI}) + \sum_{h \in H} \sum_{c \in C} A_{h,c}^{HE} \right) c^A$$
$$+ \sum_{h \in H} Q_h^{cu} \, c_h^{cu} + \sum_{c \in C} Q_c^{hu} \, c_c^{hu} \tag{1}$$

With the surface areas of the heat exchangers for hot utility ($A_h^{cu}$), cold utility ($A_c^{hu}$), hot product to heat transfer media (HTM) ($A_h^{HI}$) and cold product to HTM ($A_c^{HI}$) and the external heat exchanger ($A_{h,c}^{HE}$). The cost factor $c^A$ refers to the specific investment costs for the heat exchanger surface areas scaled down to one process run. The operational costs comprise the amount of heat supplied by the cold utility $Q_h^{cu}$ and hot utility $Q_c^{hu}$ and the specific price for cold utility $c^{cu}$ and hot utility $c^{hu}$.

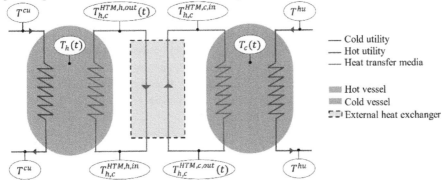

Figure 1: *Exemplary scheme of the DynHeat model for one hot and one cold product. The left vessel (orange) contains the hot product of the temperature $T_h(t)$ which can be cooled down by cold utility of the temperature $T^{cu}$ (dark blue). Analoguesly the cold product in the right vessel (light blue) of the temperature $T_c(t)$ can be heated up by hot utility (red) of the temperature $T^{hu}$. Both vessels can be connected by an external heat exchanger (grey) with heat transfer media (HTM) (green line). The temperature of the HTM at the inlet of the vessels $T_{h,c}^{HTM,h,in}$ and $T_{h,c}^{HTM,c,in}$, is constant.*

In the DynHeat model, we make the following assumptions: The vessels are perfectly mixed, and no heat losses occur. The external heat exchangers are counter-flow heat exchangers. All heat capacities, heat transfer coefficients, and the temperature of the utilities are constant. The HTM is not allowed to function as a storage, i.e., the total integrated heat flow must be transferred from the hot product to the cold product immediately, and the temperature of the HTM at the inlets of the vessels $T_{h,c}^{HTM,c,in}$ and $T_{h,c}^{HTM,h,in}$ is constant. The HTM between a hot and a cold product has the same heat capacity rate on both sides of the external heat exchanger, i.e., the temperature difference along the external heat exchanger $(T_{h,c}^{HTM,h,in} - T_{h,c}^{HTM,h,in}(t)) = (T_{h,c}^{HTM,h,out}(t) - T_{h,c}^{HTM,c,in})$ is constant along the heat exchanger surface area.

In the following, we describe the DynHeat model in detail. The most important equations are given for hot products that need cooling. The equivalent equations for cold products that need heating can be derived analogously.

The temperature profile $T_h(t)$ of a hot product $h$ with the mass $m_h$ and heat capacity $c_{p,h}$ changes due to heat transferred to cold utility $\dot{Q}_h^{cu}(t)$ or by heat integration with a cold product $\dot{Q}_{h,c}^{HI}(t)$:

$$\frac{dT_h(t)}{dt} = -\frac{\left(\sum_{c \in C} \dot{Q}_{h,c}^{HI}(t)\right) + \dot{Q}_h^{cu}(t)}{m_h \cdot c_{p,h}} \qquad \forall h \in H \qquad (2)$$

The heat flow from a hot product to the HTM $\dot{Q}_{h,c}^{HI}(t)$ is defined by

$$\dot{Q}_{h,c}^{HI}(t) = \dot{m}_{h,c}^{HTM} c_p^{HTM}\left(T_{h,c}^{HTM,h,out}(t) - T_{h,c}^{HTM,h,in}\right) \qquad \forall h \in H, \forall c \in C \qquad (3)$$

, where $\dot{m}_{h,c}^{HTM}$ is the given mass flow of the HTM between hot vessel $h$ and cold vessel $c$ and $c_p^{HTM}$ is the given constant heat capacity of the HTM.

The temperature of the HTM at the outlet of the hot vessel $T_{hc}^{HTM,h,out}(t)$ is defined by the temperature progression along the heat exchanger between the hot product and the HTM (Glück, 2017):

$$T_{h,c}^{HTM,h,out}(t) =$$

$$T_{h,c}^{HTM,h,in}(t) \cdot e^{-\frac{k\ A_{h,c}^{HTM,h}}{\dot{m}_{h,c}^{HTM}\ c_p^{HTM}}} + T_h(t) \cdot \left(1 - e^{-\frac{k\ A_{h,c}^{HTM,h}}{\dot{m}^{HTM}\ c_p^{HTM}}}\right) \qquad \forall h \in H, \forall c \in C \quad (4)$$

, where $A_{h,c}^{HTM,h}$ is the surface area of the heat exchanger between the hot product and the HTM, and $k$ is the constant heat transfer coefficient of the heat exchanger.

Finally, the required surface area of the external heat exchanger $A_{h,c}^{HE}$ can be derived by the transferred heat and the temperatures of the heat transfer medium by

$$\dot{Q}_{h,c}^{HI}(t) \geq k\ A_{h,c}^{HE}\ \Delta T_{h,c}^{HTM}(t) \qquad\qquad\qquad \forall h \in H, \forall c \in C \quad (5)$$

, where the temperature difference $\Delta T_{h,c}^{HTM}(t)$ describes the temperature difference in the external heat exchanger. As in Verheyen and Zhang (2006), we assume that the biggest surface area needed at any time is installed and that all other operation modes can be realized by bypassing a part of the streams. The heat exchanger surface area for utility supply can be derived analogously. We assume a sequential process, meaning that external utilities are only used after heat integration is complete. Logical big-M constraints denote the beginning and end of utility supply and heat integration.

To solve the resulting dynamic-algebraic optimization problem, we discretize the time by orthogonal collocation on finite elements using pyomo.dae (Nicholson et al., 2018). Through the collocation, the discretized problem is a fully algebraic mixed-integer non-linear optimization problem (MINLP) (Biegler, 2010).

## 3. Application to a Case Study

We apply the DynHeat method to a case study with one hot and one cold product. We adapt our process parameters to a milk pasteurization process, where fresh milk is first heated to a certain temperature and, afterwards, is cooled down to its final storing temperature. We assume that the heating of one batch and the cooling of another batch take place simultaneously. We adapt the process parameters from a case study in Fellows (2017) .

We compute the case study on an Intel(R) Xeon(R) CPU E5-1660 v4 with 3.30GHz running on Microsoft Windows Server 2016 Standard with kernel version 10.0.14393. We use python 3.7 as a modeling language. As a solver, we use baron version 20.4.14 (Kılınç and Sahinidis, 2018). We apply eight threads. The relative gap is set to 1E-8. For the collocation method, we choose seven finite elements and 3 collocation points per element. We set a limit of 1000 *sec* to the time horizon to facilitate the solution of the problem.

With the DynHeat model, we perform a multi-objective optimization of the given case study, minimizing the process duration and the total cost of one process run. Figure 2 (left) shows the resulting Pareto front for the selected case study. The Pareto front visualizes the trade-off between the total cost for one process run and the process duration.

In the left anchor point, the total cost is minimal. Heat integration takes place as long as possible, such that the smallest possible amount of utility is used. However, thereby the maximal allowed time horizon of 1000 *sec* is required. In contrast, the right anchor point shows the results for minimal process duration. For minimal process duration, the thermal demands are covered by utility only. By the increased use of external utility, the total cost increase by almost 60% compared to the minimal total cost. Accordingly, heat integration can significantly reduce the total cost in the regarded case study.

Furthermore, there is one solution point between the two anchor points, representing a compromise between process duration and total cost. Figure 2 (right) shows the temperature profiles and the heat flows for the compromise solution. The heat integration is stopped before the temperature of the hot and the cold product reach the same level. Instead, a temperature difference of 19.02 $K$ remains and utility is used to cover the remaining demands. This compromise increases the total cost only slightly, while reducing the process duration by almost 600 $sec$ compared to the left anchor point.

All in all, the Pareto front shows that heat integration can reduce the total cost significantly in the regarded case study. However, heat integration extends the process duration notably. Given this trade-off, the DynHeat method also offers solutions with a finite process duration that still significantly benefit from heat integration.

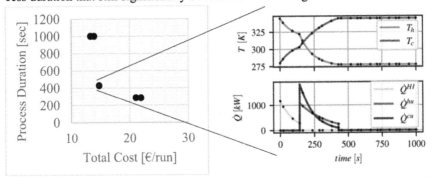

*Figure 2: Left: Resulting Pareto front of the DynHeat method for the selected case study. Right: Process operation for one middle point on the Pareto front. The upper diagram shows the temperature progression of the hot product $T_h(t)$ (orange) and the cold product $T_c(t)$ (blue) over time. The lower diagram shows the corresponding heat flows (heat integration $\dot{Q}_{h,c}^{HI}(t)$ (yellow), cold utility $\dot{Q}_h^{cu}(t)$ (blue) and hot utility $\dot{Q}_c^{hu}(t)$ (red)).*

While the orthogonal collocation in the DynHeat method allows for a more accurate representation of the dynamic temperature profiles than existing approaches, it still leads to some discretization errors. The dynamic profiles are not represented exactly but approximated by polynomials. In our case, the DynHeat method leads to a discretization error concerning the integrated heat of 1.1 %. Thus, we conclude that the chosen settings are sufficient for accurate representation of the temperature profiles. Furthermore, due to the discretization, the process can only switch from heat integration to utility supply, and also finish the utility supply, at the boundaries of a finite element of the discretized time horizon. Consequently, the obtained solutions highly depend on the number of finite elements. The discretization, thus, restricts the solution space, but all solutions of the discretized problem are feasible to the original problem.

With the chosen settings, we find that the DynHeat model does not terminate to global optimality within the allowed computing time of 3000 $sec$ for all points on the pareto front. Thus, further research on the model complexity and solvability needs to be done. However, the results show that the DynHeat model can propose reasonable solutions for heat integration in batch processes while considering dynamic temperature changes.

## 4. Conclusion

In this contribution, we introduce the DynHeat method for heat exchanger network design in dynamic batch processes. We model the temperature dynamics of the batch process and discretize the problem by orthogonal collocation to a fully algebraic MINLP. To the best of our knowledge, the DynHeat method is the first optimization method that meets the trade-off between process duration and total cost for heat integration in dynamic batch processes while taking design decisions for heat exchangers into account. We find that the DynHeat method enables us to find solutions that offer a compromise between total cost and process duration.

## Acknowledgements

This study is funded by the German Federal Ministry of Economic Affairs and Energy (ref. no.: 03EN2031D). FB received financial support from the Swiss Federal Office of Energy through the project "SWEET PATHFNDR". CR received financial support by the Ministry of Economics, Innovation, Digitalization and Energy of North-Rhine Westphalia (ref. no.: EFO 0001G). We gratefully acknowledge all the support.

## References

L.T. Biegler, 2010, Nonlinear programming. Society for Industrial and Applied Mathematics, Philadelphia, Pa.

P.M. Castro, B. Custódio, H.A. Matos, 2015, Optimal scheduling of single stage batch plants with direct heat integration, Comput Chem Eng, vol. 82, 172

C. Dowidat, M. Kalliski, G. Schembecker, C. Bramsiepe, 2016, Synthesis of batch heat exchanger networks utilizing a match ranking matrix, Appl Therm Eng, vol. 100, 78

C. Dowidat, K. Ulonska, C. Bramsiepe, G. Schembecker, 2014, Heat integration in batch processes including heat streams with time dependent temperature progression, Appl Therm Eng, vol. 70, 1, 321

P. Fellows, 2017, Food processing technology. Woodhead Publishing, Duxford, United Kingdom

B. Glück, 2017, Wärmeübertrager, Raumheizflächen, Behälteraufheizung, Verl. für Bauwesen, Berlin

I.C. Kemp, J.S. Lim, 2020, Pinch Analysis for Energy and Carbon Footprint Reduction: User Guide to Process Integration for the Efficient Use of Energy. Butterworth-Heinemann

M.R. Kılınç, N.V. Sahinidis, 2018, Exploiting integrality in the global optimization of mixed-integer nonlinear programming problems with BARON, Optimization Methods and Software, vol. 33, 3, 540

J.J. Klemeš, Z. Kravanja, 2013, Forty years of Heat Integration: Pinch Analysis (PA) and Mathematical Programming (MP), Curr Opin Chem Eng, vol. 2, 4, 461

B. Linnhoff, J.R. Flower, 1978, Synthesis of heat exchanger networks: I. Systematic generation of energy optimal networks, AIChE J, vol. 24, 4, 633

B. Nicholson, J.D. Siirola, J.-P. Watson, V.M. Zavala, L.T. Biegler, 2018, pyomo.dae: a modeling and automatic discretization framework for optimization with differential and algebraic equations, Math Prog Comp, vol. 10, 2, 187

J.A. Vaselenak, I.E. Grossmann, A.W. Westerberg, 1986, Heat integration in batch processing, Ind Eng Chem Process Des Dev, vol. 25, 2, 357

W. Verheyen, N. Zhang, 2006, Design of flexible heat exchanger network for multi-period operation, Chem Eng Sci, vol. 61, 23, 7730

T.F. Yee, I.E. Grossmann, 1990, Simultaneous optimization models for heat integration—II. Heat exchanger network synthesis, Comput Chem Eng, vol. 14, 10, 1165

Antonis Kokossis, Michael C. Georgiadis, Efstratios N. Pistikopoulos (Eds.)
PROCEEDINGS OF THE 33rd European Symposium on Computer Aided Process Engineering
(ESCAPE33), June 18-21, 2023, Athens, Greece
© 2023 Elsevier B.V. All rights reserved.  http://dx.doi.org/10.1016/B978-0-443-15274-0.50438-8

# Process Simulation Approaches to Reduce Commercial Risk of CCS Projects

Ryan Muir[a], Ralph Cos[b], Chloe Smith[b], Stelios Papastratos[c]

[a]AVEVA, Lake Forest, California, United States of America
[b]AVEVA, Munich, Bavaria, Germany
[c]AVEVA, Thessaloniki, Greece

## Abstract

Sustainability is increasingly emerging as a license to operate for Owner-Operator and EPC companies. As industry looks towards sustainable processes that reduce carbon emissions, Carbon Capture and Storage (CCS) has emerged as a viable way of increasing sustainability while reducing operational costs from emissions. For CCS technologies, process simulation is an essential tool for evaluating the economic and environmental feasibility of greenfield and retrofit projects with accelerated schedules and limited capital. When integrated with plant data, process simulation also enables real-time accounting of carbon emissions from operations. Accurate and timely accounting of process emissions is critical for justifying CCS project costs, evaluating different CCS technologies, and quantifying emission and cost savings after project execution. In this paper, we will show how this new approach enables engineers to quickly evaluate CCS alternatives by considering cost vs. relative capture rates to further reduce the commercial risk of new projects.

**Keywords**: Process simulation, sustainability, reducing commercial risk, emission monitoring, economics of CCUS.

## 1. Carbon Capture and Storage

The global carbon capture market is expected to grow from $1.9 billion in 2020 to $7.0 billion by 2030. This growth represents a Compound Annual Growth Rate (CAGR) of nearly 13.8% between 2021 and 2030 (Allied Market Research, 2021). This growth is primarily attributed to emission reduction goals set by governments around the world and the companies responsible for reducing emissions to achieve these goals. CCS technologies allow for emission reduction with limited impact on existing processes, making this technology a good candidate for reducing emissions in the short- to medium-term. For some sectors like steel and cement, where renewable technologies are not readily available or scalable, CCS may be the only cost-effective strategy for reducing emissions.

In addition to reducing emissions from existing processes, carbon capture technologies are critical for supporting the ongoing hydrogen energy transition. Green hydrogen technologies like electrolysis offer a long-term solution to decarbonization. However, many of these technologies are not mature enough today to meet the rising demand for hydrogen. In 2021, Steam Methane Reforming (SMR) of natural gas accounted for nearly 60% of hydrogen production. However, SMR can have an emission factor (kg of CO2-equivalent emissions per kg of hydrogen produced) of over 12 kg/kg (Mehmeti et al., 2018). Despite the high emission factor, SMR will be critical to meeting the short- to medium-term demands of the hydrogen market. Carbon capture offers a 'best of both worlds' approach that allows for continued use of SMR for hydrogen production while offering a path to reduce emissions from the process by up to 90% (IEAGHG, 2017).

## 2. Commercial Challenges

One common challenge of CCS projects is the cost of operating these units. The cost of CCS, measured as the cost per ton of $CO_2$ captured, is inversely related to the $CO_2$ concentration in the process streams. **Figure 1** shows the cost of carbon capture for a variety of industries (Baylin-Stern and Berghout, 2021).

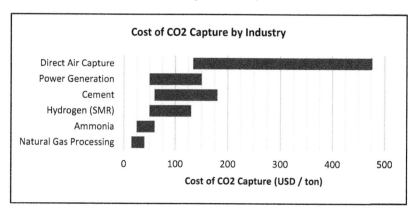

**Figure 1-** Relative cost of carbon capture by industry (Balylin-Stern and Berghout, 2021)

In addition to the operating cost of carbon capture units, companies must also weigh the capital cost and commercial risk of these projects. Recent analysis found that, on average, large capital projects overrun planned capital expenditure by 80% and are delivered 20 months beyond the original schedule (Agarwal et al., 2016). Due to the immediate need for carbon emission reduction, accelerated schedules for CCS projects will remain important for the success of this technology. Digital tools provide opportunities to reduce cost and schedule risk by integrating modern work process with next-generation modeling technologies.

## 3. Reducing Commercial Risk with Digital Tools

### 3.1. Introduction

Government incentives, the growing cost of carbon emissions from carbon tax programs, and emerging technologies have made CCS projects more feasible today than ever before. However, significant capital risk for these projects still exists. Government incentives are tied closely to current political ideology and do not provide a long-term guarantee of success; carbon tax programs are difficult to forecast throughout the length of a project; and emerging technologies are unproven and may present technical challenges that increase cost and project timelines.

Process simulation stands to reduce many of these risks by allowing owner-operator and EPC companies to gain greater insight into the technical and economic impact of decisions made while designing a new CCS unit. Solvent system, process flow (for example, pre-combustion vs. post-combustion carbon capture), and operating condition selections all impact the operating and capital cost of CCS projects. As shown in this study, the impact of these selections can be modeled and studied in detail using a next-generation process simulation platform.

### 3.2. Emission Calculations and Cost Accounting

As a first step in any CCS project, companies must understand the magnitude of their existing carbon emissions and the associated operational expenditure from these emissions. As Carbon Tax and Cap-and-Trade programs become more widespread, accurate real-time accounting of process emissions will be critical for justifying the additional capital and operational costs of CCS technologies. Many companies today rely on complex spreadsheets for this accounting. However, collecting accurate data for these spreadsheets is cumbersome and does not allow for real-time emission monitoring and accounting. Modern process simulation platforms allow engineers to easily calculate carbon emissions, operational cost, and capital expenditure for any process.

Adding both emission and cost calculations to a single process simulation model allow for process-wide optimization of both values. For example, AVEVA Process Simulation allows users to simultaneously calculate overall emissions for any process and include these emissions in the total operating cost. Alongside built-in operating and capital cost estimates, users can leverage the application's optimization features to find the ideal tradeoff between carbon capture rates and operating/capital spend for a CCS project.

These values can also be monitored in real-time without the need for additional monitoring equipment (i.e., soft sensing) by connecting the simulation to a process historian and live process data. Accurate and timely accounting of process emissions is critical for justifying CCS project costs, evaluating different CCS technologies, and quantifying emission and cost savings after project execution.

### 3.3. Digital Twins: Integrated Process Simulation Models

Process simulation has historically been used during the Conceptual Design and FEED stages of projects. At later stages of the project, simulation models remain largely disconnected from other project data and are often not used to diagnose operational issues. Next-generation simulation tools, however, break down the silos between process engineers and other project disciplines by connecting models to engineering and operational databases. These connections enable first-principle driven real-time monitoring and 'evergreen' models that receive project and asset data from common engineering databases. Interfaces between process simulation models, engineering databases, and real-time operational data are the basis for Engineering and Operating Digital Twin models. Such a unified approach to project design, with integrated simulation, engineering, and design data increases design efficiency by up to 30% and may reduce the total installed cost of a CCS project by up to 5% (AVEVA, 2020).

## 4. Process Simulation Case Study

### 4.1. Introduction

While traditional process simulation tools have been sufficient to model well-understood technologies, they have limited data and equipment models available to support emerging technologies like carbon capture and new energy markets.

Overcoming limitations of traditional process simulators developed in the 1980s, new simulation packages enable companies to explore a range of CCS technologies within a single simulation platform. New simulation platforms provide an open and extendible model writing infrastructure and customizable thermodynamic methods that can incorporate complex heat and mass transfer equations without custom programming. This infrastructure allows users to optimize the design and operation of CCS technologies using new and/or proprietary solvents and solvent systems. An open model writing framework, paired with rigorous thermodynamics and dozens of standard customizable equipment models, allows engineers to quickly study the scale-up of new process developments with limited commercial risk.

To demonstrate the utility of simulation platforms when designing carbon capture processes, a case study was performed comparing a variety of process metrics for pre-combustion and post-combustion carbon capture for a typical SMR process. The processes were modeled in AVEVA Process Simulation utilizing custom reaction submodels and thermodynamic properties for the first-generation monoethanolamine (MEA) solvent. While newer amine solvents are now available, reaction kinetics and thermodynamic property data is widely available for MEA which makes it a good candidate for this illustrative study.

For purposes of this study, three simulation models were built: a SMR process with no carbon capture, SMR with pre-combustion carbon capture, and SMR with post-combustion carbon capture. Operating parameters and Key Performance Indicators (KPIs) were compared across the three simulations. SMR process specifications, MEA loading, and CO2 capture rates were kept consistent across the simulations for easier comparison of results.

### 4.2. Modeling Methodology

One of the greatest challenges of building process simulation models for emerging technologies is the lack of thermodynamic data and unit operation models for these processes. Historically, users have leveraged CAPE-OPEN and similar interfaces to incorporate new unit operations into existing process simulation packages. However, these models often rely on expert users with programming knowledge to build and distribute the packages. This is a significant hurdle to process simulation users who would like to incorporate custom models but do not have programming expertise or the time to build such detailed models.

Next-generation process simulation tools eliminate this obstacle by providing an open modeling framework that all simulation users can access. Modern frameworks require no programming and give users access to the same model writing tools used by internal developers of the simulation platform. For this study, the kinetic rate expressions proposed by Xu and Froment (1989) are used to model the SMR reactor. The equilibrium expressions proposed by Hla et al. (2009) and Moe (1962) were used to model the high- and low-temperature water gas shift (WGS) reactions, respectively. **Figure 2** illustrates how these rate expressions were added to the open model writing framework of AVEVA Process Simulation.

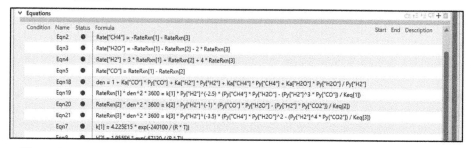

**Figure 2** – Model editor window for AVEVA Process Simulation, a next-generation process simulation application. Users define a set of variables, parameters, and conditions then write custom equations in an open modeling framework.

The simulations used the electrolyte NRTL (eNTRL) method available in AVEVA Process Simulation with custom thermodynamic parameters taken from Zhang et al. (2011). Equilibrium reactions were modeled based on the work of Bishnoi and Rochelle (2000). To account for the impact of reaction kinetics on mass-transfer in the film layer, additional enhancement factors were modeled in the Rate-based distillation column using the custom modeling framework.

*4.3. Results and Discussion*

The results of the three models built in AVEVA Process Simulation are summarized in **Table 1**. As previously noted, the design specifications for the SMR and subsequent high- and low-temperature WGS reactions were kept the same across all three simulations to facilitate easier comparison between processes. Given the wide variation in raw material and energy prices across regions, this study uses the energy intensity (GJ / tCO2 captured) and lean MEA makeup flow in place of operating cost. Sustainability metrics like Global Warming Potential (GWP) and Total CO2-equivalent (CO2e) emissions are also reported for each simulation.

**Table 1** – Results of a pre- and post-combustion carbon capture simulation built in the next-generation simulation platform AVEVA Process Simulation

| Property | Baseline SMR with no Carbon Capture | Pre-Combustion Capture using MEA | Post-Combustion Capture using MEA |
|---|---|---|---|
| *Steam Methane Reforming* | | | |
| Steam-to-carbon ratio | 2.75 | 2.75 | 2.75 |
| Natural Gas Feed [Nm3/h] | 65,000 | 65,000 | 65,000 |
| Feed Water [kg/h] | 107,730 | 107,730 | 107,520 |
| Export Steam [kg/h] | 17,150 | 17,150 | 17,180 |
| Methane Conversion | 0.870 | 0.870 | 0.867 |
| *Carbon Capture* | | | |
| Syngas Feed [Nm3/h] | - | 284,880 | 298,140 |
| CO2 Capture Rate [%] | - | 80 | 80 |
| Lean MEA Flow [m3/h] | - | 982.6 | 2,564 |
| Energy Intensity [GJ/tCO2] | - | 3.22 | 5.60 |
| Lean MEA CO2 Load | - | 0.21 | 0.21 |
| *Overall Process Sustainability Metrics* | | | |
| Global Warming Potential | 7.79 | 4.38 | 4.73 |
| Total CO2e Emissions [t/h] | 134.6 | 80.86 | 81.60 |
| Captured CO2 [Nm3/h] | - | 41,750 | 53,411 |

The results of this study illustrate the importance of process simulation when evaluating carbon capture processes. For example, the post-combustion unit in this study captures more total CO2 compared to pre-combustion capture, but results in a higher overall GWP and CO2e emission footprint due to its elevated energy intensity. The makeup MEA requirement for post-combustion capture is also 2.6x that of the pre-combustion configuration. AVEVA Process Simulation accounts for emissions from both direct and indirect sources which enables a more complete comparison between these processes. While post-combustion capture allows for capture of both flue gas and process CO2 emissions (produced as a byproduct of SMR and WGS reactions), the lower pressure flue gas stream makes the capture less efficient. A holistic simulation model that calculates process metrics alongside sustainability and economic indicators enables accurate comparison between process alternatives. Given the reduced energy intensity, GWP, and MEA requirements, the pre-combustion capture may be preferred. If the higher overall CO2 capture rate from post-combustion capture is required, sourcing steam from nearby process units could offset the additional indirect emissions from this configuration.

When designing new carbon capture processes, companies should leverage next-generation simulation tools like AVEVA Process Simulation to evaluate a variety of design alternatives. Capital cost, operating cost, and overall capture rates should be compared for a variety of solvent systems, process configurations, and operating conditions. An open modeling framework like the one shown in **Figure 2**, paired with custom thermodynamic data, allows companies to incorporate proprietary data into simulation models of CCS processes. While this study uses a first-generation MEA solvent as an illustrative example, custom thermodynamics and the open modeling framework allow for extension to modern second- and third-generation solvents.

## 5. Conclusions

Carbon Capture and Storage (CCS) projects offer a path to reduce carbon emissions with minimal changes to existing processes. Despite this prospect, CCS projects are often considered high-risk due to the uncertainty of emerging technologies and relatively high operating cost of these units. Carbon tax programs and policy decisions will continue to increase the viability of CCS projects but must be accompanied by smart project execution and operation. When used effectively, next-generation process simulation platforms reduce the capital risk of CCS projects. Applications like AVEVA Process Simulation include open modeling frameworks that allow for integration of custom and proprietary process and equipment data with no programming required. This allows for rapid comparison of a variety of solvent systems and process configurations for CCS. Next-generation simulation platforms also include built-in carbon emission calculations alongside estimates of operating and capital cost for process-wide optimization. This gives owner-operators and EPCs better insight into the tradeoff between capital expenditure, operating cost, and emission capture rates. CCS is critical to achieving short- to medium-term emission reduction goals and next-generation simulation platforms will enable the adoption of these technologies with limited commercial risk.

## References

R. Agarwal et al., 2016, Imagining construction's digital future, McKinsey & Company.

Allied Market Research, 2021, Carbon Capture, Utilization, and Storage (CCUS) Market by Service, Technology, and End-Use Industry: Global Opportunity Analysis and Industry Forecast, 2021-2030.

AVEVA, 2020, Unified Engineering: A new proposition to break down the silos between FEED and Detailed Design to minimize risk and maximize return on Capital Investment.

A. Balylin-Stern and N. Berghout, 2021, Is carbon capture too expensive?, International Energy Agency

S. Bishnoi and G. Rochelle, 2000, Absorption of carbon dioxide into aqueous peperazine: reaction kinetics, mass transfter and solubility, Chemical Engineering Science, 55, 22, 5531-5543.

S. Hla et al., Kinetics of high-temperature water-gas shift reaction over two iron-based commercial catalysts using simulated coal-derived syngases, Chemical Engineering Journal, 146, 148-154.

IEAGHG, 2017, Techno-Economic Evaluation of SMR Based Standalone (Merchant) Plant with CCS, IEA Greenhouse Gase and R&D Program, 2017-02.

A. Mehmeti et al., 2018, Life Cycle Assessment and Water Footprint of Hydrogen Production Methods: From Conventional to Emerging Technologies, Environments, 5, 2, 24.

J. Moe, 1962, Design of water-gas shift reactors, Chemical Engineering Progress, 58, 33-36

Y. Zhang et al., 2011, Thermodynamic modeling for CO2 absorption in aqueous MEA solution with electrolyte NRTL model, Fluid Phase Equilibria, 311, 67-75.

J. Xu and G. Froment, 1989, Methane Steam Reforming, Methanation and Water-Gas Shift: I. Intrinsic Kinetic, AIChE Journal, 35, 88-90.

Antonis Kokossis, Michael C. Georgiadis, Efstratios N. Pistikopoulos (Eds.)
PROCEEDINGS OF THE 33rd European Symposium on Computer Aided Process Engineering
(ESCAPE33), June 18-21, 2023, Athens, Greece

# Incorporation of non-linear efficiency constraints in green ammonia production design for cost minimisation

Nicholas Salmon,[a] René Bañares-Alcántara,[a]

*[a]Department of Engineering Science, University of Oxford, Parks Road, Oxford, OX1 3PJ, United Kingdom*

## Abstract

Affordable production of green ammonia will play a critical role in the decarbonization of fertilisers, the maritime industry, and the energy sector. Since renewable electricity can represent more than 50% of the levelised cost of ammonia, maximizing efficiency of electrolysis is an important stepping stone to achieving low costs. This paper analyses the increased efficiency which can be obtained by operating electrolysers with low throughputs, to determine the extent of the impacts on the ammonia costs. It considers both a QP and LP approach, demonstrating the computational efficiency of LP calculation in this setting. We show the cost improvements from considering low-rate operation are between 1 and 5%, and that a significant change in plant design is not likely; because electrolysers themselves are expensive, intentionally operating them at low rates costs more in wasted equipment capacity than it saves in electricity costs.

**Keywords**: Non-linear programming, Renewable Fuels, Green Hydrogen, Green Ammonia, Energy Efficiency

## 1. Introduction

The renewable energy transition will require large-scale installation of energy storage technologies in the form of chemical vectors such as green hydrogen and ammonia in order to convert variable renewables into dispatchable, portable fuels (Schmidt, 2019). The requirement that hydrogen and ammonia production be flexible to match the variable renewable power source introduces complexity into the design process, as sophisticated optimisation techniques must be used to design plants which minimise production costs.

However, variable operation also represents an opportunity for cost savings, since electrolysers operate more efficiently, and with lower degradation, at reduced load factors (Taibi, 2020). This has led some projects to pursue low-load factor operation, which enables access to free or very cheap electricity from otherwise curtailed renewables, and which can then be converted into hydrogen with high efficiency.

The opportunity of reduced load factor operation has historically been neglected by production cost prediction models due to the non-linearity of variable electrolyser efficiencies, which conflicts with the Mixed Integer Linear Programming approach that is typically adopted for optimisation of system design (Fasihi, 2021). Using Non-Linear Programming (NLP) approaches may resolve this problem technically, but typically reduces the speed at which the model solves, and the maximum amount of input weather data that the problem can handle, itself introducing error.

This study compares this non-linear approach with an alternative method for linearising this constraint without introducing integer variables, or increasing the solution time, through the introduction of a 'pseudo-power' variable. This enables the power reduction associated with increased efficiency to be approximated using a series of linear constraints.

## 2. Methodology

### 2.1. Ammonia cost estimation method

Conventional ammonia production, using natural gas, typically operates all equipment at or close to its design rate continuously, in order to extract the maximum value from the capital expenditure into equipment. This operating approach is not suitable for green ammonia production, because it depends on variable renewable energy which is not always available. Selection of equipment sizes needs to account for the possibility of using both wind and solar as an energy source, and must include sufficient back-up storage of power and hydrogen to enable continuous operation of the Haber-Bosch synthesis loop, which is only partially flexible.

The process can, mostly, be represented using linear mass and energy balances, meaning the optimal size of equipment can be determined in a straightforward fashion. The inputs to the model are the local renewable weather profiles (which here include wind, fixed solar PV and single-axis tracking PV), as well as equipment efficiencies and costs. The model can then output optimal equipment size as well as the levelised cost of ammonia. For this research, the process was modelled using pyomo, and was solved using Gurobi, which can be accessed for free under an academic license.

### 2.2. Quadratic Constraint

The electrolyser is an exception to the rule of linear constraints. Electrolyser efficiency is better at low current densities, typically because there are fewer energy losses to electrical resistance or heat loss. Here, the relationship between efficiency and current density is treated as linear, although non-linear curves are discussed in subsequent sections.

The simplest approach to modelling the efficiency is to do so directly:

$$\kappa_{H2}(t) = \kappa_{H2}(t-1) + \pi\mu_{H2} - \frac{3}{17}\dot{m}_{NH3} \tag{1}$$

$$\mu_{H2}C_{Elec} = \mu_{Best}C_{Elec} - (\mu_{Best} - \mu_{Worst})\pi \tag{2}$$

where $\kappa_{H2}$ is the amount of hydrogen stored in tons at time $t$, $\pi$ is the energy in MWh supplied to the electrolyser, $\mu_{H2}$ is the efficiency of the electrolyser in t/MWh (which in this model is a variable, not a parameter), $\dot{m}_{NH3}$ is the production rate of ammonia (in tons), $C_{Elec}$ is the capacity of the electrolyser in MW, and $\mu_{Best}$ and $\mu_{Worst}$ are, respectively, the efficiencies of the electrolyser under the best operating condition (i.e. very low current densities) and the worst operating condition (i.e. the electrolyser rated capacity).

Both equations are modelled as strict equality constraints in the LP. Equation 1 is simply a mass balance over hydrogen, with the factor $\frac{3}{17}$ representing the stoichiometric mass relationship between hydrogen and ammonia. Equation 2 is an expression relating the electrolyser efficiency to its operating rate; this is simply a linear interpolation between $\mu_{Best}$ and $\mu_{Worst}$, which depends on the operating ratio, given by $\frac{\pi}{C_{elec}}$. The operating ratio does not appear explicitly as the entire equation is multiplied by $C_{elec}$ in order to render the non-linear constraint as a quadratic.

In theory, the above reaction can be modelled by Gurobi, which can handle both convex and non-convex QPs (Quadratic problems) using a bilinear solver. However, in practice, the non-convexity of this problem makes it very challenging to solve, and significantly slows down the model solution. For that reason, using one year of data at hourly resolution, the model has over 50,000 constraints and 30,000 variables, meaning the solver was unable to identify an optimal solution within 48 hours when solved on an i7 desktop with 16 GB of RAM. Even applying a significantly reduced dataset, containing just one hundred time steps (~500 constraints, 300 variables), the model solution takes over 16 hours.

Realistically, the plant design needs to be rapid, so it can solve under a large number of conditions, such as varying locations, and equipment costs. For that reason, a linear solution needs to be found which can converge more rapidly, even though the two constraints described above do not readily linearise.

### 2.2.1. Linearisation approach

In order to resolve this problem, we introduce a new variable, $\zeta$, which we term the 'pseudopower'. The plant is then designed as normal under a linear arrangement (i.e. using equation (1) as a constraint, but not equation (2)), with $\mu_{H2}$ treated as a parameter whose value is equal to $\mu_{Worst}$. The true power consumed by the electrolyser is therefore slightly less than the power modelled by the LP. The difference between the true power and the modelled power is the pseudopower, and it is returned to the input side of the overall plant energy balance, along with the power which originates from the variable renewable supply. The optimisation solver can then reallocate the unused energy as it sees fit.

Formally, the pseudo-power is calculated by:

$$\zeta = \pi \left(1 - \frac{\eta_{H2}}{\eta_{Worst}}\right) \tag{3}$$

Note that for the definition of the pseudopower, rather than direct efficiencies, ($\mu_{H2}$ and $\mu_{Worst}$, measured in t/MWh), we use their reciprocals, $\eta_{H2}$ and $\eta_{Worst}$, measured in MWh/t. It is strictly necessary to use $\mu_{H2}$ for the non-linear modelling, and the problem can only be solved for electrolysers where the efficiency is linearly related to the operating ratio, such that the problem will be quadratic. This linearisation approach is more flexible, and we therefore use $\eta_{H2}$ in place of $\mu_{H2}$ only so that the variable $\eta_{H2}$ appears in the numerator rather than the denominator in the definition of $\zeta$. For the approximation of $\eta_{H2}$ (which we subsequently refer to as the reciprocal efficiency), a slightly wider range of input functions can be used – for demonstration, we use a linear one:

$$\eta_{H2} = \eta_{Best} + \Delta\eta\left(\frac{\pi}{C_{Elec}}\right) \tag{4}$$

where $\Delta\eta$ is the difference in the reciprocal efficiencies. Note that equation (4) is linear in the reciprocal efficiencies, rather than the efficiencies themselves, as per (2); the results will be similar, and the alternative is adopted merely for simplicity of demonstration. This results in the following expression for the pseudopower:

$$\zeta = \frac{\Delta\eta}{\eta_{Worst}}\left(\frac{-\pi^2}{C_{Elec}} + \pi\right) \tag{5}$$

This does not apparently resolve the problem, since the expression is non-linear. However, the pseudo-power, unlike the electrolyser efficiency, can be treated using inequalities, rather than strict equalities. Therefore, the acceptable region of values of the pseudopower can be defined using a series of linear constraints which are tangent to the curve, as shown in Figure 1.

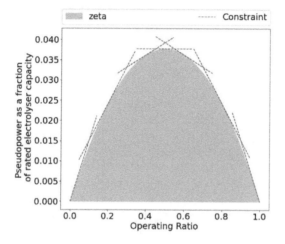

Figure 1 - Suitable region for the definition of the pseudopower. Acceptable values lie within the grey curve, and are constrained there by the linear constraints represented using dashed lines.

In general, the model will maximise the power input into the energy balance, so it will typically select the maximum value of the pseudopower as allowed within the constraint region, i.e. it will select a value on the curve, rather than underneath it. The case in which it selects a pseudopower which is less than any of the linear constraints is equivalent to curtailing electricity. The curtailed electricity is simply the slack variable in the energy balance constraint; whether the slack is allocated to the energy balance or the pseudopower constraint is arbitrary to the actual outcome. Here, the shape of the pseudopower curve is quadratic; other shapes could be used, although integer variables may need to be introduced to 'turn off' the constraints in certain parts of the operating ratio range if the pseudopower curve has a large number of critical points.

Even now, a non-linearity remains in the calculation of the operating ratio. We resolve this by pre-estimating the size of the electrolyser, $C_{elec}$ by allowing the model to run without any pseudopower. For only the constraints which consider the pseudopower, $C_{elec}$

is treated as a parameter, rather than a variable; the amount of error introduced by this adjustment is discussed in the results.

## 3. Results

The linearized model converges in around one minute using an i7 desktop and a full year of weather data. This enabled the code to be run in over 400 locations with a wide range of weather profiles, considering a case for both 2022 and 2050 (which accounts for falling costs of some equipment, as well as improving efficiencies of the electrolyser).

On average for 2020, the pseudopower represented 3% of the energy 'supplied' to the plant, with a maximum value of 4.8%. This improvement in efficiency enabled a reduction in the electrolyser size by on average 4%, and at most 11% (compared to a case without pseudopower). The results for 2050 were broadly similar to those for 2022, although the improvement is slightly smaller. This is because the general improvement in electrolyser efficiency over time, as well as the rapidly falling price of solar power, means that (i) the efficiency benefit from low power operation is smaller as a fraction of total contribution, and (ii) efficiency is a less important criteria than low capital costs for determining the optimum arrangement of the ammonia plant. For that reason, pseudopower only represents 2% of the energy supplied, and the electrolysers only decreased in size by 2.5%.

The reduced electrolyser size impacts the accuracy of the pseudopower calculation, since it depends upon the original estimate of the electrolyser size. This will cause the pseudopower to be overestimated when the operating ratio is less than ½, and will be underestimated when the operating ratio is greater than ½. To some extent, these two impacts should cancel out (since the average electrolyser load fraction is 47%, they spend roughly the same amount of time above and below this point). In any case, the error in the pseudopower will not be larger than 10%, which is fairly small in the context of large uncertainties in the equipment costs (and given that the pseudopower is a small fraction of the total input power). If the error needs to be reduced further, the high speed of solution would enable the model to be converged several times until the initial guess of the electrolyser size was within a tolerance limit of the output electrolyser size.

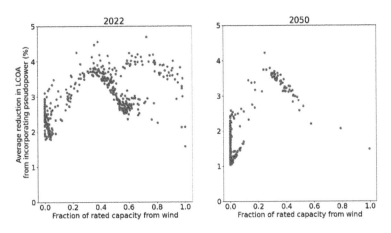

Figure 2 - Improvement in LCOA plotted against fraction of rated capacity from wind

Reducing both the electricity consumption and the electrolyser size also reduces the levelised cost of ammonia (LCOA), which is the objective of the optimisation. Unsurprisingly, the reduction in LCOA is well correlated to the amount of pseudo-power consumed.

Figure 2 shows the relationship between the size of this LCOA reduction and the fraction of the renewable energy farm which originates with wind. Very clearly for the 2050 locations, and slightly less clearly for the 2022 locations, the largest pseudo-power benefit originates at sites which use hybrid operation (i.e. rely on both wind and solar). At sites which predominantly rely on only one power source, the rated capacity of the electrolyser is similar in magnitude to the installed capacity of the renewables; this prevents excessive curtailment when the electrolyser is running without unduly oversizing it. To achieve the same outcome for the hybrid sites, the electrolyser may be larger in capacity than either of the renewables; only when they operate in tandem will the electrolyser be fully utilized. This means that the electrolyser more frequently operates at a lower rated capacity (i.e. when only one of the two installed renewables is available), and therefore benefits to a greater extent from the improved efficiency under those conditions.

Considering the efficiency as a function of electrolyser load has not radically changed system design, which is unsurprising given that it represents, proportionally, a small change in electrolyser performance. This suggests that low-load factor operation at high efficiencies is not likely to be a viable operating mode, predominantly because the electrolyser capital cost is quite high; therefore, it is better to use it at a higher rate where the availability of renewables allows it, even if doing so sacrifices some efficiency. From the perspective of design, therefore, suitable equipment sizes may be selected even without accounting for this non-linearity. However, from the perspective of comparing sites to each other, it may be necessary to consider the role of improved efficiency, since they have the greatest impact on sites with weather profiles that lend themselves to both wind and solar (as opposed to sites that rely on one particularly strong resource).

## 4. Conclusions

This report has presented a novel method for dealing with a non-linearity present within optimisation of renewable ammonia production. It compared the possibility of using a QP with a linearized LP approach, demonstrating that the errors introduced from an LP are comparatively small, and enable a far more rapid solution than a non-convex QP. The improved efficiency of electrolysers at low load factors may reduce costs between 1 and 5%; this is not sufficiently large to justify changes in the plant design, but may prove beneficial for operating plants, particularly if they use both wind and solar as power sources. Further investigation should consider the extent to which these results are affected by a connection to the electricity grid.

## References

Schmidt, J., et al., 2019, A new perspective on global renewable energy systems: why trade in energy carriers matters. Energy & Environmental Science. **12**(7): p. 2022-2029.
Fasihi, M., et al., 2021, Global potential of green ammonia based on hybrid PV-wind power plants. Applied Energy. **294**: p. 116170.
Taibi, E. et al., 2020, Green Hydrogen Cost Reduction: Scaling up electrolysers to meet the 1.5°C climate goal, IRENA. p. 45

Antonis Kokossis, Michael C. Georgiadis, Efstratios N. Pistikopoulos (Eds.)
PROCEEDINGS OF THE 33rd European Symposium on Computer Aided Process Engineering
(ESCAPE33), June 18-21, 2023, Athens, Greece
© 2023 Elsevier B.V. All rights reserved.  http://dx.doi.org/10.1016/B978-0-443-15274-0.50440-6

# Strategic participation of a gas-fired power plant in interdependent electricity and natural gas markets under carbon emission trading schemes

Christos N. Dimitriadis,[a] Evangelos G. Tsimopoulos,[a] Michael C. Georgiadis [a]

[a]*Department of Chemical Engineering, Aristotle University of Thessaloniki, University Campus, Thessaloniki, 54124, Greece*
*Corresponding author, e-mail: mgeorg@auth.gr*

## Abstract

This work considers a bi-level optimization framework to model the strategic participation and derive optimal offers for a gas-fired power plant (GFPP) in interdependent pool-based electricity and natural gas markets, under high penetration of wind power generation. The upper-level problem ensures profit maximization for the strategic agent, while the lower-level problem represents the sequential electricity and natural gas market clearing process. Considering the worldwide establishment of low-carbon policies, a carbon emission trading scheme (CETS) is also incorporated into the proposed optimization framework. The bi-level algorithm is initially transformed into a mathematical programming with equilibrium constraints model and further recast into a mixed integer linear program, using Karush-Kuhn-Tucker optimality conditions and strong duality theory. Numerical simulations illustrate that the proposed methodology is capable of effectively mimicking the actual electricity and gas market-clearing process and derive the optimal amount of carbon emission allowances and strategic offers for the gas-fired power plant.

**Keywords**: bi-level optimization, strategic offering, electricity market, natural gas market, carbon emission trading

## 1. Introduction

In recent years, the development of mathematical approaches that ensure the strategic participation of a power producer in energy markets has been of great interest. Tsimopoulos and Georgiadis (2020) studied the optimal strategies for the participation of a market agent owning a mixed portfolio of conventional and wind power generation. In addition, Dimitriadis et al. (2022) proposed a bi-level algorithm to investigate the strategic bidding decisions of an energy storage agent in a joint energy and reserve market. Natural gas is considered an efficient and clean fuel that in the long-term can sufficiently replace more polluting fuels for power generation, such as coal and oil. However, while the GFPPs hold a significant share in the market, their optimal operation as power producers and natural gas consumers has not been thoroughly studied.

In this work, a sequential clearing mechanism for interdependent electricity and gas markets is adopted (Ordoudis et al., 2019), to derive the optimal capacity and offering strategies for a GFPP. The CETS is also incorporated into the algorithm to account for the carbon emissions of each conventional producers and to investigate how carbon emission trading affects the operation of the GFPP.

## 2. Mathematical model

In this section, the bi-level formulation is presented to determine the optimal offering strategies for a strategic GFPP in interdependent electricity and gas markets, considering a cap-and-trade program for carbon emissions. As shown in (1), the hourly overall carbon emission allowances number $Q_t$ varies with the net load i.e., demand load minus wind power production, while $\eta$ represents the emission allowance factor (tCO$_2$/MW). Constraint (2) defines the number of emission allowances $Q_{h,t}^H$ that correspond to each conventional power plant $h$, depending on its allocated factor of allowances $\alpha_h$, which is calculated by (3). $\zeta_h$ comprises the emission factor of each conventional power plant.

$$Q_t = \eta \cdot \left( \sum_{d^{EL} \in D_{aN}} L_{d,t}^E - \sum_{j \in J_{aN}} w_{j,t} \right) \tag{1}$$

$$Q_{h,t}^H = \alpha_h \cdot Q_t \tag{2}$$

$$\alpha_h = \frac{\zeta_h}{\sum_h \zeta_h} \tag{3}$$

### 2.1. Upper-level problem: Profit maximization for the GFPP

$$\textbf{\textit{maximize}} \quad \sum_t \left\{ \sum_{g \in G_{aN}} \lambda_{n,t}^E \cdot v_{g,t} - \sum_{g \in G_{aR}} \lambda_{r,t}^{NG} \cdot \varphi_g \cdot v_{g,t} - cp \cdot (\zeta_g \cdot v_{g,t} \right.$$
$$\left. - Q_{g,t}^H) \right\} \tag{4}$$

Objective function (4) aims at maximizing the profit of the GFPP $g$. The first term represents its income from selling its hourly power production $v_{g,t}$, while the second term corresponds to the cost of purchasing gas, with $\varphi_g$ being the electricity-gas conversion factor for the GFPP. $\lambda_{n,t}^E$, $\lambda_{r,t}^{NG}$ and $cp$ correspond to the electricity, natural gas and carbon prices, respectively. The third term represents GFPP's carbon trading cost, depending on its allocated ($Q_{g,t}^H$) and actual ($\zeta_g \cdot v_{g,t}$) carbon emission allowances.

### 2.2. Lower-level problem: Electricity market clearing

$$\textbf{\textit{minimize}} \quad \sum_t \left\{ \sum_{g \in G_{aN}} o_{g,t} \cdot v_{g,t} + \sum_{i \in I_{aN}} C_i \cdot p_{i,t} \right.$$
$$\left. + \sum_{g \in G_{aN}} cp \cdot (\zeta_g \cdot v_{g,t} - Q_{g,t}^H) + \sum_{i \in I_{aN}} cp \cdot (\zeta_i \cdot p_{i,t} - Q_{i,t}^H) \right\} \tag{5}$$

**s.t.**

$$-\sum_{i \in IaN} p_{i,t} - \sum_{g \in GaN} v_{g,t} - \sum_{j \in JaN} w_{j,t} + \sum_{d^{EL} \in DaN} L^E_{d,t}$$

$$+ \sum_{m \in NaM} B_{n,m} \cdot (\delta_{n,t} - \delta_{m,t}) = 0 \quad : \left[\lambda^E_{n,t}\right] \quad \forall n, \forall t \tag{6}$$

$$0 \leq p_{i,t} \leq \overline{P_i} \quad : \left[a_{i,t}, \overline{a_{i,t}}\right] \quad \forall i, \forall t \tag{7}$$

$$0 \leq v_{g,t} \leq \overline{V_g} \quad : \left[\beta_{g,t}, \overline{\beta_{g,t}}\right] \quad \forall g, \forall t \tag{8}$$

$$0 \leq w_{j,t} \leq \overline{W_j} \quad : \left[\gamma_{j,t}, \overline{\gamma_{j,t}}\right] \quad \forall j, \forall t \tag{9}$$

$$-Q^H_{h,t} + \alpha_h \cdot \eta \cdot \left(\sum_{d^{EL} \in DaN} L^E_{d,t} - \sum_{j \in JaN} w_{j,t}\right) = 0 \quad : \left[\rho_{h,t}\right] \quad \forall h, \forall t \tag{10}$$

$$-\overline{T_{n,m}} \leq B_{n,m} \cdot (\delta_{n,t} - \delta_{m,t}) \leq \overline{T_{n,m}} \quad : \left[\psi_{n,m,t}, \overline{\psi_{n,m,t}}\right] \quad \forall (n,m)$$

$$\in NaM, \forall t \tag{11}$$

$$-3.14 \leq \delta_{n,t} \leq 3.14 \quad \forall n, \forall t \quad : \left[\pi_{n,t}, \overline{\pi_{n,t}}\right] \tag{12}$$

$$\delta_{n_1,t} = 0 \quad : \left[\eta^o_{n,t}\right] \quad \forall n = n_1, \forall t \tag{13}$$

Objective function (5) minimizes total operating cost and represents the electricity market clearing procedure, while $o_{g,t}$ and $C_i$ correspond to the strategic offers by the GFPP and the cost offers of non-GFPPs $i$, respectively. Constraint (6) applies the power balance at each electric bus $n$, where $L^E_{d,t}$ is the power demand load and $B_{n,m}$ the susceptance of power transmission line connecting buses $n, m$. Constraints (7) – (9) enforce the upper and lower capacity for non-gas-fired, gas-fired and wind power plants $j$, respectively. Constraint (10) derives the allocated emission allowances for each conventional power plant. Constraint (11) imposes transmission lines' capacity limits, while constraints (12), (13) limit the voltage angle $\delta_{n,t}$ range of each electric bus and establish bus A as the electric grid's slack bus.

### 2.3. Lower-level problem: Natural gas market clearing

$$\boldsymbol{minimize} \quad \sum_t \left\{\sum_{k \in KaR} C_k \cdot f_{k,t}\right\} \tag{14}$$

**s.t.**

$$-\sum_{k \in KaR} f_{k,t} + \sum_{g \in GaR} \varphi_g \cdot v_{g,t} + \sum_{d^{NG} \in DaR} L^{NG}_{d,t} = 0 \quad : \left[\lambda^{NG}_{r,t}\right] \quad \forall r, \forall t \tag{15}$$

$$\underline{F_k} \leq f_{k,t} \leq \overline{F_k} \quad : \left[\varepsilon_{k,t}, \overline{\varepsilon_{k,t}}\right] \quad \forall k, \forall t \tag{16}$$

Objective function (14) represents the natural gas clearing mechanism by minimizing total operating cost, with $C_k$ corresponding to the cost offers of each natural gas supplier $k$. Constraint (15) constitutes the gas balance at each gas node $r$ and $L_{d,t}^{NG}$ represents natural gas demand of loads $d^{NG}$. Constraint (16) imposes upper and lower capacity for the natural gas production $f_{k,t}$ of each supplier.

*2.4. Solution strategy*

Considering the convexity and continuity of the lower-level problems, the bi-level formulation is reduced to a mathematical program with equilibrium constraints (MPEC), by employing Karush-Kuhn-Tucker optimality conditions and is further recast into a mixed-integer linear program (MILP), applying disjunctive constraints and the strong duality theorem.

## 3. Application study

The proposed algorithm is applied in a modified Pennsylvania – New Jersey – Maryland (PJM) 5-bus electric network, as illustrated by **Fig.1**, and a single-node natural gas network. Six non-gas-fired power plants, the strategic GFPP and a wind farm are located at the power network, while the total electricity demand is equally distributed on three load buses. Similarly, at the natural gas network, three gas suppliers and three gas loads are established. It is important to emphasize that the GFPP is considered as the fourth gas load, the capacity of which is directly

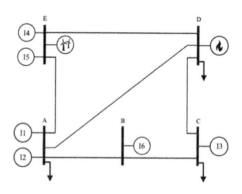

Figure 1. PJM 5-bus power network.

linked to the power that the GFPP provides to the electricity market. Carbon emission price is set at 23 $/t, while the maximum capacity and the susceptance of each power transmission line are equal to 1000 MW and 9.412, respectively.

## 4. Results and Discussion

*4.1. Uncongested power network*

The proposed MILP model is applied to the integrated electricity and natural gas system and solved using GAMS/CPLEX. The strategic gas-fired unit exerts its dominant position in the market and manipulated day-ahead prices to increase its profitability. **Fig.2** depicts the market clearing prices (MCPs) during the 24-hour horizon, both for the case where carbon emissions of conventional producer are considered and for the opposite case. It is important to point out that the wind power plants and considered both cost- and emission-free. The value of CETS-embedded MCPs is higher compared to the normal MCPs for all time periods since each conventional producer due to its carbon emissions, increases its bidding cost by $cp \cdot \zeta_h$.

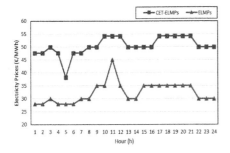

Figure 2. CETS-embedded and normal electricity MCPs.

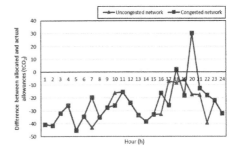

Figure 3. Net carbon emission allowances.

In the calculation of the expected profits for each conventional power plant, trading of carbon emission allowances plays a key role. The difference between the cost-free allowances provided by the government to the strategic gas-fired unit and its actual emissions based on its power production, is illustrated in **Fig. 3**. Positive values represent the number of allowances (in $CO_2$ tons) granted to the GFPP but not employed and thus constitute an income source. Conversely, negative values indicate the additional carbon allowances that the GFPP is worth paying for, in order to satisfy its desired electricity production. For the uncongested power network case, the GFPP strategically chooses to pay this extra allowance purchase cost, since the CETS-embedded MCPs are noticeably higher compared to the carbon trading price.

### 4.2. Congested power network

In this case, the capacity of lines A-B and D-E is reduced to 400 and 300 MW equivalently. As a result, the power network becomes congested and different CETS-embedded electricity MCPs arise, as shown in **Fig.4**. The GFPP acting strategically, manages to capitalize on congestion and further manipulate MCPs. Especially in bus D, where it is installed, a price cap needs to be established at 158.05 $ by the MO, to prevent its excessive speculation. Bus E remains the only bus not affected

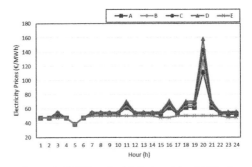

Figure 4. CETS-embedded electricity MCPs for the congested network.

by the bidding strategy of the GFPP. The reason seems to be the fact that the zero-cost wind farm is located at this bus. In fact, the wind farm generates electricity at full capacity during the 24-hour horizon and covers the largest percentage of the demand, thus holding electricity MCPs down. Furthermore, as depicted by **Table 1**, despite the fact that the GFPP generates less electricity compared to the uncongested network case, due to the significantly higher prices, manages to increase its daily profits by 21.5 %.

Table 1: GFPP's electricity production and expected profits

|  | *Electricity generation (MWh)* | *Profit ($)* |
|---|---|---|
| *Uncongested power network* | 4,394 | 122,005.53 |
| *Congested power network* | 4,153 | 148,343.96 |

### 4.3. Natural gas price increase

This case study investigates the influence of natural gas price increase on the market outcomes and the optimal strategies of the GFPP. In particular, gas suppliers rise their bidding costs by 50%, 100%, 150% and 200% and consequently the gas MCPs. In order to balance this increase in its marginal cost, the strategic GFPP bids higher. As a result, for many time periods the electricity MCPs are also affected by

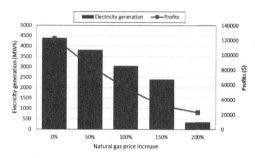

Figure 5. Power generation and profits for strategic GFPP.

following an upward trend. However, the GFPP cannot offset the rise of the gas MCPs and significantly withholds its power production experiencing a critical profit decrease, as shown in **Fig.5**.

## 5. Conclusions

In this work a bi-level mathematical algorithm is developed to derive optimal offering strategies and maximize the profit of a GFPP participating in interdependent low-carbon electricity and natural gas markets. The model derives the CETS-embedded electricity and gas MCPs and the optimal offering decisions and carbon emission management for the GFPP. Results demonstrate that power network congestion creates more arbitrage opportunities for the GFPP, compared to the uncongested network case, while an increase in gas prices leads the GFPP to withhold its production and thus experience profit losses. Future work should involve the investigation of the strategic behavior for an agent with mixed generation portfolio in an integrated electricity and gas market scheme.

## Acknowledgments

This research has been co-financed by (i) the European Union and Greek national funds through the Operational Program Competitiveness, Entrepreneurship and Innovation, under the specific call "Aquacultures" – "Industrial Materials" – "Open Innovation in Civilization" (project code: T6YBP-00251). Project title: Development of Computer-Aided Tools for Optimal Energy Consumption in Industrial Ceramics (CATOPEC-IC) and (ii) HELLENiQ ENERGY, under the framework of research program "HELLENiQ ENERGY Scholarships" (project number: 98665).

## References

Dimitriadis, C. N., Tsimopoulos, E. G., & Georgiadis, M. C. (2022). Strategic bidding of an energy storage agent in a joint energy and reserve market under stochastic generation. *Energy*, *242*, 123026. https://doi.org/https://doi.org/10.1016/j.energy.2021.123026

Ordoudis, C., Pinson, P., & Morales, J. M. (2019). An Integrated Market for Electricity and Natural Gas Systems with Stochastic Power Producers. *European Journal of Operational Research*, *272*(2), 642–654. https://doi.org/10.1016/j.ejor.2018.06.036

Tsimopoulos, E. G., & Georgiadis, M. C. (2020). Withholding strategies for a conventional and wind generation portfolio in a joint energy and reserve pool market: A gaming-based approach. *Computers and Chemical Engineering*. https://doi.org/10.1016/j.compchemeng.2019.106692

Antonis Kokossis, Michael C. Georgiadis, Efstratios N. Pistikopoulos (Eds.)
PROCEEDINGS OF THE 33rd European Symposium on Computer Aided Process Engineering
(ESCAPE33), June 18-21, 2023, Athens, Greece
© 2023 Elsevier B.V. All rights reserved.  http://dx.doi.org/10.1016/B978-0-443-15274-0.50441-8

# Modeling and optimization of hybrid P/VSA-membrane separation processes for $CO_2$ capture from post combustion flue gas

Christos C. Chatziasteriou,[a,b] Michael C. Georgiadis,[a,b] Eustathios S. Kikkinides,[a,b]

*aDepartment of Chemical Engineering, Aristotle University of Thessaloniki (AUTH), Thessaloniki 54124, Greece*
*bChemical Process and Energy Resources Insitute (CPERI) Center for Research and Technology Hellas (CERTH), 6th km Charilaou-Thermi, Thessaloniki 57001, Greece*

## Abstract

This work presents a hybrid Pressure/Vacuum Swing Adsorption (P/VSA)-membrane process for $CO_2$ capture from flue gas. The proposed process combines the advantages of each individual process. Both P/VSA-membrane and membrane-P/VSA configurations have been considered and evaluated based on a modeling and optimization framework. In addition, a two-stage P/VSA case has been considered and optimized as a reference case for comparison purposes. In all cases, the goal of optimization is to minimize total energy requirements keeping the constraints of 95% total $CO_2$ purity and 90% total $CO_2$ recovery, separating a 30/70 mol % $CO_2/N_2$ feed mixture. Optimization results demonstrate that the optimal membrane-P/VSA configuration leads to an energy requirement of 134.4 kWh/t$CO_2$, representing ~8% reduction comparing to the respective value of 145.9 kWh/t$CO_2$ for the two-stage P/VSA case.

**Keywords**: Post-combustion $CO_2$ capture. P/VSA, Membrane, Hybrid process

## 1. Introduction

The capture of the post-combustion $CO_2$ emissions that come from various industrial applications (Abanades et al., 2015) is a decisive step to the direction of reducing global warming due to the increased concentration of $CO_2$ in the atmosphere. Chemical absorption is the most mature technology for this purpose. However, it constitutes a huge thermal heat duty process. As a result, research on more efficient processes is in progress. Pressure/Vacuum Swing Adsorption (P/VSA) and membrane separation are promising alternatives to absorption (Chatziasteriou et al., 2022). Unfortunately, single-stage membrane processes are unable to achieve the target of $CO_2$ Purity $\geq$ 95% and $CO_2$ Recovery $\geq$ 90% set by US Department of Energy (DOE/NETL) (Khurana and Farooq, 2017) utilizing the currently existing materials. On the other hand, industrially unapplicable low vacuum pressures are required for efficient one-stage P/VSA process configurations. Accordingly, two-stage P/VSA processes and three-stage or even four-stage membrane configurations have been studied to overcome the abovementioned limitations, resulting in significant increase in the capital expenditure (CAPEX) and the operational expenditure (OPEX) of the process (Chatziasteriou et al., 2022; Zanco et al., 2017).

An integrated or hybrid membrane-P/VSA separation process (Figure 1) may be capable of combining the advantages of each individual process and, at the same time, be a more efficient alternative to the abovementioned for the effective post-combustion $CO_2$ separation. P/VSA and membrane process are connected in such way that they constitute the two stages of the hybrid process. The flue gas is partially separated in the first stage and the $CO_2$ enriched product enters the second stage where the separation is completed. In this work, both P/VSA-membrane and membrane-P/VSA configurations are examined.

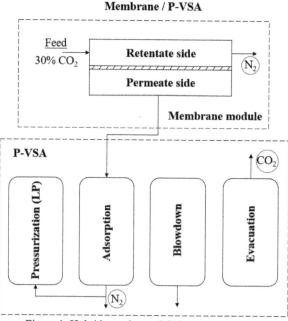

Figure 1. Hybrid membrane-P/VSA representation

## 2. Process modeling

### 2.1. Pressure/Vacuum Swing Adsorption

As partial separation of $CO_2$ is required in each one of the two stages, a simple 4-step P/VSA process has been considered in the present study, due to its high efficiency and the reduced computational cost compared to more complex cycles. The present 4-step cycle consists of an adsorption step, a co-current blowdown step, a counter-current evacuation step and a counter-current pressurization with light product (LP) step. A set of partial differential equations (Haghpanah et al., 2013) describes the whole process, while each step differs from the others due to its unique boundary conditions. The conditions at the end of each step are considered as the initial conditions of the next step. Zeolite 13X is considered as the adsorbent, as this is the most mature and efficient material used for $CO_2/N_2$ mixtures separation at an industrial scale. Note that adsorbate/adsorbent equilibrium is described by the dual-site Langmuir isotherm.

#### 2.1.1. P/VSA Model Equations

Mass balance of component i:

$$\frac{\partial y_i}{\partial t} + \frac{y_i}{P}\frac{\partial P}{\partial t} - \frac{y_i}{T}\frac{\partial T}{\partial t} = \frac{T}{P}D_z\frac{\partial}{\partial z}\left(\frac{P}{T}\frac{\partial y_i}{\partial z}\right) - \frac{T}{P}\frac{\partial}{\partial z}\left(\frac{y_i P}{T}u\right) - \frac{R_g T}{P}\frac{(1-\varepsilon_b)}{\varepsilon_b}\frac{\partial q_i}{\partial t} \quad (1)$$

Mass transfer rate of component i (LDF model):

$$\rho_p \frac{\partial q_i}{\partial t} = \frac{c_{pi}}{q_i^*} k_{ci}(q_i^* - q_i)$$

(2)

Bed energy balance:

$$\left[ (1 - \varepsilon_b)\rho_p c_{ps} + (1 - \varepsilon_b)\rho_g c_{pa} \sum_{i=1}^{2} \frac{\rho_p q_i}{c_f} \right] \frac{\partial T}{\partial t}$$

$$= \frac{\lambda_e}{\varepsilon_b} \frac{\partial^2 T}{\partial z^2} - \frac{c_{pg}}{R_g} \frac{\partial}{\partial z}(uP) - \frac{c_{pg}}{R_g} \frac{\partial P}{\partial t} - \frac{(1 - \varepsilon_b)}{\varepsilon_b} c_{pa} T \sum_{i=1}^{2} \frac{\partial q_i}{\partial t}$$

$$+ \frac{(1 - \varepsilon_b)}{\varepsilon_b} \sum_{i=1}^{2} (-\Delta H_i) \frac{\partial q_i}{\partial t} - \frac{2 h_{w,in}}{\varepsilon_b r_{in}} (T - T_w)$$

(3)

Momentum balance (Darcy's law):

$$-\frac{\partial P}{\partial z} = \frac{150\mu(1 - \varepsilon_b)^2}{4 R_p^2 \varepsilon_b^2} u$$

(4)

A wall energy balance is also used in order to describe the heat transfer between the column and the environment. In the above set of equations, $y_i$ is the molar fraction of the component i, P and T are the operating pressure and temperature, respectively, t and z are the time and the column's length, $D_z$ is the axial dispersion coefficient, $R_g$ is the universal gas constant, $\varepsilon_b$ is the bed porosity, $q_i$ is the concentration in the solid phase of the component i, $\rho_p$ is the adsorbent density, $c_{pi}$ is the concentration of the component i in the adsorbent pores, $q_i^*$ is the solid phase equilibrium concentration, $k_{ci}$ is a mass transfer coefficient, $c_{ps}, c_{pa}, c_{pg}$ are the specific heat capacities of the adsorbent, the adsorbed phase and the gas phase, respectively, $\rho_g$ is the gas phase density, $c_f$ is the feed concentration, $\lambda_e$ is the gas axial thermal conductivity, $\Delta H_i$ is the component i heat of adsorption, $h_{w,in}$ is the heat transfer coefficient form the column to wall, $r_{in}$ is the inner bed radius, $T_w$ is the bed wall temperature, $\mu$ is the gas viscosity and $R_p$ is the solid particles radius.

### 2.1.2. P/VSA boundary conditions

The mass and energy balances boundary conditions constitute the most significant boundary conditions (BCs) that correspond to the inlet process streams and they are expressed as

$$u(y_i|_z - y_{i,f}) = D_z \frac{\partial y_1}{\partial z}\Big|_z \quad (5) \quad \text{and} \quad \rho_g c_{pg} u \varepsilon_b (T|_z - T_f) = \lambda_e \frac{\partial T}{\partial z}\Big|_z \quad (6)$$

At the outlet streams, the operating pressure is set to the desired value, $\boldsymbol{P = P_t}$. Finally, at the column's closed ends, the gas velocity, is set $\boldsymbol{u = 0}$.

### 2.2. Membrane process

In general, several types of flow models of various complexity have been proposed to describe gas separation by permeation through membranes (Geankoplis, 2003). In the present study we employ the cross-flow model which gives a high efficiency separation performance, that is very close to the more rigorous, but much more expensive computationally, counter-current flow model (Geankoplis, 2003).

### 2.2.1. Membrane model equations

Mass balance:

$$y_p = \frac{x_f - x_{ret}(1 - \theta)}{\theta}$$

(7)

Connection between retentate and permeate equation:

$$\frac{y}{1-y} = \frac{a^*[x - (P_L/P_h)y]}{(1-x) - (P_L/P_h)(1-y)} \tag{8}$$

where $y_p$ is the permeate exit molar fraction, $x_f$ is the feed molar fraction, $x_{ret}$ is the retentate exit molar fraction, $\theta$ is the membrane stage cut, $y$ and $x$ are the permeate and retentate molar fractions, respectively, $a^*$ is the membrane permselectivity and $P_L$ and $P_h$ are the permeate and the retentate operating pressures, respectively.

### 2.3. Hybrid P/VSA – Membrane process

The hybrid process consists of a P/VSA and a membrane stage. In the present work, two potential configurations are examined: P/VSA-membrane and membrane-P/VSA configuration. The separation of 30 mol % $CO_2$ post combustion flue gas mixture from the cement industry is considered. The low pressure, that is, the pressure at the evacuation step in the P/VSA process and the permeate pressure in the membrane process, is fixed at 0.1 bar as this is the lowest applicable pressure at an industrial scale. The efficiency indicators in a two-stage configuration are described below (Haghpanah et al., 2014). The indicator indices represent the stage number, while the output of the first stage is the input of the second one.

$$Purity_{total} = Purity_2 \tag{9}$$

$$Recovery_{total} = Recovery_1 \cdot Recovery_2 \tag{10}$$

$$Energy_{total} = \frac{Energy_1}{Re_2} + Energy_2 \tag{11}$$

### 2.3.1. Optimization problem

Optimization aims at investigating the optimal variable values which lead to the most efficient process performance. The separation processes energy requirement is one of the most significant indicators and as such, energy minimization is the target of the present optimization studies. The constraints and the decision variable bounds are summarized in Table 1 and Table 2.

Table 1. Optimization constraints and decision variables of the P/VSA process

|                       | Stage 1 | Stage 2 |
|-----------------------|---------|---------|
| **Objective function** | Min Energy consumption | Min Energy consumption |
| **Constraints** | $Purity_{CO2} = 48.4\%$ <br> $Recovery_{CO2} = 100\%$ | $Purity_{CO2} \geq 95\%$ <br> $Recovery_{CO2} \geq 95\%$ |
| **Decision variables** | $1.0\ bar \leq P_h \leq 1.5\ bar$ <br> $0.15\ bar \leq P_l \leq 0.95\ bar$ <br> $0.5\ m/s \leq u_f \leq 0.9\ m/s$ | $1.0\ bar \leq P_h \leq 1.5\ bar$ <br> $0.2\ bar \leq P_l \leq 0.95\ bar$ <br> $0.3\ m/s \leq u_f \leq 1.2\ m/s$ |

Table 2. Optimization constraints and decision variables of the membrane separation process

|                       | Stage 1 | Stage 2 |
|-----------------------|---------|---------|
| **Objective function** | Min Energy consumption | Min Energy consumption |
| **Constraints** | $Purity_{CO2} = 48.4\%$ <br> $Recovery_{CO2} = 95.5\%$ | $Purity_{CO2} \geq 95\%$ <br> $Recovery_{CO2} \geq 90\%$ |
| **Decision variables** | $1.0\ bar \leq P_h \leq 1.5\ bar$ <br> $0.1\ bar \leq P_l \leq 1.0\ bar$ <br> $0.0 \leq x_{ret} \leq 0.3$ | $1.0\ bar \leq P_h \leq 1.5\ bar$ <br> $0.1\ bar \leq P_l \leq 1.0\ bar$ <br> $0.0 \leq x_{ret} \leq 0.3$ |

### 2.3.2. Numerical solution

The mathematical model of the P/VSA process consists of a set of partial differential and algebraic equations (PDAE). The system of PDAEs has been solved using a 2$^{nd}$ order

Orthogonal Collocation on Finite Elements Method (OCFEM) and/or Centered Finite Difference Method (CFDM) of $2^{nd}$ order over a discretization grid of 150 intervals for the simulation and the optimization of the P/VSA process. For the case of the membrane cross-flow model, a semi-analytical solution has been employed (Geankoplis, 2003).

The model is implemented in the gPROMS™ modeling environment, which has been previously proven to be a very efficient tool for simulation and optimization of P/VSA or membrane processes (Chatziasteriou et al., 2022).

### 2.4. Optimization of the two-stage P/VSA process

Two-stage P/VSA processes have extensively been developed as promising alternatives to deep vacuum single-stage P/VSA separations. As a result, such a process has been used as reference in the present work. The results of this optimization study are presented in Table 3.

Table 3. Optimization results of the two-stage P/VSA reference case

| Stage | $P_L$ (bar) | $P_I$ (bar) | $P_h$ (bar) | $t_{ads}$ (s) | $u_f$ (m/s) | Purity (%) | Recovery (%) | Energy (kWh/t) |
|---|---|---|---|---|---|---|---|---|
| $1^{st}$ | 0.1 | 0.92 | 1.2 | 30 | 0.69 | 48.4 | 100 | 85.4 |
| $2^{nd}$ | 0.1 | 0.82 | 1.0 | 60 | 0.66 | 95.0 | 91.0 | 52.1 |
| Total | - | - | - | - | - | 95.0 | 91.0 | 145.9 |

It is seen that a two-stage P/VSA process can produce CO₂ meeting the DOE targets employing an industrially acceptable vacuum pressure of 0.1 bar. However, the use of two P/VSA units significantly increases the CAPEX and the OPEX of the process.

### 2.5. Hybrid process optimization

Since a membrane unit has a lower capital and operating cost compared to a P/VSA unit, a two-stage process where a membrane unit replaces either the first or the second P/VSA stage of the reference case, may provide a more cost-effective total process, while the total energy requirement may be improved, as well. In the present work, we have examined the above design alternatives by simulation and optimization studies.

#### 2.5.1. Optimization of a P/VSA-membrane hybrid process

Optimization results of the membrane process and the total performance indicators of the P/VSA-membrane hybrid process are presented in Table 4. The total energy requirement is slightly larger than the reference case. As a result, the two configurations are comparable and they can provide the bases for further design and operating improvements.

Table 4. Optimization results of the P/VSA-membrane process

| 1st stage | $P_L$ (bar) | $P_I$ (bar) | $P_h$ (bar) | $t_{ads}$ (s) | $u_f$ (m/s) | Purity (%) | Recovery (%) | Energy (kWh/t) |
|---|---|---|---|---|---|---|---|---|
| | 0.1 | 0.92 | 1.2 | 30 | 0.69 | 48.4 | 100 | 85.4 |
| **2nd stage** | $P_L$ (bar) | $P_h$ (bar) | Permelectivity (-) | | $\theta$ (-) | Purity (%) | Recovery (%) | Energy (kWh/t) |
| | 0.11 | 1.2 | 90 | | 0.46 | 95 | 90 | 71.5 |
| Total | - | - | - | | - | 95 | 90 | 166.4 |

#### 2.5.2. Optimization of a membrane-P/VSA hybrid process

In the case of the membrane-P/VSA configuration (Table 5), the energy requirements are significantly lower comparing with both the reference process and the previously studied hybrid process. The energy reduction can be attributed to the lower energy needed by the first stage membrane compared to the P/VSA of the reference case, as well as the greater recovery index of the second stage which affects the total energy demand. Note that the membrane's selectivity is, also, much lower in this case.

Table 5. Optimization results of the membrane-P/VSA process

| 1st stage | $P_L$ (bar) | $P_h$ (bar) | Permelectivity (-) | | $\theta$ (-) | Purity (%) | Recovery (%) | Energy (kWh/t) |
|---|---|---|---|---|---|---|---|---|
| | 0.23 | 1.0 | 25 | | 0.59 | 48.4 | 95.5 | 73.9 |
| 2nd stage | $P_L$ (bar) | $P_I$ (bar) | $P_h$ (bar) | $t_{ads}$ (s) | $u_f$ (m/s) | Purity (%) | Recovery (%) | Energy (kWh/t) |
| | 0.1 | 0.43 | 1.0 | 60 | 0.4 | 95.4 | 94.7 | 56.4 |
| **Total** | - | - | - | - | - | **95.4** | **90.4** | **134.4** |

## 3. Conclusions

A hybrid P/VSA-membrane process is a promising alternative for post-combustion $CO_2$ capture compared to a two-stage P/VSA process. Two different hybrid process configurations examined in this work provide high separation efficiency with low energy requirements. Specifically, the P/VSA-membrane configuration leads to a process with energy consumption of 166.4 kWh/tCO$_2$ (equivalent to 0.599 GJ/tCO$_2$), greater than the reference two-stage P/VSA 145.9 kWh/tCO$_2$ (0.525 GJ/tCO$_2$). However, the energy consumption in this case is not considerably higher. On the other hand, the membrane-P/VSA configuration results to an energy demand of 134.4 kWh/t $CO_2$ (0.484 GJ/tCO$_2$), which is lower than the reference case. The results illustrate that a P/VSA process is more efficient for the separation of high $CO_2$ concentration mixtures, while membranes are preferable at $CO_2$ dilute mixtures. Combining the advantages of the two individual processes it can is revealed that a hybrid membrane-P/VSA process can be more efficient in terms of CAPEX and OPEX compared to the standard two-stage P/VSA process.

## Acknowledgements

The research project was supported by the Hellenic Foundation for Research and Innovation (H.F.R.I.) under the "1st Call for H.F.R.I. Research Projects to support Faculty Members and Researchers and the procurement of high-cost research equipment grant" (project number 2090).

## References

Abanades J.C., Arias B., Lyngfelt A., Mattisson T., Wiley D.E., Li H., Ho M.T., Mangano E., Brandani S., 2015. Emerging $CO_2$ capture systems. Int. J. Greenh. Gas Control. 40, 126-166.

Chatziasteriou C.C., Kikkinides E.S., Georgiadis M.C., 2022, Recent advances on the modeling and optimization of $CO_2$ capture processes, Comput. Chem. Eng., 165, 107938.

Geankoplis C. J., 2003, Transport Processes and Separation Process Principles, Prentice Hall PTR, Upper Saddle River, New Jersey.

Haghpanah R., Majumder A., Nilam R., Rajendran A., Farooq S., Karimi I. A., Amanullah M., 2013, Multiobjective Optimization of a Four-Step Adsorption Process for Postcombustion $CO_2$ Capture Via Finite Volume Simulation, Ind. Eng. Chem. Res. 52, 11, 4249-4265.

Haghpanah, R., Rajendran, A., Farooq, S., Karimi, I. A., 2014, Optimization of One- and Two-Staged Kinetically Controlled $CO_2$ Capture Processes from Postcombustion Flue Gas on a Carbon Molecular Sieve, Ind. Eng. Chem. Res. 53 (22): 9186-9198

Khurana M., Farooq S., 2017, Integrated adsorbent-process optimization for carbon capture and concentration using vacuum swing adsorption cycles. AIChE J., 63, 7, 2987–2995

Zanco S.E., Joss L., Hefti M., Gazzani M., Mazzotti M., 2017, Addressing the criticalities for the deployment of adsorption-based $CO_2$ capture processes, Energy Procedia, 114, 2497-2505

Antonis Kokossis, Michael C. Georgiadis, Efstratios N. Pistikopoulos (Eds.)
PROCEEDINGS OF THE 33rd European Symposium on Computer Aided Process Engineering
(ESCAPE33), June 18-21, 2023, Athens, Greece

# Integration of renewable energy and CO₂ capture and utilization technologies for decarbonization of energy intensive process industries

Calin-Cristian Cormos [a], Letitia Petrescu [a], Ana-Maria Cormos [a], Simion Dragan [a], Cristian Dinca [b], Marius Sandru [c]

[a] *Babes-Bolyai University, Faculty of Chemistry and Chemical Engineering, 11 Arany Janos, Cluj-Napoca, Postal code: RO-400028, Romania*
[b] *University Politehnica of Bucharest, Faculty of Power Engineering, 313 Splaiul Independentei, Postal code: RO-060042, Bucharest, Romania*
[c] *Sintef Industry, Sem Sælands vei 2 A, Trondheim, Norway*

## Abstract

Renewable energy sources and $CO_2$ utilization technologies are predicted to play an important role in achieving the climate neutrality by the half of this century. This work evaluates from technical and environmental point of view the integration of renewable energy and $CO_2$ capture and utilization technologies for production of sustainable energy carriers / chemicals. As illustrative cases, Synthetic Natural Gas (SNG) and methanol production using renewable-based hydrogen and captured $CO_2$ were assessed at 100 MW thermal output. The overall processes have significant technical advantages (e.g., high overall energy efficiency up to 60%, more than 97% $H_2$ and $CO_2$ utilization yields etc.) as well as environmental benefits in term of reducing specific $CO_2$ emissions (nearly zero carbon emissions at the plant level and an overall negative emissions to contribute to the reduction of atmospheric $CO_2$ concentration), but significant scale-up efforts are required.
**Keywords**: Renewable energy; Green hydrogen; $CO_2$ capture and utilization; Decarbonized energy carriers; Technical and environmental analysis.

## 1. Introduction

Currently the energy-intensive industrial processes are facing significant economic and environmental challenges. The large-scale utilization of renewable energy sources (e.g., solar, wind, biomass) and their integration with $CO_2$ Capture and Utilization (CCU) technologies are predicted to play an important role for development of low carbon economy to achieve the global climate neutrality (Alok et al., 2022). Figure 1 presents the overall integration of renewable energy sources and $CO_2$ capture and utilization technologies for production of sustainable carbon-neutral energy carriers / chemicals.

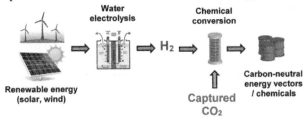

Figure 1. Integration of renewable power and $CO_2$ capture and utilization technologies

This work evaluates the potential decarbonization of several industrial processes (e.g., power generation, cement, petro-chemistry) by integration of renewable energy sources and the $CO_2$ capture and utilization technologies. As investigated systems, methanol and synthetic methane production were evaluated from captured $CO_2$ and green hydrogen (generated from water electrolysis using renewable power) were assessed at relevant industrial sizes (100 MW thermal output for both evaluated options). As key novelty aspects, the overall technical and environmental implications of integrated renewable and $CO_2$ utilization technologies at relevant industrial scales were evaluated using process modeling, model validation and thermal integration for global energy optimization (Szima and Cormos, 2018). For comparison reason, the current non-capture fossil-based processes were also considered to assess the overall benefits of proposed CCU systems.

## 2. Plant configurations and main design assumptions

The first investigated system integrating green hydrogen (produced from renewable power) and captured $CO_2$ from various energy-intensive industrial applications refers to the production of Synthetic Natural Gas (SNG) according to Sabatier chemical reaction:

$$CO_2 \ + \ 4H_2 \ \leftrightarrow \ CH_4 \ + \ 2H_2O \qquad \Delta H = -165.0 \ kJ/mole \qquad (1)$$

The conceptual layout of SNG plant from renewable power (wind and solar) and captured $CO_2$ is presented in Figure 2. The methanation reaction is strongly exothermic and the reaction heat is recovered as steam which is then expanded to produce electricity. The produced electricity is totally covering the ancillary plant consumption and the excess is exported to the grid. This co-generation capability of SNG and power is a particular important aspect of this process contributing to the optimization of plant performances.

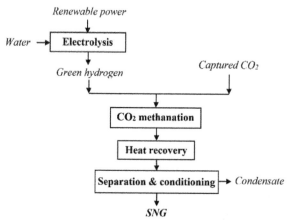

Figure 2. Conceptual layout of Substitute Natural Gas (SNG) plant

The second investigated system involving renewable-based green hydrogen and captured $CO_2$ is referring to the production of methanol that can be used both as energy carrier and chemical. The chemical reaction for producing methanol from is presented below:

$$CO_2 \ + \ 3H_2 \ \leftrightarrow \ CH_3OH \ + \ H_2O \qquad \Delta H = -49.2 \ kJ/mole \qquad (2)$$

The conceptual layout of methanol plant from renewable power (wind and solar) and captured $CO_2$ (from various energy-intensive processes) is presented in Figure 3.

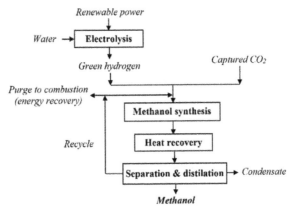

Figure 3. Conceptual layout of methanol plant

As in the case of SNG, the methanol plant has also available heat that is converted into steam and then in electricity to cover the ancillary consumption and the excess was used for export to the grid. The main design assumptions of SNG and methanol plants are presented in Table 1. Both $CO_2$ utilization systems were simulated using process flow modeling - ChemCAD, then systems were subject to detailed thermal integration analysis.

Table 1. Key design assumptions of SNG / methanol plants

| Unit | Design parameters |
|---|---|
| Captured $CO_2$ composition (vol.) | 99.00% carbon dioxide, 0.99% non-condensable gases (nitrogen, argon), 0.01% water |
| Water electrolysis unit | Power consumption: 54 kWh/kg |
| | Hydrogen purity: 99.90% vol. |
| $CO_2$ methanation unit | Ni-based catalyst |
| | Reactor temperature & pressure: 300°C & 50 bar |
| | Kinetic reactor |
| | Thermal mode: heat exchanger type |
| | Pressure drop: 1 bar |
| Methanol synthesis unit | Cu/ZnO/Al$_2$O$_3$ catalyst |
| | Reactor temperature & pressure: 220°C & 80 bar |
| | Kinetic reactor |
| | Thermal mode: heat exchanger type |
| | Pressure drop: 1 bar |

| SNG compression unit | Delivery pressure: 60 bar |
| --- | --- |
| | Compressor efficiency: 85% |
| Methanol distillation unit | Methanol purity: 99.90% |
| | Distillation column: 12 stages |
| | Column feed temperature: 80°C |
| Heat recovery and steam cycle | Steam temperature & pressure: 200 - 280°C & 3 bar |
| | Condensation pressure: 0.046 bar |
| | Steam turbine efficiency: 86% |
| | Turbine steam wetness: max. 10% |
| Heat exchangers | $\Delta T_{min.} = 10°C$ |
| | Pressure drop: 2 - 5% of inlet pressure |
| Thermodynamic package | Soave-Redlich-Kwong (SRK) |

## 3. Results and discussions

After modeling and simulation, the developed models were subject to model validation in comparison to experimental / industrial data. The model validation was done only for the methanation and methanol reactors since the rest of the processes (e.g., heat recovery, gas separation, distillation) is already common in chemical applications. The main simulated performance indicators (e.g., $H_2$ and $CO_2$ conversion rates) were fully in line with experimental data (Koytsoumpa and Karellas, 2018; Lombardelli et al., 2022).

For optimization of overall energy efficiency, the thermal integration analysis using pinch methodology was used (Smith, 2016). For SNG plant, the composite curves are presented in Figure 4 showing a significant heat recovery potential in form of steam generation.

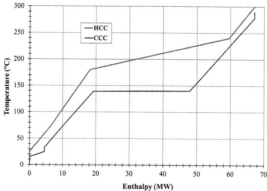

Figure 4. Thermal integration analysis of SNG plant

The main performance indicators of SNG plant are presented in Table 2. One can noticed the high conversion rates (>98%) of both used reactants ($CO_2$ and $H_2$), a promising overall energy efficiency of the global system as well as an almost zero specific $CO_2$ process emissions at the plant level. In fact, considering the renewable nature of the power used for water electrolysis to produce the required green hydrogen stream, the overall $CO_2$ emissions are negative (contributing to reduction of $CO_2$ concentration from atmosphere).

Table 2. Main performance indicators of SNG plant

| Parameter | Unit | Value |
|-----------|------|-------|
| $CO_2$ flowrate | t/h | 18.45 |
| $CO_2$ conversion yield | % | 98.90 |
| $H_2$ flowrate | t/h | 3.38 |
| $H_2$ conversion yield | % | 98.10 |
| Specific power consumption for water electrolysis | kWh/kg | 54.00 |
| Power consumption for $H_2$ production | $MW_e$ | 182.52 |
| | | |
| SNG production capacity | t/h | 6.88 |
| SNG lower heating value | MJ/kg | 52.30 |
| SNG thermal output | $MW_{th}$ | 100.00 |
| Gas decompression | $MW_e$ | 0.60 |
| Gross power output | $MW_e$ | 5.95 |
| Net power output | $MW_e$ | 6.55 |
| Overall energy efficiency | % | 58.37 |
| Specific $CO_2$ emissions | kg/kg SNG | 0.05 |

Similar for methanol synthesis, the thermal integration was used for overall energy optimization (see Figure 5 for hot and cold composite curves). One can noticed comparing Figures 4 and 5 that the SNG case has the available heat sources at higher temperature than for the methanol case which will have an influence on the overall energy efficiency.

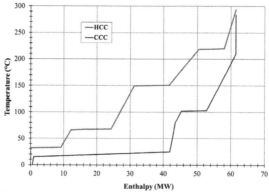

Figure 5. Thermal integration analysis of methanol plant

The main performance indicators of methanol plant are presented in Table 3. As in the case of SNG plant, high conversion rates for both reactants as well as overall energy efficiency coupled with almost zero $CO_2$ emissions were reported. For comparison reason, the conventional methanol process starting from natural gas (fossil source) without carbon capture has a specific $CO_2$ emission of about 95 - 110 kg/GJ which correspond to about 0.5 - 0.6 kg/kg (IRENA, 2021; Khojasteh-Salkuyeh et al., 2021). Comparing both investigated $CO_2$ utilization processes, one can noticed that the methanol plant has a slightly less overall energy efficiency which can be explained by lower temperature of available heat sources (as discussed above) as well as a more complex design of the overall system (e.g., involving a distillation of raw methanol which requires additional thermal energy for separation) with inherent higher energy consumptions.

Table 3. Key technical performance indicators of methanol plant

| Parameter | Unit | Value |
|---|---|---|
| $CO_2$ flowrate | t/h | 25.50 |
| $CO_2$ conversion yield | % | 97.35 |
| $H_2$ flowrate | t/h | 3.50 |
| $H_2$ conversion yield | % | 99.85 |
| Specific power consumption for water electrolysis | kWh/kg | 54.00 |
| Power consumption for $H_2$ production | $MW_e$ | 187.20 |
| Methanol production capacity | t/h | 18.07 |
| Methanol lower heating value | MJ/kg | 19.92 |
| Methanol thermal output | $MW_{th}$ | 100.00 |
| Plant ancillary consumption | $MW_e$ | -4.95 |

| Gross power output | $MW_e$ | 6.00 |
|---|---|---|
| Net power output | $MW_e$ | 1.05 |
| Overall energy efficiency | % | 53.98 |
| Specific $CO_2$ emissions | kg/kg MeOH | 0.04 |

Although very promising in delivering better technical and environmental performance indicators, the evaluated $CO_2$ capture and utilization (CCU) systems still requires significant scale-up efforts from the current development level (up to several MW) to full industrial sizes (Bailera et al., 2017). In addition, the utilization of green hydrogen as raw material for $CO_2$ utilization technologies requires an efficient energy storage facility considering the time intermittency of solar and wind resources (Miehling et al., 2022).

## 4. Conclusions

The present work evaluates the potential benefits of integration the renewable energy sources with $CO_2$ capture and utilization (CCU) technologies for production of sustainable carbon-neutral fuels at industrial level capacities. As illustrative cases, substitute natural gas and methanol production from green hydrogen and captured $CO_2$ were assessed using process modeling and thermal integration. As the results show, the integration of renewable energy and $CO_2$ capture and utilization technologies brings significant technical advantages (e.g., high overall energy efficiency 54 - 58%, more than 97% hydrogen and $CO_2$ utilization yields etc.) as well as positive environmental benefits in term of reducing specific $CO_2$ emissions (nearly zero carbon emissions at the plant level and overall negative emissions to contribute to the reduction of atmospheric $CO_2$ concentration) compared to the current non-capture fossil-based concepts. However, significant scale-up is still needed to deploy these technology to relevant industrial level.

## Acknowledgements

This work was supported by the NO Grants 2014 - 2021, under project contract no. 13/2020 and a grant of the Romanian Ministry of Education and Research, CCCDI - UEFISCDI, project number PN-III-P4-ID-PCE-2020-0032, within PNCDI III.

## References

A. Alok, R. Shrestha, S. Ban, S. Devkota, B. Uprety, R. Joshi, 2022, Technological advances in the transformative utilization of $CO_2$ to value-added products, Journal of Environmental Chemical Engineering, 10, 106922

M. Bailera, P. Lisbona, L.M. Romeo, S. Espatolero, 2017, Power to Gas projects review: Lab, pilot and demo plants for storing renewable energy and $CO_2$, Renewable and Sustainable Energy Reviews, 69, 292-312

International Renewable Energy Agency (IRENA), 2021, Innovation outlok - Renewable methanol

Y. Khojasteh-Salkuyeh, O. Ashrafi, E. Mostafavi, P. Navarri, 2021, $CO_2$ utilization for methanol production; Part I: Process design and life cycle GHG assessment of different pathways, Journal of $CO_2$ Utilization, 50, 101608

E.I. Koytsoumpa, S. Karellas, 2018, Equilibrium and kinetic aspects for catalytic methanation focusing on $CO_2$ derived Substitute Natural Gas (SNG), Renewable and Sustainable Energy Reviews, 94, 36-50

G. Lombardelli, M. Mureddu, S. Lai, F. Ferrara, A. Pettinau, L. Atzoric, A. Conversano, M. Gatti, 2022, $CO_2$ hydrogenation to methanol with an innovative Cu/Zn/Al/Zr catalyst: Experimental tests and process modeling, Journal of $CO_2$ Utilization, 65, 102240

S. Miehling, S. Fendt, H. Spliethoff, 2022, Optimal integration of Power-to-X plants in a future European energy system and the resulting dynamic requirements, Energy Conversion and Management, 251, 115020

R. Smith, 2016, Chemical process design and integration, second edition, Wiley, Hoboken, USA

S. Szima, C.C. Cormos, 2018, Improving methanol synthesis from carbon-free $H_2$ and captured $CO_2$: A techno-economic and environmental evaluation, Journal of $CO_2$ Utilization, 24, 555-563

Antonis Kokossis, Michael C. Georgiadis, Efstratios N. Pistikopoulos (Eds.)
PROCEEDINGS OF THE 33rd European Symposium on Computer Aided Process Engineering
(ESCAPE33), June 18-21, 2023, Athens, Greece

# Simultaneous optimisation of energy recovery and water recirculation in a ceramic plant

Miguel Castro Oliveira,[a,b] Muriel Iten,[a] Henrique A. Matos,[b]

[a] *Low Carbon and Resource Efficiency, R&Di, Instituto de Soldadura e Qualidade, 4415 491 Grijó, Portugal*

[b] *Centro Recursos Naturais e Ambiente (CERENA), Department of Chemical Engineering, Instituto Superior Técnico, Universidade de Lisboa, Avenida Rovisco Pais 1, 1049-001 Lisboa, Portugal*

## Abstract

The ongoing energy crisis and water shortages occurring in many EU Member countries have reinforced the importance of the achievement of the aims associated to sustainability policies. In this work, a non-linear programming (NLP) model developed with the Python language for the virtual implementation in a ceramic plant of a Water and Energy Integration System (WEIS). This is an innovative process integration and system retrofitting-based concept aiming for simultaneous energy efficiency improvement and water minimisation in industry. A set of indicators were assessed in post-processing for the results obtained to the ceramic plant WEIS project, namely a payback period of about 1 year and 4 months and an emission reduction level of 2.97 kton $CO_{2,eq}$/ year. These are highly favourable compared to industrial benchmarks. The developed optimisation model is part of a research & development initiative designated ThermWatt, set to create a customised computational tool for water, energy and waste management in end-use sectors and an Engineering consultancy service around it.

**Keywords**: Water and Energy Integration Systems, energy efficiency, water minimisation, ceramic industry, Python NLP-model.

## 1. Introduction

The improvement of water and energy efficiency is an important concern in the context of the most recent sustainable development requirements in the world. In the scope of the reduction of the significant use of both energy and water in end-use sectors, the authors have developed the innovative concept of Water and Energy Integration Systems (WEIS) (Castro Oliveira et al., 2022). These are types of systems that include a certain number of water-using processes and combustion-based thermal processes and all potential stream recirculation between these processes.

Several theoretical approaches have been proposed in academia for the problems related to heat recovery systems (fuel and electricity use reduction) (Castro Oliveira et al., 2022a) and water allocation and heat exchanger networks (freshwater and hot/ cold utilities use reduction) (Ibrić et al., 2016). While the first one has been proved theoretically and practically implemented (although not in a holistic perspective, considering all potential technologies and scenarios), the latter has been essentially studied in theory only, with the existing studies only focusing on a small number of end-use sectors.

The concept of WEIS has been introduced to encompass both the phenomenon of waste heat stream recirculation to produce fuel savings in combustion-based processes (as well as electricity generation in thermodynamic cycles) and the concept of water allocation and heat exchanger network mentioned afore. Furthermore, it also includes the integration of energy recovery from wastewater technologies for the production of additional fuel quantities to be fed to combustion-based processes. The wastewater treatment units to be included within water systems are heat-driven ones (such as Multi-effect distillation) (Castro Oliveira et al., 2022b), so to make possible the allocation of enthalpy from waste heat streams originating from combustion-based processes. The conceptualization of WEIS consists on the analysis of all potential interdependencies between water and energy streams to generate savings in both, thus subsisting on the promotion of the water-energy nexus character associated to this type of process (Castro Oliveira et al., 2019).

This work presents the development of an optimisation model considering simultaneous energy recovery and water recirculation in a ceramic plant. A post-processing assessment is performed based on the determination of indicators associated to economic and environmental impact viabilities.

## 2. Contextualization of the Case-study

The case-study is set within a ceramic industry plant installed in Portugal. The plant is characterized by the existence of 2 combustion-based processes (tunnel kilns) and 4 water-using processes (each one being set to remove a determinate quantity of salt contaminant). In Table 1, the operational data for the case-study is presented.

**Table 1.** Operational data for each combustion-based process and water-using line

| | | Combustion-based processes | | | | |
|---|---|---|---|---|---|---|
| Process | Natural gas flow rate (kg/h) | Hot Air | | Exhaust gases | | |
| | | Flow rate (kg/h) | Temp. (°C) | Flow rate (kg/h) | Temp. (°C) | |
| Kiln 1 | 196.5 | 20711.7 | 193.2 | 16480.5 | 230.0 | |
| Kiln 2 | 103.5 | 23583.1 | 95.0 | 14454.5 | 159.3 | |

| | | | | Water system | | | | |
|---|---|---|---|---|---|---|---|---|
| Water-using Lines | Water | | | Salt | | | Hot Utility (MJ/year) | Cold Utility (MJ/year) |
| | Flow rate (kg/h) | Final Temp. (°C) | Flow rate (kg/h) | Salt Concentration (ppm) | | | | |
| | | | | WP Inlet | WP Outlet | | | |
| | | | | Max. | Min. | Max. | | |
| Line 1 | 474.83 | 95 | 0.47483 | 200 | 800 | 1000 | 495.00 | |
| Line 2 | 477.12 | 95 | 0.47712 | 200 | 800 | 1000 | 495.00 | |
| Line 3 | 365.43 | 95 | 0.36540 | 200 | 800 | 1000 | 495.00 | |
| Line 4 | 58.79 | 100 | 0.05873 | 200 | 800 | 1000 | 130.00 | |
| Discharge | | | | | 0.00 | 1000 | | 396.00 |
| Total | 1376.17 | | | | | | 1615.00 | 396.00 |

The presented data is the foundation for the project of a WEIS in the ceramic plant. In terms of hot air/ exhaust gas streams allocation, the configuration may be described by the following sequence steps: a part of the hot air stream at the outlet of a kiln may be recirculated to the same kiln or the other as part of the total combustion air; the remaining quantities of the two hot air streams are mixed and then directed to the water system, with the stream being divided for each water-using line, and in its turn for each heater and saline water treatment Multi-effect distillation (MED) unit (5 effects and 1 condenser); the hot air streams at the heaters and MED's outlets are mixed with themselves and the two exhaust gas stream from each kiln and then directed to the HRSG unit of an Organic Rankine cycle (ORC) electricity generation; an Electrolysis unit is installed to produced hydrogen fuel from discharge water stream from the water system, which is then feed as additional fuel to each kiln in the form of hydrogen-enriched natural gas (HENG).

The allocation of water streams (recycling, reuse and by-pass) occurs as follows: from the water-using process (WP) to the MED unit inlet, heater inlet, cooler inlet, the water system outlet, other 3 heaters and other 3 coolers; from the MED unit to water-using line inlet, heater inlet, cooler inlet, the water system discharge, other 3 heaters and other 3 coolers; from the heater to water-using line inlet, MED unit inlet and water system discharge; from the cooler to water-using line inlet, MED unit inlet and water system discharge. The described strategy (in the form of stream allocation-based superstructure) is pictorially represented in Figure 1.

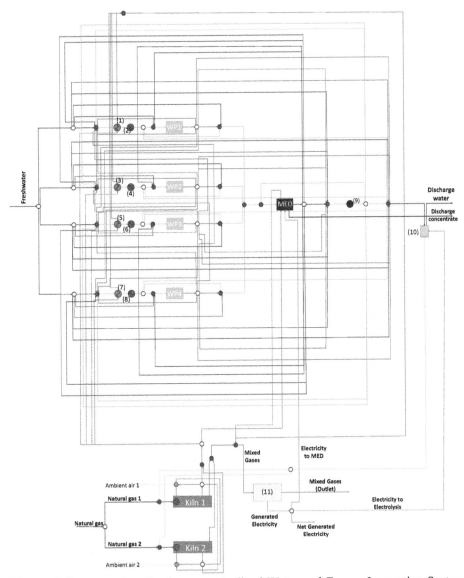

**Figure 1.** Superstructure for the conceptualized Water and Energy Integration System. Legend: ●-stream mixing; ○ -stream splitting ; — Exaust Gases ; — Hydrogen; — hot air; (1) – Economiser 1; (2) – Heater 1; (3) – Economiser 2; (4) – Heater  2 ; (5) – Economiser  3; (6) – Heater 3; (7) – Economiser 4; (8) – Heater 4; (9) – Cooler; (10) – Electrolysis Unit; (11) – Organic Rankine Cycle

## 3. Optimisation Model

The optimisation model approached in this work was developed using the non-linear programming (NLP) methodology, with the GEKKO package built in the Python language. In Table 2, the developed NLP model is characterized, with the decision variables and constraints being presented in an aggregated and generic manner. The optimal solution in the form of the optimal WEIS scenario flowsheet is presented in Figure 2, considering all the results for stream allocation and sizing parameters.

**Table 2.** Characterization of the optimisation problem

**Combustion-based Processes System**

**Decision Variables**

- Natural gas flow rates ($M_{Fuel}$)
- Ambient air flow rates ($M_{Amb.Air}$)
- Exhaust gases flow rates ($M_{Ex.}$)
- Exhaust gases specific enthalpies ($h_{Ex.}$)
- Exhaust gases temperatures ($T_{Ex.}$)
- Hot air flow rates ($M_{Hot\ Air}$)
- Hot air specific enthalpies ($h_{Hot\ Air}$)
- Hot air specific temperatures ($T_{Hot\ Air}$)

- Recirculated air flow rates ($M_{Rec.Air}$)
- Recirculated air specific enthalpies ($h_{Rec\ Air}$)
- Recirculated air temperatures ($T_{Rec\ Air}$)
- Air-to-fuel ratios (AF)
- Fuel lower heating value ($LHV_{Fuel}$)
- Generated Electricity (Elec)
- Appreciably Generated Electricity ($Elec_{eff}$)
- Electricity used in Electrolysis ($Elec_{Eletrolysis}$)

**Relevant Inequality Constraints**

$$T_{Ex} \le 75°C$$

**Relevant Equality Constraints**

$$M_{Fuel,Baseline} \cdot LHV_{Natural\ Gas} = M_{Fuel} \cdot LHV_{Fuel} + M_{Comb.Air} \cdot (h_{Comb.Air} - h_{Comb.Air,Baseline}) \qquad (1)$$

$$M_{Comb.Air} = M_{Recyc.Air} + M_{Amb.Air} \qquad (2)$$

$$M_{Comb.Air} \cdot h_{Comb.Air} = M_{Recyc.Air} \cdot h_{Recyc.Air} + M_{Amb.Air} \cdot h_{Amb.Air} \qquad (3)$$

$$M_{Fuel} + M_{Comb.Air} = M_{Ex.} \qquad (4)$$

$$M_{Fuel} \cdot AF = M_{Comb.Air} \qquad (5)$$

$$AF \cdot LHV_{Natural\ Gas} = AF_{Baseline} \cdot LHV_{Fuel} \qquad (6)$$

$$LHV_{Fuel} = y_{Natural\ Gas} \cdot LHV_{Natural\ Gas} + y_{Hydrogen} \cdot LHV_{Hydrogen} \qquad (7)$$

$$M_{gas,in,ORC} \cdot (h_{gas,in,ORC} - h_{gas,out,ORC}) \cdot 0.06 = Elec \cdot 3600 \qquad (8)$$

$$Elec = Elec_{eff} + Elec_{Electrolysis} \qquad (9)$$

**Water System**

**Decision Variables**

- Freshwater mass flow rate ($M_{FW}$)
- Each water stream mass flow rate ($M_w$)
- Each water stream specific enthalpy ($h_w$)
- Each water stream temperatures ($T_w$)
- Each water stream contaminant concentration ($C_w$)
- Heat transfer areas (A)
- Withdrawn enthalpy from hot air ($q_{with.}$)
- Treated water mass flow rate produced in the second-to-last effects and condenser of the MED unit ($M_{TW}$)

- Vapour mass flow rate from a MED unit effect ($M_V$)
- Concentrate water mass flow rate from a MED unit effect ($M_{Conc.}$)
- Discharged water mass flow rate from the water system ($M_{Disch.}$)
- Produced vapour (MED unit outlet) specific enthalpy ($h_V$)
- Produced hydrogen mass flow rate ($M_{Hydrogen}$)
- Water-to-hydrogen conversion ratio ($X_{Hydrogen}$)

**Relevant Inequality Constraints**

$$C_{w,WP,inlet} \le 200\ ppm$$
$$C_{w,WP,outlet} \ge 800\ ppm$$
$$C_{w,WP,outlet} \le 1000\ ppm$$

**Relevant Equality Constraints**

$$M_{W,to-be-splitted} = \sum_{i=1} M_{W,split,i} \qquad (10)$$

$$h_{W,to-be-splitted} = h_{W,split,i} \qquad (11)$$

$$C_{W,to-be-splitted} = C_{W,split,i} \qquad (12)$$

$$\sum_{i=1} M_{W,to-be-mixed,i} = M_{W,mixed} \qquad (13)$$

$$\sum_{i=1} M_{W,to-be-mixed,i} \cdot h_{W,to-be-mixed,i} = M_{W,mixed} \cdot h_{W,mixed} \qquad (14)$$

$$\sum_{i=1} M_{W,to-be-mixed,i} \cdot C_{W,to-be-mixed,i} = M_{W,mixed} \cdot C_{W,mixed} \qquad (15)$$

$$M_{W,in,Eff} \cdot \frac{1}{5} = M_{T\ W,Eff} + M_{Conc,Eff} \qquad (16)$$

$$q_{with,MED} = M_{V,Eff1} \cdot (h_{V,Eff1} - 418.896) + M_{w,in,Eff1} \cdot \frac{1}{5} \cdot (418.896 - h_{w,in,Eff}) \qquad (17)$$

$$M_{TW,Eff\ k-1} \cdot (h_{V,Eff\ k-1} - 418.896) = M_{V,Effk} \cdot (h_{V,Eff\ k} - 418.896) + M_{w,in,Eff\ k} \cdot \frac{1}{5} \cdot (418.896 - h_{w,in,Eff}) \qquad (18)$$

$$M_{TW,Eff} \cdot (2675.43 - 418.896) = M_{w,in,Eff} \cdot \frac{1}{5} \cdot (h_{V,Eff} - 418.896) \qquad (19)$$

$$M_{TW,Eff\ 5} \cdot (h_{V,Eff\ 5} - 418.896) = M_{w,in,MED} \cdot \frac{1}{5} \cdot (h_{w,in,Eff} - h_{w,in,MED}) \qquad (20)$$

$$q_{with.} = 400 \cdot A \cdot \left((T_{Air,in} - T_{w,out}) \cdot (T_{Air,out} - T_{w,in}) \cdot ((T_{Air,in} - T_{w,out}) + (T_{Air,out} - T_{w,in})) \cdot 0.5\right)^{1/3} \qquad (21)$$

$$\frac{M_{Disch.,Eff}}{0.01801528} \cdot X_{Hydrogen} = \frac{M_{Hydrogen}}{0.002016} \qquad (22)$$

$$\frac{M_{Disch.,Eff}}{0.01801528} \cdot 285.85 \cdot X_{Hydrogen} = Elec_{Electrolysis} \qquad (23)$$

**Objective-function (€/h)** (Natural gas, Electricity and Freshwater unitary prices for Portugal)

$$\min \left( \left( 23.66(\text{€/GJ}) \cdot 0.0451(\text{GJ/kg}) \cdot M_{\text{Natural Gas}}(\text{kg/h}) + 1.8499(\text{€/m}^3) \cdot \frac{1}{999}(\text{m}^3/\text{kg}) \cdot M_{\text{FW}}(\text{kg/h}) + 23.66(\text{€/GJ}) \right. \right.$$
$$\left. \left. \cdot \, q_{\text{Hot Utility}}(\text{GJ/h}) + 7.389(\text{€/GJ}) \cdot q_{\text{Cold Utility}}(\text{GJ/h}) + 0.1459(\text{€/kWh}) \cdot \text{Elec}_{\text{eff}}(\text{kWh/h}) \right) \right) \quad (24)$$

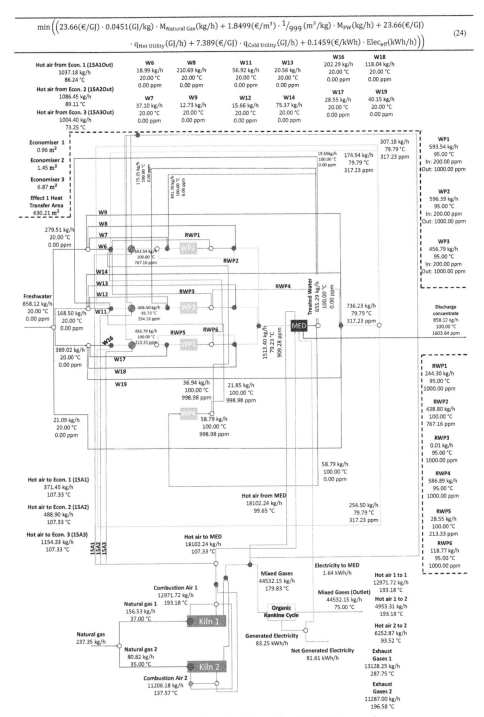

**Figure 2.** Flowsheet for the optimal WEIS scenario

## 4. Post-processing: Economic and Environmental Impact Assessments

In Table 3, the results for economic and environmental impact assessment are presented.

**Table 3.** Economic and Environmental Impact Reduction Assessments

| Natural gas consumption (kg/h) | | | | |
|---|---|---|---|---|
| Process | Initial | Improved | Relative Savings Share | Savings (€/h) |
| Kiln 1 | 196.50 | 156.53 | 20.34% | 44.54 |
| Kiln 2 | 103.50 | 80.82 | 21.91% | 25.27 |
| Hot and Cold utilities consumption (MJ/h) | | | | |
| Heater 1 | 495.00 | 0.00 | 100.00% | 11.71 |
| Heater 2 | 495.00 | 0.00 | 100.00% | 11.71 |
| Heater 3 | 495.00 | 0.00 | 100.00% | 9.55 |
| Heater 4 | 130.00 | 0.00 | 100.00% | 3.08 |
| Cooler | 396.00 | 0.00 | 100.00% | 16.04 |
| Water consumption (m³/h) | | | | |
| | Initial | Improved | Relative Savings Share | Savings (€/h) |
| | 1.38 | 0.86 | 23.50% | 0.96 |
| Electricity Balances (kWh/h) | | | | |
| | Net Electricity Generation (kWh/h) | | | Savings (€/h) |
| | 81.61 | | | 16.04 |
| Final assessment | | | | |
| CAPEX (k€) | OPEX (k€/year) | Savings (k€/year) | Payback Time (Years) | CO$_{2,eq}$ emissions reduction (kton/year) |
| 1241.86 | 84.31 | 1054.47 | 1.28 | 2.97 |

## 5. Conclusions

This work approaches the assessment of potential improvements of the overall water and energy efficiencies in a ceramic industry plant through the development and further use of an optimisation model using the Python language. The model was developed with the aim to apply the newly created methodology of Water and Energy Integration Systems (WEIS), which has only yet been proved in concept. The model proved to be valuable for the achievement of the proposed objective of reducing overall water and energy-related costs and associated pollutant emissions generated by water discharge and combustion gases discharge. A set of indicators were assessed in post-processing, having been obtained a payback period of about 1 year and 4 months and an emission reduction level of 2.97 kton $CO_{2,eq}$/year, which are highly favourable compared to industrial benchmarks.

## Acknowledgements

The publishing procedure and conference participation have received funding through ISQ – Instituto de Soldadura e Qualidade through Programa Interface/ CIT – Centro de Interface Tecnológicos and CERENA under grant UIDB/04028/2020_UIDP/04028/2020.

## References

M. Castro Oliveira, M. Iten, H.A. Matos, J. Michels, 2019, Water-energy nexus in typical industrial water circuits, Water 11 (4), 699.

M. Castro Oliveira, M. Iten, H.A. Matos, 2022, Review on Water and Energy Integration in Process Industry: Water-Heat Nexus, Sustain., 14, 7954.

M. Castro Oliveira, M. Iten, H.A. Matos, 2022a, Simulation and assessment of an integrated thermal processes and Organic Rankine Cycle (ORC) system with Modelica, 8, 764 – 770.

M. Castro Oliveira, P. Coelho, M. Iten, H.A. Matos, 2022b, Modelling of Heat-Driven Water Treatment Systems: Multi-Effect Distillation (MED) model in Modelica. Comput. Aided Chem. Eng., 51, 397– 402.

N. Ibrić, E. Ahmetović, Z. Kravanja, 2016, Mathematical programming synthesis of non-isothermal water networks by using a compact/reduced superstructure and an MINLP model. Clean Technol. Environ. Policy, 18, 1779–1813.

Antonis Kokossis, Michael C. Georgiadis, Efstratios N. Pistikopoulos (Eds.)
PROCEEDINGS OF THE 33rd European Symposium on Computer Aided Process Engineering
(ESCAPE33), June 18-21, 2023, Athens, Greece

# Embedding Flexibility to the Design of Pressure-Vacuum Swing Adsorption Processes for $CO_2$ Capture

Steven Sachio[a,b], Adam Ward[a,b], Ronny Pini[a,b], Maria M. Papathanasiou[a,b]

[a]Sargent Centre for Process Systems Engineering, Imperial College London, London, United Kingdom SW72AZ
[b]Department of Chemical Engineering, Imperial College London, London, United Kingdom SW72AZ

## Abstract

Capture of carbon dioxide ($CO_2$) from post-combustion flue gases is an engineered solution to enable global transition to a sustainable energy system. For this, typically, pressure-vacuum swing adsorption (PVSA) is used. The design of PVSA processes traditionally relies on solving complex, constrained multi-objective optimization problems for the identification of good candidate operating points. Such processes are not agile as they are constrained to operate around a single optimal point. Examining process flexibility underpins the identification of suitable control strategies that handle disturbances. In this work, we deploy a machine learning-aided design space identification framework for simultaneous quantification of process flexibility and preliminary Pareto front identification to design flexible and controllable PVSA processes. The framework enables reducing the number of simulations required to identify good candidate operating points by 77%, with a difference of 1.1% in the cost optimum solution compared to performing rigorous optimization by NSGA-II. Additionally, the framework identifies that the cost optimal operation is highly non-flexible, suggesting that new design approaches are required to allow for the design of efficient and controllable PVSA processes.

**Keywords**: computing and systems engineering, process design, carbon capture

## 1. Introduction

One of the most significant contributions to anthropogenic carbon dioxide ($CO_2$) emissions is the elution of flue gases from fossil fuel-fired power plants. It is likely that the combustion of fossil fuels will remain in widespread use over the next several decades while the world undergoes a transition to a sustainable energy system. Therefore, there is a need to design efficient processes for removing $CO_2$ from such flue gases to reduce emissions to the environment. Gas-phase separation by pressure-vacuum swing adsorption (PVSA) is a promising technology for performing post-combustion $CO_2$ capture (Raganati et al, 2021). In a PVSA process, flue gas is exposed to a fixed bed of solid adsorbent material to selectively remove $CO_2$. The fixed bed then elutes a $CO_2$ deficient effluent stream which can be vented to the atmosphere. The $CO_2$ which has been adsorbed in the bed can be subsequently recovered at high purity to be sent for downstream utilization or geological sequestration. The computational design of PVSA processes for $CO_2$ capture is typically quite challenging (Balashankar et al, 2019). First, description of the highly non-linear process dynamics with a suitable mathematical model requires a significant amount of computational time to evaluate the process performance for a given set of operating conditions. Second, the design problem requires the solution of constrained multi-objective optimization to find a Pareto front of optimum productivity/energy usage, while satisfying regulatory requirements on the purity and recovery of the extracted $CO_2$ (Haghpanah et al, 2013). Both factors together mean that several days of CPU time are required to design a single adsorbent material/process cycle PVSA configuration. Additionally, the status-quo approach for design of such processes does not account for the flexibility of the optimal process design. Assessment of the flexibility of a process is an underpinning element to understanding its controllability, which could prove to be an important factor in discrimination between competing PVSA configurations. Particularly, assessment of new configurations based on flexibility could improve robustness of process operations to disturbances in the flue gas feed conditions.

In this work, we present a framework for simultaneous design and flexibility assessment of PVSA processes applied to post-combustion $CO_2$ capture. The approach utilizes a high-fidelity dynamic process model as a virtual experimentation platform. In conjunction with quasi-random sampling, an artificial neural network (ANN) model, and an alpha shapes approach, we use the virtual experimentation environment to efficiently identify an initial set of Pareto fronts for the process, the design space of operating parameters where all the process constraints are satisfied and quantify the flexibility around the nominal operating point (NOP). The proposed methodology is both significantly more efficient than the status-quo design approach for PVSA presented in the literature and additionally generates a much richer set of outputs to inform the design and control of such systems.

## 2. The system

We consider a four-step PVSA process with feed pressurization for post-combustion $CO_2$ capture from a dry coal fired power plant flue gas using a fixed bed of zeolite 13X adsorbent. The feed gas is a binary mixture of $CO_2/N_2$ with a molar composition of 15/85% which is available at ambient conditions. Regulatory requirements constrain the operation of the process to recover greater than 90% of the $CO_2$ fed to the process at a product purity of greater than 95%. The process has been described using a mathematical process model developed in a previous study, which is taken as a virtual experimentation platform for the purposes of this work (Ward & Pini, 2022a). Briefly, the model comprises a coupled system of partial differential and algebraic equations (PDAEs) which represent the governing balances of mass, momentum, and energy in the adsorption column. The PDAE system is solved in MATLAB using a finite volume scheme. The model equations are solved subject to a set of time-varying boundary conditions which describe the four-step adsorption cycle. The mathematical model has been validated against both experimental measurements (Ward & Pini, 2022b) and independent simulations conducted in the literature (Ward & Pini, 2022a). Design of such systems is cumbersome because simulation of the process performance for a given set of operating parameters takes up to several minutes of computational time.

As inputs, the process model requires specification of the operating parameters of the PVSA cycle. These are the intermediate operating pressure achieved in the blowdown step ($p_I$), as well as the high operating pressure ($p_H$) and the flow rate ($v_F$) at which flue gas is fed to the bed during the adsorption step. For a given set of operating conditions, the process performance is simulated and a set of five key performance indicators (KPIs) are calculated. We evaluate the purity and recovery of the $CO_2$ extracted from the flue gas to allow us to assess compliance with the regulatory constraints on the operation of the process. We also evaluate the productivity of the process and its specific energy usage to assess the efficiency of the process. The productivity specifies the capture rate of $CO_2$ per unit volume of the bed and the specific energy usage specifies the amount of energy consumed per tonne of $CO_2$ captured. Additionally, the dynamic process simulator is also coupled to a detailed techno-economic assessment framework. This allows for calculation of the capture cost associated with each set of operating parameters, given as the cost per tonne of $CO_2$ captured.

The design of PVSA processes for post-combustion $CO_2$ capture is classically conducted in three stages. First, the purity and recovery of $CO_2$ extracted from the flue gas is maximized. This allows for confirmation that the chosen process configuration has a design space for which the regulatory requirements on the purity/recovery of the extracted $CO_2$ are satisfied. Second, the productivity of the process is maximized while minimizing the specific energy usage, subject to the above regulatory constraints. In this step, we assess the efficiency of the process for capturing $CO_2$ from the flue gas. Third, a capture cost minimization is conducted subject to the purity/recovery constraints. The cost minimum point is usually taken to be the nominal operating point (NOP) of the process. The design of these systems is challenging because it requires constrained multi-objective optimization coupled with a detailed process simulation and economic assessment framework. The new approach presented in this study aims to significantly streamline the design by conducting all three design stages simultaneously, whilst also explicitly obtaining the design space and quantifying the flexibility of the NOP.

## 3. The framework

The framework has three main steps: problem formulation, design space identification, and design space analysis.

### 3.1. Problem Formulation

The objective of this case study is to identify good candidate process operating points and assess their flexibility. As detailed in Section 2, the manipulated variables of the considered PVSA system are $p_H$, $p_I$ and $v_F$. The bounds of the manipulated variables are provided in Table 1 and were chosen based on good practice in the literature on PVSA process design. The KPIs of interest are the purity and recovery of $CO_2$ extracted from the flue gas, as well as specific energy consumption, productivity, and capture cost. The process must satisfy regulatory constraints on the $CO_2$ product stream with a purity > 95% and a recovery > 90%. Additionally, the operating conditions are constrained such that the intermediate pressure is always less than high pressure ($p_I \leq p_H$).

Table 1. Bounds of the manipulated variables.

|  | $p_I$ (bar) | $p_H$ (bar) | $v_F$ (m/s) |
|---|---|---|---|
| Lower bound | 0.05 | 1 | 0.1 |
| Upper bound | 3.00 | 10 | 2.0 |

### 3.2. Design Space Identification

The quasi-random Sobol sequence is used to generate 4,096 parameter combinations within the parameter bounds. Owing to the constraint imposed on the operating pressures, only 3,458 of the sampled parameter combinations were feasible for use in virtual experimentation. The process model was evaluated at the operating point corresponding to each parameter combination to generate a dataset. Using this data, an artificial neural network is trained, and an additional 260,000 samples are generated. This allows for the characterization of the design space with a fine alpha shape.

### 3.3. Design Space Analysis

Based on the model outputs for each of the Sobol sampled parameter combinations, we select the nominal operating point (NOP) for the process as that which minimizes the capture cost. Starting from the NOP, a uniform cube with respect to the parameter axes is formed and expanded until one of its vertices intersects the design space boundary. The resulting region is the uniform acceptable operating region (AOR). This allows for the extraction of acceptable operating ranges of the different parameters with respect to the NOP used, which is an underpinning element for analyzing process controllability.

### 3.4. Optimality-Related Analysis

In addition to the systematic design space and flexibility analysis, the framework also offers information regarding good candidate operating conditions and Pareto fronts. For benchmarking, we also perform rigorous optimization using the non-dominated sorting genetic algorithm II (NSGA-II). We solve to obtain purity/recovery and productivity/energy Pareto fronts, as well as a point of minimum capture cost. The productivity/energy and capture cost optimization problems are constrained by the purity/recovery requirements using a penalty function approach. For each problem, we use a population size of 72 with a maximum of 70 generations. Therefore, the solution of the three design problems requires $72 \times 70 \times 3 = 15{,}120$ forward simulations by rigorous optimization, as compared to only 3,458 simulations by the proposed framework.

## 4. Results and Discussion

First, before performing design space and flexibility analysis, the dataset generated by virtual experimentation with the Sobol sequence can be used to obtain a first approximation of the Pareto fronts for the design problem. To this end, purity/recovery and productivity/energy Pareto fronts, as well as a cost-optimal point are identified and compared with the outputs of rigorous optimization using NSGA-II. Second, we present the design space analysis and associated flexibility analysis of the cost-optimal point.

### 4.1. Optimality-Related Analysis

The comparison between the Sobol sampled data points and the Pareto front obtained from the rigorous optimization with NSGA-II is shown in Figure 1. The boundary outlined by the data points obtained from the Sobol sampling shows strong agreement with the Pareto fronts obtained from the rigorous optimization using NSGA-II. Further, the cost-optimal point obtained from Sobol sampling is in very good agreement with the

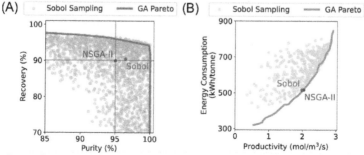

Figure 1. Pareto front comparison (A: purity-recovery and B: energy-productivity), solid lines: genetic algorithm, points: Sobol sampling. Red point is the cost-optimal point of NSGA-II and green is that of the Sobol sampling.

solution obtained using NSGA-II, as detailed in Table 2. The cost optimal point obtained from NSGA-II has a capture cost which is 1.1% lower than that obtained by Sobol sampling. However, solution of the set of design problems using NSGA-II requires greater than 4x the computational time to obtain the optimal process design as compared to Sobol sampling. This highlights a key advantage of the proposed framework, which is that it is effective at identifying good candidate process performance while requiring significantly less computational effort. In practical terms, the good candidate points obtained by Sobol sampling could be used to significantly tighten the parameter bounds before applying rigorous optimization to the system, which can reduce the burden of formal optimization quite significantly.

Table 2. Cost-optimal solution from NSGA-II and Sobol sampling.

|  | NSGA-II | Sobol sampling |
|---|---|---|
| $p_H$ (bar) | 3.56 | 3.55 |
| $p_I$ (bar) | 1.72 | 1.25 |
| $v_F$ (m/s) | 1.44 | 1.40 |
| Capture cost (\$/tonne) | 61.67 | 62.35 |

### 4.2. Design Space Identification & Analysis

The design space is identified and shown in Figure 2. The samples which violate the constraints are hidden to improve the clarity of the figure. We can see that at feed velocities greater than 1.5 m/s there are no samples which satisfied the purity and recovery constraints. Starting at low velocities, the design space is quite narrow. As the velocity increases, the size of the design space increases. However, after reaching a certain value, the design space reduces in size until the process becomes infeasible at higher velocities. The same can be seen when considering the other two manipulated variables. This is because there are trade-offs between achieving higher recovery or higher purity. Due to the non-linearity of the phenomena and highly coupled parameters affecting the process, it remains challenging to identify general heuristics for design. The proposed framework highlights these trade-offs through a systematic, data-supported methodology.

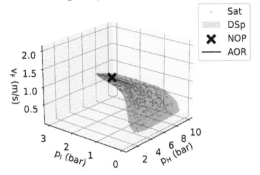

Figure 2. Identification of the optimal point acceptable operating region. Flexibility is very low therefore the AOR is not visible in the plot.

In Figure 2, the NOP used is the cost-optimal point obtained from Sobol sampling. The flexibility of the point is examined and an AOR is defined. Table 3 provides quantitative metrics from analysis of the design space. We can see that the process is non-flexible as only very small variabilities in the operating conditions are permissible without violation of the constraints. When the point of minimum capture cost is chosen to be the NOP the purity/recovery constraints are active at the NOP, meaning that it lies near the edge of the design space and the process has very poor flexibility. Therefore, in practice, the process would be challenging to control while maintaining operation in compliance with regulatory constraints on the $CO_2$ product stream extracted from the flue gas. This insight remains unaccounted for in the adsorption process design literature, and we contend based on this case study that this is a central point of importance for the practical application of adsorption-based separations for $CO_2$ capture.

Table 3. Design space analysis metrics.

|                                        | Value              |
|----------------------------------------|--------------------|
| DSp size (bar$^2$ m/s)                 | 4.25               |
| Minimum capture cost (\$/tonne)        | 62.35              |
| Average capture cost (\$/tonne)        | 76.41              |
| Maximum capture cost (\$/tonne)        | 302.14             |
| AOR size (bar$^2$ m/s)                 | $8.6 \times 10^{-5}$ |
| Acceptable range $p_H$ (bar)           | $3.55 \pm 0.054$   |
| Acceptable range $p_I$ (bar)           | $1.25 \pm 0.018$   |
| Acceptable range $v_F$ (m/s)           | $1.40 \pm 0.011$   |

## 5. Conclusion

In this work, a framework for flexible process design using design space identification has been presented and applied to an adsorption-based post-combustion $CO_2$ capture process. The proposed framework facilitates integrated analysis to quantify flexibility metrics with respect to any of the process KPIs and provide good candidate operating conditions. Acceptable operating regions and ranges of operating parameters based on any nominal point can be quantified. We used the framework to identify a good candidate operating point with a very similar capture cost to that obtained by rigorous optimization while requiring 77% fewer forward model evaluations. We show that the status-quo design approach of minimizing capture cost leads to a non-flexible design which would be challenging to operate within regulatory requirements on the $CO_2$ product stream. Herein, we provide a framework for efficiently evaluating process flexibility of any NOP which can therefore be used to assess new design approaches which account for flexibility from an early stage. Thereby, we will ultimately be able to design more highly controllable PVSA $CO_2$ capture processes and accelerate the propagation of this technology from research into industry. Future work on this framework includes the exploitation of the Sobol sequence for the identification of better bounds for rigorous optimization.

## References

Riganati et al. (2021): "Adsorption of carbon dioxide for post-combustion capture: A review". Energy & Fuels (35).

Balashankar et al. (2019): "Analysis of a batch adsorber analogue for rapid screening of adsorbents for postcombustion $CO_2$ capture". Industrial & Engineering Chemistry Research (58).

Haghpanah et al. (2013): "Multiobjective optimization of a four-step adsorption process for post combustion $CO_2$ capture via finite volume simulation". Industrial & Engineering Chemistry Research (52)

Ward & Pini (2022a): "Efficient bayesian optimization of industrial-scale pressure-vacuum swing adsorption processes for CO2 capture". Industrial & Engineering Chemistry Research (61).

Ward & Pini (2022b): "Integrated uncertainty quantification and sensitivity analysis of single-component dynamic column breakthrough experiments". Adsorption (28).

Antonis Kokossis, Michael C. Georgiadis, Efstratios N. Pistikopoulos (Eds.)
PROCEEDINGS OF THE 33rd European Symposium on Computer Aided Process Engineering
(ESCAPE33), June 18-21, 2023, Athens, Greece

# Multiple-Model Fault Detection of PEMFC

A. Allam[a], M. Mangold[b], P. Zhang[a]

[a] *Institute of Automatic Control, Technische Universität Kaiserslautern,
aallam@rhrk.uni-kl.de,  pzhang@eit.uni-kl.de, Kaiserslautern, 67653, Germany*
[b] *Bingen University of Applied Sciences, m.mangold@th-bingen.de, Bingen 55411,
Germany*

## Abstract

Catalytic degradation and flooding are classified as critical cell failures that significantly impact the durability of proton exchange membrane fuel cells (PEMFC). Delayed detection of both failures can have detrimental effects on the fuel cell. The purpose of this work is to achieve early fault detection by integrating a fault diagnosis system onto a PEMFC degradation model. The framework of the diagnosis system is based on the concept of multiple-model fault detection with a main task of selecting the underlying model which most likely represents the current operating condition of the system. Primarily, optimal state estimates are computed using the Square Root Unscented Kalman filter. Then fault indication signals are generated by the Bayes' Rule updated with conditional probabilities propagated by each filter model. Finally, a threshold function is derived based on the fault indication signals. Simulation results demonstrate that the proposed strategy successfully achieves fault detection and isolation.

**Keywords**: PEMFC, Fault Diagnosis, Multiple Model, Catalytic Degradation, Flooding

## 1. Introduction

Favorable characteristics of Proton Exchange membrane fuel cells (PEMFC), such as low operating temperature and compact design, enable them as an alternative solution in the electrification of the transportation sector. However, PEMFCs exhibits performance limitations when implemented as electric propulsion systems. A main contributing factor is load cycling which are rapid transient operating conditions that are unsustainable by the slow internal dynamical behavior of the fuel cell. Experiments have demonstrated that load cycling is a root cause of accelerated cell deterioration (Steiner, 2009).

Flooding and induced catalytic degradation are both symptoms of improper management of load cycling. Extreme conditions of both failures disrupt the chemical stability of the fuel cell and can lead to the loss of electrochemically active surface area (ECSA). Therefore, integrating an effective diagnosis system is key to enhance cell durability and to maintain optimal stack performance.

Several studies have considered the task of fault diagnosis in PEMFCs. In (Aitouche, 2011; Escobet, 2008; Lira, 2012) model-based approaches are adopted to detect flooding and catalytic degradation. Meanwhile, Hernandez (2010) constructs an equivalent circuit model and achieves fault detection through parameter identification of critical system parameters. In (Ibrahim, 2015; Zheng, 2014) fault diagnosis of flooding is accomplished by analyzing experimental data using the Discrete Wavelet Transform and a Clustering double-fuzzy approach respectively.

Motivated by recent developments in fault diagnosis (Dinge, 2013), in this paper the diagnosis of flooding and catalytic degradation in PEMFCs is investigated. Primarily, a PEMFC multiscale catalytic degradation model is developed based on the radii of platinum particles and the surficial coverage of platinum oxide. Principally, in multiple-model fault detection the main task of the diagnosis system is to accurately distinguish the correct model (nominal or faulty behavior) which most likely represents the current operating condition of the system. At first, optimal state estimates of a bank of models under different assumptions are obtained using the Square Root Unscented Kalman filter (SRUKF) given in (Merwe, 2001). Then the Bayes' Rule is implemented to generate fault indication signals based on the conditional posteriori probabilities of each model. A decision logic is then derived to determine the current operating condition of the system.

The paper is organized as follows. In section 2 a 5-state PEMFC multiscale catalytic degradation model is presented. The framework of the diagnosis system is developed in Section 3. Finally, simulation results are demonstrated in Section 4 to evaluate the performance of the diagnosis system under the events of flooding and catalytic degradation.

## 2. PEMFC Multiscale Degradation Model

Testing the developed diagnosis system requires reference data from specific failures. As it is quite hard to induce desired types of failures to a real system, simulated measurement data are used in this work, which are generated by a reference PEMFC model. The model consists of a macroscopic part derived from macroscopic mass and charge balances and of a microscopic kinetic model accounting for changes in the morphology of the catalytic structure.

Without loss of generality, the macroscopic part of model is based on the following assumptions: 1) Gases behave like ideal gases. 2) PEMFC is an isothermal system 3) The anodic reaction is fast enough and is not considered as a rate determining step. The macroscopic model has three states: the molar concentration of oxygen in gas flow channels ($x_1$) and in the catalyst layer ($x_2$) and the cathodic activation losses ($x_3$). The model is a multiple-input multiple-output (MIMO) system with three inputs, the current ($u_1$), the inlet air flow ($u_2$) and the partial molar concentration of oxygen in the supplied air ($u_3$). The two measurements are the molar concentration of oxygen in the catalyst layer ($y_1$) and the cell voltage ($y_2$).

From mass conservation principles, the molar concentrations of oxygen in the gas flow channel is computed by,

$$\dot{x}_1 = \frac{1}{V_C}\left(u_2(u_3 - x_2) - A_E \beta(x_1 - x_2)\right) \tag{1}$$

where $V_C$ is the cathode bulk volume, $A_E$ is the area of mass exchange and $\beta$ is the mass transfer coefficient of the gas diffusion layer. The molar concentration of oxygen in the catalyst layer is derived from

$$\dot{x}_2 = \frac{1}{V_{CL}}\left(A_E \beta(x_1 - x_2) - k_{CD}\frac{i_{c,o} A_E}{4F}\left(1 - e^{\frac{-2Fx_3}{RT}}\frac{x_2}{u_3}\right)\right), \tag{2}$$

where $V_{CL}$ is the volume of the catalyst layer, $i_{c,o}$ is the exchange current density, $F$ is the Faraday constant, $R$ is the universal gas constant and $T$ is stack temperature. The final state is the cathodic activation loss $x_3$, defined as the energy required to overcome the ionic energy barrier to initiate the electrochemical reaction

$$\dot{x}_3 = \frac{1}{\phi_C}\left(-u_1 - k_{CD}\frac{i_{c,o} A_E}{F}\left(1 - e^{\frac{-2Fx_3}{RT}}\frac{x_2}{u_3}\right)\right) \tag{3}$$

The microscopic model is motivated by the work in (Darling, 2003). An assumption imposed on the microscopic model characterizes the catalyst layer as finely distributed uniformly sized spherically shaped carbon-supported platinum (Pt) particles. Suboptimal operating conditions in the catalyst layer induce morphological changes to the Pt particles and imminently lead to loss of ECSA. The proposed model consists of two states: PtO coverage on the spherical Pt particle ($x_4$) and the Pt particle radius ($x_5$), which are computed from

$$\dot{x}_4 = \left(\frac{r_2 - r_3}{\Gamma_{max}}\right) - \left(\frac{2x_4}{x_5}\right)\dot{x}_5 \tag{4}$$

$$\dot{x}_5 = -\frac{M}{\rho}(r_1 - r_2), \tag{5}$$

where $r_1$ and $r_2$ expresses the rate of the electrochemical reactions of Pt ionization and PtO formation respectively and $r_3$ is the rate of the overall electrochemical reaction. Due to limitation of space the electrochemical reactions of Pt dissolution and PtO formation ($r_1$, $r_2$ and $r_3$) described by the Butler Volmer kinetics equation are not covered. Both sub-models are connected by the degradation rate $k_{cd}$ which is defined as the ratio between current particle radius $x_5$ and initial radius $x_{5,0}$.

Finally, the two system measurements are the molar concentration of oxygen in the catalyst layer $y_1 = x_2$ and the cell voltage. The latter is calculated by subtracting the activation losses $x_3$ and the ohmic resistance losses $R_{ohm}$ from the open circuit voltage $U_0$,

$$y_2 = U_0 + x_3 - R_{ohm}u_1 \tag{6}$$

## 3. Fault Diagnosis Approach

### 3.1. Fault Analysis and Modelling

Determining the correct system parameters to model the multiplicative faults of flooding and catalytic degradation is essential for the proposed diagnosis system. In literature various studies investigate the impact of both failures on the transient behavior

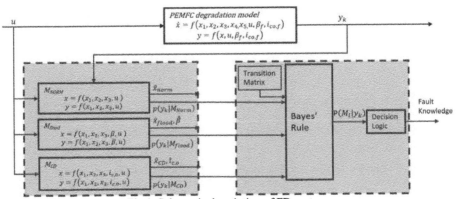

Fig 1. Schematic description of FD system

of PEMFCs. It is determined that early stages of flooding result in the accumulation of water within the porous structure of the gas diffusion layer compromising its diffusive properties (Grotsch, 2008). Accordingly, the parameter chosen to model flooding is $\beta$ which influences the mass flux of oxygen within the stack. The asserted assumption is that the cell loses 50% of its diffusive properties defined as $\beta_f$ as illustrated in Fig.1.

Meanwhile, a qualitative analysis was conducted by Steiner et al (2008) to identify the various mechanisms of catalytic degradation. Severe conditions of the failure induce a non-uniform current distribution which is attributed to the exchange current density $i_{c,o}$. The fault is provoked by reducing $i_{c,o}$ from its original and is assigned as $i_{co,f}$.

### 3.2. Fault Diagnosis Scheme

In this subsection the proposed fault diagnosis system will be developed. Unlike in (Blackmore, 2006) where a set of finite models are differentiated by their operating state (normal or faulty conditions), the presented diagnosis system is based on a bank of models that are distinguished by a desired system parameter $\gamma$ to be estimated, i.e. $\gamma = \beta$ or $\gamma = i_{c,o}$. The system parameter $\gamma_i$ is derived from the analysis conducted on the multiplicative fault and is described as an additional state in the system model with zero dynamics i.e. $\dot{\gamma}_i = 0$. Consider that the system dynamics of a bank of models $M_i$ are described by,

$$M_i : \dot{x}^i(t) = f_i(x^i(t), u(t), \gamma_i) + w^i(t)$$
$$y_k^i = h(x^i(t_k), u(t_k), \gamma_i) + v_k^i \qquad (7)$$

where $i=0$ represents the normal macroscopic three-state model with $\gamma_i=0$ (no additional state or system parameter to be estimated), $i=1,2,\ldots,\alpha$ represents $i$-th multiplicative fault described by the $\gamma_i$ system parameter to be estimated, $x^i(t)$, $u(t)$, $y_k^i$, $w^i(t)$, $v_k^i$ are respectively, the state vector, the control input vector, the output vector, the process noise and the measurement noise when the system incorporates the $i$-th multiplicative fault. As shown in Fig.1, $M_0=M_{norm}$ represents a model with nominal system parameters with no additional state. $M_1=M_{flood}$ is a model that incorporates flooding through the additional system state $\beta$. $M_2=M_{CD}$ describes catalytic degradation which does not define a specific mechanism but is manifested as a deprecation of the exchange current density $i_{c,o}$.

The proposed diagnosis strategy is composed of two parts as mapped in Fig 1. Primarily, the SRUKF is adopted to compute optimal state estimates of each model $M_i$ and to predict the probability density function of the output conditioned by each model

$$p(y_k|M_i) = \frac{1}{(2\pi)^{\frac{\alpha}{2}} |S_{yy_i}|} \exp\left(-\frac{\left(y_k - \bar{y}^i{}_k\right)^T S_{yy_i}^{-1} \left(y_k - \bar{y}^i{}_k\right)}{2}\right), \qquad (8)$$

where $\alpha$ is the number of models, $\bar{y}^i{}_k$ is the estimated output mean and $S_{yy_i}$ is output estimation error covariance matrix of the $i$-th SRUKF of $M_i$. Secondly, the Bayes' Rule is implemented to update the propagated prior information and to compute the conditional posteriori probability that $M_i$ is true given the current measurement $y_k$,

$$P(M_i \mid y_k) = \frac{p(y_k \mid M_i)P(M_i \mid y_{k-1})}{\sum_{j=1}^m p(y_k \mid M_j)P(M_j \mid y_{k-1})}, i = 1, \ldots, m \qquad (9)$$

A probability transition matrix is introduced to define the likelihood of the different models to transition among each other. Finally, to classify each failure the decision logic is derived as,

$$i = \arg\max_i P(M_i \mid y_k) \text{ and } P(M_i \mid y_k) > J_{th} \qquad (10)$$

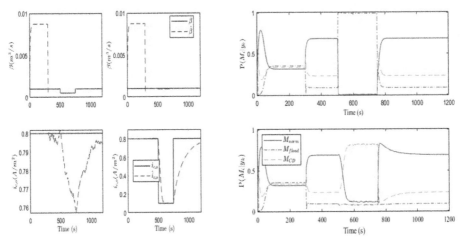

Fig 2. Parameter estimation provided by $M_{flood}$ (top figures) and $M_{CD}$ (bottom figures) under flooding (left) and catalytic degradation (right)

Fig 3. Posteriori Probabilities for the case of flooding (top) and catalytic degradation (bottom)

where $J_{th}$ is a threshold introduced to increase the reliability of the diagnosis system. Specifically, satisfying both conditions indicates that the PEMFC system is operating under the $i$-th condition. In the presented case $J_{th} = 0.7$.

## 4. Simulation Results

In this section the validity of the developed fault diagnosis system is evaluated in the MATLAB environment. Accurate fault detection of the proposed diagnosis system significantly relies on correct parameter estimation ($\beta$, $i_{c,o}$) provided by the SRUKF. The initial conditions of both system parameters are assumed to be equal to the nominal values.

Figure 2 plots the system parameters $\beta$ and $i_{c,o}$ and their respective estimates based on $M_{flood}$ and $M_{CD}$ in response to a step change input current from 0 to 1 $A$ at 300s, a failure event introduced at 500s and cell recovery at 750s. Specifically, the left plots illustrate the response of both models to a flooding event between 500s and 750s. During the first 300s, the fuel cell is in idle conditions and due to the electrochemical inactivity the SRUKF diverges and fails to estimate $\beta$. However, after the introduction of the unity step input current the SRUKF identifies the system parameter and converges to its true value. At 500s, it can be observed that $M_{flood}$ reacts to the failure event and correctly estimates $\beta$. Meanwhile, the SRUKF based on $M_{CD}$ weakly recognizes the failure and a slight decrease in $\hat{\imath}_{c,o}$ can be observed. A similar behavior is also exhibited by both models under the event of catalytic degradation (right plots of Fig.2). The SRUKF of $M_{CD}$ reacts to the failure event of catalytic degradation and correctly estimating $i_{c,o}$. However, the filter model based on $M_{flood}$ weakly responds to the induced failure event.

The diagnosis of the failure events is demonstrated in Fig 3. using the posteriori probabilities given by (9) and the decision logic derived in (10). For the first 300s the stack is in idle conditions and the three models share a relatively similar probability. As current is introduced at 300s the fuel cell is electrochemically activated and the diagnosis system is able to distinguish between the models with $P(M_{norm} \mid y_k) > 0.7$ correctly indicating that the system is operating under fault-free conditions. The top plot demonstrates that flooding was successfully detected and isolated at 505s with

$P(M_{flood} \mid y_k) > 0.7$ and a detection delay of 5s. Meanwhile, the bottom plot indicates that catalytic degradation was detected at 553s with a detection delay of 53s.

A challenging task when implementing the proposed diagnosis scheme is maintaining the stability of the multiple Kalman filter models. Under certain failure events often the Kalman filter exhibits unstable dynamics and diverge. For instance, under catalytic degradation the SRUKF based on $M_{flood}$ would diverge while estimating $\beta$. Two solutions were implemented to overcome this problem. Firstly, by tuning the parameters of the Kalman filter (system and measurement noise) according to the transient impact of the failure on the fuel cell system. Secondly, a constrained SRUKF is constructed based on bounding the additional state within a feasible range. Imposed by these constraints a new Kalman gain is computed by solving an optimization problem based on the unconstrained estimated states and covariance matrices using *fmincon* on MATLAB. Then an updated constrained state space is constructed using the new Kalman gain.

## 5. Conclusion

In this paper, a fault diagnosis scheme based on multiple-model fault detection is developed to classify two major PEMFC failures, namely flooding and catalytic degradation. Models are distinguished by an additional system state which represents a predefined system parameter corresponding to the multiplicative fault under consideration. Therefore, the effectivity of the diagnosis system significantly relies on the correct state estimation provided by the SRUKF. The Bayes' Rule is then implemented to generate fault indication signals to achieve fault detection and isolation.

## References

A. Aitouche, Q. Yang, and B. O. Bouamama, 2011, Fault detection and solationof PEM fuel cell system based on nonlinear analytical redundancyan application via parity space approach, The European Physical Journal Applied Physics, 54, 2, 23408.

T. Escobet et al., 2009, Model-based fault diagnosis in PEM fuel cell systems, Journal of Power Sources, 192, 1, 216–223.

A. Hernandez, D. Hissel, and R. Outbib, 2006, Fuel cell fault diagnosis: A stochastic approach, in Proc. IEEE Int. Symposium on Industrial Electronics, 1984–1989.

M. Ibrahim et al. 2015, Signal-based diagnostics by wavelet transform for proton exchange membrane fuel cell, Energy Procedia, 74, 1508-1516.

Z. Zheng, et al., 2014, A double-fuzzy diagnostic methodology dedicated to online fault diagnosis of proton exchange membrane fuel cell stacks. Journal of Power Sources, 271, 570-581.

S. X. Ding, 2013, Model-based fault diagnosis techniques: design schemes, algorithms, and tools. Springer.

R. Van Der Merwe and E. A. Wan, 2001, The square-root unscented kalman filter for state and parameter-estimation, in Proc. IEEE Int. Conf. on Acoustics, Speech and Signal Processing, 3461–3464.

R.Darling and J. Meyers, 2003, Kinetic model of platinum dissolution in PEMFCs. Journal of the Electrochemical Society, 150, 11, A1523

M. Groetsch, R. Hanke-Rauschenbach, and M. Mangold, 2008, Bifurcation analysis of a two-phase PEMFC model, Journal of Fuel Cell Science and Technology, 5, 2.

N. Yousfi-Steiner et al., 2009, A review on polymer electrolyte membrane fuel cell catalyst degradation and starvation issues: Causes, consequences and diagnostic formitigation, Journal of Power Sources, 194, 1, 130–145.

L. Blackmore and B.Williams, 2006, Finite horizon control design for optimal discrimination between several models, Proceedings of the IEEE Conference on Decision and Control, 45, 1147-1152.

Antonis Kokossis, Michael C. Georgiadis, Efstratios N. Pistikopoulos (Eds.)
PROCEEDINGS OF THE 33rd European Symposium on Computer Aided Process Engineering
(ESCAPE33), June 18-21, 2023, Athens, Greece

# Implications of Heat and Work Integration in Biomass to Fischer-Tropsch Fuels: A simulation Approach

Samukeliso Dube[*], Baraka Celestin Sempuga, Xinying Liu

*Institute for Development of Energy for African Sustainability (IDEAS), University of South Africa, Private Bag X6, Florida, Johannesburg, South Africa*

## Abstract

The sustainability of biomass and biogas use relies on the efficiency of conversion processes and produced products. This work determines specific process targets that have the highest efficiency in terms of material, energy, and work balances. Many authors have suggested biomass and biogas to be sustainable sources of hydrogen. However, the analysis in this work shows that conversion of these to hydrogen has fundamental drawbacks because of the inevitable $CO_2$ emissions and zero carbon efficiency. Co-production of hydrogen with methanol and/or Fischer-Tropsch fuels can significantly increase the efficiency but maximizing the carbon, energy and work efficiencies requires zero hydrogen production, with the potential to achieve net $CO_2$ consumption. There is need to rigorously integrate heat and work energies between the gasification/reformer and synthesis section. We propose the use of heat engine-heat pump configuration with a theoretical Carnot efficiency of 0.43. We also explore using solar energy to maximize $CO_2$ consumption.

**Keywords**: Biomass, Biogas, Fischer Tropsch synthesis, Targeting techniques, Process synthesis.

## 1. Introduction

Solid and gas bio-energy resources, are relatively evenly distributed across the globe and have been identified as renewable resources from which hydrogen and hydrocarbons can be produced sustainably. However, hydrogen production from biomass can be considered inefficient because of the $CO_2$ emissions which, from a material balance perspective, are a result of feeding material containing carbon, hydrogen and oxygen to only make hydrogen. Consequently, $CO_2$ is the preferred product to get rid of carbon and oxygen. Lepage et al. (2021) reviewed biomass-to-hydrogen production routes and concluded that biomass conversions need improvements and adaptations to be implemented at a larger scale  (Lepage et al., 2021). Therefore, one needs to understand how to maximize the potential of biomass by utilizing all its components namely, carbon, hydrogen, and oxygen, and minimize $CO_2$ emissions. A system's approach, adopted in this work, can give a better understanding of the process options and assist in setting specific performance targets which will guide the development and design of the process. Performance targets may be understood as theoretical process performance in terms of material, energy, and work balances, indicating the best feasible options against which a process can be measured or as an indication of opportunities for improvement. Patel et al.

(Patel et al., 2005) pointed out that a high level mass and energy flow analysis across a process is a pre-cursor to designing processes that are cost- and energy- efficient. When dealing with carbonaceous feedstocks, it is imperative to consider the H/C and O/C ratios, both in the feed and the product streams; this has an impact on the hydrogen and carbon efficiencies (Liu & Patel, 2017) and will also impact the energy and work flows across the process. Therefore, in this work, we co-feed biomass with biogas as an alternative renewable source of hydrogen and carbon elements which allows varying their ratios in the feed and also provides more degrees of freedom and a much bigger region where we can set the optimisation targets.

## 2. Methodology

The high-level analysis of a process starts by developing its material balance attainable region. To develop the material balance attainable region of the biomass to hydrogen and hydrocarbons process we start by the overall material balance that includes all the components we have identified.

$$aCH_{1.4}O_{0.6} + bCO_2 + cCH_4 + dH_2O + eO_2 + fH_2 + gC + hCO + iCH_3OH + kCH_2 = 0 \quad (1)$$

From this, we deduce the atomic species balances with three independent equations and 10 variables; thus, the system has 7 degrees of freedom. However, too many degrees of freedom make it difficult identifying optimal targets as it leads to searching within a multidimensional region. To systematically narrow down the attainable region into sub-regions of interest we only specify a limited number of variables representing the main targets and then use an optimization method to determine the rest of the variables to meet a specific objective function. Thus, in this method, the objective function and the constraints will represent the main targets for the process and then the optimization variables will be solved to meet these targets. We can express an optimization problem where we vary the ratio of biomass to biogas in the feed as follows:

| | | |
|---|---|---|
| for $R_{B/BG} = [0:1]$ ; $max\ N_{CH2}$ subject to $\begin{cases} A.N_d^T \leq 0 \\ A_{eq}.N^T = b_{eq} \\ \sum N_i \Delta H_{T_o} \leq 0 \\ \sum N_i \Delta G_{T_o} \leq 0 \\ CO = 0 \end{cases}$ | | (2) |

Where:
$R_{B/BG}$, is the ratio of biomass to biogas in the feed, $A.N_d^T \leq 0$ is the inequality constraint; $A_{eq}.N^T = b_{eq}$ is the material balance constraints in equations; $\sum N_i \Delta H_{T_o} \leq 0$ and $\sum N_i \Delta G_{T_o} \leq 0$ are the energy and work constraints, respectively.

We determined the extent to which a non-idealised process deviates from the optimal targets by simulating the process in Aspen Plus® and the flowsheet is shown in Figure 1 below.

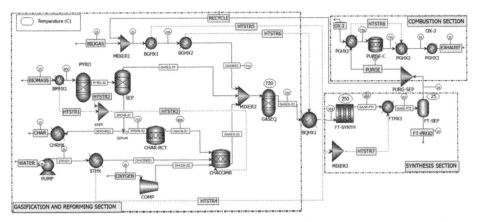

*Figure 1: FT-synthesis from a mixture of biomass and biogas feedstock: Aspen Plus Simulation*

## 3. Results and Discussions

### 3.1 MATLAB Results

We targeted maximising the hydrogen and carbon efficiences of the system by matching the H/C and the O/C ratios in the feed to the H/C and O/C ratios in the valuable product streams, respectively. These produce a broad product spectrum. Matching the H/C ratios produced $CH_3OH$, char, $H_2O$ (when the $CH_4$ fraction < 0.4), $H_2$ and $CH_2$ products. Significant amounts of $O_2$ and $H_2O$ are consumed and $CO_2$ is consumed from a $CH_4$ fraction of 0.2. This produces less amounts of $CH_2$, but favours $CH_3OH$ production. The amount of $CH_3OH$ produced increases with an increase in the $CH_4$ fraction, this is due to the increase in the H/C ratio in the feed. At a $CH_4$ fraction of 0.4, only $CH_3OH$ and char are produced and this is the best achievable target in terms of mass, energy and work efficiencies; results are shown in Figure 2a. Furthermore, both the hydrogen and carbon efficiences are 100% at this point. Most of the chemical potential potential of the system is conserved (-10 kJ/mol) and the enthalpy change is zero, hence no energy is lost to or required from the surroundings as shown in Figure 2b.

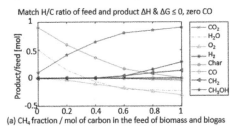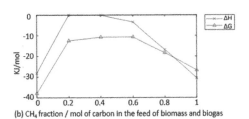

*Figure 2: (a) Material targets and (b) energy and work targets that match the H/C ratio in the feed to the H/C ratio in the products*

Figure 3a shows that matching the O/C ratio in the feed to the O/C ratio in the valuable product streams favours the production of, mainly Fischer-Tropsch hydrocarbons ( -$CH_2$), $H_2O$ and char. $CH_3OH$ and $H_2$ start being produced at a $CH_4$ fraction of 0.2. $CH_2$ production increases with an increase in the $CH_4$ fraction. $CO_2$ and $O_2$ are consumed within such a process. The system achieves 100% carbon efficiency and 67% hydrogen efficiency because some of the hydrogen is oxidised to $H_2O$ to get rid of the oxygen in the system. Both the enthalpy and Gibbs free energy are negative throughout, as illustrated in Figure 3b, therefore, neither energy nor work input is required to achieve such a target. This makes the production of FT-fuels an attractive target that needs to be maximised.

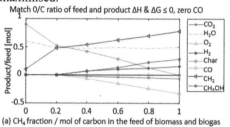
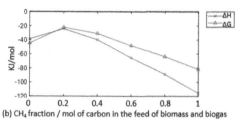

(a) $CH_4$ fraction / mol of carbon in the feed of biomass and biogas      (b) $CH_4$ fraction / mol of carbon in the feed of biomass and biogas

Figure 3: *(a) Material targets and (b) energy and work targets that match the O/C ratio in the feed to the O/C ratio in the products*

Setting the target to maximise the production of $CH_2$ led to consumption of a significat amount of $CO_2$ from a methane fraction of 0.4 and less $O_2$ is required as illustrated in Figure 4a. $CH_2$, $H_2O$ and char are the only products obtained and $CH_2$ production increases with an increase in the fraction of $CH_4$ in the feed. From Figure 4b, we concluded that the process is thermodynamically feasible. Both the enthalpy and the Gibbs free energy are less or equal to zero throughout the system. A zero Gibbs free energy means that the process fully utilises the chemical potential of the feed material (Sempuga et al., 2010).

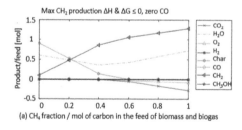
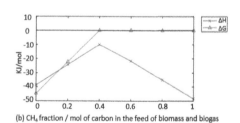

(a) $CH_4$ fraction / mol of carbon in the feed of biomass and biogas      (b) $CH_4$ fraction / mol of carbon in the feed of biomass and biogas

Figure 4: *(a) Material targets and (b) energy and work targets that maximize the production of $CH_2$*

### 3.2 Aspen Plus Simulation Results
The results from the simulation on Aspen Plus, shown in Table 1, show that it is not possible to achieve a net $CO_2$ consumption unless we rigorously integrate the heat and work energies within the system, particularly, between the reformer and the synthesis reactors. Case0 shows a system with no energy integration, the energy realeased from the FT-synthesis (-53.26kW) reactor is simple lost, and it can be seen that the process deviates by approximately 200% from the theoretical $CO_2$ consumption target of 0.17kmol and the carbon and hydrogen efficiencies are significantly low, 84% and 48%, respectively.

Table 1: Results obtained when the thermal efficiency is varied from 0 to 43% at a synthesis operating pressure of 1 bar.

|  | Case0 | Case1 | Case2 | Case3 | Case4 | Case5 | Target |
|---|---|---|---|---|---|---|---|
| **Carnot-eff** | 0,00 | 0,10 | 0,25 | 0,35 | 0,43 | 0,43 |  |
| **Q-Sythesis (kW)** | -53,26 | -55,26 | -58,57 | -61,07 | -63,33 | -75,10 |  |

| Q-Gas_Ref (kW) | 51,93 | 53,93 | 57,26 | 59,76 | 62,01 | 73,63 | |
|---|---|---|---|---|---|---|---|
| Q-Combustion (kW) | -51,93 | -46,03 | -36,35 | -29,23 | -23,10 | -5,79 | |
| Qdeff @ 720 (kW) | 0,00 | 0,00 | 0,00 | 0,00 | 0,00 | 21,69 | |
| Recycle fr | 0,61 | 0,65 | 0,71 | 0,75 | 0,78 | 0,92 | |
| $CH_4$ | -0,80 | -0,80 | -0,80 | -0,80 | -0,80 | -0,80 | -0,80 |
| $H_2$ | 0,00 | 0,00 | 0,00 | 0,00 | 0,00 | 0,00 | 0,00 |
| $CO$ | 0,00 | 0,00 | 0,00 | 0,00 | 0,00 | 0,00 | 0,00 |
| $CO_2$ | 0,16 | 0,13 | 0,07 | 0,03 | 0,00 | -0,10 | -0,17 |
| $H_2O$ | 0,80 | 0,77 | 0,70 | 0,66 | 0,62 | 0,51 | 0,57 |
| $O_2$ | -0,50 | -0,45 | -0,36 | -0,30 | -0,24 | -0,09 | -0,06 |
| $CH_2$ | 0,84 | 0,87 | 0,93 | 0,97 | 1,00 | 1,10 | 1,17 |
| Biomass | -0,20 | -0,20 | -0,20 | -0,20 | -0,20 | -0,20 | -0,20 |
| Ceff | 0,84 | 0,87 | 0,93 | 0,97 | 1 | 1 | 1 |
| Heff | 0,48192 | 0,50108 | 0,53259 | 0,5557 | 0,5755 | 0,6311 | 0,671 |
| Delta H | -223,66 | -200,51 | -162,46 | -135 | -111 | -43 | -35,01 |
| Delta G | -187.45 | -165.14 | -128.45 | -102 | -78 | -13 | 0 |

A heat engine and heat pump configuration, as shown in Figure 5, is adopted to integrate the heat from a low temperature exorthemic process to a high temperature endothermic process.

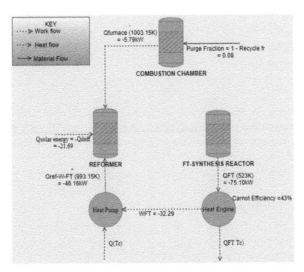

*Figure 5: Illustration of the heat engine-heat pump configuration*

A 19% decrease in $CO_2$ production was achieved when the heat engine was operated at a carnot efficiency of 10%, shown in Case1. As the carnot efficiency is increased from 10% to 43%, $CO_2$ production decreases while the carbon and hydogen efficiencies increase significantly. A net-zero $CO_2$ production was obtained at Carnot efficiency of 0.43 as shown in Table 1, Case4. However, the system still deviates by 100% from the 0.17 kmol $CO_2$ consumption target. This is because, at 43% Carnot efficiency, the synthesis section cannot fully supply the heat energy needed in the reformer, therefore, some of the hydrocarbon product is burnt to provide the additional heat, hence, produces $CO_2$. The only way the target can be achieved is through integration of solar energy as a clean, renewable energy source to compensate for the energy shortfall, shown as 21.69kW in

Case5, Table 1. Case5 is illustrated in Figure 5 and shows heat integration from the FT-synthesis reactor, combustion chamber and solar energy.

## Conclusions

Biomass and biogas are considered to be green and sustainable sources of hydrogen. In this work, we show that the process suffers a significantly low carbon efficiency and we propose the production of methanol and/or Fischer-Tropsch fuel instead of hydrogen to achieve higher conversion efficiencies. The production of methanol and FT-fuels is an attractive target and is thermodynamically feasible throughout the biogas to biomass ratios considered ($CH_4$ fraction). There is potential to achieve a net $CO_2$ consumption in the biomass to FT-fuels process, however Aspen Plus® simulation clearly shows that without energy integration throughout the system, the process will always emit $CO_2$ and have low carbon and hydrogen efficiencies. A zero net $CO_2$ emission can be attained when the synthesis heat, converted to work at the maximum Carnot efficiency, is integrated into the reformer. Furthermore, the simulation clearly shows that introduction of external energy is necessary to attain a net $CO_2$ consumption even if the process is fully energy integrated. This is a direct consequence of reaction kinetics and equilibrium limitations. In this instance, solar is considered as a renewable energy source. During the targeting analysis, we noted that matching the H/C ratio in the feed to H/C ratio in the products favours the production of methanol. This process should be investigated further to gain insight on the effect of heat and work integration in the biomass to methanol process. The methanol can be used in blended fuels to improve the octane number and hence, the quality of the fuel.

## References

Lepage, T., Kammoun, M., Schmetz, Q., & Richel, A. (2021). Biomass-to-hydrogen: A review of main routes production, processes evaluation and techno-economical assessment. *Biomass and Bioenergy, 144*(December 2020), 105920. https://doi.org/10.1016/j.biombioe.2020.105920

Liu, X., & Patel, B. (2017). Carbon efficiency targets for methanol production from a hybrid solar-carbonaceous feedstocks process. *AIP Conference Proceedings, 1850*(June 2017). https://doi.org/10.1063/1.4984471

Patel, B., Hildebrandt, D., Glasser, D., & Hausberger, B. (2005). Thermodynamics analysis of processes. 1. Implications of work integration. *Industrial and Engineering Chemistry Research, 44*(10), 3529–3537. https://doi.org/10.1021/ie048787f

Sempuga, B. C., Hausberger, B., Patel, B., Hildebrandt, D., & Glasser, D. (2010). Classification of chemical processes: A graphical approach to process synthesis to improve reactive process work efficiency. *Industrial and Engineering Chemistry Research, 49*(17), 8227–8237. https://doi.org/10.1021/ie100288h

Antonis Kokossis, Michael C. Georgiadis, Efstratios N. Pistikopoulos (Eds.)
PROCEEDINGS OF THE 33rd European Symposium on Computer Aided Process Engineering
(ESCAPE33), June 18-21, 2023, Athens, Greece

# Modeling and Assessment of Electrochemical Reduction of $CO_2$ in Amine-based Capture Solvents

Alexios-Spyridon Kyriakides,[a] Panagiotis Kazepidis,[a] Athanasios I. Papadopoulos,[a] Panos Seferlis[b]

[a]*Chemical Process & Energy Resources Institute (C.P.E.R.I.), Center for Research and Technology Hellas (CE.R.T.H.), P.O. Box 60361, 57001, Thermi-Thessaloniki, Greece*

[b]*Department of Mechanical Engineering, Aristotle University of Thessaloniki, P.O. Box 484, 54124 Thessaloniki, Greece*

*alexkyr@certh.gr*

## Abstract

Electrochemical $CO_2$ reduction is a promising utilization process. The use of amine solvents to deliver the captured $CO_2$ into the cell is receiving experimental attention, but models are also needed to investigate the performance of such systems. This work aims to model and assess the performance of the electrochemical reduction of $CO_2$ into CO in an amine capture solvent. The developed process model is validated using a conventional electrolyte ($KHCO_3$), exhibiting good match and low deviation from experimental data. The process is evaluated for monoethanolamine (MEA), and compared to $KHCO_3$ within a range of 2-20 $cm^3$/min of total inlet cell flow. MEA enables lower undesirable $H_2$ formation (less than 5% of the total current density) and faster reaction, as implied by the higher CO current density (from 45%, up to 98.7% within the considered flow range). $KHCO_3$ exhibits higher conversion rates than MEA, but MEA's higher CO production rate within the entire inlet flow range reaches a value of 30.8% at the lower flow end.

**Keywords**: $CO_2$ utilization, electrochemical reduction of $CO_2$, CO2RR, amines

## 1. Introduction

Solvent-based, post-combustion $CO_2$ capture is a mature technology for short-term industrial implementation (Nessi et al., 2021). The high capture costs that mainly result from the intense, thermal solvent regeneration prohibit its wide deployment. Electrochemical $CO_2$ reduction processes for the production of valuable products (e.g., CO, $CH_3OH$, etc.) are gaining attention as a means of off-setting the capture costs (De Luna et al., 2019). These systems enable the *in situ* production of $H_2$, which reacts with $CO_2$ over catalysts to attain the desired products. Conventionally, the $CO_2$ is transferred into the electrochemical cell in a purely aqueous solution. The low solubility of $CO_2$ in water and the mass transfer and kinetic limitations result in low production rates and conversion of feedstock. Experimental reports propose the use of an amine solvent (e.g., monoethanolamine (MEA)-Lee et al., 2020; and 1-cyclohexylpiperidine (CHP)-Diaz et al., 2018) directly from the absorber of the capture process to transfer the captured $CO_2$ into the electrochemical cell. There the $CO_2$ may be released and react with hydrogen, while the solvent is regenerated. This approach enables the delivery of a richer $CO_2$ stream, than using water as the carrier, and allows the complete replacement of the thermal solvent regeneration process.

The mathematical models developed for the electrochemical $CO_2$ reduction process largely focus on aqueous $CO_2$ solutions as feedstock, whereas additives like KOH (Weng et al., 2019) or $KHCO_3$ (Kotb et al., 2017) are also used as electrolytes to increase performance. Although there are several studies on the experimental evaluation of electrochemical reduction of $CO_2$ in amine-based media, there are no studies on the mathematical modeling of the process, that could aid in process design and optimization. The aim of this study is the development and validation of a mathematical model for the electrochemical reduction of $CO_2$ into CO (selected due to the availability of experimental data), using an aqueous amine-$CO_2$ mixture as feedstock, with the model also used to compare the amine performance with $KHCO_3$ solutions. The evaluation considers process indicators such as partial current densities, Faradaic efficiency and $CO_2$ conversion.

## 2. Model Development

This section aims to discuss the modeling approach, governing equations, occurring reactions and boundary conditions. First, the one-dimensional, isothermal model of the planar electrochemical cell configuration is presented, followed by the governing equations of all underling physicochemical phenomena (mass and current balances, Nernst-Planck and Ohm). Then all reactions taking place both in the electrolyte and electrodes (charge transfer reactions) are described, followed by the boundary conditions.

### 2.1. Cell Configuration

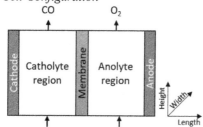

CO₂ saturated electrolyte solution ($KHCO_3$ or MEA)

**Figure 1.** Schematic representation of the electrochemical $CO_2$ reduction cell configuration.

The electrochemical cell (Figure 1) is composed of two electrodes and a proton exchange membrane. A channel filled with the $CO_2$-saturated electrolyte solution separates the cathode and anode electrodes and the membrane, namely the catholyte and anolyte regions. Both regions are considered to be well-mixed and are constantly fed with a $CO_2$-saturated electrolyte solution (either $KHCO_3$ or MEA in this work, but the model is generic), whereas the proton exchange membrane separates the two regions.

### 2.2. Governing Equations

In both electrolyte channels (anolyte and catholyte), mass continuity is considered:

$$\frac{\partial C_i}{\partial t} + \nabla . N_i = R_i \tag{1}$$

where $N_i$ is the species molar flux $[mol/(m^2 s)]$, and $R_i$ is the source term $[mol/(m^3 s)]$, for $i = CO_2, H^+, OH^- HCO_3^-, CO_3^{2-}, K^+, RNH_2, RNHCOO^-, CO, O_2, H_2$. At steady state the first term is equal to zero, whereas only the distance between the two electrodes is considered, in terms of spatial dimensions. The species flux is computed with the Nernst-Planck equations, which consider diffusion, electric migration and convection transportation, as described by Eq. (2):

$$N_i = -D_i \nabla C_i - z_i u_{mi} F C_i \nabla \varphi_l + \boldsymbol{u} C_i, \quad u_{mi} = \frac{D_i}{RT} \tag{2}$$

where $D_i$ is the diffusion coefficient $[m^2/s]$, $C_i$ is the species concentration $[mol/m^3]$, $z_i$ is the species charge number, $u_{mi}$ is the mobility of ions $[(s\ mol)/kg]$, $F$ is the Faraday constant $[C/mol]$, $\varphi_l$ is the electrolyte potential $[V]$, and $\boldsymbol{u}$ is the velocity vector $[m/s]$. The ionic mobility is based on the Nernst-Einstein relation (Eq. (2)), where $R$ is the universal gas constant $[J/(K\ mol)]$, $T$ is the temperature $[K]$. The charge conservation at the electrolyte is considered, while the current density is described by Ohm's law:

$$\nabla . \boldsymbol{i}_l = 0, \ \boldsymbol{i}_l = -\sigma_l \nabla \varphi_l, \ \sigma_l = \frac{F^2}{RT} \sum_i z_i^2 D_i C_i \tag{3}$$

where $\boldsymbol{i}_l$ is the electrolyte current density $[A/m^2]$, and $\sigma_l$ is the electronic conductivity at the electrolyte $[S/m]$. The source term in Eq. (1) is given by the following equation:

$$R_i = R_{CT,i} + R_{EL,i} \tag{4}$$

where $R_{CT,i}$ is related to the charge transfer reactions, and $R_{EL,i}$ is related to the electrolyte reactions (described in detail in section 2.3).

### 2.3. Charge Transfer (Anode and Cathode) and Electrolyte Reactions

Hydrogen (HER, Eq. (5)) and carbon evolution reactions (COER, Eq. (6)), and the anode-related reaction is the oxygen evolution reaction (OER, Eq. (7)).

$$2H_2O + 2e^- \rightarrow H_2 + 2OH^- \tag{5}$$

$$CO_2 + H_2O + 2e^- \rightarrow CO + 2OH^- \tag{6}$$

$$4OH^- \rightarrow O_2 + 2H_2O + 4e^- \tag{7}$$

The reaction kinetics are assumed to follow the Tafel kinetics. The reaction current densities ($i_k$) are calculated by Eq. (8),(9) and (10), for the three reactions, respectively.

$$i_{HER} = i_{o,HER} \ exp \left( \frac{-\alpha_{HER} F \eta_{HR}}{RT} \right) \tag{8}$$

$$i_{COER} = i_{o,COER} \frac{C_{CO_2}}{C_{CO_2,ref}} exp \left( \frac{-\alpha_{COER} F \eta_{COER}}{RT} \right) \tag{9}$$

$$i_{OER} = exp \left( \frac{\alpha_{OER} F \eta_{OER}}{RT} \right) \tag{10}$$

where $i_{o,k}$ is the exchange current density, $\alpha_k$ is the charge transfer coefficient, $C_{CO_2,ref}$ is the saturation concentration of dissolved $CO_2$ at ambient conditions, and $\eta_k$ is the overpotential for reaction $k$ $[V]$, given by Eq. (11):

$$\eta_k = \varphi_s - \varphi_l - E_k^0 \tag{11}$$

where $\varphi_s$ is the solid phase (cathode or anode) applied potential, and $E_k^0$ is the reaction equilibrium potential $[V]$. The charge transfer reaction source term is defined as:

$$R_{CT,i} = \sum_k \frac{v_i i_k}{n_k F} \tag{12}$$

where $v_i$ is the stoichiometric coefficient of component $i$ in reaction $k$, and $n_k$ is the number of electrons transferred in reaction $k$.

*2.3.1. Utilization of KHCO₃ as an electrolyte*

For KHCO₃ the following reactions are considered at the electrolyte phase:

$$CO_2 + H_2O \xrightleftharpoons{k_1,k_{-1}} H^+ + HCO_3^- \tag{13}$$

$$HCO_3^- \xrightleftharpoons{k_2,k_{-2}} H^+ + CO_3^{2-} \tag{14}$$

$$CO_2 + OH^- \xrightleftharpoons{k_3,k_{-3}} HCO_3^- \tag{15}$$

$$HCO_3^- + OH^- \xrightleftharpoons{k_4,k_{-4}} H_2O + CO_3^{2-} \tag{16}$$

Additionally, water dissociation reaction takes place:

$$H_2O \xrightleftharpoons{k_w,k_{-w}} H^+ + OH^- \tag{17}$$

*2.3.2. Utilization of MEA as an electrolyte*

For aqueous MEA solution additional reactions are considered for the equilibrium at the electrolyte solution. Primary amines capture $CO_2$ by reacting with it to form carbamic acid, carbamate ion and bicarbonate through the following reaction mechanism:

$$RNH_2 + CO_2 \xrightleftharpoons{k_5,k_{-5}} RN^+H_2COO^- \tag{18}$$

$$RN^+H_2COO^- + RNH_2 \xrightleftharpoons{k_6,k_{-6}} RNHCOO^- + RN^+H_3 \tag{19}$$

$$RNHCOO^- + H_2O \xrightleftharpoons{k_7,k_{-7}} RNH_2 + HCO_3^- \tag{20}$$

Then, bicarbonate ($HCO_3^-$) reacts with $H^+$ (Eq. (13)) in both electrolyte channels to produce $CO_2$ to be used for the reduction reactions taking place on the electrodes. The bulk reaction source term for component $i$ is defined as:

$$R_{EL,i} = \sum_n v_i \left( k_n \prod_{v_j<0} C_j - k_{-n} \prod_{v_j>0} C_j \right) \tag{21}$$

where $k_n$ and $k_{-n}$ is the forward and backward reaction rate of the $n^{th}$ reaction.

*2.4. Boundary Conditions*

At the boundary between the electrode and the electrolyte, current conservation applies:

$$\nabla(-\sigma_l \nabla \varphi_l) = S_l, \; S_{l,c} = \alpha_{COER} i_{o,COER} + \alpha_{HER} i_{o,HER}, \; S_{l,a} = -\alpha_{OER} i_{o,OER} \tag{22}$$

where $S_l$ is the current source term resulting from the electrochemical reactions occurring at each electrode.

## 3. Results and discussion

The electrochemical cell dimensions are 3.4×3.4×8.1 cm in height, width and length, with a membrane of 1.5 mm thickness (Verma et al., 2016). The electrolyte flowrate is equal to 20 cm³/min, at 298.15 K and 1 atm. 0.5 M KHCO₃ and 30% w/w MEA aqueous solutions are considered. Reaction kinetics and constants are from Borhani et al. (2018), Gupta et al. (2013) and Hebelmann et al. (2022).

### 3.1.1. Partial Current Density vs Applied Potential

The model is validated for $KHCO_3$ with experimental data from Verma et al. (2016) (Figure 2a and Figure 2b). The partial CO (Figure 2a) and $H_2$ (Figure 2b) current densities are presented as a function of applied cathode potential. The simulated results are in good agreement with the experimental data. Higher discrepancies are observed at higher applied potential for the CO partial current density. In both cases, both CO and $H_2$ partial current densities increase when the applied potential in the cathode is increased (becomes more negative). Higher partial current densities are observed in the case of MEA, resulting in higher reaction rates. The undesirable $H_2$ formation is less than 10% of the total current density for all potentials tested for $KHCO_3$ and less than 5% for MEA, although for higher applied potential, the $H_2$ current density percentage increases.

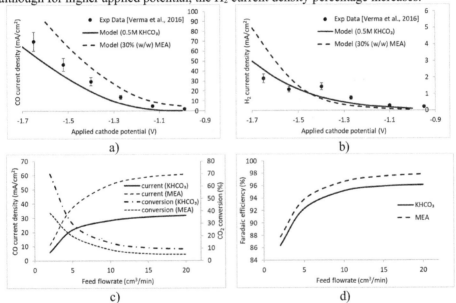

**Figure 2.** Comparison between experimental and simulation results for a) CO and b) $H_2$ partial current densities as a function of applied cathode potential. Effect of feed flowrate on c) CO current density and $CO_2$ conversion rates and d) on Faradaic efficiency.

### 3.1.2. Effect of MEA solution feed flowrate

The effect of the feed flowrate on electrochemical cell performance is shown in Figure 2c and Figure 2d. As the flowrate increases (2 to 20 cm³/min), the current density and Faradaic efficiency increase too, whereas the $CO_2$ conversion decreases. At flowrates higher than 10 cm³/min, the $CO_2$ concentration near the electrode is higher, resulting in higher reaction rates, current density and Faradaic efficiency. However, the effect of mass transport limitation increases, resulting in marginal increase in current density and Faradaic efficiency for further flowrate increase. Higher flowrate results in lower residence time, which affects the overall $CO_2$ conversion rate. At flowrates higher than 10 cm³/min, the current density achieved in the MEA solution is significantly higher than that achieved when $KHCO_3$ is used as an electrolyte. An increase between 45% and 98.7% in observed for 2 and 20 cm³/min, respectively. The $CO_2$ conversion is lower by 40% on average. However, the lower conversion rate when combined with the higher inlet molar flowrate of $CO_2$ (0.77 and 0.40×10⁻³mol/s for MEA and $KHCO_3$) results in higher CO production rates. For example, the outlet CO flowrates for MEA are 0.34 and

$0.06 \times 10^{-3}$mol/s, whereas for $KHCO_3$ they are 0.28 and $0.04 \times 10^{-3}$mol/s (for 2 and 20 $cm^3$/min). At the higher flowrate range, the conversion is similar for both electrolytes, however the higher $CO_2$ concentration and reaction rate that MEA exhibits result in 30.8% higher CO production rate than $KHCO_3$. The Faradaic efficiency presents similar behavior for both solutions.

## 4. Conclusions

The comparative study and the parametric analysis indicate that higher CO and lower $H_2$ current densities are observed for MEA compared to $KHCO_3$, implying higher reaction rates and less undesirable product. Lower $CO_2$ conversion ratios are observed for MEA, attributed to higher initial $CO_2$ quantities and mass transport limitations. However, when these are combined with the initial higher $CO_2$ concentration at the inlet streams, they result in higher CO production for MEA. In future work, optimization studies should investigate the existence of an intermediate optimal potential, flowrate pair and electrochemical cell dimensions, such that a trade-off between operating cost (Faradaic efficiency) and capacity cost (flowrate, conversion, dimensions) can be achieved.

## Acknowledgements

This research has been co-financed by the European Union and Greek national funds under the call ERANET 2021a-European E&T Cooperation in European Network ACT, Project T12EPA5-00040.

## References

Borhani T.N., Oko E., Wang, M., 2018. Process modelling and analysis of intensified $CO_2$ capture using monoethanolamine (MEA) in rotating packed bed absorber. Journal of Cleaner Production, 204, pp.1124-1142.

De Luna P., Hahn C., Higgins D., Jaffer S.A., Jaramillo, T. F., Sargent, E. H., 2019. What would it take for renewably powered electrosynthesis to displace petrochemical processes? Science, 364 (6438), eaav3506.

Diaz L.A., Gao N., Adhikari B., Lister T.E., Dufek E.J. and Wilson A.D., 2018. Electrochemical production of syngas from $CO_2$ captured in switchable polarity solvents. Green Chemistry, 20(3), pp.620-626.

Gupta M., da Silva E.F., Hartono A., Svendsen, H.F., 2013. Theoretical Study of Differential Enthalpy of Absorption of $CO_2$ with MEA and MDEA as a Function of Temperature. The Journal of Physical Chemistry B, 117(32), pp.9457-9468.

Hebelmann M., B.C. Bräsel B.C., R.G. Keller R.G., M. Wessling M., 2022, Simulation-based guidance for improving $CO_2$ reduction on silver diffusion electrodes, Electrochemical Science Advances, 2100160.

Kotb Y., Fateen S.E.K., Albo J. and Ismail I., 2017. Modeling of a Microfluidic Electrochemical Cell for the Electro-Reduction of $CO_2$ to $CH_3OH$. Journal of The Electrochemical Society, 164(13), p.E391.

Lee G., Li, Y.C., Kim J.-Y., Peng T., Nam D.-H., Rasouli., A.S., Li F., Luo M., Ip A.H., Joo Y.-C., Sargent E.H., 2021, Electrochemical upgrade of $CO_2$ from amine capture solution. Nature Energy, 6, p46-53.

Nessi E., Papadopoulos A.I., Seferlis P., 2021, A Review of Pilot and Commercial Plants for Post-Combustion $CO_2$ Capture: Packed Bed, Phase-Change and Rotating Processes, International Journal of Greenhouse Gas Control , 111, 103474.

Verma S., Lu X., Ma S., Masel R.I., Kenis P.J.A., 2016, The effect of electrolyte composition on electroreduction of $CO_2$ to CO an Ag based gas diffusion electrodes. Physical Chemistry Chemical Physics, 18 p.7075.

Weng L.-C.. Bell A.T., Weber A.Z., 2019, Towards membrane-electrode assembly systems for $CO_2$ reduction: a modeling study. Energy & Environmental Science, 12, p.1950.

Antonis Kokossis, Michael C. Georgiadis, Efstratios N. Pistikopoulos (Eds.)
PROCEEDINGS OF THE 33rd European Symposium on Computer Aided Process Engineering
(ESCAPE33), June 18-21, 2023, Athens, Greece
© 2023 Elsevier B.V. All rights reserved.  http://dx.doi.org/10.1016/B978-0-443-15274-0.50448-0

# Design of $CO_2$ Capture and Mineralization Systems: Integrated Process Optimization and Controllability Assessment in Parallel Infrastructures

Thomas Prousalis[a], George Gkizas[b], Athanasios I. Papadopoulos[b], Panos Seferlis[c]

[a]*Y Squared P.C., 57019, Perea, Greece*
[b]*Chemical Process and Energy Resources Institute, Centre for Research and Technology Hellas, 57001, Thermi, Thessaloniki, Greece*
[c]*Department of Mechanical Engineering, Aristotle University of Thessaloniki, 54124, Thessaloniki, Greece*
*spapadopoulos@@certh.gr*

## Abstract

This work presents the use of an optimization algorithm with approximate computing capabilities in the simultaneous $CO_2$ capture (CC) and utilization (CU) process design and controllability assessment. The CC design problem includes 6 solvent and process flowsheet combinations, followed by the use of a Rotating Packed Bed (RPB) process for the production of precipitated calcium carbonate (PCC) minerals as the CU option. The algorithm employs memoization and task dropping to accelerate execution in a high-performance cluster. The results indicate up to 141.7 h of saved CPU time due to the use of the approximate computing techniques. When the CC and CU processes are considered simultaneously, the generated Pareto front changes compared to the one of the CC process. The 2-Aminoethanol 30 wt. % solvent with intercooling and side feeds in the desorber results in almost equally profitable PCC production to the 3-Amino-1-Propanol 35 wt. % solvent in simpler flowsheets.

**Keywords**: $CO_2$ capture and utilization, process optimization, controllability assessment.

## 1. Introduction

$CO_2$ capture (CC) technologies promise to help mitigate the effects of global warming, but their wide industrial deployment is elusive due to high costs (Bui et al., 2018). The latter can be offset by the profitability induced by $CO_2$ utilization (CU) processes. The transformation of $CO_2$ into carbonated salts (minerals) is a mature technology and there is a wide market for products such as precipitated calcium carbonate (PCC) (Jimoh et al., 2018). Such CC and CU systems need to be designed simultaneously, considering their performance under disturbances, but the calculations are challenging. The combination of algorithms for process design and control with parallelization techniques could accelerate the computations and widen the scenarios leading to superior designs.

In the area of $CO_2$ capture, there are published approaches for integrated process design and control (Sahraei and Ricardez-Sandoval, 2014), while advanced control approaches have also been presented (Jung et al., 2020). A framework for integrated process design and control has also been proposed where parallel capabilities were considered, without specific application details or benefits (Miller et al., 2017). Multi-scale design frameworks for CC, CU and sequestration have been proposed (Hasan et al., 2015), without considering the controllability of the CC or CU systems. The effects of different capture materials (e.g., solvents) and process flowsheets in the simultaneous design and controllability assessment of CC and CU systems have not been reported previously. Vasilas et al. (Vasilas et al., 2022) developed an algorithm for simultaneous process design and controllability in distributed and heterogeneous infrastructures, applying it to the design of CC systems. The work showed the benefits that can be attained when several decision levels are addressed simultaneously and also exhibited significant reductions in the computational effort due to the use of advanced parallelization tools.

Building on these developments, this paper incorporates for the first time in the above algorithm a mineralization process that uses the captured $CO_2$ as raw material to produce PCC in a rotating packed bed (RPB). The latter is another innovation introduced here, as PCC production and CC process design have never been integrated for different solvents and process layouts or operating variability. The innovation is enhanced by the use of an RPB, which is an intensified reactor in terms of size and efficiency (Borhani et al., 2019).

## 2. Models and methods

### 2.1. Algorithm and problem formulation

The proposed algorithm (Figure 1) comprises an outer loop that handles discrete design parameters through Simulated Annealing (SA) (Kirkpatrick et al., 1983) and two inner loops, whereby steady-state process optimization is performed, followed by process optimization under the influence of disturbances. Two vectors $D_{CC}$ and $D_{CU}$ with the discrete model input parameters are generated for both the CC and CU processes. The CC model undergoes optimization for the given $D_{CC}$ within the IPOPT block (Wächter and Biegler, 2006), which considers only the continuous parameters as design variables (vector $C$), targeting the minimization of the objective function $OF_{CC,ss}$. The optimized state variables $X_{CC,ss}^{opt}$ and the $OF_{CC,ss}$ from IPOPT, as well as the $D_{CU}$ vector from SA are used as input to the CU model that generates the $OF_{CU,ss}$. This block is designated as "NW-ODE-SS", representing the inclusion of a Newton-based (NW) step and an ordinary differential equations (ODE) solution step for the steady-state (SS) case. The $OF_{CC,ss}$ value is the cost per ton of captured $CO_2$ that is used in the CU model as raw material. These two blocks represent the SS instance of the CCU system in each SA iteration.

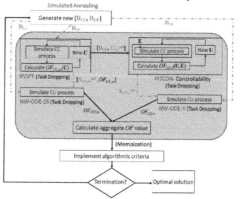

**Figure 1:** Main algorithmic steps. Vector $D$ represents the discrete variables, vector $C$ the continuous variables, vector $X$ the state variables, vector $E$ the disturbances, vector $E$ the manipulated variables, $OF$ the objective function, $ss$ is steady state, and $v$ variability.

Vector $C_{CC,ss}^{opt}$ of the continuous variables and $D_{CC}$ of the discrete variables are passed to the PITCON block (Rheinboldt and Burkardt, 1983) for the controllability assessment of the CC process. The latter is achieved through a non-linear sensitivity analysis approach (Seferlis and Grievink, 2004) and implemented in an integrated design fashion (Vasilas et al., 2022). The model is simulated under the effect of disturbances to calculate the CC process performance under variability, represented through $OF_{CC,v}$. The latter expresses the deviation of the operating point of the CC process from the set-point and the resources required to maintain this set-point under the effect of exogenous disturbances. Then, the $D_{CU}$ vector, the CC model state variables $X_{CC,v}^{opt}$ and the calculated cost per ton of CO₂ under variability are passed to the CU process (NW-ODE-V block). The CU model is simulated for the optimum solution that was attained by the CC model under the influence of disturbances, providing the $OF_{CU,v}$ value which is different than the corresponding $OF_{CU,ss}$ one. The effects of the disturbances on the CC process are therefore propagated indirectly to the CU model calculations.

The optimum design and controllability assessment problem formulation is represented through the objective functions shown below. The addition of equality and inequality constraints are omitted due to space restrictions. Details for the CC part are reported in Vasilas et al. (2022), and for the CU part in Dimoliani et al. (2021). The overall $OF$ of Eq. (1) represents maximization of the profit from selling the product, considering the maximization of the sum of the steady-state and under variability profits. For a vector of disturbances that induce deterioration of the $OF_{CU,v}$ it is desired to target a value that is as close as possible to the $OF_{CU,ss}$. The CC optimization and controllability assessment objective functions are shown in Eq. (2) and (3).

Overall optimization problem (SA loop), considering the CU model:

$$max \quad OF = OF_{CU,ss} + OF_{CU,v} \tag{1}$$

Optimization of the CC process at steady-state (IPOPT block):

$$min \quad OF_{CC,ss} = \frac{TAC_{CC}}{\dot{m}_{CO_2} \cdot t_a} \tag{2}$$

Controllability assessment of CC process (PITCON block):

$$min \quad OF_{CC,v} = \left(Y - Y_{sp}\right)^T W_Y \left(Y - Y_{sp}\right) + (U - U_{ss})^T W_U (U - U_{ss}) \tag{3}$$

where $TAC_{CC}$ is the total annual cost (M€), $\dot{m}_{CO_2}$ is the flow rate of the captured CO₂ (t/h), $t_a$ is the annual equipment deployment (h/y), $Y$ is the vector of controlled variables and $Y_{sp}$ the vector of set-points. $W_Y$ and $W_X$ are the weight matrices (Vasilas et al., 2022). $OF_{CC,ss}$ is used as input to simulate the CU model at steady-state, whereas the same term as that of Eq. (2) is calculated based on the result of the PITCON block (it is the cost per ton of CO₂ for the CC process under variability) and used as input to the CU model in the NW-ODE-V block. The objective functions of the CU process are the following:

$$OF_{CU,i} = \left(SP - CP_{Prod,i}\right) \cdot P \text{ (NW-ODE-i block), } i=\{ss, v\} \tag{4}$$

where $SP$ is the product selling price (€/t), $CP_{Prod}$ is the product cost (€/t) and $P$ is the total yearly production (t/y).

## 2.2. Acceleration and parallelization

The algorithm implements the approximate computing techniques of memoization and task dropping (Mittal, 2016) to accelerate the execution, on top of the parallelization. Memoisation refers to the development of a stored record of already visited and converged designs. The record is used to directly attain the stored solutions when the corresponding designs are re-visited by SA (a typical feature in this algorithm), instead of repeating the time-consuming simulations. Task dropping refers to avoiding tasks which incur intense computational effort. These include the IPOPT, PITCON and NW-ODE algorithms, that take longer to converge or do not converge as the values of the discrete variables shift the simulations away from the fixed starting point used here. A task is automatically dropped as unconverged when a time threshold, set from offline tests, is overcome. Vectors $D_{CC}$ and $D_{CU}$ are distributed to an equivalent number of parallel computing units which execute the IPOPT, PITCON and NW-ODE algorithms.

## 3. Implementation

We consider 6 cases that result from the combination of 2 solvents (Sol1 and Sol2) and 3 process structures (Proc1, Proc2, and Proc3) for the CC case. Sol1 and Sol2 are aqueous 2-Aminoethanol 30 wt. % and 3-Amino-1-Propanol 35 wt. %. Proc1 is the conventional absorption/ desorption flowsheet, in Proc2 the rich $CO_2$ stream enters the desorber at different locations, and Proc3 is a combination of Proc2 with cooling along the absorber height (Damartzis et al., 2014). The absorber and the stripper are divided in 3 elements, using the orthogonal collocation on finite elements method (Damartzis et al., 2014). The length of each element (ranging between 1-20) is considered in vector $D_{CC}$, whereas $D_{CU}$ includes the inner radius of the RPB (0.2-1.2 m, with step of 0.1 m). Vector $C$ (IPOPT) includes the solvent make-up flowrate (50-140 mol/s), the reboiler temperature (363-393 K), the absorber and desorber pressure (1-3 bar), the stream split ratios (0-100%), and the duties of the cooler and of the two intercoolers (0-2 MW). The controlled variables $Y$ are the percentage of captured $CO_2$, the lean stream loading, and the column temperatures. The manipulated variables $U$ are all the continuous variables, except for pressures. The disturbance $E$ is on the $CO_2$ concentration in the feed stream, that is allowed to be up to 2% lower than the nominal value of a feed stream with 12 % vol. $CO_2$ and a total flow of 320.22 mol/s. A 10 wt. % aqueous $Ca(OH)_2$ is the raw material for RPB-based PCC production (Dimoliani et al., 2021). The number of packing layers is 10, the packing specific area and porosity are 2,500 $m^2/m^3$ and 0.76, and the rotating speed is 3,000 rpm. The $t_a$ is 8,000 h/y and the $SP$ is 1,000 €/t. The implemented annual variability scenario (VS-A) considers that 20 % of the yearly operation is at nominal operating conditions and 80 % under variability. The latter includes 24 %, 19.2 %, 16%, 12.8% and 8% of the time, disturbance of -0.4%, -0.8%, -1.2%, -1.6% and -2%, respectively.

## 4. Results and discussion

### 4.1. Algorithmic scalability

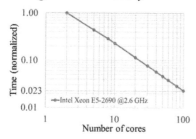

**Figure 2:** (a) Scalability analysis of the proposed algorithm as computation time against number of cores utilized.

The computational time from execution in 100 CPU cores was up to 72,000 s (20.0 h) for the performed runs. Memoization and task dropping, reduced the computational time of the algorithm by up to 510,000 s (141.7 h), by avoiding the repetitive simulations of already tested discrete variable combinations and computationally intensive tasks. Figure 2 exhibits a desirable scalability trend, as the computational time decreases linearly with the addition of parallel cores. Utilizing up to 100 CPU cores, we gradually achieve a 97.5 % reduction in execution time, compared to

*Design of CO₂ Capture and Mineralization Systems: Integrated Process*
*Optimization and Controllability Assessment in Parallel Infrastructures*

2819

running in 2 cores.

### 4.2. CC results

Figure 3a illustrates a Pareto analysis of the cost per ton of $CO_2$ at steady-state ($OF_{CC,SS}$) vs. under VS-A ($Q_{CC,VS-A}$) for all of the CC solvent-process combinations. The Pareto front indicates that Sol2-Proc2 achieves the best trade-off between operation at steady-state and under variability, overcoming the reference Sol1-Proc1. Sol2-Proc2 achieves a cost of 38.62 €/t at nominal conditions and 38.92 €/t $CO_2$ under VS-A. Sol2-Proc1 achieves very similar values, but is not Pareto optimal.

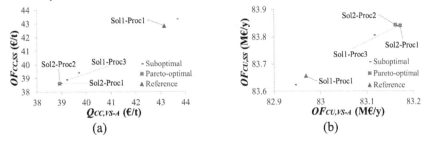

(a)                   (b)

**Figure 3:** Pareto analysis of designed **(a)** CC process cost per ton $CO_2$ at steady-state vs. operation under VS-A (both OFs are minimized), **(b)** CU process annual profit at steady-state vs. operation under VS-A (both OFs are maximized). $Q_{CC,VS-A}$ stands for cost per ton of $CO_2$ under VS-A.

### 4.3. CU results

Figure 3b illustrates a Pareto analysis for the annual profit of the CU process (tailored after each tested CC process case) at steady-state vs. operation under VS-A. The reference case Sol1-Proc1 results again in suboptimal behavior. The Pareto front indicates that Sol2-Proc2 remains Pareto optimal, but Sol2-Proc1 is now part of the Pareto front. The latter may be considered the best choice for the CU process, due to its higher annual profit under variability (83.171 M€/y vs. 83.160 M€/y for Sol2-Proc2, although the values are very close). Even more pronounced is the case of Sol1-Proc3 that was clearly suboptimal in the CC process (Figure 3a) and has moved between the two Pareto optimum systems in Figure 3b. These changes can be explained based on the results of Figure 4. Although all of the tested solvent-process combinations have the same captured $CO_2$ flowrate at steady-state, disturbances may cause the captured $CO_2$ to deviate from case to case. For instance, Sol2-Proc1 captures about 25 tons of $CO_2$ per year more than Sol2-Proc2 in the disturbance magnitude of -0.4 %, and about 16 tons of $CO_2$ less in the magnitude of -2 %. Similar differences are observed for Sol1-Proc3. This behavior changes the annual profit, as $CO_2$ is the raw material in PCC production.

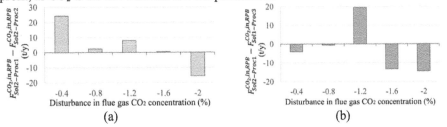

(a)                   (b)

**Figure 4:** Deviation of CC process captured $CO_2$ flow vs. disturbance range in VS-A between a) Sol2-Proc1 and Sol2-Proc2, and b) Sol2-Proc1 and Sol2-Proc3. $F_i^{CO_2,in,RPB}$ stands for the mass flow rate of captured $CO_2$ fed to the RPB reactor.

## 5. Conclusions

The presented work has illustrated the use of a parallel algorithm for solvent selection, CC and CU process design and controllability assessment, considering an RPB process as a $CO_2$ utilization option for production of PCC. The results showed that the proposed algorithm exhibits excellent scalability and significant acceleration is attained due to the use of approximate computing techniques. The Pareto optimal solvent-process structure combinations that were attained in the CC process exhibits differences with the Pareto front attained when the CU process is considered simultaneously, highlighting the need for algorithms for such complex design problems.

## Acknowledgements

The experiment "CCUPAR" has received funding from the European High-Performance Computing Joint Undertaking (JU) through the FF4EuroHPC project under grant agreement No 951745. The JU receives support from the European Union's Horizon 2020 research and innovation programme and Germany, Italy, Slovenia, France, Spain.

## References

T.N. Borhani, E. Oko, M. Wang, 2019. Process modelling, validation and analysis of rotating packed bed stripper in the context of intensified $CO_2$ capture with MEA, J. Ind. Eng. Chem., 75, 285–295.

M. Bui, C.S. Adjiman, A. Bardow et al., 2018, Carbon capture and storage (CCS): The way forward, Energy Environ. Sci., 11, 1062–1176.

T. Damartzis, A.I. Papadopoulos, P. Seferlis, 2014, Optimum synthesis of solvent-based post-combustion $CO_2$ capture flowsheets through a generalized modeling framework, Clean Technol. Environ. Policy, 16, 1363–1380.

M. Dimoliani, A.I. Papadopoulos, P. Seferlis, 2021, Modeling and Parametric Investigation of Rotating Packed Bed Processes for $CO_2$ Capture and Mineralisation, Chem. Eng. Trans., 88, 187–192.

M.M.F. Hasan, E.L. First, F. Boukouvala, C.A. Floudas, 2015, A multi-scale framework for $CO_2$ capture, utilization, and sequestration: CCUS and CCU, Comput. Chem. Eng., 81, 2–21.

O.A. Jimoh, K.S. Ariffin, H.B. Hussin, A.E. Temitope, 2018, Synthesis of precipitated calcium carbonate: a review, Carbonates and Evaporites, 33, 2, 331-346.

H. Jung, D. Im, S. Heo, B. Kim, J.H. Lee, 2020, Dynamic analysis and linear model predictive control for operational flexibility of post-combustion $CO_2$ capture processes, Comput. Chem. Eng., 140, 106968.

S. Kirkpatrick, C.D. Gelatt, M.P. Vecchi, 1983, Optimization by simulated annealing, Science, 220, 671–680.

D.C. Miller, D. Agarwal, D. Bhattacharyya et al., 2017, Innovative Computational Tools and Models for the Design, Optimization and Control of Carbon Capture Processes, in: Papadopoulos, A.I., Seferlis, P. (Eds.), Process Systems and Materials for $CO_2$ Capture, John Wiley and Sons Ltd, Chichester, West Sussex, 311–339.

W.C. Rheinboldt, J.V. Burkardt, 1983, A Locally Parameterized Continuation Process, ACM Trans. Math. Softw., 9, 215–235.

M.H. Sahraei, L.A. Ricardez-Sandoval, 2014, Simultaneous design and control of the MEA absorption process of a $CO_2$ capture plant, Energy Procedia, 63, 1601–1607.

P. Seferlis, J. Grievink, 2004, Process design and control structure evaluation and screening using nonlinear sensitivity analysis, Comput. Aided Chem. Eng., 17, 326-351.

N. Vasilas, A.I. Papadopoulos, L. Papadopoulos et al., 2022, Approximate computing, skeleton programming and run-time scheduling in an algorithm for process design and controllability in distributed and heterogeneous infrastructures, Comput. Chem. Eng., 164, 107874.

A. Wächter, L.T. Biegler, 2006, On the implementation of an interior-point filter line-search algorithm for large-scale nonlinear programming, Math. Program., 106, 25–57.

Antonis Kokossis, Michael C. Georgiadis, Efstratios N. Pistikopoulos (Eds.)
PROCEEDINGS OF THE 33rd European Symposium on Computer Aided Process Engineering
(ESCAPE33), June 18-21, 2023, Athens, Greece
© 2023 Elsevier B.V. All rights reserved.  http://dx.doi.org/10.1016/B978-0-443-15274-0.50449-2

# Accurately Modeling Hydropower in the USA

Amanda Farnsworth,[a,b] Emre Gençer,[a]

[a] *MIT Energy Initiative, Massachusetts Institute of Technology, 400 Main Street, Cambridge, MA 02142, USA*
[b] *Department of Chemical Engineering, Massachusetts Institute of Technology, 25 Ames Street, Cambridge, MA 02142, USA*

## Abstract

This study marks the first comprehensive evaluation of hydropower across the US. Both installation limits and capacity factor profiles were extracted and processed from a variety of sources and incorporated into a capacity expansion model. Life-cycle assessment strategies were used to fairly assesses the three types of hydropower: conventional, run-of-river, and pumped storage. When only operational emissions are considered, 30-63% of system emissions go unaccounted for. As emissions caps become stricter, hydropower is relied upon more heavily. At a 50 gCO2-eq/kWh emissions limit, seven out of nine regions analyzed reach their installation limit in at least one hydropower technology type. Lastly, a carbon neutral power sector requires carbon negative technologies.

**Keywords**: hydropower, LCA, optimization, decarbonization, power sector

## 1. Introduction

Currently in the US, hydropower capacity is 80.25 GW, outputting 274 TWh of energy annually. This contribution accounts for 6.7% of generation capacity, and 6.6% overall power production and 38% of renewable power production (Uría-Martínez 2021). Around this technology, there is a heated debate regarding its value and impacts. It has been shown that hydropower can be leveraged to lower the cost of decarbonization, where hydropower integration provides increasing value to the system as decarbonization targets become more stringent (Dimanchev 2021, Bain 2018). Conversely, another faction of researchers emphasize that hydropower can damage the social and ecological ecosystems of a region, and that these impacts are not accurately captured in power system expansion and planning (Williams 2020, Moran 2018). This study aims to fairly assess the value of hydropower while penalizing it appropriately for its direct and indirect emissions.

The term "hydropower" primarily refers to a dammed river because the vast majority of hydropower resources are this type. However, hydropower technologies can fit into 3 main categories. Dammed hydropower will hereafter be referred to as "conventional." Run-of-river hydropower (RoR) does not incorporate any water storage, so power generation is intermittent and non-dispatchable as it depends solely on river flowrate. Pumped hydropower storage (PHS) requires two nearby reservoirs at varying heights. Water is pumped up or drained down to the respective higher or lower reservoir to convert electricity to and from gravitational potential energy.

This study uses a capacity expansion model (CEM) to optimize power sector buildout by minimizing system cost while simultaneously reaching specific decarbonization targets. Life Cycle Assessment (LCA) and Technoeconomic Analysis (TEA) techniques are used to track emissions and cost values throughout the life cycle. The last consideration of this study is that hydropower capacity buildout is limited in each region based on local geography and weather patterns.

## 2. Methodology

This section focuses on hydropower-related data and constraints, rather than overall model structure.

### 2.1. Ideal Grid

Ideal Grid (IG) is a capacity expansion model built within MIT's Sustainable Energy System Analysis Modelling Environment (SESAME). SESAME is a pathway analysis tool which utilizes LCA and TEA techniques to estimate the emissions and costs of producing a particular unit of product within the overall energy system, such as steel, hydrogen, gasoline, etc (Gençer 2020). IG references the electricity production pathways, so external LCA and TEA evaluation of technologies is not needed. Eleven different generator types are represented: wind, solar, RoR hydropower, conventional hydropower, 3 types of natural gas (combustion turbine, combined cycle, and combined cycle with carbon capture), 3 types of coal (boiler, IGCC, and boiler with carbon capture), and nuclear fission. Two different storage options are included: lithium-ion batteries (LIB), and PHS. Single-nodal, deterministic optimization is performed over a year, at an hourly timestep. Figure 1 shows the nine regions explored, roughly along the North American Electric Reliability Corporation boundary lines for convenience.

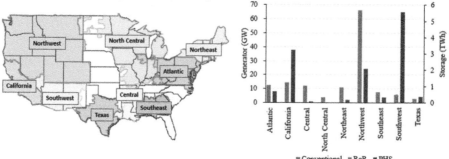

Figure 1. Regions and their respective hydropower capacity limits

### 2.2. Regional Capacity Limits

As mentioned above, hydropower adds an additional constraint to the optimization because its buildout is limited. Conventional hydropower is estimated by obtaining current capacity values from *Electric Power Annual* and adding upgrade and non-powered potentials from *Hydropower Vision* and *An Assessment of Energy Potential at Non-Powered Dams in the US*, respectively. Data is provided on a state-by-state basis, but is easily aggregated to represent regional potential. RoR regional potential is sourced from *New Stream-reach Development* assessment. This comprehensive review identified potential RoR hydropower sites across the US while eliminating sites which are close to national parks, wild and scenic rivers, and wilderness areas. Again, capacity estimates are provided in a state-by-state basis and aggregated to represent regional potential. PHS potential can be downloaded from NREL's *Closed-Loop Pumped Storage Hydropower Resource Assessment for the US*. Sites are aggregated into regional groups based on their latitudes and longitudes. The generation and storage potential of each region can be compared in Figure 1.

### 2.3. Hydropower Generation Profiles

Conventional hydropower generation is a dispatchable generation source, but must be balanced periodically to account for reservoir size. To account for this, monthly capacity factors (CFs) are calculated based on existing nameplate hydropower capacity and monthly power output, both sourced from EIA's *Electric Power Monthly* reports. Equation (1) shows the simple relation used to track monthly CF, and Equation (2) shows how this CF is enforced within the model

$$CF_{m,y} = \frac{E_{m,y}}{24*n_m*C_y} \qquad \forall\ m \in jan, feb \ldots dec \wedge y \in 2007, 2008 \ldots 2013 \quad (1)$$

$$CF_{m,y} = \frac{\sum_{d=st*24}^{d=end*24} E_d}{C} \qquad \forall\ m \in jan, feb \ldots dec \wedge y \in 2007, 2008 \ldots 2013 \quad (2)$$

where $E$ is energy output in MWh, $C$ is capacity in MW, $n$ is days in the month, and *st* and *end* reflect the first and last day of each month.

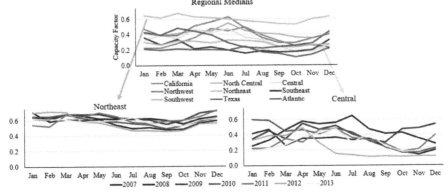

Figure 2. Conventional Hydropower CF Profiles

Figure 2 compares the conventional hydropower CF trends for all nine regions. Table A shows the standard deviation in CFs for each region, which reflects conventional hydropower resource predictability. Figure 2 also includes the yearly variation for the most and least predictable regions. This variability trend has a very low correlation with installed capacity with an $R^2$ value of 0.1046, meaning that site aggregation is not the main reason for this high range of CF consistency.

Table A. Standard Deviation of CF in Each Region

|  | Atlantic | California | Central | North Central | Northeast | Northwest | Southeast | Southwest | Texas |
|---|---|---|---|---|---|---|---|---|---|
| Conventional | 7.4% | 8.8% | 12.1% | 9.7% | 5.2% | 6.7% | 9.9% | 5.4% | 9.8% |
| RoR | 17.6% | 10.7% | 13.8% | 12.4% | 9.9% | 7.8% | 17.6% | 8.1% | 24.6% |

RoR CF curves are calculated based off daily river flowrate data from the United States Geological Survey (USGS). USGS provides data on over 1.9 million water-resources within the US. Each stream-site is aggregated into its respective region to produce a daily conglomerate river flowrate in each region. Equation (3) shows the calculation used to convert regional river flowrate to daily CF

$$CF_d = \begin{cases} \frac{Q_d}{Q_{max}} * \eta_{turb} & for \quad Q_d \leq Q_{max} \\ \\ \eta_{turb} & for \quad Q_d > Q_{max} \end{cases} \qquad (3)$$

where $Q_d$ is hourly flowrate, $Q_{max}$ is the flowrate which 30% of the hours exceed, and turbine efficiency, $\eta_{turb}$, is 85%. The values calculated with this method match the estimated values published in the *New Stream-reach Development* assessment with less than 15% discrepancy. Figure 3 shows regional RoR CF trends. Also, the yearly variation in the most and least predictable regions is shown, based on average standard deviation values provided in Table A. Just as in the conventional hydropower case, available river data is not the cause of variation, resulting in an $R^2$ value of 0.0190. Lastly, PHS is assumed to have dispatchable operation, limited only by energy and power capacities.

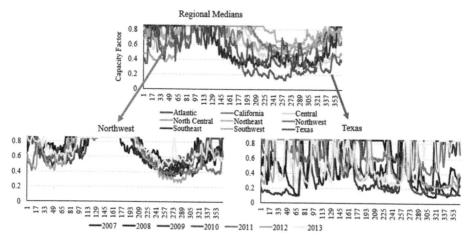

Figure 3. RoR Hydropower CF Profiles

## 2.4. Solar and Wind Generation Profiles and Demand Profiles

Regional solar and wind CF curves are generated through the aggregation of 169 equidistant site-specific CF profiles in each region, spaced 30 miles apart. Hourly site-specific solar and wind outputs are sourced from ZEPHYR (Zero-emissions Electricity system Planning with HourlY operational Resolution) repository. ZEPHYR accesses weather data from NREL's *Wind Integration National Dataset* (WIND) Toolkit and NREL's *National Solar Radiation Database* (NSRDB), and calculates power output.

2021 regional demand profiles are sourced from the EIA *Hourly Electric Grid Monitor*. Demand curves were scaled down to 8760 kWh annually so that decarbonization strategies can be directly compared inter-regionally. This also allows for an easier evaluation of overbuilding where a generation capacity of 1kW means that all generators are operating at 100% capacity factor for all hours and no electricity is curtailed. This is only possible if demand is perfectly flat, or if there is ample energy storage without the consideration of charging/discharging or parasitic efficiency losses.

## 2.5. LCA and TEA

Both construction and operational costs and emissions are considered in this model, so as to fairly assess hydropower. Most importantly, an estimation for emissions from inundated areas from conventional hydropower are tracked. Figure 4 maps the emissions-cost space of generators and storage technologies based on the construction and operational emissions and cost values which are combined based on median CF for renewables and 100% CF for fossil fuel generators.

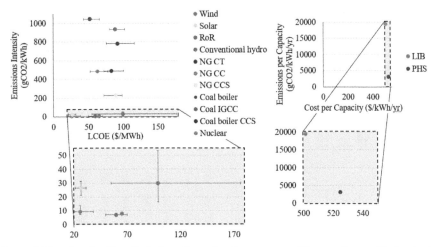

Figure 4. Mapping the Cost-Emissions Space for Generators and Energy Storage Technologies

Upon first glance, it seems that solar, wind, RoR, and nuclear are far better decarbonization options than conventional hydropower or any fossil fuel generators. This comparison is not fair because conventional hydropower and fossil fuel generators provide dispatchability to the grid which reduces energy storage requirements and limits overbuilding and curtailed energy. Additionally, fossil fuel generators costs and emissions are largely based on operation, so adjusting the power output level of these resources greatly impacts their location on the Figure 4 mapping.

## 3. Case Study

A simple case study illustrates the importance of LCA in assessing hydropower, and other decarbonization options. Figure 5 compares decarbonization strategies depending on differing emissions tracking schemes. First, it is clear that ignoring emissions from stages of the life-cycle outside operation allows for a significant increase in emissions, ranging from 30-63% increase depending on the region. The majority of this decarbonization from LCA enforcement comes from a reduction of natural gas operation, and carbon capture technologies introduced in the Atlantic, Southeast, Southwest, and Texas. Wind and solar technologies are increased by up to 25%, seeing a decrease in only the Californian region. This standalone decrease is due to the introduction of nuclear which supplies 18% of noncurtailed electricity. This shift to LCA increases system price by 1.7-3.9% depending on region. Lastly, it is shown that LIBs are not installed until PHS capacity is maximized.

LCA increases system reliance on hydropower in all regions, causing seven out of the nine regions to maximize their installation capacity in at least one of the hydropower technologies. When tracking only operational emissions, conventional hydropower is maxed out in three regions (Atlantic, North Central, and Northeast), but when LCA is applied, it is maximized in three additional regions (Central, Southeast and Southwest), while also increasing by significant amounts in two others (California and Northwest). LCA increases RoR in California and the Southwest. Also, LCA increases PHS by a significant amount in almost every region. When regional hydropower capacity limits are ignored, installed hydropower generator capacity increases by 102% and PHS decreases by 16%, resulting in a price decrease of about 1%. Lastly, this study shows that a truly carbon neutral power sector requires some carbon capture or carbon negative technologies.

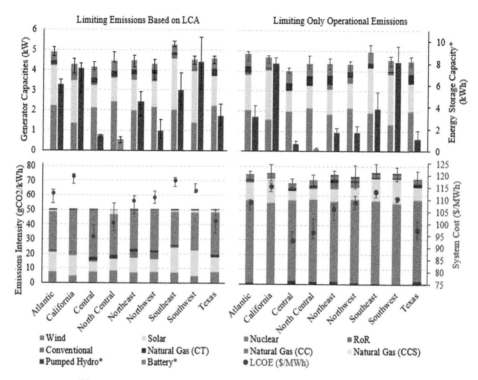

Figure 5. Decarbonization Strategies Depend on Emissions Tracking

## 4. Conclusion

A wide range of sources are used to comprehensively evaluate hydropower resources across the USA. Regional capacity limits and performance profiles are identified for conventional, RoR, and PHS resources. LCA techniques are used to show that the optimal decarbonization strategy for every region involves the leveraging of at least one hydropower resource. Also, only monitoring operational emissions can lead to up to 63% error. Lastly, carbon negative technologies are needed to reach net neutrality.

## References

Bain, Dominique M, and Thomas L Acker. 2018. "Hydropower Impacts on Electrical System Production Costs in the Southwest United States." https://doi.org/10.3390/en11020368.

Dimanchev, Emil G., Joshua L. Hodge, and John E. Parsons. 2021. "The Role of Hydropower Reservoirs in Deep Decarbonization Policy." *Energy Policy* 155 (August): 112369. https://doi.org/10.1016/j.enpol.2021.112369.

Gençer, Emre, Sarah Torkamani, Ian Miller, Tony Wenzhao Wu, and Francis O'Sullivan. 2020. "Sustainable Energy System Analysis Modeling Environment: Analyzing Life Cycle Emissions of the Energy Transition." *Applied Energy* 277 (November). https://doi.org/10.1016/j.apenergy.2020.115550.

Moran, Emilio F., Maria Claudia Lopez, Nathan Moore, Norbert Müller, and David W. Hyndman. 2018. "Sustainable Hydropower in the 21st Century." *Proceedings of the National Academy of Sciences of the United States of America* 115 (47): 11891–98. https://doi.org/10.1073/pnas.1809426115.

Uría-Martínez, Rocío, Megan M. Johnson, Rui Shan. 2021. "U.S. Hydropower Market Report."

Williams, Jessica M. 2020. "The Hydropower Myth." *Environmental Science and Pollution Research* 27 (12): 12882–88. https://doi.org/10.1007/s11356-019-04657-6.

Antonis Kokossis, Michael C. Georgiadis, Efstratios N. Pistikopoulos (Eds.)
PROCEEDINGS OF THE 33rd European Symposium on Computer Aided Process Engineering
(ESCAPE33), June 18-21, 2023, Athens, Greece

# Biogas valorisation to liquid fuels: modelling and setting up process targets.

Selusiwe Ncube,[a*] Baraka C Sempuga,[a] Xinying Liu[a]

[a]*Institute for the Development of Energy for African Sustainability (IDEAS) Research Unit, University of South Africa (UNISA), Florida, Johannesburg,1710, South Africa.*

## Abstract

The concept of attainable region and targeting techniques is used to explore the feasibility of co-producing Fischer-Tropsch (FT) fuels and methanol through biogas valorisation. The interest is particularly in sub-regions with a net consumption of $CO_2$ as we are aiming for a carbon negative process. One of the requirements to achieve a net $CO_2$ consumption is to be able to fully integrate the energy within the process. Heat integration between the reformer and the synthesis reactors is one of the factors that cause significant deviations from the target, especially the energy target. Adding large amounts of feed to compensate for the heat required would not be practical and the process would be a net $CO_2$ producer instead of a net $CO_2$ consumer. Comparatively, a heat pump uses as less power as possible. Thus, we propose the addition of a heat engine to the simulation process to maximise the efficiency of the process and improve $CO_2$ utilisation. A heat pump is needed to pump heat between the FT and methanol synthesis section to the reformer because of the temperature gradient. We compute the theoretical targets using MATLAB and then validate the theoretical solutions by modelling the processes using Aspen Plus®. A match of the mass balance simulation results with the theoretical stoichiometry showed a good correspondence. For heat integration, it was shown that 12.19 kW of heat can be absorbed from the synthesis reactor at 230 °C to put in 13.81 kW of work for the supply of 26 kW of heat required at the reformer which is at 801 °C for a carbon negative process.

**Keywords**: Biogas, Targeting techniques, Fischer-Tropsch fuels, Methanol, Simulation

## 1. Introduction

The abundance of carbon dioxide and methane either as flared gases or emissions from industrial sectors propels their use as raw materials. These greenhouse gases can be utilised in the form of biogas, a low-cost renewable resource [1]. There is a drive for converting $CO_2$ to fuel and chemicals such as methanol, FT (Fischer-Tropsch) fuels and ethanol [2], [3]; hence biogas is a cost and energy effective source of $CO_2$ ready to be utilised. However, the efficiency of the processes involved in valorising biogas to different fuels has to be taken into account while ascertaining that the process is carbon negative (net $CO_2$ consumption). The simulation process is a facile way to determine the heat or work that is required or can be expended by a process. One way in which work can be transferred to processes to make them feasible without altering their net energy requirement is using the Carnot temperature concept [4]. This paper unfolds from a process synthesis perspective through the use of graphical targeting techniques where we set theoretical targets in MATLAB to valorise biogas to FT fuels and methanol. The study is substantiated by a modelling process in Aspen Plus® to validate the theoretical targets and a heat pump is introduced for heat and work integration purposes to try and improve the efficiency of the process while maintaining an overall carbon negative process.

## 2. Methodology

The methodology section is divided into two sections that include the theoretical and the simulation.

### 2.1. Setting up process targets

We first look at the theoretical approach which allows us to optimise certain targets called the Attainable Regions (AR) using MATLAB. We regard the overall process as a 'black box' by looking at only the input and output of the system as shown in Figure 1.

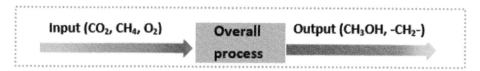

Figure 1: A schematic representation of the overall process

The basis for the production of the products (methanol and FT fuels) was set as 1 mol of methane. The targets identified in MATLAB were then simulated in Aspen Plus®.

### 2.2. Simulation process

The NRTL-RK thermodynamic property method was used for all the reactors used in the simulation process to allow for an accurate description of the phase equilibrium. The reformer was simulated as an equilibrium reactor, an RGibbs reactor model. The methanol synthesis reactor was modelled as an RPLUG model using a kinetic model derived from Skrzypek et al. [5]. The model has the form of the Langmuir–Hinshelwood–Hougen–Watson (LHHW) reaction Figure 2 illustrates the implemented flowsheet.

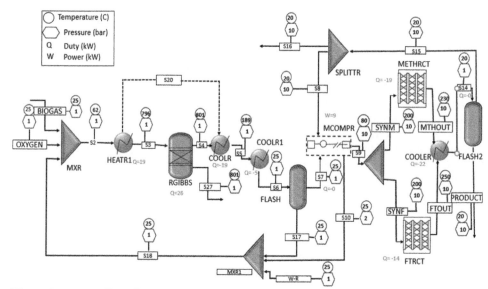

Figure 2: Process flow diagram for the synthesis of methanol and FT from biogas.

### 2.2.1. Heat integration computations

A heat pump will be included in the simulation process to integrate the heat between the reformer and the synthesis reactor. To use a heat pump, it is imperative to determine the amount of work needed to put into the pump to draw heat at a lower temperature (Tc) and pump the resultant heat to a much higher temperature (Th) to supply the required heat. Given Qh (heat load), Th and Tc obtained from the simulation, the work (W) required is calculated as shown in Equation 1.1.

$$W = Qh * \left(1 - \frac{T_c}{T_h}\right)$$

(1.1)

The amount of heat (H) to be absorbed from the synthesis reactor is computed as shown in Equation 1.2.

$$H = Q_h - W$$

(1.2)

## 3. Results and Discussion

Figure 3 shows the different production rates of $CH_2$ where $CH_3OH$ production is maximized using the MATLAB software. Point A illustrates the desired target.

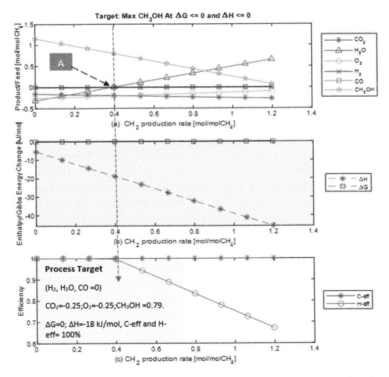

Figure 3: Process material balance targets (a) and their associated energy and work balances (b), and carbon and hydrogen efficiencies (c) for biogas conversion to FT-fuel at various production rates per mole of $CH_4$ consumed and maximum $CH_3OH$ consumption.

Tables 1 and 2 show the results obtained from MATLAB (Target) and Aspen Plus®.
Table 1: Global Mass balance

| Component | Inlet (kmol/h) | Simulation Outlet (kmol/h) | Simulation (Net)(kmol/h) | Target (kmol/h) |
|-----------|----------------|----------------------------|--------------------------|-----------------|
| CO | 0.00 | 0.00 | 0.00 | 0.00 |
| $CO_2$ | 0.25 | 0.11 | -0.14 | -0.25 |
| $H_2O$ | 0.27 | 0.27 | 0.00 | 0.00 |
| $O_2$ | 0.25 | 0.00 | -0.25 | -0.25 |
| $CH_4$ | 1.00 | 0.05 | -0.95 | -1.00 |
| $CH_3OH$ | 0.00 | 0.73 | 0.73 | 0.79 |
| $-CH_2-$ | 0.00 | 0.31 | 0.31 | 0.40 |

Table 2: Global Energy balance

| | Heat Duty/Energy (Q) (kW) | | Power (kW) | |
|---|---|---|---|---|
| | Theoretical Target (MATLAB) | Simulation | Theoretical Target (MATLAB) | Simulation |
| Net Energy/Power | -18 | -34 | 0 | 9 |

The simulation results achieved 78% of the theoretical target of $-CH_2-$ production while 92% was achieved for methanol production indicating a small deviation from the theoretical targets as shown in Table 1. As per the target, there was net $CO_2$ consumption. However, the slight discrepancy was that only 0.14 moles of $CO_2$ were consumed instead of 0.25 moles due to limitations in driving forces such as entropy generation and temperature approaches across heat exchangers. Considerable deviations were observed in the energy balance between the simulation (net) and the target results from MATLAB as shown in Table 2. The theoretical targeted $\Delta \hat{H}$ value was -18 kJ/mol. Therefore, it is critical to ensure that $\Delta H$ is recovered as work, which is high-quality energy. If it is recovered as heat, the quality of the recovered energy is poor, and the process is inefficient. However, the theoretical value for work ($\Delta \hat{G}$) was 0 kJ/mol and a value of 9 kW was obtained from the simulation process as a result of the work required by the compressor (MCOMPR) to supply high pressure needed at the methanol synthesis reactor to increase chemical driving reaction forces which are one of the major sources of entropy generation and thus work losses. To supply some of the work needed by the process, a heat pump is needed to integrate the temperature gradient from low to high instead of burning an external energy source such as $CH_4$ in order to generate enough work. The consequence of burning $CH_4$ is that the process would be a net $CO_2$ producer instead of a net $CO_2$ consumer. As an optimisation strategy, the heat generated in situ was used for heat integration within the simulation process. Heat integration was carried out between the two heat exchangers at the inlet and outlet of the reformer and the minimum temperature approach was set at 5°C (801°C-796°C) as shown in Figure 4.

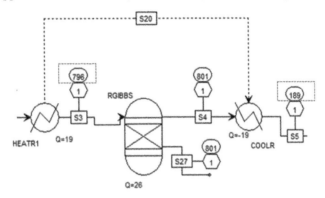

Figure 4: Heat integration between the heater and the cooler in the reformer unit (extracted from the process flowsheet in Aspen Plus®).

The overall process consisted of the reforming and the synthesis stage that could be optimised for energy integration.

> The reforming stage (RGIBBS) is endothermic at high temperatures hence the heat carries work into the process.
> The synthesis stage (METHRCT) is exothermic at lower temperatures and work is rejected from the process.

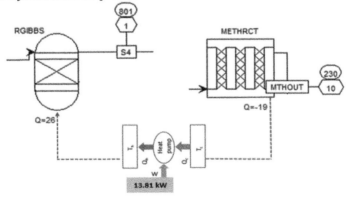

Figure 5: Heat integration between the reformer and the synthesis reactor using a heat pump (extracted from a process flowsheet in Aspen Plus®).

One would need a heat pump to integrate the heat between the reformer and the synthesis reactor because of the temperature gradient as a hot stream at 230 or 250 °C cannot be used to heat a cold stream at 801 °C as shown in Figure 5. Therefore, work is needed to pump heat in the opposite direction of its normal flow. Therefore, from the computations (Equations 1.1 and 1.2), 12.19 kW of heat can be absorbed from the synthesis reactor at 230 °C to put in 13.81 kW of work for the supply of 26 kW of heat required at the reformer which is at 801 °C. It should be noted that from a practical point of view, there are currently no heat pump technologies that are capable of reaching such high temperatures;

however, we seek to determine what is required in order to achieve the heat integration within the process or a carbon negative overall process.

## 4. Conclusions

Simulated mass balance targets extrapolated to conventional methanol and FT fuels synthesis conditions were in good agreement with the results obtained from the theoretical targets. Of particular significance is that the process revealed a net $CO_2$ consumption, meaning that the overall process is carbon negative. However, to achieve a zero net $CO_2$ consumption negative process, it is necessary to fully integrate energy within the process. In this case, there is a need to integrate the heat and work between the synthesis reactors ($CH_2$ and Methanol) and the reformer. However, a heat pump is needed to overcome the heat flow temperature gradient from low to high. The simulation reveals that in order to get close to the target, external work supply to the process is required. This is one of the major deviations from the target which is 0 work requirement due to the work needed at the heat pump to integrate heat between the low temperature synthesis section to the high temperature reformer section; also due to the high pressure required at the methanol synthesis reactor which is essentially reaction driving forces to obtain high conversions for methanol synthesis. Thus, the additional work must be supplied from a renewable source to achieve a truly carbon negative process. In essence, heat integration between the reformer and the synthesis reactors is one of the factors that causes significant deviations from the target, especially the energy target, and therefore, should be a subject of optimisation. These limitations are a result of lack of better technologies or better catalysts to improve the efficiencies in processes. The discrepancies in this work can be taken as a reference point for future work.

## References

[1]     Rahul Kadam, N. L. Panwar, "Recent advancement in biogas enrichment and its applications," *Renew. Sustain. Energy Rev.*, vol. 73, no. September 2016, pp. 892–903, 2017, doi: 10.1016/j.rser.2017.01.167.

[2]     Daniele Previtali, Antonio Vita, Andrea Bassani, Cristina Italiano, Andrè Furtado Amaral, Carlo Pirola, Lidia Pino, Alessandra Palella, *and others*, "Methanol synthesis: A distributed production concept based on biogas plants," *Chem. Eng. Trans.*, vol. 65, pp. 409–414, 2018, doi: 10.3303/CET1865069.

[3]     Borja Hernandez, Mariano Martin, "Optimization for biogas to chemicals via tri-reforming. Analysis of Fischer-Tropsch fuels from biogas," *Energy Convers. Manag.*, vol. 174, no. August, pp. 998–1013, 2018, doi: 10.1016/j.enconman.2018.08.074.

[4]     Baraka Celestin Sempuga, Diane Hildebrandt, Bilal Patel, David Glasser, "Work to chemical processes: The relationship between heat, temperature, pressure, and process complexity," *Ind. Eng. Chem. Res.*, vol. 50, no. 14, pp. 8603–8619, 2011, doi: 10.1021/ie2004785.

[5]     J. Skrzypek, M. Lachowska, H. Moroz, "Kinetics of methanol synthesis over commercial copper/zinc oxide/alumina catalysts," *Chem. Eng. Sci.*, vol. 46, no. 11, pp. 2809–2813, 1991, doi: 10.1016/0009-2509(91)85150-V.

Antonis Kokossis, Michael C. Georgiadis, Efstratios N. Pistikopoulos (Eds.)
PROCEEDINGS OF THE 33rd European Symposium on Computer Aided Process Engineering
(ESCAPE33), June 18-21, 2023, Athens, Greece

# Modeling Commercial Fleet Charging and Regulation Strategies via Data-driven Optimization

James Owens[a,b], Emre Gençer[a]

[a]MIT Energy Initiative, Massachusetts Institute of Technology, 400 Main Street, Cambridge, MA 02142, USA
[b]Department of Chemical Engineering, Massachusetts Institute of Technology, 25 Ames Street, Cambridge, MA 02142, USA

## Abstract

While vehicle electrification offers an opportune path to transportation decarbonization, current tariffs can make the transition cost prohibitive for commercial fleets. To this end, providing frequency regulation has been proposed as a means for fleets to generate revenues while parked. However, regulation dispatch uncertainty can make participation difficult for fleets with strict schedules, and assuming a deterministic dispatch profile tends to overestimate a fleet's flexibility and underestimate the financial risk of its bids. Moreover, the most efficient retail rate and strategy for providing regulation, or simply charging alone, highly dependends on fleet schedule and demand relative to other loads a fleet owner may have. Thus, we pose a two-stage, stochastic model, informed by real-world data, to realistically determine optimal charging and regulation behavior under different tariffs. A case study demonstrates model utility in analyzing a last-mile delivery truck fleet housed at a large shipping warehouse.

**Keywords**: vehicle, electrification, grid, tariffs, optimization

## 1. Introduction

As the world marches toward a net-zero future, transportation is poised to electrify. Apart from personal vehicles, light truck and bus fleets are anticipated to undergo a rapid transition. In addition to reducing fossil fuel consumption, electrified truck fleets can provide demand response and ancillary services to the grid, known as "Vehicle-to-Grid" (V2G). For example, commercial delivery fleets are prime V2G candidates given their large batteries, predictable schedules, and overnight co-location at shipping depots. Moreover, V2G revenues can be used to offset costs of fleet electrification. For the grid, V2G increases system flexibility, ultimately reducing firm generator emissions (Owens, 2022). However, traditional U.S. retail rates are not conducive to affordable EV charging and V2G for commercial entities. Monthly demand charges, which recoup fixed delivery costs and are determined by peak consumption over a 15-minute period, can represent as much as 75% of an EV fleet operator's bill despite relatively low consumption and demand peaks the remainder of the month (He, 2019). This can discourage charging or performing V2G at opportune times, or even make electrification prohibitively expensive.

While literature has probed the issue, limitations include (1) A lack of real regulation data or ignoring uncertainty, which overestimates performance, and (2) Optimizing charging subject to current retail rates, which limits cost-optimal outcomes. For example, DeForest et al. (2018) pose a charging and ancillary service optimization model for a 29-vehicle fleet housed within a U.S. Air Force base. The authors conduct scenario analysis to assess optimal bidding strategy and its sensitivities to resource utilization, local load conditions, and retail electricity prices. However, the study's deterministic approach and parametric nature limit insights into hedged bid behavior and market outcomes. Likewise, Al-Hanahi et al. (2022) pose an integrated charging and routing optimization problem for commercial vehicles traveling to both public and depot charging stations. The model considers both demand charges and time-of-use tariffs, but also takes a deterministic approach and does not consider ancillary service participation. Neither study considers the implications of alternative tariffs.

Here we pose a stochastic, two-stage charging and frequency regulation (the ancillary service with the most earning potential) bidding model to more accurately assess realistic smart charging and regulation opportunities for commercial EV fleets. Of particular note, the model considers the risks and rationale of a standalone fleet owner and utilizes random regulation signals derived from actual EVs, which are a significant source of uncertainty and key to informing hedged regulation bids (DeForest, 2018). The mixed-integer model, subject to different market prices and rules, makes depot level and single vehicle decisions over multiple time scales to minimize costs and maximize frequency regulation revenues. Informing the high-resolution model with real world delivery truck data and the nuances of corresponding warehouse load profiles, we demonstrate the model's utility by evaluating different EV charging tariffs – from longstanding industrial rates to newly proposed, separately metered EV rates – and how they may enable V2G.

## 2. Methodology

The depot-centered model framework is tariff and fleet-agnostic, making it extendable to several combinations of fleets, building loads, time horizons, and charging schemes. As an illustrative case study, we formulate the optimization to minimize monthly demand charges and net energy costs for the overnight charging of a last-mile delivery fleet. Given the "return-to-base" nature and predictability of these fleets, the model uses data from an average summer day in 2022 and optimizes decisions for a single overnight (one day-ahead market settlement) period and assumes known vehicle arrival states. In the day-ahead (DA) stage, depot-wide charging demand is scheduled and regulation bids are submitted on behalf of the entire depot. The recourse stage sees to real time (RT) charge and capacity management, subject to stochastic regulation signals. For model tractability, the RT step resolution is taken to be 1-minute. Since regulation capacity is bid by the hour (market rules) and baseline charging is scheduled in 15-minute intervals, the DA capacity commitments and charging plan are mapped to the RT scale with additional constraints.

### 2.1. Nomenclature
**Indices and Sets**

| | |
|---|---|
| $h/t$ | Time step index |
| $T_H, T_b, T_m$ | Optimization horizon in hours, quarter-hours (b), minutes (m) |
| $i/V$ | Vehicle index / Set of vehicles |
| $s/S$ | Scenarios index / Set of scenarios |

**Parameters**

| | |
|---|---|
| $\omega_s$ | Probability of scenario $s$ |
| $p_D(t), p_U(t)$ | DA regulation prices, down, up ($/kW) |
| $p_{E,ret}(t), p_{E,inj}(t)$ | Price of retail electricity, Payment for injection ($/kWh) |
| $p_{RD,vio}(t), p_{RU,viol}(t)$ | Costs of violating regulation cap commitment down, up ($/kW) |
| $p_{S,vio}(t)$ | Costs of violating SOC departure targets ($/kWh) |
| $p_{deg}$ | Degradation cost associated with cycling from injection ($/kWh) |

| | |
|---|---|
| $p_{demand}(d)$ | Charge for peak demand during period $d$ (\$/kW) |
| $f_D^s(t), f_U^s(t)$ | AGC utilization factor down, up |
| $\eta$ | One-way charger efficiency (0.94, up and down) |
| $P_{max}$ | Maximum charge/discharge power of individual vehicle (kW) |
| $S_{travel}$ | Energy consumed in daily travel (kWh) |
| $SOC_{min}, SOC_{max}$ | Vehicle state-of-charge minimum, maximum (kWh) |

**Decision Variables**

| | |
|---|---|
| $R_D(h), R_U(h)$ | DA bid/commitment regulation capacity down, up (kW) |
| $P_{Plan}(t)$ | DA scheduled charging of full fleet (kW) |
| $dP^s(t)$ | RT deviation from $P_{Plan}$ in scenario $s$ (kW) |
| $P_{RT}^s(t), R_{inj}^s(t)$ | RT charging, injection of full fleet in scenario $s$ (kW) |
| $q_i^s(t), r_i^s(t)$ | RT charging, injection of vehicle $i$ in scenario $s$ (kW) |
| $SOC_i^s(t)$ | State-of-charge of vehicle $i$ in scenario $s$ (kWh) |
| $R_{D,RT}^s(t), R_{U,RT}^s(t)$ | RT depot reserve availability in scenario $s$ down, up (kW) |
| $R_{D,vio}^s(t), R_{U,vio}^s(t)$ | RT violation of cap commitment in scenario $s$ down, up (kW) |
| $D^s(d)$ | Peak demand during period $d$ in scenario $s$ (kW) |

## 2.2 Objective and Constraints

The model objective maximizes revenues from participation in the wholesale frequency regulation market while minimizing real-time charging costs and demand charges.

$$max \sum_{h \in T_H} R_D(h) * p_D(h) + R_U(h) * p_U(h) - \sum_{t \in T_b} \frac{1}{4} P_{Plan}(t) * p_{E,ret}(t) \quad (1a)$$

$$+ \sum_{s \in S} \frac{\omega_s}{60} \left( \sum_{t \in T_m} R_{inj}^s(t) * \left( p_{E,inj}^s(t) - p_{Deg} \right) - \left( R_{ch}^s(t) + dP^s(t) \right) * p_{E,ret}(t) \right) \quad (1b)$$

$$- \sum_{s \in S} \omega_s \left( S_{vio}^s * p_{S,vio} + \sum_{t \in T_H} R_{D,vio}^s(t) * p_{RD,vio}(t) + R_{U,vio}^s(t) * p_{RU,vio}(t) \right) \quad (1c)$$

$$- \sum_{s \in S} \omega_s * \sum_{d \in D} D^s(d) * p_{demand}(d) \quad (1d)$$

In the DA stage, revenue is earned by offering up and down regulation capacity and a baseline charging plan is determined (1a). It is assumed that the depot operates as a price taker, submitting quantity-only capacity offers that optimally respond to deterministic regulation price forecasts and are accepted. In RT, the depot can deviate from baseline charging or discharge to the grid to satisfy regulation dispatch signals each minute (1b). Here we consider the fact that vehicles dispatching up regulation (discharging) can satisfy other depot loads/baseloads (instantaneously reducing metered load is identical to injection in this regard) and in turn further reduce demand charges. The EVs earn the retail energy rate when covering the baseload and the wholesale price for injection that exceeds the baseload ($p_{E,inj}^s(t)$ is governed by unlisted constraints), but also incurs the cost of accelerated aging from increased battery cycling, $p_{deg}$ (1b). For this study, per the California Public Utilities Commission, the EVs/depot participate in the wholesale regulation market, but all energy consumed by the EVs is settled at the local retail rate (DeForest 2018). If DA capacity commitments are unmet or SOC departure targets are violated, penalty charges are incurred (1c). Demand charges are set across one or more demand periods, depending on the specific tariff (1d). Since demand charges are applied once per month, price terms (1a-1c) are all scaled to a one-month basis in the objective.

The charge/discharge decisions of individual vehicles are bound by their battery capacities and charging infrastructure as well as their state-of-charge upon arrival and energy requirements for the next day travel (Eq. 2-5). $P_{RT}^s(t)$ and $R_{reg}^s(t)$ are the RT charging and net regulation of all vehicles, respectively (Eq. 6-7).

$$SOC_i^s(t) = SOC_i^s(t-1) + [q_i^s(t) + r_i^s(t)]/60, t \in T_m, i \in V, s \in S \tag{2}$$
$$SOC_i^s(t_F) = SOC_i^s(t_0) + S_{travel}, \quad t \in T_m, i \in V, s \in S \tag{3}$$
$$-P_{max} \leq q_i^s(t) + r_i^s(t) \leq P_{max}, \quad t \in T_m, i \in V, s \in S \tag{4}$$
$$SOC_{min} \leq SOC_i^s(t) \leq SOC_{max}, \quad t \in T_m, i \in V, s \in S \tag{5}$$
$$P_{RT}^s(t) * \eta = \sum_{i \in V} q_i^s(t), \quad t \in T_m, s \in S \tag{6}$$
$$R_{reg}^s(t) = \sum_{i \in V} r_i^s(t), \quad t \in T_m, s \in S \tag{7}$$

Available regulation capacity is governed by battery SOC, maximum energy capacity, charger capacity, and planned baseline charging level (Eq. 8-11). Per market regulations, the fleet must bid a minimum capacity into the regulation market, $R_{Min}$ (i.e. 100 kW in California, binary constraints not shown for brevity), and is required to maintain the bid capacity over the entire hour in real-time. If the day-ahead commitments are not satisfied by the grid-connected vehicles in RT, the shortfall is acquired on the spot market (for the entire hour) and is reflected as a penalty in the objective ($R_{D,viol}^s$ and $R_{U,viol}^s$).

$$R_{D,RT}^s(t) \leq \sum_{i \in V} SOC_{max} - SOC_i^s(t)) - P_{Plan}^s(t) + R_{D,viol}^s(t_h), \quad t \in T_m, s \in S \tag{8}$$
$$R_{D,RT}^s(t) \leq N_V * P_{max} - P_{Plan}^s(t) + R_{D,viol}^s(t_h), \quad t \in T_m, s \in S \tag{9}$$
$$R_{U,RT}^s(t) \leq \sum_{i \in V}(SOC_i^s(t) - SOC_{min}) + P_{Plan}^s(t) + R_{U,viol}^s(t_h), \quad t \in T_m, s \in S \tag{10}$$
$$R_{U,RT}^s(t) \leq N_V * P_{max} + P_{Plan}^s(t) + R_{U,viol}^s(t_h), \quad t \in T_m, s \in S \tag{11}$$

RT frequency regulation signal response is satisfied through a combination of deviation from the scheduled baseline charging, $R_{chg}^s(t)$, and energy injection into the depot or grid, $R_{inj}^s$ (Eq. 13). When not providing regulation, the fleet can increase its rate of charge in real time, $dP^s(t)$, to meet future capacity commitments and/or SOC targets. Additional constraints govern the signs and distribution of regulation between $R_{chg}^s(t)$ and $R_{inj}^s(t)$.

$$R_{D,RT}^s(t) * f_D^s(t) - R_{U,RT}^s(t) * f_u^s(t) = R_{reg}^s(t), \quad t \in T_m, s \in S \tag{12}$$
$$R_{reg}^s(t) = R_{chg}^s(t) * \eta + R_{inj}^s(t) * (1/\eta), \quad t \in T_m, s \in S \tag{13}$$
$$P_{RT}^s(t) = P_{Plan}^s(t) + dP^s(t), \quad t \in T_m, s \in S \tag{14}$$
$$-P_{Plan}(t) \leq R_{chg}^s(t), \quad t \in T_m, s \in S \tag{15}$$
$$-P_{Plan}(t) \leq dP_{chg}^s(t), \quad t \in T_m, s \in S \tag{16}$$

Finally, for each demand period, containing time steps $d$, peak demand is set as a function of the net load from the depot baseload, charging, and regulation.

$$\max \left(P_{base}(t) + P_{RT}^s(t) + R_{reg}^s(t)\right) \leq D^s(d), \quad t \in d, s \in S \tag{17}$$

### 2.2. Stochastic Signal Data

Coupled frequency regulation signals, $f_D^s(t)$ and $f_U^s(t)$, are uniformly sampled from a set of 500 synthetic 10-hour profiles generated using the SynAS Python module (Gehbauer 2020). The SynAS module was developed using 143 days of CAISO dispatch signals (4 second resolution) for a V2G field demonstration at the Los Angeles Air Force Base. The demo comprised a fleet of bi-directional EVs that bid 100 kW of symmetric regulation into the market. The synthetic profiles are statistically similar to the actual signals.

## 3. Case Study and Results

To demonstrate the model's utility, we compare both regulation opportunities and net charging costs under two commercial electricity tariffs offered by the Pacific Gas & Electric (PG&E) company in California, USA. The "B-20" is a traditional rate offered to customers with peak loads over 500 kW. Customers are billed on the basis of energy consumption and maximum demands across "peak", "part-peak" and "off-peak" periods, each with its own energy cost (Fig. 1a). B-20 demand charges are \$30.06/kW, \$6.13/kW, \$28.04/kW for maximum peak, part-peak, and overall demand. The BEV demand charge is \$1.91/kW for maximum overall demand only. Depot and EV loads are *not* separately metered. Designed to undue cost burdens from brief peaks in charging profiles, the "Business Electric Vehicle" (BEV) rate rolls delivery costs into volumetric energy prices with higher, more aggressive time-of-use rates, resulting in monthly charges more commensurate with overall consumption. Under this rate, EV loads are separately metered. Details of both rates can be found at pge.com/tariffs. While the BEV rate will theoretically always outperform B-20 for standalone fleet charging, we uncover the nuances that emerge when considering corresponding warehouse/depot load profiles.

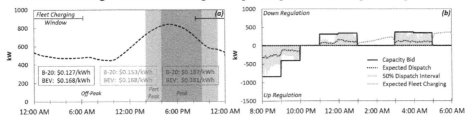

**Figure 1.** Depot baseload profile and time-of-use energy prices for each rate **(a)** Regulation and charging behavior for a 10-truck fleet under B-20 (Case A) **(b)**

We consider electrified delivery trucks charging overnight at an 800,000 square foot shipping depot/warehouse during summer months. The depot's load profile shape and magnitude (Fig. 1a) are informed by publicly available data from the U.S. government's National Renewable Energy Laboratory (NREL) and Energy Star program. The model's energy prices are informed by the PG&E rates and the hourly wholesale regulation prices are the California Independent System Operator's (CAISO) median day-ahead clearing prices for June-September 2022 (Fig. 1a). Capacity and SOC violation costs are tuned to reasonably minimize violations. All trucks are assumed to have 200 kWh batteries and 100 kW DC fast chargers, with 100-mile daily routes (~60 kWh overnight recharging for a 1.75 mi/kWh efficiency). For simplicity, all trucks are assumed to be available for charging/regulation strictly between 8PM and 6AM (based on a 75% vehicle availability threshold using NREL's Fleet DNA data) and weekend activity is not considered. The number of EVs is varied across cases, from 10 to 50 trucks, and both "Smart Charge Only" and "Smart Charge + Regulation" scenarios are considered. The departing truck SOC is left to be optimized for the most profitable regulation capacity. When including regulation, sampling 50 regulation dispatch scenarios was found to sufficiently characterize the distribution. Key results are presented in the Table 1.

We begin our analysis examining the regulation and charging behavior of a 10 EV truck fleet under the B-20 rate (Case A, Fig. 1b). In this case, the EV charging load is small relative to depot load, meaning the fleet can leverage pre-existing peak depot demands. Fig. 1b shows the optimal DA bid profile and expected RT dispatch and charging behaviors. Up regulation is bid in the earliest hours, when prices are at their highest and the EVs still have several hours to regain discharged energy. Likewise, these bids are backed by an optimum departure SOC at full charge. Having to recover discharged energy, down regulation is bid in the hours immediately following, when overnight energy prices are low, and with the last hour left available for additional charging corrections. Notice that existing depot peaks enable fleet charging on the order of 300 kW without incurring increased demand charges. Compared to the "Smart Charging Only" case in Table 1, regulation offers considerable net cost savings (43.4%). In addition to DA capacity revenues, savings are achieved by providing energy to the depot (reducing its overall demand) in early evening hours when retail rates are high. We also appreciate the more realistic (i.e. hedged) bidding behavior that the stochastic data offers. For instance, the expected value of perfect information (EVPI) for Case A is 452.8 – which would yield a 51.5% underestimate of net cost. In contrast to Case A, the fleet in Case B is separately metered (BEV) and thus cannot leverage the depot's baseload peaks, which makes it the inferior option for smart charging alone. Still, the relatively low demand charges enable regulation participation that offers significant savings (63%) and net savings comparable to Case A.

**Table 1.** Scenarios Results for Monthly Fleet Charging Costs

| Case | Fleet Size | Tariff | Smart Charging Only | | Smart Charging + Regulation | | | | | Savings via Regulation |
|---|---|---|---|---|---|---|---|---|---|---|
| | | | Δ Demand Charge ($) | Net Fleet Cost ($) | Δ Demand Charge ($) | RU Bid (MW) | RD Bid (MW) | DA Cap. Revs ($) | Net Fleet Cost ($) | |
| A | 10 | B-20 | 0 | 1551 | 0 | 1.2 | 1.4 | 508.9 | 878 | 43.4% |
| B | 10 | BEV | 136 | 2283 | 217 | 0.9 | 0 | 306.3 | 856 | 63% |
| C | 20 | B-20 | 0 | 3102 | 107 | 2.1 | 0 | 629 | 2265 | 27% |
| D | 20 | BEV | 271 | 4566 | 424 | 1.9 | 0 | 612.6 | 1894 | 59% |
| E | 50 | B-20 | 102 | 8376 | 102 | 0 | 0 | 0 | 8375 | 0% |
| F | 50 | BEV | 677 | 11416 | 1039 | 4.7 | 0 | 1531.5 | 4977 | 56% |
| G (no depot) | 10 | B-20 | 2423 | 4046 | 2423 | 0 | 0 | 0 | 4046 | 0% |

Cases C and D for a 20-truck fleet tell a similar story for only smart charging, but the doubled EV demand forces more conservative bids and therefore fewer net savings under the B-20 rate. We observe, however, that the V2G bids enabled by BEV rate scales linearly, with comparable overall savings due to the low marginal demand charge. We explore this trend up to 50 trucks, at which point no capacity is bid under B-20 due to the increased demand charges. Rather than fleet size, the outcome depends on vehicle loads relative to flexibility from the depot. For example, 10 standalone trucks see no regulation bids under B-20 (Case G) since all marginal demand peaks come at a prohibitive cost.

## 4. Conclusions

A two-stage stochastic model is posed for assessing charging and regulation bid behavior under different tariffs. It is used to demonstrate that the most effective fleet charging strategies and tariffs are not one-size-fits-all, but context dependent. The model is easily adapted to other technologies and scenarios and can readily accommodate additional uncertainties (i.e. vehicle schedules, prices) in future work.

## References

J. Owens et al., 2022. Can vehicle-to-grid facilitate the transition to low carbon energy systems?. Energy Advances, 12.

Y. He et al., 2019. Fast-charging station deployment for battery electric bus systems considering electricity demand charges. Sustainable Cities and Society, 48.

C. Gehbauer et al., 2020. Synthetic CAISO Frequency Regulation Signal, The American Modelica Conference 2020.

N. DeForest et al., 2018. Day ahead optimization of an electric vehicle fleet providing ancillary services in the Los Angeles Air Force Base vehicle-to-grid demonstration, Appl. Energy, 210.

Al-Hanahi, Bassam, et al., 2022. An optimal charging solution for commercial electric vehicles. IEEE Access, 10.

Antonis Kokossis, Michael C. Georgiadis, Efstratios N. Pistikopoulos (Eds.)
PROCEEDINGS OF THE 33rd European Symposium on Computer Aided Process Engineering
(ESCAPE33), June 18-21, 2023, Athens, Greece
© 2023 Elsevier B.V. All rights reserved.  http://dx.doi.org/10.1016/B978-0-443-15274-0.50452-2

# Economic Benefits from Planned Renewable Installations in the US using Hydrogen and Modular Ammonia Production Units

Apoorv Lal, Fengqi You

*Cornell University, Ithaca, New York 14853, USA*

## Abstract

Planned installations for renewable power generation are often associated with significant economic risks for the investors and thus require specific policies, incentives by the government, and risk reduction mechanisms in place. Each installation for renewable power generation has a period before its integration with the grid, which involves initiating and completing regulatory approvals and the construction phase. In the current scenario, a given installation generates no revenue before its commercial operation, even when it can produce power at less than its nameplate capacity. This study has analyzed the possibility of extracting added profits from planned installations which could negate the significant economic risks borne by the investors. Two chemical-based energy storage options, namely hydrogen and ammonia, have been evaluated in this work to harness economic benefits during the installation period of planned renewable energy systems.

**Keywords**: renewable installations, hydrogen, ammonia, modular manufacturing

## 1. Introduction

The substantial dependence on fossil fuels to meet the ever-increasing energy demand is one of the burning questions the world is trying to answer (Kim et al., 2014). Accordingly, many countries incentivize renewable energy production to limit carbon emissions and facilitate the transition toward a more sustainable energy matrix (Tian et al., 2020). Despite the continued efforts by governments to facilitate the development of new facilities for renewable power generation (Sun et al., 2021), significant issues in operations and investment risk management, both pre and post-commercial operations, hinder an accelerated adoption of renewable power (Pistikopoulos et al., 2022). The anticipated expansion of renewable energy capacity is crippled by factors including high capital expenditure and the transient nature of renewable sources of energy (Ajagekar et al., 2022), which are considered two major roadblocks in its contribution to affordable electricity (Zhao et al. 2020). In the current scenario, before the commercial operation, a given installation generates no revenue even when it can produce power at lesser than nameplate capacity. This implies that a significant amount of renewable energy can be hedged into profits. The energy utilization can be localized at the installation sites or with minimal infrastructure to direct the power to the use site. To the best of our knowledge, previous works have not evaluated the possibility of extracting added profits during the installation period of planned renewable energy systems. Therefore, this paper proposes a framework for added profits from planned installations using simultaneous investment in energy storage options, thus, creating incentives for early investment in planned installations in the US. Two scenarios for chemical-based energy storage, namely, hydrogen and ammonia, have been evaluated to harness economic benefits during the installation period of planned renewable energy systems.

## 2. Preliminaries

### 2.1. Electrolyzer and Hydrogen Tank

An electrolyzer (ELE) takes power as input and produces hydrogen. The electrolyzer considered in this study is an alkaline electrolyzer (AWE), a relatively mature and commercially available technology. AWE is capable of producing at large capacities with a life span of around 80,000 hrs (Bhandari and Shah, 2021). In addition to its economic viewpoint (Thomassen et al., 2019), AWE can withstand low current densities, making it flexible, so it can easily accommodate the dynamic nature of electrolyzers (Shams et al., 2021). Hydrogen produced can be stored in a hydrogen tank at high pressures, which comes in various sizes depending on the application.

### 2.2. Ammonia Production

Ammonia is an essential feedstock for fertilizer production, with the global annual demand expected to touch 230 Mt by 2025 (Apodaca, 2022). It is regarded as a potential carrier for "green hydrogen" owing to its higher energy density and easier storage and transport than gaseous hydrogen (Giddey et al., 2017; Hank et al., 2020). Nitrogen required to produce ammonia can be obtained using a cryogenic air separation unit (ASU). The Haber-Bosch (H-B) process can be used to combine the reactants to produce ammonia. This study evaluates ammonia production using an AWE electrolyzer to produce hydrogen and nitrogen from the ASU unit combined in the H-B loop. Modular manufacturing unit specifications for ammonia production are considered in this study.

## 3. Model Formulation

The proposed formulation aims to maximize the profitability for the different scenarios implemented for all the planned renewable installations considered in the study. The profit for different scenarios is defined based on the revenue generated for the entire life of the project and the associated costs during this period. The general equation to calculate the $PROFIT$ for both scenarios can be defined as:

$$MAX(PROFIT) = REVENUE - CAPEX - O\&M - FC + SAL \tag{1}$$

where $REVENUE, CAPEX, O\&M, FC,$ and $SAL$ represent the revenue, total capital expenditure, operation and maintenance, fixed cost, and salvage value for the investment at the end of project life, respectively, for the scenarios considered. The generic form for total revenue for the project can be calculated as the summation of the revenue for the hourly resolution considered in the study, represented as follows:

$$REVENUE = \sum_{t} PRODUCT(t) \tag{2}$$

where $PRODUCT(t)$ represents the revenue generated in different time intervals for the respective scenarios. The following equation can describe the total load balance of the available power:

$$Pavailable(t) = Putilized(t) + Psurplus(t) \tag{3}$$

where $Pavailable(t)$, $Putilized(t)$, and $Psurplus(t)$ represent the available power from planned renewable installation, utilized power, and surplus power at different time intervals, respectively.

### 3.1. Hydrogen scenario

In the case of the hydrogen scenario, a combination of electrolyzer which splits water into hydrogen and oxygen (Zhao and You, 2021b, 2021c), and hydrogen tanks has been used to utilize the available power from the planned installations. The following equation can represent the total balance for the power which has been utilized:

$$Putilized(t) = Pele(t) + Pstorage(t) \tag{4}$$

where $Pele(t)$ and $Pstorage(t)$ refers to the power consumed by the electrolyzer and storing the produced hydrogen. Corresponding to the power which has been utilized in the electrolyzer, the hydrogen produced ($h2ele(t)$) can be calculated as follows (Niaz, Shams, et al., 2022):

$$h2ele(t) = Pele(t) \cdot \eta^{ELE} / LHV \tag{5}$$

where $\eta^{ELE}$ and $LHV$ represent the efficiency of the electrolyzer and the lower heating value for hydrogen in kWh/kg of $H_2$ (Ahmed and Krumpelt, 2001). The power consumed in storing the produced hydrogen depends on the amount produced in the given time interval. Thus, Eq.(6) calculates the storage power based on the hourly data for the hydrogen produced by the electrolyzer (Niaz, Liu, et al., 2022).

$$Pstorage(t) = P^{HTANK} \cdot h2ele(t) \tag{6}$$

where $P^{HTANK}$ is the factor showing the amount of power consumed to store the hydrogen produced. The total capital expenditure is the summation of capital expenditure on electrolyzer and storage units. The total capital expenditure on hydrogen storage can be calculated using a certain percentage of the capital expenditure on the electrolyzer unit (Lal and You, 2022). Based on the total life for the electrolyzer and storage units, the salvage value for both units can be calculated using the double declining depreciation method. The total operating expenditure ($OPEX^{ELE}$) is the summation of the operating cost of the electrolyzer ($O\&M^{ELE}(t)$) for all the time intervals considered in the study, as depicted below (Zhao and You, 2021a):

$$OPEX^{ELE} = \sum_t O \& M^{ELE}(t) \tag{7}$$

The fixed cost for the facility (*FC*) is essentially the fixed cost for the total electrolyzer units in operation, which can be calculated using the number of electrolyzer units, the maximum capacity of each electrolyzer, and the project life.

### 3.2. Ammonia scenario

The ammonia scenario requires power utilization in three main processes, i.e., producing hydrogen using the electrolyzer, generation of nitrogen in ASU, and combining the produced hydrogen and nitrogen in the HB-loop (Cheema and Krewer, 2018; Rouwenhorst et al., 2021). Thus, the total load balance of utilized power can be described using Eq.(8).

$$Putilized(t) = Pasu(t) + Pele(t) + Pmodular(t) \tag{8}$$

where $Pasu(t)$ and $Pmodular(t)$ represents the power consumed in the ASU and modular ammonia manufacturing unit, respectively. The amount of ammonia generated (*NH3(t)*) can be calculated using the power given to the modular manufacturing unit using Eq.(9).

$$NH3(t) = Pmodular(t) \cdot \alpha_{NH3} \tag{9}$$

where $\alpha_{NH3}$ refers to the factor for conversion between the power consumed in the modular unit (Gao and You, 2017). Using similar factors to convert the power consumption to the production rate in the electrolyzer and the ASU (Yang et al., 2018), we can get the amount of hydrogen and nitrogen needed. Now, the distribution of the total consumed power among the electrolyzer, ASU, and manufacturing unit depends on their respective ratios ( $\mu_1^{NH3}$, $\mu_2^{NH3}$, $\mu_3^{NH3}$ ) for the ammonia generation process (Wang et al., 2021).

$$Pele(t) = Putilized(t) \cdot \mu_1^{NH3} \tag{10}$$

$$Pasu(t) = Putilized(t) \cdot \mu_2^{NH3} \tag{11}$$

$$Pmodular(t) = Putilized(t) \cdot \mu_3^{NH3} \tag{12}$$

The total capital expenditure is the summation of capital expenditure on the electrolyzer, ASU, and modular units for ammonia production, which can be obtained using the respective number of units employed. Based on the total life of the equipment used, the salvage value can be calculated using the double-declining depreciation method, similar to the hydrogen scenario. The total operating expenditure for the ammonia scenario ( $O \& M^{NH3}$ ) is the summation of the operating cost of the electrolyzer and the storage cost for the hydrogen and ammonia produced for all the time intervals considered in the study, as depicted below:

$$O\&M^{NH_3} = \sum_t \left( O\&M^{ELE}(t) + O\&M^{HTANK}(t) + O\&M^{NH3TANK}(t) \right) \tag{13}$$

The storage cost for the hydrogen produced ($O\&M^{HTANK}(t)$) by the electrolyzer unit can be calculated based on the hydrogen production in the given interval and the per-unit storage cost. Similarly, the ammonia storage cost ($O\&M^{NH3TANK}(t)$) can be calculated based on the ammonia production in the given interval and the per unit storage cost. The fixed cost for the facility ( $FC$ ) is essentially the fixed cost for the total electrolyzer units in operation, like the hydrogen scenario, which can be calculated using the number of electrolyzer units, the maximum capacity of each electrolyzer, and the project life.

## 4. Results and Discussion
The hydrogen scenario was found to be profitable for the planned renewable installations of most counties considered in the study, with the maximum profit observed for the Texas-Roseland Solar Project and the Texas Atkina Solar project. These cases have a renewable power utilization of around 0.86 with 165 MW of electrolyzers. A scenario can lead to more profit considering the demand for its generated product is higher, which drives up the revenue generated. In contrast to the ammonia scenario, hydrogen has a relatively higher selling price, thus, making its profit margins much higher. It was observed that planned installations with higher nameplate capacity resulted in higher utilization rates. The lowest utilization rate for the hydrogen scenario was 12%. The planned renewable installation in Oregon was the only case that did not result in any profit generation, reflecting it not being an appropriate state due to a lower wind potential. In the case of the ammonia scenario, the planned renewable installations were profitable; however, the profitability in comparison to hydrogen was relatively lower, as depicted in Figure 1. Texas-Roseland Solar Project was found to be a prominently profitable installation for both hydrogen and the ammonia scenario. The most profitable installations in the ammonia scenario had the majority of their utilization ranging from 50%-59%, with only one touching the 70% mark. In contrast to the hydrogen scenario, there is no clear trend of similarity between the profitability and the investment in electrolyzers and ammonia production units. The cost-intensive nature of ASU and H-B units can be attributed to the ammonia scenario being less profitable for the planned installations considered in the study. The project life of the pre-operational planned installation was two years, which is small compared to the normal project life of 30 years for an ammonia production unit, thus aggravating the relatively fewer profit margins for many installations in this scenario.

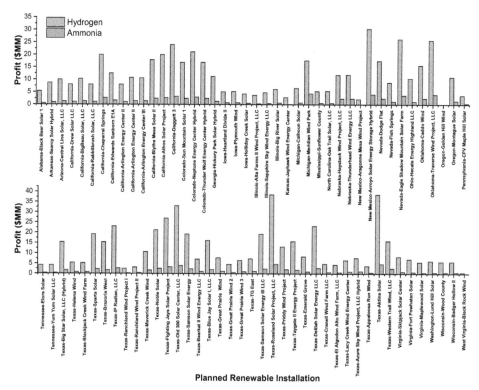

Figure 1. Profit generated from different planned renewable installations based on hydrogen and ammonia scenarios for utilizing the available renewable energy.

## 5. Conclusion

In the current practice, the planned installations for upcoming renewable projects like wind and solar power do not generate any revenue before they are integrated with the grid for commercial operation. This study has examined the potential economic benefits of 83 planned renewable installations in the US before supplying electricity to the grid. It has been analyzed if it can be profitable to operate the planned installations at less than nameplate capacity utilizing two chemical-based energy storage options, namely, hydrogen and ammonia. Results suggest that producing hydrogen using the available renewable power from the planned installations was more profitable due to the higher selling price of the green hydrogen in the market, coupled with the cost-intensive nature of the equipment required to produce ammonia.

## References

S. Ahmed and M. Krumpelt, 2001. Hydrogen from hydrocarbon fuels for fuel cells. International Journal of Hydrogen Energy, 26, 291-301.

A. Ajagekar, F. You, 2022, Quantum computing and quantum artificial intelligence for renewable and sustainable energy: A emerging prospect towards climate neutrality. Renewable & Sustainable Energy Reviews, 165, 112493.

L. Apodaca, 2022. Nitrogen Statistics and Information. https://www.usgs.gov/centers/national-minerals-information-center/nitrogen-statistics-and-information#

R. Bhandari and R. R. Shah, 2021. Hydrogen as energy carrier: Techno-economic assessment of decentralized hydrogen production in Germany. Renewable Energy, 177, 915-931.

I. I. Cheema and U. Krewer, 2018. Operating envelope of Haber-Bosch process design for power-to-ammonia. RSC Adv, 8, 34926-34936.

J. Gao, F. You, 2017, Can Modular Manufacturing Be the Next Game-Changer in Shale Gas Supply Chain Design and Operations for Economic and Environmental Sustainability? ACS Sustainable Chemistry & Engineering, 5, 10046-10071.

S. Giddey, S. P. S. Badwal, C. Munnings, and M. Dolan, 2017. Ammonia as a Renewable Energy Transportation Media. ACS Sustainable Chemistry & Engineering, 5, 10231-10239.

J. Gong, F. You, 2015, Sustainable design and synthesis of energy systems. Current Opinion in Chemical Engineering, 10, 77-86.

C. Hank, A. Sternberg, et al., 2020. Energy efficiency and economic assessment of imported energy carriers based on renewable electricity. Sustainable Energy & Fuels, 4, 2256-2273.

K. T. Kim, D.J. Lee, and S.J. Park, 2014. Evaluation of R&D investments in wind power in Korea using real option. Renewable and Sustainable Energy Reviews, 40, 335-347.

A. Lal and F. You, 2022. Targeting climate-neutral hydrogen production: Integrating brown and blue pathways with green hydrogen infrastructure via a novel superstructure and simulation-based life cycle optimization. AIChE Journal, 69, e17956.

H. Niaz, J. J. Liu, et al., 2022. Can Texas mitigate wind and solar curtailments by leveraging bitcoin mining? Journal of Cleaner Production, 364, 132700.

H. Niaz, M. Shams, et al., 2022. Mining Bitcoins with Carbon Capture and Renewable Energy for Carbon Neutrality Across States in the USA. Energy & Environmental Science, 15, 3551-3570.

E.N. Pistikopoulos, A. Barbosa-Povoa, J.H. Lee, et al., 2021, Process systems engineering – The generation next? Computers & Chemical Engineering, 147, 107252.

K. H. Rouwenhorst, A. G. Van der Ham, and L. Lefferts, 2021. Beyond Haber-Bosch: the renaissance of the Claude process. International Journal of Hydrogen Energy, 46, 21566-21579.

M. H. Shams, H. Niaz, J. Na, A. Anvari-Moghaddam, and J. J. Liu, 2021. Machine learning-based utilization of renewable power curtailments under uncertainty by planning of hydrogen systems and battery storages. Journal of Energy Storage, 41, 103010.

L. Sun, F. You, 2021, Machine Learning and Data-Driven Techniques for the Control of Smart Power Generation Systems: An Uncertainty Handling Perspective. Engineering, 7, 1239-1247.

X. Tian, T. Meyer, H. Lee, et al., 2020. Sustainable design of geothermal energy systems for electric power generation using life cycle optimization. AIChE Journal, 66, e16898.

G. Thomassen, M. Van Dael, S. Van Passel, et al., 2019, How to assess the potential of emerging green technologies? Towards a prospective environmental and techno-economic assessment framework. Green Chemistry, 21, 4868-4886.

M. Wang, M. A. Khan, et al., 2021. Can sustainable ammonia synthesis pathways compete with fossil-fuel based Haber–Bosch processes? Energy & Environmental Science, 14, 2535-2548.

M. Yang, F. You, 2018, Modular methanol manufacturing from shale gas: Techno-economic and environmental analyses of conventional large-scale production versus small-scale distributed, modular processing. AIChE Journal, 64, 495-510.

N. Zhao, F. You, 2020, Can renewable generation, energy storage and energy efficient technologies enable carbon neutral energy transition? Applied Energy, 279, 115889.

X. Zhao and F. You, 2021. Consequential Life Cycle Assessment and Optimization of High-Density Polyethylene Plastic Waste Chemical Recycling. ACS Sustainable Chemistry & Engineering, 9, 12167-12184.

X. Zhao and F. You, 2021. Waste respirator processing system for public health protection and climate change mitigation under COVID-19 pandemic: Novel process design and energy, environmental, and techno-economic perspectives. Applied Energy, 283, 116129.

X. Zhao and F. You, 2021. Waste high-density polyethylene recycling process systems for mitigating plastic pollution through a sustainable design and synthesis paradigm. AIChE Journal, 67, e17127.

Antonis Kokossis, Michael C. Georgiadis, Efstratios N. Pistikopoulos (Eds.)
PROCEEDINGS OF THE 33rd European Symposium on Computer Aided Process Engineering
(ESCAPE33), June 18-21, 2023, Athens, Greece
© 2023 Elsevier B.V. All rights reserved.  http://dx.doi.org/10.1016/B978-0-443-15274-0.50453-4

# Data-Driven Robust Model Predictive Control on Building Climate Control with Renewable Energy

Wei-Han Chen, Fengqi You

*Cornell University, Ithaca, New York, 14853, USA*

## Abstract

In this work, we propose a data-driven robust model predictive control (DDRMPC) framework to address building climate control with renewable hybrid energy systems under weather forecast uncertainty. The control and energy system configurations include heating, ventilation, and air conditioning, geothermal heat pump, photovoltaic panel, and electricity storage battery. Historical weather forecast and measurement data are gathered from weather station to identify the forecast errors and for the use of uncertainty set construction. The data-driven uncertainty sets are constructed with multiple machine learning techniques, including principal component analysis with kernel density estimation, K-Means clustering, density based spatial clustering of applications with noise, and Dirichlet process mixture model. Lastly, a data-driven robust optimization problem is developed to obtain the optimal control inputs for a building with renewable energy systems. A case study on controlling a building with renewable energy located on the Cornell campus is used to demonstrate the advantages of the proposed framework.

**Keywords**: building climate control, data-driven robust MPC, renewable energy systems.

## 1. Introduction

While the implementation of renewable energy systems and model predictive control (MPC) could reduce the non-renewable energy consumption (Killian and Kozek, 2016), one challenge to building climate control using MPC is the weather forecast uncertainty. A deterministic predictive control framework to regulate the climate of a sustainable building using hybrid energy systems has been developed (Chen and You, 2022). However, thermal comfort would violate the constraints if uncertainties in weather forecasts are not effectively accounted for. Robust MPC (RMPC) could protect the system states from violating the constraints (Yang et al., 2019). Although RMPC could protect the indoor climate from becoming uncomfortable to occupants, it may lead to over-conservative results. To reduce the conservatism of RMPC, data-driven RMPC (DDRMPC) is a popular approach that adopts machine learning techniques or statistical hypothesis tests to construct uncertainty sets that capture high-density regions of the uncertain forecast errors from historical weather data (Shang and You, 2019). Therefore, DDRMPC is an appropriate approach to ensure building climate by taking account of uncertainties within weather forecast errors.

## 2. Building Climate Dynamic Model and RMPC Framework

The overview of the DDRMPC framework for building climate control with the adoption of renewable energy systems is presented in Fig. 1. Temperature, humidity, and predicted mean vote index are the controlled variables in this control framework. The predicted mean vote index, which is derived from temperature, humidity, and other indoor factors, is regulated to ensure the occupants' thermal comfort. The renewable energy systems adopted in this work include ground source heat pumps, photovoltaic panels, and battery energy storage.

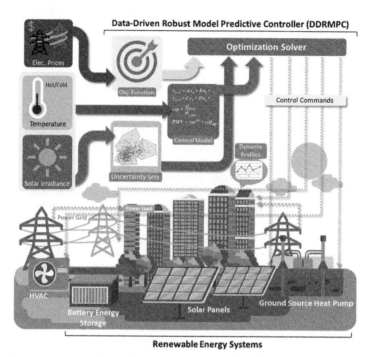

Figure 1. The overview of data-driven robust model predictive control framework for building climate control utilizing renewable energy sources considering weather forecast uncertainties and dynamic pricing.

The most important factor for thermal comfort is indoor temperature. A dynamic temperature model is needed for the DDRMPC to predict future temperatures (Hu and You, 2022). A popular approach to constructing a building dynamic temperature model is to take building components analogous to resistances and capacitances within an electric circuit. The dynamic temperature model for a multi-zone building is generated through Building Resistance-Capacitance Modeling (BRCM) Toolbox in this work (Sturzenegger et al., 2016). The dynamic temperature model for a multi-zone building generated by BRCM is based on the building materials, structures, and geometry.

Another important factor in building climate relating to thermal comfort is humidity. The dynamic model for absolute humidity can first be developed using the mass balance equation on water. The equation considering the water amount through ventilation, respiration, and control actuators is given as,

$$\rho V \frac{dh_i}{dt} = m_{vent} + m_{res} + m_{hum} \tag{1}$$

where $h_i$ denotes absolute humidity, $m_{vent}$ represents the ventilation, $m_{res}$ is the occupant respiration, and $m_{hum}$ denotes the net flow of control actuators for humidity.

Many studies on building energy control only measure thermal discomforts for occupants by the difference between the set point temperature and the room temperature, where other factors that would affect thermal comfort (e.g., humidity, wind speed, occupant's activity level) are neglected. To address this issue, the predicted mean vote index is adopted in this work to better measure the thermal comfort of the occupants (Enescu, 2017). The predicted mean vote index is estimated by temperature, humidity, clothing, action level of occupants, airspeed, and mean radiant temperature (Yang et al., 2018),

$$PMV = (ae^{bM} + c)Q_{diff} \tag{2}$$

where $Q_{diff}$ is the net heat of the occupant's body; $M$ is the occupant's metabolic rate (Yang et al., 2022). The dynamic models are first linearized, and the linearized state-space model for building energy control can be expressed in a compact form with the prediction horizon $H$,

$$\mathbf{x} = \mathbf{A}x_0 + \mathbf{B}_u\mathbf{u} + \mathbf{B}_v\mathbf{v} + \mathbf{B}_w\mathbf{w} \tag{3}$$

where $\mathbf{A}$, $\mathbf{B}_u$, $\mathbf{B}_v$, and $\mathbf{B}_w$ are the system matrices with the size according to prediction horizon $H$. $\mathbf{x}$, $\mathbf{u}$, $\mathbf{v}$, and $\mathbf{w}$ are the sequence vectors of the system state, control input, weather forecasts that are known a priori, and disturbances from forecast errors.

The uncertain disturbances in this work are weather forecast errors. Since weather forecast errors have a disjoint structure, clustering the data has been proven helpful and could be adopted (Zhao and You, 2022). One effective clustering technique is K-means clustering. The forecast errors of temperature, humidity, and solar radiation are first clustered by K-means clustering. Principal component analysis with density estimation (PCADE), which can capture the shape of weather forecast error distributions, is then adopted to construct the data-driven uncertainty sets (Chen and You, 2021). The PCADE-based data-driven uncertainty set for weather forecast errors is given by,

$$D^{PCADE} = \left\{ \mathbf{w} \left| \begin{array}{l} \mathbf{w} = \boldsymbol{\mu}_0 + \mathbf{P}\boldsymbol{\eta}, \; \boldsymbol{\eta} = \overline{\boldsymbol{\eta}}z^+ + \underline{\boldsymbol{\eta}}z^- \\ z^+ + z^- \leq \mathbf{1}, \; 0 \leq z^+, z^- \leq \mathbf{1}, \; \mathbf{1}^T\left(z^+ + z^-\right) \leq \boldsymbol{\phi} \\ \underline{\boldsymbol{\eta}} = \left[\hat{F}_{KDE}^{(1)-1}(\alpha), ..., \hat{F}_{KDE}^{(m)-1}(\alpha)\right]^T \\ \overline{\boldsymbol{\eta}} = \left[\hat{F}_{KDE}^{(1)-1}(1-\alpha), ..., \hat{F}_{KDE}^{(m)-1}(1-\alpha)\right]^T \end{array} \right. \right\} \tag{4}$$

Another popular machine learning approach, Dirichlet process (DP) mixture model, has gained interest in density estimation and clustering (Ning and You, 2019). The DP mixture model approach has the advantage of systematically determining the number of clusters without specifying by users in advance. The data-driven uncertainty set constructed by DP mixture model with a variational inference algorithm is shown as,

$$D^{DPMM} = \left\{ \mathbf{w} \left| \mathbf{w} = \boldsymbol{\mu} + s\boldsymbol{\psi}^{1/2}\boldsymbol{\Lambda}\mathbf{z}, \; \|\mathbf{z}\|_\infty \leq 1, \|\mathbf{z}\|_1 \leq \boldsymbol{\phi} \right. \right\} \tag{5}$$

The DDRMPC adopts the affine disturbance feedback policy to obtain the optimal control inputs. However, the problem might be infeasible. The feasibility issue can be handled by softening the system state constraints (Lu et al., 2020). The control input constraints should remain hard constraints as the control input cannot surpass the designed limit. The objective function of this work is a linear cost function formulated by the dynamic electricity pricing and the consumption of the actuators. The goal is to minimize the total electricity costs. The soft-constrained data-driven robust optimization problem is presented as,

$$\min_{\mathbf{M},\mathbf{h},\boldsymbol{\varepsilon}} \mathbf{cc}^T\mathbf{h} + \boldsymbol{\varepsilon}^T\mathbf{S}\boldsymbol{\varepsilon}$$

$$\text{s.t. } \mathbf{G}_x\left[\mathbf{A}x_0 + \mathbf{B}_u\mathbf{h} + \mathbf{B}_v\mathbf{v} + (\mathbf{B}_u\mathbf{M} + \mathbf{B}_w)\mathbf{w}\right] \leq \mathbf{g}_x + \boldsymbol{\varepsilon}, \forall \mathbf{w} \in D \tag{6}$$

$$\mathbf{G}_u\left[\mathbf{M}\mathbf{w} + \mathbf{h}\right] \leq \mathbf{g}_u, \forall \mathbf{w} \in D$$

$$\boldsymbol{\varepsilon} \geq 0$$

where **cc** denotes the electricity costs of the actuators. **S** and **ε** are the matrix of penalty weight and the vector of slack variable added to soften the problem.

## 3. Case Study on a Campus Building Adopting Renewable Energy Systems

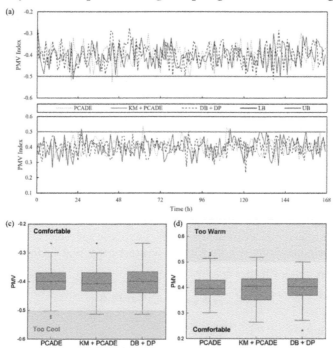

Figure 2. Predicted mean vote index profiles under clustering-based robust MPC comparing three uncertainty sets, including PCADE, K-means followed by PCADE, and DBSCAN followed by DP mixture model, in (a) winter and (b) summer. Box charts that show the maximum, 75th quantile, median, 25th quantile, and minimum of predicted mean vote index with three different data-driven sets in (c) winter and (d) summer.

**Table 1.** Control Performance of DDRMPC with data-driven uncertainty sets using PCA with KDE, K-means followed by PCA with KDE, DBSCAN, and by DPMM.

|                        | PCA-KDE | KM + PCA-KDE | DB + DPMM |
|------------------------|---------|--------------|-----------|
| Electricity cost ($)   | 20,016  | 18,914       | 18,629    |
| Savings                | -       | -5.5%        | -6.9%     |
| Violation percentage   | 0.36%   | 0.32%        | 0.34%     |

We consider a multi-zone campus building using renewable energy sources at Cornell University in Ithaca, New York, following the proposed DDRMPC framework. Carpenter Hall, which has two stories and multiple zones, is selected as the target building with the goal of decarbonizing the energy systems of the building. The uncertainty sets of weather forecast errors are clustered by different machine learning techniques including PCADE, K-Means clustering, density based spatial clustering of applications with noise (DBSCAN) (Hu and You, 2023), and DP mixture model. Fig. 2(a) and 2(b) show the predicted mean vote index profile of three different approaches, including PCADE, K-

Means coupled with PCADE, and DBSCAN coupled with DP mixture model (Ning and You, 2016) in winter and summer. Fig. 2(c) and 2(d) are the box charts that show the maximum, 75th quantile, median, 25th quantile, and minimum of predicted mean vote index using data-driven robust MPC approach with three different data-driven sets, including PCADE, K-Means coupled with PCADE, and DBSCAN followed by DP mixture model in winter and summer. The constraints of the predicted mean vote index are set to between 0.5 and -0.5. The indoor climate would be cool if the predicted mean vote index is below -0.5 and too warm if the predicted mean vote index is above 0.5. During the winter, heat pumps frequently operate to ensure the indoor climate is warm enough for the occupants. The adoption of geothermal energy could effectively decarbonize building energy. The predicted mean vote index is mostly above -0.5, the lower bound. However, when forecast errors are too large, the predicted mean vote index constraints are occasionally violated. The DBSCAN followed by DP mixture model approach has the least violation among the three approaches. The reason is that the outliers are handled best with the help of the DBSCAN approach.

Table 1 presents the control performances of three approaches, including PCADE, K-means coupled with PCADE, and DBSCAN coupled with DP mixture model in terms of electricity cost, savings compared with the PCDE approach, and violation percentage. Constraint violations occasionally occur due to the slight chances of forecast errors not within the constructed uncertainty sets. While all three approaches avoid the constraint violation most of the time with 0.36% 0.32, and 0.34% of constraint violations under PCADE, K-means coupled with PCADE, and DBSCAN coupled with DP mixture model, respectively, the DBSCAN coupled with DP mixture model approach results in the least electricity cost and PCADE approach ends up the most. The DBSCAN coupled with the DP mixture model approach achieves 6.9% less electricity cost than the PCADE approach. The least electricity cost under similar constraint violation percentages of DBSCAN coupled with the DPMM approach suggests that DBSCAN is able to better capture the shape of uncertainty data and handle the outliers more efficiently.

## 4. Conclusion

In this work, we developed a DDRMPC framework for a multi-zone building with renewable energy systems to address weather forecast uncertainties, reduce electricity costs, and ensure occupants' thermal comfort. Instead of regulating the temperature solely, humidity and predicted mean vote index were also considered to better ensure the occupants' thermal comfort. Machine learning techniques, including DBSCAN and K-means clustering, were first adopted to cluster the weather forecast data. Uncertainty sets of temperature, humidity, and solar radiation forecast errors with a disjunctive structure were then constructed using PCADE and DP mixture model. Finally, a data-driven robust optimization problem was formulated and could be solved to yield the optimal inputs for control actuators at each time step. A year-round simulation case of regulating the temperature, humidity, and predicted mean vote index in a two-story multi-zone campus building in Ithaca, New York was studied to demonstrate the effectiveness of the developed energy optimization framework. The control performances of the uncertainty sets constructed by different machine learning approaches were compared. The proposed DDRMPC framework could effectively minimize the total control cost and ensure the predicted mean vote index within the region. The advantage of DBSCAN coupled with DP mixture model was shown with a smaller constraint violation percentage and less electricity cost than the approach without clustering methods.

# References

W.-H. Chen, F. You, 2021, Smart greenhouse control under harsh climate conditions based on data-driven robust model predictive control with principal component analysis and kernel density estimation, Journal of Process Control, 107, 103-113.

W.-H. Chen, F. You, 2022, Semiclosed Greenhouse Climate Control Under Uncertainty via Machine Learning and Data-Driven Robust Model Predictive Control. Ieee Transactions on Control Systems Technology, 30, 1186-1197.

W.-H. Chen, F. You, 2022, Sustainable building climate control with renewable energy sources using nonlinear model predictive control, Renewable and Sustainable Energy Reviews, 168, 112830.

D. Enescu, 2017, A review of thermal comfort models and indicators for indoor environments, Renewable and Sustainable Energy Reviews, 79, 1353-1379.

G. Hu, F. You, 2022, Renewable energy-powered semi-closed greenhouse for sustainable crop production using model predictive control and machine learning for energy management, Renewable and Sustainable Energy Reviews, 168, 112790.

G. Hu, F. You, 2023, Multi-zone building control with thermal comfort constraints under disjunctive uncertainty using data-driven robust model predictive control. Advances in Applied Energy, 9, 100124.

M. Killian, M. Kozek, 2016, Ten questions concerning model predictive control for energy efficient buildings, Building and Environment, 105, 403-412.

S. Lu, J.H. Lee, et al., 2020, Soft-constrained model predictive control based on data-driven distributionally robust optimization. AIChE Journal, 66, e16546.

C. Ning, F. You, 2017, Data-Driven Adaptive Nested Robust Optimization: General Modeling Framework and Efficient Computational Algorithm for Decision Making Under Uncertainty. AIChE Journal, 63, 3790-3817.

C. Ning, F. You, 2018, Data-driven decision making under uncertainty integrating robust optimization with principal component analysis and kernel smoothing methods. Computers & Chemical Engineering, 112, 190-210.

C. Ning and F. You, 2019, Data-driven adaptive robust unit commitment under wind power uncertainty: A bayesian nonparametric approach, IEEE Transactions on Power Systems, 34, 2409-2418.

C. Ning, F. You, 2019, Optimization under uncertainty in the era of big data and deep learning: When machine learning meets mathematical programming. Computers & Chemical Engineering, 125, 434-448.

C. Shang, F. You, 2019, Data analytics and machine learning for smart process manufacturing: Recent advances and perspectives in the big data era, Engineering, 5, 1010-1016.

C. Shang, F. You, 2019, A data-driven robust optimization approach to scenario-based stochastic model predictive control. Journal of Process Control, 75, 24-39.

D. Sturzenegger, D. Gyalistras, M. Morari and R. S. Smith, 2016, Model predictive climate control of a Swiss office building: Implementation, results, and cost–benefit analysis, IEEE Transactions on Control Systems Technology, 24, 1-12.

S. Yang, M. P. Wan, B. Ng, et al., 2018, A state-space thermal model incorporating humidity and thermal comfort for model predictive control in buildings, Energy and Buildings, 170, 25-39.

S. Y. Yang, M. P. Wan, W. Y. Chen, et al. 2019, An adaptive robust model predictive control for indoor climate optimization and uncertainties handling in buildings, Building and Environment, 163.

S. Yang, H. Oliver Gao, et al., 2022, Model predictive control in phase-change-material-wallboard-enhanced building energy management considering electricity price dynamics. Applied Energy, 326, 120023.

S. Yang, H. Oliver Gao, et al., 2022, Model predictive control for Demand- and Market-Responsive building energy management by leveraging active latent heat storage. Applied Energy, 327, 120054.

N. Zhao, F. You, 2022, Sustainable power systems operations under renewable energy induced disjunctive uncertainties via machine learning-based robust optimization, Renewable and Sustainable Energy Reviews, 161, 112428.

Antonis Kokossis, Michael C. Georgiadis, Efstratios N. Pistikopoulos (Eds.)
PROCEEDINGS OF THE 33rd European Symposium on Computer Aided Process Engineering
(ESCAPE33), June 18-21, 2023, Athens, Greece

# Thermodynamic Modelling and Performance Analysis of Power Plant for Switching from Coal to Biomass

Romuald Coupan,[a,*] Ahmed Baccouche,[a] Pierre Szymanski,[a]

[a]ALBIOMA, Tour Opus 12 – La Défense 9, 77 Esplanade du Général de Gaulle, La Défense F-92914, France

## Abstract

Converting coal plants to biomass is an economical and environmental solution to continue power generation operations with former coal power plants. Indeed, such fuel change allows significant reduction in greenhouse gas emissions. Switching from coal to biomass, impacts however the process operating conditions and it is required to understand how to adjust these parameters. In this work, we present both modelling, calibration, and simulation of the 60 MW twin thermal power plant of Albioma Bois Rouge (ABR) at La Reunion Island (a French overseas territory). The ABR power plant is currently achieving the replacement of coal by biomass, and a detailed process model of ABR is useful to predict the future performances of the plant. The process model is achieved by using Ebsilon® Professional, a computational thermodynamic modelling software. Process simulations allow obtaining the plant performances in terms of boiler efficiency, overall plant energy efficiency, and specific fuel consumption. A comparison of the main process parameters is also discussed for both coal and biomass process operations.

Keywords: Power Plant, Energy Efficiency, Biomass, Process Modelling.

## 1. Introduction

The main goal of the energy transition is to fight against global warming. All energy and industry sectors have thus to address plant conversion in an environmentally responsible manner that ensure minimizing greenhouse gas emissions. Accordingly, fossil fuels are being abandoned in favour of renewable energy sources such as solar, wind, hydraulic, and biomass. The energy transition is country specific. For instance, France has set an ambitious goal of increasing its installed renewable energy capacity by 50% by 2023. Accordingly, Albioma – a French independent renewable energy producer, actor in solar, geothermal and biomass energies with more than 1 GW installed capacity – is currently achieving fuel switch [1] of its main fired thermal power plant assets located in French overseas territories. Albioma has reached 75% of renewable energy in its energy production and is also phasing out coal to 100% by 2025 using sustainable biomass. The fuel substitution aims at maintaining power production with former coal power plants with significant reduction in carbon footprint [2]. About 130 to 420 g-$CO_2$ equivalent per kWh are emitted from biomass power plants whereas 740 to 910 g-$CO_2$ equivalent per kWh are measured from coal power plant.

Biomass energy is one of the ways to produce renewable and low-carbon electricity by mean of thermal power plant. In this latter, biomass is first burned in presence of air comburant to provide heat which allows the generation of high-pressure steam. This steam then drives a turbine to produce work. The rotation of the turbine shaft finally drives an alternator, which generates electricity. In this process, we can distinguish different successive stages in which chemical energy is first converted into thermal energy, then kinetic energy, mechanical energy, and at this end into electric energy.

To achieve such process, a thermal power plant comprises four main subsystems: (i) the boiler section corresponding to the hot source, (ii) the turboalternator section, (iii) the condenser section corresponding to the cold source, and (iv) the so-called balance-of-plant (BOP) where the feed water is set at suitable operating conditions.

In this work, we present both modelling, calibration, and simulation of the 60 MW twin thermal power plant (2 units of 30 MW each) of Albioma Bois Rouge (ABR) at La Reunion Island (a French overseas territory). A detailed process model of ABR is useful to predict the future performances of the plant with only biomass as fuel, especially for different load cases since the island situation imposed the variation of load every hour. Switching from coal to biomass, impacts indeed the process operating conditions. Process simulations allow obtaining the plant performances in terms of boiler efficiency, overall plant energy efficiency, and specific fuel consumption. A comparison of the main process parameters (e.g., steam turbine inlet flowrate, exhaust turbine condenser pressure, outlet flue gas temperature, etc.) is also discussed for both coal and biomass process operations.

## 2. Process Modelling, Calibration and Validation

The ABR process model is achieved by using Ebsilon® Professional, a computational thermodynamic modelling software [3]. The fluids considered in the model are water, steam, flue gas, air, and fuel (i.e., coal and solid matter). Water and steam are considered pure streams. Their thermodynamic properties are given by the revised formulation of 1997 of The International Association for the Properties of Water and Steam (IAPWS-IF97) [4]. The other flue gas, air and fuel are characterized by their composition (see **Table 1**). Low heating value (LHV) is also specified for the fuel. The model is based on a thermodynamic Hirn cycle with steam extraction. Each system of the power plant – boiler, turbine, condenser, pump – is described according to available input design and process data. The model calibration is realized thanks to real coal-based power generation operations.

*Table 1: Fuels parameters.*

| Raw material properties | Coal | Biomass |
|---|---|---|
| Carbon (wt.%) | 67.1 | 25.1 |
| Hydrogen (wt.%) | 3.8 | 1.8 |
| Oxygen (wt.%) | 6.4 | 9.6 |
| Nitrogen (wt.%) | 1.6 | 0.2 |
| Sulfur (wt.%) | 0.6 | 0.1 |
| Chlorine (wt.%) | 0.007 | 0.000 |
| Ash (wt.%) | 12.6 | 1.0 |
| Water (wt.%) | 7.9 | 62.2 |

| LHV (kJ/kg) | 26215 | 7935 |
|---|---|---|

The power plant is modelled by using predefined blocks and objects for each process conditions changes (see **Figure 1**). The steam once produced is discharged in two successive steam turbine blocks (**1** and **2**) both connected to alternator (**3**) and generator blocks (**4**). The gross electric production stream is obtained from the generator block. A medium-pressure (MP) steam extraction from the first turbine block (**1**) feeds three different blocks corresponding to an air preheater (**5**), a heat consumer (**6**) and a thermal deaerator (**7**). The heat consumer block (**6**) is a way to consider the cogeneration mode in which both electricity and heat can be produced. The exhaust steam from the second turbine block (**2**) feeds a condenser block (**8**), where the steam is fully condensed to water and directed to the deaerator (**7**) via a pump block (**9**). The condensation is ensured by mean of circulating cooling water from a cooling tower block (**10**) fed with ambient air. At the deaerator, four streams are thus recovered: (i) the condensed water from the steam turbine condenser, (ii) the MP steam extraction from the turbine, (iii) the condensate water from the air preheater, and (iv) the return condensate water from the heat consumer. The water stream exiting the deaerator is compressed via a pump block (**11**) and is directed to a heat exchanger economizer block (**12**). The economizer allows preheating the water by recovering heat from flue gas. The hot water from economizer can be used in a second air preheater (**13**) before being vaporized and superheated in a steam generator block (**14**). Optionally, an amount of water from the feed water pump (**11**) is used as de-superheating water stream in the steam generator (**14**). This latter is linked to a combustion zone block (**15**) where fuel reacts with the preheated air to provide useful heat. A controller block (**16**) calculates the suitable fuel flowrate to ensure the equalization of heat flux at both combustion zone and steam generator blocks.

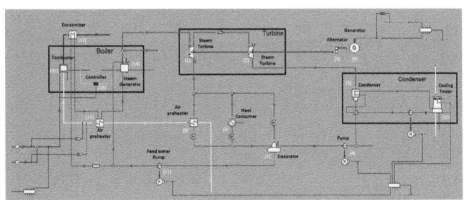

*Figure 1: Ebsilon® process model of the ABR power plant. Flowsheet showing (yellow objects) equipment and process streams: (red line) steam, (blue line) liquid water, (yellow line) air, (brown line) coal or biomass fuel, (green line) work, (pink line) electricity, (black line) logic connection.*

According to the type of blocks or objects, specific parameterizations are performed. Heat exchanger blocks (economizer, air preheater, condenser, heat consumer) are modelled as counter-current flow exchangers and are specified by terminal temperatures (i.e., either cold or hot outlet temperatures). Pump blocks are specified by their suction and discharge pressures. Turbine blocks are characterized by their discharge ratio and isentropic efficiency. For the steam generator, the pressure drops, and the steam specifications are filled. For the combustion zone block, it is specified the exhaust gas temperature, the slag temperature, the air / fuel ratio, the thermal and the combustion efficiency. Note that these combustion parameters are dependent on the fuel input. The main process parameters of the ABR plant are given in **Table 2**.

To calibrate and represent part-load mode (operation at flowrate conditions below the nominal case), specific parameters and characteristic curves are applied to turbine, heat exchanger, and boiler blocks. In non-nominal operating cases, the turbine model follows the Stodola's cone law, and it is applied an isentropic efficiency curves function of either mass flowrate, volume flowrate or pressure discharge ratio [5]. Furthermore, pre-established performance curves of steam turbines can be used. These are the basis of a so-called SCC turbine model developed by Spencer, Cotton, and Cannon in 1962 and revised in 1974. Note that it however exists a limitation for the SCC model where it is not valid for powers lower than 16.5 MW and for turbine bodies with an inlet pressure lower than 1.34 bar [6]. For heat exchangers, a characteristic curve is given to represent heat transfer coefficients function of either cold or hot flowrate. For the boiler, the exhaust flue gas temperature is determined with a characteristic curve function of the air flowrate.

*Table 2: Main process parameters of the ABR power plant.*

| Process specifications | Nominal parameters |
|---|---|
| Gross electric production | 30 MW |
| Steam turbine admission pressure | 81 bara |
| Steam turbine admission temperature | 525°C |
| Turbine exhaust pressure | 0,10 bara |
| Water condenser outlet temperature | 50°C |
| Deaerator pressure | 2.3 bara |
| Fluegas economizer outlet temperature | 150°C |
| Fluegas boiler outlet temperature | 400°C |
| Ambient temperature | 27°C |

From all the used input measurement data, an average uncertainty of 3% is estimated on the output values of the model. Moreover, a validation step is performed to assess the reliability of the simulated performances. To do so, the evolution of a performance index named "specific fuel consumption" (SFC) – corresponding to the equivalent mass of a standard coal required for 1 kWh net electric production – is tracked and compared with real data from the production site. In the range of 5 to 30 MW, it is thus found 2% of deviation between the simulated and the real SFC. Accordingly, this deviation being inferior to the average uncertainty, the model is validated for the corresponding electric production range. Note that the model validation is only done for coal operations according to the data availability. Fuel switch being in progress, the results for biomass are still subject to validation.

## 3. Results and discussions

The model once build, is used to simulate SFC of the power plant for two different fuels: coal and biomass. Switching from coal to biomass, implies some changes in the operating conditions, but also impacts the performances. This modification of operating conditions is considered via the combustion parameters specifications such as the exhaust gas temperature, the air / fuel ratio, and the thermal / combustion efficiency.

The simulated performances are given in term of SFC function of the net electric production (**Figure 2 – a**) and energy efficiency (EE) function of the thermal power input (**Figure 2 – b**). Note that EE is the ratio between the net electric power production and the thermal power input. The SFC of coal is thus found lower than the SFC of the biomass for all the covered range of net electric production. It is observed a difference of about 3% to 6% of SFC from low to high net electric production. The same trend is obtained for EE in the range of thermal power input. The biomass power plant operation is less energy-efficient compared to coal operation. Accordingly, to produce the same amount of electricity than coal operation, more energy is needed with biomass as fuel.

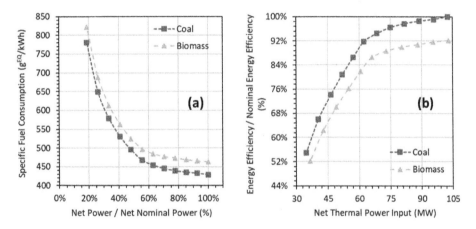

*Figure 2: Simulation of (a) the specific fuel consumption function of the net electric production and (b) the energy efficiency function of the net thermal power input of the ABR power plant: (red) coal, (yellow) biomass.*

Knowing that the turbine, condenser, and BOP sections are not affected by fuel changes, only the boiler efficiency can be pointed out to explain the SFC reduction by switching from coal to biomass. The boiler efficiency is defined as the ratio of the useful heat output to the total energy input. From the simulations in the range of 10 to 30 MW, the boiler efficiencies are calculated at about 92% and 88% for coal and biomass operations respectively. These values are in line with those observed in literature [7]. When the boiler efficiency decreases, more fuel must be burned to reach the steam specifications for the electricity production.

Working with biomass instead of coal, several observations can be done: (i) the air / fuel ratio is higher, leading to dilution of the heat produced; (ii) the thermal and combustion efficiency are lower, mainly due to less carbon content, high moisture content and heterogeneous size of the biomass; and (iii) the exhaust flue gas temperature is higher, as it is correlated to the former coal-fired boiler design. Therefore, the main reason for poorer performance of biomass boiler is the thermal losses and depends on the fuel composition.

The main loss of the boiler being the flue gas losses, a particular attention is generally addressed for heat exchanger economizer design [8-9]. The economizer allows the heat recovery from hot exhaust flue gas to preheat the feed water addressing operating constraints such as: the variation of hot and cold flowrates and temperature profiles, the dust content, the limit temperature on both sides i.e., the flue gas acid dew point and the water vaporization temperature [9].

The biomass composition and particularly its high moisture content, imply a very low LHV. Higher is the moisture content, lower the LHV. Significant effects can thus be expected on the boiler efficiency according to the typical variation of moisture content of biomass with the different sources and seasons. Note that biomass energy density can be improved by mean of a biomass dryer upstream the boiler.

## 4. Conclusion

In this study, coal-to-biomass power plant conversion is assessed by mean of process modelling using the computational thermodynamic modelling software Ebsilon® Professional. Switching from coal to biomass fuels, requires changing the operating conditions, and leads to modifications of the power plant performances. A process model is thus built, calibrate, and validate to simulate the specific fuel consumption of the plant on different load cases. Using this model, the biomass operations is found less energy efficient than coal operations. The boiler efficiency is pointed out with explanations based on the increase of heat losses with biomass as fuel. With these considerations, process intensification strategy will be proposed to improve the efficiency.

From energy efficiency aspect, this analysis does not point to positive considerations for switching from coal to biomass. However, one must remind that the main objective of this fuel substitution is the environmental aspects to continue power generation operations with former coal power plants with significant reduction in greenhouse gas emissions. The carbon footprint of biomass power plants is about 130 to 420 g-$CO_2$ equivalent per kWh compared to coal power plant with about 740 to 910 g-$CO_2$ equivalent per kWh [2].

## References

[1] D. W. Bunn, J. Redondo-Martin, J. I. Muñoz-Hernandez, P. Diaz-Cachinero, **2019**, Analysis of coal conversion to biomass as a transitional technology, *Renewable Energy, 132*, 752 – 760.

[2] Steffen Schlömer (ed.), **2014**, Technology-specific Cost and Performance Parameters, Annex III of Climate Change 2014: Mitigation of Climate Change. Contribution of Working Group III to the Fifth Assessment Report of the Intergovernmental Panel on Climate Change.

[3] P. Madejski, P. Zymełka, **2020**, Calculation methods of steam boiler operation factors under varying operating conditions with the use of computational thermodynamic modeling, *Energy, 197*, 117221 – 117232.

[4] The International Association for the Properties of Water and Steam (IAPWS), **2007**, Revised Release on the IAPWS Industrial Formulation 1997 for the Thermodynamic Properties of Water and Steam, Lucerne, Switzerland.

[5] S. Naderi, M. Banifateme, O. Pourali, A. Behbahaninia, I. MacGill, G. Pignatta, **2020**, Accurate capacity factor calculation of waste-to-energy power plants based on availability analysis and design/off-design performance, *Journal of Cleaner Production, 275*, 123167 – 123170.

[6] R. C. Spencer, K. C. Cotton, C. N. Cannon, **1974**, A method for predicting the performance of steam turbine-generators…16500kW and larger.

[7] Esa Kari Vakkilainen (Ed.), **2017**, 3 – Boiler processes, Steam Generation from Biomass, Butterworth-Heinemann, 57 – 86.

[8] V. D. Stevanovic, M. M. Petrovic, T. Wala, S. Milivojevic, M. Ilic, S. Muszynski, **2019**, Efficiency and power upgrade at the aged lignite-fired power plant by flue gas waste heat utilization: High pressure versus low pressure economizer installation, *Energy, 187*, 115980 – 115992.

[9] G. Miliauskas, E. Puida, R. Poskas, V. Ragaisis, L. Paukstaitis, H. Juhara, L. Mingilaite, **2022**, Experimental investigations of water droplet transient phase changes in flue gas flow in the range of temperatures characteristic of condensing economizer technologies, *Energy, 256*, 124643 – 124655.

Antonis Kokossis, Michael C. Georgiadis, Efstratios N. Pistikopoulos (Eds.)
PROCEEDINGS OF THE 33rd European Symposium on Computer Aided Process Engineering
(ESCAPE33), June 18-21, 2023, Athens, Greece

# Bottleneck-identification methodology and debottlenecking strategy for heat exchanger network with disturbance

Liwen Zhao,[a] Guilian Liu,[a]

[a]School of Chemical Engineering and Technology, Xi'an Jiaotong University, Xi'an, Shaanxi Province, 710049, China

## Abstract

In chemical processes, source/sink parameters of the HEN change due to catalyst deactivation, industrial restructuring, and other reasons. The bottleneck of energy utilization exists and changes with these parameters. A general bottleneck-identification method and the corresponding debottleneck strategy are proposed. Based on topology analysis and algebraic reasoning, feasible Disturbance Response Schemes (DRSs) of the system and load-shift rules of heat exchangers under single-stream heat capacity flowrate disturbance are clarified. Relations among the overall thermal conductance demands, total annualized cost (TAC), and parameter fluctuation are deduced. Corresponding diagrams are constructed to identify the bottleneck, and the TAC is taken as the evaluation index to target the optimal scheme for eliminating the bottlenecks. The proposed method is intuitive and efficient and can guide the design, optimization, or retrofit of chemical processes. A benzene alkylation process is analyzed to illustrate its application.

**Keywords**: heat exchanger network, bottleneck, debottleneck, economy

## 1. Introduction

Along with the process improvement and product/raw material adjustment, the streams related to the reactor and separator will change in composition and flowrate, leading to constant changes in their heat capacity flowrates ($CP$). These streams are generally sources and sinks of the Heat Exchanger Network (HEN) and form multiple heat flow paths with utilities (Smith, 2010). System disturbances transfer along these paths, affecting the utility consumption, the heat load requirements, and the overall thermal conductance demands $(UA)^{req}$ of some heat exchangers. In this process, the $UA$ of some heat exchangers may be insufficient, resulting in bottlenecks restricting energy utilization and even affecting the feasibility of the process. Identifying the locations of these bottlenecks and proposing economic debottleneck strategies is of great significance to the optimization of HENs and stable production of a chemical process.

Towards practical chemical processes with disturbances, approaches and algorithms were proposed for matching heat transfer areas in a multiperiod HEN retrofit (Kang and Liu, 2014), optimizing topology and handling continuous heat load variables (Pavao et al., 2017), and optimizing the placement of the heater/cooler and relocating utilities within HEN (Zamora et al., 2020). These optimization/retrofit methods rely heavily on topology modifications, might result in a long-retrofit duration, and could be impractical. To overcome this disadvantage, heat transfer enhancement technology was deployed in the HEN retrofit (Klemes et al., 2020). However, the heat exchanger's area demand is generally set as a constant to reduce the difficulty in solving, and this conflicts with the actual production condition (Tian et al., 2018) and may lead to unreasonable retrofit. Besides, the best location in which to implement the retrofit and the treatment of downstream effects after the retrofit are left out of consideration.

This paper aims to study the locations of energy bottlenecks under disturbance and propose the corresponding debottlenecking strategy. The disturbance response scheme and the change rules of load-shift and $(UA)^{req}$ will be studied in Section 2. In Section 3, methods are developed for identifying bottlenecks and debottlenecking strategy. A case is investigated in Section 4 to illustrate the proposed method.

## 2. Disturbance response scheme and load-shift rules

For a disturbed stream ($S_D$), variations in flow rate and composition cause its $CP$ changes from $CP^{ini}$ to $\alpha CP^{ini}$, affecting the system's utility consumption. The variations in heating and cooling utilities are related to the position and properties of $S_D$ in the temperature-enthalpy (T-H) diagram and can be determined according to the location rules of sources and sinks (Zhang and Liu, 2017), as shown in Table 1. In this table, $\Delta H$ denotes the enthalpy change of the disturbed stream and can be calculated by Eq. (1); $\Delta H_1$ and $\Delta H_2$ represent the enthalpy change above and below the pinch and equal $(\alpha-1)CP^{ini}(T^S - T^P)$ and $(\alpha-1)CP^{ini}(T^P - T^T)$, respectively.

Table 1 Variation of utilities when $CP$ of $S_D$ changes

| Cases | Disturbed stream | | Variation of utility | |
|-------|------------------|--|----------------------|--|
|       | Position | Property | Heating utility ($\Delta Q_H$) | Cooling utility ($\Delta Q_C$) |
| Case 1 | Above the pinch | Source/sink | $-\Delta H$ | 0 |
| Case 2 | Below the pinch | Source/sink | 0 | $\Delta H$ |
| Case 3 | Across the pinch | Source | $-\Delta H_1$ | $\Delta H_2$ |
| Case 4 | Across the pinch | Sink | $-\Delta H_2$ | $\Delta H_1$ |

$$\Delta H = \Delta H_1 + \Delta H_2 = (\alpha-1)CP^{ini}(T^S - T^P) + (\alpha-1)CP^{ini}(T^P - T^T) \tag{1}$$

Where $T$ is the temperature of $S_D$; superscripts $S$ and $T$ represent the supply and target values; $T^P$ is the average pinch temperature; superscript *ini* denotes the initial value; $\alpha$ represents the fluctuation coefficient of $CP$.

### 2.1. Disturbance response scheme

The heat balance of the disturbed process can be maintained by controlling the flow rate of the cooler or heater's medium, which is defined as a Response Variable (RV). The heater/cooler whose heat duty changes under disturbance is defined as a Response Object (RO) located at the response stream $S_R$. This scheme responding to the disturbance by adjusting the RV is called the Disturbance Response Scheme (DRS). The fewer the ROs, the lower the scheme's operational complexity.

The disturbance propagates through downstream paths, which are uninterrupted and have a mature determination procedure (Zhu et al., 1996). In a DRS, the shortest path connecting $S_D$ and $S_R$ is defined as the Disturbance Propagation Path (DPP). It is worth mentioning that, affected by the topology structure of the HEN, there may be no DPP between $S_D$ and $S_R$. In this case, the RO on $S_R$ and the DRS are invalid.

For the HEN with $n$ heaters and $m$ coolers, if $S_D$ lies above the pinch, there are at most $n$ DRSs. When heater $HE_i$ ($i$=1, 2..., $n$) is taken as the RO, the DRS is recorded as $DRS_i$, and the corresponding disturbance propagation path is marked as $DPP_i$. Similarly, if $S_D$ locates below the pinch and cooler $CE_j$ ($j$=1, 2..., $m$) is set as the RO, the response scheme and propagation path are recorded as $DRS_j$ and $DPP_j$, and there are at most $m$ valid DRSs; if $S_D$ crosses the pinch, the maximum number of possible DRSs is $(n \cdot m)$

since the disturbed system has two ROs, one heater, and one cooler, and the variations of their duties are $\Delta Q_H$ and $\Delta Q_C$, respectively. If $HE_i$ and $CE_j$ are taken as ROs, the control scheme is $DRS'_{i,j}$, corresponding to two disturbance propagation paths, $DPP'_i$ and $DPP'_j$.

### 2.2. Load-shift rules of heat exchangers

With disturbance migration, the duty of heat exchangers on the DPP will change. By referring to the analysis methods proposed by Zhao and Liu (2022), the load variation of each heat exchanger under various disturbance-response cases is investigated, and general load-shift rules of heat exchangers along the DPP are summarized.

If $S_D$ lies above or below the pinch, a DRS has a single RO and DPP. The $K$ heat exchangers in $DPP_i$ or $DPP_j$ are numbered and divided into odd and even groups. Load-shift rules inside and outside the disturbance propagation path are as follows:
(1)  If $K$ is even (odd), the heat load variation of the odd (even) group's heat exchanger is $\Delta Q_H$ or $\Delta Q_C$, and that of the even (odd) group is $-\Delta Q_H$ or $-\Delta Q_C$.
(2)  The heat load of RO changes by $\Delta Q_H$ or $\Delta Q_C$, and that of the heat exchanger outside the path remains unchanged.

For $S_D$ crosses the pinch, a DRS has two ROs and DPPs, and the device's load variation follows the rules introduced above. It is worth noting that if a heat exchanger locates on $DPP'_i$ and $DPP'_j$ simultaneously, its heat load variation equals the superposition of those in two paths.

## 3. Heat transfer bottleneck identification and debottleneck strategy

### 3.1. Changes in the overall thermal conductance of heat exchangers

According to the heat transfer equation shown in Eq. (2), $UA$ needs to be changed to meet the heat transfer requirements of the heat exchanger. However, Eq. (2) cannot determine the dynamic change of the $(UA)^{req}$ under disturbance due to its strong temperature dependence. In this case, the heat transfer efficiency, $\varepsilon$, is introduced. It is the ratio of the heat exchanger's actual heat transfer rate to the maximum value, $Q_{E,\,max}$, and can be transformed into Eq. (3) for a counterflow heat exchanger. Besides, $\varepsilon$ can be expressed by Eq. (4) (Incropera and Dewitt, 1996).

$$Q_E = UA\Delta T_m = UA\left[(T_{hi}-T_{co})-(T_{ho}-T_{ci})\right]/\ln\left[(T_{hi}-T_{co})/(T_{ho}-T_{ci})\right] \qquad (2)$$

$$\varepsilon = Q_E/Q_{E,max} = (Q_E/CP_{min})/(Q_E/CP_{min}+\Delta TE_{min}) \qquad (3)$$

$$\varepsilon = \left|\mathrm{sgn}\left(1-\frac{CP_{min}}{CP_{max}}\right)\right|\frac{CP_{max}-CP_{max}\exp\left[(UA)^{req}(1/CP_{max}-1/CP_{min})\right]}{CP_{max}-CP_{min}\exp\left[(UA)^{req}(1/CP_{max}-1/CP_{min})\right]} + \frac{(UA)^{req}}{(UA)^{req}+CP_{min}} \qquad (4)$$

Where $U$ is the heat transfer coefficient; $A$ indicates the heat exchange area; $\Delta T_m$ denotes the logarithmic mean temperature difference; subscripts $h$ and $c$ denote the hot and cold stream; subscripts $i$ and $o$ indicate the inlet and outlet stream; $CP_{max}$ and $CP_{min}$ indicate the maximum and minimum one between $CP_h$ and $CP_c$; $\Delta TE_{min}$ denotes the minimum temperature difference of a heat exchanger and remains unchanged. $\mathrm{sgn}(x)$ is a sign function, and it equals -1, 0, and 1 when $x$ is less, equal, and greater than 0.

With Eq. (3) and Eq. (4) combined, relations among $(UA)^{req}$, $CP$, and $Q_E$ are deduced, as shown in Eq. (5). According to section 2, $Q_E$ can be described as a function of $\alpha$, i.e., $Q_E=Q(\alpha)=r+q\alpha$, where $r$ and $q$ are constants and can be calculated based on Table 1. In addition, different initial relations between $CP_h$ and $CP_c$ result in different representations of $CP_{max}$ and $CP_{min}$, which will change as the variation of $\alpha$. This leads to four possible initial-disturbed combinations, as shown in Figure 1.

$$(UA)^{req} = \left| \text{sgn}\left( 1 - \frac{CP_{min}}{CP_{max}} \right) \right| \frac{CP_{min} \cdot CP_{max}}{(CP_{min} - CP_{max})} \ln \frac{\Delta TE_{min}}{Q_E / CP_{min} - Q_E/CP_{max} + \Delta TE_{min}} + \frac{Q_E}{\Delta TE_{min}} \quad (5)$$

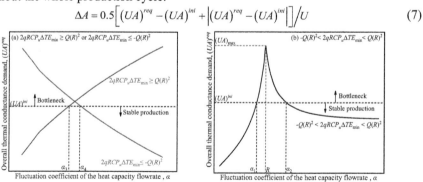

Figure 1 Four initial-disturbed cases and the representation of $CP_{min}$ under different ranges of $\alpha$

The relationship between $(UA)^{req}$ and $\alpha$ is analyzed for each combination based on Eq. (5), and the general correlation is summarized and shown in Eq. (6).

$$(UA)^{req} = \left| \text{sgn}(\alpha - R) \right| \left\{ \frac{\alpha CP_u}{|\alpha - R|} \ln\left[ \frac{|\alpha - R|Q(\alpha)}{\alpha CP_u \Delta TE_{min}} + 1 \right] - \frac{Q(R)}{\Delta TE_{min}} \right\} + \frac{Q(R)}{\Delta TE_{min}} \quad (6)$$

Where $R$ denotes the ratio between the initial $CPs$ of streams $u$ and $v$ and is a constant; $u$ and $v$ represent streams with constant and changing $CP$.

### 3.2. Identification of heat exchange bottleneck and debottleneck strategy

With the monotonicity of $(UA)^{req}$ analyzed, the $(UA)^{req}\sim\alpha$ curve can be constructed, as shown in Figure 2. For an actual process, the curve can be plotted to intuitively illustrate the variation of $(UA)^{req}$ along with the disturbance, find out the bottleneck restricting energy utilization, and lay a foundation for proposing the debottleneck strategy. $(UA)^{req}\leq(UA)^{ini}$ indicates that the designed heat exchanger can meet the heat exchange demand, and there is no need to retrofit this equipment. If $(UA)^{req}>(UA)^{ini}$, the heat exchanger's initial overall thermal conductance is insufficient and cannot meet the heat exchange demand, and it needs to be modified. A common modification strategy is to increase its area, and the area increment ($\Delta A$) can be calculated by Eq. (7) in the case of constant $U$. This figure can also be applied in the design stage to determine the optimal $UA$ of the installed heat exchanger, i.e., $(UA)_{max}$, to satisfy the heat transfer requirements throughout the whole production cycle.

$$\Delta A = 0.5\left[ (UA)^{req} - (UA)^{ini} + \left| (UA)^{req} - (UA)^{ini} \right| \right]/U \quad (7)$$

Figure 2 $(UA)^{req}$ versus $\alpha$ curves

In summary, multiple DRSs exist when the system fluctuates and correspond to different ROs and DPPs. For different DRSs, the system's utility demands are different, as well as the annual operation cost ($Co$). With singe-stream $CP$ disturbance, the change in $Co$ can be expressed by Eq. (8). With the relation between $\Delta Q_H/\Delta Q_C$ and $\alpha$ substituted, the relation between $Co$ and $\alpha$ is determined. Besides, changes in the $(UA)^{req}$ of each heat exchanger lead to variations in the annual investment cost (*Ci*). For HEN containing *X* heat exchangers, the serial number of each heat exchanger is denoted as E*x* (*x*=1, 2…, *X*). On the basis of Eq. (7), *Ci* can be calculated by Eq. (9), consisting of the purchase and the installation costs (Al-Riyami et al., 2001).

$$Co = t_A \left[ p_{HU} \left( \Delta Q_H + Q_H^{ini} \right) + p_{CU} \left( \Delta Q_C + Q_C^{ini} \right) \right] \tag{8}$$

$$Ci = \left\{ a \cdot Y + \sum_{x=1}^{X} 0.5^c b \left[ (UA)_{Ex}^{req} - (UA)_{Ex}^{ini} + \left| (UA)_{Ex}^{req} - (UA)_{Ex}^{ini} \right| \right]^c \middle/ U^c \right\} \middle/ D_P \tag{9}$$

Where $t_A$ is the annual running time, h·year$^{-1}$; $p$ denotes the price of the utility, USD·kJ$^{-1}$; *a*, *b*, and *c* are cost coefficients; *Y* indicates the number of heat exchangers with $(UA)^{req}$ greater than $(UA)^{ini}$; $D_P$ represents the depreciable period of heat exchangers, year.

With Eq. (8) and Eq. (9) superimposed, the relationship between TAC and α can be deduced for each DRS of a disturbed system (with *z* DRSs), and the economic variation diagram can be plotted on this basis. For a given α, the DRS with the smallest TAC should be chosen as the optimal bottleneck-solving strategy.

## 4. Case study

For a simplified alkylation process (Zhao and Liu, 2022), there are one source, three sinks, and five heat exchangers (including two heaters) in the HEN; their initial data are displayed in Figure 3. As the catalyst deactivates, the heat capacity flowrate of the reactor's outlet stream (H1), located above the pinch, changes. In this case, the disturbed system has two DRSs, DRS$_1$ (HE1 and C1 are RO and $S_R$) and DRS$_2$ (HE2 and C2 are RO and $S_R$).

According to Table 1, the cooling utility keeps unchanged while the heating utility changes as $CP_{H1}$ fluctuates and $\Delta Q_H = 4706(1-\alpha)$. Based on load-shift rules deduced in section 2.2, relations between the $Q_E$ and α of each heat exchanger are determined for DRS$_1$ and DRS$_2$, also shown in Figure 3.

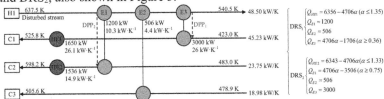

Figure 3 Simplified HEN of the alkylation process from benzene to ethylbenzene

With these initial data substituted into Eqs. (6)~(9), relations among heat exchanger's $(UA)^{req}$, *Co*, *Ci*, TAC, and α can be clarified for DRS$_1$ and DRS$_2$. Based on this, the **$(UA)^{req}$~α curves and the economic variation diagram are plotted, as shown in** Figure 4, **where ΔTAC indicates the difference between TAC$_{DRS1}$ and TAC$_{DRS2}$.**

Figure 4 (a) shows that when α changes to different values, the bottlenecks of the system are different. Besides, different DRS corresponds to different bottlenecks. For example, when α equals 0.75, E1, E2, and HE1 are bottlenecks for DRS$_1$ due to the insufficient *UA*, but for DRS$_2$, E2 and HE2 are bottlenecks; when α varies to 1.33, the bottlenecks of DRS$_1$ and DRS$_2$ are E3 and E1. Affected by this characteristic, the variations of *Ci* and TAC, along with α, are discontinuous, as shown in Figure 4 (b). When α locates in the interval [0.91,1.09], *Ci* is zero, indicating that the initial *UA* of heat exchangers can satisfy the heat exchange demands of the system. According to the ΔTAC~α curve, if α lies in the interval [0.75,0.88], DRS$_2$ should be chosen as the debottleneck strategy since ΔTAC>0. Compared to DRS$_1$, this scheme can save up to 19,400 USD·year$^{-1}$ (point A$_1$). When α

locates at the interval [0.88,1.33], ΔTAC≤0. From an economic point of view, DRS₁
should be selected as the bottleneck-solving strategy and can save up to 24,024 USD·year⁻
¹ (point A₂) compared with DRS₂.

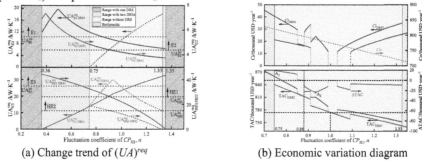

(a) Change trend of $(UA)^{req}$                    (b) Economic variation diagram

Figure 4 Dynamic change diagram of $(UA)^{req}$ and system cost

## 5. Conclusions

Locations of energy bottlenecks under system disturbance are studied with the constraint
of the overall thermal conductance considered, and the corresponding debottlenecking
strategy is proposed. The method can be applied in the design, optimization, or
modification stage to evaluate the system's operational flexibility, determine the energy
bottlenecks, and propose the optimal bottleneck elimination scheme without complex
simulation and calculation. For the studied case, optimal bottleneck elimination schemes
are determined when $\alpha$ is in different intervals. Although the study aims at a single
stream's $CP$ fluctuation, the method can be extended to analyze other critical parameters,
which will be studied in future work.

## References

Al-Riyami BA, Klemes J, Perry S, 2001, Heat integration retrofit analysis of a heat exchanger
     network of a fluid catalytic cracking plant, *Applied Thermal Engineering*, 21, 13/14, 1449.
Incropera FP, Dewitt DP, 1996, Fundamentals of heat and mass transfer, Wiley, New York.
Kang LX, Liu YZ, 2014, Target-oriented methodology on matching heat transfer areas for a
     multiperiod heat exchanger network retrofit, *Industrial & Engineering Chemistry Research*,
     53, 45, 17753-17769.
Klemes JJ, Wang QW, Varbanov PS, Zeng M, Chin HH, Lal NS, Li NQ, Wang BH, Wang XC,
     2020, Heat transfer enhancement, intensification and optimisation in heat exchanger network
     retrofit and operation, *Renewable & Sustainable Energy Reviews*, 120, 109644.
Pavao LV, Costa CBB, Ravagnani M, 2017, Heat exchanger network synthesis without stream
     splits using parallelized and simplified simulated annealing and particle swarm optimization,
     *Chemical Engineering Science*, 158, 96-107.
Smith R, 2010, Chemical process design and integration, Wiley, West Sussex, England.
Tian X, Yin CF, Lv DH, Wang P, Liu GL, 2018, Effect of catalyst deactivation on the energy
     consumption of gasoline-diesel hydrotreating process, *Energy & Fuels*, 32, 10, 10879-10890.
Zamora JM, Hidalgo-Munoz MG, Pedroza-Robles LE, Nunez-Serna RI, 2020, Optimization and
     utilities relocation approach for the improvement of heat exchanger network designs,
     *Chemical Engineering Research & Design*, 156, 209-225.
Zhang D, Liu GL, 2017, Integration of heat exchanger network considering the pressure variation
     of distillation column, *Applied Thermal Engineering*, 116, 777-783.
Zhao LW, Liu GL, 2022, Dynamic coupling of reactor and heat exchanger network considering
     catalyst deactivation, *Energy*, 260, 125161.
Zhu J, Han Z, Rao M, Chuang K, 1996, Identification of heat load loops and downstream paths in
     heat exchanger networks, *The Canadian Journal of Chemical Engineering*, 74, 6, 876-882.

Antonis Kokossis, Michael C. Georgiadis, Efstratios N. Pistikopoulos (Eds.)
PROCEEDINGS OF THE 33rd European Symposium on Computer Aided Process Engineering
(ESCAPE33), June 18-21, 2023, Athens, Greece

# A Power-to-Gas energy system: modeling and operational optimization for seasonal energy supply and storage

Yifan Wang,[a] Luka Bornemann,[a] Christiane Reinert,[a] Niklas von der Aßen[a,*]

[a]Institute of Technical Thermodynamics, RWTH Aachen University, Schinkelstr. 8, 52062 Aachen, Germany

## Abstract

Power-to-Gas (PtG) technologies show high potential as a long-term solution for future energy systems to compensate for seasonal fluctuations in energy demand and renewable energy supply. Despite growing attention to PtG technologies, their modeling is typically simplified during energy system optimization for computational tractability.

This work mathematically describes a power-to-gas energy system for seasonal energy supply and storage (ES$^4$) with great technical and temporal detail based on a real-world pilot PtG ES$^4$. The proposed optimization model is highly transparent and versatile in its adjustability for various applications and solution methodologies.

We use the model to evaluate the operational performance of the PtG ES$^4$, considering energy prices of the German day-ahead markets since the energy crisis in late 2021, and find that 36% of the overall methane consumption comes from PtG technologies. Additionally, the PtG ES$^4$ can achieve net-zero direct greenhouse gas emissions with a cost increase of a factor of 2.3.

**Keywords**: low-carbon, long-term, large-scale MI(N)LP, linearization, decomposition.

## 1. Introduction

Future energy systems typically have a high need for energy storage, specifically long-term energy storage, to account for seasonal fluctuations in energy demand and renewable energy supply. Due to their capability to shift energy on seasonal time scales, Power-to-Gas (PtG) technologies show high potential (Blanco and Faaij, 2018). Through electrolysis and methanation, electricity can be chemically stored for later use, including reconversion to electricity.

In the literature, PtG technologies are receiving increased attention in the community of energy system modelers. Wang and Yuan (2020) build an operational optimization model for integrated electrical and natural-gas systems with PtG. In their work, however, the PtG technologies are modeled with low levels of technical detail and optimized with low temporal resolution. Gabrielli et al. (2018) propose a detailed mixed-integer linear programming (MILP) formulation of PtG technologies to design multi-energy systems with an hourly resolution of an entire year but do not count methanation options in. Zhang and Zhang (2020) present a detailed scheduling model for integrated energy systems, including an electrolyzer, a methanation reactor, and a carbon capture process with carbon dioxide ($CO_2$) storage. Yet, they still use a typical day with an hourly resolution.

The description of seasonal cycles requires a time horizon of one year, while the operation decisions call for hourly resolution (Gabrielli et al., 2018). Still, PtG technologies are often considered with limited technical or temporal detail to balance the model complexity and computational effort.

In this contribution, we mathematically describe a power-to-gas energy system for seasonal energy supply and storage (ES$^4$) with great technical and temporal detail. Firstly, we propose a mixed-integer nonlinear programming (MINLP) formulation for operational optimization. Then, the MINLP problem is automatically linearized. In this way, the mathematical formulation can be well adapted to suit different solution approaches for computational tractability. Finally, we solve the resulting large-scale MILP problems via a decomposition-based method. Section 2 explicates the modeling and optimization of the PtG ES$^4$. Accordingly, in Section 3, we analyze how the economic competitiveness of PtG technologies has evolved since the energy crisis started in late 2021. Section 4 concludes the work.

## 2. Modeling of a Power-to-Gas energy system

### 2.1. Structure of a PtG ES$^4$

Figure 1 shows the structure of a PtG ES$^4$, which aims to fulfill electricity (e-) and heating (h-) demands via energy conversion or purchase from electricity and gas (g-) grids.

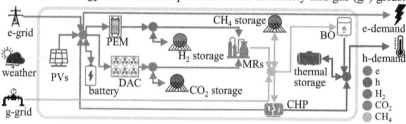

Figure 1: Structure of a PtG ES$^4$.

In total, there are 11 components inside the PtG ES$^4$: Photovoltaic panels (PVs) generate electricity under different weather conditions. The electricity can be used to cover the e-demand directly, be stored in a battery, or be utilized to operate a proton exchange membrane electrolyzer (PEM) and a direct-air-capture plant (DAC). The hydrogen (H$_2$) and CO$_2$ produced by the PEM and the DAC can be fed into methanation reactors (MRs) for methane (CH$_4$) production. Three gas tanks are available to store H$_2$, CO$_2$, and CH$_4$, respectively. Via a boiler (BO) and a combined heat and power system (CHP), CH$_4$ can be burnt to provide the heat (h), which can be used to satisfy the h-demand or be stored in a thermal storage for later use. Another product of the CHP is electricity. Five buses indicate five balance constraints for the product e, h, H$_2$, CO$_2$, and CH$_4$, respectively.

The described PtG ES$^4$ is based on a real-world pilot energy system located in Duisburg, Germany (Leitmarkt Agentur.NRW, 2019). We increase the nominal size of the components ($\dot{E}_i^N$ and $E_i^N$) to allow energy supply and storage on a seasonal scale, as summarized in Table 1. Please note that this work focuses on the components reflected in a real-world energy system. Further decarbonization potentials, such as heat integration and alternative CO$_2$ supply technologies, are outside the scope of this study but can be implemented with ease.

### 2.2. Mathematical description of the PtG ES$^4$

#### 2.2.1. Exogenous inputs

Exogenous inputs encompass all external energy supply and demand: e- and g-grid, weather, e- and h-demand, as shown in Figure 1. They serve as time-dependent input data for the energy system optimization. This work uses an hourly resolution with a time horizon of one year beginning on September 1$^{st}$, 2021, as shown in Figure 2.

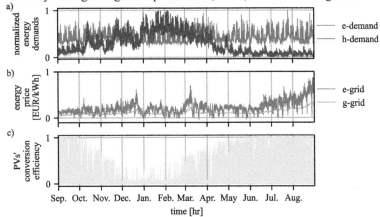

Figure 2: Input time series from September 1, 2021 to August 31, 2022: a) normalized energy demands, b) energy prices $c_{b,t}^{buy}$ (EEX, 2022, SMARD.de, 2022), c) conversion efficiency of the photovoltaic panels (PVs) $\eta_{PVs,t}$ (Perez et al., 1987, Eicker, 2003, Leuchner and Ketzler, 2022).

In our mathematical implementation, $\dot{E}_{b,t}^{D}$ is used to indicate exogenous demands for each product $b$ ($\forall b \in B = \{e, h, H_2, CO_2, CH_4\}$) at every time step $t$ ($\forall t \in T$). Here, $\dot{E}_{e,t}^{D}$ and $\dot{E}_{h,t}^{D}$ are measured data of an office building; $\dot{E}_{H_2,t}^{D}$, $\dot{E}_{CO_2,t}^{D}$ and $\dot{E}_{CH_4,t}^{D}$ equal zero. We take the energy prices from the German day-ahead markets (EEX, 2022, SMARD.de, 2022) as energy buying prices $c_{b,t}^{buy}$, where $\forall b \in B' = \{e, CH_4\}$. We apply the measured weather data from Leuchner and Ketzler (2022), and directly process the data to obtain the conversion efficiency of photovoltaic panels $\eta_{PVs,t}$ (Perez et al., 1987, Eicker, 2003).

### 2.2.2. Conversion components

Conversion components include all components that convert one product to any other product(s) ($\forall i \in I \backslash I^S$), where $I = \{PVs, PEM, DAC, MRs, BO, CHP, battery, thermal storage, H_2 storage, CO_2 storage, CH_4 storage\}$ and $I^S = \{battery, thermal storage, H_2 storage, CO_2 storage, CH_4 storage\}$. We use input-output relationships to model the performance of conversion components in the PtG ES[4]. The main parameters, adapted models and their references are summarized in Table 1 (1a - 1h). $\dot{E}_{i,b,t}^{in}$ and $\dot{E}_{i,b,t}^{out}$ express the input and output of each component $i$ ($\forall i \in I \backslash I^S$) at each time step $t$ ($\forall t \in T$). The index $b \in B$ indicates if there is more than one input-output relationship for the component $i$. $\eta_i^N$ is the nominal conversion efficiency. Besides, the performance of each component is limited by its minimal and maximal part-load fraction $p_i^{min}$ and $p_i^{max}$.

### 2.2.3. Storage components

Storage components transport products from one time step to other time steps ($\forall i \in I^S$). The mathematical description of the five storage components is shown in Table 1 (1i - 1m). The state of charge ($SOC$) of a storage component $i$ ($\forall i \in I^S$) at the time step $t + 1$ depends on its' $SOC_{i,b,t}$, product input $\dot{E}_{i,b,t}^{in}$ and product output $\dot{E}_{i,b,t}^{out}$ at the last time step $t$ considering the efficiency of self-discharge $\eta_i^{self}$, charging $\eta_i^{in}$ and discharging $\eta_i^{out}$, respectively (1i). The so-called cycling constraint ensures that the product is conserved (1j). At the same time, the product input and output flow is limited by the charging and discharging rate $c_i^{in}$, $c_i^{out}$ (1k, 1l). Also, the binary variables $\delta_{i,t}^{in}$ and $\delta_{i,t}^{out}$ prevent the charging and discharging behavior from occurring at the same time step (1m).

Table 1: Mathematical models of components inside the PtG ES[4]: photovoltaic panels (PVs), a proton exchange membrane electrolyzer (PEM), a direct-air-capture plant (DAC), methanation reactors (MRs), a combined heat and power system (CHP), a boiler (BO), and five storage technologies for electricity, heat, $H_2$, $CO_2$ and $CH_4$, respectively.[a]

| $i \in \Gamma^S$ | $E_i^N$ | $E_{i,b,t}^{out}$ | $E_{i,b,t}^{in}$ | $\eta_i^N$ | $p_i^{min}, p_i^{max}$ | Input-output relationship(s) | Ref. |
|---|---|---|---|---|---|---|---|
| PVs | 900 $kW_e$ | e | - | 1 | 0 , 1 | $E_{i,e,t}^{out} \le \eta_{PVs,t}(weather) \cdot E_i^N$ (1a) | Baumgärtner et al. (2020) |
| PEM | 900 $kW_e$ | $H_2$ | e | 0.63 | 0.2 , 1.2 | $E_{i,H_2,t}^{out} = \eta_{i,H_2,t} \cdot E_{i,e,t}^{in}$, with $\eta_{i,H_2,t} = \frac{607.68p^4+1100.79p^3-52.60p^2+1.49p}{1041.50p^4+686.68p^3+10.90p^2-2.33p+0.12}\eta_i^N$, $p = \frac{E_{i,e,t}^{in}}{E_i^N}$ (1b) | Kopp et al. (2017)[b] |
| DAC | 250 $kg_{CO_2}$/hr | $CO_2$ | e | 0.5 $kg_{CO_2}$/$kWh_e$ | 0 , 1 | $E_{i,CO_2,t}^{out} = \eta_i^N \cdot E_{i,e,t}^{in}$ (1c) | Fasihi et al. (2019) |
| MRs | 1500 $kW_{CH_4}$ | $CH_4$ | $H_2$, $CO_2$ | 0.78 | 0 , 1 | $E_{i,CH_4,t}^{out} = \eta_i^N E_{i,H_2,t}^{in}$ (1d); $E_{i,CO_2,t}^{in} = 0.178 E_{i,CH_4,t}^{out}$ (1e) | Gorre et al. (2020) |
| CHP | 800 $kW_h$ | h, e | $CH_4$ | 0.87 (0.47 for h, 0.4 for e) | 0.5 , 1 | $E_{i,h,t}^{out} = \eta_{i,h,t} E_{i,CH_4,t}^{in}$ (1f); $E_{i,e,t}^{out} = \eta_{i,e,t} E_{i,CH_4,t}^{in}$, with $\eta_{i,h,t} = -0.135p^2 + 0.605p$, $\eta_{i,e,t} = -0.12p^2 + 0.52p$, $p = \frac{E_{i,h,t}^{out}}{E_i^N}$ (1g) | Baumgärtner et al. (2020) |
| BO | 500 $kW_h$ | h | $CH_4$ | 0.9 | 0.001 , 1 | $E_{i,h,t}^{out} = \eta_{i,h,t} \cdot E_{i,CH_4,t}^{in}$, with $\eta_{i,h,t} = \frac{84.35p^3-18.34p^2+2.68p}{79.14p^3-10.39p^2-0.79p+0.73}\eta_i^N$, $p = \frac{E_{i,CH_4,t}^{out}}{E_i^N}$ (1h) | Baumgärtner et al. (2020) |

| $i \in \Gamma^S$ | $E_i^N$ | $E_{i,b,t}^{in/out}$ | $\eta_i^{self}$ | $\eta_i^{in} = \eta_i^{out}$ | $c_i^{in} = c_i^{out}$ | Input-output relationship(s) | Ref. |
|---|---|---|---|---|---|---|---|
| battery | 5000 $kWh_e$ | e | 0.000042 1/hr | 0.92 | 0.36 1/hr | $SOC_{i,b,t+1} = SOC_{i,b,t}(1 - \eta_i^{self}\Delta t_t)$ $+ \Delta t_t\left(\eta_i^{in} E_{i,b,t}^{in} - \frac{E_{i,b,t}^{out}}{\eta_i^{out}}\right)$ (1i) | Baumgärtner et al. (2020) |
| thermal storage | 5000 $kWh_h$ | h | 0.005 1/hr | 0.95 | 1 1/hr | $SOC_{i,b,t=1} = SOC_{i,b,t=\|T\|+1}$ (1j) | Baumgärtner et al. (2020) |
| gas tanks[c] | 5000 $kWh_{H_2}$, 5000 $kg_{CO_2}$, 5000 $kWh_{CH_4}$ | $H_2$, $CO_2$, $CH_4$ | 0 1/hr | 1 | 0.25 1/hr | $0 \le E_{i,b,t}^{in} \le \delta_{i,t}^{in} c_i^{in} E_i^N$, $0 \le E_{i,b,t}^{out} \le \delta_{i,t}^{out} c_i^{out} E_i^N$ (1k,1l); $\delta_{i,t}^{in} + \delta_{i,t}^{out} \le 1$ (1m) | Gabrielli et al. (2018) |

[a] Index $H_2$ and $CH_4$ indicate that the value is related to the high heating value of $H_2$ and $CH_4$, respectively.

[b] The model is based on measured data in Kopp et al. (2017).

[c] We assume that the efficiencies, charging and discharging rates of the $CO_2$ and $CH_4$ storage tanks are equal to those of the $H_2$ storage tank.

### 2.3. MINLP formulation of the operational optimization problem

In Eqs. (1), we state the generic operational optimization problem using an MINLP formulation. Given the input time series (Section 2.2.1), technical constraints of each energy system component (Section 2.2.2 and Section 2.2.3) and other limitations (1p), the energy system aims to minimize the operational expenditures (1n) while fulfilling the energy demands at each time step (1o). $\Delta t_t$ denotes the length of each time step $t$. All decision variables are summarized in (1q). The surrogate vectors $x$ and $y$ represent other decision variables that are not specified here, including on/off decisions of components.

$$\min \text{OpEx}^{\text{ES}} = \sum_{t \in T} \Delta t_t (\sum_{b \in B'} (c_{b,t}^{\text{buy}} \dot{E}_{b,t}^{\text{buy}})) \tag{1n}$$

s.t. $\quad \sum_{i \in I} (\dot{E}_{i,b,t}^{\text{out}} - \dot{E}_{i,b,t}^{\text{in}}) + \dot{E}_{b,t}^{\text{buy}} = \dot{E}_{b,t}^{\text{D}} \qquad \forall b \in B, \forall t \in T \tag{1o}$

$\quad h(\dot{E}_{i,t}^{\text{in}}, \dot{E}_{i,t}^{\text{out}}, SOC_{i,b,t}, \delta_{i,t}^{\text{in}}, \delta_{i,t}^{\text{out}}, x, y) \leq 0 \qquad \forall i \in I, \forall b \in B, \forall t \in T \tag{1p}$

$\quad \dot{E}_{i,b,t}^{\text{in}}, \dot{E}_{i,b,t}^{\text{out}} \in \mathbb{R}^+; 0 \leq SOC_{i,b,t} \leq E_i^{\text{N}}; \delta_{i,t}^{\text{in}}, \delta_{i,t}^{\text{out}} \in \{0,1\}; \qquad \forall i \in I, \forall b \in B, \forall t \in T \tag{1q}$
$\quad x \in \mathbb{R}^{N_x}; y \in \{0,1\}^{N_y}$

### 2.4. Implementation and Solution

We model the PtG ES[4] on the COMANDO platform (Langiu et al., 2021). The MINLP formulation is transformed into an MILP formulation via the COMANDO built-in linearization function. We implement a decomposition-based method (Baumgärtner et al., 2020) to solve the resulting large-scale MILP problem with an optimality gap of 2 %.

We assess the PtG ES[4] from an economical and environmental perspective using two scenarios: with (1) and without (2) exogenous methane supply.

## 3. Results and discussion

Figure 3 illustrates the resulting operational performance of the PtG ES[4] of Scenario 1. The left side shows the energy consumption from the grids and the part-load fraction of the PtG components. At the beginning and end of the time horizon, where sufficient electricity of PVs is available, PtG components are operated frequently. In particular, after $t = 7000$ hr (around April 8th, 2022), when energy prices increase dramatically, gas supply via PtG dominates. Overall, 36% of the total gas supply is from PtG components.

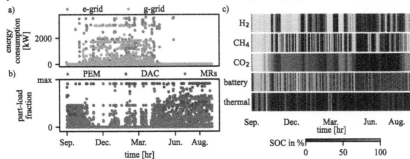

Figure 3: Operational performance: a) energy consumption from electricity and gas grid; b) part-load fraction of PtG components; c) state of charge (SOC) behavior of all storage components.

The right side shows the SOC behavior of storage components. Gas storage tanks perform as expected on large time scales. The battery is preferred over thermal storage systems. In our analysis, the current energy crisis makes PtG technologies economically viable. Please note that this work focuses on the operation of an existing energy system and thus does not consider capital costs.

The optimal operational performance in Scenario 2 shows a similar pattern to Scenario 1. As the exogenous energy supply is solely from PVs and the e-grid, the PtG $ES^4$ achieves net-zero direct greenhouse gas emissions; however, the cost increases by a factor of 2.3. Each computation involved in this work includes over 890 000 variables and 1 000 000 constraints after linearization. The computational time varies between 30 minutes to 2 hours depending on the configuration.

## 4. Conclusions

PtG technologies are promising candidates for seasonal energy supply and storage for future energy systems. However, due to seasonal fluctuations, optimizing the operation of a PtG $ES^4$ is computationally challenging. We introduce a modeling and optimization approach based on a real-world PtG $ES^4$. The proposed model involves large-scale operational decisions with great technical and temporal detail. Meanwhile, the resulting operational problems remain computationally tractable.

Considering the energy crisis since late 2021, we find that the natural gas supply from PtG has become economically competitive due to the dramatic increase in energy prices. We also show that a net-zero direct greenhouse gas emissions energy system is possible with a cost increase by a factor of 2.3. Overall, we expect our modeling and operational optimization approach to be transferable to other cases with different exogenous inputs.

## Acknowledgments

This study is funded by the 'Europäischer Fonds für regionale Entwicklung (EFRE)' (EFRE-0801844). The support is gratefully acknowledged.

## References

N. Baumgärtner, D. Shu, B. Bahl, M. Hennen, D.E. Hollermann, A. Bardow, 2020, DeLoop: Decomposition-based Long-term operational optimization of energy systems with time-coupling constraints, Energy, vol. 198, 4, p. 117272

H. Blanco, A. Faaij, 2018, A review at the role of storage in energy systems with a focus on Power to Gas and long-term storage, Renewable and Sustainable Energy Reviews, vol. 81, p. 1049

EEX, 2022, Natural Gas Day Ahead Market data: GASPOOL and THE, https://www.eex.com/en/market-data/natural-gas/spot. Accessed 2022.10.13

U. Eicker, 2003, Solar technologies for buildings. John Wiley & Sons

M. Fasihi, O. Efimova, C. Breyer, 2019, Techno-economic assessment of CO2 direct air capture plants, Journal of Cleaner Production, vol. 224, 3, p. 957

P. Gabrielli, M. Gazzani, E. Martelli, M. Mazzotti, 2018, Optimal design of multi-energy systems with seasonal storage, Applied Energy, vol. 219, 7, p. 408

J. Gorre, F. Ruoss, H. Karjunen, J. Schaffert, T. Tynjälä, 2020, Cost benefits of optimizing hydrogen storage and methanation capacities for Power-to-Gas plants in dynamic operation, Applied Energy, vol. 257, 1–2, p. 113967

M. Kopp, D. Coleman, C. Stiller, K. Scheffer, J. Aichinger, B. Scheppat, 2017, Energiepark Mainz: Technical and economic analysis of the worldwide largest Power-to-Gas plant with PEM electrolysis, International Journal of Hydrogen Energy, vol. 42, 19, p. 13311

M. Langiu, D.Y. Shu, F.J. Baader, D. Hering, U. Bau, A. Xhonneux, D. Müller, A. Bardow, A. Mitsos, M. Dahmen, 2021, COMANDO: A Next-Generation Open-Source Framework for Energy Systems Optimization, Computers & Chemical Engineering, vol. 152, 11, p. 107366

Leitmarkt Agentur.NRW, 2019, Projekt PtG-MSE: Power to Gas-Modellvorhaben für sektorübergreifende Energiesysteme, https://www.leitmarktagentur.nrw/lw_resource/datapool/_items/item_763/pdb_kesw-1-2-006.pdf. Accessed 2020 -10-15

M. Leuchner, G. Ketzler, 2022, Klimamessstation Aachen-Hörn - Monatsbericht 2021-2022. RWTH Aachen University. Department of Geography. Physical Geography and Climatology Group. ISSN 1861-3993

R. Perez, R. Seals, P. Ineichen, R. Stewart, D. Menicucci, 1987, A new simplified version of the perez diffuse irradiance model for tilted surfaces, Solar Energy, vol. 39, 3, p. 221

SMARD.de, 2022, Strommarkt, https://www.smard.de/home/downloadcenter/download-marktdaten. Accessed 2022.09.01

S. Wang, S. Yuan, 2020, Interval optimization for integrated electrical and natural-gas systems with power to gas considering uncertainties, International Journal of Electrical Power & Energy Systems, vol. 119, 1, p. 105906

X. Zhang, Y. Zhang, 2020, Environment-friendly and economical scheduling optimization for integrated energy system considering power-to-gas technology and carbon capture power plant, Journal of Cleaner Production, vol. 276, 3, p. 123348

Antonis Kokossis, Michael C. Georgiadis, Efstratios N. Pistikopoulos (Eds.)
PROCEEDINGS OF THE 33rd European Symposium on Computer Aided Process Engineering
(ESCAPE33), June 18-21, 2023, Athens, Greece

# Liquid organic hydrogen carriers (LOHC) as a solution for the energy transition: a reactor design assessment

Carlos Prieto[a], Antonio Sánchez[a], Mariano Martín[a]

[a]*Department of Chemical Engineering, University of Salamanca, Salamanca, 37003, Spain*

## Abstract

Liquid organic hydrogen carriers (LOHCs) use for green hydrogen storage has become a promising option for an effective decarbonization. The core of the process relies on the hydrogenation/dehydrogenation reaction, therefore rigorous reactor models are required. In this work, slurry and trickle bed reactors are modelled for LOHCs hydrogenation/dehydrogenation. Kinetic models as well as mass, energy, and momentum transfer are considered. The influence of operational variables was evaluated jointly with design parameters. The benefits and limitations of each design were highlighted discovering in some cases the presence of two regions: mass controlling and a second where kinetic begins to contribute. For dehydrogenation reactors, the main barrier is the high endothermicity of the reaction limiting the kinetic step of the entire process.

**Keywords**: energy storage, energy carriers, green hydrogen, LOHC, reactor design.

## 1. Introduction

The introduction of renewable resources is essential to decarbonize the energy system which, including transportation, is responsible for around 2/3 of global greenhouse gas emissions. As a result, deployment of renewables will play an important role in the sustainable energy transition. The two most important renewable sources in the near future are expected to be wind and solar. Nevertheless, both are highly fluctuating, which unavoidably introduces a new challenge in a system with high penetration of renewables. Therefore, to achieve an effective decarbonization, the use of energy storage systems and energy carriers is mandatory.

At this point, green hydrogen emerges as one of the most important actors in the new energy system. This energy carrier can be used efficiently to decarbonize different energy demands that are hard to directly electrify, for example, heavy or maritime transport. In addition, hydrogen is also proposed as an energy storage system on a seasonal horizon. A major barrier is the difficulties regarding hydrogen storage and transportation as it is one of the lightest chemicals with a low volumetric energy density. To overcome these issues, different hydrogen storage technologies are available. Some of them are conventional such as high pressure or liquified hydrogen, although there also exist other arising options as metal hydrides or metal organic frameworks. Among the novel alternatives, liquid organic hydrogen carriers (LOHCs) are emerging as a promising option. The idea behind LOHCs is to hydrogenate a liquid chemical to improve the storage and transportation of hydrogen. Then, when hydrogen is required, the liquid is dehydrogenated. The main advantages of LOHCs are the reaction reversibility, moderate reaction temperatures, commercial availability of LOHCs, and compatibility with the existing oil infrastructure

(He et al., 2015). Different LOHCs have been proposed such as n-ethylcarbazole or dibenzyltoluene looking for the ideal one with good manageability at liquid conditions, reduced cost, safety, and non-toxicity (Niermann et al., 2021).

Different research works have investigated the use of LOHCs from two different perspectives. Firstly, different authors have explored the hydrogenation/dehydrogenation reactions from a kinetic point of view to determine the kinetic rate for the different LOHCs because reaction step is the core section since only additional stream conditioning is required in the process (Salman et al., 2022). In addition, the global performance of these LOHCs has also been evaluated from a process perspective (Niermann et al., 2019). But the details of the chemical hydrogenation/dehydrogenation reactions beyond kinetics have not been addressed. In this work, an intermediate step between these areas is explored focusing on the reactor design of the hydrogenation/dehydrogenation unit. Thus, an accurate assessment can be performed at process scale using realistic data of the reactor performance. Therefore, this evaluation is essential to support deployment of LOHCs for hydrogen storage systems. Particularly, in this work, the most extended three-phase reactor designs have been analyzed: trickle bed and slurry. For both, a rigorous model is developed including principles of mass, energy, and momentum transfer to describe the complex system of a hydrogenation/dehydrogenation reactor. Using this model, it is possible to determine the main variables that affect the design and performance of the LOHCs reactors determining the best operating conditions of each of the alternatives. Specifically, two of the most promising LOHCs systems are evaluated: dibenzyltoluene and a mixture of 1,2-dimethylindol and 7-ethylindole. However, this analysis can be easily extended to other LOHCs systems.

## 2. Reactor modelling

### 2.1 Trickle bed reactor model

Trickle bed reactors can be applied for both hydrogenation and dehydrogenation reactions. This is because liquid-to-particle mass transfer is intensified under trickle and high interaction conditions and a hydrogen gas acceptor will favor hydrogen transference to the gas phase, avoiding hydrogen accumulation in the liquid media.

The design complexity of trickle bed reactors is found in the operating regimes. They mainly depend on the gas and liquid flows. The most common regimes are high interaction and the transition between high interaction and trickle, which are used in industrial activities and, also, in the proposed model. Its flow can be co and counter-current, although in general, co-current with downward flow is the preferred option.

The performance of trickle bed reactors can be assumed to be a plug flow model with no axial dispersion. Also, the consideration that both phases remain at the same temperature is well accepted. With these assumptions, the mass transfer between phases and the chemical reaction and diffusion inside catalyst pores can be described given by Eqs (1-3) for hydrogen reaching the catalyst active center. Liquid species such as LOHCs are assumed not to be transferred to the gaseous phase because of their low volatility. They will only transfer into catalyst surface and then will perform parallel mechanisms of diffusion and reaction. Because of that, only Eqs (2-3) will be applied.

$$\frac{(dF_{H_2})_g}{dW} = (k_l a_g)_{H_2} \cdot \left( \left( C_{H_2} \right)^*_g - \left( C_{H_2} \right)_l \right) \tag{1}$$

$$\frac{(dF_i)_l}{dW} = (k_m a_m)_i \cdot ((C_i)_l - (C_i)_s) \quad \forall i \tag{2}$$

$$(k_m a_m)_i \cdot ((C_i)_l - (C_i)_s) = \eta \cdot r_{surface} \quad \forall i \tag{3}$$

F represents the molar flow rate of each component i, C is the concentration in the gas (g) or liquid (l) phase, denoting with an asterisk the equilibrium concentration, $k_l a_g$ is the mass transfer coefficient for the gas-liquid transport and $k_m a_m$ for the liquid-solid transport. Finally, $r_{surface}$ is the surface reaction rate corrected using the effectiveness factor ($\eta$). It must be noticed, that for the reaction to occur, both reactants must reach the catalytic center. Otherwise, the reaction cannot progress. Because of that, the model accounts for the transfer of both species and reaction velocity taking the lowest as the overall rate, assuring that all reactants are transferred. Additionally, it must be considered that ideally, catalyst particles will be surrounded by the liquid phase. However, to describe the actual situation, wetting factor is required to account for the catalyst real effectiveness.

Related to heat transfer, an adiabatic operation is selected, and the temperature radial gradient can be discarded. Also, the intraparticular gradient can be neglected, although others such as longitudinal (Eq.4) and interparticular (Eq.5) cannot be removed.

$$\frac{dT}{dW} = \frac{r \cdot (-\Delta Hr)}{\sum_{i=1}^{n} F_i \cdot cp_i} \tag{4}$$

$$h \cdot a_m \cdot (T_s - T_b) = r \cdot (-\Delta Hr) \tag{5}$$

In these equations, h is the convection heat transfer coefficient and Ts and Tb the temperatures in the surface of the particle (s) and bulk liquid (b). To predict pressure drop along the bed, a modification of the Ergun's equations for a two-phase flow is selected. Another relevant parameter is the reactor volume fraction occupied by liquid, defined as liquid hold-up. It can be divided into internal and external, and this last into static and dynamic.

## 2.2 Slurry reactor model

In slurry reactors, a liquid phase holds finer particles than those in the trickle bed, thanks to the action of a bubbled gas introduced at the bottom and dispersed with a gas sparger. Slurry reactors hydrodynamics can be divided into slug flow, churn turbulent, and homogeneous. Industrial columns tend to prefer churn-turbulent, at large diameter and superficial gas velocities, as heat and mass transfer are intensified.

Slurry reactors are known to be well-mixed units. As a result, liquid and solid phases can be understood as a pseudo-phase and modelled considering perfect mixture. Nevertheless, the hydrogen is better described as a plug flow since it is not mixed with the liquid. Variables such as gas hold-up and bubble diameter have a great influence on hydrogen transference from the gas to the liquid. This mandates to characterize the features of the bubble. For the sake of simplicity, a bi-modal distribution (large and small bubbles) is considered. Thus, gas-to-liquid hydrogen transfer can be modelled with Eq.6. Assuming steady-state, reaction velocity can be computed following Eq.7. As same as with trickle bed reactors, the slurry model must assure that all species are able to perform all transfer steps. For that, both reactive velocities are calculated and the slowest is taken.

$$-\frac{(dF_{H_2})_g}{dV} = \left(kla_{g\,small} + kla_{g\,large}\right)_{H_2} \cdot \left(\left(C_{H_2}\right)^*_g - \left(C_{H_2}\right)_l\right) \tag{6}$$

$$(k_m a_m)_i \cdot ((C_i)_l - (C_i)_s) = \eta \cdot r_{surface} \quad \forall i \tag{7}$$

Where $kla_{g\,small}$ and $kla_{g\,large}$ are the gas-liquid transfer coefficient for the two bubble sizes. Slurry reactors are considered to have proper temperature control; therefore, an isothermal operation can be performed if heat transfer internals are used. Gas sparger design is also required. In general, it is preferred to use pipe spargers for higher diameter reactors. Its design is limited by weeping phenomena, fixing minimum hole velocity.

## 3. Results

With the proposed models, it is possible to simulate both reactor performance: trickle beds and slurry ones, for hydrogenation and dehydrogenation and evaluate how operational and design parameters impact on LOHCs conversion.

Hydrogenation reactors account for velocities of both reactants. In general, when LOHCs concentration is higher, the limiting step is hydrogen gas-liquid transfer. Figure 1 presents the results for the dibenzyltoluene hydrogenation slurry reactor. A first gas-to-liquid hydrogen transfer controlling region can be distinguished accounting for nearly 75-85% of the total resistance. The superficial gas velocity (directly related with the excess of hydrogen) seems to have beneficial effects on conversion as gas holdup and mass transfer coefficients are enhanced while kinetics has negligible influence. Mass transfer from bulk liquid to particle is responsible for the remaining 15-20%. This behavior ends up with a second tendency, in which, hydrogen transference reduces its importance and LOHCs concentration depletion becomes responsible for increasing kinetic contribution. This change of behavior ends up with all superficial gas velocity lines converging, which means that its influence becomes negligible.

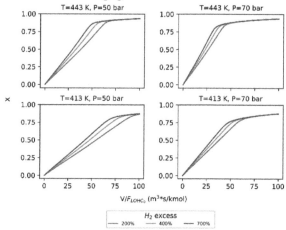

Figure 1 Hydrogenation conversion against normalized volume for dybenzyltoluene on slurry reactor with 100 kg/m³ catalyst load

Temperature and pressure influence can be also evaluated from Figure 1. Both will increase hydrogen solubility in the proposed liquid systems. Higher gas solubility favors the mass transfer, increasing conversion, and reaching the second operating window earlier. Higher conversions could be obtained if normalized volume increases. Nevertheless, it is preferred to avoid unit oversizing since the second region is not as favorable as the first one. In general, perfect mixture reactors are usually employed for intermediate-high conversions. In this specific case, conversion can range within 75-90% if the reactor works in the gas-liquid mass transfer controlling region. In fact, the first region slope is 12 times higher than the second one for dibenzyltoluene, and 17 and 3 times for 1,2-dimethylindole and 7-ethylindole respectively. It clearly indicates a better catalyst use and the convenience to operate and design the reactor in the first zone. Working on this region, expected capital costs range from 1.5 to 2.5 MM\$·s/kmol $H_2$.

Related to trickle bed reactors, the conversion is plotted against normalized catalyst weight for 1,2-dimethylindole and 7-ethylindole system hydrogenation in Figure 2. In general, trickle bed reactors are considered for applications with low reaction velocities. Thus, feed is preferred not to be pure. In addition, temperature rise can damage the catalyst if there is an inadequate heat removal from catalyst particles. For that, a molar relation of reactant to product of 1:4 is fed to the reactor.

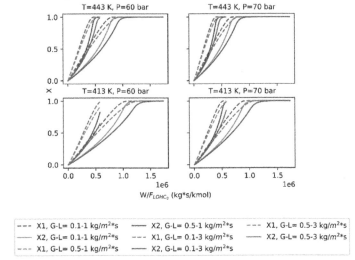

Figure 2 Hydrogenation conversion against normalized catalyst weight for 1,2-dimethylindole and 7-ethylindole 1:1 mixture on trickle bed reactor

Although LOHCs concentrations are lower, from this analysis, the gas-to-liquid step is attributed to be the main resistance contributor with approximately 95%. The remaining 5%, corresponds to liquid-to-particle transference. Only in the end, trickle bed reactors find a sharp increase in kinetic resistance due to extremely lower concentrations, becoming the main limiting step (60-80%). This fact is captured in Figure 2 with a change of tendency on conversion pattern. Notwithstanding, liquid-to-particle transference will be still relevant (20-40%).

Gas and liquid flowrates for a given diameter can be varied to determine their effect on conversion. While increasing liquid flows has evident benefits, the gas flow rate will have a contrary effect. Higher liquid flows increase mass transfer coefficients. It results in better catalyst use for the same amount of reactive. However, at upper gas flowrates, the catalyst bed pressure drop will be higher. It will cause a faster reduction of hydrogen solubility in the liquid phase. Undoubtedly, catalyst usage per hydrogenated LOHC is considerably higher on trickle beds than on slurry reactors. It has a clear impact on the global reactor cost, as from 20 to 40 MM\$·s/kmol $H_2$ are estimated.

However, as it can be seen in Figure 2, this kind of reactor allows to reach higher conversions with lower concentrations of reactants as the kinetic controlling region is only found at the end of the reaction. Therefore, a proper combination of both designs can be explored to take advantage of the benefits of the reaction technologies. For instance, a first slurry reaching almost 80% conversion before the flattened curve region can be set, and then a trickle bed reactor to fully hydrogenate the LOHC.

During dehydrogenation, hydrogen transfer no longer limits reaction progress. Nonetheless, proper hydrogen mass transfer to gas must be assured to avoid accumulation. In general, it is easy to accomplish as lower pressures are used, which considerably reduces its solubility. Slurry dehydrogenation reactors are clearly limited in both systems by kinetics. Thus, the main variables affecting conversion are temperature and catalyst load. As dehydrogenation kinetics are considerably lower than hydrogenation, a great unit oversizing is required compared with previous designs. To achieve similar conversions of 80%, higher particle concentrations are used. Related to trickle bed dehydrogenation reactors, kinetics is also the main resistance. Reaction endothermicity highly limits the rate as the temperature is reduced through the catalyst bed. It makes necessary to introduce a high fraction of dehydrogenated LOHC to avoid higher temperature drops. In this case, the molar relationship between reactive and product is increased to 1:9. Both 1,2-dimethylindol and 7-ethylindole can be almost fully dehydrogenated with 10000 kg·s/mol. Nevertheless, reaching higher conversions is not possible for dibenzyltoluene as kinetics are slow, and is not possible to introduce higher catalyst weight without higher pressure drop in systems operating at lower pressures. It limits conversions to values up to approximately 25-40%.

## 4. Conclusions

A detailed reactor modelling was performed for hydrogenation and dehydrogenation of LOHCs with slurry and trickle bed designs. Hydrogenation slurry was characterized by having two differentiated zones: a mass transfer controlled region where gas superficial velocity has a positive influence, and a second where kinetics increases its contribution to the total resistance and superficial gas velocity no longer has effect. It was found that operating in the first region will work from 3 to 17 times better than in the second one. Therefore, a combination of both designs could be explored in order to maximize the global rate in each design avoiding slurry oversizing. A similar configuration could be proposed for dehydrogenation reactors. Dehydrogenation-associated endothermicity is one of the bottlenecks for LOHCs deployment, from an energetic point of view but also due to a kinetic reduction as temperature falls. The study shows that trickle bed reactors will have worse catalyst use than slurry and the unit oversizing when dehydrogenation reactors are compared to hydrogenation ones. On the whole, this work shows the great importance of the transfer phenomena in the design of LOHCs reactor and the need to go beyond traditional kinetic studies for an accurate analysis of them.

## Acknowledgments

The authors acknowledge H2MetAmo project by the financial support.

## References

T. He, Q. Pei, P. Chen, 2015, Liquid organic hydrogen carriers, Journal of Energy Chemistry, 24(5), 587-594.

M. Niermann, S. Drünert, M. Kaltschmitt, K. Bonhoff, 2019, Liquid organic hydrogen carriers (LOHCs)–techno-economic analysis of LOHCs in a defined process chain, Energy & Environmental Science, 12(1), 290-307.

M. Niermann, S. Timmerberg, S. Drünert, M. Kaltschmitt, 2021, Liquid Organic Hydrogen Carriers and alternatives for international transport of renewable hydrogen, Renewable and Sustainable Energy Reviews, 135, 110171.

M.S. Salman, N. Rambhujun, C. Pratthana, K. Srivastava, K.F. Aguey-Zinsou, 2022, Catalysis in Liquid Organic Hydrogen Storage: Recent Advances, Challenges, and Perspectives, Industrial & Engineering Chemistry Research, 61(18), 6067-6105.

Antonis Kokossis, Michael C. Georgiadis, Efstratios N. Pistikopoulos (Eds.)
PROCEEDINGS OF THE 33rd European Symposium on Computer Aided Process Engineering
(ESCAPE33), June 18-21, 2023, Athens, Greece

# Powering Clean and Affordable Energy through Geothermal Integration: A Case Study on Dominica.

## Keeara Bhagaloo[a], Rehannah Ali[a], Anastasia Baboolal[a] and Keeran Ward*[b,]

[a]Department of Chemical Engineering, The University of the West Indies, St. Augustine, Trinidad and Tobago.

[b]School of Chemical and Process Engineering (SCAPE), University of Leeds, Leeds, UK, LS2 9JT.

## Abstract

Caribbean economies are particularly vulnerable to climate change. While developed nations are actively making strides in becoming more sustainable, small island developing states in the Caribbean face many hurdles. Hence, this study presents techno-economic and environmental assessments to inform on sustainable options for affordable and clean energy on the island of Dominica. Four cases were explored using both current and future indicators: levelized electricity (LCOE) costs, product annualized costs (TAC) and environmental impacts. Our results illustrate that with 100% deployment of geothermal energy, greenhouse gas (GHG) emissions and LCOE can be reduced by 99.5% and 70% respectively. Furthermore, diversification linked to production of methanol and ammonia gave environmental benefits, but were infeasible based on current fossil-based prices. Ultimately, the most sustainable option was energy exportation from Dominica to Martinique via subsea transmission, leading to a 20% decrease in LCOE and 2.5 million tonne $CO_2$-eq/year avoided emissions.

**Keywords:** Geothermal Energy, Small Island Developing States, Sustainable Energy, Techno-economics, Life Cycle Assessments.

## 1. Introduction

The Organisation of the Eastern Caribbean States (OECS)- an 11-member group of islands within the easternmost region of the Caribbean Sea, is an inter-governmental association which aims to enhance regional integration by promoting trade along with economic, environmental, and social resilience[1]. The organisation has thus prioritised long-term use of renewable energy-namely geothermal energy, with which the region is endowed[2,3]. Transitioning to renewable energy for power generation is especially important given the region's vulnerability to the effects of climate change, such as rising sea levels and increased occurrence of intense weather systems such as hurricanes[4]-coupled with the longstanding issue of dependence on a volatile oil sector with high prices on the global market, making power generation expensive even at low production capacities[5]. Additionally, energy security is limited by aging infrastructure[2]- which in the face of natural disasters, puts a strain on reliant sectors.

Owing to its geographical location, many forms of renewable energy exist in the Eastern Caribbean region such as wind, solar and hydroelectric power[6]. These sources are dependent on weather conditions and may be intermittent in supply and thus, require other dispatchable power systems for island-wide power distribution. Geologically, the region is an active volcanic region, wherein geothermal energy, independent of weather and climatic situations, can be harnessed[6]. Also, the abundance of untapped geothermal allows for large-scale power generation while simultaneously eliminating the need for fossil fuel. Islands such as Guadeloupe (15 MW installed capacity) and Dominica (up to 1390 MW potential)[6] have begun exploring geothermal energy, with ambitions to reduce emissions from local power sectors. Dominica's geothermal potential surpasses its national demand, allowing neighbouring islands with higher energy needs to benefit by the creation of an interconnected grid via subsea transmission[2]. Furthermore, the island's high geothermal energy potential allows for considerable energy storage systems.

Six of the eleven OECS nations are involved in the Paris Agreement, which aims to increase renewable energy penetration and reduce greenhouse gas emissions. Thus, our study utilizes multiple decision criteria using techno-economic and environmental assessments to advise on sustainable operations of the OECS power sector through a case study approach. We propose case-specific scenarios for Dominica in achieving increased renewable energy penetration. By disseminating evidence-based results, solutions can be provided to aid OECS to promote sustainable development through the deployment of clean and affordable energy (SDG 7)[8].

## 2. Methodology

The following cases are aligned to Dominica's national commitment targets on the integration of renewable energy sources by 2030, Each case is evaluated based on techno-economic and environmental assessments aligned to process design, economic viability and life cycle analysis.

### 2.1 Case 1: Dominica 2030 Outlook- 100% RE Deployment

This case explores the feasibility of utilising a fraction of Dominica's geothermal potential to replace the 63% grid share dominated by fossil fuels by 2030, while power from existing hydroelectric plants constitute the remaining 37%; thereby fulfilling 100% (27MW) renewable power.

### 2.2 Cases 2 and 3: Energy Storage Platforms: MeOH and NH₃ Production

These cases explore the sustainable production of Methanol (MeOH) and Ammonia ($NH_3$), using electrochemical production of hydrogen via water electrolysis, using Polymer Electrolyte Membrane (PEM) technologies. The power required for the process was derived from geothermal energy integration on the island by 2030.

For Case 2, our renewable MeOH flowsheet was designed using Aspen Plus V10 in accordance with past studies done by some of us[10, 11], utilizing renewable $H_2$ and $CO_2$ from Direct air capture (DAC). For Case 3, the Haber process was considered whereby $NH_3$ was produced from renewable $H_2$ and $N_2$ from cryogenic air separation-modelled using Aspen Plus V10.

### 2.3 Case 4: Geothermal Energy Exportation: Martinique 2030 Outlook

Case 4 explores the feasibility of Dominica exporting power to Martinique through sub-sea cable transmission while sustaining their own geothermal energy grid by 2030.

### 2.4 Economic Feasibility

The economic feasibility was assessed by evaluating the levelized cost of electricity (LCOE) for all four cases as well as the Total Annualized Cost (TAC) for Cases 2 and 3. The LCOE for each case was determined using **Eq (1)** where $P_{ij}$ represents the energy (MWh) derived from technology j, and $LCOE_j$ is the fixed LCOE (USD/MWh) associated with technology j.

$$LCOE = \frac{\sum_j^n (P_{ij} \times LCOE_j)}{\sum_j^n P_{ij}} \tag{1}$$

Total Annualized Cost (TAC) was computed by estimating the capital (CAPEX) and operating costs (OPEX) associated with MeOH and $NH_3$ operations. CAPEX was calculated using bare module costing parameters, with purchased equipment costs extrapolated for the cost year 2020 using Chemical Engineering Plant Cost Index (CEPCI). OPEX was estimated from fixed costs (FC) using cost allocations and variable costs (VC) such as raw material prices based on current and future market analysis. TAC scores were subsequently compiled using **Eq 2**, whereby the annualized fixed costs (AFC) were calculated using the annual capital cost ratio (**Eq 3**) and a 330 day yearly on-stream factor.

$$AFC = FCI \times \frac{(1+i)^n \times i}{(1+i)^n - 1} \tag{2}$$

where, FCI -Fixed Capital Investment (CAPEX), interest rate i = 7% and the designated plant lifetime, n = 20 years

$$TAC = \frac{AFC + OPEX}{Yearly\ production\ rate} \tag{3}$$

### 2.5 Life Cycle Assessment (LCA) Framework

A consequential cradle-to-power generation gate, as outlined in accordance with the ISO 14040:2006 methodology[12] was employed. The functional unit for all cases was set as 1MWh of energy production. Case-specific life cycle inventories were defined by mass and energy balances across system boundaries, and included electrical production from deep geothermal wells, hydroelectric run-of-river, petrol/oil, biomass, solar and wind supply chains, deionized water, natural gas (heating purposes) and flue gas emissions (MeOH/NH₃ process). The inventories associated with raw materials and utilities were obtained from Ecoinvent v3.4 databases. For Cases 2-4, a substitution allocation approach was employed to distribute environmental burdens among all products. Environmental benefits were evaluated at the midpoint level using ReCiPe 2016 hierarchist (H)[10] method within the SimaPro v9 LCA modelling platform -with global warming potential ($GWP_{100a}$) as the main impact category. Finally, the LCA results were interpreted to provide sufficient evidence supporting the transition towards greater sustainable power generation.

## 3. Results and Discussion

### 3.1 Environmental Performance

Dominica currently requires a peak demand output of 20MW (63% from diesel and 37% from hydroelectric sources)[9]. The business-as-usual (BAU) case assumes that existing hydroelectric power plants maintain operations at current capacity while diesel generation increases to satisfy a growing energy demand in the following years up to 2030. Increased fossil fuel use to satisfy this increasing demand leads to a 62% observed increase in GHG emissions from 90,366 tonnes $CO_2$ eq/year in 2019 to 146,831 tonnes $CO_2$ eq/year in 2030 as shown in **Figure 1**.

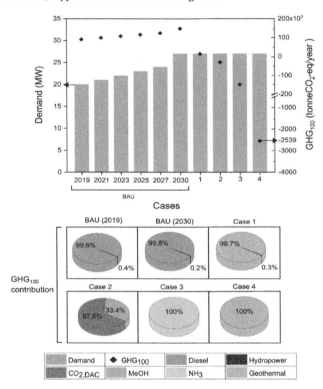

**Figure 1: Case specific Life Cycle GHG emission quotas (tonne $CO_2$-eq/year) for Dominica as a function of peak power demand over the period 2019-2030.**

In Case 1, power from fossil fuels is completely substituted by geothermal sources, supporting a decline in total emission quotas to 734 tonnes $CO_2$ eq/year.

Cases 2 and 3 which explore opportunities for excess energy storage in the form of MeOH and $NH_3$ respectively achieve negative carbon emissions through avoided burdens- avoiding 36,871 and 149,013 tonnes $CO_2$-eq/year respectively. Avoided burdens were mainly attributed to lower fossil fuel utilization- through the absence of conventional energy intensive steam methane reforming for hydrogen production as well as $CO_2$ utilization through direct air capture (DAC) operations. Case 4, which investigates the option of a RE export supply chain from Dominica to Martinique by harnessing geothermal energy to fulfil both countries' peak demand in 2030, shows an avoided life cycle GHG emission quota of 2.5 million tonnes $CO_2$-eq- the highest amongst all scenarios investigated. Thus, Case 4 can significantly contribute to GHG emission reduction efforts for both countries under the Paris Agreement.

### 3.2 Economic Performance

The economic feasibility of all cases was assessed by utilizing current and projected LCOE data for each technology as well as energy storage potential in the form of MeOH and $NH_3$ grassroots operations. For the BAU case, the LCOE for Dominica increased from 153 USD in 2019 to 175 USD/MWh in 2030 due to a 35% increase in power demand –resulting in an increase in diesel share contribution from 87% to 92%, shown in **Figure 2**. Although hydropower maintains 44% of the grid in 2019, it accounts for only 13% of the LCOE due to its lower energy costs over diesel.

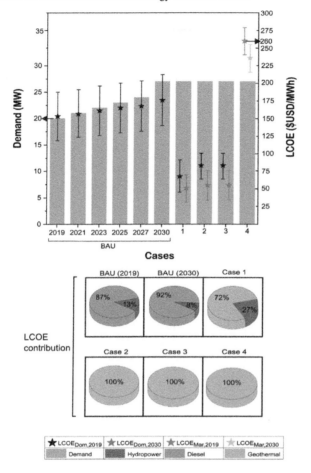

**Figure 2: Case-specific LCOE as a function of net energy demand for 2019-2030, given with respect to technology grid share.**

The technology is, however, constrained by high reliance on weather events- impeding on its potential for dispatchable power generation and leading to a possible decrease in energy share to 33% in 2030.

Across Cases 1-3, our results show a drastic decrease in LCOE for Dominica. For Case 1, a 62% decrease in LCOE to 69 USD/MWh is attributed to the complete substitution of diesel power generation by geothermal energy- representing a 100% renewable grid; with 67% of the demand fulfilled by geothermal power. Cases 2 and 3 were analysed using TAC as a key performance indicator. **Figure 3** describes the respective current and future economic feasibility for each power-to-fuel scenario. Results illustrate TAC ranges for MeOH and $NH_3$ from 1.22 to 2.07 USD/kg$_{MeOH}$ and 1.07 to 1.61 USD/kg$_{NH3}$ respectively. Thus, our data shows MeOH production to be the more expensive of the two scenarios-mainly attributed to energy and capital-intensive operations surrounding electrolysis and DAC. Overall, cost contributions to TAC for each process show major expenses attributed to geothermal electricity utilization (48%-51%) - with fixed and capital costs giving 9%-31% and 21%-22% respectively. Furthermore, DAC operations accrued up to 16% of the total TAC for MeOH production. Comparing current prices for both MeOH and $NH_3$ markets, green production routes utilizing geothermal energy can be regarded as uncompetitive - with 75-80% higher costs compared to fossil-based technologies[13,14]. However, with future reduction in electrolyser CAPEX and geothermal energy costs by 2030, TAC scores reveal strong MeOH and $NH_3$ competitiveness at near market value.

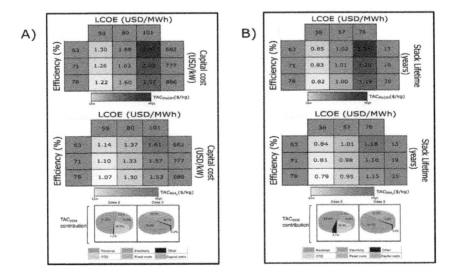

**Figure 3: Current-2020 (A) and future-2030 (B) TAC for MeOH (blue) and NH₃ (green) production as a function of LCOE (geothermal power), electrolyser efficiency, capital cost and stack lifetime. Costs associated with the category 'other' are natural gas fuel, process water, wastewater and catalyst charges.**

Lastly, the economic feasibility of Case 4- wherein Dominica exports power to the neighbouring island of Martinique- was assessed. Apart from achieving 100% RE penetration for both Dominica and Martinique by the exportation of 434MW of geothermal power via subsea transmission, the projected $LCOE_{Mar}$ (**Figure 2**) was found to be 259 USD/MWh- 11% lower than the current consumer price in Martinique. Furthermore, with lower geothermal costs expected in the future, a further 20% decrease in $LCOE_{Mar}$ to 236 USD/MWh in 2030 is anticipated. Among the case-specific cost contributions, subsea transmission accounts for 75% of the $LCOE_{Mar}$. Considering the vast energy losses during electrolysis when compared to transmission losses, energy exportation was found to be the most economically viable option. Notwithstanding, that the projected geothermal energy potential of Dominica surpasses the total deployment covered in this study (Proven potential = 1390 MW[5]), the nation can realize increased economic advantages from energy exportation and storage activities in the future. While our results do support a sustainable geothermal energy transition for Dominica, it accompanies several hurdles for the island linked to high capital investment such as upgrading of current power grid infrastructure, maintenance logistics linked to sub-sea transmission to Martinique and finally, exploration and geothermal production costs. Thus, to achieve its sustainable energy transition, Dominica will need to seek public and private sector investment while advocating for changes in current energy policies which align to strategic benefits for the country.

## 4. Conclusion

A study on the island-nation of Dominica was conducted utilising techno-economic and environmental assessments to determine ways in which the nation can reduce anthropogenic emissions via the deployment of geothermal energy to fulfil its growing energy demand. Four cases were evaluated using LCA framework, LCOE and TAC with sensitivity to assess the most sustainable options for Dominica. Our results indicate that by 2030, without further renewable penetration, the island will see a 62% increase in GHG emissions together with an increase in $LCOE_{2030}$ up to 175 USD/MWh. However, with a 100% renewable grid supported by power generation from geothermal and hydropower sources, GHG emissions can be reduced by 99.5%, allowing the nation to meet its GHG commitments and achieve clean and affordable energy with a $LCOE_{2030}$ of 53 USD/MWh. While the production of MeOH and $NH_3$ allows for significant environmental benefits, TAC shows infeasibility compared to current market prices. Ultimately, the most sustainable case was the exportation of geothermal energy to fulfil 100% grid capability of neighbouring Martinique, resulting in a 20% decrease in LCOE and 2.5 million tonne $CO_2$-eq/year avoided emissions.

## References

1. Organisation of Eastern Caribbean States (OECS), OECS Strategic Objectives, https://www.oecs.org/en/who-we-are/strategic-objectives. (Accessed June, 2021).

2. OECS, Energy Issues and Options (2006)., https://openknowledge.worldbank.org/bitstream/handle/10986/17975/esm3170PAPER0OECS0energy01PUBLIC1.pdf?sequence=1&isAllowed=y.

3. Joseph EP. Geothermal Energy Potential in the Caribbean Region. Retrieved July 4, 2021, from https://sustainabledevelopment.un.org/content/documents/3339energy_joseph.pdf.

4. Glenn E, Comarazamy D, González JE, Smith T. Detection of recent regional sea surface temperature warming in the Caribbean and surrounding region. Geophys Res Lett 2015;42:6785–92. https://doi.org/10.1002/2015gl065002.

5. Manijean L, Saffache P. Geothermal energy slowly makes its entrance in the caribbean region. Dynenviron 2016:108–19. https://doi.org/10.4000/dynenviron.695.

6. Koon Koon R, Marshall S, Morna D, McCallum R, Ashtine M. A Review of Caribbean Geothermal Energy Resource Potential. WIJE. 2020;42(2):37-43.

7. Savaresi A. The Paris Agreement: a new beginning? J. Energy Nat. Resour. Law, 34;1:16-26. DOI: 10.1080/02646811.2016.1133983.

8. United Nations, Goal 7: Ensure access to affordable, reliable, sustainable and modern energy for all, https://sdgs.un.org/goals/goal7.

9. U.S Department of Energy- Energy Transition Initiative, Energy Snapshot: Dominica, https://www.nrel.gov/docs/fy15osti/62704.pdf. [accessed 7 July 2021].

10. Narine K, Mahabir J, Koylass N, Samaroo N, Singh-Gryzbon S, Baboolal A, et al. Climate smart process design for current and future methanol production. J. CO2 Util 2021;44:101399. https://doi.org/10.1016/j.jcou.2020.1013

11. Mahabir J, Bhagaloo K, Koylass N, Boodoo MN, Ali R, Guo M, et al. What is required for resource-circular CO2 utilization within Mega-Methanol (MM) production? J. CO2 Util 2021;45:101451. https://doi.org/10.1016/j.jcou.2021.101451

12. International Organization for Standardization, Environmental management -Life cycle assessment - Requirements and guidelines; ISO 14044:2006 c2006 [updated 2016; cited 2020 December].

13. Zhang H, Wang L, Van herle J, Maréchal F, Desideri U. Techno-economic comparison of green ammonia production processes. Appl Energy 2020;259:114135. https://doi.org/10.1016/j.apenergy.2019.114135.

14. IRENA and Methanol Institute, Innovation Outlook: Renewable Methanol, International Renewable Energy Agency, 2021; ISBN 978-92-9260-32.

Antonis Kokossis, Michael C. Georgiadis, Efstratios N. Pistikopoulos (Eds.)
PROCEEDINGS OF THE 33rd European Symposium on Computer Aided Process Engineering
(ESCAPE33), June 18-21, 2023, Athens, Greece

# Optimal design of a water energy food nexus system through a multi-objective approach

Daniel Peña-Torres[a], Marianne Boix[a], Ludovic Montastruc[a]

[a] LGC, UMR 5503, Toulouse INP – CNRS – Université Toulouse 3, 4 allée Emile Monso
31432 Toulouse, France

## Abstract

Water, energy, and food resources have seen a growth in their global demand in the last decade and it is expected to continue for the year 2030 (National Intelligence Council, 2012). During the last 20 years, the scientific community have deeply studied the relations between these resources. Although it is at the center of governmental concerns, there is still a lack of studies regarding the WEFN systems with a nexus approach (FAO, 2021). Multi-objective optimization methods have the potential to conceive in a sustainable manner these complex systems. This study aims to design water, energy, and food optimal connections where different agents interact with each other. Two objective functions are taken into account for the model: total $CO_2$ emissions and net economic benefit. When minimizing total $CO_2$ emissions, the results indicate a total of 1 046 711 t $CO_2$e and costs of 26 510 million USD. When minimizing net economic benefit, the emissions increase 2 000 times its ideal value, and the system perceives an economic benefit of 29 941 million USD. For future work it is expected to do a sensitivity analysis varying certain system parameters, as well as separating the economic objective function (one for each agent of the system), in order to study the competition that may exist among them.

**Keywords**: multi-objective optimization, decision support tool, water-energy-food nexus.

## 1. Introduction

Over the last decade, water, energy, and food resources grown in their global demand and it is expected that this tendency will continue for the year 2030 (FAO et al., 2021). Indeed, the reliance on water, energy, and food is projected to increase by 40, 50, and 35 percent, respectively, compared to their 2012 values (National Intelligence Council, 2012). The increment in the resources demand is attributable to the climate change that the earth is currently going through and rapid global population growth, which is expected to increase by 50% for the year 2050 (Ferroukhi et al., 2015). Given the above, there is a great pressure on these 3 resources. Therefore, in order to ensure safe access to water, energy, and food source, it is necessary to develop further studies for insuring a responsible resource management (Peña-Torres et al., 2022).

On the other hand, water, energy, and food are highly interrelated, presenting both synergisms and trade-offs along their supply chains. In the food production chain, the use of water and energy is necessary, from planting and feeding in agriculture and livestock, respectively, to cooking food in homes. Energy generation requires over half of the freshwater resources used (Bauer et al., 2014), which is transformed into steam to turn turbines, for example. It is also possible to use by-products of the food industry as biomass to generate energy. Both water treatment and water transport require the use of energy.

The interconnection of these three resources is referred in literature as the Water Energy Food Nexus (WEFN). This concept considers that, when a decision is taken for the management of one of the three, it will necessarily impact the decisions that will be taken for the two other resources. A recent report of the Food and Agriculture Organization of the United Nations (FAO et al., 2021) pointed out the negative effects of considering these three resources not-interconnected:

- Insecurity of access of water, energy, and food.
- Economic crises, geopolitical conflicts, public health concerns.
- Environmental impacts greater than expected.

The design of resources allocation systems through the nexus approach also addresses the use of land and soils by taking into account socio-economic factors. According to Carvalho et al. (2022), there is a real need for systemic thinking to achieve multipurpose design dedicated to WEFN. A systemic approach could also help to consider important indicators such as sustainability and resilience in terms of connections across different domains rather than just as individual components (Huntington et al., 2021). WEFN systems should then be conceived with a holistic approach so that they are resilient, durable, and organized to respond to current societal problems. Multi-objective optimization methods and tools have the potential to conceive in a sustainable manner these complex systems.

This study aims to design water, energy, and food optimal connections at a given territorial scale where different agents interact with each other.

## 2. Problem definition

The overall goal of this study is to design water, energy, and food optimal connections at a given territorial scale, with two conflicting objectives: maximizing net economic benefit and minimizing total Greenhouse Gas (GHG) emissions. To optimize them, it is necessary to go through a step of modeling, formalization and formulation of optimization criteria. Based on a case study, we propose to optimize a territory in order to make it more respectful towards resource consumption, especially water, which is itself highly interconnected with energy generation and food production.

The optimization model describes every possible exchange with mass balance and conservation equations, and demand satisfaction restrictions. Linear models represent every material to energy conversion. The epsilon constraint method was used to obtain different points between the maximization of the net economic benefit (scenario A) and the minimization of the GHG emissions (scenario E). Three intermediate net economic benefit points were established between these two scenarios, minimizing the GHG emissions in each one of them to generate scenarios B, C, and D. The resulting mixed integer linear programming (MILP) model was solved using CPLEX v.20.1.0.1 solver (IBM, 2021) for GAMS 38.2.1 (General algebraic modeling system) (Bussieck and Meeraus, 2004).

## 3. Case Study

This study describes the problem of water, energy, and food distribution at a macro level in the hydrological region of Sinaloa (58 000 km² approx.), located in the northwestern part of Mexico, and it is based on the previous work of Núñez-López et al. (2021). Within this region, four power plants satisfy the energy demand by burning natural gas or agricultural wastes. Aquifers, dams, and wells satisfy the water demand of the different sectors (agriculture, livestock, domestic needs and industries). The total domestic food demand is fixed and obtained from agriculture, livestock or industrially processed food, or a combination of these three. In the system there is also the option of installing new actors:

- Three new desalinization plants can be installed that can provide water and energy to different agents of the system.
- New rainwater collecting units for agriculture, livestock farmers, and the domestic sector that provide water to each one of them, respectively.
- New water treatment plants that offer fresh water to agriculture, industries and the domestic sector.
- A solar energy system for the domestic sector that offers energy outside of the power plants.
- A new gasification system that handles domestic waste and produces gas that feeds power plants and new desalinization plants.

In a WEFN system, different types of resources are exchanged between different agents. In the water layer of the nexus, the power plants receive water from the sea and send it to livestock farmers, the agriculture sector, industries, the domestic sector, dams and aquifers. The same connections are proposed for the desalinization plants. Dams receive from these two plants, in addition to water received from precipitations, and they send water to aquifers, livestock farmers, agriculture, industries, and the domestic sector. Aquifers receive water from dams, natural precipitations, and from water treatment units installed for the domestic, agricultural and industrial sector. Wells receive water only from aquifers, and they send water to livestock farmers, agriculture, industries and the domestic sector.

In the energy layer, power plants and desalinization plants send energy to livestock farmers, the agriculture sector, industries and the domestic sector, while receiving fuel from natural gas suppliers, gasification system installed for domestic waste treatment, and agricultural wastes.

In the food layer of the system, livestock farmers, agriculture, and industries send food to the domestic sector. They have the option as well to sell their products to an external market. Agriculture sends its waste to the livestock sector in order to feed the cattle. Industries receive vegetables from agriculture to produce food. Finally, in order to grow the food in the agricultural sector industries sell fertilizer to them.

## 4. Results

The results are summarized in Table 1. In order to detail its analysis five different scenarios were selected. The extreme points A and E correspond to the results of the model when maximizing the net economic benefit and when minimizing GHG emissions respectively. The scenarios B, C, and D are obtained varying the trade-of index, which represents the importance of the economic goal in the multi-objective optimization problem, over the environmental goal (the importance of the environmental objective is obtained by subtracting this value from 1).

Comparing the scenarios, A and E, it can be seen that the economic function goes from 26 000 million USD of costs to 30 000 million of economic benefits. On the other hand, the environmental function increases 2 000 times its value from scenario E to scenario A.

Table 1: Objective function values when addressing economic and environmental goals.

| Scenarios | Trade-off index | GHGC / t CO₂e | Net economic benefit / 10⁶ USD |
|---|---|---|---|
| Maximizing Net Economic Benefit (A) | 1 | 2 804 999 808 | 29 941 |
| Scenario B | 0.8 | 1 802 450 000 | 19 234 |
| Scenario C | 0.6 | 1 040 490 000 | 8 804 |
| Scenario D | 0.4 | 311 635 000 | -1 627 |
| Minimizing GHGC (E) | 0 | 1 046 711 | -26 510 |

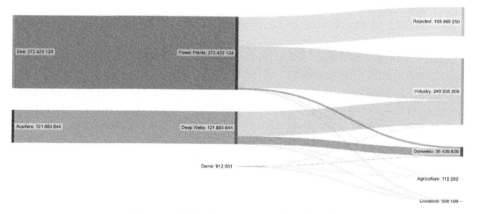

Figure 1: Water flows in scenario A (in m³).

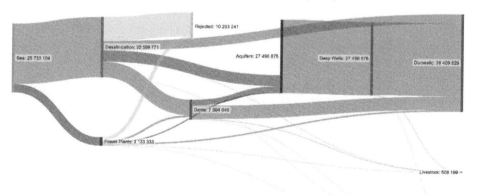

Figure 2: Water flows in scenario E (in m³).

The main changes between the system configuration in scenarios A and E are the installation of 3 new desalinization plants and 3 new gasification systems, both for scenario E (Figures 2 and 4). The installation of the new desalinization plants entails the reduction of GHG emissions of 1 245 448 330 t CO₂e, whereas the installation of gasification system accounts for a reduction of 311 564 647 t CO₂e. On the other hand, the cost for the installation and operation of the new desalinization plants is 21 564 million USD, and the profit of it is 9 million USD, meaning that the installation of new desalinization plants implies a negative net economic benefit 21 555 million USD. This new additions to the system also affect the number of connections within it. As it can be seen from Figures 1 and 2, when having desalinization plants as a water source, the number of connections is higher, and therefore the cost for the system increases.

As the net economic benefit increases, the fertilizer production inside the system also does. When minimizing the GHG emissions, the fertilizer production within the system is 0, and the emissions related to its production are from the importation of fertilizer. When maximizing the net economic benefit, the fertilizer production increases up to 89 000 000 t, entailing an increase of GHG emissions of 1 247 848 375 t $CO_2$e (Figures 3 and 4), but also an increase of the profits of 62 300 million USD.

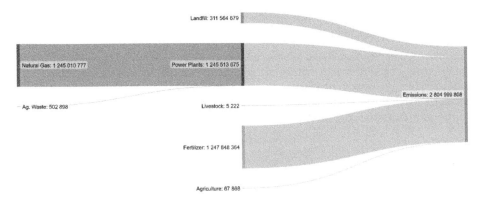

Figure 3: GHG emissions in scenario A (in t $CO_2$e).

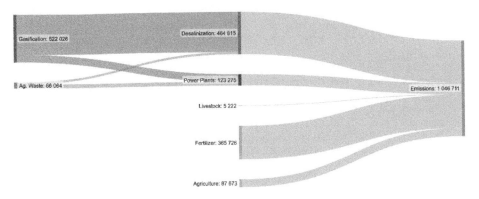

Figure 4: GHG emissions in scenario E (in t $CO_2$e).

It is also possible to notice that between the points D and C the net economic benefit of the system changes sign, passing from costs to benefits. This means that when increasing the environmental function between 300 and 1 000 times its ideal value, the system already starts perceiving economic benefits. Between points D and C, a balanced solution could be obtained. For that it is necessary to include other indicators in the analysis, such as net present value and water footprint.

## 5. Conclusions

In this work, a MILP model is developed to design water, energy, and food optimal connections at a given territorial scale. The model considers energy flows coming from power plants; water flows from deep wells, dams, and aquifers; and food flows from agriculture, livestock and industrial processed food. It also considers the installation of new desalinization plants for energy and water supply.

The model is applied to the design and plan of a WEFN system in Sinaloa, Mexico. Different scenario points were obtained using the epsilon constraint method between the maximization of the net economic benefit and the minimization of the GHG emissions. When minimizing the environmental objective function, the system configuration generates 1 046 711 t $CO_2$e and has a cost of 26 510 million USD. When maximizing the economic objective function, the emissions result in 2 000 times its ideal value, and the economic benefit for the system is 29 941 million USD. The main difference between the system configuration of these two scenarios (A and E), is the installation of three new desalinization plants and three new gasification systems, both in scenario E.

For future work, it is intended to explore other scenarios in the model and do a sensitivity analysis, varying certain parameters of the system, such as domestic food demand and total rainfall in the region. It is also expected to consider and economic objective function for each one of the agents present in the system, thus analyzing the behavior and competition that may exist among these agents.

## References

D. Bauer, M. Phillbrick, B. Vallario, H. Battey, Z. Clement, F. Fields, 2014. The water-energy nexus: Challenges and opportunities. US Department of Energy

M. R. Bussieck, A. Meeraus, 2004. General algebraic moedling system (gams). In: Modeling languages in mathematical optimization. Springer, pp. 137-157.

P. N. Carvalho, D. C. Finger, F. Masi, G. Cipolletta, H. V. Oral, A. Tóth, M. Regelsberger, A. Exposito, 2022. Nature-based solutions addressing the water-energy-food nexus: Review of theoretical concepts and urban case studies. Journal of Cleaner Production 338, 130652.

FAO, IFAD, UNICEF, WFP, WHO, 2021. The State of Food Security and Nutrition in the World 2021. FAO, Rome, Italy.

R. Ferroukhi, D. Nagpal, A. Lopez-Peña, T. Hodges, R. H. Mohtar, B. Daher, S. Mohtar, M. Keulertz, 2015. Renewable energy in the water, energy and food nexus. Internationa Renewable Energy Agency (January), 1-125.

H. P. Huntington, J. I. Schmidt, P. A. Loring, E. Whitney, S. Aggarwal, A. G. Byrd, S. Dev, A. D. Dotson, D. Huang, B. Johnson, J. Karenzi, H. J. F. Penn, A. Salmon, D. J. Sambor, W. E. Schnabel, R. W. Wies, M. Wilober, 2021. Applying the food-energy-water nexus concept at the local scale. Nature Sustainability 4(8), 672-679. URL https://doi.org/10.1038/s41893-021-00719-1

IBM, 2021. IBM ILOG CPLEX 20.1 User's Manual.

National Intelligence Council, 2012. Global Trend: Alternative Worlds. URL www.dni.gov/nic/globaltrends

J.M. Núñez-López, E. Rubio-Castro, J. M. Ponce-Ortega, 2021. Involving resilience in optimizing the water-energy-food nexus at a macroscopic level. Process Safety and Environmental Protection 147, 259-273.

D. Peña-Torres, M. Boix, L. Montastruc, 2022. Optimization approaches to design water-energy-food nexus: A litterature review. Computers & Chemical Engineering, 108025.

Antonis Kokossis, Michael C. Georgiadis, Efstratios N. Pistikopoulos (Eds.)
PROCEEDINGS OF THE 33rd European Symposium on Computer Aided Process Engineering
(ESCAPE33), June 18-21, 2023, Athens, Greece

# Techno-economic comparison of peaking power plants: OCGT+CCS vs Lithium-ion batteries

Mathew Dennis Wilkes,[a] Diarmid Roberts,[a] Solomon Brown,[a]

*a Department of Chemical and Biological Engineering, University of Sheffield, Sheffield, S1 3JD, United Kingdom,*

## Abstract

To ensure electricity system security dispatchable power generation is required to provide balancing capacity in times of need, such as providing diurnal peak power supply. In order to achieve a cost-effective transition to Net Zero, these peaking power plants need to be low-cost and low-carbon. Herein, we compare two forms of dispatchable power: open-cycle gas turbine (OCGT) with carbon capture and storage (CCS), and Lithium-ion battery energy storage system (BESS). The results highlight the lower cost of BESS compared to OCGT+CCS, although this is only for systems that provide <8h duration. Hence, both forms of dispatchable power generation will be required in future resilient energy systems.

**Keywords**: CCS, Energy, Energy Storage, Energy Grid

## 1. Introduction

As we move towards Net-Zero emissions by 2050, all forms of power generation need to have low, zero, or negative carbon emissions. With an anticipated growth in variable renewable energy (VRE) (Heptonstall & Gross, 2021), Energy System Operators (ESOs) across the world are strengthening their balancing capacity. These services ensure a constant balance between supply and demand of energy, providing crucial system security and reliability of supply (NGESO, 2018). Balancing services include dispatchable power generation (peaking plants), demand side response, interconnectors, and frequency response (NGESO, 2022). Within the UK, the National Grid (NG) expects an increase in dispatchable electricity supply, which is currently dominated by gas turbines but by 2050 they will be replaced by energy storage, interconnectors, and hydrogen (NGESO, 2021). Similarly, the Australian Energy Market Operator (AEMO) has anticipated a 57 GW growth in dispatchable resources to enable an additional 125 GW of large-scale VRE's. Traditionally, Australia has relied on gas-fired generators for peaking plants but there is a growing interest in energy storage solutions (AEMO, 2022).

Australia's Clean Energy Council compared battery storage to gas turbines, and highlighted the batteries are superior peaking plant in terms of cost, flexibility, emissions, and the range of network services it can provide (CEC, 2021). The study did not include $CO_2$ abatement/tax, which will have a major impact on the cost of electricity from gas turbines. Also, the economics of energy storage is dependent on the mode of operation, capacity factor, electricity price, and location-based factors.

### 1.1. Aims and Objectives

Currently, dispatchable gas turbines are the main form of peaking technology; however, in order to meet Net-Zero targets their emissions need to be reduced. Hence, this study makes a techno-economic comparison of open-cycle gas turbine (OCGT) power generation with Carbon Capture and Storage (CCS), and a Lithium-ion battery energy storage system (BESS), specifically for operation in the UK. Herein, we utilize process models developed in our earlier studies to provide the necessary design and operating parameters which are then used within the economic models. The main study objectives are:

- Utilize process modelling to identify key design/operating parameters.
- Define economic assumptions for both dispatchable UK power plants.
- Techno-economic comparison of **OCGT+CCS** against **BESS**.

## 2. Methodology

This section highlights the process design, costing methodology, and economic assumptions, for both dispatchable technologies (OCGT+CCS and BESS).

*2.1. Process design*

For the OCGT+CCS power plant, the gas turbine is a Siemens SGT-400 producing 10.4 MWe and 33.8 kg/s flue gas containing 6.78 wt.% $CO_2$. In order to be low-carbon, the flue gas needs post-combustion $CO_2$ capture using the benchmark Monoethanolamine (MEA) process. More information on the power generation, capture plant design, and process model can be found in our previous study (Wilkes, et al., 2021a). The $CO_2$ stream is then conditioned ready for pipeline transportion, at 111 bar and 50 ppm moisture. More information on the conditioning train design and process model can be found in our previous study (Wilkes, et al., 2021b).

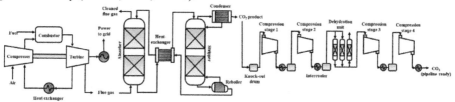

*Figure 1: OCGT+CCS power plant flowsheet*

The BESS is modelled as a turnkey stationary grid-connected system of 10 MWe rating, using the definitions in Mongird et al. (2020). The round-trip efficiency is set at 86%. The BESS generates revenue by charging the battery during periods of low price and supplying electricity to the grid when the price is high.

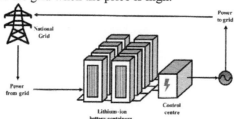

*Figure 2: BESS plant flowsheet*

*2.2. Economic costing metric*

In this study we use the levelized cost of electricity (LCOE) for the OCGT+CCS plant and the levelized cost of storage (LCOS) for the BESS. The LCOE is the breakeven point at which the electricity must be sold to counteract the cost of constructing and operating the plant. The LCOE is the sum of the net present value (NPV) of costs divided by the sum of the NPV of electricity generated then sold, shown in Equation 1 (BEIS, 2020).

$$LCOE = \frac{NPV_{total\ costs}}{NPV_{generation}} = \frac{\sum_n \left( \frac{TCC_n}{(1+r)^n} + \frac{FOM_n}{(1+r)^n} + \frac{VOM_n}{(1+r)^n} \right)}{\sum_n \frac{E_n^{Out}}{(1+r)^n}} \qquad (1)$$

Where TCC is the total capital costs, FOM is the fixed operating and maintenance costs, VOM is the variable operating and maintenance costs, $E_t^{Out}$ the total electricity generated, $r$ is the discount rate, and $n$ is the time period.

For the OCGT+CCS cost model, the TCC is calculated using correlations from Chauvel et al. (1981) and is based on the purchased equipment cost (PEC):

$$PEC = \sum_1^{total} E_i \qquad (2)$$

This is for all of the major pieces of equipment ($i$) identified in the process model, and are shown in Figure 1. The individual equipment cost ($E_i$) is based on the correlation from Towler & Sinnott (2012):

$$E_i = a + bS^n \qquad (3)$$

Where $S$ is the sizing factor specific to each piece of processing equipment, and $a$, $b$, and $n$ are cost factors. The costs are scaled to the present day using Turton et al. (2018):

$$E_i^{2019} = E_i^{2010} \left( \frac{F^{2019}}{F^{2010}} \right) \qquad (4)$$

The Chemical Engineering Plant Cost Index (CEPCI) for 2010 is 551 ($F^{2010}$) and for 2019 is 607.5 ($F^{2019}$) (Jenkins, 2020). The VOM and FOM are also calculated using correlations from Chauvel et al. (1981). Table 1 shows the economic assumptions for the OCGT+CCS plant. Table 3 shows the utilities prices used to calculate the VOM.

The LCOS is very similar to LCOE, in that the NPV of all costs is divided by the NPV of the electricity output. They can hence be used for a like-for-like comparison. LCOS is defined by:

$$LCOS = \frac{NPV_{total\ costs}}{NPV_{generation}} = \frac{TCC + \sum_n \left( \frac{VOM_n}{(1+r)^n} \right)}{\sum_n \frac{E_n^{Out}}{(1+r)^n}} \qquad (5)$$

Which is adapted from Julch (2016), where it is assumed that $TCC$ are accrued in year 0. $VOM_n$, the variable operating costs are further defined by:

$$VOM_n = OPEX_n + CAPEX_{re,n} + \bar{c}_{elec.,n} \frac{E_n^{Out}}{\eta} - R_n \qquad (6)$$

Where $OPEX_n$ is the fixed operational cost (excluding degradation and charging) $CAPEX_{re,n}$ covers any re-investments in equipment to maintain capacity following degradation, $\bar{c}_{elec.,n}$ is the average price of electricity used to charge the BESS, $\eta$ the round-trip efficiency of the BESS, and $R_n$ the residual value of the equipment. Table 2 shows the economic assumptions for the BESS facility.

This analysis neglects additional revenue that could be generated using the BESS for arbitrage, or ancillary services such as frequency response, and which would reduce the LCOS for the peaking application. This is done under the assumption that the pivotal role of the BESS is to provide incremental peaking capacity, and that performing other roles may push other capacity out of the market.

*Table 1: OCGT power plant economic assumptions*

| Assumption | Description |
|---|---|
| Plant location | Yorkshire, England |
| Power rating | 10 MWe |
| Plant lifetime | 25 years |
| Construction time | 2 years |
| Start of construction | 2019 |
| Discount rate | Proven technology = 7.8% (BEIS, 2018) |
| | Higher risk technology = 8.9% (BEIS, 2018) |
| Capacity factor | 1500 annual operating hours (Millbrook Power Ltd., 2017) |
| Carbon price (CP) | £21.70/tCO$_2$ (BEIS, 2018) |

*Table 2: Li-ion BESS economic assumptions*

| Parameter | Description |
|---|---|
| Plant location | Yorkshire, England |
| Power rating | 10 MWe |
| Project life | 10 years |
| Start of operation | 2021 |
| $r$ | 7.8 % proven technology rate from Table 1. |
| $TCC$ | £784-3825/kW, 2020 data in (Mongird, et al., 2020) |
| $OPEX_n$ | £4.20/kW/year (Mongird, et al., 2020) |
| $\bar{c}_{elec.,n}$ | £100/MWh. Mean N2EX 2021 day-ahead price 20:00-07:00. |
| $CAPEX_{re,n}$ | The system is assumed to last for the entire project life; therefore, this value is 0 (Roberts & Brown, 2022). |
| $R_n$ | There is no value in the equipment once it has been used. |
| $\eta$ | 0.86 (Mongird, et al., 2020) |

*Table 3: Utility prices*

| Assumption | Description |
|---|---|
| Natural gas | 33 £/MWh (Global Petrol Prices, 2021) |
| Electricity | 140 £/MWh (BEIS, 2021) |
| Cooling water | 1.39 £/m3 (Yorkshire Water, 2021) |
| MEA solvent | 5.0 £/L (Mistral Industrial Chemicals, 2013) |

## 3. Results

The LCOE of the OCGT+CCS plant and the LCOS of the BESS are shown in Figure 5. For each technology, the levelized cost (£/MWh) drops as the operational hours increase, as the CAPEX is spread over a greater electricity output. It does not drop to zero, as there are variable operating costs in both cases. The operating hours range between 250-4,000 hours annually for both technologies.

The OCGT+CCS plant is considerably more expensive than unabated OCGT. It is also more expensive than BESS except when the required duration of daily response is greater than 8 h and less than 1000h per year. In this case, the TCC associated with the BESS is prohibitive. The results show that a BESS is more suitable than OCGT+CCS as a low carbon solution for a diurnal peaking application where power must be provided for 2-4h every day. This situation will arise in grids predominantly powered by PV, such as those in Australia or California. In the UK in the future however, it is likely that wind power supply variation will mean that multi-day back-up power is more important than peaking power (Drax, 2022). It is clear from Figure 5 that BESS with sufficient duration will be more expensive than OCGT+CCS.

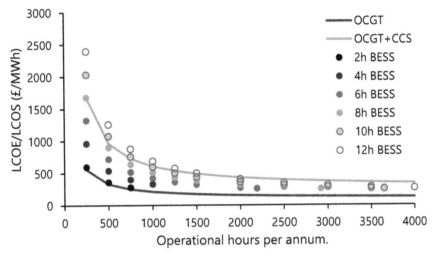

*Figure 3: Modelled LCOE and LCOS for OCGT, OCGT+CCS, and BESS versus operational hours per year. For the BESS the operational hours are capped by assuming that the BESS performs 1 cycle per day.*

Based on predicted pathways for future energy scenarios from NGESO (NGESO, 2022), natural gas peakers are expected to decrease in line with Net Zero scenarios; however, the results in this study show they will still have a role to play. Depending on the NGESO pathway, the Gas-CCS share of dispatchable electricity supply ranges between 3.2 to 20.8% or 3.3 GW to 23.1 GW. All NGESO pathways show a large portion of flexibility will be provided by energy storage. The results shown in Figure 3 highlight the slightly lower cost of BESS (276-2,393 £/MWh) compared to Gas-CCS (290-1,675 £/MWh), but only for systems designed for <8h duration. Therefore, future work should focus on reducing the cost of BESS for long duration systems, and reducing the cost of dispatchable Gas-CCS by identifying low energy capture solutions, thermal integration potential, and $CO_2$ utilization options.

## 4. Conclusion

Future energy systems that incorporate a high proportion of variable renewable energy technologies require balancing capacity to ensure security of electricity supply. This study is a techno-economic comparison of two forms of dispatchable power generation used during periods of peak power demand: OCGT+CCS and BESS. Including CCS for the OCGT plant significantly increase the LCOE, as the additional capital costs associated with capturing, transporting, and storing the $CO_2$ exacerbate the issues of small plant size and low capacity factor. Interestingly, the results show the lower cost of BESS, but only for low duration (<8h) operation. Therefore, future work is required to ensure the cost of longer duration BESS is lower than Gas-CCS, i.e., investigating alternate BESS technologies or medium-duration storage technologies (compressed air or pumped hydro). Thus, leading to a cost-effective Net Zero transition in the power sector.

## 5. References

AEMO, 2022. *2022 Intergrated System Plan,* Melbourne, Australia: Australian Energy Market Operator.

BEIS, 2018. *Assessing the Cost Reduction Potential and Competitiveness of Novel (Next Generation) UK Carbon Capture Technology,* s.l.: UK Department for Business, Energy & Industrial Strategy.

BEIS, 2020. *Electricty Generation Costs 2020,* London: Department for Business, Energy & Industrial Strategy.

BEIS, 2021. *Quarterly Energy Prices: UK January to March 2021,* s.l.: The Department for Business, Energy and Industrial Strategy.

CEC, 2021. *Battery Storage: The new, clean peaker,* s.l.: Clean Energy Council.

Chauvel, A. et al., 1981. *Manual of Economic Analysis of Chemical Processes: Feasibility Studies in Refinery and Petrochemical Processes..* s.l.:McGraw-Hill.

Drax, 2022. *Electric Insights 24-11-22 to 01-12-22.* [Online]
Available at: https://www.electricinsights.co.uk/#/dashboard?period=7-days&start=2022-11-24&&_k=xw6no5
[Accessed 1 December 2022].

Global Petrol Prices, 2021. *United Kingdom natural gas prices.* [Online]
Available at: https://www.globalpetrolprices.com/United-Kingdom/natural_gas_prices/
[Accessed April 2021].

Heptonstall, P. J. & Gross, R. J. K., 2021. A systematic review of the costs and impacts of integrating variable renewables into power grids. *Nature Energy,* Volume 6, pp. 72-83.

Jenkins, S., 2020. *2019 CHEMICAL ENGINEERING PLANT COST INDEX ANNUAL AVERAGE.* [Online]
Available at: https://www.chemengonline.com/2019-chemical-engineering-plant-cost-index-annual-average/
[Accessed 25 October 2021].

Julch, V., 2016. Comparison of electricity storage options using levelized cost of storage (LCOS) method. *Applied Energy,* Volume 183, pp. 1594-1606.

Millbrook Power Ltd., 2017. *The Millbrook Power (Gas Fired Power Station) Order,* s.l.: Parsons Brinckerhoff.

Mistral Industrial Chemicals, 2013. *MONOETHANOLAMINE MEA 2-AMINOETHANOL.* [Online]
Available at: https://mistralni.co.uk/products/mea-monoethanolamine
[Accessed October 2021].

Mongird, K. et al., 2020. *2020 Grid Energy Storage Technology Cost and Performance Assessment,* s.l.: US DOE.

NGESO, 2018. *ESO Balancing Services: A guide to contracting, tendering and providing response and reserve services,* Warwick, England: National Grid ESO.

NGESO, 2021. *Operability Strategy Report,* London, England: National Grid ESO.

NGESO, 2022. *List of all balancing services.* [Online]
Available at: https://www.nationalgrideso.com/industry-information/balancing-services/list-all-balancing-services
[Accessed 11 November 2022].

Roberts, D. & Brown, S., 2022. The economics of firm solar power from Li-ion and vanadium flow batteries in California. *MRS Energy & Sustainability.*

Towler, G. & Sinnott, R., 2012. *Chemical Engineering Design: Principles, Practice and Economics of Plant and Process Design.* 2nd ed. Oxford: Elsevier.

Turton, R., Shaeiwitz, J. A., Bhattacharyya, D. & Whiting, W. B., 2018. *Analysis, Synthesis, and Design of Chemical Processes.* 5th ed. s.l.:Pearson Eduction Inc..

Wilkes, M. D., Mukherjee, S. & Brown, S., 2021a. Transient CO2 capture for open-cycle gas turbines in future energy systems. *Energy,* p. 119258.

Wilkes, M. D., Mukherjee, S. & Brown, S., 2021b. Linking CO2 capture and pipeline transportation: sensitivity analysis and dynamic study of the compression train. *International Journal of Greenhouse Gas Control,* Volume 111, p. 103449.

Yorkshire Water, 2021. *Charges for customers with a meter.* [Online]
Available at: https://www.yorkshirewater.com/bill-account/how-we-work-out-your-bill/customers-with-a-meter/
[Accessed October 2021].

Antonis Kokossis, Michael C. Georgiadis, Efstratios N. Pistikopoulos (Eds.)
PROCEEDINGS OF THE 33rd European Symposium on Computer Aided Process Engineering
(ESCAPE33), June 18-21, 2023, Athens, Greece

# Bioenergy with carbon capture and storage (BECCS) – power generation coupled with hydrogen production

Mathew Dennis Wilkes,[a] Oludayo Asuni,[a] Solomon Brown,[a]

[a] *Department of Chemical and Biological Engineering, University of Sheffield, Sheffield, S1 3JD, United Kingdom,*

## Abstract

Achieving Net Zero emissions by 2050 requires the utilization of negative emissions technologies such as Bioenergy with Carbon Capture and Storage (BECCS), as well as hydrogen to decarbonize challenging industrial $CO_2$ emitters. Within this paper we develop a BECCS-Power-Hydrogen process model in Aspen Plus. The analysis shows the key operating parameters and key performance indicators for the process. The base case electrical efficiency is very low (18.4%) but including the hydrogen production increases the overall system efficiency to 52%. Also included in this study is a sensitivity analysis investigating the effect gasification temperature has on the hydrogen production and net system efficiency.

**Keywords**: BECCS, Hydrogen, Energy, Gasification, Aspen.

## 1. Introduction

Bioenergy coupled with Carbon Capture and Storage (BECCS) is a negative emissions technology that can be applied to power (BECCS-Power) and hydrogen production (BECCS-Hydrogen). BECCS is featured heavily in energy scenarios designed to achieve Net-Zero, alongside the use of hydrogen to decarbonize power, industry, heating, and transportation (CCC, 2020; BEIS, 2021).

One option for generating hydrogen from biomass is via gasification, whereby the product syngas components are separated to produce high purity $H_2$. Several review papers have highlighted the current state-of-the-art of biomass gasification technologies (Lepage, et al., 2021; Tezer, et al., 2022), including the integration of carbon capture, utilization and storage (CCUS) technologies (Shahbaz, et al., 2021) and the possibility of bio-renewable hydrogen production (Cao, et al., 2020). Mutlu and Zeng (Mutlu & Zeng, 2020) highlighted the challenges and opportunities of modelling biomass gasification. Process simulation tools such as ChemCAD, Matlab, gPROMS, Aspen, GAMBIT, and Fluent, can allow users to identify process limitations and optimize operation.

There are studies that have focused on modelling BECCS-Hydrogen in Aspen Plus (Marcantonio, et al., 2019; Safarian, et al., 2022) and the possibility of including heat integration to incorporate BECCS-Power (Cohce, et al., 2011; Ishaq & Dincer, 2020). Cohce et al. (2011) evaluated biomass gasification-based hydrogen production, with waste heat recovery and electricity generation to improve overall system efficiency (energy efficiency = 33% and exergy efficiency = 29%). Ishaq and Dincer (2020) showed an integrated energy system design for heat, electricity, and hydrogen production, based on biomass gasification and water electrolysis. The process model uses 0.4 kg/s of biomass feedstock and has the potential to produce 1.4 MW of energy and 10.74 mol/s $H_2$. The overall energy efficiency is 53.7 2%; however, there is a very high capital investment required for the cryogenic air separation unit, quantity of turbines, proton exchange membrane electrolyzer, and entrained flow gasifier.

Therefore, this study investigates the thermochemical conversion of biomass for the co-production of power and hydrogen. Utilizing process models developed in Aspen Plus to identify the processes key operating parameters (KOPs) and key performance indicators (KPIs). The relatively simplistic design, biomass gasification for hydrogen production coupled with heat recovery for power generation, provides a baseline for the conversion of biomass to power and hydrogen. A sensitivity analysis on the identified KOPs will enable effective process optimization and highlight potential process limitations. The key objectives are:

- Develop a process model, in Aspen Plus® v11.1, for BECCS-Power-Hydrogen.
- Highlight and analyze the processes KOPs and KPIs.
- Identify process limitations and options for optimization.

## 2. Process design and modelling

The process design is separated into five main sections: biomass gasification, heat recovery and steam cycle, syngas cleaning and upgrading, hydrogen separation, and $CO_2$ conditioning. The flowsheet is shown in the model topology (Figure 1) in Section 2.6.

### 2.1. Biomass Gasification

The biomass gasification and syngas production in a downdraft gasifier is based on the experiments conducted by Wei et al. (2009) using hardwood chips (Tauqir, et al., 2019), the key operating parameters are shown in Table 1. The proximate and ultimate analysis of the chips is shown in Table 2.

Table 1: Operating conditions for the gasification unit for run #14 from Wei et al. (2009)

| Parameter | Value |
|---|---|
| Biomass feed flowrate (kg/hr) | 20.58 |
| Moisture content (wt.%) | 10.05 |
| Gasifying temperature (°C) | 789 |
| Air flowrate (m³/hr) | 46.05 |
| Equivalence ratio | 0.289 |

Table 2: Hardwood chips proximate and ultimate analysis (Tauqir, et al., 2019)

| Proximate Analysis | Value (wt.%) |
|---|---|
| Moisture | 25 |
| Fixed Carbon | 79.85 |
| Volatile Material | 19.031 |
| ASH | 1.119 |
| **Ultimate Analysis** | |
| Carbon | 49.817 |
| Hydrogen | 5.556 |
| Nitrogen | 0.078 |
| Chlorine | 0.000 |
| Sulfur | 0.005 |
| Oxygen | 43.425 |
| HHV (MJ/kg) | 18.58 |

### 2.2. Power generation

Within the steam cycle, water is pumped to 125 bar and passes through a heat recovery steam generator (HRSG) unit, where the hot gases from the gasifier heat the steam to approximately 565°C (Chiesa, et al., 2005). The isentropic and mechanical efficiency of the high pressure (HP), intermediate pressure (IP), and low pressure (LP) steam turbines is 80% and 95%, respectively (Cohce, et al., 2011).

### 2.3. Syngas upgrading

The syngas upgrading using the water-gas shift (WGS) reaction unit is based on Marcantonio et al. (2019) and Moneti et al. (2016), both of which simulated the experiments conducted within the UNIfHY project (UNIfHY, 2016). The WGS reaction favors the production of CO and $H_2O$ at high temperatures, thus the UNIfHY project looked at high temperature shift (HTS) at 400°C and low temperature shift (LTS) at 200°C. Both HTS and LTS reactors are operated at 27 bar (Cohce, et al., 2011).

### 2.4. $H_2$ production

Sulfur within the biomass is converted into $H_2S$ and COS in the gasification unit, and all of the COS is converted in $H_2S$ in the WGS units. Therefore, prior to $H_2/CO_2$ separation $H_2S$ is removed using Selexol, which also co-captures $CO_2$. The separation efficiency for $H_2S$ is 100% and for $CO_2$ it is 95%. High purity $H_2$ (99.99%) is separated using a Pressure Swing Adsorption (PSA) unit (Chiesa, et al., 2005). Modelling the Selexol process and PSA units for $H_2$ production is possible in Aspen Plus (Zhu, et al., 2020), however, for this study we assume set separation efficiencies to reduce the complexity of the model.

### 2.5. $CO_2$ conditioning

The $CO_2$ conditioning unit ensures the $CO_2$ stream is ready for pipeline transportation, it uses sub-critical liquefaction (at 66 bar) and liquid pumping (111 bar) to reduce the energy consumption (Wilkes, et al., 2021).

### 2.6. Process model

The process model is developed in Aspen Plus® v11.1, the model topology is shown in Figure 1. Wet biomass enters and **DRYER** unit and the output moisture content is set to 10.05 wt.%. Within Aspen, biomass is a non-conventional solid and needs to be decomposed (**DECOMP**) into its constituent elements before gasification (**GASI**). An RGibbs reactor is chosen for the gasification unit, which calculates chemical equilibrium based on Gibbs free energy minimization (Tauqir, et al., 2019). The high temperature (**HT-WGS**) and low temperature (**LT-WGS**) WGS units are REquil reactors (Marcantonio, et al., 2019). The Selexol and $H_2$-PSA processes are modelled as separation units (**SELEXOL1, SELEXOL2,** and **PSA**), with the separation efficiencies specified in Section 2.4. Heat is recovered in the **HRSG** unit, and the high-pressure steam produces power in the **HP-ST, IP-ST,** and **LP-ST** turbines.

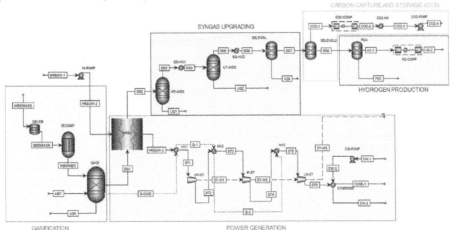

*Figure 1: Biomass gasification for $H_2$ and power production, model topology using Aspen Plus*

## 3. Results

### 3.1. Validation

The validation is carried out on the gasification unit, based on the downdraft gasifier experiments (run #14) conducted by Wei et al. (Wei, et al., 2009), the key operating conditions are shown in Table 1. The comparison between the gas compositions in the experiment and simulation is shown in Figure 2. The experimental study only investigated the composition of $CH_4$, $CO_2$, CO and $H_2$, on a dry basis. The first simulation (Simulation #1) used the same ER and air flowrate as Wei et al. (Wei, et al., 2009), which resulted in underestimating the CO and $H_2$ composition and overestimating the $CO_2$ composition. As this study focusses on $H_2$ production, it is imperative the $H_2$ composition is accurate. Therefore, we modified the ER in Simulation #2 to 0.214 or 34.12 m3/hr of air. This is still within the range (0.2 to 0.28) specified in Wei et al. (Wei, et al., 2009). In Simulation #2, the composition of $CO_2$, CO, and $H_2$ deviate 3.61%, 3.70%, and 0% compared to the experiment. The composition of $CH_4$ is much lower (0.0013 vol.%) than shown in Wei et al. (Wei, et al., 2009), this is due to the use of thermodynamic equilibrium calculations within Aspen's RGibbs reactor (Tauqir, et al., 2019). As the model underpredicts the quantity of $CH_4$, the simulations syngas LHV (4.58 MJ/Nm3) is 26% lower than expected (6.17 MJ/Nm3).

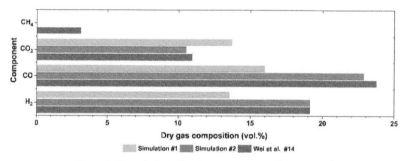

*Figure 2: Downdraft gasification syngas composition comparison*

It is also important to ensure the correct ratio of $H_2$/CO is achieved after the WGS units. Typically, the syngas $H_2$/CO ratio should range between 1.5:1 to 2:1, this is suitable for further processing in methanol or Fischer-Tropsch synthesis (Binder, et al., 2018). For this simulation the $H_2$/CO ratio is 1.79, therefore, the model is in good agreement with experimental data and within the acceptable syngas composition range.

### 3.2. Base case

To ensure enough steam can be generated to power the turbines, the process is scaled to use 3600 kg/hr of biomass (hardwood chip analysis is shown in Table 2) and ER=0.214. The energy flows through the process are shown in Figure 3. The KOPs are shown in Table 3 and the KPI's are shown in Table 4.

The gasifier heat duty is 5,023 kW and the turbines combined power output is 3,846 kW. Chiesa et al. (2005) showed the electrical efficiency of the steam cycle (based on manufacturer quotes) is approximately 18.1-19.1%. In this study, the electrical efficiency of the gasification plant is 18.4%. Therefore, the process design is comparable to sources within the literature and industry. The power generation and electrical efficiency is low compared to conventional biomass combustion technologies, due to the much lower ER which reduces the amount of heat recoverable in the HRSG.

The thermal efficiency is based on the amount of hydrogen produced, which is 185 kg/hr or 6,176 kW. The net efficiency is the combination of the electrical and thermal conversion of the biomass feedstock, for this plant design it is 51.65%, similar to Ishaq and Dincer (2020).

Table 3: Key operating parameters

| KOP | Value |
|---|---|
| Biomass input (kg/s) | 3,600 |
| Biomass energy (kW) | 18,580 |
| Air flowrate (kg/s) | 6934 |
| Equivalence Ratio | 0.214 |
| HRSG flowrate (kg/s) | 10,497 |
| Syngas/HRSG stream ratio | 1 |

Table 4: Key performance indicators

| KPI | Value |
|---|---|
| Power demand (kW) | 425 |
| Power generated (kW) | 3,846 |
| Net power output (kW) | 3,421 |
| Hydrogen output (kW) | 6,176 |
| Electrical efficiency (%) | 18.41 |
| Thermal efficiency (%) | 33.24 |
| Net efficiency (%) | 51.65 |

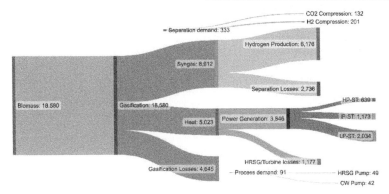

Figure 3: Sankey diagram showing energy flows

## 3.3. Sensitivity Analysis

The gasification process is one of the most important units, especially in terms of exergy destruction (Cohce, et al., 2011). Therefore, we investigated the effect of varying the gasification temperature from 700°C to 1000°C. Interestingly, the $H_2$ concentration in the syngas decreases due to an increase in combustion components, but the concentration post-WGS increases. Thus, more $H_2$ is produced which increase the net efficiency, as shown in Figure 4. More energy is available to recover in HRSG; however, this requires re-adjusting the syngas/HRSG steam ratio, and only the gasification temperature was modified in this study. Future work should focus on global optimization and maximizing the net efficiency without minimizing hydrogen production.

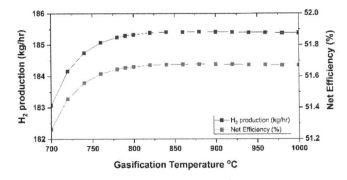

Figure 4: Effect of varying the gasification temperature on the $H_2$ production and net efficiency

## 4. Conclusion

In order to achieved Net Zero targets by 2050, two important pathways are negative emissions with BECCS and industrial decarbonization via hydrogen. Within the study we evaluate a process for BECCS-Hydrogen-Power, using process modelling in Aspen Plus to identify the key operating parameters and key performance indicators. Using 3,600 kg/hr of wood chips can produce 185 kg/hr of $H_2$, with an overall net efficiency of 52%. Within the study we also highlight the effects of increasing the gasification temperature. Future work should investigate additional heat integration options at high gasification temperatures, as well as analyze the effect of different separation technologies post-WGS.

## 5. References

BEIS, 2021. *Net Zero Strategy: Build Back Greener,* s.l.: Crown copyright.

Binder, M., Kraussler, M., Kuba, M. & Luisser, M., 2018. *Hydrogen from biomass gasification,* s.l.: IEA Bioenergy.

Cao, L. et al., 2020. Biorenewable hydrogen production through biomass gasification: A review and future prospects. *Environmental Research,* Volume 186, p. 109547.

CCC, 2020. *The Sixth Carbon Budget: The UK's path to Net Zero,* s.l.: Committee on Climate Change.

Chiesa, P., Consonni, S., Kreutz, T. & Williams, R., 2005. Co-production of hydrogen, electricity and CO2 from coal with commercially ready technology. Part A: Performance and emissions. *International Journal of Hydrogen Energy,* Volume 30, pp. 747-767.

Cohce, M. K., Rosen, M. A. & Dincer, I., 2011. Efficiency evaluation of a biomass gasification-based hydrogen production. *International Journal of Hydrogen Energy,* 36(17), pp. 11388-11398.

Ishaq, H. & Dincer, I., 2020. A new energy system based on biomass gasification for hydrogen and power production. *Energy Reports,* Volume 6, pp. 771-781.

Lepage, T., Kammoun, M., Schmetz, Q. & Richel, A., 2021. Biomass-to-hydrogen: A review of main routes production, processes evaluation and techno-economical assessment. *Biomass and Bioenergy,* Volume 144, p. 105920.

Marcantonio, V. et al., 2019. Process analysis of hydrogen production from biomass gasification in fluidized bed reactor with different separation systems. *International Journal of Hydrogen Energy ,* Volume 44, pp. 10350-10360.

Moneti, M. et al., 2016. Influence of the main gasifier parameters on a real system for hydrogen production from biomass. *International Journal of Hydrogen Energy,* 41(28), pp. 11965-11973.

Mutlu, Ö. Ç. & Zeng, T., 2020. Challenges and Opportunities of Modeling Biomass Gasification in Aspen Plus: A Review. *Chemical Engineering & Technology,* 43(9), pp. 1674-1689.

Safarian, S., Unnthorsson, R. & Richter, C., 2022. Performance Investigation of Biomass Gasification for Syngas and Hydrogen Production Using Aspen Plus. *Open Journal of Modelling and Simulation,* Volume 10, pp. 71-87.

Shahbaz, M. et al., 2021. A comprehensive review of biomass based thermochemical conversion technologies integrated with CO2 capture and utilisation within BECCS networks. *Resources, Conservation and Recycling,* Volume 173, p. 105734.

Tauqir, W., Zubair, M. & Nazir, H., 2019. Parametric analysis of a steady state equilibrium-based biomass gasification model for syngas and biochar production and heat generation. *Energy Conversion and Management,* Volume 199, p. 111954.

Tezer, Ö. et al., 2022. Biomass gasification for sustainable energy production: A review. *International journal of Hydrogen Energy ,* Volume 47, pp. 15419-15433.

UNIfHY, 2016. *Final Report Summary - UNIFHY (UNIQUE gasifier for hydrogen Production),* s.l.: s.n.

Wei, L. et al., 2009. Syn-Gas Quality Evaluation for Biomass Gasification with a Downdraft Gasifier. *Transactions of the American Society of Agricultural and Biological Engineers,* 52(1), pp. 21-37.

Wilkes, M. D., Mukherjee, S. & Brown, S., 2021. Linking CO2 capture and pipeline transportation: sensitivity analysis and dynamic study of the compression train. *International Journal of Greenhouse Gas Control,* Volume 111, p. 103449.

Zaman, S. A. & Ghosh, S., 2022. Thermo-economic and environmental performance analyses of a biomass-based carbon negative system integrating externally fired gas turbine and molten carbonate fuel cell. *Energy Conversion and Management: X,* Volume 14, p. 100187.

Zhu, X. et al., 2020. Application of elevated temperature pressure swing adsorption in hydrogen production from syngas. *Adsorption,* Volume 26, pp. 1227-1237.

Antonis Kokossis, Michael C. Georgiadis, Efstratios N. Pistikopoulos (Eds.)
PROCEEDINGS OF THE 33rd European Symposium on Computer Aided Process Engineering
(ESCAPE33), June 18-21, 2023, Athens, Greece
© 2023 Elsevier B.V. All rights reserved.   http://dx.doi.org/10.1016/B978-0-443-15274-0.50462-5

# Optimizing the Sustainable Energy Transition: A Case Study on Trinidad and Tobago

Sherard Sadeek,[a] Dhurjati Chakrabarti,[a] Maria M. Papathanasiou,[bc] Keeran Ward[d]

[a] Department of Chemical Engineering, The University of the West Indies, St. Augustine, Trinidad and Tobago.
[b] Sargent Centre for Process Systems Engineering (SCPSE), Imperial College London, South Kensington Campus, London SW7 2AZ, UK
[c] Department of Chemical Engineering, Imperial College London, South Kensington Campus, London SW7 2AZ, UK;
[d] School of Chemical and Process Engineering (SCAPE), University of Leeds, Leeds, LS29JT, UK;

## Abstract

Trinidad and Tobago is one of the largest emitters of $CO_2$ per capita globally, with a significant reliance on oil and gas sectors. With the country's commitment, as a small island developing state (SIDS), to sustainable development goals and climate change agreements, rapid redesign of Trinidad and Tobago's power sector is critical to promoting a sustainable energy transition. Hence this study implements a mixed-integer linear programming model (MILP) to assess the levelized cost of electricity (LCOE) and life-cycle greenhouse gas emissions ($GHG_{LC}$) across five scenarios. The results illustrate that with an improvement in power generation technology and resource efficiency, reduction of LCOE and $GHG_{LC}$ of up to 40% and 24% respectively are possible. For 2030, our results indicate an estimated increase of 29% and 5% for LCOE and $GHG_{LC}$, respectively compared to the equivalent scenarios in 2019. Ultimately, through a multi-objective optimisation framework, our results highlight the value of systems-based planning and implementation in the sustainable energy transition across the Caribbean region, in accordance with sustainable development goals (SDGs).

**Keywords**: Sustainable development goals, Power generation, Multiple decision criteria, Life cycle assessment, Small Island Developing States.

## 1. Introduction

The Caribbean comprises of 13 island nations-most of which are classed as developing states[1]. Across the Caribbean archipelago, energy is an expensive necessity as most of the region is heavily reliant on fossil fuels and current market demand in meeting its energy needs. The deployment of clean and affordable energy (SDG 7) is integral in combatting the effects of climate change and promoting climate action (SDG 13). A holistic approach is required to aid in this transition, considering all aspects of a robust and sustainable energy system supporting the development of sustainable cities and communities (SDG 11)[2]. This transition, however, remains a challenging task as both economic and environmental constraints need to be optimized to guarantee SDGs are met across the wider global population.

Despite being a small island developing state (SIDS), Trinidad and Tobago is endowed with natural resources and is a net producer of energy, with an emphasis on - natural gas and oil. The country also relies heavily on its petrochemical sector (including methanol (MeOH) and ammonia ($NH_3$)), which utilizes steam reforming to produce hydrogen ($H_2$), along with significant amounts of grid electricity. This results in alarming rates of $CO_2$ at a national level and the country must emphasize sustainable forms of energy to meet its 15% GHG reduction pledge[3].

By utilizing a multi-objective optimization framework, guidance on achieving clean and affordable energy through whole systems thinking can be fostered and utilized locally or domestically across the Caribbean Region, and globally among several SIDS. Hence, our work aims to utilise mixed integer linear programming (MILP) methodologies to minimize both levelized electricity costs (LCOE) and overall life-cycle greenhouse gas emissions ($GHG_{LC}$). One of the key novelties of the presented work is that our MILP framework is tailored to resource availability, local infrastructure, and energy system capabilities of SIDS. This is of critical importance as previous works focused on developed nations.

## 2. Methodology

### 2.1. Overview

This work employs MILP to investigate LCOE and $GHG_{LC}$ in Trinidad and Tobago. The model involves the use of binary integer variables to represent each power plant, thus allowing the model the opportunity to select which ones can be used. Each plant was constrained to a minimum capacity factor of 0.3. The key variables used included the energy required by each plant for both peak and normal times (assumed to be 12 hours each), along with the natural gas utilized. These variables link directly with costs and emissions as seen in **Sections 2.6 and 2.7**. The system was constrained to meet the national electricity demand of 8.87 TWh (2019), with a daily peak load of 1350 MW. These factors are examined for various scenarios including the production of $H_2$ from polymer electrolyte membrane electrolysis (PEM) to provide an alternative to present reforming practices linked to the petrochemical sector for downstream products like MeOH and $NH_3$.

### 2.2. Scenario 1A & 1B: Business-as-Usual (BAU)

This case examines the present power generation system in Trinidad and Tobago, with four natural gas-based power plants. There is a total power capacity of 1950MW, with two single cycle (SC) and two combined-cycle (CC) plants accounting for 990MW and 960MW, respectively. Scenario 1A highlights the use of the current take or pay power purchase agreement (PPA), ensuring that all power plants were online. Scenario 1B optimizes the present system without this PPA, which allows the model the choice of online power plants, if possible.

### 2.3. Scenario 2: Upgrade of Plant Efficiency

Currently, the largest power plant (Plant A) in the country employs SC gas turbine technology, with an installed capacity of 765 MW and an average efficiency of 23% [4]. The upgrade of this plant, results in a total of 1725 MW of CC grid power available, with Plant B (225 MW) being the sole SC plant serving the national power grid.

## 2.4. Scenario 3: $H_2$ Production

Scenarios 3,4 and 5 examine the production of downstream products into the power sector supply and its ability to reduce LCOE and $GHG_{LC}$. Scenario 3 employs $H_2$ generation via PEM. PEM is used as it is more efficient versatile, and commercial feasible over alkaline electrolysis and solid oxide electrolysis[5]. The power demand of this process is exclusively supplied by the upgraded CC plant (Plant A) mentioned in Scenario 2.

## 2.5. Scenario 4 and 5: MeOH Production and $NH_3$ Production

The production of MeOH and $NH_3$ is explored via electrolytic $H_2$ as highlighted in Scenario 3. MeOH and $NH_3$ production, via $CO_2$ hydrogenation and the Haber-Bosch process respectively, was modelled in accordance to previous work [6-7]. Production of these downstream commodities with electrolytic $H_2$ provides a comparison between the country's use of resources (especially natural gas), costs and environmental impact, presently with this alternative method.

## 2.6. Economic Feasibility

The economic impact of each scenario was defined by the levelized cost ($\$_{USD}$ per MWh), computed by estimating the total capital (CAPEX) and operating (OPEX) expenditure, for each process, *r*, in a given scenario. CAPEX costs were derived from literature[6,8] for each process technology while OPEX [7-9] was calculated from fixed and variable costs associated with maintenance, labour, capital overheads, purchasing feedstocks (including natural gas), insurance, royalties and other process-based costs. These costs were levelized based on the grid energy required for the national grid, on a yearly basis. This is shown in **Equation 1.**

$$LCOE = CAPEX_r + OPEX_r \quad \forall\, r \tag{1}$$

## 2.7. Environmental Impact

A consequential life cycle assessment (LCA) was used to examine the environmental impacts related to $GHG_{LC}$ for a function unit of 1MWh of energy produced. A cradle-to-power generation gate approach was followed using the ISO 14040:2006 methodology [10]. Mathematically, each process *r* for a given scenario consumes feedstocks $P_i$ (*kg* $p_i$/MWh) while emitting waste streams, $W_r$ (*kg* $w_r$/MWh). Furthermore, each feedstock and waste stream is linked to a characterized environmental impact ($GWP_{100}$) $I_i^{IN}$ (kg $CO_2eq$/kg$P_i$) and $I_r^{OUT}$ (kg $CO_{2eq}$/kg$W_r$), respectively. For multiple product systems (Scenarios 3-5), avoided burdens $I_r^{COMM}$ (kg $CO_{2eq}$/kg $pc_r$) relative to the BAU downstream processes, $PC_r$(kg$pc_r$/MWh) were recorded using Ecoinvent v3.4. The environmental impact, described as $GHG_{LC}$ represents the total life cycle GHG emissions corresponding to the summation of embodied feedstock impacts and the impacts of each scenario as well as avoided burdens associated with the substitution of low carbon $H_2$, MeOH and $NH_3$ and the utilization of $CO_2$. This is seen in **Equation 2.**

$$GHG_{LC} = \sum_i P_i I_i^{IN} + \sum_r W_r I_r^{OUT} - PC_r I_r^{COMM} \quad \forall\, r, i \tag{2}$$

## 3. Results and Discussion

### *3.1. 2019 SOO Outlook*

Initially, our model was optimized using SOO with a focus on the LCOE. This is in line with the current national perspective on decision making.

Scenarios 1A and 1B employ the use of the present power generation grid technology. However, Scenario 1B explores the removal of the current take or pay PPA which results in an approximate LCOE reduction of $\$_{USD}$ 18 per MWh (29% decrease) compared to Scenario 1A ($\$_{USD}$ 61.72 per MWh). As seen in **Figure 1**, the elimination of the PPA allows the grid demand to be satisfied by only 3 power plants. The use of more efficient power plants also resulted in a reduction of $GHG_{LC}$ from 756 $kgCO_{2eq}$ to 743 $kgCO_{2eq}$.

Scenario 2 resulted in a reduction of LCOE of approximately $\$_{USD}$ 25 per MWh (40% decrease) and $GHG_{LC}$ decreased to 572 $kgCO_{2eq}$ (24% reduction) compared to Scenario 1A. These improved results were as a result of the improved efficiency due to technological improvements on the power grid.

Scenarios 3-5 demonstrated a similar LCOE reduction as Scenario 2. However, these cases required improved commodity prices ($H_2$, MeOH and $NH_3$) for the production of downstream products to be considered feasible in this system. Also, $GHG_{LC}$ increased by 8 – 12% when compared to Scenario 2. Thus, it can be noted that Scenario 2 is the best performing case for both economic and environmental in assessment despite the use of single objective optimization (SOO).

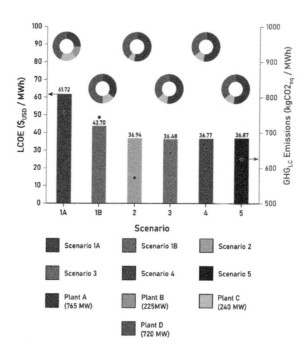

**Figure 1: SOO 2019 highlighting LCOE, GHG$_{LC}$ and Grid share attributed to each Power Plant. Bars show LCOE prices while ● illustrates GHG$_{LC}$.**

### 3.2. 2030 MOO Outlook

The MOO analysis for 2030 (**Figure 2**) allows for insight into the current power system's outlook and assessment with respect to the national goals. Due to the projected increase in grid demand and peak loads, four power plants were online across all scenarios. The results for 2030 followed a similar trend to 2019. However, there was an approximate increase in LCOE of $\$_{USD}$ (8.5 – 14) per MWh compared to the equivalent scenarios in 2019 SOO. The $GHG_{LC}$ increased by approximately (8 – 27) $kgCO_{2eq}$, when compared to 2019 equivalent, with Scenario 3 being an exception. Scenario 3 demonstrated a reduction in the $GHG_{LC}$ of approximately 39 $kgCO_{2eq}$ when comparing 2030 to 2019. This was due to a reduction in electrolyser capacity, as a result of grid constraints. Overall, our results indicate an estimated increase of 29% and 5% for LCOE and $GHG_{LC}$, respectively compared to the equivalent scenarios in 2019.

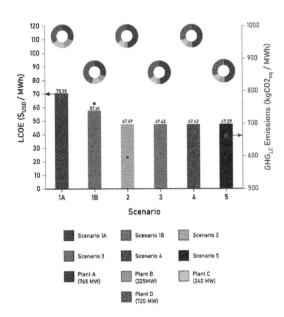

**Figure 2: MOO 2030 highlighting LCOE, GHG$_{LC}$ and Grid share attributed to each Power Plant. Bars show LCOE prices while ● illustrates GHG$_{LC}$.**

## 4. Conclusion

We present the use of multiple decision criteria, through multi-objective optimization, and its relevance in promoting clean and affordable energy among SIDS, using Trinidad and Tobago as a case study. This work demonstrates the ability to link energy supply chains for less developed countries in the Caribbean and globally, thus linking to sustainable development. Five scenarios were explored, utilizing MILP while incorporating a LCA framework, with LCOE and GHG$_{LC}$ in mind. Our results illustrate that the most optimal scenario would be the improvement of gas turbine technology from

SC to CC for the nation's largest power plant. This resulted in a LCOE reduction (for 2019) of 40% compared to BAU while $GHG_{LC}$ reduces by 24% to 572 $kgCO_{2eq}$ per MWh. The introduction of downstream chemicals- $H_2$, MeOH and $NH_3$ within the national energy system shows to be infeasible at current market prices. For 2030, our results indicate an estimated increase of 29% and 5% for LCOE and $GHG_{LC}$, respectively compared to the equivalent scenarios in 2019. These results validate the need for new policies linked to active decarbonisation such as CCS frameworks and carbon taxes, along with the reconsideration of present power purchase agreements. Our results underpin viable solutions-driving impact and distributing guidance on the sustainable energy transition across the Caribbean Region, through the deployment of clean and affordable energy.

## References

United Nations, 2022, Office of the High Representative for the Least Developed Countries, Landlocked Developing Countries and Small Island Developing States. https://www.un.org/ohrlls/content/list-sids

United Nations, 2019, Take Action for the Sustainable Development Goals https://www.un.org/sustainabledevelopment/sustainabledevelopment-goals/.

National Renewable Energy Laboratory, Energy Transition Initiative, 2015. Energy Snapshot Trinidad and Tobago. https://www.nrel.gov/docs/fy15osti/64117.pdf

Inter-American Development Bank, 2015. A Unique Approach for Sustainable Energy in Trinidad and Tobago, https://publications.iadb.org/en/publication/12365/unique -approach-sustainable-energy-trinidad-and-tobago.

International Renewable Energy Agency, 2020, Green Hydrogen Cost Reduction Scaling up Electrolysers to Meet the 1.5 °C Climate Goal https://irena.org/-/media/Files/IRENA/Agency/Publication/2020/Dec/IRENA Green hydrogen cost 2020.pdf.

Narine, K., Mahabir, J., Koylass, N., Samaroo, N., Singh-Gryzbon, S., Baboolal, A., Guo, M., Ward, K., 2021, Climate smart process design for current and future methanol production. J.CO2 Util. 41, 101399, http://dx.doi.org/10.1016/J.JCOU.2020.101399.

Bhagaloo, K., Ali, R., Baboolal, A., Ward, K., 2022b, "Powering sustainable transition with geothermal energy: A case study on Dominica," Sus. Ener. Tech. Assess. 51. https://doi.org/10.1016/j.seta.2021.101910.

Bhagaloo, K., Baboolal, A., Ali, R., Razac, Z., Lutchmansingh, A., Mangra, A., Muhammad, T., Ward, K.. 2022a. "Resource efficiency as a guide to clean and affordable energy: A case study on Trinidad and Tobago," Chem. Eng. Res. Des. 178: 405-420. https://doi.org/10.1016/j.cherd.2021.12.026.

U.S Energy Information Administration, 2020, Capital Cost and Performance Characteristic Estimates for Utility Scale Electric Power Generating Technologies.

International Organization for Standardization, 2016, Environmental Management – Life Cycle Assessment – Requirements and Guidelines. ISO 14044.

Antonis Kokossis, Michael C. Georgiadis, Efstratios N. Pistikopoulos (Eds.)
PROCEEDINGS OF THE 33rd European Symposium on Computer Aided Process Engineering
(ESCAPE33), June 18-21, 2023, Athens, Greece

# Optimal operation of a sustainable water desalination unit integrated a green energy system

Ali Ahmadian,[a] Ali Almansoori,[b] Ali Elkamel,[c]

*aDepartment of Electrical Engineering, University of Bonab, Bonab, Iran.*
*bDepartment of Chemical Engineering, Khalifa University, Abu Dhabi 127788, United Arab Emirates*
*cDepartment of Chemical Engineering, University of Waterloo, 200 University Avenue West, Waterloo, ON, N2L 3G1, Canada*

## Abstract

In this paper, an optimization framework is proposed in order to optimal operation of a water desalination unit in a sustainable green energy network. The operation problem is modeled as a mixed integer linear programming (MILP) and optimized using a mathematical based optimization algorithm. In order to increase the flexibility of the studied sustainable energy system, a fuel cell unit and hydrogen-based vehicles have been included in the system. Moreover, the uncertainty of stochastic parameters has been considered and a machine learning based method namely long short term memory (LSTM) algorithm is utilized for forecasting of the parameters. The proposed methodology is applied on a typical case study and the simulation results are extracted and discussed.

**Keywords**: Water desalination unit, sustainable green energy, smart cities.

## 1. Introduction

Todays, the water demand addressing is a challenge in development countries and the poly makers and governments have been trying to increase the water resources. One of the main approach is utilization of water desalination units to produce water for domestic and industries. The water desalination units should be operated optimally in order to increase their benefits [1]. Several approaches have been proposed in the literature in order to increase the benefits of water desalination units. In [2], the renewable energy resources have been integrated with the water desalination units for producing a sustainable system. A geothermal energy based hybrid system in proposed in [3] and an experimental investigation is carried out in [4].

In this paper, the optimal utilization of desalination units and their interaction with the electricity network is implemented. In addition, to increase the flexibility of the proposed method fuel cell units and hydrogen-based vehicles are modeled. The optimization problem is a mixed-integer linear programming method that has the ability to solve large-scale problems efficiently and can be solved with well-known solvers such as CPLEX. Owing to the fact that uncertainty parameters especially those of RESs and load demand plays a decisive effect on the total cost of the system. In this paper, a deep learning-based method known as long short-term memory networks (LSTMs) a well-known method in time series forecasting is implemented for modeling different stochastic parameters.

## Nomenclature

| $n, m$ | Indices of buses |
|---|---|
| $e$ | Index of emission types |

| | |
|---|---|
| $dg, r, es$ | Index for DGs, RESs, and ESs |
| $t$ | Index for time |
| $des$ | Index for desalination unit |
| $\alpha_{dg}, \beta_{dg}, \gamma_{dg}$ | DGs cost coefficients |
| $\Gamma_{e,dg}$ | Emission factor of different emission types (\$/lb) |
| $G_{n,m}, B_{n,m}$ | Conductance and susceptance of lines (p.u.) |
| $PD_{n,t}, QD_{n,t}$ | Active and reactive load demands |
| $EP_t$ | Electricity price (\$/kWh) |
| $PDG_{dg}^{MIN}, PDG_{dg}^{MAX}$ | Minimum and maximum output power of DGs (kW) |
| $PCH_{es}^{MAX}, PDS_{es}^{MAX}$ | Maximum charging and discharging power of ESs (kW) |
| $S^{BASE}$ | Base apparent power (kVA) |
| $SL_{n,m}^{MAX}$ | The maximum thermal limit of lines (kVA) |
| $SES_{es}^{MIN}, SES_{es}^{MAX}$ | Minimum and maximum SOC od ESs (kWh) |
| $V_n^{MIN}, V_n^{MAX}$ | Minimum and maximum voltage magnitude (p.u) |
| $V_{des}^{T,MAX}$ | Maximum volume of the tank (m$^3$) |
| $V_{des}^{DES,MIN}, V_{des}^{DES,MAX}$ | Minimum and maximum treated water by desalination unit (m$^3$) |
| $W_t^D$ | Water demand (m$^3$) |
| $D^{EF}$ | Efficiency of WDs |
| $\zeta_{dg}$ | Externality emission cost of DGs (lb/kWh) |
| $\alpha_{es}^{ES}$ | Degradation factor of ESs |
| $\alpha_r^{RES}$ | Cost factor of RESs (\$/kW) |
| $\Delta t$ | Length of time interval |
| $\varrho_{n,m,t}$ | Linear load flow constant |
| $\eta_{es}^{CH}, \eta_{es}^{DCH}$ | ES's charging and discharging efficiency |
| $\theta_n^{MIN}, \theta_n^{MAX}$ | Minimum and maximum voltage angle (rad) |
| $PCH_{es,t}, PDS_{es,t}$ | ES charge and discharge (kW) |
| $UP_t$ | Exchanged power with the upstream network (kW) |
| $PDG_{dg,t}, PES_{es,t}, PRES_{r,t}$ | Generated power by DG, ES, and RESs (kW) |
| $PDS_{des,t}$ | Consumed power by WD unit (kW) |
| $PG_{n,t}, QG_{n,t}$ | Generated active and reactive powers in each bus |
| $P_{n,m,t}, Q_{n,m,t}, S_{n,m,t}$ | Active, reactive, and apparent power flow (kW) |
| $SES_{es,t}$ | SOC of ESs (kWh) |
| $I_{es,t}^{CH}, I_{es,t}^{DIS}$ | Binary variables for ESs |

| $U_{dg,t}$ | Binary variables for on/off of DGs |
|---|---|
| $V_{n,t}$ | Voltage magnitude (p.u.) |
| $V_{des,t}^{T}$ | The volume of stored water in the tank (m³) |
| $V_{des,t}^{T,INP}$ | Input water to the tank (m³) |
| $\theta_{n,t}$ | Voltage angle (rad) |

## 2. Problem Formulation

Due to the water crisis in the world, this paper aims to find optimal management for a smart city to satisfy the electric and water demand of residents. In the proposed method we consider water desalination units besides renewable energy resources (RESs). In this regard, we can get the most out of RESs by using their surplus power for making drinking water. The main objective is minimizing cost as demonstrated in equation (1).

$$Minimizing\ Cost = \sum_t UP_t\ EP_t + \sum_t \sum_{dg}((\alpha_{dg}PDG_{dg,t}^2 + \beta_{dg}PDG_{dg,t} + \gamma_{dg})U_{dg,t} + \sum_e \zeta_{dg}\ \Gamma_{e,dg}\ PDG_{dg,t}) + \sum_t \sum_{es} \alpha_{es}^{ES}PES_{es,t} + \sum_t \sum_r \alpha_r^{RES}PRES_{r,t} \tag{1}$$

The total cost consists of the cost of exchanging power with the upstream network, the cost of DGs considering their emission cost, the degradation cost of ESs, and the RESs cost. DGs constraints for the maximum and minimum generated active power is shown in (2). The other constraints such as ramp rate and on/off limits are modeled based on reference [5].

$$PDG_{dg}^{MIN}\ U_{dg,t} \le PDG_{dg,t} \le PDG_{dg}^{MAX}\ U_{dg,t} \tag{2}$$

Equations (3)-(8) show the operational constraints of ESs. (3) show the level of energy stored in the ES. The amount of power delivered or injected into the grid is calculated based on (4). Equations (5)-(7) demonstrate the charging and discharging state of these units. Finally, (8) restricts the state of charge of ESs.

$$SES_{es,t} = SES_{es,t-1} + (PCH_{es,t}\eta_{es}^{CH} - PDS_{es,t}/\eta_{es}^{DCH})\Delta t \tag{3}$$

$$PES_{es,t} = PDS_{es,t} - PCH_{es,t} \tag{4}$$

$$0 \le PCH_{es,t} \le PCH_{es}^{MAX}\ I_{es,t}^{CH} \tag{5}$$

$$0 \le PDS_{es,t} \le PDS_{es}^{MAX}\ I_{es,t}^{DIS} \tag{6}$$

$$I_{es,t}^{CH} + I_{es,t}^{DIS} \le 1 \tag{7}$$

$$SES_{es}^{MIN} \le SES_{es,t} \le SES_{es}^{MAX} \tag{8}$$

In order to model the water desalination units (WDs) equations (9)-(12) are taken into account. To increase the flexibility of WDs a tank for storing water is considered. The volume of water stored in this tank is calculated based on (9). The volume of input water and the minimum and maximum of stored water in this unit are controlled by (10) and (11). (12) indicate the relation between purified water and the power consumed by WD.

$$V_{des,t}^T = V_{des,t-1}^T + V_{des,t}^{T,INP} - WD_t \tag{9}$$

$$0 \le V_{des,t}^T \le V_{des}^{T,MAX} \tag{10}$$

$$V_{des}^{DES,MIN} \le V_{des,t}^{T,INP} \le V_{des}^{DES,MAX} \tag{11}$$

$$V_{des,t}^{T,INP} = PDS_{des,t}D^{EF} \tag{12}$$

For modeling the load flow constraints a linearized load flow method based on [6] is used. Active and reactive power balances are checked by (13) and (14). Equations (15)-(17) express active, reactive, and apparent power flows through the network. Equations (18)-(20) are used to control network limits.

$$(PG_{n,t} - PD_{n,t})/S^{BASE} = (2V_{n,t} - 1)G_{n,n} + \sum_{m \ne n} G_{n,m}(V_{n,t} + V_{m,t} - 1) + B_{n,m}(\theta_{n,t} - \theta_{m,t}) \tag{13}$$

$$(QG_{n,t} - QD_{n,t})/S^{BASE} = -(2V_{n,t} - 1)B_{n,n} + \sum_{m \ne n} -B_{n,m}(V_{n,t} + V_{m,t} - 1) + G_{n,m}(\theta_{n,t} - \theta_{m,t}) \tag{14}$$

$$P_{n,m,t} = G_{n,m}(V_{n,t} - V_{m,t}) + B_{n,m}(\theta_{n,t} - \theta_{m,t}) \tag{15}$$

$$Q_{n,m,t} = -B_{n,m}(V_{n,t} - V_{m,t}) + G_{n,m}(\theta_{n,t} - \theta_{m,t}) \tag{16}$$

$$S_{n,m,t} = P_{b,\bar{b},t} + \varrho_{n,m,t} Q_{n,m,t} \tag{17}$$

$$V_n^{MIN} \le V_{n,t} \le V_n^{MAX} \tag{18}$$

$$\theta_n^{MIN} \le \theta_{n,t} \le \theta_n^{MAX} \tag{19}$$

$$|S_{n,m,t}| \le SL_{n,m}^{MAX} \tag{20}$$

### 2.1. Uncertainty Modeling

Nowadays, due to access to big data in power systems. Data-driven-based approaches especially deep-learning-based approaches known as promising tools for modeling different stochastic parameters. One of the well-known methods for forecasting time series stochastic parameters is long-short-term memory networks (LSTMs). The fundamentals and formulation of LSTMs are presented in [7].

## 3. Numerical results and discussion

### 3.1. Input data

To evaluate the proposed method a network as presented in Fig. 1 is considered. As shown in Fig. 1 the system contains two wind turbines (WTs), two photovoltaic panels (PVs), two WDs, and three DGs. Input data related to DG and ES and other data are extracted from reference [8] and the emission data are obtained based on [9].

### 3.2. Simulation Results

After running the optimization problem based on the above-mentioned data. The results for the study case are as follows. The amount of consumption power by WD units is illustrated in Fig. 2. As stated in this figure and fig. 4 to utilize the maximum benefit of RESs, WDs are used during hours when the total power of RESs is high which proves the good performance of the proposed method.

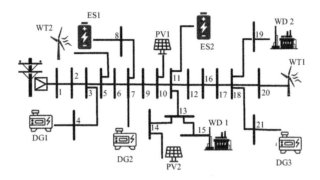

Fig. 1. Single-line diagram of the case study.

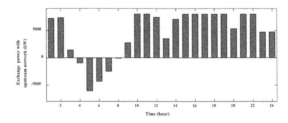

Fig. 2. Consumed power by WD units.

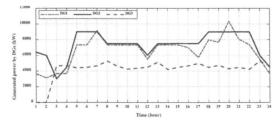

Fig. 3. exchange power with the upstream network.

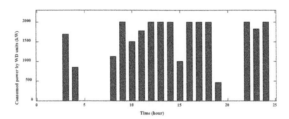

Fig. 4. Generated power by DGs.

Fig. 3 shows the amount of power exchange with the upstream network. By comparing this result with Fig. 2 it is obvious that the algorithm adjusts its power based on the electricity price, RESs generation, and water demand. Fig. 4 indicates the output power of each DG during different hours. A detail of the resources' cost is depicted in Table 1.

**Table 1: Detail of distribution network cost.**

| Parameters | Cost ($) |
|---|---|
| DG cost | 25509 |
| Power exchange cost | 9483 |
| Total emission cost | 720 |
| RESs cost | 1045 |
| Total Cost | 36757 |

## 4. Conclusion

In this paper, a water desalination unit is operated optimally in a sustainable green energy system. The uncertainty of stochastic parameters has been considered using a machine learning based approach and the operation problem is solved as a mixed integer linear programming (MILP) using a mathematical based optimization algorithm. The simulation results verified the effectiveness and robustness of the proposed approach in reducing the operation cost of the sustainable energy system and the emission pollution.

## References

[1]     Peng, Wanxi, Akbar Maleki, Marc A. Rosen, and Pouria Azarikhah. "Optimization of a hybrid system for solar-wind-based water desalination by reverse osmosis: Comparison of approaches." Desalination 442 (2018): 16-31.

[2]     Bundschuh, Jochen, Michał Kaczmarczyk, Noreddine Ghaffour, and Barbara Tomaszewska. "State-of-the-art of renewable energy sources used in water desalination: Present and future prospects." Desalination 508 (2021): 115035.

[3]     Okati, V., Amir Ebrahimi-Moghadam, A. Behzadmehr, and Mahmood Farzaneh-Gord. "Proposal and assessment of a novel hybrid system for water desalination using solar and geothermal energy sources." Desalination 467 (2019): 229-244.

[4]     Mostafa, Marwa, Heba M. Abdullah, and Mohamed A. Mohamed. "Modeling and experimental investigation of solar stills for enhancing water desalination process." IEEE Access 8 (2020): 219457-219472.

[5]     Gougheri SS, Dehghani M, Nikoofard A, Jahangir H, Golkar MA. Economic assessment of multi-operator virtual power plants in electricity market: A game theory-based approach. Sustain Energy Technol Assessments 2022;53:102733.

[6]     Sadeghi S, Jahangir H, Vatandoust B, Golkar MA, Ahmadian A, Elkamel A. Optimal bidding strategy of a virtual power plant in day-ahead energy and frequency regulation markets: A deep learning-based approach. Int J Electr Power Energy Syst 2021;127:106646. https://doi.org/https://doi.org/10.1016/j.ijepes.2020.106646.

[7]     Jahangir H, Tayarani H, Gougheri SS, Golkar MA, Ahmadian A, Elkamel A. Deep Learning-based Forecasting Approach in Smart Grids with Micro-Clustering and Bi-directional LSTM Network. IEEE Trans Ind Electron 2020.

[8]      Gougheri SS, Jahangir H, Golkar MA, Ahmadian A, Golkar MA. Optimal participation of a virtual power plant in electricity market considering renewable energy: A deep learning-based approach. Sustain Energy, Grids Networks 2021;26:100448.

[9]      Mohamed FA, Koivo HN. System modelling and online optimal management of microgrid using mesh adaptive direct search. Int J Electr Power Energy Syst 2010;32:398–407.

Antonis Kokossis, Michael C. Georgiadis, Efstratios N. Pistikopoulos (Eds.)
PROCEEDINGS OF THE 33rd European Symposium on Computer Aided Process Engineering
(ESCAPE33), June 18-21, 2023, Athens, Greece

# Optimal production of green hydrogen with grid assistance for enhanced flexibility

Christopher Varela,[a,b,c] Mahmoud Mostafa,[a] Edwin Zondervan,[d]

[a]*Laboratory of Process Systems Engineering, University of Bremen, Leobener Str. 6, 28359 Bremen, Germany*
[b]*Facultad de Ciencias Naturales y Matemáticas, Escuela Superior Politécnica del Litoral, ESPOL, Campus Gustavo Galindo, Km. 30.5 Vía Perimetral, Guayaquil P.O. Box 09-01-5863, Ecuador*
[c]*Centro de Energías Renovables y Alternativas, CERA, Escuela Superior Politécnica del Litoral, ESPOL, Campus Gustavo Galindo, Km. 30.5 Vía Perimetral, Guayaquil P.O. Box 09-01-5863, Ecuador*
[d]*SPT-PSE, University of Twente, 7522NB Enschede, The Netherlands*

## Abstract

The use of grid power to compensate for shortages of renewable energy results in higher profit at electrolysis facilities. However, the carbon footprint of hydrogen increases in regions where fossil sources have a significant share in the energy mix. This contribution seeks to balance profit with carbon footprint through mathematical programming. The case study comprises a 100-$MW_p$ wind power plant, and data on electricity price and $CO_2$-emissions content in the grid, covering a full-year of operation in northern Germany. The results show that the highest profit is attained at maximum load, with a minor influence of the electricity price (<75 €/MWh) and no influence of the $CO_2$-emissions content of the grid. In this scenario, approximately 50% of the power stems from conventional sources. Therefore, a cost penalty is proposed to the use of fossil power to limit the grid assistance. This further reduces the grid contribution to around 30%, still allowing for a high profit.

**Keywords**: Energy transition, green hydrogen, Power-to-X, MILP.

## 1. Main Text

The main text can start here. Next paragraphs should start with heading as given in below example.

## 2. Introduction

The efficient conversion and long-term storage of renewable energy is a key aspect within the energy transition concept. This can be achieved by for example Power-to-X (PtX) technologies, using green hydrogen as renewable energy carrier. It is expected that green hydrogen will meet a global demand of 74 exajoules per year by 2050, with a production cost below 1.25 $/kg [1]. While the economic figures seem promising, scaling-up the production of green hydrogen requires operation strategies to deal with volatile renewable energy and the dynamics of energy markets.

In earlier work a method to determine the optimal number of electrolyzers and their optimal operation schedule for an off-grid electrolysis facility was presented [2].

However, the connection to power grids provides additional flexibility to move the operation of electrolyzers towards more favorable conditions. This comprises demand-side management and provision of grid services [3]. On the other hand, loading power beyond the available renewable capacity increases the carbon footprint of hydrogen, especially in periods with low share of renewables in the energy mix. This work includes the grid power in the scheduling program of alkaline water electrolysis (AEL). The grid is expected to participate mainly in periods of low $CO_2$-emissions content, low electricity prices, and to avoid unnecessary shutdowns. In addition, the program includes a penalty to avoid intensive use of the grid. This penalty is based on a time-variant profile of $CO_2$-emissions content in the grid. In such way, the grid assists the PtX facility maximizing the profit with minimum carbon footprint.

## 3. Methodology

The water electrolysis optimization program (available in [2], [4]) determines the optimal schedule of electrolyzers with profiles of renewable energy and electricity price. It is based on a timed-automaton model that represents the states and power load of a commercial electrolysis stack. The constraints describe the physical and technical restrictions of the system (startup/shutdown time, load range, etc.). The current case study considers a reference 100-$MW_p$ wind power supply (Figure 1) and the power grid with a theoretical unlimited capacity. Agorameter [5] reports time-variant data on electricity price and $CO_2$-emissions content in the grid for Germany. Data of the year 2019 was considered. The objective function is set to maximize the profit with a penalty on the fossil power loaded from the grid.

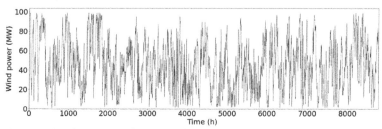

*Figure 1. Wind power supply (54°10'29.2"N 9°03'51.9"E, Vestas V150, 80 m hub height) [6], [7]*

The results are obtained for a base case scenario that reflects the operation of PtX within the current energy market and AEL performance. Furthermore, a sensitivity analysis allows estimating the effect on the profit and carbon footprint of the process for other scenarios. Such scenarios reflect different operation goals, technological development, and market trends. The selected parameters are shown in Table 1.

*Table 1. AEL-model parameters*

| Parameter | Base case | Sensitivity analysis |
|---|---|---|
| Annual production (MNm³) | 110 | 50 – 200 |
| Investment cost per 3.5-MW electrolyzer (M€) | 1.96 | 0.5 – 2.0 |
| Penalty cost of $CO_2$ emissions (€/t$_{CO2}$) | 40 | 0 – 200 |

The annual demand is set to around 60% of the maximum production capacity for the base case, with an evenly distributed production per month. An increased demand of hydrogen requires either adding more electrolyzers or making intensive use of the grid. The investment cost of electrolyzers is expected to decrease in the next few years, for which lower values are mainly considered. The penalty on $CO_2$-emissions is a cost, which is set to around the order of magnate of values reported by the European Trading System.

## 4. Results and discussion

The program is solved using the optimizer GUROBI/PYTHON [8]. The number of variables is in the order of 1.6 million, as it considers a full-year horizon with time intervals of 1 hour and several electrolysis stacks. Despite the large extension of the program, finding optimal solutions in a few seconds is feasible due to its linear structure.

The program finds the optimal schedule for each electrolyzer considering the whole time horizon, while the number of installed electrolyzers has to be fixed at first. The base case scenario presents the solution with 27 installed electrolyzers of 3.1 MW with load ranges from 10 to 100% each. The sensitivity analysis, on the other hand, includes MILP-solutions generated by setting the number of electrolyzers from 20 to 34, while varying the parameters mentioned in Table 1.

### 4.1. Base case scenario

The optimal solution shows that the facility should mainly operate at full capacity to increase the profit, despite the penalty added for the grid use. Figure 2 contains the load of the electrolysis facility (almost constant profile), while the available renewable power appears in the background. It shows many periods in which the facility uses the grid to compensate for the lack of renewable power. The grid contributed around 46.8% of the total power, while the overall production cost and carbon footprint were estimated to be 2.46 €/kg$_{H2}$ and 10.83 kg$_{CO2}$/kg$_{H2}$, respectively. Since fossil hydrogen (from SMR) has an approximate production cost of 1.5 €/kg$_{H2}$ and a carbon footprint of 10 kg$_{CO2}$/kg$_{H2}$, AEL with major grid assistance is economically and environmentally unviable under the case study conditions. Similar results were obtained with a different number of electrolyzers added to the facility.

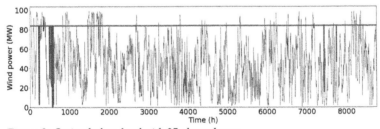

*Figure 2: Optimal plant load with 27 electrolyzers*

Moreover, there are few periods where the process undergoes a partial or total shutdown. These periods coincide with periods of electricity prices greater than 75 €/MWh. Thus, periods of high electricity price trigger total or partial shutdown of electrolyzers, regardless of the renewable power availability or $CO_2$-emissions content in the grid. The process response to such scenario is shown in Figure 3, which contains the load of electrolyzers in the time interval of 500 to 600 hours. Few electrolyzers report partial loads, keeping rather their operation at maximum capacity or shutdown.

### 4.2. Sensitivity analysis

The sensitivity analysis is performed to explore optimal solutions under more optimistic conditions to the energy transition, namely lower investment cost of electrolyzers or restricted use of fossil-based power. It is of special interest to identify under which scenarios the process remains cost-competitive while the carbon footprint considerably decreases as compared to the base case scenario. The MILP considers 20 to 34 installed electrolyzers and parameter values within the range shown in Table 1. The sensitivity analysis is locally performed, meaning that it determines the individual influence of the parameters. The surface of the objective function in relation to the parameters are projected in the subplots of Figure 4, with the inline figure indicating the objective value in M€/a.

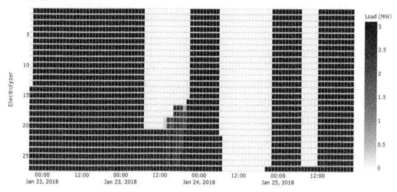

*Figure 3: Optimal schedule of electrolyzers during the time 500 to 600 h*

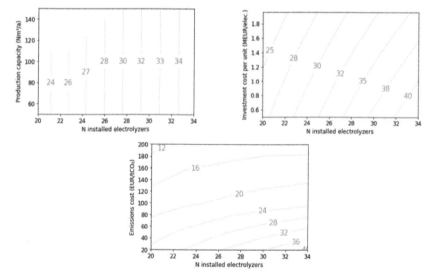

*Figure 4: Parameters sensitivity to the objective function in M€/a: (top left) production capacity, (top right) purchasing cost of electrolyzers, and (bottom) cost of $CO_2$ emissions.*

The effect of the production capacity is negligible, as the electrolysis facility always load at its full capacity to increase the profit. This means that optimal solutions correspond to steady-state operations with few executed startup/shutdown cycles, major grid assistance, and production rate that exceeds the monthly demand. The purchasing cost of electrolyzers has a relevant impact on the objective function. For the most optimistic scenarios (low capital cost) the objective value increases by around 15% as compared to the base case. This can be possible considering the expected technological developments in future years. However, both parameters have no effect on the production schedule, keeping the loading of electrolyzers always at their full capacity. On the other hand, the objective function presents a high sensitivity to the $CO_2$-emissions cost. For values lower than 40 €/$t_{CO2}$, the facility opts operations at full capacity, similarly to the base case scenario. While for costs higher than 40 €/$t_{CO2}$, lower carbon footprints are computed with considerably lower annual production of hydrogen. The results are shown in Table 2.

*Table 2: Sensitivity analysis results*

| | $CO_2$-emissions penalty cost (€/$t_{CO2}$) | | | | |
|---|---|---|---|---|---|
| | **0** | **20** | **40** | **100** | **200** |
| Annual production (MNm³) | 156.10 | 155.83 | 155.46 | 135.29 | 110.00 |
| Production cost (€/$kg_{H2}$) | 2.47 | 2.46 | 2.46 | 2.43 | 2.52 |
| Carbon footprint ($kg_{CO2}$/$kg_{H2}$) | 20.34 | 10.88 | 10.83 | 8.57 | 5.27 |
| Annual profit without penalty (M€) | 35.55 | 35.54 | 35.51 | 31.23 | 24.49 |
| Grid assistance (%Power) | 95.43 | 46.96 | 46.84 | 39.84 | 27.29 |
| Operation strategy | Full load | Full load | Full load | Partial load | Load following |

It is noted that the demand constraint (at 110 MNm³/a, evenly distributed each month) restricts the carbon footprint to a minimum of 5.27 $kg_{CO2}$/$kg_{H2}$. This also means that the grid had to provide at least 27.29% of the total power to cover the hydrogen demand. The operation however presents a different load profile as compared to the base case, as shown in Figure 5, for a snapshot of the operation for the period from 2000 to 3000 h.

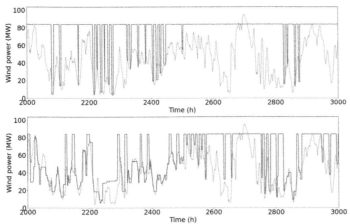

*Figure 5: Load profile of the AEL facility for (top) emission cost of 100 €/$t_{CO2}$, and (bottom) emission cost of 200 €/$t_{CO2}$*

This result shows how the penalty allowed moving the operation strategy from a steady-state load profile to a load-following profile (same behavior as the renewable power). An intermediate profile, denoted in this work as to partial load (Figure 5, top), is still a profit-driven operation in which the electricity price has a major influence as compared to the emissions content in the grid. The load-following profile (Figure 5, bottom) attempts to reduce the grid assistance but still exploits periods of low electricity price to increase the profit. The carbon footprint of the load-following operation decreases by almost a half of the estimated value at the base case, while the profit presents a reduction of 31%.

## 5. Conclusions and outlook

The operation of electrolysis facilities at their full capacity (renewable power plus grid compensation) is the most beneficial operation strategy in terms of profit, and therefore the most obvious choice to industry nowadays. However, it substantially differs from a renewable-based operation, for instance, load-following operations with a reference renewable power plant.

This work presented an approach to restrict the grid assistance to specific scenarios, namely avoiding unnecessary shutdowns and benefit from periods of low electricity prices or low emissions content in the grid. It is to remark that the demand of hydrogen (model constraint) posed a minimum limit to the grid participation. In the case study, the grid contributed to at least 30% of the total power supply to the AEL facility, while the wind power plant of reference supplied the major part. Although green hydrogen plants are expected to fully operate on renewables, an efficient use of the grid could enhance the process economics while keeping a high renewable content in the product. In this study, the optimization was driven by including a cost penalty to the emissions content in the grid, which can be consider a carbon tax. This is an indirect form to promote the grid use when the renewable content in the grid is high, regardless the specific location, capacity and generation profile of those renewable power facilities. An alternative approach would be to add a constraint that restricts the $CO_2$ content to a certain level, for instance, to participate in green or low-carbon hydrogen markets.

There is still the opportunity to analyze the effect of hydrogen storage in such systems, as a buffer could reduce the extent of the grid assistance. Yet it is to remark that on-grid operations of PtX facilities should estimate the carbon footprint due to the emissions content in the grid, with its spatial and temporal distribution. In addition, this work suggests that a regulatory framework to support PtX projects is required to favor load-following operations. This can include establishing preferential electricity tariffs, markets for the provision of grid services, or taxes when using grid power at periods with a high emission factor.

## References

[1]     IRENA, *Global hydrogen trade to meet the 1.5°C climate goal: Part III – Green hydrogen cost and potential.* 2022.

[2]     C. Varela, M. Mostafa, and E. Zondervan, "Modeling alkaline water electrolysis for power-to-x applications: A scheduling approach," *Int. J. Hydrogen Energy*, vol. 46, no. 14, pp. 9303–9313, 2021, doi: 10.1016/j.ijhydene.2020.12.111.

[3]     A. Gitis, M. Leuthold, and D. U. Sauer, "Chapter 4 - Applications and Markets for Grid-Connected Storage Systems," in *Electrochemical Energy Storage for Renewable Sources and Grid Balancing*, P. T. Moseley and J. Garche, Eds. Amsterdam: Elsevier, 2015, pp. 33–52.

[4]     J. Bartels, C. Varela, T. Wassermann, W. Medjroubi, and E. Zondervan, "Integration of water electrolysis facilities in power grids: A case study in northern Germany," *Energy Convers. Manag. X*, vol. 14, no. March, p. 100209, 2022, doi: 10.1016/j.ecmx.2022.100209.

[5]     Agora Energiewende, "Agorameter," 2019.

[6]     S. Pfenninger and I. Staffell, "Long-term patterns of European PV output using 30 years of validated hourly reanalysis and satellite data," *Energy*, vol. 114, pp. 1251–1265, Nov. 2016, doi: 10.1016/j.energy.2016.08.060.

[7]     I. Staffell and S. Pfenninger, "Using bias-corrected reanalysis to simulate current and future wind power output," *Energy*, vol. 114, pp. 1224–1239, Nov. 2016, doi: 10.1016/j.energy.2016.08.068.

[8]     Gurobi Optimization LLC, "Gurobi Optimizer Reference Manual." 2022.

Antonis Kokossis, Michael C. Georgiadis, Efstratios N. Pistikopoulos (Eds.)
PROCEEDINGS OF THE 33rd European Symposium on Computer Aided Process Engineering
(ESCAPE33), June 18-21, 2023, Athens, Greece

# Water sources evaluation for green hydrogen production: a case study in Brazil

Leonardo O. S. Santana,[a]  Artur S. Bispo,[a] Gustavo S. Santos,[a]  Chrislaine B. Marinho,[a] Ewerton E. S. Calixto,[a] José L. G. Almeida,[a] Fernando L. P. Pessoa[a,b]

[a] *SENAI CIMATEC university center, Avenida Orlando Gomes, Salvador 41650-010, Brazil*
[b] *Federal University of Rio de Janeiro (UFRJ), Av. Athos da Silveira Ramos, Rio de Janeiro 21941-909, Brazil.*
*leosantana049@gmail.com*

## Abstract

A proper sustainability analysis must include technical, economical, environmental, and social criteria. In this regard, a look at the water consumption in the green hydrogen process is essential to guarantee that the process is indeed sustainable. This work presents an approach to evaluate the suitability of water sources (WS) for hydrogen production via water electrolysis. The approach was applied to a designed 1 MW green hydrogen cluster to be in the future in SENAI-CIMATEC Park in Brazil. Five different WS were evaluated; seawater, treated industrial wastewater, tap water, rainwater, and groundwater. 12 criteria were considered, and economical calculations were performed to evaluate each source. The sum of each measure defined the best and worst water source for the case study. The results have shown that the best WS where tap and rainwater and the worst was seawater, mainly due to the elevation of the hydrogen plant.

**Keywords**: Green hydrogen production, water electrolysis, water treatment, water scarcity, sustainable value.

## 1. Introduction

The production of green hydrogen from the electrolysis of water using renewable energy sources is essential. Beswick, et al. (2021) indicate that in a renewable future the need for hydrogen would be 2.3 Gt per year, where the carbon emissions from the energy sector could be reduced by up to 10,2Gt annually. However, according to Newborough & Cooley (2021), if the green hydrogen replaces all fossil fuels, the water requirement for electrolysis would be near 1x1014 kg per year (1.8% of present global water consumption). T and, as a result, water ecosystems can be under significant pressure if not well managed. With this, the scarcity of water, both in quality and quantity, generates the need to assess the adequacy of the sources. (Woods, et al. 2022)

The use of quantitative resources and qualitative factors becomes a priority. Competing with human uses, such as agriculture and urban consumption, requires alternative water sources, such as seawater or industrial wastewater, which have great potential for large-scale production of green hydrogen. The study of these potential WS can lead to a more sustainable one, creating the opportunity for support water security and reducing environmental contamination. (Winter et al., 2022)

Ultrapure water is required for electrolysis, typically water type I or II, as defined by the American society for testing and materials (ASTM) with ionic conductivity < 5μS/cm (ISO 2696) and this water quality must be guaranteed regardless the source of water otherwise water impurities can lead to irreversible damage to the electrolyzer. Thus, designing a water treatment plant to meet the electrolyzer's requirements is crucial. (Woods, et al. 2022; Simões et al. 2021)

This work presents an approach to assessing the suitability of WS for hydrogen production via water electrolysis, applying a Sustainable Value methodology and an optimization method for aqueous liquid effluent treatment systems to support decision making, combining economic, environmental, and social criteria. The approach is applied to an 1MW green hydrogen cluster on SENAI-CIMATEC Park in Brazil. WS are evaluated for water availability, quality, transport options, abstraction costs, treatment, regulatory needs (including environmental restrictions), and social acceptance. The WS selected were grid water, seawater, rainwater, industrial wastewater (from a near centralized effluent treatment plant), and good quality groundwater (from the São Sebastião aquifer). The necessary treatments were optimally generated using a decision support tool based on heuristic rules for water and effluent treatment, and the water Quality Specification (pre- purification) was established according to the electrolyzer data (according to Directive (EU) 2020/2184- quality of water for human consumption).

## 2. Methodology

The methodology presented herein is based on the multi-criteria approach of sustainable value methodology proposed by Simões (2021). It was developed by integrating different concepts from distinct subjects such as value analysis, ecoefficiency, energy efficiency and cleaner production.

The first step was to identify and mapping all potential WS that can input the electrolyzer which were available around the green hydrogen cluster, and then information about distance and elevation (between the water source and the hydrogen plant) and treatment needs where summarized.

Five potential WS were identified (grid "Tap" water (TW), treated industrial wastewater (IW), sea water (SW), rainwater (RW), and ground water (GW)). The CAPEX and OPEX information were calculated taking in account captation, collection, transport. The table 1 presents investment costs for water captation, storage for each water source, and an overall water loss of 10% was taking in account (due to evaporation, leaks, etc.); water treatment (including installation costs, terrain preparation, etc.) were considered for supplying 700 m3/day. The individual treatment technologies where: Reverse Osmosis (RO); Reverse Osmosis (seawater) (RO*); Ultrafiltration (MF); Fine screening (FS) and Filtration/Coagulation (Chempre), and heuristics from literature were used to create the best treatment train.

**Table 1** – Treatment and captation costs

| WS | Treatment train | W. loses | Process CAPEX (€) | Energy consumption kWh/m3 | Captation (€) | Captation OPEX kW/m3 |
|----|----|----|----|----|----|----|
| TW | RO | 10% | 500,000.00 | 4.5000 | 0.00 | 0 |
| IW | FS→MF→RO | 25% | 776,000.00 | 4.5635 | 25,000.00 | 180.0000 |
| GW | Chempre→RO | 20% | 580,000.00 | 4.5500 | 150,000.00 | 600.0000 |
| RW | FS→MF | 10% | 201,000.00 | 0.0635 | - | - |
| SW | FS→RO* | 37% | 576,000.00 | 4.5010 | 80,000.00 | - |

For investment costs calculations for water transport, the specific distances and elevation from each potential WS to SENAI CIMATEC Park cluster (as in Table 4) were considered. For water transport via pipelines, purchase costs of welded and screwed pipe per unit length were assumed based in the equation on table 3. The construction of pipeline (considering the different transport distances in Table 2) includes stainless steel piping with an internal diameter of 50 cm.

**Table 2** – Considered distances and elevation for water transport

| Potential water source | CIMATEC Park cluster (m) |
|---|---|
| Ground water | On site |
| Industrial wastewater | 5.247/13 |
| Seawater | 4.686/40 |
| Water grid | On site |
| Rainwater | On site |

Water costs were calculated based on the work of Joksimovic (2007) and McGivney & Kawamura (2008) as shown by the equations on table 3.

**Table 3** – Water costs equations

| | **CAPEX** | **OPEX** |
|---|---|---|
| **Water transport** | $CC = 21{,}715 \cdot H \cdot Q^{0,52}$ <br><br> $CP = C_1 \cdot e^{c_2 \cdot D}$ <br><br> CC is the pumping station capital cost (R\$), H is the required pumping head (m) and Q the design flow rate. CP is the pipe unit cost (R\$/m), D is the diameter (m) and $C_i$ is the cost coefficients from literature. | $CE = \theta_{hp} \cdot C_e \cdot (V_{ann} \cdot H/2{,}7 \cdot \eta)$ <br><br> CE is the annual cost of energy required for pumping (R\$); $\theta_{hp}$ is a conversion factor to kWh $\theta_{hp} = 0{,}746$; $C_e$ is the electricity price [R\$/kWh]; $V_{ann}$ the volume of water pumped annually (m³) and $\eta$ the pump efficiency (65 %). |
| **Storage** | $UCS = C_1 \cdot V^{C_2}$ <br><br> UCS is the CAPEX unit cost of storage facility (R\$/m³); $C_i$ is the cost coefficients from literature and V is the storage volume (m³). | |
| **Treatment** | $CT = Cost_{(1)} \cdot f$ <br><br> CT is the capex cost for the treatment plant; $Cost_{(1)}$ is the sum of CAPEX cost of individual treatment process and f is the factor that includes other capex cost of treatment plat (f =1,8226 ) | $OT_{El} = E \cdot C_e$ <br><br> $OT_{Total} = OPEX_{El} /0{,}275$ <br><br> OT is the OPEX of treatment plant in function of electricity and the total OPEX; E is the energy consumption [kWh/m³] and $C_e$ the electricity price [R\$/kWh] |

For this study, values of 10.00 L per kg produced H2 are considered as required to input for 1MW PEM electrolyser, and 25401,6 kWh per day of electricity consumption. The values are based on information publicly available from electrolyser suppliers.

After cost calculations each of the potential WS (Table 5) was qualitatively assessed for each site adopting a functional value approach where the function is to supply water for hydrogen production. For this, the following criteria were identified: a) Short-term reliability of availability (effect of weather factors on WS as droughts); b) Long-term reliability of availability which can affect authorization on water use by environmental authorities (perceived future impact of climate change on water source); c) Reliability of supply (possibility for non-weather-related intermittencies, such as maintenance pauses, that could damage ensuring continuity of water supply); d) Competition with other uses (at water abstraction/collection level); e) Complexity of abstraction/collection (number of involved entities and existence of previous experience with this type of water for a similar use); f) Transport distance from water source to $H_2$ production plant site; g) Degree of water treatment needed up to electrolyser input requirements; h) Social acceptance; i) Complexity of the permitting process required (number of involved entities and existence of previous experience with this type of water for a similar use, including transport). j) Proportional cost related to CAPEX; k) Proportional cost related to OPEX and l) Electricity consumption. The performance level of the qualitative assessment of water sources for Criteria A to I was taken from Simões, et al (2021), with exception of criteria J, K and L.

**Table 4** – Criteria for Sustainable Value analysis of water sources.

| Criteria | Performance Level | | | |
|---|---|---|---|---|
| | **1** | **2** | **3** | **4** |
| **J** | 75-100% of H2 plant CAPEX | 50-74% of H2 plant CAPEX | 25-49% of H2 plant CAPEX | 0-24% of H2 plant CAPEX |
| **K** | 75-100% of H2 plant OPEX | 50-74% of H2 plant OPEX | 25-49% of H2 plant OPEX | 0-24% of H2 plant OPEX |
| **L** | 75-100% of H2 plant electricity consumption | 75-100% of H2 plant electricity consumption | 75-100% of H2 plant electricity consumption | 75-100% of H2 plant electricity consumption |

## 3. Main results

The performed cost of the different water sources shown that the more expensive source is sea water, specially in terms of OPEX, this is regarding the greater distance between the source and the treatment plant. Again because of transporting the treated industrial wastewater is also an expensive source.

**Figure 1** – Water sources CAPEX and OPEX

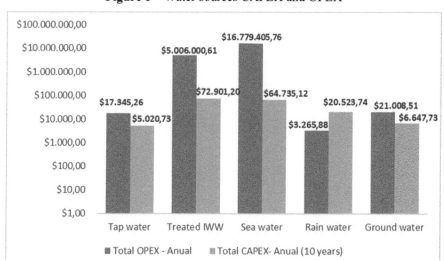

The analysis of the distributed costs of water presented in Figure 2. shows that costs related to transport (where necessary, for example sea water and treated IWW) are the most relevant in a general context. Another high cost is the cost of water treatment itself.

**Figure 2** – Water sources distributed costs.

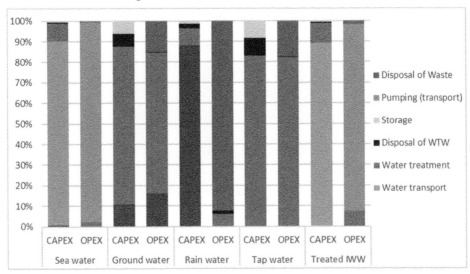

The results of the qualitative criteria are shown in Table 5, in which the grading (1–4 points) follows the criteria presented in Table 3. The best qualitative water source performance was obtained for rainwater followed by treated industrial wastewater and grid water. The water options with lower performance values for the site is sea water.

**Table 5** – Sustainable Value analysis of water sources.

| Weight | Criteria | TW | IW | SW | RW | GW |
|---|---|---|---|---|---|---|
| 2 | A | 3 | 4 | 4 | 1 | 2 |
| 1 | B | 4 | 4 | 4 | 1 | 2 |
| 2 | C | 4 | 4 | 4 | 2 | 2 |
| 2 | D | 1 | 4 | 4 | 4 | 1 |
| 1 | E | 4 | 2 | 1 | 2 | 2 |
| 2 | F | 4 | 2 | 2 | 4 | 4 |
| 1 | G | 4 | 1 | 1 | 3 | 3 |
| 4 | H | 1 | 4 | 4 | 4 | 2 |
| 1 | I | 4 | 3 | 1 | 3 | 2 |
| 1 | J | 4 | 1 | 1 | 4 | 4 |
| 3 | K | 4 | 3 | 1 | 4 | 4 |
| 4 | L | 4 | 3 | 1 | 4 | 4 |
| **Total points** | | 76 | 76 | 59 | 79 | 67 |

The Rainwater shown to be low costing easy to handle and abundant in the local of study.

It's important to take in account that these results represents the best water source for this specific study case, once the performance level are location and capacity dependent, for example, the high proportional capital and operational cost, the high energy consumption and the complexity of collection make the seawater be a bad choice for the study case plant, however, as the hydrogen capacity increases and the hydrogen cluster is constructed near from the sea, the proportional cost decreases, making sea water being a better option.

**Figure 3** – Results of water sources evaluation

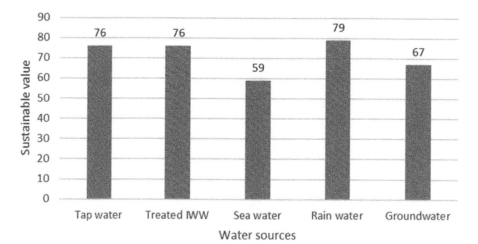

## 4. Conclusion

A sustainable value indicator allows a relative quantitative comparison of the performance of different water sources for electrolysis and the costs involved. It appears that for this case study rainwater is the most suitable source of water for electrolysis due to the lower risk of supply, lower costs, and avoids complex licensing processes. Likewise, grid water and effluent from the effluent treatment plant proved to be possible sources of water, where the factors that most affect suitability are the costs of transporting water and disposing of waste from effluent treatment.

## References

M. Newborough & G. Cooley, 2021, Green hydrogen: water use implications and opportunities, Fuel Cells Bulletin, Volume 2021, Issue 12 , p 12-15.

P. Woods, H. Bustamente, K. Zinsou, 2022, The hydrogen economy- where is the water? Energy nexus, volume 7.

S. Simoes, J. Catarino, A. Picado, T. Lopes, S. di Berardino, F. Amorim, F. Gírio, C. Rangel, T. Ponce de Leão, 2021, Water availability and water usage solutions for electrolysis in hydrogen production, Journal of Cleaner Production, 315, p 128124.

R. Beswick, A. Oliveira, Y. Yan, 2021, Does the green hydrogen economy have a water problem?, ACS energy letters, 6, p 3167-3169.

D. Joksimovic, 2007. Decision support system for planning of integrated water reuse projects.

W. McGivney, S. Kawamura, 2008, Cost estimating manual: for water treatment facilities. New Jersey: Hoboken

Antonis Kokossis, Michael C. Georgiadis, Efstratios N. Pistikopoulos (Eds.)
PROCEEDINGS OF THE 33rd European Symposium on Computer Aided Process Engineering
(ESCAPE33), June 18-21, 2023, Athens, Greece

# Sustainable Development Goals assessment of carbon capture on-board

Valentina Negri, Margarita A. Charalambous, Juan D. Medrano-García, Gonzalo Guillén-Gosálbez

*Institute for Chemical and Bioengineering, Department of Chemistry and Applied Biosciences, ETH Zürich, Vladimir-Prelog-Weg 1, Zürich 8093, Switzerland*
gonzalo.guillen.gosalbez@chem.ethz.ch

## Abstract

The shipping industry of cargo containers is a very efficient freight mode, yet it is still entirely reliant on fossil fuels. While sustainable fuels penetrate the market, carbon capture and storage has been proposed as an interim solution for low-carbon shipping. In this work, we assess the technical feasibility, economic and environmental performance of a cargo ship with a retrofitted carbon capture plant on-board that captures 94 % of direct emissions at 85 $\$_{2019}$/tCO$_2$. Compared to the current scenario, our solution reduces climate change by 50 %, while the direct air capture technology stands at a 45 % reduction. Our environmental assessment is based on absolute thresholds to quantify the impacts relative to the Earth's carrying capacity and shows that burden-shifting occurs in all the categories but climate change. Finally, the results are analyzed in light of five Sustainable Development Goals using 16 life cycle impact assessment metrics and their associated absolute thresholds.

**Keywords**: container ship, maritime emissions, carbon capture on-board, life cycle assessment, Sustainable Development Goals.

## 1. Introduction

The shipping industry is one of the most efficient transportation modes: it only contributed to approximately 3 % of the global GHG emissions in 2018 (IMO, 2021) while moving 80 % of the total cargo by sea (Istrate et al., 2022). Nonetheless, this sector is still heavily reliant on fossil fuels and its decarbonization was never part of the goals set in the Paris Agreement (Rogelj et al., 2016). Despite the measures adopted to reduce the environmental impact of the shipping industry (IMO, 2022), its emissions are still projected to increase due to population and consequent freight demand growth. Long-term solutions are based on a complete switch of the current fleet to low- or zero-carbon fuels, with a non-negligible change in the infrastructure, i.e., they require compatible engines and bigger fuel storage tanks on-board to compensate for the lower volumetric energy densities. While these sustainable fuels, such as hydrogen, ammonia and methanol, are introduced into the market, interim solutions based on carbon (CO$_2$) captured directly at the source (DNV, 2022) or from the air (DAC) could be deployed in parallel.

We conduct a comprehensive techno-economic and environmental assessment of a carbon capture plant retrofitted on-board a cargo ship. While the concept was first proposed by Det Norske Veritas and Process Systems Enterprise in 2013 and recently evaluated by Feenstra and co-workers (Feenstra, 2019), its absolute environmental footprint remains unclear. Additionally, we compare this solution with the current business-as-usual scenario (BAU) and DAC as an alternative emissions abatement technology.

In this work, life cycle assessment (LCA)-based absolute sustainability methods quantify impacts relative to the planet's carrying capacities using environmental thresholds to interpret the results on a global scale. These methods are rooted in the planetary boundaries (PBs) concept introduced in the work by Rockström et al. (2009), where for the first time, a set of Earth system biophysical limits that should never be surpassed to operate our planet safely were defined. Later, Sala and co-authors (2020) built on the existing literature connecting 16 indicators of the Environmental Footprint (EF) method to five Sustainable Development Goals (SDGs), which is the approach followed here and the focus of this work.

## 2. Methodology

### 2.1. Reference ship

We consider an 8500 twenty-foot equivalent units (TEU) cargo ship powered by a standard internal combustion engine with heavy fuel oil. The reference vessel travels fixed routes and distances between commercial ports at an assumed speed of 26.5 knots. We retrofit a standard carbon capture process on-board the reference ship to reduce the direct emissions considering a week-long trip. We perform a detailed modeling of the system in Aspen HYSYS v11, which includes three main sections, namely the exhaust gas cleaning, $CO_2$ capture and its liquefaction, as displayed in Figure 1, that are heat-integrated.

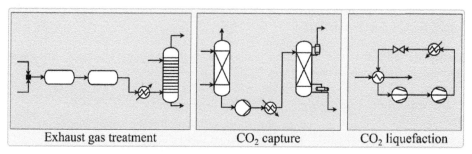

| Exhaust gas treatment | $CO_2$ capture | $CO_2$ liquefaction |

Figure 1. Sketch of the process modeling sections. The exhaust gas treatment, $CO_2$ capture and $CO_2$ liquefaction are heat-integrated on-board the vessel.

The pre-treatment section includes a scrubber for the removal of nitrogen and sulfur oxides from the combustion of the heavy fuel oil, as well as a particulate matter abatement technology to comply with the current regulations.

We retrofit a standard post-combustion carbon capture plant on the vessel. Among all the available options, absorption-based $CO_2$ capture is characterized by the highest technology readiness level, which leads to an easy installation on-board and high efficiency. However, this solution comes at the expenses of considerable space reduction on-board mainly allocated to the absorption and desorption column and the natural gas furnace needed to supply heat to the desorber reboiler. Alternative technologies for $CO_2$ capture might be considered to overcome these challenges; however, their assessment is not included in this work.

The exhaust gas coming out from the cleaning section is put in counter-current contact with a 30 % wt. monoethanolamine aqueous solution that absorbs the $CO_2$ and leaves from the bottom of the first column. The clean gas containing less than 1 % mol. $CO_2$ is vented to the atmosphere. The $CO_2$ absorbed by the solvent is stripped in the second column employing heat supplied by the furnace and it is sent to the liquefaction section. Here, it is cooled with natural gas and an ammonia refrigeration cycle to storage conditions (22.0 bar and −16.6 °C) in commercial tanks until it can be unloaded at the port and transported to storage sites via pipelines. We note that the emissions of the furnace are combined with the exhaust gas, so the plant on-board captures the net $CO_2$ emissions of the system.

Further details about the techno-economic analysis summarized in the sections below can be found in Negri et al. (2022) where we report capital and operating costs of the capture plant, as well as a full LCA study based on Rockström et al. PBs.

### 2.2. Feasibility study

Firstly, we assess the technical feasibility of the configuration proposed to ensure that there is enough space on-board to retrofit the capture plant. In this step, we determine the weight and volume of each piece of equipment required on-board in addition to the ones already usually present on vessels, which are not accounted for. Then, we relate this information to the cargo displaced by the plant. Lastly, we calculate the number of extra ships that will be required to transport the cargo displaced in order to keep the total weight of the ship unchanged.

### 2.3. Economic assessment

The economic assessment is performed in accordance with the correlations in Towler and Sinnot for chemical plants (Towler, 2013), given the large scale of the equipment installed. We calculate the cost of each unit, considering installation and material factors, for the reference year 2019. The electricity required to drive pumps and compressors is given by the generator, while freshwater is supplied directly from the sea using a desalinator at no additional cost.

### 2.4. Absolute environmental assessment

We perform an absolute environmental sustainability assessment following the four phases of the LCA methodology where we quantify the total impact of the system on 16 LCA metrics based on the Environmental Footprint (European Commission, 2013) and updated LANCA (Bos et al., 2018 and Laurentiis et al., 2019) methods connected to the nine PBs and five SDGs. Then, we compare the environmental performance to the threshold values reported by Sala et al., where we updated the human health-related effects according to the population of 2019. The functional unit of the study is the global annual cargo demand (36 trillion tkm in 2019) with a well-to-propulsion scope. The life cycle inventory (LCI) phase is carried out in SimaPro v.9.2.0.2, combining data of the foreground from the process simulation and background system from the Ecoinvent v3.5 database. During the last LCA phase, where the results are interpreted, we analyze the relative impacts of the system in the full safe operating space (SOS %). Therefore, an impact above 100 % implies a transgression of the corresponding PB. By using the full SOS, we avoid allocating a share of the PBs to the container ships industry, which is often a controversial step.

The life cycle impacts are calculated for each flow $i$ ($imp_k$), based on the characterization factors ($CFs_{ik}$) of each elementary flow ($E_1$) with respect to k PBs categories. The impact is then compared to the threshold values reported in Sala et al. ($PB_k$) to determine the transgression level ($tl_k$) according to Eq. (1). The LCA inventories include all the activities from the capture to the storage of the $CO_2$.

$$tl_k = \frac{imp_k}{PB_k} = \frac{\sum_i CF_{ik} E_i}{PB_k} \quad \forall \, k \in K \tag{1}$$

The analyses performed in this study and the main findings that are discussed in the following paragraph are summarized in Figure 2.

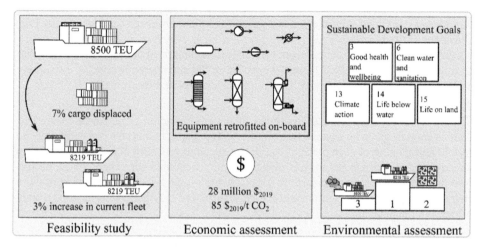

Figure 2. Analyses performed in this study: feasibility study based on the weights of the equipment retrofitted on-board, economic assessment of the units required for the $CO_2$ capture and absolute environmental assessment linked to the PBs and SDGs.

## 3. Results and discussion

The carbon capture plant on-board cargo vessels is a technically feasible and economically appealing solution to abate direct emissions compared to the current scenario and the alternative emissions reduction technology DAC.

The plant designed has an overall efficiency of 94 %, with a total cost of 85 $\$_{2019}$/tCO$_2$ captured, without considering the capital expenses for the construction of the additional vessels. Given its lower technology maturity level and the low concentration of $CO_2$ in the air, DAC is still a more expensive option with estimates at 300-600 $/tCO$_2$ captured (Fuss et al., 2018 and DAC, 2021). The total equipment required on-board displaces 7 % of the cargo on a mass-basis for a week-long trip, which implies an increase of 3 % in the current fleet to fulfill the annual cargo demand of 2019. The $CO_2$ captured during the trip is stored on-board until the vessel has reached the port, where it is unloaded and transported to saline aquifers storage sites.

We assess the environmental performance of the system with respect to the full SOS and we note that none of the categories is transgressed (Figure 3). The impact on climate change [kg CO$_{2\text{-eq}}$] is reduced by 50 % in the capture on-board compared to BAU, while DAC reduces it by 45 % due to the capture of direct $CO_2$ emissions in both scenarios. Although the two alternatives to the BAU contribute to mitigating climate change, significant burden-shifting occurs in the other categories. Eutrophication freshwater, marine and terrestrial are the most affected by burden shifting, where capture on-board performs significantly worse than DAC in the last two. Resource use energy carriers, and minerals and metals also increase compared to BAU, in particular in the DAC scenario due to the additional energy inputs required by the capture process. If we considered downscaling of the SOS to allocate a portion of it to the shipping industry only, e.g., using the sector GVA (3 % of the global GVA in 2010, OECD 2016), some of the categories such as respiratory inorganics and resource use energy carriers would show a transgression level above 95 %. On a broader perspective, trade-offs within SDG 3, SDG 13 and 14 appear when trying to reduce climate change. Respiratory inorganics, i.e., particulate matter, is the most impactful category in SDG 3 good health and wellbeing, where capture on-board performs worse than the BAU scenario. SDG 13 climate action benefits from the $CO_2$ emissions reduction, however, resource use energy carriers increases with both capture on-board and DAC. Lastly, SDG 14 life below water is affected by the eutrophication freshwater category, where both capture on-board and DAC perform worse than BAU, with DAC showing the worst performance.

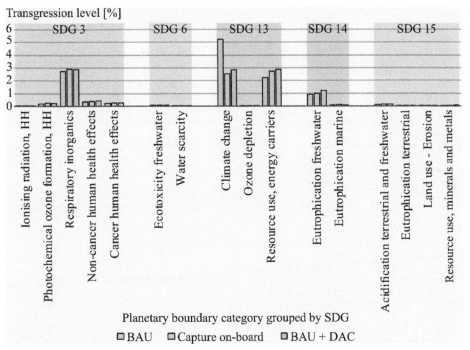

Figure 3. Environmental assessment results: planetary boundaries transgression [%] with respect to the full space and respective Sustainable Development Goals mapping.

## 4. Conclusions

An interim solution to reduce direct emissions from the cargo shipping industry based on a retrofitted carbon capture plant on-board was proven to be technically feasible, economically competitive and environmentally appealing. The scenario presented is compared to the business as usual where no measures are implemented and direct air capture.

The plant achieves 94% net capture efficiency displacing 7% of the cargo on a mass-basis, which is transported by additional ships corresponding to a 3% increase in the current fleet in 2019. The cost of capture is 85 $\$_{2019}/tCO_2$, which is considerably cheaper than removing the same amount of $CO_2$ from the air using direct air capture technologies.

The absolute environmental assessment reveals that none of the categories is transgressed compared to the full safe operating space. While capture on-board reduces climate change by 50% compared to the business-as-usual, direct air capture achieves a 45 % reduction. However, burden-shifting occurs in all the other categories in both scenarios, although the scenarios assessed occupy only a small percentage of the full safe operating space. In particular, capture on-board performs the worst in eutrophication marine and terrestrial. The resource use categories are also exacerbated compared to the current scenario, particularly using direct air capture.

In order to implement this solution, social and political barriers still exist regarding abatement technologies and should be overcome by putting legal frameworks in place. Additionally, the capital expenses faced by the shipping industry to retrofit the plant on-board and build new vessels that satisfy the demand should be supported by public incentives.

## References

U. Bos, R. Horn, T. Beck, J. P. Lindner, M. Fischer, 2018, LANCA®-Characterization Factors for Life Cycle Impact Assessment, Version 2.5, Fraunhofer Verlag

DAC, Direct Air Capture Summit 2021, 2021, https://www.youtube.com/watch?v=ZoMz7dmfitY&t=1039s

DNV, 2022, Maritime Forecast to 2050

European Commission, 2013, Recommendation 2013/179/EU on the use of common methods to measure and communicate the life cycle environmental performance of products and organisations

M. Feenstra, J. Monteiro, J. T. van den Akker, M. R. M. Abu-Zahra, E. Gilling; E. Goetheer, 2019, Ship-Based Carbon Capture Onboard of Diesel or LNG-Fuelled Ships, International Journal of Greenhouse Gas Control, 85, 1–10

S. Fuss, W. F. Lamb, M. W. Callaghan, J. Hilaire, F. Creutzig, T. Amann, T. Beringer, W. De Oliveira Garcia, J. Hartmann, T. Khanna, G. Luderer, G. F. Nemet, J. Rogelj, P. Smith, J. V. Vicente, J. Wilcox, M. Del Mar Zamora Dominguez, J. C. Minx, 2018, Negative Emissions - Part 2: Costs, Potentials and Side Effects, Environmental Research Letter, 13 (6)

Á. Galán-Martín, V. Tulus, I. Díaz, C. Pozo, J. Pérez-Ramírez, G. Guillén-Gosálbez, 2021, Sustainability Footprints of a Renewable Carbon Transition for the Petrochemical Sector within Planetary Boundaries, One Earth, 4, 565–583

IMO, Initial IMO Strategy on Reduction of GHG Emissions from Ships, https://www.imo.org/en/MediaCentre/HotTopics/Pages/Reducing-greenhouse-gas-emissions-from-ships.aspx

IMO, 2021, Fourth IMO GHG Study 2020

I. Istrate, D. Iribarren, J. Dufour, R. Ortiz Cebolla, A. Arrigoni, P. Moretto, F. Dolci, 2022, Quantifying Emissions in the European Maritime Sector

V. De Laurentiis, M. Secchi, U. Bos, R. Horn, A. Laurent, S. Sala, 2019, Journal of Cleaner Production, 215, 63–74

V. Negri, M. A. Charalambous, J. D. Medrano-García, G. Guillén-Gosálbez, 2022, Navigating within the safe operating space with carbon capture on-board, ACS Sustainable Chemistry & Engineering, 10, 51, 17134–17142

OECD, 2016, The Ocean Economy in 2030; OECD Publishing Paris, Ed.

J. Rockström, W. Steffen, K Noone, Å. Persson, F. Stuart III Chapin , E. Lambin, T. M. Lenton, M. Scheffer, C. Folke, H. Joachim Schellnhuber, B. Nykvist, C. A. de Wit, T. Hughes, S. van der Leeuw, H. Rodhe, S. Sörlin, P. K. Snyder, R. Costanza, U. Svedin, M Falkenmark, L. Karlberg, R. W. Corell, V. J. Fabry, J. Hansen, B. Walker, D. Liverman, K. Richardson, P. Crutzen, J. Foley, 2009, Planetary boundaries: Exploring the safe operating space for humanity, Ecology and Society, 14

J. Rogelj, M. Den Elzen, N. Höhne, T. Fransen, H. Fekete, H. Winkler, R. Schaeffer, F. Sha, K. Riahi, M. Meinshausen, 2016, Paris Agreement Climate Proposals Need a Boost to Keep Warming Well below 2 °C, Nature, 534, 631–639

M. W. Ryberg, M. Owsianiak, K. Richardson, M. Z. Hauschild, 2018, Development of a Life-Cycle Impact Assessment Methodology Linked to the Planetary Boundaries Framework, Ecological Indicators, 88, 250–262

S. Sala, E. Crenna, M. Secchi, E. Sany-Mengual, 2020, Environmental sustainability of European production and consumption assessed against planetary boundaries, Journal of Environmental Management, 269, 110686

G. Towler, R. K. Sinnott, 2013, Chemical Engineering Design; Elsevier

Antonis Kokossis, Michael C. Georgiadis, Efstratios N. Pistikopoulos (Eds.)
PROCEEDINGS OF THE 33rd European Symposium on Computer Aided Process Engineering
(ESCAPE33), June 18-21, 2023, Athens, Greece

# Parametric study of the reactive absorption of $CO_2$ for soda ash production

Maria F. Gutierrez,[a] Peter Schulze,[a] Andreas Seidel-Morgenstern[a], Heike Lorenz[a]

[a]*Max Planck Institute for Dynamics of Complex Technical Systems, Sandtorstr. 1, 39106 Magdeburg, Germany*

## Abstract

The design of carbon-negative processes replacing traditional energy-intensive processes is desirable to achieve the UN sustainability goals. The CODA project aims to develop a sustainable process to produce soda ash by capturing airborne $CO_2$ using NaOH followed by a crystallization sequence. This work aimed to analyze the influence of three process variables, namely the $Na_2CO_3$ concentration, the temperature and air humidity in the absorber. The $CO_2$ capture rate, the energy consumption and the water loss in the absorber were considered as process performance variables. High $Na_2CO_3$ concentrations result in small capture rates in the absorber, which is directly related with larger absorbers and higher energy consumption for pumping. Absorption is favored at low temperatures because the $Na_2CO_3$ saturation concentration is smaller and water loss is reduced. The assessment of two downstream schemes in terms of energy led to the identification of opportunities for further process optimization.

**Keywords**: absorption, carbon dioxide, capture, soda ash.

## 1. Introduction

The development of processes for carbon capture and utilization is one of the pathways that could help to limit global warming. To contribute to this goal, the new CODA (Carbon-negative sODA ash) project has the aim to develop a sustainable process to produce soda ash (FONA, 2022). In the classical Solvay process, the carbonate ion is obtained from lime stone in an energy-intensive reaction that finally generates ~500 kg $CO_2$/ton soda. In contrast, the carbonate source in the CODA process is $CO_2$ captured directly from air using a NaOH solution. Soda ash (from this point mentioned as *soda* in this document) is crystallized from the obtained sodium carbonate solution.

The implementation of the CODA process requires technical studies allowing the design and optimization of a reactive absorber to capture $CO_2$ using a NaOH solution. Theoretical and experimental studies have reported the average $CO_2$ flux and potential costs of this operation (Keith et al., 2018; Mazzotti et al., 2013). However, some design variables important for the CODA process have not been studied in detail, e.g. the influence of the $Na_2CO_3$ concentration on the absorption performance. The possibility of soda crystallization in the absorber sets new challenges for the equipment design, and the influence of other variables such as weather conditions become worth to study.

Our goal is to study the influence of the $Na_2CO_3$ concentration, relative air humidity and temperature on the reactive absorption of $CO_2$ in an alkaline solution and on the downstream processing of the resulting liquid stream or slurry. To deal with the possible crystallization of soda inside the absorber, we studied the absorption in a column of droplets and without any packing material that could be blocked by crystals (similar to

(Cho et al., 2018)). The flow of droplets and the air are arranged in a co-current mode, in which no fan is required because the falling droplets induce the airflow inside the absorber, in a similar way that in an ejector venturi scrubber (Atay et al., 1987). A rate-based model capable to describe the reactive absorption of $CO_2$ in a NaOH solution was established using thermodynamic, kinetic and property parameters reported in the literature.

## 2. Mathematical model

### 2.1. Droplet absorber

The absorption of $CO_2$ in droplets of aqueous NaOH was modeled using the differential equation describing the concentration of $CO_2$ along the absorber (Eq. 1). The water loss was calculated using the differential equation describing the concentration of water in the gas phase along the absorber (Eq. 2) and the differential equation describing the temperature along the absorber (Eq.3). These equations were obtained from the component mass balance and the energy balance in the gas phase. The energy balance neglects the enthalpy of $CO_2$ dissolution and enthalpy of reaction because both enthalpies are less than 1% of the evaporation enthalpy. Table 1 presents a list of symbols used for these equations.

$$\frac{dy_{CO_2}}{dz} = -\frac{K_{G,CO_2}^c a}{\dot{G}'}\left(y_{CO_2} - y_{CO_2}^*\right)\frac{P}{RT} \tag{1}$$

$$\frac{dy_w}{dz} = \frac{k_{G,w}^c a}{\dot{G}'}\left(y_w^* - y_w\right)\frac{P}{RT} \tag{2}$$

$$\frac{dT}{dz} = -\frac{dy_w}{dz}\frac{\Delta H_{vap} M_w}{C_{p,G} M_G} \tag{3}$$

Table 1: List of symbols used in equations 1, 2 and 3

| Symbol | Meaning | Symbol | Meaning |
|---|---|---|---|
| $y_{CO_2}$ | molar concentration of $CO_2$ in the gas phase | $y_w^*$ | molar concentration of water in the gas phase in equilibrium with the liquid |
| $z$ | height of the absorber from top to bottom | $y_w$ | molar concentration of water in the gas phase |
| $K_{G,CO_2}^c$ | overall mass transfer coefficient of $CO_2$ in the gas phase (in m/s) | $k_{G,w}^c$ | local mass transfer coefficient of water in the gas phase (in m/s) |
| $a$ | specific surface area (in m²/m³) | $\Delta H_{vap}$ | Enthalpy of vaporization (in kJ/kg) |
| $\dot{G}'$ | molar flow per cross sectional area (in kmol/h/m²) | $C_{p,G}$ | Heat capacity of the gas phase (in kJ/(kg°C)) |
| $y_{CO_2}^*$ | $CO_2$ gas concentration in equilibrium with the $CO_2$ liquid bulk concentration | $M_w$ | Molecular weight of water |
| $P$ | pressure of the system | $M_G$ | Molecular weight of the gas phase |
| $T$ | temperature of the system | $R$ | universal gas constant |

Following assumptions were made:

- The change of the flow rate of gas due to the absorption and water loss is negligible. Due to the small concentration of $CO_2$ in the gas phase, if all the $CO_2$ on the gas stream would be absorbed, the molar flow rate would be reduced approx. by 0.0004%. In the worst-case scenario, the change in the molar flow rate of gas due to water evaporation is around 0.0043%.

- The equilibrium concentration is calculated from the isofugacity equation ($y_{CO_2}^* P = H_{v,CO_2} c_{CO_2}$), which requires the bulk concentration of $CO_2$ in the liquid phase (calculated from the mass balance in the liquid phase considering the flux of $CO_2$ into the liquid phase and the amount of $CO_2$ reacting with NaOH).

- The equilibrium concentration $y_w^*$ is calculated from the isofugacity equation ($y_w^* P = a_w p_s$), which requires the activity of water ($a_w$) and the vapor pressure of pure water ($p_s$), both functions of the temperature.
- The reaction is irreversible because the hydroxide ions concentration is always much higher than the concentration of the dissolved CO₂ (Danckwerts, 1970).
- The droplet diameter, number of droplets and gas and liquid velocities are constant along the absorber. No coalescence is considered. Results of the model are somehow ideal in this sense.

The overall mass transfer coefficient was calculated using the two-resistance theory, which requires to compute the local mass transfer coefficients in the liquid and in the gas phase (see Eq. 4). The Enhancement factor ($E$) was used to calculate the liquid mass transfer coefficient due to the reaction taking place in the liquid phase ($CO_2 + 2NaOH \rightarrow Na_2CO_3 + H_2O$). This factor is a function of the Hatta number ($Ha$ in Eq. 5) and depends on how fast is the reaction relative to the mass transfer. Our previous studies showed that the droplet absorber remains in the intermediate-fast reaction regime, where the penetration theory can be applied (Danckwerts, 1970). The equation to calculate $E$ is reported in literature (van Swaaij & Versteeg, 1992).

$$\frac{1}{K_{G,CO_2}^c} = \frac{1}{k_{G,CO_2}^c} + \frac{H_{v,CO_2}}{E k_{L,CO_2}^c RT} \tag{4}$$

$$Ha = \frac{\sqrt{k' D_{CO_2,L}^m}}{k_{L,CO_2}^c} \tag{5}$$

Local mass transfer coefficients were calculated with Eq. 6 and Eq. 7 for the gas and liquid phase, respectively. The equation for the gas phase is used for convective flow surrounding spheres, while the equation for the liquid phase is based on the penetration theory. The Henry volatility constant ($H_{v,CO_2}$) and the second order kinetic constant ($k'$) were calculated as a function of the solution ionic strength (Gondal, 2014). For the diffusivity of CO₂ in the liquid mixture ($D_{CO_2}^m$), a function of the viscosity. (Kucka et al., 2002) was used. The specific surface area was calculated with Eq. 8 (Dimiccoli et al., 2000). In this equation, the liquid volumetric flow rate ($\dot{q}_L$), the absorber diameter ($D$), the droplet diameter ($d$) and the liquid velocity ($v_L$) are required. Geometric, hydrodynamic and some operational variables of the absorber were constant in the parametric study (Table 2). Some of these variables were fixed based on our previous experimental studies. The differential-algebraic equation system was solved with Python.

$$k_{G,CO_2}^c = \frac{D_{CO_2}^m}{d} \left( 2 + 0.6 Re^{0.5} Sc^{1/3} \right) \tag{6}$$

$$k_{L,CO_2}^c = 2\sqrt{\frac{D_{CO_2,L}^m v_L}{\pi d}} \tag{7}$$

$$a = \frac{24 \dot{q}_L}{\pi d D^2 v_L} \tag{8}$$

Table 2: Variables kept constant in the parametric study

| Absorber variable | Units | Value | Absorber variable | Units | Value |
|---|---|---|---|---|---|
| Absorber diameter | mm | 28.4 | Pressure | kPa | 101.325 |
| Absorber height | m | 1.4 | Concentration of NaOH | wt.% | 5 |
| Liquid velocity | m/s | 2.38 | Inlet concentration of CO₂ | ppm | 400 |
| Gas velocity | m/s | 2.56 | Gas molar flow ($\dot{G}'$) | kmol/s/m² | 0.109 |
| Droplet diameter | μm | 333 | Liquid volumetric flow rate | mL/min | 922.4 |
| Specific surface area | m²/m³ | 182.7 | Pressure drop of liquid | mbar | 129 |

*2.2. Downstream processes*

The solution out of the absorber should be processed to obtain anhydrous sodium carbonate ($Na_2CO_3$). Different processing strategies can be used depending on the final concentrations obtained in the absorber. Here, two strategies were identified and evaluated. In the first strategy, the absorption is carried out until sodium hydroxide is completely consumed and $Na_2CO_3$ concentration is below saturation (because the sodium hydroxide inlet concentration is set to 5 wt.% and the corresponding soda concentration is below the saturation condition). Then, anhydrous soda is obtained from an evaporative crystallization, using mechanical vapor recompression (MVR) for heat integration and reducing the primary energy demand.

In the second strategy, the absorption is carried out using a NaOH solution saturated with $Na_2CO_3$, in the metastable zone where no crystals are formed. Then, a crystallization of decahydrate ($Na_2CO_3 \cdot 10H_2O$) at ambient conditions will follow. This scheme implies that the liquid out of the crystallizer (saturated in $Na_2CO_3$) is recycled to the absorber. In this way, most of the water in the solution is eliminated from the product by crystallization (without evaporation), and only 10 moles of water remain with the product. Finally, decahydrate crystals undergo melting, followed by evaporative crystallization with MVR to obtain anhydrous soda ash.

## 3. Parametric study

Three parameters were changed in this study of reactive absorption of $CO_2$ with NaOH: $Na_2CO_3$ concentration in the inlet of the absorber, ambient temperature at the inlet and relative humidity of air.

Aiming to evaluate the performance of the absorber, the specific capture rate was calculated along the absorber using Eq. 9. This value expresses the flow of $CO_2$ captured (kg/h) in one cubic meter of absorber. The smaller the capture rate, the bigger the absorber should be to achieve a certain capture demand. Based on our previous studies, the pump energy was related to the capture rate to obtain the energy consumption in the absorber (in kWh/kg $CO_2$ captured). Using a carbon dioxide equivalency of 0.1237 kg of $CO_2$ emitted per kWh electricity consumed (maximal value for onshore wind power (Amponsah et al., 2014)); the energy consumption was transformed into kg $CO_2$ equivalent/kg of $CO_2$ captured. Values of the capture rate reported and used here after correspond to the arithmetic average along the absorber (valid due to low $y_{CO2}$).

$$r = \frac{K_G^c a y_{co_2} P}{RT} \tag{9}$$

Some water is also evaporated in the absorber depending on the conditions of the inlet air. The saturation concentration of water in the air was calculated with the isofugacity equation, which requires the activity of water in the liquid (with ions) and the vapor pressure of pure water at the system temperature. The water loss per mass of $CO_2$ captured was calculated with Eq. 10.

$$W_{loss} = \frac{\dot{G}(y_w^{out} - y_w^{in})}{r V_{abs}} \tag{10}$$

The power consumed by the MVR compressors in each strategy was calculated using the amount of water needed to be evaporated and the enthalpy difference for the vapor in the MVR blower (compression ratio of 1.5). This energy was related with the amount of $CO_2$ capture by stoichiometry (1 mol of $CO_2$ should be captured to obtain 1 mol of $Na_2CO_3$).

## 4. Results and Discussion

The capture rate and emission of $CO_2$ in the absorber due to pumping are presented in Figure 1 as a function of the system outlet temperature, $Na_2CO_3$ inlet concentration and inlet air humidity. The highest $Na_2CO_3$ concentration on each temperature and humidity case changes because it corresponds to the saturation concentration. The decrease in the capture rate when the $Na_2CO_3$ concentration increases can be related with the decrease of $CO_2$ solubility in the liquid due to the presence of the carbonate ions in the solution (salting-out effect). Results show that the absorption using a liquid feed saturated in $Na_2CO_3$ is favored at lower temperatures because the $Na_2CO_3$ saturation concentration is smaller. The air humidity does not affect considerably the capture rate in the low temperature range. On the other hand, the $CO_2$ emission in the absorber is heavily affected (Figure 1b is in logarithmic scale) by the temperature and $Na_2CO_3$ concentration in the absorber. According to our results, the maximal emission of this absorption process occurs at 30°C when the liquid is almost saturated with $Na_2CO_3$ (smallest capture rate).

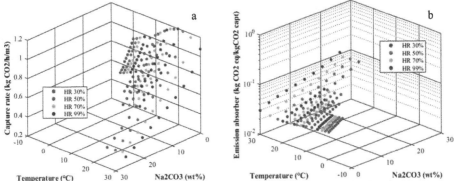

Figure 1: Results of the parametric study in the absorber (5 wt% NaOH) regarding a) CO₂ capture rate and b) emission of CO₂ due to energy consumption in the absorber.

The water loss in absorber is heavily affected by relative humidity and air (see Figure 2a). Processes at lower temperature and high humidity present the smallest water loss (~0.00024 kg water/kg $CO_2$ captured). Since the water used in the process should be highly pure (to achieve pure crystals), it is recommended to include an upstream humidifying tower, in which the air can be saturated with low grade water (cheaper) prior to the absorption (at dry and warm weather conditions).

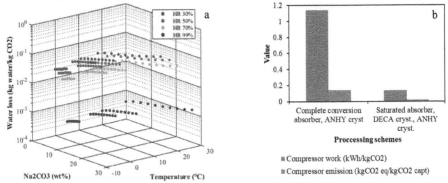

Figure 2: Results of the parametric study in the absorber (5 wt% NaOH) regarding a) water loss in the absorber and b) emission of CO₂ due to energy consumption in the downstream process.

Analysis of the downstream process shows in Figure 2b that the second strategy has a smaller energy consumption compared to the first strategy. Even though both downstream processing schemes are carbon-negative, the second strategy avoids the emission of around 0.123 kg CO₂ per kg of CO₂ captured.

However, the second strategy also implies to operate at smaller capture rates resulting in bigger absorbers and higher energy consumption in the absorber. An opportunity for process synthesis by optimization is evidenced from our results.

## 5. Conclusion and Outlook

The reactive absorption of $CO_2$ from air with carbonated NaOH has been analyzed using a parametric study in which the $Na_2CO_3$ concentration and the temperature and humidity of air were varied. The effect of these parameter on the capture rate, water loss and energy consumption in the absorber were evaluated. In addition, two downstream processing schemes to obtain anhydrous soda were assessed in terms of energy consumption. The presence of high concentration of $Na_2CO_3$ in the absorber reduces considerably the capture rate; but at the same time, this is required in the downstream process with the lowest energy consumption. The results also showed that absorption is favored at low temperatures, where the saturation concentration is smaller (the capture rate is higher) and the water loss is minimized. Under dry and warm weather scenarios, a pre-humidification process should be added to avoid the loss of high-quality (distilled) water. Analysis of the energy consumption in terms of $CO_2$ emitted per $CO_2$ captured allowed to identify scenarios in which the operation of absorber emits around 10% of the $CO_2$ captured. The results of this study will be used to optimize the conceptual design of the CODA process.

## References

Amponsah, N.Y., Troldborg, M., Kington, B., Aalders, I., Hough, R.L., 2014. Greenhouse gas emissions from renewable energy sources: A review of lifecycle considerations. Renewable and Sustainable Energy Reviews 39, 461-475.

Atay, L., Lewandowski, G., Trattner, R., 1987. Fluid Flow and Gas Absorption in an Ejector Venturi Scrubber. Environmental Progress 6, 198–203.

Cho, M., Lee, S., Choi, M., & Lee, J. W. (2018). Novel Spray Tower for CO2 Capture Using Uniform Spray of Monosized Absorbent Droplets. Industrial and Engineering Chemistry Research, 57(8), 3065–3075

Danckwerts, P. v., 1970. Gas-Liquid Reactions. McGraw-Hill, New-York.

Dimiccoli, A., di Serio, M., Santacesaria, E., 2000. Mass transfer and kinetics in spray-tower-loop absorbers and reactors. Ind Eng Chem Res 39, 4082–4093.

FONA, 2022. CODA – Development of an environmentally friendly process for the production of soda. URL https://www.fona.de/en/measures/funding-measures/KlimPro/coda.php

Gondal, S., 2014. Carbon dioxide absorption into hydroxide and carbonate systems (Ph. D. Thesis). NTNU-Trondheim, Trondheim.

Keith, D.W., Holmes, G., Angelo, D. st., Heidel, K., 2018. A Process for Capturing CO2 from the Atmosphere. Joule 2, 1573–1594.

Kucka, L., Kenig, E.Y., Górak, A., 2002. Kinetics of the gas-liquid reaction between carbon dioxide and hydroxide ions. Ind Eng Chem Res 41, 5952–5957.

Mazzotti, M., Baciocchi, R., Desmond, M.J., Socolow, R.H., 2013. Direct air capture of CO2 with chemicals: Optimization of a two-loop hydroxide carbonate system using a countercurrent air-liquid contactor. Clim Change 118, 119–135.

Stolaroff, J.K., Keith, D.W., Lowry, G. v., 2008. Carbon dioxide capture from atmospheric air using sodium hydroxide spray. Environ Sci Technol 42, 2728–2735.

van Swaaij, W.P.M., Versteeg, G.F., 1992. Mass Transfer Accompanied With Complex Reversible Chemical Reactions In Gas-Liquid Systems: An Overview, Chemical Engineering Science 47, 3181-3195.

Antonis Kokossis, Michael C. Georgiadis, Efstratios N. Pistikopoulos (Eds.)
PROCEEDINGS OF THE 33rd European Symposium on Computer Aided Process Engineering
(ESCAPE33), June 18-21, 2023, Athens, Greece

# Machine learning enabled modelling and sensitivity analysis for the power generation from a 660 MW supercritical coal power plant

Waqar Muhammad Ashraf, Vivek Dua*

*Sargent centre for Process Systems Engineering, Department of Chemical Engineering, University College London, Torrington Place, London WC1E 7JE, UK*

* Corresponding Author: v.dua@ucl.ac.uk

## Abstract

The modelling of large-scale industrial power generation system is a challenging task owing to the hyperdimensional input space of the variables and the non-linear interactions among them. In this work, the power production operation from 50% to 100% generation capacity of a 660 MW supercritical coal power plant is modeled on almost three months' operational data by artificial neural network (ANN). The hyperparameters of the ANN model are optimized, an effective ANN model is developed and validated on the power generation conditions. The partial derivative-based sensitivity analysis is carried out and it reveals that main steam flow rate is the most significant input variable on the power production followed by coal flow rate, reheat steam temperature and main stem temperature. This research work presents a reliable utilization of ANN model for the modelling of large capacity power plants that can be extended to conduct the enterprise-level performance enhancement analytics.

**Keywords**: power generation modelling; machine learning; net-zero; coal power plants

## 1.0 Introduction

The power generation from a large-scale industrial complex is maintained under the synchronized operation of several devices and systems having associated non-linearities and interactions. The development of first principles to model the power generation under various operational constraints and state of equipment availability is a challenging task, and model-based optimization can be computationally prohibitive. Artificial neural network is a powerful modelling algorithm that is widely used in the area of machine learning, and it can effectively approximate nonlinear function constructed on hyperdimensional input space with reasonable accuracy. Moreover, ANN can build an effective functional map between the input and output variables of the given system, and thus, it can be deployed to model the complex power generation operation of the coal power plants.

Researchers have developed machine learning models for modelling the power generation operation from the coal-based power plants. A comprehensive review of the application of various machine learning models for fuel combustion to generate power is presented by (Mohammadi, Immonen et al. 2022). (Blackburn, Tuttle et al. 2022) presented the study on the machine learning assisted optimization of the coal power plant using nine input variables. An optimized model for the improved coal combustion in the boiler with respect to power generation and quality of coal is presented by (Li and Yao

2017). In another work, (Safdarnejad, Tuttle et al. 2019) presented the recurrent neural network assisted dynamic modelling and optimization of a coal-based furnace for the minimization of $NO_x$ and CO emissions.

In the research studies reported in literature, many operating variables are deployed to model coal power plant's operation that can be reduced by considering the operational relevance and variables' independence. The application of ANN for modelling the power generation from a 660 MW power plant under reduced input space has not been fully explored. Moreover, the sensitivity of the input variables on the power generation is also required to be investigated that is potentially lacking in literature and can be of interest to the industrial community operating the coal-based power generation systems.

In this work, data from a 660 MW supercritical coal power plant is utilized to model the complex and multivariable dependent power generation operation under reduced but relevant input variables. Furthermore, the partial-derivative based sensitivity analysis of the input variables is performed to evaluate their significance on the power production. This research work demonstrates the reliable utilization of machine learning algorithm for the industrial relevance and competitiveness that can contribute to smart operation management of industrial complexes supporting the net-zero goal.

## 2.0 Variables identification, data-collection, visualization and pre-processing

A generic schematic diagram of a 660 MW coal power plant operation is presented in Figure 1, whereas the detailed description on the schematic is provided in (Muhammad Ashraf, Moeen Uddin et al. 2020). Four critically controlled and operational-relevant input variables, i.e., coal flow rate ($\dot{m}_f$), main steam temperature (MST), main steam flow rate (MSF) and reheat steam temperature (RHT), which are backed by domain-knowledge and literature survey (Tunckaya and Koklukaya 2015, Kumar, Nikam et al. 2020), are identified to model the power generation from a 660 MW

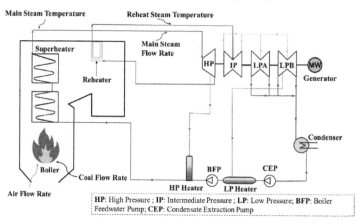

Figure 1. Schematic diagram of a coal power plant operation.

supercritical coal power plant. The selected input variables are strictly controlled within their operating ranges during ramp-up and ramp-down operation of the power plant. It is important to mention here that the sustained power production from the power plant contributes to the frequency control of the nearby connected grid thereby security and safety of the grid is critical to ensure the smooth power production and transmission. Almost 2000 hourly averaged observations (i.e., almost three months) from 50 % to 100 % power generation capacity of the power plant are taken for all operating variables. The visualization of the input and output data-distribution space for the variables is presented in Figure 2. Continuous data-distribution of the input variables, i.e., $\dot{m}_f$, MST, MSF, RHT as well as output variable (Power) can be observed for their operating ranges. The data-distribution of the variables is reasonably good that possesses information about the operating values for the variables under different power generation capacity and is essentially beneficial for the development of a well-performing machine learning model.

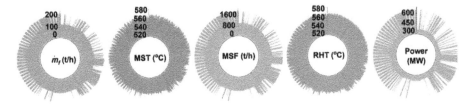

Figure 2. Data-visualization of the operation control parameters; $\dot{m}_f$, MST, MSF, RHT and power. Good data-distribution space is observed for the selected variables.

The operating ranges of the variables are significantly different which can affect the generalization and prediction efficacy of the machine learning model. Therefore, the data of all variables is transformed into an equal range. The mathematical expression for the data-transformation into [a,b] scale is given as:

$$X_i' = \frac{(X_i - X_{min})(b-a)}{X_{max} - X_{min}} + a \tag{1}$$

Here, $X_i$ is the value of the original variable that is transformed into $X_i'$. $X_{min}$ and $X_{max}$ are the minimum and maximum value of $X$; $a$ and $b$ are taken as -1 and 1 respectively that represents the scale of the data transformation for the variables.

## 3.0 Development of Artificial Neural Network Model

Artificial neural network, commonly known as multi-layered perceptron, is one amongst the powerful modelling algorithms widely deployed to approximate the non-linear functions constructed on high-dimensional input space (Gueddar and Dua 2012). The working of ANN is inspired by the functioning of human brain and the details can be found in the reported work (Muhammad Ashraf, Moeen Uddin et al. 2020, Ashraf, Uddin et al. 2021).

In this work, three layered shallow ANN architecture is constructed. The number of neurons in the hidden layer are varied from 4 to 10 (1 ~ 2.5 times of input layer neurons) to find an optimal configuration of ANN network. Tangent hyperbolic and linear activation function is applied on the hidden and output layer respectively. Levenberg-Marquardt algorithm is used for the parametric optimization of ANN architecture. The performance metrics built on coefficient of determination ($R^2$), mean absolute error (MAE) and root mean square error (RMSE) are deployed for evaluating the training performance of the ANN. The mathematical expression of the performance metrics adopted in this work is given as:

$$R^2 = 1 - \frac{\sum_i^N (y_i - \hat{y}_i)^2}{\sum_i^N (y_i - \bar{y}_i)^2}, \quad 0 \le R^2 \le 1 \tag{2}$$

$$MAE = \frac{1}{N}\sum_{i=1}^N |y_i - \hat{y}_i| \tag{3}$$

$$RMSE = \sqrt{\frac{1}{N}\sum_{i=1}^N (\hat{y}_i - y_i)^2} \tag{4}$$

here, $y_i$, $\hat{y}_i$ and $\bar{y}_i$ are the actual value, model projected value, and mean of actual values, with $i$ = 1, 2, 3..., N being the number of observations.

Figure 3 shows the pictorial representation of the trained ANNs with different number of hidden layer neurons (from 4 to 10). The performance matrix constructed on $R^2$, MAE and RMSE is computed for the developed networks. The performance metrics corresponding to the trained ANNs are compared to find the ANN model having optimal hidden layer neurons. It is found that ANN built on nine neurons in the hidden layer has comparatively better values for performance metrices with $R^2$ = 0.99, MAE = 3.22 MW and RMSE = 4.43 MW. Therefore, ANN model with nine neurons in the hidden layer is deployed to undergo external validation test as described in the next section.

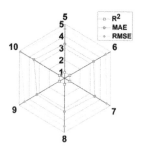

Figure 3. The training performance of ANN with different number of hidden layer neuron (5,6,…,10) is measured on $R^2$, MAE, and RMSE. ANN with nine neurons in the hidden layer has demonstrated comparatively better performance.

## 4.0 Validation of the developed ANN model

The validation of the developed ANN model is a crucial step towards the applicability of the machine learning algorithms in the large-scale industrial complexes. In this regard, the external validation test is performed to check the efficacy of the developed ANN model towards the prediction of unseen operating conditions of the industrial complexes. Therefore, the developed ANN model is deployed for the external validation test to evaluate its generalization and modelling performance for predicting the power generation from the power plant. The external validation dataset consists of 134 randomly selected observations for the operating variables corresponding to 50% to 100% power generation capacity of the power plant. Subsequently, the external validation dataset is deployed to be predicted from the developed ANN model. The performance metrics of the ANN network for the external validation dataset is calculated: $R^2$ = 0.99, MAE = 2.35 MW and RMSE = 3.08 MW which are comparable with the results reported in literature (Ashraf, Uddin et al. 2022). The performance of the developed ANN network in the external validation test confirms the good generalization and modelling ability of the model, and thus the operational insights about the power plant operation using the ANN model can be developed.

## 5.0 Partial-derivative based sensitivity analysis of ANN model

Partial-derivative based sensitivity analysis technique is utilized to evaluate the significance of the input variables on the power generation. The partial derivative-based sensitivity analysis computes the partial derivative of the output variable with respect to the input variable at each sample of the dataset. Thus, the explicit expression for the sensitivity analysis of the ANN model can provide robust diagnostic information about the variable significance on the output variable.

The mathematical expression for partial derivative-based sensitivity of input variable ($X_p$) on the output variable (Y) for the ANN model is given as (Nourani and Fard 2012):

$$\frac{\partial Y}{\partial X_p} = \sum_{h=1}^{nh} W_2(1 - M^2)W_1 \tag{5}$$

here, $W_2$ is the weight matrix built on the weight connections from the hidden layer to output layer neuron; $W_1$ is the weight connections from the particular input variable ($X_p$) to the hidden layer neurons; $(1 - M^2)$ is the partial derivative of the activation function applied on the hidden layer with respect to the summation computed at the hidden layer neuron.

The variance produced in the output variable with respect to the input variable is calculated using Eq. 5 and the procedure is repeated for the remaining input variables. Subsequently, the variance computed for all the input variables is normalized to account for the percentage significance of the input variable towards the prediction of output variable. Higher the value of percentage significance is for an input variable, the more significant the input variable is towards the output variable and vice versa. The mathematical expression of percentage significance is given as:

$$Percentage\ Significance = \frac{\sigma_{y_i|x_i}^2}{\sum_{i=1}^{d} \sigma_{y_i|x_i}^2} 100 \tag{6}$$

here, $\sigma_{y_i|x_i}^2$ refers to the variance produced in output variable $y_i$ with respect to the input variable $x_i$; $\sum_{i=1}^{d} \sigma_{y_i|x_i}^2$ is the summation of the variance produced in the output variable with respect to input variables; $i = 1, ..., d$ equals to number of input variables.

Figure 4 shows the percentage significance of the input variables on the power production from the coal power plant. MSF turns out to be the most significant variable contributing the percentage significance of 67. The second most sensitive input variable towards the power generation is $\dot{m}_f$ followed by RHT and MST having a percentage significance value of 23.5, 7.05 and 2.34 respectively. The order of significance of the input variables on the power production is similar to the reported research in literature in

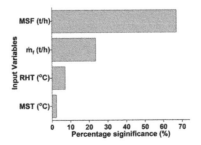

Figure 4. Percentage significance of the input variables for the power generation operation of coal power plant.

which response surface methodology was conducted to evaluate the variables' significance (Ashraf, Uddin et al. 2022). Furthermore, the significance order of the variables on the power production is also explainable as per the operational knowledge of the power plant.

## 6.0 Conclusion

In this work, ANN model is trained on the data taken from a 660 MW supercritical coal power plant to model the power production from 50% to 100% generation capacity. ANN model having nine neurons in the hidden layer is developed after rigorous hyperparameters tuning and the model has presented excellent performance metrics in the external validation test ($R^2 = 0.99$, MAE = 2.35 MW and RMSE = 3.08 MW). The partial derivative-based sensitivity analysis of ANN model is performed, and it is found that MSF is the most significant input variable towards the power production having a percentage significance value of 67. Whereas, percentage significance value for $\dot{m}_f$, RHT and MST is 23.5, 7.05 and 2.34 respectively. The effective utilization of ANN model for the complex and large-scale industrial power generation operations is presented in this study and the enterprise-level performance enhancement using machine learning based analytics would be investigated in the future studies to quantify the energy efficiency improvement and reduction in emissions footprint from the energy sector.

## Reference

Ashraf, W. M., G. M. Uddin, H. A. Ahmad, M. A. Jamil, R. Tariq, M. W. Shahzad and V. Dua (2022). "Artificial intelligence enabled efficient power generation and emissions reduction underpinning net-zero goal from the coal-based power plants." Energy Conversion and Management **268**: 116025.

Ashraf, W. M., G. M. Uddin, S. M. Arafat, J. Krzywanski and W. Xiaonan (2021). "Strategic-level performance enhancement of a 660 MWe supercritical power plant and emissions reduction by AI approach." Energy Conversion and Management **250**: 114913.

Blackburn, L. D., J. F. Tuttle, K. Andersson, A. Fry and K. M. Powell (2022). "Development of novel dynamic machine learning-based optimization of a coal-fired power plant." Computers & Chemical Engineering **163**: 107848.

Gueddar, T. and V. Dua (2012). "Novel model reduction techniques for refinery-wide energy optimisation." Applied energy **89**(1): 117-126.

Kumar, R., K. Nikam and R. Jilte (2020). A simulation model to predict coal-fired power plant production rate using artificial neural network tool. Applied Computer Vision and Image Processing, Springer: 150-160.

Li, Q. and G. Yao (2017). "Improved coal combustion optimization model based on load balance and coal qualities." Energy **132**: 204-212.

Mohammadi, K., J. Immonen, L. D. Blackburn, J. F. Tuttle, K. Andersson and K. M. Powell (2022). "A review on the application of machine learning for combustion in power generation applications." Reviews in Chemical Engineering.

Muhammad Ashraf, W., G. Moeen Uddin, A. Hassan Kamal, M. Haider Khan, A. A. Khan, H. Afroze Ahmad, F. Ahmed, N. Hafeez, R. Muhammad Zawar Sami and S. Muhammad Arafat (2020). "Optimization of a 660 MWe supercritical power plant performance—a case of Industry 4.0 in the data-driven operational management. Part 2. Power generation." Energies **13**(21): 5619.

Nourani, V. and M. S. Fard (2012). "Sensitivity analysis of the artificial neural network outputs in simulation of the evaporation process at different climatologic regimes." Advances in Engineering Software **47**(1): 127-146.

Safdarnejad, S. M., J. F. Tuttle and K. M. Powell (2019). "Dynamic modeling and optimization of a coal-fired utility boiler to forecast and minimize NOx and CO emissions simultaneously." Computers & Chemical Engineering **124**: 62-79.

Tunckaya, Y. and E. Koklukaya (2015). "Comparative prediction analysis of 600 MWe coal-fired power plant production rate using statistical and neural-based models." Journal of the Energy Institute **88**(1): 11-18.

Antonis Kokossis, Michael C. Georgiadis, Efstratios N. Pistikopoulos (Eds.)
PROCEEDINGS OF THE 33rd European Symposium on Computer Aided Process Engineering
(ESCAPE33), June 18-21, 2023, Athens, Greece

# Hydrogen production using renewable energy: solar PV and offshore wind power – An economic evaluation in Bahia.

Gustavo de S. dos Santos[a], Chrislaine do B. Marinho[a], Leonardo O. S. Santana[a], Artur S. Bispo[a], Fernando L. P. Pessoa[a,b], José L. G. Almeida[a], Ewerton E. S. Calixto[a]

[a] Centro Universitário SENAI CIMATEC, Avenida Orlando Gomes, Salvador 41650-010, Brazil
[b] Universidade Federal do Rio de Janeiro, Av. Athos da Silveira Ramos, Rio de Janeiro-RJ 21941-909, Brazil
gustavo.eqrj@gmail.com

**Abstract**
Green hydrogen is an interesting and sustainable alternative capable of diversifying the energy grid and reducing the dependency on fossil fuels, contributing to decarbonizing the global economy. Despite being widely applied on an industrial scale, hydrogen still faces major challenges, mainly due to the high cost incurred in its production, storage, transport, and the electricity required. Thus, the objective of this study was to evaluate the levelized cost of Hydrogen (LCOH) of offshore wind power and solar photovoltaic energy sources in the state of Bahia located in the northeast of Brazil. The two scenarios were created for a PEM electrolysis plant: 50 MW and 100 MW. As a result, for the LCOH, we got, as a result, 2.28 US\$/kg $H_2$ and 2.16 US\$/kg $H_2$ for solar PV, and 3.81 US\$/kg $H_2$ and 3.57 US\$/kg $H_2$ for offshore wind unit in the 50 MW and 100 MW systems, respectively. Despite the lower cost, the intermittency of renewable sources must be considered for the operation of solar PV and wind power plants. Offshore wind plants have the advantage of being installed near the main source for electrolysis – water – and of having a large space available, but with a trade-off on cost. The results show that a hybrid system uniting has the potential to be the most viable strategy.

**Keywords**: hydrogen production, water electrolysis, economic evaluation, renewable energy, PEM electrolysis.

## 1. Introduction

The development of sustainable energy generation requires technological changes, which revolve around three pillars: economy on production and demand, increased efficiency on production, and the use of clean energy sources to replace fossil fuels (Lund, 2007). In this sense, green hydrogen emerges as a viable and sustainable alternative capable of diversifying the energy matrix and reducing the dependence on fossil fuels, contributing to decarbonizing global economies. For this, by achieving global targets for reducing greenhouse gas (GHG) emissions and increasingly adopting the use of clean sources in the energy matrix, such as wind and solar photovoltaic (Nikolaidis e Poullikkasop, 2017).

Green hydrogen is produced through an electrolysis process, which uses electricity from a renewable source to split up the water molecule. Despite of already being widely applied on an industrial scale, this technology still faces major challenges, mainly due to the high cost related to its production, storage, transport, and the required electrical energy. With regard to energy and technological advances, wind and solar PV have increased their efficiency and capacity factor through the years and reduced the final price.

In Brazil, mainly in the Northeast Region, a variety of natural resources is available for the production of electricity with a great generation potential in using water sources, wind, solar PV, among others. In view of the global trend towards decarbonizing its economy, as well as diversifying its energy matrix, Brazil has made large investments and developed public policies for the use of new and sustainable technologies, such as wind turbines and electrolysis on hydrogen production, and improved efficiency of the existing ones.

Bahia is the fifth largest state in terms of territory and has geographic and meteorological characteristics that favor the development of these renewable sources (Atlas solar, 2018; Atlas eólico, 2013). Furthermore, it has an industrial pool capable of meeting the required demands. Currently, the State of Bahia is the second generator of wind energy and eighth in solar PV (distributed generation), with an installed capacity of wind and solar PV of 6.46 GW and 621.4 MW, respectively (Abeeólica, 2022; Absolar, 2022). Its industrial complex of Camaçari has already started the project for producing Green Hydrogen, demonstrating the State's maturity in the face of technological advances aimed at these segments. In this sense, the present article proposes a comparative study between two sources of clean energy – offshore wind and solar photovoltaic – to identify which of these has greater economic attractiveness for producing green hydrogen in the state of Bahia. For this purpose, two scenarios were created for a hydrogen plant with different configurations of electricity supply (offshore wind and solar photovoltaic) and a capacity of 50 MW and 100 MW of the PEM electrolysis unit, simultaneously, the potential of the renewable energy generation and application was studied. The work assumes average demands and does not consider dynamic elements.

## 2.    Methodology

### 2.1.    Geographic localization

In the present work, geographic location was determined in two instances. One for the Solar PV Plant (SPVP) and the other for the Offshore Wind Power Plant (OWPP). As the scope of the study uses the state of Bahia as a case, the peculiarities of the region were considered so the modeling could represent the desired scenario and the evaluation of potential hydrogen production. The data and calculations assume average demands as a preliminary analysis for this study, if the results conclude the real potential considering all infrastructure necessary, dynamics elements should be implemented in future work.

The SPVP uses the data from *Bahia's Solar ATLAS* (2018), a document from the government of Bahia, in partnership with the SENAI CIMATEC, that shows and details the solar energy potential of the state. Protection and agriculture areas, forestry formation, lakes and reservoirs, and areas with a land inclination bigger than 3% were excluded. Thus, the useful and free space could be evaluated and compared with the results of the modeling calculations, being a parameter limitation. Hence, the SPVP localization considered the average Global Horizontal Irradiation (GHI) potential of all region and the area available for implementation of the solar panels. Further implementation of the plant, in this case, should consider areas of *Bahia's Solar ATLAS* with the availability of water in order to determine the exact location in the state.

In the other case, the OWPP was located in a region of the cost of Bahia that first satisfied the technical calculations, second the proximity with a port and infrastructure, and third the environmental sustainability. So, the best area chosen with aid of GLOBAL WIND ATLAS (GWP, 2022), was 13 km from Ilhéus city, which has proximity to a port, gives an average wind velocity in the year that satisfy the modeling, and avoids the Abrolhos Bank and Vitória-Trindade Chain, an important region with marine biodiversity, coral reefs, endemic and endangered marine species. It is important to note, however, that other areas could be evaluated with good potential for the installation of the OWPP, as the coast of Bahia extends for more than 1000 km.

### 2.2.    Proposed scheme of modeling

In order to calculate the LCOH from the proposed scenario, this study considers the modeling according to Figure 1. The demand and cost of energy source, compression, storage, transport, and treated water (in the case of desalinization for OWPP) are a function of the power of the electrolysis plant, which presents the major demand for energy.

In the case of SPVP, it was considered that the solar panels and the entire solar energy production infrastructure are close to the electrolysis production area. However, for the OWPP, each turbine was considered to produce hydrogen coupled with the turbine using water from desalinization for the PEM electrolysis, therefore, hydrogen is transported through a pipeline and main storage occurs onshore (Groenemans, 2022). Transport for SPVP was considered as the number of compressed hydrogen trucks necessary to handle the daily production of the electrolysis plant (Mints, 2006). On the other hand, transport for OWPP was considered as the use of a pipeline to the near harbor and assumed an existing infrastructure available to distribute the hydrogen (Groenemans, 2022).

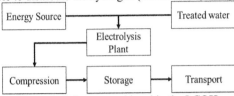

Figure 1: Scheme considered in the LCOH.

### 2.2.1.　Solar

The model of the SPVP was developed, as aforementioned, as a function of the electrolysis plant. Thus, the energy that solar PV power should deliver needs to satisfy all the demands of the electrolysis unit and compression in this study. For this, the average GHI of Bahia was taken into account for the capacity of solar energy production (Atlas solar, 2018). A model of a photovoltaic monocrystalline module with 670 W, a dimension of 3.1 m², and 21.5 % efficiency were considered to compose the plant.

The annual energy production was calculated according to Equation 1 (Hyjack, 2022):

$$Solar\ PV\ production\ \left(\frac{kWh}{year}\right) = GHI\left(\frac{\frac{kWh}{m^2}}{year}\right) * Area(m^2) * Module\ Efficiency \qquad (1)$$

Then, using the tool Solver in Excel, the energy demand and solar PV production converged by alternating the area required for the unit. After this, the number of required PV modules was calculated so the costs could be evaluated.

### 2.2.2.　Offshore Wind Power Plant

The Wind Farm modeling was structured first considering the potential of the selected region. For this, the annual average of wind velocity was considered using the Global Wind Atlas (GWP, 2022). It considered a height of 200 m for the tower, swept area of 38,000 m², and blades with 107 m length, the air density used was 1.225 kg/m³ (Groenemans, 2022). So, it was possible to calculate the power that the model of the wind turbine could generate in such conditions of operation using Equation 2 (Catrinus, 2017):

$$P(W) = \frac{1}{2}\rho A v^3 C_p \qquad (2)$$

where, P is the power in W, $\rho$ the air density in kg/m³, A the swept area in m², $\upsilon$ is the wind speed in m/s, and $C_p$ is the power coefficient, considered 0.65.

Since the OWPP provides all the energy, the power required accounts for the energy demand of the electrolysis unit, compression unit, and desalination unit.

### 2.3.　PEM Electrolysis

The electrolysis unit data was obtained from the software "Size and Costing" in Hyjack (Hyjack, 2022). It compiles different suppliers to inform the energy consumption, hydrogen production, and efficiency as a function of the desired power of the electrolysis plant. The platform was created to assist projects of hydrogen and work as a regularly updated software package to help with analysis and information from specialized workers in the area.

Finally, to select the plant balance data, a useful life of 90,000 h of the pile was considered as a base criterion (Macedo, 2022). In this study, a 50 MW and 100 MW system was considered, with hydrogen output of 40 bar and 70 °C.

### 2.4.　Compression

The compression unit considers the specific work necessary for a reciprocating compressor to compress hydrogen from the output pressure of the PEM unit to up 350 bar, the same pressure of storage. For this, Equation 3 is used (Hyjack, 2022):

$$Specific\ Work\left(\frac{J}{kg}\right) = \frac{\frac{\gamma}{\gamma-1}*\frac{R*T_1}{M}*[\left(\frac{P2}{P1}\right)^{\frac{\gamma-1}{\gamma}}-1]}{isentropic\ efficiency} \tag{3}$$

Where $\gamma$ is isentropic coefficient assumed 1.4, R is the universal law constant, $T_1$ the initial temperature, $P_2$ and $P_1$, output pressure and inlet pressure, respectively, and M the molar mass of hydrogen. Isentropic efficiency, in turn, is calculated according to Equation 4 (Hyjack, 2022).

$$Isentropic\ Efficiency = -2.3082*r^2 + 20.717*r + 40.719 \tag{4}$$

The ratio between the discharge and suction pressure is $r$. After this, it is possible to calculate the power required for the system to compress the mass of hydrogen to the desired pressure. Equation 5, considers (Hyjack, 2022):

$$Power\ (kW) = \frac{Q*\left(\frac{\rho}{3600*1000}\right)*Work*(1+leaks)}{Mechanical\ efficiency*Electrical\ efficiency} \tag{5}$$

Q is the flow rate in kg/h, $\rho$ the relative density obtained by data regression from Hyjack (2022), leaks assumed 3%, mechanical and electrical efficiencies assumed 79% and 95%, respectively.

### 2.5. Storage

Hydrogen storage was assumed in tanks of compressed gas of 350 bar with a capacity of 90 kg according to supplier information (FIBA, 2022). Furthermore, the quantity necessary to store the daily production was calculated according to the balance of mass of the system.

### 2.6. LCOH evaluation and economic assessment

In order to determine the comparison between the two strategies of hydrogen production, levelized cost of hydrogen was estimated according to the following Equation 6 (Macedo, 2022).

$$LCOH\left(\frac{\$}{kg}\right) = \frac{Total\ Costs(\$)}{Total\ hydrogen\ production(kg)} \tag{6}$$

The costs and data necessary to estimate total CAPEX and O&M are presented in Table 1:

| | CAPEX | O&M (%CAPEX) | Notes | Reference |
|---|---|---|---|---|
| Total PEM | $C(\text{€}) = 1.7*Power*(6046*Power^{-0.2})$ | 4% | Power in kW | Hyjack (2022) |
| Replacement | N/A | 20% Total PEM | N/A | Singlitico (2021) |
| Compressor | $C(\text{€}) = (75700*Power^{-0.62})*Power$ | 8% | Power in kW | Hyjack (2022) |
| Storage | $C(\text{€}) = Cap*N*(0.0015*P^2 + 0.2521*P + 448.54)$ | 5% | Cap = capacity of tank; N = number of tanks; P (bar) | Hyjack (2022) |
| Transport | $C(\$) = N*CHT$ | - | N = number of trucks; CHT = cost of hydrogen truck | Mintz (2006) |
| SPVP | $C(\$) = N*Pot*Cm$ | 6% | N = number of modules; Pot = Power in Watt of each module; Cm = cost of each module ($/W) | - |
| Desalination | $C(\text{€}) = 61200*\left(\frac{Water\ demand(L/h)}{2000}\right)^{0.6}$ | 2,50% | N/A | Catrinus (2017) |
| Pipeline | $C(M\$) = A + 0.3555*A + 0.57125*A$ | 2% | $A = 13.3*\left(\frac{D(km)}{16}\right)^{0.6}$ | - |
| OWPP | $C(\$) = Pot_{req}*N*3*10^6$ | 3% | $Pot_{req}$ = Power required in MW; N = number of wind turbine | McDonagh (2020) |
| Eolic DECEX | N/A | 10% | N/A | McDonagh (2020) |

**Table 1:** Economic data.

With regard to economic assumptions, it was estimated the lifetime of the plant for the SPVP and OWPP, of 25 and 30 years respectively (Gutiérrez, 2021; Singlitico 2021). Besides, the cash flow of each strategy was calculated, considering the first year of implementation of the plant, replacement of equipment necessary each 10 years, and the decommissioning at the end of lifetime expected. Therefore, after annualizing the results for the year 2022, it was possible to estimate the LCOH in the state of Bahia using the potential of renewable sources.

## 3. Results

As a result of the methodology applied, Figure 2 shows the LCOH calculated.

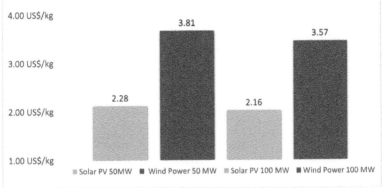

**Figure 2:** LCOH Solar PV and Offshore Wind Power 50 MW and 100 MW.

As observed, solar photovoltaic strategy shows the best performance in the levelized cost of hydrogen. However, it is important to note the advantages and disadvantages of each proposal. Solar PV power requires a larger area than offshore wind power, and this could be a constraint on the operation of a power plant. Moreover, offshore wind power is still in process of being more competitive in the next years, and despite the higher cost in the year analyzed, the technology has the advantage of a large area available at sea (McDonagh, 2020). Also, with the goal of the Brazilian government to expand decarbonization projects, political decisions, and regulatory marks can enable the implementation of strategy and reduce costs.

In addition, even Solar PV power having the lowest cost in this analysis, it is important to note the intermittent availability of this source during the day as the wind power (Minutillo, 2021). Hence, this should be a constraint in a project. In this case, a hybrid scheme with Wind Power should satisfy this problem that also affects the OWPP with the velocity varying along the day. In this way, both strategies could complement the lack of energy source during a cloudy day or a period with lower wind speed, for example.

## 4.    Conclusions

Following the study of previous years, the feasibility of renewable projects is becoming more real, especially in countries like Brazil where renewable sources are abundant. The LCOH calculated is already reaching the current price of steam methane reform which is the leading technology to produce hydrogen nowadays. Nevertheless, the intermittence of solar and wind energy is still a challenge. Therefore, in order to nearly fully decarbonize the energy source in a hydrogen production plant, the intermittence of renewable energy should be overcome. For example, a hybrid system of solar PV and wind power could minimize this challenge and can improve the level of dependency from grid energy for operation in a place that provides a good renewable potential.

## 5.    References

Associação brasileira de energia eólica (Abeeólica). InfoVento 28. São Paulo, nov., 2022. Disponível em: <https://abeeolica.org.br/energia-eolica/dados-abeeolica/>.

Associação brasileira de energia solar fotovoltaica (ABSOLAR). Energia solar fotovoltaica no Brasil: infográfico Absolar. nov., 2022. Disponível em: <https://www.absolar.org.br/mercado/infografico/>.

AWS Truepower, Camargo Schubert Engenheiros Associados, Fieb/Senai Cimatec. Atlas solar: Bahia. Curitiba: Camargo Schubert; Salvador: Secti: Seinfra: Cimatec/Senai. 76 p. 2018.

Catrinus Jepma, Gert-Jan Kok, Malte Renz, Miralda V. Schot, Kees Wouters. Towards sustainable energy production on the North Sea - Green hydrogen production and CO2 storage: onshore or offshore? North Sea Energy, 2017.

GWP - Global Wind Atlas. Energy data info. Available at: <globalwindatlas.info/en>. Access in: October, 2022.

Groenemans, H., Saur, G., Mittelsteadt, C., Lattimer, J., & Xu, H. (2022). Techno-economic analysis of offshore wind PEM water electrolysis for H2 production. Current Opinion in Chemical Engineering, 37, 100828. https://doi.org/10.1016/j.coche.2022.100828

Gutiérrez-Martín, F., Amodio, L., & Pagano, M. (2021). Hydrogen production by water electrolysis and off-grid solar PV. International Journal of Hydrogen Energy, 46(57), 29038–29048. https://doi.org/10.1016/j.ijhydene.2020.09.098

Lund H. Renewable energy strategies for sustainable development. Energy 2007;32(6):912–9.

Macedo, S. F., & Peyerl, D. (2022). Prospects and economic feasibility analysis of wind and solar photovoltaic hybrid systems for hydrogen production and storage: A case study of the Brazilian electric power sector. International Journal of Hydrogen Energy, 47(19), 10460–10473. https://doi.org/10.1016/j.ijhydene.2022.01.133

McDonagh, S., Ahmed, S., Desmond, C., & Murphy, J. D. (2020). Hydrogen from offshore wind: Investor perspective on the profitability of a hybrid system including for curtailment. Applied Energy, 265, 114732. https://doi.org/10.1016/j.apenergy.2020.114732

Mintz, M., Gillette, J., Elgowainy, A., Paster, M., Ringer, M., Brown, D., & Li, J. (2006). Hydrogen Delivery Scenario Analysis Model for Hydrogen Distribution Options. Transportation Research Record: Journal of the Transportation Research Board, 1983, 114–120. https://doi.org/10.3141/1983-16

Minutillo, M., Perna, A., Forcina, A., di Micco, S., & Jannelli, E. (2021). Analyzing the levelized cost of hydrogen in refueling stations with on-site hydrogen production via water electrolysis in the Italian scenario. International Journal of Hydrogen Energy, 46(26), 13667–13677. https://doi.org/10.1016/j.ijhydene.2020.11.110

Nikolaidis, Pavlos; Poullikkas, Andreas. Uma visão comparativa dos processos de produção de hidrogênio. Revisões sobre energia renovável e sustentável, v. 67, p. 597-611, 2017.

Schubert, Camargo. Atlas Eólico: Bahia. Governo do Estado da Bahia, 2013.

Singlitico, A., Østergaard, J., & Chatzivasileiadis, S. (2021). Onshore, offshore or in-turbine electrolysis? Techno-economic overview of alternative integration designs for green hydrogen production into Offshore Wind Power Hubs. Renewable and Sustainable Energy Transition, 1, 100005. https://doi.org/10.1016/j.rset.2021.100005.

Sizing and Costing. Hyjack Hydrogen Tech Online. Available at: <hyjack.tech/components>. Access in: October, 2022.

Antonis Kokossis, Michael C. Georgiadis, Efstratios N. Pistikopoulos (Eds.)
PROCEEDINGS OF THE 33rd European Symposium on Computer Aided Process Engineering
(ESCAPE33), June 18-21, 2023, Athens, Greece

# Resilience-aware multi-scale integration of distributed energy systems

Natasha J. Chrisandina[a], Shivam Vedant[b,c], Eleftherios Iakovou[b,d], Efstratios N. Pistikopoulos[a,b], Mahmoud M. El-Halwagi[a,b,g]

[a]Artie McFerrin Department of Chemical Engineering, Texas A&M University, 3122 TAMU, 100 Spence St., College Station, TX 77843, USA

[b]Texas A&M Energy Institute, Texas A&M University, College Station, TX, 77843, USA

[c]Department of Multidisciplinary Engineering, Texas A&M University, College Station, USA

[d]Department of Engineering Technology and Industrial Distribution, Texas A&M University, College Station, USA

[g]Gas and Fuels Research Center, Texas A&M Engineering Experiment Station, College Station, USA

el-halwagi@tamu.edu

## Abstract

To cost-competitively harness both renewable and traditional energy sources, the use of large-scale facilities should be considered along with distributed energy systems (DESs), which are networks of small-scale energy production facilities and their associated suppliers, intermediaries, end users, and transportation links. Furthermore, to accurately capture the different operational scales in a DES and integrate long-term planning decisions alongside short-term scheduling decision, a multi-scale approach may be utilized. In this work, we present a multi-scale framework for the design and analysis of cost-competitive and resilient DESs. To this end, the framework integrates: 1) facility location decisions to achieve specified threshold service level; 2) quantitative reliability analysis on individual process modules; and 3) considerations of tradeoff between multiple objectives such as cost, resilience, and sustainability. The framework is applied to a biomass value chain that uses various agricultural waste materials to produce a range of biofuels.

**Keywords**: distributed energy system, multi-scale engineering, resilience, supply chain, sustainability

## 1. Introduction

As the energy sector moves away from predominant use of fossil fuels to a more diverse suite of sources, two great challenges have emerged. First, new energy sources such as solar power, biomass, and wind display significant geo-temporal variability. Second, energy systems have been under great strain in the face of disruptions such as natural disasters, geopolitical conflicts, and global pandemics (Kakodkar et al., 2022). To simultaneously address both these challenges, distributed energy systems (DESs) have been proposed as a promising pathway (Yang and You, 2018). To enable cost-competitive utilization of locally available energy sources, DESs integrate small-scale modular energy production facilities across geographical locations with other key stakeholders along the supply chain, including traditional large-scale facilities.

In the current literature, there has been growing interest in DESs and their capability to provide operational flexibility and resilience benefits in an uncertain world (Allen et al., 2019; Al-Fadhli et al., 2019). Utilizing modular facilities within a DES can also reduce set-up and maintenance time, and provide flexibility in the form of mobile modular units (Baldea et al., 2017). However, a major question is how to balance the multiple objectives that need to be considered: cost-competitiveness, sustainability, and resilience. In this work, a multi-scale approach is employed to accurately capture the various spatio-temporal scales of operation prevalent in energy systems to allow discovery of potential synergies that can be leveraged to achieve win-win solutions. Building on this approach, we propose a framework that integrates planning and operational decisions – production facility design and facility location-allocation – to achieve a resilience-aware DES in a cost-competitive manner. The proposed methodology is demonstrated through a case study for planning and scheduling of a biomass value chain.

## 2. Methodology

### 2.1. Framework summary

In this work, a two-step procedure is presented wherein: 1) given the process flow diagram (PFD) for a modular unit, major process equipment selections are made to maximize the modular unit availability subject to a cost constraint, 2) a network is designed using the modular units from the previous stage to maximize the total system profit subject to a minimum reliability at every location. The framework is modeled as two mixed-integer programs (MIP) to represent each step independently.

#### 2.1.1. Nomenclature

The nomenclature used in the rest of this section is outlined below.

Table 1: Sets

| Notation | Description | Notation | Description |
|---|---|---|---|
| $\mathcal{K}$ | Set of modules | $\mathcal{F}$ | Set of all feedstock resources |
| $\mathcal{L}$ | Set of potential facility locations | $\mathcal{Y}$ | Set of years in the planning horizon |
| $\mathcal{I}$ | Set of source locations | $\mathcal{P}$ | Set of all product resources |
| $\mathcal{J}$ | Set of sink locations | $\mathcal{M}$ | Set of months in one year |
| $\mathcal{V}$ | Set of vehicles for transport | $\mathcal{U}$ | Set of all utility resources |
| $\mathcal{E}$ | Set of equipment | $\mathcal{B}$ | Set of equipment types |

Table 2: Parameters

| Notation | Description | Notation | Description |
|---|---|---|---|
| $p_e$ | CAPEX of equipment $e$ | $cap_k$ | Maximum capacity of module $k$ |
| $p_k$ | Annual CAPEX of module $k$ | $qty_{b,k}$ | Number of unit type $b$ used in module $k$ |
| $p_k^{max}$ | Maximum CAPEX for module $k$ | $type_{e,b}$ | 1 if unit $e$ is of type $b$, 0 otherwise |
| $capex_k$ | CAPEX multiplier for module $k$ | $life_k$ | Lifetime of module $k$ (years) |
| $MTBF_e$ | Maximum MTBF of equipment $e$ | $m_{x,l}$ | Distance between location $x$ and facility $l$ (where $x \in \mathcal{I}$ or $\mathcal{J}$) |
| $MTTRes_e$ | Minimum MTTRes of equipment $e$ | $Re_l^{min}$ | Minimum availability allowable in facility $l$ |
| $conv_{f.k}$ | Conversion rate of feedstock $f$ by module $k$ | $conv_{p.k}$ | Yield of product $p$ by module $k$ |

| conv$_{u.k}$ | Conversion rate of utility $u$ by module $k$ | $r_p$ | Revenue from product $p$ |
| $c_f$ | Cost of feedstock $f$ | $sc_p$ | Shipping cost of product $p$ per mile per ton |
| $c_u$ | Cost of utility $u$ | $sc_f$ | Shipping cost of feedstock $f$ per mile per ton |

Table 3: Variables

| Notation | Description | Notation | Description |
|---|---|---|---|
| $p_k$ | CAPEX of module $k$ | | Binary variables |
| qty$_{e,k}$ | Number of unit $e$ used in module $k$ | $y_{e,k}$ | 1 if unit $e$ is chosen for module $k$, |
| $Re_k$ | Availability of module $k$ | $y_{k,l}$ | 1 if module $k$ is chosen for location $l$, 0 otherwise |
| prod$_{k.l}$ | Actual production by module $k$ in facility $l$ | $x_l$ | 1 if location $l$ is chosen for the network, 0 otherwise |
| qty$_{k,l}$ | Number of module $k$ used in facility $l$ | | |
| $Re_l$ | Availability of facility $l$ | | |

## 2.2. Stage 1: Process module design

Modular unit reliability is estimated using the methodology outlined by Al-Douri et al. (2021). In this methodology, PFDs of the modular units are assumed to be known. The MTBF, which is the inverse of the failure rate, and MTTRes data for every equipment are derived from the 2015 edition of the OREDA Handbook for Onshore and Offshore Reliability Data. Modular unit availability, used here as a proxy metric for reliability, is then calculated as follows:

$$Re_k = \prod_B \left( \frac{\text{MTBF}_b}{\text{MTTRes}_b + \text{MTBF}_b} \right) \tag{1}$$

The availability of each modular unit is then used to modify profit calculation to express the fact that no revenue and operating expenses are applicable when the unit is non-operational.

### 2.2.1. Constraints

There are three groups of constraints that are needed in this stage of the model. The first group of constraints limits the number and type of units used per operation called for by the PFD:

$$\sum_{\mathcal{E} \text{ if type}_{e,b}=1} y_{e,k} \leq 1 \quad \forall\, k \text{ in } \mathcal{K} \tag{2}$$

$$\sum_{\mathcal{E} \text{ if type}_{e,b}=1} \text{qty}_{e,k} = \text{qty}_{b,k} \quad \forall\, k \text{ in } \mathcal{K} \tag{3}$$

The second group of constraints restricts the total CAPEX of the module constructed based on the maximum CAPEX allowable:

$$\frac{\text{capex}_k \times \sum_{\mathcal{E}} \text{qty}_{e,k} \times p_e}{\text{life}_k} \leq p_k^{max} \quad \forall\, k \text{ in } \mathcal{K} \tag{4}$$

The third group of constraints calculates the aggregate availability of each module based on the availabilities of the units chosen for the module:

$$Re_k = \prod_{\mathcal{B}} \left( \sum_{\mathcal{E} \text{ if type}_{e,b}=1} y_{e,k} \times \left( \frac{\text{MTBF}_e}{\text{MTTRes}_e + \text{MTBF}_e} \right) \right)^{\text{qty}_{b,k}} \quad \forall\, k \text{ in } \mathcal{K} \tag{5}$$

*2.2.2. Objective functions*
The objective function in this stage is to maximize the total availability of every module being constructed:

$$\max \sum_{\mathcal{K}} Re_k \tag{6}$$

*2.3. Stage 2: facility location-allocation*
Mass balance constraints for this stage of the model is outlined in Chrisandina et al. (2022). Additional constraints to specify aggregate availability for each potential location are outlined below.

*2.3.1. Constraints*
The availability of each location is calculated as an aggregate of the availability of all modules selected for that location, assuming that the modules run in parallel:

$$Re_l = 1 - \prod_{\mathcal{K}} (1 - Re_k)^{\text{qty}_{k,l}} \quad \forall\, l \text{ in } \mathcal{L} \tag{7}$$

The annual profit per location is calculated as follows, where the location availability is used to modify both the revenue and operating cost factors:

$$\text{profit}_l = Re_l(\text{rev}_l - \text{OPEX}_l) - \sum_{\mathcal{K}} y_{k,l} \times \text{CAPEX}_k, \quad \forall\, l \text{ in } \mathcal{L} \tag{8}$$

where the revenue, operating and capital costs are expressed below:

$$\text{rev}_l = \sum_{\mathcal{K}} \sum_{\mathcal{P}} r_p \times \text{conv}_{p,k} \times \text{prod}_{k,l} \times \text{qty}_{k,l} \quad \forall\, l \text{ in } \mathcal{L} \tag{9}$$

$$\text{OPEX}_l = \sum_{\mathcal{K}} \left( \begin{array}{l} \sum_{\mathcal{F}} c_f \times \text{conv}_{f,k} \times \text{qty}_{k,l} + \sum_{\mathcal{U}} c_u \times \text{conv}_{f,k} \times \text{qty}_{k,l} \\[8pt] + \sum_{\mathcal{J}} \sum_{\mathcal{F}} sc_f \times m_{i,l} \times \text{conv}_{f,k} \times \text{prod}_{k,l} \\[8pt] + \sum_{\mathcal{J}} \sum_{\mathcal{P}} sc_p \times m_{j,l} \times \text{conv}_{p,k} \times \text{prod}_{k,l} \end{array} \right)$$
$$\forall\, l \text{ in } \mathcal{L} \tag{10}$$

$$\text{CAPEX}_l = \sum_{\mathcal{K}} p_k \times \text{qty}_{k,l} \quad \forall\, l \text{ in } \mathcal{L} \tag{11}$$

*2.3.2. Objective function*
The objective of this stage is to maximize the total profit obtained by the system, with consideration of location availability:

$$max \sum_{\mathcal{L}} profit_l \qquad (12)$$

## 3. Case study

### 3.1. Setup

The framework is applied towards the simultaneous design and schedule optimization of a new multi-city biomass value chain to meet a monthly demand for several value-added products. A set of microbiorefineries (MBRs) are available to produce different products, and the PFDs for each MBR are fixed. The case study considers three biomass resources (cassava, banana, and mango) and three products (biogas, methanol, and mango oil). Agricultural cities which supply each resource also act as potential locations for placing MBRs. The availability of the resources fluctuates monthly based on local harvest patterns, while the demand for products remains constant year-round.

### 3.2. Results & discussion

In the first stage of the framework, MBRs are constructed given their PFDs and a selection of possible equipment units to purchase with associated costs, MTBF, and MTTRes values. It can be observed that purchasing more reliable units increases both the cost and availability of an MBR. However, there is a point of diminishing return (see Fig. 1) after which additional investment in costly but higher-performing units do not significantly increase aggregate MBR availability. MBR manufacturers can utilize this insight to decide on the level of investment into reliable units based on the desired performance. Furthermore, it is also possible to conduct sensitivity analysis on the major components within an MBR to determine the contribution of each equipment to overall reliability and direct targeted investments towards the most critical components.

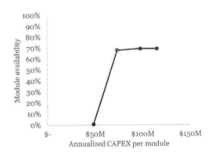

Figure 1: Pareto front for annualized CAPEX per process module vs module availability

In the second stage of the framework, a supply chain network using MBRs, designed in the previous stage, was constructed. Two separate scenarios were generated: one scenario using lower-cost and less reliable MBRs, and one scenario using higher-cost and more reliable MBRs. As shown in Fig. 2, higher profit is achievable when more reliable MBRs are used despite the higher capital cost per module installed in this scenario. This is due to the fact that fewer MBRs need to be installed at each location to meet the minimum availability requirement per location, leading to lower total capital costs. Furthermore, the installed MBRs

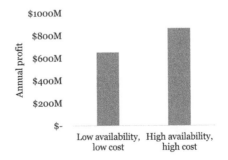

Figure 2: Comparison of total network profit based on the availability and cost of MBRs installed in each location

are operational for a longer proportion of the year which leads to higher revenue generating potential.

## 4. Conclusion

DESs offer a potential pathway towards a more resilient energy system due to their flexibility in responding to fluctuating supply or demand patterns. Utilization of modular production units can also provide additional benefits since units can be designed to enhance overall system resilience. This work has presented a two-stage framework to integrate modular production facility design with supply chain network optimization. It was observed that designing modular units to maximize reliability contributes to increased network profit compared to purchasing cheaper but less reliable modular units. Depending on the risk tolerance and budget constraints of the decision-maker, the limits on modular unit cost and location reliability can be adjusted. In this work, modular units are considered as stationary during the planning horizon. However, modular units can be transported between locations to limit idle time if feedstock supply is unavailable at a particular location. To address this limitation, the framework can be extended to account for modular unit transport. Some idle time during transport needs to be considered, as well as the effect of transportation-related wear and tear on the performance and reliability of the units.

*References*

R. Kakodkar, G. He, C.D. Demirhan, M. Arbabzadeh, S.G. Baratsas, S. Avraamidou, D. Mallapragada, I. Miller, R.C. Allen, E. Gençer, and E.N. Pistikopoulos, 2022, A review of analytical and optimization methodologies for transitions in multi-scale energy systems, Renewable and Sustainable Energy Reviews, 160, 112277.

M. Yang, F. You, 2018, Modular methanol manufacturing from shale gas: Techno-economic and environmental analyses of conventional large-scale production versus small-scale distributed, modular processing, AIChE Journal, 64, 495-510.

R. C. Allen, D. Allaire, and M.M. El-Halwagi, 2019, Capacity planning for modular and transportable infrastructure for shale gas production and processing, Ind. Eng. Chem. Res, 58, 5887–5897.

F.M. Al-Fadhli, H. Baaqeel, and M.M. El-Halwagi, 2019, Modular design of carbon-hydrogen-oxygen symbiosis networks over a time horizon with limited natural resources. Chem. Eng. Process. Process Intensif. 141, 107535.

M. Baldea, T.F. Edgar, B.L. Stanley, and A.A. Kiss, 2017, Modular manufacturing processes: Status, challenges, and opportunities. AIChE Journal, 4262-4272.

N.J. Chrisandina, S. Vedant, E. Iakovou, E.N. Pistikopoulos, and M.M. El-Halwagi, 2022, Multi-scale Integration for Enhanced Resilience of Sustainable Energy Supply Chains: Perspectives and Challenges, Computers & Chemical Engineering, 107891.

OREDA, 2015, Offshore and Onshore Reliability Data Handbook Vol. 1.

Antonis Kokossis, Michael C. Georgiadis, Efstratios N. Pistikopoulos (Eds.)
PROCEEDINGS OF THE 33rd European Symposium on Computer Aided Process Engineering
(ESCAPE33), June 18-21, 2023, Athens, Greece

# Techno-enviro-economic analysis of H₂ economy in China from H₂ production to utilization

Xiaodong Hong[a]\*, Zuwei Liao[b]\*, Yao Yang[a,b], Jingdai Wang[b], Yongrong Yang[b]

[a]*ZJU-Hangzhou Global Scientific and Technological Innovation Center, Hangzhou 311215, China*
[b]*State Key Laboratory of Chemical Engineering, College of Chemical and Biological Engineering, Zhejiang University, Hangzhou 310027, China*
\**hongxiaodong@zju.edu.cn*

## Abstract

China, the world's largest $CO_2$ emitter, has promised to achieve carbon neutrality before 2060. The hydrogen economy is one of the most promising alternatives to cut emissions. The planning of the hydrogen economy should consider the diversity of China, such as renewable energy distribution, industry distribution, etc. In this work, the impact of renewable energy availability on the production cost of hydrogen and the impact of hydrogen transport are explored on a national scale. A comprehensive techno-enviro-economic analysis of the hydrogen economy in China from its production to utilization is carried out. A mixed integer linear programming (MILP) model is developed to optimize the levelized cost of hydrogen (LCOH) and $CO_2$ emissions of hydrogen (CEOH) utilizing local solar, wind, and grid electricity. Key questions, such as import $H_2$ from where via which form for what application, are answered for each province. These are crucial and useful for decision-makers to plan hydrogen economy development.

**Keywords**: techno-enviro-economic, hydrogen economy, carbon neutrality.

## 1. Introduction

With the world's population growing, human energy demand keeps rising, which has caused climate change and environmental degradation and threatened the way of life. Over the past decades, the world has devoted significant efforts to developing renewable energy technologies. The renewables in the global power generation energy mix have been rising rapidly. However, the developments in renewable energy technologies also reveal the critical lack of transportable forms of energy has become the main bottleneck in a global shift toward renewables. Growing adoption of grid-connected photovoltaic systems caused in advertent stress on the electrical grid (Obi et al., 2016). A chemical form of energy storage, simply like fossil fuel storing energy over millions of years, is needed to compensate for the intermittent nature of solar and wind. This throws the spotlight onto the hydrogen economy (Majumdar et al., 2021), where hydrogen has dual properties of energy carrier and material carrier.

Much research has been carried out to reveal the role of different hydrogen production technologies, hydrogen transport carriers, and hydrogen applications in a hydrogen-based low-carbon society. Staffell et al. (2019) review the challenges of the hydrogen economy, showing considerable improvements are still required for hydrogen to become truly competitive. Parkinson et al. (2019) evaluated 12 different hydrogen production techniques from technical, economic, and environmental aspects. The results show that the most cost-effective methods of decarbonization still utilize fossil feedstocks, and methane pyrolysis may be the most cost-effective short-term abatement solution. The cost of renewable electrolytic routes is high, while they offer significantly higher emissions reduction. Hong et al. (2021) studied four hydrogen carriers and two hydrogen end-use scenarios. Results showed that liquid hydrogen is preferred for road transport application. Sunny et al. (2020) studied the regional transition of the heating sector from natural gas-based infrastructure to $H_2$ by a supply chain optimization model. They found that the synergistic deployment of autothermal reforming of methane and biomass gasification with $CO_2$ capture and storage (CCS) is critical in achieving cost-effective decarbonization.

The impact of renewable energy availability on the production cost of hydrogen, such as solar radiation and wind speed, has been studied. Al-Sharafi et al. (2017) investigated the potential of power generation and hydrogen production via solar and wind energy resources at five different locations in the Kingdom of Saudi Arabia, Toronto, and Sydney. Pan et al. (2020) studied the levelized cost of hydrogen in 31 provinces considering provincial differences in electricity prices, shares of renewables in power grids, and solar radiations in China. The cost varies from 31.5 ¥ per kg to 46.8 ¥ per kg. However, the impact of hydrogen transmission and delivery on the hydrogen cost and carbon footprint has not been explored. Relatively cheap hydrogen produced in renewable energy abundant regions can lead to higher landed costs higher than hydrogen produced locally, and an even higher carbon footprint depending on its supply chain.

In light of the aforementioned concerns, we first develop an optimization model of Hybrid Power-to-Hydrogen System, which can design a cost-minimal or emission-minimal system considering solar and wind resource availability and time-of-use grid power prices. Then, a systematical study and comparison of levelized cost of hydrogen (LCOH) and carbon emissions of hydrogen (CEOH) are presented for the 31 provinces of mainland China studied in Pan et al. (2020). $H_2$ via local production and provincial transport are all compared for each province.

## 2. Hybrid Power-to-Hydrogen System

A $H_2$ supply chain is constructed as shown in Figure 1, considering local production by a hybrid power-to-hydrogen system (HPtoH). The water electrolyzer (WE) is the main component, which adopts power from solar photovoltaic panels (PV), wind turbines (WT), utility-scale lithium batteries (BT), and power grids (GRID). In the study, proton exchange membrane (PEM) electrolysis is adopted, due to its higher efficiency and flexibility than alkaline electrolysis.

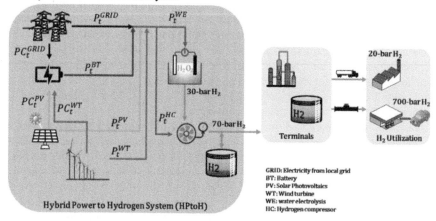

Figure 1. Illustration of Hybrid Power-to-Hydrogen System (HPtoH).

In Figure 1, it is assumed that 30-bar $H_2$ is produced, and then compressed to 70 bar for transport. Considering the intermittent nature of solar and wind, a utility-scale lithium battery storage and buffer storage tank (ST) are adopted to ensure the system could have steady daily output. Batteries can store the excess generated electricity of PV and WT while charging batteries during valley-time-price hours and discharging batteries during peak-time-price hours are also considered. After 70-bar $H_2$ is delivered to terminals, it will be further compressed to 540 bar for truck delivery as 540-bar $H_2$ (CH540) and liquefied for truck delivery as liquid hydrogen (LH2) (Hong et al., 2021). Besides, 70-bar $H_2$ can also be directly transported by pipelines.

## 3. Model Description

The objective of the developed model is to minimize the levelized cost of hydrogen (LCOH, ¥/kg), as shown by Eq. 1. LCOH is obtained by the annual output of the system and the annual cost. The annual cost consists of three parts, the capital cost of facilities (*CAPEX*), fixed operation and maintenance cost (*FOM*), and variable operation cost (*VOP*). CAPEX is obtained by the annualized factor, the unit capital investment cost, and the capacity of the facility (PV, WT, WE, BT, ST). The annualized factor is derived from the lifetime of the facility and the discount rate. The overall $CO_2$ emissions of hydrogen (CEOH) can be obtained by summing up emissions in the entire supply chain, including grid electricity consumption and truck fuel consumption. Note that, the CEOH can also be adopted as an objective.

$$LCOH = \frac{CAPEX+FOM+VOP}{\lambda \times 1000 \times 365} \tag{1}$$

The model also includes energy balance equations for PV, WT, WE, and BT, mass balance equations for WE and ST, constraints on daily $H_2$ output and energy availability, etc. The techno-economic parameters are obtained from the literature (Terlouw et al., 2022; Wiser et al., 2021; Feldman et al., 2021), as shown in Table 1.

Table 1. Techno-economic parameters.

| Item | Unit | Value |
|---|---|---|
| Photovoltaic (PV) investment cost | ¥/kW | 5477.4 |
| Fixed operation and maintenance (O&M) cost of PV | ¥/kW-year | 547.74 |
| Wind turbine (WT) investment cost | ¥/kW | 10087.8 |
| Fixed operation and maintenance (O&M) cost of WT | ¥/kW-year | 296.7 |
| Water electrolyzer (WE) investment cost | ¥/kW | 9213.98 |
| Fixed operation and maintenance (O&M) cost of WE | ¥/kW-year | 212.63 |
| Battery (BT) investment cost | ¥/kW | 9522.0 |
| Fixed operation and maintenance (O&M) cost of BT | ¥/kW-year | 69 |
| Hydrogen storage (HS) investment cost | ¥/kg $H_2$ | 3588 |
| Fixed operation and maintenance (O&M) cost of HS | ¥/kg $H_2$-year | 35.8 |
| Hydrogen compressor (HC) investment cost | ¥/kW | 27887.8 |
| Fixed operation and maintenance (O&M) cost of HC | ¥/kW-year | 1115.5 |
| Fixed operation and maintenance (O&M) cost of GRID | ¥/kW-year | 336~576 |
| Conversion efficiency of water electrolyzer | - | 60.5% |
| Discount rate | - | 4% |

### 3.1. Renewable energy availability

In this study, hourly solar power data are collected from the PVWatts Calculator developed by National Renewable Energy Laboratory (NREL). A PV module with a two-axis tracking system (dual-axis tracking system) is considered to calculate the power generation capacity. For power generation by wind turbines, the data of wind speed at 50 meters is obtained from NASA by API. The wind speed at 80 meters can be obtained by the following Eq. 2.

$$v = v_{ref} \times \left(\frac{H}{H_{ref}}\right)^{\alpha} \ \forall t \in T \tag{2}$$

where $v_{ref}$ and $v$ represents the wind speed at the height of $H_{ref}$ and $H$ and $\alpha$ is surface roughness (0.14). Based on the hourly wind speed at 80 meters, the turbine power can be obtained based on the turbine power curve.

### 3.2. Grid electricity

In China, industrial consumers can choose the single electricity price and the time-of-use price. In this study, the time-of-use price is adopted. The electricity prices are categorized into the rush, peak, flat, and valley time prices. The valley time price could be as low as only 40% of the flat price, while the peak time price could be 150% of the flat price. And the rush time price can be even 20% higher than the peak time price. The rush time price is mostly only available in specific hours in a few months with extremely cold or hot weather (e.g. July, August, December). With the time-of-use price and intermittent nature of solar and wind, the optimization model will find the optimal operating strategy of the HPtoH system, by minimizing LCOH and/or CEOH.

## 4. Results and Discussion

Provincial economic and environmental analysis of $H_2$ produced by the HPtoH system is presented in a case study. LCOH and CEOH of locally produced $H_2$ and delivered $H_2$ in each province are obtained. In each province, at least five locations are chosen for analysis. Solar and wind resource availability is obtained for each location, and production cost and emissions of $H_2$ are obtained via the HPtoH model (by Pyomo). The optimal system size, including water electrolysis, battery, $H_2$ storage, and compressor, is also determined. With the production cost of $H_2$, the LCOH and CEOH can be calculated for various end users via different transport pathways.

Figure 2 shows the LCOH matrix, where the LCOH of 20-bar $H_2$ received by end-users is shown for each province. $H_2$ can be locally produced or by provincial transportation via the 70-bar pipeline. For the locally produced $H_2$, we assume a transmission distance of 50 kilometers and a distribution distance of 15 km, from the producers to end-users. For the provincial transportation, distances between any two provinces are calculated. In Figure 2, each column represents the LCOH in each province. For example, the first column indicates the LCOH of 20-bar $H_2$ in Beijing. The First row is the one for the locally produced $H_2$. The second one is from Tianjin. Only the LOCH lower than local production in each province is represented in the Figure. All blank blocks mean uneconomical supply chains. For the columns where most of the blocks are blank, local production is the most economical path, such as Inner Mongolia, Qinghai, and Xinjiang. On the contrary, these provinces tend to have fewer blank blocks, from the perspective of rows. Mongolia, Qinghai, Xinjiang, Ningxia, and Shanxi all have the potential to provide $H_2$ for many neighboring provinces.

It is worth mentioning that Figure 2 shows the case study where the LCOH is minimized. Thus, the HPtoH systems tend to use grid electricity if the valley time price is low. As a result, the CEOH of the produced $H_2$ is relatively high for most of the provinces, since the renewable energy share of the grid is still low. In another case, the CEOH is minimized for the HPtoH system. A similar plot of Figure 2 is obtained, which indicates the LOCH varies from 40 ¥/kg $H_2$ to 66 ¥/kg $H_2$. Given the length of the article, the results are not provided.

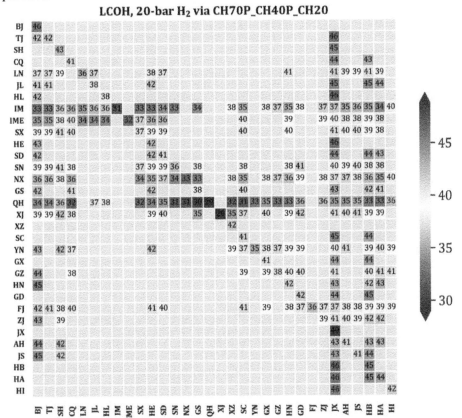

Figure 2. LCOH (¥/kg $H_2$) of 20-bar $H_2$ received end users. (BJ: Beijing, TJ: Tianjin, SH: Shanghai, CQ: Chongqing, LN: Liaoning, JL: Jilin, HL: Heilongjiang, IM: Inner Mongolia West; IME: Inner Mongolia East; SX: Shanxi; HE: Hebei, SD: Shandong, SN: Shaanxi, NX: Ningxia, GS: Gansu, QH: Qinghai, XJ: Xinjiang, XZ: Tibet, SC: Sichuan, YN: Yunnan, GX: Guangxi, GZ: Guizhou, HN: Hunan, GD: Guangdong, FJ: Fujian, ZJ: Zhejiang, JX: Jiangxi, AH: Anhui, JS: Jiangsu, HB: Hubei, HA: Henan, HI: Hainan)

## 5. Conclusions

This study presents a comprehensive techno-enviro-economic analysis of hydrogen economy, to evaluate the competitiveness of hydrogen in each province of China. Hydrogen production, hydrogen delivery, and hydrogen utilization are considered simultaneously. A mixed integer linear programming (MILP) model is developed to optimize the levelized cost of hydrogen (LCOH) and $CO_2$ emissions of hydrogen (CEOH). The landed cost of $H_2$ from any other provinces in China and the carbon footprint are obtained for each province. Provinces in western China, including Inner Mongolia, Qinghai, Xinjiang, Ningxia, and Shanxi, have a higher potential to provide low-cost hydrogen for other provinces, as they have more abundant renewable energy sources. Many key questions still need to be answered with further research.

- Importing H2 via liquid hydrogen, ammonia, and liquid organic carriers will be compared with local production
- High-pressure gas hydrogen (e.g. 100 bar, 300 bar) directly produced via PEM WE will be considered for other hydrogen applications, such as refueling stations.

- Off-shore wind will be considered for coastal provinces.
- Sensitivity analysis will be carried out to evaluate the impact of uncertainties.
- A multiperiod supply chain model will be developed for the planning of the hydrogen economy considering all provinces simultaneously.

## Acknowledgment

We gratefully acknowledge the financial support of the National Natural Science Foundation of China (U22A20415) and ZJU-Hangzhou Global Scientific and Technological Innovation Center.

## Nomenclature

LCOH    Levelized cost of hydrogen, ¥/ kg $H_2$
CEOH    $CO_2$ emissions of hydrogen, kg $CO_2$/kg $H_2$
CAPEX  Annual capital cost of the hydrogen system, ¥/year
FOM      Annual fixed operation and maintenance cost of the hydrogen system, ¥/kW
VOP      Annual variable operation cost of the hydrogen system, ¥/kW
$\lambda$          Average daily $H_2$ production capacity, tonne per day
$v_{ref}/v$       Wind speed at the height of $H_{ref}/H$
$\alpha$          Surface roughness (0.14)

## References

M. Obi, R. Bass, 2016, Trends and Challenges of Grid-Connected Photovoltaic Systems – A Review. Renewable and Sustainable Energy Reviews, 58, 1082–1094.

A. Majumdar, J. M. Deutch, R. S. Prasher, T. P. Griffin, 2021, A Framework for a Hydrogen Economy. Joule, 5 (8), 1905–1908.

I. Staffell, D. Scamman, A.Velazquez Abad, P. Balcombe, P. E. Dodds, P. Ekins, N. Shah, K. R. Ward, 2019, The Role of Hydrogen and Fuel Cells in the Global Energy System. Energy & Environmental Science, 12 (2), 463–491.

B. Parkinson,; P. Balcombe, J. F. Speirs, A. D. Hawkes, K. Hellgardt, 2019, Levelized Cost of CO2 Mitigation from Hydrogen Production Routes. Energy & Environmental Science, 12 (1), 19–40.

X. Hong, V. B. Thaore, I. A. Karimi, S. Farooq, X. Wang, A. K. Usadi, B. R. Chapman, R. A. Johnson, 2021, Techno-Enviro-Economic Analyses of Hydrogen Supply Chains with an ASEAN Case Study. International Journal of Hydrogen Energy, 46 (65), 32914–32928.

N. Sunny, N. Mac Dowell, N. Shah, 2020, What Is Needed to Deliver Carbon-Neutral Heat Using Hydrogen and CCS? Energy & Environmental Science, 13 (11), 4204–4224.

A. Al-Sharafi, A. Z. Sahin, T. Ayar, B. S. Yilbas, 2017, Techno-Economic Analysis and Optimization of Solar and Wind Energy Systems for Power Generation and Hydrogen Production in Saudi Arabia. Renewable and Sustainable Energy Reviews, 69, 33–49.

G. Pan, W. Gu, Q. Hu, J. Wang, F.Teng, G. Strbac, 2021, Cost and Low-Carbon Competitiveness of Electrolytic Hydrogen in China. Energy & Environmental Science, 14 (9), 4868–4881.

T. Terlouw, C. Bauer, R. McKenna, M. Mazzotti, 2022, Large-Scale Hydrogen Production via Water Electrolysis—a Techno-Economic and Environmental Assessment. Energy & Environmental Science, 15, 3583-3602

R. Wiser, M. Bolinger, B. Hoen, D. Millstein, J. Rand, G. Barbose, N. Darghouth, W. Gorman, S. Jeong, A. Mills, B. Paulos, 2021, Land-Based Wind Market Report: 2021 Edition. 87.

D. Feldman, V. Ramasamy, R. Fu, A. Ramdas, J. Desai, R. Margolis, 2021, U.S. Solar Photovoltaic System and Energy Storage Cost Benchmark: Q1 2020. Renewable Energy, 120.

PVWatts Calculator. https://pvwatts.nrel.gov/ (accessed 2022-07-21).

POWER | Data Access Viewer. https://power.larc.nasa.gov/data-access-viewer/ (accessed 2022-07-29).

Antonis Kokossis, Michael C. Georgiadis, Efstratios N. Pistikopoulos (Eds.)
PROCEEDINGS OF THE 33rd European Symposium on Computer Aided Process Engineering
(ESCAPE33), June 18-21, 2023, Athens, Greece

# Towards a novel concept for solid energy storage

Adrian Straub[a], Bogdan Dorneanu[a], Harvey Arellano-Garcia[a]

[a]*LS Prozess- und Anlagentechnik, Brandenburgische Technische Universität Cottbus-Senftenberg, Cottbus, D-03046, Germany*
*arellano@b-tu.de*

## Abstract

In this contribution, the model-based development of a novel process concept for the storage and release of ammonia in solids is proposed. The concept is validated by means of the Aspen Plus® process simulator. As a promising prospect, Hexaaminenickel(II) chloride is selected. After a preparative stage, the process can cycle between the storage and release of energy. The process is split in a reaction and a separation section, in such a way that the same equipment is used for both storage and release steps. Sensitivity analysis and design parameter optimization are used to determine key process parameters. The operation ranges from standard conditions (25 °C and 1 atm) to temperatures not higher than 120 °C. Moreover, the simulation results show that it is possible to store over 50% of the base material in form of ammonia, equivalent to almost 10 wt.% hydrogen, placing the concept within the specific system targets set by the U.S. Department of Energy.

**Keywords**: Process design, Process modelling, Aspen Plus®

## 1. Introduction

Climate change and energy supply count amongst the most important issues of our time. The focus of many countries and companies has shifted from the use of fossil fuels as an energy source to renewable energies (Sterner, 2019). In 2021, 42.4 % of the German electricity came from renewable energy sources. With the increasing number of green energies, the variability of technologies based on wind or solar caused by changes in weather can impact the electricity grid. Achieving a reliable power delivery to satisfy changing supply and demand is crucial for a modern economy (Ausfelder et al., 2017). This calls for strategies to ensure stability of the grid during times of low power production or high demand. Apart from a sophisticated grid structure, the storage of energy is important. Whilst there are already established approaches, such as mechanical (pumped hydroelectric storage), thermal (sensible heat storage) or chemical (hydrogen in gaseous or liquefied form), most of them are geo-limited or require adverse operating conditions (*e.g.,* high pressure, high and low temperature, etc.) (Koohi-Fayegh, 2020). In recent years the interest in hydrogen has increased, with many nations striving towards a hydrogen economy. Figure 1 gives an overview of the different storage technologies currently available for hydrogen.

To determine the best suited material for hydrogen storage, certain properties, such as the gravimetric and volumetric hydrogen density, decomposition temperature, reusability and production cost, need to be evaluated and taken into account. To this end, the U.S. Department of Energy (DOE) has set targets for solid hydrogen storage used in cars, albeit these are not restricted to the automotive sector. Those main goals are (Rather, 2020):

- Gravimetric energy density:     1.5 kWh/kg system (4.5 wt.% hydrogen)
- Volumetric energy density:     1.0 kWh/L system (0.030 kg hydrogen/L)

- Cost per stored energy:                $10/kWh    ($333/kg    stored    hydrogen
  capacity)

In addition, the materials should be acceptable from the point of view of health and safety and the environment.

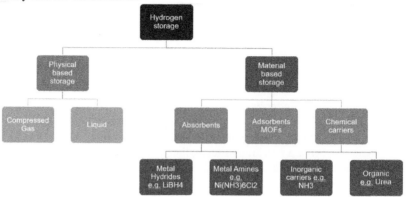

*Figure 1: Overview of hydrogen storage technologies*

In recent years the application of many different materials for solid energy storage has been investigated (Amiri and Shahbazian-Yassar, 2021). However, these new materials are lacking a process design concept to be applied at commercial scale. The focus of this work is the development of such a novel concept by means of the Aspen Plus® process simulator. It has been chosen over other process simulators due to its flexibility, extensive component and physical properties database, and advanced solids handling capabilities. These include an extensive library of physical properties (e.g., SOLIDS, ELECNRTL, etc.) and equipment models for solid processing (e.g., fluidized bed reactor, cyclone, classifiers, crystallizer, dryer, filter, centrifuge, etc.). Furthermore, it allows solids to take part in reactions, and detailed description of granular solids (e.g., particle size distribution, sub-streams of different solid phases, etc.). Another novel aspect of this work is the use the resources provided by Aspen Plus in the context of solid-solid separations and reactions beyond typical operations such as gasification.

## 2. Process design

### 2.1. Storage material

After investigating several options, an ammonia salt, Hexaaminenickel(II) chloride (HEX), is chosen as the energy storage material. A blue/violet solid, the component is an indirect hydrogen storage solution, capable of storing up to 44.1 wt.% $NH_3$ (Kojima and Yamaguchi, 2020). Unlike the group of adsorbing materials, such as metal and covalent organic frameworks (MOF's/COF's) or intermetallic alloys and metal hydrides on the absorbing side, ammonia salts have received less attention in the pursuit of materials for solid energy storage. For the production of HEX, larger-scale production has not yet been proposed. The starting point is absorption by introducing $NH_3$ gas to nickel chloride ($NiCl_2$). HEX can additionally be prepared in liquid form by mixing aqueous solutions of $NiCl_2$ and $NH_4Cl$ with subsequent crystallisation (Leineweber and Jacobs, 2000). However, this reaction path is not chosen for the conceptual design discussed in this work, for it would require additional equipment like crystallisers and dryers, and, apart from being energy intensive, these units would not be used in other processing steps. When HEX is subjected to heat it releases $NH_3$, decomposing into Diaminenickel(II) chloride (DIA). Ultimately, with more heat added, DIA decomposes back to $NiCl_2$.

The reactions discussed above obey the following stoichiometry:

$$NiCl_2 + 6\,NH_3 \rightarrow Ni(NH_3)_6Cl_2 \tag{1}$$
$$Ni(NH_3)_6Cl_2 \rightarrow Ni(NH_3)_2Cl_2 + 4\,NH_3 \tag{2}$$
$$Ni(NH_3)_2Cl_2 \rightarrow NiCl_2 + 2\,NH_3 \tag{3}$$
$$Ni(NH_3)_2Cl_2 + 4\,NH_3 \rightarrow Ni(NH_3)_6Cl_2 \tag{4}$$

Table 1 shows the different reactions as well as their temperatures and kinetic parameters as they were determined by researchers at the Nagoya University of Japan (Kubota et al., 2014).

*Table 1: Summary of the reaction steps, their reaction kinetics and conditions.*

| Step | Reaction equation | T [K] | k [-] | $E_A$ [kJ/mol] | n [-] |
|---|---|---|---|---|---|
| Preparation | (1) | 323 | $6.82\times10^5$ | 66.6 | 2.3 |
| Desorption | (2) | 383 | $3.80\times10^4$ | 50.5 | 0 |
| Complete desorption | (3) | 413 | NA | NA | NA |
| Absorption | (4) | 303 | $4.85\times10^0$ | 24.7 | 0 |

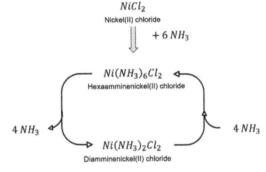

*Figure 2: Concept of cycling between desorption (left) and absorption (right) to release and store ammonia after initial preparation from NiCl₂.*

By cycling through the Absorption and Desorption steps, as shown in Figure 2, $NH_3$ can be repeatedly released and stored. The Complete desorption step in Reaction (3) is not considered in the current work.

### 2.2. Process concept

The flowsheet for the proposed process concept based on the reaction pathways for the production and decomposition of HEX is illustrated in *Figure 3*.

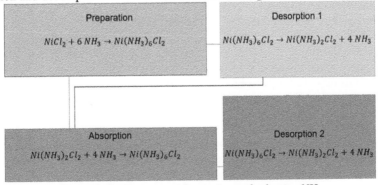

*Figure 3: Design concept for storing and releasing NH₃.*

The starting point is NiCl$_2$, assumed to be broadly available. Beginning with the initial Preparation step (purple), in which NH$_3$ is stored as HEX, a first stage of releasing NH$_3$, in which DIA is produced – Desorption 1 (green) – is considered. The main storage and release cycle starts with an Absorption step (blue), in which NH$_3$ reacts with DIA, and its release in the Desorption 2 step (red). In each of these four process steps considered, gas-solid reactions occur. In order to facilitate them, suitable equipment must be selected.

To this end, the proposed concept considers, for each of the four steps described above, a Reaction section, in which solid and gas reactants come into contact, and a Separation section, in which solid-solid and solid-gas components are separated, as illustrated in the block diagram in *Figure 4*.

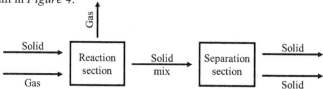

*Figure 4: Block diagram of the process concept stages.*

For the storage and release reactions, a fluidized bed reactor (FBR) is chosen. The liquid-like behaviour of the FBR eases the transport of solids and, due to its turbulent nature, eliminates the need for other mixing equipment. Furthermore, this turbulence favours heat transfer and leads to a uniform product (Reschetilowski, 2020). Since no conclusive particle size distribution (PSD) is available for the solid materials considered for this process (HEX and DIA, respectively), an assumption based on scanning electron microscope (SEM) imagery (Rejitha et al., 2011) is made.

Thus, it is assumed that all solid materials present in the system will have the same PSD. Moreover, to simplify further the process simulation, only one class of particles – of 50 μm – is considered, meaning that all particles will have the same diameter. Hence, in the Separation section a separation of the solid materials based on density is proposed.

### 2.3. *Process concept development procedure*

The process concept design is developed in Aspen Plus v12. Initially, the storage of NH$_3$ is simulated using a continuously stirred tank reactor (CSTR), with a volume determined for a lab size scale design. The starting point for the feed flowrates of reactants is selected using a sensitivity analysis. This was used in the selection of an efficient production target, under constraints of low corresponding feed flowrates of DIA and NH$_3$. Subsequently, these flowrates are minimized to still meet the selected production target.

For the implementation of in Aspen Plus, some settings are already given by the process at hand, others are carefully picked and designed. This is done to ensure a compact reactor (in terms of size) for reduced material cost, as well as a low pressure drop to cut down on operational costs – while obtaining the maximum possible amount of the product.

Among the fixed settings, the possible desired and undesired reactions, the temperature of the favoured reaction (see Table 1), the fluidization behaviour and the PSD of the produced solids (assumed to be constant) need to be specified. Based on density and the PSD assumption, all solid materials are Geldart A solids (Geldart, 1973).

For determining the geometry of the FBR, an optimization is conducted with the objective of maximising the production of HEX, whilst minimizing the column. Since Aspen Plus cannot perform multiobjective optimizations, an equation is used to combine both targets using weights, with higher weighting assigned to the maximisation of the main product. The reactor diameter, height and the solid discharge location are varied to find the best solution. To ensure a feasible result, some additional constraints are added. These include defined targets for the HEX production, ratios for the FBR geometry, etc. To maintain a FBR typical shape, the height is to be bigger than the diameter.

In the Separation section, common equipment is used to perform the solid-solid and solid-gas separations. These processes are designed to be as sharp as possible, while maintaining industry standard flowrates and dimensions. The calculations are performed using the standard calculation methods of the respective unit (e.g., cyclone, sifter, etc.) implemented in Aspen Plus.

In contrast to the simulation of two phase separations of solids (gas-solid, liquid solid), the separation of multiple solids requires a different stream setup. Each solid component is assigned its own sub stream in order to facilitate different PSDs and enable the separation of the streams.

## 3. Results

The results are presented as rounded component units (CU) based on the molar flowrate of the initial reactant, $NiCl_2$. At the beginning of the Preparation stage, 1 CU of $NiCl_2$ reacts with 4.6 CU ammonia, producing HEX and a small amount of DIA, following Reaction (1). In the following stage, Desorption 1, the HEX gets desorbed to DIA, following Reaction (2), and releasing 2.6 CU of $NH_3$. Subsequently, the DIA streams produced during the first and second stages are mixed together, resulting in a flowrate of 1.4 CU. The stream is then introduced in the Absorption stage, where it absorbs 4 CU of $NH_3$, producing HEX, following Reaction (4). In the final stage (Desorption 2), 1 CU of HEX releases 4 CU of ammonia, according to Reaction (2).

This marks the success of the proposed concept. Starting out form the broadly available $NiCl_2$, ammonia is stored and released in several stages. The temperature of each step is not exceeding 120 °C (393 K). The optimizations regarding the reactor geometry reveal the FBR to have a height – diameter ratio of 4.5, while the overall pressure drop of all reactors registers below 25 mbar. Thus, the simulated separation processes produced results that are within the range of the established guidelines.

In the resulting process simulation, the $NiCl_2$ is able to store 52.50 % of its weight in ammonia. This is equivalent to 9.31 wt.% hydrogen, placing the concept within the guidelines (> 4.5 wt.% hydrogen) of the U.S. Department of Energy. Furthermore, the design is set up in such a way that the same equipment is used for both the Storage and Release steps, potentially reducing the equipment cost of the pilot plant.

The complete desorption to $NiCl_2$ requires significantly higher heat compared to the desorption step of HEX to DIA. If only this part is to be considered, the storage capacity must then be based on the 1 CU of HEX entering the Desorption 2 stage. This results in 3.67 wt.% hydrogen being stored, fulfilling only 81.6 % of the target. However, the targets are set for the automotive industry. With the current reactor dimensions, its use in the automotive industry is not viable. The aim is to combine the proposed process in a power-to-ammonia (P2A) concept. Nonetheless, this integration of the solid storage with the utilization of green ammonia and ammonia to power processes (e.g., solid oxide fuel cell) is expected to result in additional losses, due to the conversion efficiency (Jeerh et al., 2021). Hence the DOE targets are formulated for the produced energy, which needs to be evaluated once all the various elements are integrated in the final process concept.

## 4. Conclusion

A novel process concept for solid energy storage has been introduced. In line with advances in hydrogen technology, ammonia as an indirect hydrogen carrier is used, considering safety aspects as well. As a storing compound, the metal ammine halide

Hexaamminenickel(II) chloride is chosen, due to its relatively high hydrogen density (7.81 wt.%) and kinetic data available in the public domain. The concept is developed around the cyclical storage (Absorption) and release (Desorption) of ammonia. For the gas solid reactions, a fluidized bed reactor is used. After the reaction, several separation steps of the different solids present in the reactor streams, as well as of solids and gas, are needed. The process design is set up to have four stages, each at a specific temperature, to favour the desired reaction. Extensive model-based analyses have been conducted in Aspen Plus to validate the proposed process concept. This has been shown to store an equivalent of 9.31 wt.% hydrogen. Furthermore, the operating conditions of the process are within a normal range, with temperatures below 120 °C, and the predominant pressure of one bar. Thus, no costly temperature resistant or pressure specific equipment is needed. In both the reaction and the separation sections, industry standard equipment can be used. This marks a step up from the analytical equipment used for investigating the storage materials and offers the possibility of scaling up in the later stage of process development. Improvements can be made for the simulation in Aspen Plus, as well as on the practical/experimental side of the process. Regarding the simulation further, optimization of the models can be done. In addition to fine-tuning flow rates and equipment in the case of the reactor, or using a custom model for the separation, switching to a dynamic simulation can bring further insight on the practical operation and stability of the system. Furthermore, information regarding the start-up and shut-down of the various cycles, as well as the control strategies can be investigated with the aid of a dynamic model that can be constructed in Aspen Plus Dynamics. Material investigations with a broader temperature and pressure ranges, either in a thermogravimetric analyser or a FBR, can improve on the reaction kinetics or could provide further knowledge on the process conditions.

## References

A. Amiri and R. Shahbazian-Yassar, 2021, Recent progress of high-entropy materials for energy storage and conversion, Jorunal of Materials Chemistry A 9, pp. 782-823

F. Ausfelder et al., 2017, Energy storage as part of a secure energy supply, ChemBioEng Reviews 4 (3), pp. 144-210

D. Geldart, 1973, Types of gas fluidization, Powder Technology 7 (5), pp. 285-292

G. Jeerh et al., Recent progress in ammonia fuel cells and their potential applications, Journal of Materials Chemistry A 9, pp. 727-752

Y. Kojima and M. Yamaguchi, 2020, Ammonia storage materials for nitrogen recycling hydrogen and energy carriers, International Journal of Hydrogen Energy 45 (16), pp. 10233–10246

S. Koohi-Fayegh, 2020, A review of energy storage types, applications and recent developments, Journal of Energy Storage 27, 101047

M. Kubota et al., 2014, Absorption and desorption characteristics of NH3 with metal chlorides for ammonia storage, Journal of Chemical Engineering of Japan 47 (7), pp. 542–548

A. Leineweber and H. Jacobs, 2000, Preparation and crystal structures of Ni(NH3)2Cl2 and of two modifications of Ni(NH3)2Br2 and Ni(NH3)2I2, Journal of Solid State Chemistry 152 (2), pp. 381–387

S.U. Rather, 2020, Preparation, characterization and hydrogen storage studies of carbon nanotubes and their composites: A review, International Journal of Hydrogen Energy 45, 4653-4672

K. Rejitha et al., 2011, Thermal decomposition studies of [Ni(NH3)6]X2 (X = Cl, Br) in the solid state using TG-MS and TR-XRD, Journal of Thermal Analysis and Calorimetry 103 (2), pp. 515–523

W. Reschetilowski, 2020, Handbuch Chemische Reaktoren, Springer Spektrum Berlin, Heidelberg

M. Sterner, 2019, Handbook of energy storage: Demand, technologies, integration, Springer-Verlag Berlin, Heidelberg

Antonis Kokossis, Michael C. Georgiadis, Efstratios N. Pistikopoulos (Eds.)
PROCEEDINGS OF THE 33rd European Symposium on Computer Aided Process Engineering
(ESCAPE33), June 18-21, 2023, Athens, Greece

# Multiobjective optimization of distributed energy systems design through 3E (economic, environmental and exergy) analysis

Bogdan Dorneanu,[a] Sayeef Miah,[b] Evgenia Mechleri,[b] Harvey Arellano-Garcia,[a]

[a]*LS Prozess- und Anlagentechnik, Brandenburgische Technische Universität Cottbus-Senftenberg, Cottbus D-03046, Germany*
[b]*Department of Chemical and Process Engineering, University of Surrey, Guildford GU27XH, United Kingdom*

## Abstract

Distributed energy systems (DES) are promising alternative to conventional centralized generation, with multiple financial incentives in many parts of the world. Current approaches focus on the design optimization of a DES through economic and environmental cost minimization. However, these two criteria alone do not satisfy long-term sustainability priorities of the system. The novelty of this paper is the simultaneous investigation of economic, environmental and exergetic criteria in the modelling of DES through the two most commonly used solution methodologies for solving multi-objective optimization problems – the weighted sum and the epsilon-constraint methods. Out of the set of Pareto optimal solutions, a best-compromised solution is chosen using the fuzzy-based method. Numerical results reveal reduction of around 93% and 89-91% in environmental and primary exergy input, respectively.

**Keywords**: Multiobjective optimization, Distributed energy systems, Exergy, Mixed-integer linear programming, Fuzzy-based methods.

## 1. Introduction

Due to the commitments set through the Paris Agreement, many countries are implementing plans to reduce greenhouse gas emissions relative to the 1990 baseline. To facilitate this, the utilization of renewable energy systems (DES), as well as a shift from centralized to distributed generation using distributed energy systems plays a key role (Clarke et al., 2021). Thus, a lot of work has been focused in recent years on the development of models that can optimally design the layout of DES, which show significant savings in cost and a low carbon impact (Sidnell et al., 2021). However, considering only the economic and environmental cost of the DES does not satisfy the long-term sustainability priorities. The evaluation of the impact that exergy has on the DES must be considered, as well to make the rational use of available energy (Zhao et al., 2022).
Di Somma et al. (2015) first study the use of exergy analysis within DES, where a model for the optimal operational strategy of a DES is proposed, with a multi-objective whereby cost and exergy efficiency are considered. In terms of optimal DES layout, the focus is on minimization of annual operating and investment costs (Yang et al., 2017, Sidnell et al., 2021). Additionally, environmental cost, as carbon emissions or carbon tax, is taken as a second objective function alongside annual cost in a multi-objective approach (Jing et al., 2018, Karmellos & Mavrotas, 2019). The majority focus on two objective functions,

with a single study considering annual cost, $CO_2$ emissions and electrical system unavailability (Wouters et al., 2017). However, the three objective functions are never simultaneously solved.

The novelty of this paper is twofold, with the first being the investigation of exergy with DES design optimization through a multi-objective approach, whilst considering economic and environmental cost, thus simultaneously minimizing three objectives in the context of DES. The second is the use and comparison of two most commonly used methodologies for solving multi-objective optimization problems, namely the weighted sum (WSM) and the epsilon constraint method (ECM).

## 2. Methodology

Multiple technologies are available for the generation and use of energy, such as photovoltaic panels (PV), natural gas boilers, combined heat and power (CHP) units, or the national grid. A multiobjective optimization problem (MOP) is developed with the aim to optimally select the type and number of technologies within the DES, as well as the layout of the heating pipeline network, and the operation of the system.

The economic objective is equated to the total annual cost, made up of the annualized investment and operational costs, respectively. The environmental objective is equal to the total carbon emissions multiplied by the carbon tax. Finally, the exergetic objective is equal to the primary exergy input to the DES.

The resulting model is applied to a calendar year split into 24 different periods – 6 periods per day for 4 representative seasons.

### 2.1. Problem formulation

The structure of the DES with all the available technologies is shown in Figure 1. The three most common technologies are chosen to complement the national grid – CHPs, PVs and gas fired boilers.

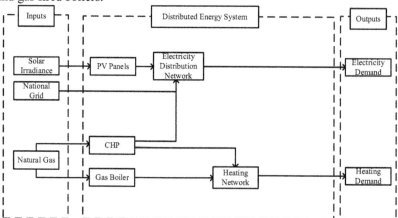

*Figure 1: Energy flows of the DES*

In detail, the national grid, PV panels and CHP units meet the customer electricity demand, while the heating demand is satisfied by gas fired boilers and CHP units.

The *economic objective* is the minimization of the total annualized cost of the DES, $C_{ANNUAL}$, which includes the investment cost, $C_{INV}$, the operational and fuel cost, $C_{OP}$, the annual cost for purchasing energy from the grid, $C_{PUR}^{GRID}$, as well as the income from selling energy back to the grid $C_{SAL}^{GRID}$, and the feed-in tariffs, $FIT$. All costs are in British Pounds (£).

$$C_{ANNUAL} = C_{INV} + C_{OP} + C_{PUR}^{GRID} - C_{SAL}^{GRID} - FIT^{PV} - FIT^{CHP} \tag{1}$$

The *environmental objective* is the minimization of environmental cost of the DES, $C_{ANNUAL}$, which contains carbon emissions arising from the combustion of natural gas within the CHP units and gas boilers, as well as the carbon emissions related to the national grid:

$$C_{ENV} = CT \cdot \left\{ \Sigma_{i,m,p} \left[ E_{i,m,p}^{GRID} \cdot CI_{ELEC} \cdot day(m) \cdot hours(p) \cdot season(m) \right] + \right.$$

$$\Sigma_{i,m,p,k} \left[ \frac{(E_{i,m,p,k,SAL}^{CHP} + E_{i,m,p,k,SELF}^{CHP})}{\eta_k^{CHP}} \cdot CI_{GAS} \cdot day(m) \cdot hours(p) \cdot season(m) \right] + \Sigma_{i,m,p} \left[ \frac{H_{i,m,p}^{B}}{\eta^{B}} \cdot CI_{GAS} \cdot \right.$$

$$\left. \left. day(m) \cdot hours(p) \cdot season(m) \right] \right\} \tag{2}$$

Where $CI_{ELEC}$ and $CI_{gas}$ are the carbon intensities of the national grid and natural gas $[kg_{CO2}/kWh$, respectively, while $CT$ is the carbon tax $[£/kg_{CO2}]$.

The *exergetic objective* is the maximization of the exergy efficiency of the DES, $\varphi$, given as the total exergy output, $Ex^{out}$[kWh], divided by the primary exergy input, $Ex^{in}$ [kWh] (Di Somma et al., 2015):

$$\varphi = \frac{Ex^{out}}{Ex^{in}} \tag{3}$$

The total annual exergy output is the annual exergy required to meet the customer electricity and heating demand, as given by:

$$Ex^{out} = \Sigma_{i,m,p} \left[ CLoad_{i,m,p}^{ELEC} \cdot day(m) \cdot hours(p) \cdot season(m) \right] +$$

$$\Sigma_{i,m,p} \left[ CLoad_{i,m,p}^{HEAT} \cdot F_{i,m,p}^{HEAT} \right] \tag{4}$$

Where $CLoad$ refers to the customer demand at a given month and period, while $F_{i,m,p}^{HEAT}$ is the Carnot factor.

The primary exergy input rate of the DES consists of the exergy from the national grid, $Ex^{GRID}$[kWh], natural gas, $Ex^{NG}$ [kWh] and solar energy, $Ex^{PV}$[kWh], given by:

$$Ex^{in} = Ex^{GRID} + Ex^{NG} + Ex^{PV} \tag{5}$$

Constraints related to the energy balance, design and operation of the various technologies (PV, CHP, heating pipeline network), and interaction with the national grid as described in Clarke et al. (2021) are added to the model.

## 2.2. Optimization methods

Two of the most commonly used optimization methodologies for solving multiobjective linear problems (MOLP), the WSM and the ECM are utilized.

Applying the *WSM* results in a single objective function that is a linear combination of the three objective function in Eqs. (1)-(3):

$$Weighted_{Obj} = \alpha \cdot \frac{C_{ANNUAL}}{C_{ANNUAL}^{REF}} + \beta \cdot \frac{C_{ENV}}{C_{ENV}^{REF}} + \gamma \cdot \frac{Ex^{in}}{Ex^{in,REF}} \tag{6}$$

Where α, β and γ are weighting factors that translate to the relative importance of each objective function; their sum should be equal to 1.

As all three objectives have different orders of magnitude, the value of each is divided by its respective reference value. The reference is equal to the value of the cost or exergy input when considering pure optimization for the corresponding objective term ($\alpha = 1$, $\beta = 1$, or $\gamma = 1$, respectively). The Pareto frontier is obtained by varying all three weighting factors such that the sum of all weights remains equal to 1.

For the ECM, the improved version of the augmented version, AUGMECON2 is used. In AUGMECON2, a single function is chosen as the main objective to be optimized whilst the remaining are applied as constraints (Mavrotas & Florios, 2013). By varying the right-hand side of the constraints parametrically, the Pareto optimal solutions are found. For the MOLP presented here, the annual cost – Eq. (1) – is chosen as the main objective function, whilst Eq. (2)-(3) are applied as constraints.

The solution of the multiobjective problem results in a set of Pareto efficient solutions, all of which are said to be optimal. To choose the best solution out of the Pareto set, a fuzzy based method is used (Yalcin & Erginel, 2011).

*2.3. Case study*

As an illustrative example, the model is applied to a cluster of 5 houses in Bristol, UK. Figure 2 illustrates the system, with available technologies for each house, as well as the heating pipeline network.

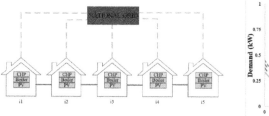

*Figure 2: Layout of the DES*                                            *Figure 3: Electricity demand profile*

Electricity usage for each house is a percentage of the UK average based on 250 houses and is illustrated in Figure 3. Heating demand is calculated using the heating degrees hour method applied to air temperature recorded by the Filton weather station (Met Office, 2006). Likewise, hourly solar irradiance is obtained from radiation observations recorded by the Liscombe weather station (Met Office, 2006).

Heating and electricity loads are distributed across the five houses (80%, 90%, 100%, 110% and 120%), such that the average of the loads is equal to the baseline.

## 3. Results and discussion

The problem formulated in Section 2 is implemented using the Branch and cut algorithm and the CPLEX solver in GAMS 25.1.2 on a PC with an AMD FX-8350 4 GHz processor and 8 GB of RAM. The full calendar year is represented as 6 hourly periods per day for 4 representative seasons: winter (December – February), spring (March – May), summer (June – August) and autumn (September – November).

In case of the WSM, Four scenarios are represented on the Pareto set (Figure 4a), namely optimization with high preference to annual cost ($\alpha = 0.8, \beta = 0.1, \gamma = 0.1$), high prefer-ence to environmental cost ($\alpha = 0.1, \beta = 0.8, \gamma = 0.1$), high preference to primary exergy input, and equal preference to all objectives ($\alpha = 0.33, \beta = 0.33, \gamma = 0.33$). The total time taken to run all four scenarios to full optimality is 11 minutes.

Using AUGMECON2 at full optimality with all three objective functions active for the ECM returns a set of Pareto optimal solutions (Figure 4b) is 1 hour and 20 minutes with weakly optimal and repeated results avoided.

The best-compromised solutions obtained by applying the fuzzy based method are summarized in Table 1, while the layout of the resulting networks are illustrated in Figure 5. For comparative purposes, the above results are compared to a conventional design whereby there are no DER technologies within the neighborhood, nor does a heating pipeline network exist. Instead, the electricity demand is fully met by the national grid, while the heating demand is satisfied by gas-fired boilers.

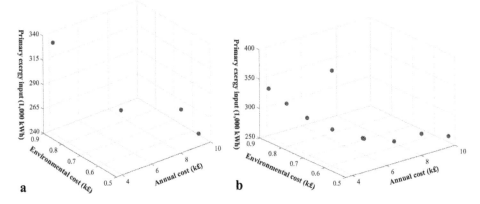

*Figure 4: Pareto optimal set for (a) WSM and (b) ESM*

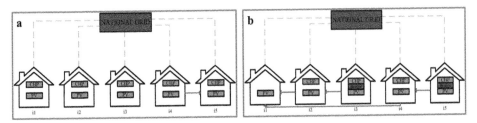

*Figure 5: DES layout for (a) WSM and (b) ECM*

*Table 1: Best compromised solutions*

| Design | Economic cost (£) | Environmental cost (£) | Primary exergy input (kWh) |
|---|---|---|---|
| Conventional | 1,237 | 7,699 | 2,481,000 |
| WSM | 10,930 | 519.3 | 213,000 |
| ECM | 9,836 | 552.8 | 287,000 |

In case of the WSM, the best-compromised solution reveals considerable reduction in both environmental cost (93%) and primary exergy input (91%). However, the annual cost increases by 784% due to the capital and operational cost of using the distributed energy resources technologies. A similar behavior is observed by applying the ECM, as seen in Table 1.

## 4. Conclusions

This paper investigates the impact of exergy on the design and operation of a DES via a multiobjective optimization approach that includes annual economic and environmental costs, and considering both the weighted sum and the epsilon-constraint methods for the solution of the resulting MOLP. A best-compromised solution is produced using the fuzzy-based method. The proposed procedure is applied on a case study, showing significant reductions (of around 90%) in both environmental and primary exergy input for both approaches. Furthermore, the results show that the use of exergy analysis is a powerful tool towards the rational use of fossil fuels.

Future work will consider the addition of more renewable generation technologies, such as wind turbines, biomass boilers, heat pumps or solar thermal collectors. Additionally, a microgrid, which enables the exchange of electricity between the dwellings, will be included in the network design. These will provide further understanding on the exergy analysis within DES.

The application of different methods for the selection of the best-compromised solutions, such as the min-max (Kparib et al., 2019) or the R-method (Rao et al., 2021) and the comparison with the fuzzy-based method in the context of DES design optimization will also be investigated.

## References

M. Di Somma et al., 2015, Operation optimization of a distributed energy system considering energy costs and exergy efficiency, Energy Conversion and Management 103, 739-751

F. Clarke et al., 2021, Optimal design of heating and colling pipeline networks for residential distributed energy systems, Energy 235, 121430

R. Jing et al., 2018, A multi-objective optimization and multicriteria evaluation integrated framewrok for distributed energy system optimal planning, Energy Conversion and Management 166, 445-462

M. Karmellos, G. Mavrotas, 2019, Multi-objective optimization and comparison framework for the design of distributed energy systems, Energy Conversion and Managemetn 180, 473-495

D.Y. Kparib et al., 2019, A min-max strategy to aid decision making in a bi-objective discrete optimization problem using an improved ant colony algorithm, American Journal of Operations Research 9, 161-174

G. Mavrotas, K. Florios, 2013, An improved version of the augmented $\varepsilon$-constraint method (AUGMECON2) for finding the exact Pareto set in multi-objective integer programming problems, Applied Mathematics and Computation 219, 9652-9669

Met Office, 2006, MIDAS: Global radiation observations and UK daily temperature data, NCAS British Atmospheric Data Centre

R.V. Rao et al., 2021, Ranking of Pareto-optimal solutions and selecting the best solution in multi- and many-objective optimization problems using R-method, Soft Computing Letters 3, 100015

T. Sidnell et al., 2021, Optimal design and operation of distributed energy resources systems for residential neighbourhoods, Smart Energy 4, 100049

C. Wouters et al., 2017, A policy-based multi-objective optimization framework for residential distributed energy system design, Renewable Energy and Environmental Sustainability 2, 5

G.D. Yalcin, N. Erginel, 2011, Determioning weights in multi-objective linear programming under fuzziness, London

H. Zhao et al., 2022, Economy-environment-energy performance evaluation of CCHP microgrid system: A hybrid multi-criteria decision-making method, Energy 240, 122830

Antonis Kokossis, Michael C. Georgiadis, Efstratios N. Pistikopoulos (Eds.)
PROCEEDINGS OF THE 33rd European Symposium on Computer Aided Process Engineering
(ESCAPE33), June 18-21, 2023, Athens, Greece

# Calcium looping for $CO_2$ capture, $H_2$ and electricity coproduction in coal fired power plants

B. Basant Kumar Pillai, Ramsagar Vooradi, Sarath Babu Anne*

*National Institute of Technology, Warangal, TG State - 506004, India*
*sarat@nitw.ac.in*

## Abstract

In recent years, global warming has become one of the most important concerns in the world. To achieve net zero carbon emissions by 2050, fossil fuel-based power plants must be integrated with suitable carbon capture and sequestration/utilization technologies. Currently, more attention is given to the looping technologies for post combustion $CO_2$ capture as it has the advantage of low efficiency penalty. In this work, a coal fired power plant configuration is integrated with double calcium looping system for $CO_2$ capture, production of electricity and hydrogen. The overall assessment of the developed configuration is carried out on the basis of energy, exergy and environmental parameters and compared with conventional coal power plant configuration. The thermal integration strategy adopted in the configuration of double calcium looping and gasification integrated power plant contributes an energy and exergy gain of 1.4% and 1.2% respectively as compared to conventional coal power plant configuration.

**Keywords**: Double calcium looping, coal fired power plant, carbon capture and sequestration, hydrogen production, energy and exergy analysis.

## 1. Introduction

Energy plays a very critical role in the socio-economic development of any country. At present, a major part of this energy demand is fulfilled by fossil fuels such as coal, oil, and natural gas. However, these fossil fuels are also a major source of Green House Gas (GHG) emissions (mostly $CO_2$) that cause climate change. Among all the fossil fuels, coal is widely used around the world. India's coal consumption in 2018 contributes to around 45% of the country's total energy consumption and is the second largest coal consuming country after China. While coal is fully combusted for power generation, it can also be converted into $H_2$ through the gasification process. It has been reported that around 27% of all the hydrogen in the world is produced by coal gasification alone (Hydrogen from coal., 2021).

Researchers are currently working on developing different carbon capture technologies that can be integrated with coal-based power generation and hydrogen production systems. Second generation $CO_2$ capture technologies are being developed to further reduce the energy penalty and economic costs. Globally, calcium looping has been proven to be a viable method of capturing $CO_2$ in a number of successful demonstration projects (Hanak et al., 2015). It is one of the attractive sustainable $2^{nd}$ generation $CO_2$ capture options due to its ability to retrofit with the existing plants with lower economic and energy penalties.

Over the last decade, most of the research in calcium looping has been focused mainly on enhancing its feasibility to capture $CO_2$. Several intensification strategies have been proposed in the last decade for reducing calcium looping technology's energy penalty

(Duan et al., 2016). Some studies have also been carried out to co-produce hydrogen along with $CO_2$ capture. Chen et al., 2011 proposed a calcium looping based novel reactor configuration involving a compact fluidized bed for $CO_2$ capture and hydrogen cogeneration. The parametric study revealed that the hydrogen production rate and purity were reduced when pressure was increased from 1 bar to 10 bar. Shaikh et al., 2022 proposed a biomass-based calcium looping configuration for power generation and hydrogen production to achieve a net zero or negative $CO_2$ emission. However, these configurations require pure $O_2$ to function and thus needs an Air Separation System (ASS) that consumes high energy. In this aspect, the Ca-Cu looping and double calcium looping configuration are some of the distinctive configurations that completely eliminates the use of ASS and thus have the potential to reduce the energy penalty significantly (Diego et al., 2016). An advantage of double calcium looping over Ca-Cu looping is its ability to operate with single sorbent (calcium) that is widely available at low cost in many countries. Over the years, several research studies have been conducted on the integration of carbon capture with hydrogen and electricity generation (Lin et al., 2002; Florin and Harris., 2008; Dean et al., 2011). However, there is still a scope to enhance performance through effective integration by utilizing double calcium looping schemes. Further, limited studies are available in the literature on overall energy, exergy, and environmental assessment with high ash coal.

Therefore, the main aim of the present research work is to propose a novel double calcium looping and coal gasification integrated power plant configuration (HDCFPP) for power and hydrogen coproduction along with $CO_2$ capture. A conventional coal fired power plant (CFPP) and double calcium looping integrated coal fired power plant (DCFPP) are also developed in this research work. This is done to demonstrate the performance of the proposed HDCFPP against DCFPP and CFPP configurations. Both configurations are evaluated based on energy, exergy and environmental parameters.

## 2. Methodology

A coal-fired power plant with operating conditions of 450 kg/s of live steam (at 590 $^0$C, 300 bar) and a double calcium looping process are developed and validated against the literature models using aspenONE software (Reddy et al., 2013; Diego et al., 2016). Using the validated process models, a CFPP, DCFPP and HDCFPP configuration are synthesized as shown in Figure 1. Thermodynamic and environmental analyses are carried out to investigate the performance of the proposed HDCFPP against DCFPP and CFPP configurations. As a part of the study, the following characteristics of Indian high ash coal are considered: carbon 39.16%, ash 48.87%, oxygen 7.92%, hydrogen 2.76%, sulfur 0.51%, nitrogen 0.78 and high heating value 15.83 MJ/kg. The assumptions considered to simplify the analyses of this research work are:

1. Process is operating in steady state.
2. Thermal loss and pressure drop in pipes (streams) are not considered.
3. Around 1.5% of input fuel energy is lost through convection and radiation in the combustor.
4. The auxiliary power consumption ($W_{aux}$) is assumed to be 9% of the gross power output of the power plant that includes lighting and control systems, transformer losses, heating, ventilation and air conditioning systems etc.
5. The overall plant life of all the configurations are 25 years and operate for 7008 hours per year.

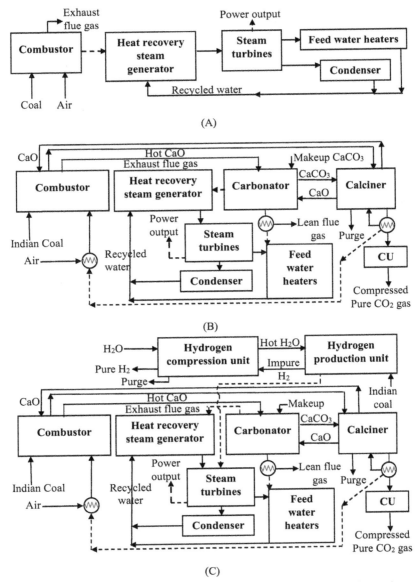

Figure 1: Layout of (A) CFPP, (B) DCFPP and (C) HDCFPP configurations

### 2.1. Coal fired power plant (CFPP)

The construction of a supercritical CFPP based on the Rankine cycle developed in aspenONE is shown in Figure 1A. The low-ash coal feed is replaced with Indian (high-ash) coal, and the operating parameters are considered in accordance with the Indian climatic conditions (Suresh et al., 2010).

### 2.2 Double calcium looping integrated coal fired power plant (DCFPP)

The double calcium looping process consists of two calcium loops instead of one in the conventional calcium looping process as shown in Figure 1B. The primary loop between the calciner and carbonator is used to separate $CO_2$ from the hot flue gas. The secondary loop between the combustor and calciner is used to transfer the required heat energy from the combustor to the calciner to carry out the calcination reaction. This configuration helps to avoid the need of ASS for calcium looping system and ensures high $CO_2$ capture efficiency.

### 2.3 Hydrogen production and double calcium looping integrated CFPP (HDCFPP)

A calcium looping gasification-based hydrogen production unit (HPU) is integrated with double calcium looping CFPP for producing concentrated $H_2$ along with $CO_2$ capture and electricity generation as shown in Figure 1C.

### 2.4 Thermodynamic and environmental analysis

The proposed configurations are assessed based on thermodynamic and environmental parameters. The techno-economic analysis of calcium looping processes has been carried out by considering key performance indicators such as energy efficiency, exergy efficiency, $CO_2$ capture efficiency and specific $CO_2$ emissions. The plant efficiency $\eta_{ele}$ on the basis of net electrical energy output is estimated using Equation 1. In this $W_{aux}$, $W_{ASS}$, $W_{pump}$, $W_{comp}$ and $W_{gross}$ are sum of all auxiliary power consumptions, energy consumption by ASS, centrifugal pumps, air compressor and gross power output produced by the turbines respectively The EXERGYMS property set provided by aspenONE is used to estimate exergy of all streams (Olaleye et al., 2015). Using this exergy data, the exergy efficiency$\psi_\eta$ and exergy destruction ratio $(\lambda_n)$ of a unit is calculated with the help of Equations 2 and 3. In these equations, $Ex_{in}$, $(Ex_{dest})_n$ and $(Ex_{out})_n$ are the exergy input, exergy destruction and exergy output flowrates for each single unit $n$, respectively and $\Sigma Ex_{dest}$ represents the overall exergy destruction of the configuration. Specific $CO_2$ emission is assessed in terms of kg $CO_2$ emitted per MWh of net energy generation. $CO_2$ capture efficiency is calculated as the ratio of $CO_2$ captured and $CO_2$ generated during coal combustion and hydrogen production.

$$\eta_{ele} = \frac{W_{gross} - W_{comp} - W_{pump} - W_{ASS} - W_{aux}}{m_{fc} \times HHV_{fc}} \tag{1}$$

$$\psi_n = \frac{(Ex_{out})_n}{(Ex_{in})_n} = 1 - \frac{(Ex_{dest})_n}{(Ex_{in})_n} \tag{2}$$

$$\lambda_n = \frac{Ex_{dest.n}}{\Sigma Ex_{dest}} \tag{3}$$

## 3. Results and Discussion

In this section, the performance of the proposed DCFPP and HDCFPP configurations are analyzed and compared with the conventional CFPP on the basis of overall energy, exergy and environmental parametric indicators. Table 1 represents the overall comparative evaluation based on energy and exergy. The higher amount of input energy and exergy in the HDCFPP configuration is because of the additional coal used for the production of hydrogen. CFPP, DCFPP, and HDCFPP configurations are found to generate 515.3 MW, 507.8 MW, and 476.31 MW of net electrical power, respectively. The net energy and exergy efficiencies of DCFPP configuration are 35.4% and 32.4%. The DCFPP configuration has very low energy and exergy penalties as compared with CFPP configuration. Further, its performance is much better than the MEA integrated Indian coal fired power plant (Karmakar et al., 2013) having an energy efficiency of 28.7% only. The performance of the proposed HDCFPP is found to be thermodynamically better than DCFPP. The results revealed that the HDCFPP configuration has an energy and exergy gain of 1.4% and 1.2% respectively as compared to the CFPP due to electric power and hydrogen cogeneration.

$CO_2$ emissions reduction is also one of the primary objectives of this work, so an evaluation is performed based on environmental parameters such as $CO_2$ capture efficiency, specific $CO_2$ emissions, and lifetime $CO_2$ emissions. A $CO_2$ capture efficiency of 91.05% is used as a benchmark in DCFPP and HDCFPP for environmental analysis. From the environmental analysis, it is observed that the HDCFPP configuration has the lowest specific $CO_2$ emission of 78.57 kg/MWh as compared to DCFPP and CFPP configurations that are having emissions of 82.94 kg/MWh and 885.17 kg/MWh respectively. It is estimated that the lifetime $CO_2$ emissions of the CFPP configuration is around 7,99,16,195 Mg, whereas the DCFPP and HDCFPP configurations have considerably lower emissions of 73,79,424 Mg and 77,95,699 Mg, respectively.

Table 1 Plant performance of CFPP, DCFPP and HDCFPP based on energy and exergy analysis

| Parameters | Energy Analysis | | | Parameters | Exergy Analysis | | |
|---|---|---|---|---|---|---|---|
| | CFPP | DCFPP | HDCFPP | | CFPP | DCFPP | HDCFPP |
| Input (MW) | 1432 | 1432 | 1511 | Input (MW) | 1565 | 1565 | 1651 |
| Gross power output MW) | 590 | 591 | 570 | | | | |
| Electricity consumption (MW) | 75.25 | 83.85 | 94.06 | | 75.25 | 83.85 | 94.06 |
| Net electricity output MW | 515.3 | 507.8 | 476.3 | | 515.3 | 507.8 | 476.3 |
| Energy from $H_2$ (MW) | | | 89.18 | Exergy from $H_2$ (MW) | | | 87.99 |
| Net electrical efficiency (%) | 35.98 | 35.46 | 31.51 | Net electrical efficiency (%) | 32.92 | 32.44 | 28.84 |
| Net energy efficiency (%) | 35.98 | 35.46 | 37.41 | Net exergy efficiency (%) | 32.92 | 32.44 | 34.16 |
| Energy efficiency penalty (%) | | 0.52 | -1.43 | Exergy efficiency penalty (%) | | 0.48 | -1.24 |
| Energy consumption by CU (MW) | | | 55.3 | | | 52.75 | 55.3 |

The exergy analysis for individual units/modules is performed to investigate the thermal losses due to process irreversibilities. The analysis not only identifies the location of losses but also helps to determine the maximum scope of improvement possible in the system. Figure 2A shows the exergy efficiency of main units/modules and Figure 2B shows the improvement potential of the same. The DCaL represents a complete module of combustor, calciner and carbonator and SPGU represents the module of HRSG, steam turbines, condenser and FWH. The results also revealed that the air preheater (HE3), CU and HCU although holds quite low exergetic efficiency, the scope of exergetic improvement potential in these respective units is found to be very less.

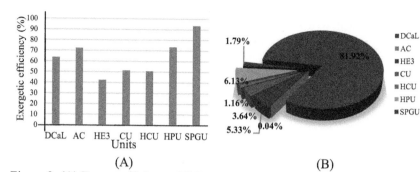

Figure 2: (A) Exergy efficiency (B) Improvement potential of HDCFPP configuration

## 4. Conclusions

The conventional CFPP configuration is integrated with double calcium looping and gasification units for $CO_2$ capture and hydrogen production. The energy and exergy analyses reveal that the net plant efficiency of the proposed DCFPP configuration is higher than the conventional MEA integrated power plant reported in the literature. Extending this DCFPP for hydrogen production by integrating it further with calcium looping gasification process enhanced the process performance. The HDCFPP configuration has an energy and exergy gain of 1.4% and 1.2% respectively as compared to the CFPP due to electric power and hydrogen cogeneration. The proposed schemes can be adopted for sustainable electricity and hydrogen cogeneration in the current crisis due to global warming and can be used as a bridging measure until the green technology becomes a more feasible option in the future.

## References

VS. Reddy, SC. Kaushik, SK. Tyagi, 2013, Clean technologies and environmental policy, 15, 1, 133-145.

SY. Lin,Y. Suzuki, H. Hatano, M. Harada, 2002, Energy conversion and management, 1, 43(9-12), 1283-1290.

S. Karmakar, MV. Suresh, AK. Kolar, 2013, International journal of green energy,10, 10,1011-1025.

S. Chen, D. Wang, Z. Xue, X. Sun, W. Xiang, 2011, International journal of hydrogen energy, 36, 8, 4887-4899.

NH. Florin, AT. Harris, 2008, Chemical engineering science, 1, 63(2), 287-316.

ME. Diego, B. Arias, JC. Abanades, 2016, Journal of cleaner production, 117, 110-121..

L. Duan, T. Feng, S. Jia, X. Yu, 2016, Energy, 115, 942-953.

IEA, Key World Energy Statistics, IEA, Paris. 2020, https://www.iea.org/reports/key-world-energy-statistics-2020.

Hydrogen from coal, Coal Age, 2021, https://www.coalage.com/features/hydrogen-from-coal/.

G. Fytianos, S. Ucar, A. Grimstvedt, A. Hyldbakk, HF. Svendsen, HK. Knuutila, 2016, International journal of greenhouse gas control, 46, 48-56.

DP. Hanak, EJ. Anthony, V. Manovic, 2015, Energy and environmental science, 8, 8, 2199-2249.

CC. Dean, J. Blamey, NH. Florin, MJ. Al-Jeboori, PS. Fennell, 2011, Chemical engineering research and design, 1, 89(6), 836-855.

AR. Shaikh, Q. Wang, L. Han, Y. Feng, Z. Sharif, Z. Li, J. Cen, S. Kumar, 2022, Sustainability,14, 4, 2189.

AK. Olaleye, M. Wang, G. Kelsall, 2015, Fuel, 151.

Antonis Kokossis, Michael C. Georgiadis, Efstratios N. Pistikopoulos (Eds.)
PROCEEDINGS OF THE 33rd European Symposium on Computer Aided Process Engineering
(ESCAPE33), June 18-21, 2023, Athens, Greece
© 2023 Elsevier B.V. All rights reserved. http://dx.doi.org/10.1016/B978-0-443-15274-0.50475-3

# 3-E (Energy, Exergy & Ecological) analyses of Chemical Looping Air Separation integrated Oxy-Coal Combustion based Power plant

Agarwal Shruti Sumankumar, Venkata Suresh Patnaikuni, Praveen Kumar Bommineni

*National Institute of Technology Warangal, Warangal – 506004, India*
*Email of the Corresponding Author: pvsuresh@nitw.ac.in*

## Abstract

Chemical looping Air Separation (CLAS) is an efficient and economic oxygen supply method for integration into oxy-fuel combustion plants for producing power with $CO_2$ capture. The present work deals with comprehensive analysis in terms of energy, exergy, and ecological parameters of the CLAS integrated oxy-coal plant using high ash coal and Indian environmental conditions. In this study, steady-state simulation of (i) conventional supercritical powerplant without capture (ii) oxy-coal combustion plant with conventional ASU, and (ii) CLAS integrated oxy-coal plant using manganese oxide as oxygen carrier, has been carried out. Comparative analysis for all three plants conducted based on 3-Es (energy, exergy, and ecological) shows that net efficiency of CLAS-based plant is higher by 7.05% and 8.36% respectively compared to conventional CFPP without capture and ASU based plant. The study concluded that CLAS integrated oxy-coal plant is energetically, energetically, and ecologically efficient compared to its counterparts.
**Keywords**: $CO_2$ capture; Chemical looping air separation; CLAS; Oxy-coal combustion

## 1. Introduction

Global warming caused by greenhouse gases is a global concern because of its detrimental impact on climate change. Emissions of $CO_2$ are increasing because of rising energy demands. Coal-fired power plants (CFPPs) are still significant sources of power generation in many countries and have become primary sources of $CO_2$ emissions. With almost a trillion tonnes of known reserves worldwide, coal is the most commonly used fossil fuel. Around 40% of world's electricity is produced using coal-based plants. The conventional CCS need to contribute to roughly 20% of emission reductions across all sectors to achieve a global reduction of 50% in $CO_2$ emissions by 2050. But the existing post combustion capture methods are expensive. Hence, there is need to create advanced, affordable $CO_2$ capture technology. Chemical looping, one of the recent technological options, can aid in adoption of low-emission technologies and provide advantages in applications involving production of fuels, chemicals, and power. Oxy-fuel combustion is one of the efficient ways to reduce $CO_2$ emission, but conventional air separation units (ASUs) are usually energy intensive and result in high energy penalties (Shah et al., 2012). Chemical looping air separation (CLAS) is a potential alternative method to separate oxygen from air. This process consists of an oxygen carrier that releases oxygen in reduction reactor and absorbs oxygen in oxidation reactor (Qing et al., 2020).

Some of the simulation and thermodynamic studies on CLAS are reviewed here. Manganese, cobalt, and copper oxides were found to be the most suited carriers for CLAS procedure (Moghtaderi, 2010; Shah et al., 2012). Shah et al., 2013a studied the impact of flue gas pollutants on oxygen carriers in integrated CLAS and reported that addition of flue gas pollutants raises the operating temperature. However, this method can produce $O_2$ at lower costs compared to cryogenic ASUs (Shah et al., 2013b). The production of electricity and $CO_2$ from the oxy-fuel combustion of lignite was studied by Tagliaferri et al., 2018. Three oxy-fuel IGCC power plants were simulated by Shi et al., 2019 using various ASUs to provide power systems with almost no $CO_2$ emissions. Aspen Plus software was used to simulate CLAS based on a dual fluidized bed with Mn-based oxygen carrier by Cao et al., 2019. Qing et al., 2020 determined the impact of recycling position for oxy-combustion power plants integrating CLAS. $SiO_2$, $ZrO_2$, $TiO_2$, and $MgAl_2O_4$ were used as inert binders for Cu-based oxygen carriers by Wang et al., 2019 and determined stability of these composites in a packed bed facility.

As observed from the literature, thermodynamic evaluation of CFPPs based on high-ash coal and sophisticated steam boilers is scarce. A comprehensive study involving 3-E (energy, exergy, and ecological) assessments is not available for direct comparison of CLAS based CFPPs with SupC steam boiler parameters using coal, even though a few studies on energy and exergy analyses are available on CLAS as discussed above. Such a study is crucial while choosing the best technology in meeting increasing clean energy demand, especially in developing nations, where coal is the primary energy source. Main goal of this work is to present a comprehensive theoretical analysis of the viability of integrating CLAS in SupC coal-based power plants using high ash coal. Performance of the CLAS integrated oxy-coal plant is also compared against that of conventional CFPP without capture and oxy-coal plant with conventional ASU for oxygen supply.

## 2. Methodology

In this study, steady-state process simulation of three types of coal-fired power plants was carried out using aspenONE software – (i) conventional SupC coal-fired power plant without capture (ii) oxy-coal combustion plant with conventional ASU, and (iii) CLAS integrated oxy-coal fired power plant using manganese oxide as the oxygen carrier. The first two plants were adopted from Suresh et al., 2010 and Suresh et al., 2011, while flowsheet of the third plant was developed by integrating the CLAS into conventional oxy-coal combustion plant. The first two plants were simulated, validated and considered as reference plants in the current study for comparing performance of the synthesized CLAS integrated oxy-coal fired power plant. All the three plants were simulated for the same fuel energy input of 1628.91 MW based on HHV (equivalent to the coal input of 102.9 kg/s). Indian coal with high ash content having the following characteristics was considered as the fuel in this study - carbon 39.16%, ash 48.87%, oxygen 7.92%, hydrogen 2.76%, sulfur 0.51%, nitrogen 0.78 and high heating value 15.83 MJ/kg. The conventional fluids were defined by stream classes MIXED, whereas conventional and unconventional solids were defined by the stream classes CIPSD and NCPSD, respectively. For estimation of properties of solids, air, flue gases, steam, and water, Peng Robinson and Boston Mathias (PR-BM), Soave Redlich Kwong (RKS), ideal gas, and STEAMNBS were used. Comparative performance analysis for all three plants was conducted based on the 3-Es (energy, exergy, and ecological). Following is the brief description of each of the above plants.

### 2.1. Description of conventional SupC CFPP without $CO_2$ capture

A typical CFPP consisting of a combustor, feed water heaters (FWHs), condenser, steam turbine units, sizing and drying, and heat recovery steam generation

(HRSG) was considered with feed-water temperature of 280°C and steam parameters of high, intermediate and low-pressure steams of 242.2 bar/537°C, 42.0 bar/565°C, and 2.9 bar/215.6°C, respectively (Suresh et al., 2010). Three high-pressure FWHs and four low-pressure FWHs make up this plant. After being crushed and dried with air present, coal was put into the combustion chamber. In the HRSG unit, steam is produced and heat is recovered from the hot flue gas produced by the combustor. The model built in the present work was validated using operational data for 660MW plant reported by Suresh et al., 2010. No $CO_2$ capture was considered in this reference case.

### 2.2. Description of SupC oxy-coal combustion plant with conventional ASU

Sizing and drying unit, Air separation unit, combustor unit, HRSG, FWHs, condenser units, $CO_2$ compressor and storage units are the key parts of this plant. The number of high-pressure and low-pressure FWHs for these plants is the same as that of the traditional CFPPs. The steam parameters (temperature and pressure) are used as 290 bar/600°C, 61 bar/620°C, and 3 bar/211.3°C, respectively, for HP, IP, and LP steams as specified in Suresh et al., 2011. With a final feed-water temperature of 305°C, the facility also includes a single stage of reheating. The oxygen required for combustion is obtained from air separation unit which consists of two stage compression with intermediate cooling of air and then air goes through cryogenic column for separation of air. This plant is simulated and validated with the results of the 800 MW conventional SupC oxy-fuelled power plant reported by Suresh et al., 2011.

### 2.3 CLAS integrated oxy-coal fired power plant

This plant flowsheet is synthesized by replacing the conventional ASU in the oxy-coal combustion plant described in section 2.2 with CLAS by ensuring proper heat integration. Additionally, this flowsheet is connected with the $CO_2$ capture and compressor unit. Manganese oxide ($Mn_2O_3$) is used as the oxygen carrier for the CLAS process. CLAS unit contains heat exchanger (heatX and heater), two Gibbs reactors for oxidation and reduction reaction, two stream splitters (Ssplit), one mixer, one splitter and flash separator to remove water. Air and oxygen carrier first enter oxidation reactor and then after reaction (eq. 1), it goes to solid separator where the reduced air is removed and goes through the heat exchanger to heat the inlet air. The solid goes to reduction reactor and reduces (eq. 2) in the presence of steam. Solid is then separated in the separator and again recycled whereas oxygen with water stream goes through flash separator to remove water. Pure oxygen is then mixed with recycled flue gas before it enters the combustor unit.

$$\text{Oxidation: } 4Mn_3O_4(s) + O_2(g) \rightarrow 6Mn_2O_3(s) \qquad (1)$$
$$\text{Reduction: } 6Mn_2O_3(s) \rightarrow 4Mn_3O_4(s) + O_2(g) \qquad (2)$$

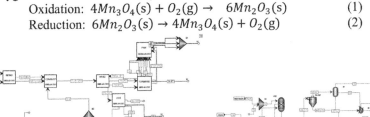
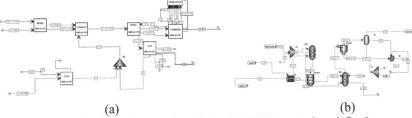

(a)                                             (b)

Fig. 1. Aspen plus flow diagram for (a) the CLAS integrated coal-fired power plant and (b) detailed flowsheet of CLAS hierarchy block

### 2.4 3-E analyses

Assessment of the environmental impact is crucial for any power production system's evaluation, in addition to the thermodynamic analysis. Hence, in the current study, the 3-E (energy, exergy and ecological) analyses were carried out to examine the performance of all the cases. Below is a brief presentation of the performance indicators for each of these analyses (Surywanshi et al, 2019).

### 2.4.1 Energy analysis

The gross energy efficiency ($\eta_{Gross}$) and the net energy efficiency ($\eta_{Net}$) are calculated by the ratio of the plant's gross or net power output ($W_{Gross}$ or $W_{Net}$) to the energy input (which is the product of coal mass flow rate ($\dot{m}_{coal}$) and HHV of the coal)

$$\eta_{Gross} = \frac{W_{Gross}}{\dot{m}_{coal} \times HHV\ of\ the\ coal} \quad (3) \qquad \eta_{Net} = \frac{W_{Net}}{\dot{m}_{coal} \times HHV\ of\ the\ coal} \quad (4)$$

### 2.4.2 Exergy analysis

To measure the exergy flow rate of specific streams, EXERGYFL property set is added to aspenONE. Exergy destruction and efficiency of each unit in the plant are calculated using eq. 5 & 6 apart from calculating net exergy efficiency of overall plant (eq.7)

$$Ex_d = \sum Ex_{in} - \sum Ex_{out} \quad (5) \qquad \varepsilon_{unit} = \frac{\sum Ex_{out}}{\sum Ex_{in}} = 1 - \left(\frac{Ex_d}{\sum Ex_{in}}\right) \quad (6)$$

$$\varepsilon_{Net} = \frac{Net\ power\ output}{\dot{m}_{coal} \times Specific\ exergy\ of\ the\ coal} \quad (7)$$

### 2.4.3 Ecological analysis

An yearly $CO_2$ emission as the product of 7000 operating hours per unit of fuel ($\varepsilon^a_{f\ CO_2}$) is calculated using eq. 8 as ratio of the yearly energy intake to the power plant in ($E^a_{chf}$ in $MW.h$) and the annual $CO_2$ emissions from plant into the atmosphere ($\dot{m}^a_{CO_2\ emit}$ in kg)

$$\varepsilon^a_{f\ CO_2} = \frac{\left(\dot{m}^a_{CO_2\ emit}\right)}{\left(3.6 \times E^a_{chf}\right)} \quad (8) \qquad CO_2 \text{capture efficiency} = \frac{\left(\dot{m}_{CO_2\ captured}\right)}{\left(\dot{m}_{CO_2\ prior\ to\ capture}\right)} \times 100 \quad (9)$$

## 3. Results and Discussion

Parametric analysis was conducted to fix operating parameters for the synthesized CLAS integrated Oxy-coal plant, while other plants were analysed with conditions given in the reference plants (Suresh et al., 2010, 2011). Operating pressure of oxidation and reduction reactors was maintained at 1.01325 bar, and other parameters of the CLAS integrated plant obtained from sensitivity analysis were as follows: air flow rate – 632.4 kg/s; reduced carrier flow rate – 4090 kg/s, temperatures of reduction & oxidation reactors as 850°C & 640°; steam flow rate, temperature and pressure– 1260 kg/s, 980°C, 1.01325 bar.

### 3.1 Energy analysis

The three plants were simulated for constant fuel energy input of 1628.91 MW (based on HHV). The power output, power consumption, and gross & net plant efficiency for each plant were calculated and are summarised in Table 1. Gross power output of CLAS integrated plant was more than that of other two plants. Improved steam parameters at superheater and reheater's outlet increased steam turbine output of ASU based and CLAS based oxy-coal plants compared to that of the conventional CFPP, which boosted up the gross power production. The net power consumption in ASU based plant was almost 3 times higher than that of conventional CFPP, while it was 1.68 times the traditional CFPP's power consumption in case of CLAS integrated plant. Subsequently, the net efficiency of all the three plants was calculated. The net energy efficiency of CLAS integrated plant was found to be higher than that of the traditional CFPP and ASU based plant by 7.05% and 8.36% , while an energy penalty of 1.3% was observed in ASU based plant compared to traditional CFPP because of addition of cryogenic air separation unit.

### 3.2 Exergy analysis

CLAS based oxy-coal power plant was found to have higher net exergy efficiency (calculated using eq. 7) compared to the other two plants. The exergy efficiency of ASU based Oxy-coal plant was slightly lower than that of the conventional plant because of the greater exergy destruction in the $CO_2$ compressor and air compressor (5.52 bar in ASU vs. 1.04 bar in conventional CFPP) (not present in conventional CFPP). All the three plants were subjected to component-wise exergy analysis in order to identify the units that experience the most exergy loss or destruction. The % contribution to exergy destruction by significant units of CLAS based oxy-coal plant was shown in Figure 2. Due to higher operating conditions (T and P) and heat transfer processes, the boiler section accounted for more energy destruction than other units. Table 2 lists the exergy and energy losses, as well as the improvement potential (IP) of key units of the plant. Boiler with highest exergy destruction contributed to 81% of total exergy destruction of the plant, while other units showed less improvement potential even though their energy losses were high (for e.g., condensers, HPFWH, ST, CLAS etc. as can be seen from Table 3). These results showed that boiler and CLAS are the units to be focused to further improve overall plant efficiency.

Table 1. Energy analysis of conventional, oxy-coal and CLAS based oxy-coal plants

| Parameter | Conv. SupC CFPP without capture | ASU based oxy-coal plant | CLAS integrated oxy-coal plant |
|---|---|---|---|
| Fuel input energy (MW) | 1628.91 | 1628.91 | 1628.91 |
| Steam Turbine output (MW) | 659.53 | 702.77 | 716.06 |
| Auxiliary loss (MW) | 49.46 | 52.71 | 53.70 |
| Gross power output (MW) | 610.06 | 650.06 | 662.35 |
| Net power consumption (MW) | 81.08 | 259.27 | 136.66 |
| Net power output (MW) | 464.53 | 443.50 | 579.40 |
| Gross electric efficiency (%) | 37.45 | 39.91 | 40.66 |
| Net electric efficiency (%) | 28.52 | 27.21 | 35.57 |

Table 2. Energy loss, exergy destruction and exergetic improvement potential for the CLAS integrated SupC oxy-coal plant.

| Unit/block | Energy loss (MW) | Exergy destruction (MW) | IP (MW) |
|---|---|---|---|
| Boiler | 19.89 | 899.60 | 308.35 |
| Steam Turbine | 204.56 | 97.11 | 4.99 |
| Condenser | 808.20 | 21.67 | 13.07 |
| LPFWH | 171.82 | 39.45 | 16.17 |
| HPFWH | 211.30 | 14.62 | 0.42 |
| Deaerator | 26.05 | 21.37 | 5.45 |
| Pumps | 24.67 | 2.49 | 0.07 |
| Compressors | 36.11 | 12.47 | 2.70 |
| CLAS | 137.95 | 312.13 | 95.90 |

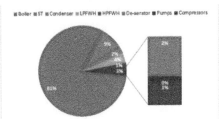

Fig. 2. Exergy destruction % contribution of key units of CLAS integrated oxy-coal plant

*3.3 Ecological analysis*

Apart from energy and exergy analyses, ecological analysis was carried out to see the effect of these plants on the environment. Table 3 provides comparison of different ecological parameters for all the three plants. Because of the absence of capture unit, the conventional CFPP displayed about $3.27 \times 10^9$ kg annual $CO_2$ emissions into the atmosphere, while the other two plants are able to capture all the $CO_2$ in the flue gas. However, the net electric output per kg of $CO_2$ captured was found to be higher for CLAS integrated plant compared to ASU based plant because of the its higher energy efficiency.

Table 3. Comparative ecological analysis of the three plants

| Parameter | Conv. SupC CFPP without capture | ASU based oxy-coal plant | CLAS integrated oxy-coal plant |
|---|---|---|---|
| $CO_2$ emission (kg/s) | 129.78 | ~0.00 | ~0.00 |
| $CO_2$ captured (kg/s) | 0.00 | 129.79 | 129.75 |
| $CO_2$ capture efficiency (%) | 0.00 | ~100 | ~100 |
| Specific $CO_2$ emission (kg/MWh) | 1005.77 | 0.01 | 0.00 |
| Annual $CO_2$ emission (kg) | $3.27 \times 10^9$ | ~0.00 | ~0.00 |
| Net electric output per kg of $CO_2$ captured (MW/kg) | - | 3.41 | 4.47 |

## 4. Conclusions

The study demonstrated the feasibility of integrating chemical looping air separation in oxy-coal power plant utilizing high ash Indian coal for generating power with $CO_2$ capture. The performance of the integrated plant was assessed using 3-E (energy, exergy, and ecological) analyses and compared against that of conventional SupC CFPP and ASU based oxy-coal plant. The key conclusions of the study are: The net efficiency of the $Mn_3O_4$-based CLAS integrated SupC oxy-coal plant was higher by 7.05% and 8.36% compared to that of the conventional SupC CFPP and oxy-coal SupC plant with ASU. Exergy analysis revealed the highest exergy destruction rate and improvement potentials occurred in the boiler unit followed by CLAS reactors in case of the integrated plant. CLAS integrated oxy-coal power plant would eliminate the annual $CO_2$ release of $3.27 \times 10^9$ kg from a 716 MW power plant (based on coal input). Based on the 3-E analyses study, it can be concluded that the CLAS based oxy-coal combustion fired power plant is energetically, exergetically and ecologically efficient.

## References

K. Shah et al., 2012, Energy Fuels, 26, 4, 2038-2045.
M. Qing et al., 2020, Energy, 206, 118136.
B. Moghtaderi, 2010, Energy Fuels, 24, 1, 190-198.
K. Shah et al., 2013a, Fuel, 103, 932–942.
K. Shah et al., 2013b, Fuel, 107, 356–370.
C. Tagliaferri et al., 2018, Chemical Engineering Research and Design, 131, 686–698.
B. Shi et al., 2019, Energy Conversion and Management, 195, 290–301.
Y. Cao et al., 2019, Energy Conversion and Management, 196, 286–295.
M. Qing et al., 2020, Energy, 206, 118136.
K. Wang et al., 2019, Powder Technology, 343, 40–48.
MVJJ. Suresh et al., 2010, International Journal of Energy Research, 34, 716–735.
MVJJ. Suresh et al., 2011, Journal of Engineering for Gas Turbines and Power, 133, 063001-1.
G. Surywanshi et al., 2019, Energy Conversion and Management, 200, 112050.

Antonis Kokossis, Michael C. Georgiadis, Efstratios N. Pistikopoulos (Eds.)
PROCEEDINGS OF THE 33rd European Symposium on Computer Aided Process Engineering
(ESCAPE33), June 18-21, 2023, Athens, Greece
© 2023 Elsevier B.V. All rights reserved.  http://dx.doi.org/10.1016/B978-0-443-15274-0.50476-5

# Reliability analysis for robust power-to-X design and storage sizing under renewable uncertainty

Jeongdong Kim[1], Meng Qi [1], Il Moon[*]

*ª Department of Chemical and Biomolecular Engineering, Yonsei University, Seoul 03722, Republic of Korea*
*1These authors contributed equally to this study*

## Abstract

During the operation of power-to-X system (PtX), the renewable profile strongly fluctuated according to its geographical and seasonal factors. Under the uncertainty of the renewable profile, the economic performance and renewable power penetration of the PtX can be enhanced by regulating two variables in design level; LCES size, renewable power plant scale. In this study, we firstly proposed the overall framework for data-driven-based reliability analysis of the PtX. First, using the pre-trained generator network in the GAN, the noise vector can be converted into the annual renewable profile. Given the generated renewable profiles, the scheduling model calculates the two performances; levelized cost of X production (LCOX), renewable power penetration. Integration of two formulated model enables us to infer the distribution of the performance via uncertainty propagation. During the propagation, the reliability analysis calculates the probability of failure (POF), which is defined as the constraint violation of renewable penetration. Conclusively, the overall framework can predict the LCOX distribution and calculate the POF of the system with constrained renewable penetration.

**Keywords**: Power-to-X, chemical energy storage, data-driven approach, power generation uncertainty

## 1. Problem statement

As shown in Fig. 1, the PtX process is composed of following unit: an electrolyzer, an intermediate hydrogen storage, and an electrified "X" production unit

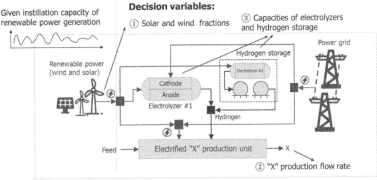

Fig. 1 Decision variables in PtX system.

Under the uncertainty of the renewable profile, the economic performance and renewable power penetration of the PtX can be enhanced by regulating design variables: installation capacity of renewable power generation, solar and wind fractions, "X" production capacity, and hydrogen storage capacities.

Sustaining economic feasibility of the PtX system in design level, minimization of the production cost (LCOX) is important issue. Additionally, for decarbonization, the consideration of the constraining the grid energy penetration rate (GD) is also crucial factor in design level, and low GD rate prevent the additional carbon emission accompanied by the grid power utilization. In this situation, it is important to investigate the impact of the design variables on the performance while considering the uncertainty of time-series renewable profile.

Considering the uncertainty of time-series in PtX system was conducted via two main model: data-driven renewable profile generator, mathematical power allocation model. In case of the first model, the adversarial generative network (GAN) is firstly pretrained using the real historical data of wind and solar profile. After the training, Using the generator network in the GAN, the Gaussian noise vector can be converted into the annual renewable profile which follows the distribution of real historical data. Given the generated renewable profiles, the formulated scheduling model determines the hourly allocation of the renewable and grid power of the PtX in one-year period, and calculates the two performances; Levelized cost of X production (LCOX), annually averaged renewable power penetration. The linkage between the generator network and process scheduling model enables us to infer the probability density distribution of the PtX performance via uncertainty propagation of renewable profile. During the propagation, the reliability analysis calculates the probability of failure (POF), which is defined as the constraint violation of renewable penetration.

## 2. Methodology

### 2.1. Data-driven renewable profile generator

Due to the nature of intermittency and temporal dynamics of renewable, the model-based approach is not feasible option for uncertainty modeling of the renewable (Pinson et al., 2009; Lee et al., 2016). Thus, in this study, the profile generator is derived from the training GAN with real historical data of wind and solar (Chen et al., 2018).

The objective function $V(G, D)$ of GAN training is defined as following:

$$\min_{\theta^{(G)}} \max_{\theta^{(D)}} V(G, D) = \underbrace{\mathop{\mathrm{E}}_{\tilde{x} \sim P_g} [D(\tilde{x})] - \mathop{\mathrm{E}}_{x \sim P_r} [D(x)]}_{Critic\ loss} + \underbrace{\lambda \mathop{\mathrm{E}}_{\hat{x} \sim P_{\hat{x}}} [(\|\nabla_{\hat{x}} D(\hat{x})\|_2 - 1)^2]}_{Gradient\ penalty} \quad (1)$$

where $\theta$ represents parameter, $\tilde{x}$ is fake sampled from the noise $P_g$, $x$ is real sampled from the historical distribution $P_r$, $\lambda$ is gradient penalty coefficient, $\hat{x}$ is the sampled from the uniform distribution $P_{\hat{x}}$ formed by the $P_g$ and $P_r$

For GAN training, the NASA POWER Data, which provides application programming interface, is used to download the temporal data of wind speed and solar irradiance in certain time period and geographical site. In this study, the Jeju Island, Korea is considered as the geographical site. The noise vector of 1,000 dimensionality was considered, real data was sampled from the batch size of 25, and the training was conducted by 1,000 epochs. The training result of wind speed and solar irradiance based GAN were shown in Fig. 2.

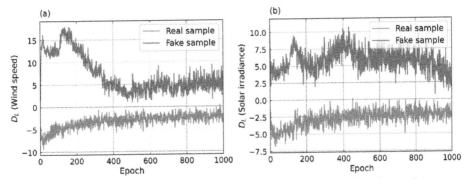

Fig. 2 Training result of GAN, (a) wind speed data, (b) solar irradiance data.

### 2.2. Formulating power allocation model

First, the wind and solar data are converted into power generation outputs by calculating the capacity factors for solar PV and wind turbines.

Given a instillation capacity, the wind ($P_W(t)$) and solar ($P_S(t)$) power profiles are first defined at an hourly resolution. Then the total renewable power profile is calculated by $P_{ren}(t) = P_W(t)f_W + P_S(t)f_S$, where $f_W$ and $f_s$ are the fractions of wind and solar power. Assuming the production flowrate of "X" is $F_x$, the mismatch of power between the renewable and PtX power load, $P_{mis}(t)$, can defined as:

$$P_{mis}(t) = P_W(t)f_W + P_S(t)f_S - P_{ptx} - P_{H2} \tag{9}$$
$$P_{ptx} = SP_{ptx}F_x \tag{10}$$
$$P_{H2} = F_{H2}F_x \tag{11}$$
$$F_{H2} = SP_{H2}\gamma_{H2} \tag{12}$$

where $P_{ptx}$ and $P_{H2}$ are power consumptions of the process and the electrolyzer, respectively, kW. $SP_{ptx}$ and $SP_{H2}$ are specific power consumptions of the "X" production process and the electrolyzer, respectively. $F_{H2}$ is the required hydrogen flowrate, and $\gamma_{H2}$ is the specific ratio of the required hydrogen flowrate to the "X" product flowrate.

Based on the mismatch profile of power, the mathematical model of power allocation can be formulated.

According to the formulated model, the time series profile of renewable and grid power, and storage profiles can be calculated as shown in Fig. 3. Conclusively, given the generated scenario and design variables, the allocate power profile can be converted in to the important performance indicator: production cost, grid penetration, and thermal efficiency of the PtX system.

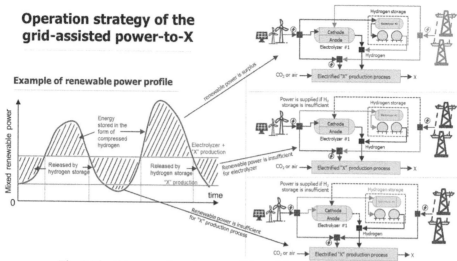

Fig. 3 Flexible operation strategy of the grid-assisted PtX process.

### 2.3. Uncertainty propagation model: PtX evaluation model

Using the formulated generator and power allocation model, the PtX evaluation model can be constructed as shown in Fig. 4. In the model, the noise vector firstly sampled from the multivariate standard normal distribution via the Monte-Carlo Sampling (MCS). The batch of noise sample transfer to the generator network, and finally converted in to batch dataset of annual profile of wind speed and solar irradiance. The mixture of renewable profile transfer to the power allocation model (operation model), and the model solves the power allocation problems via the mathematical approach, and converted into the production cost and grid penetration of each generated renewable profiles. Conclusively, using the PtX evaluation model, the uncertainty propagation of the complex renewable uncertainty can be simplified as the uncertainty of the noise with MCS. As a result, the PtX model can generate the distribution of the cost and penetration under the given design variables.

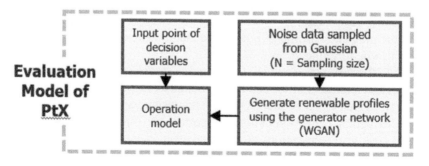

Fig. 4 proposed PtX evaluation model

## 3. Results and discussion

To test constructed PtX model, we conducted the uncertainty propagation in three different design variables, and the results are shown in Figs. 5 to 7.

As shown in the distribution, increasing the wind fraction effectively reduce the variance of the both production cost and grid penetration rate. Meanwhile, the range of production costs itself dramatically increased. The case study proves that the determined design variables has high impact on the probabilistic distribution of the PtX performance. Thus, using the constructed PtX model, the PtX design problem can be expanded into the robust optimization problem in future work.

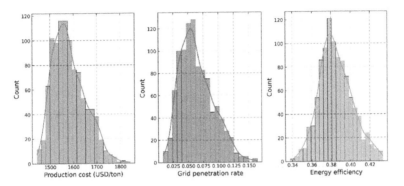

Fig. 4 Uncertainty propagation at wind fraction of 0.64, "X" flowrate of 1905, and hydrogen storage size of 38848

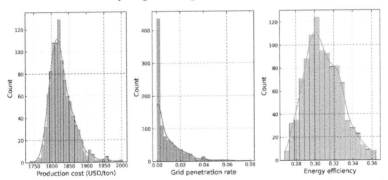

Fig. 5 proposed PtX evaluation model at wind fraction of 0.47, "X" flowrate of 1312, and hydrogen storage size of 40477

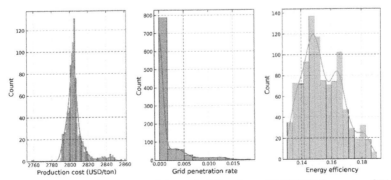

Fig. 6 proposed PtX evaluation model at wind fraction of 0.99"X" flowrate of 716 and hydrogen storage size of 39656

# References

Z inson P, Madsen H, Nielsen HA, Papaefthymiou G, Klöckl B. From probabilistic forecasts to statistical scenarios of short-term wind power production. Wind Energy: An International Journal for Progress and Applications in Wind Power Conversion Technology. 2009;12:51-62.Y. Brown, Lee D, Baldick R. Load and wind power scenario generation through the generalized dynamic factor model. IEEE Transactions on power Systems. 2016;32:400-10.

Meng Y, Wang Y, Kirschen D, Zhang B. Model-free renewable scenario generation using generative adversarial networks. IEEE Transactions on Power Systems. 2018;33:3265-75

Antonis Kokossis, Michael C. Georgiadis, Efstratios N. Pistikopoulos (Eds.)
PROCEEDINGS OF THE 33rd European Symposium on Computer Aided Process Engineering
(ESCAPE33), June 18-21, 2023, Athens, Greece

# Systematic Development of Strategies for the Decarbonization of Process Utility Systems

Julia Jiménez-Romero,[a] Adisa Azapagic,[a] Robin Smith,[a]

[a]*Department of Chemical Engineering, The University of Manchester, Oxford Road, Manchester M13 9PL, United Kingdom*

## Abstract

This paper describes an optimization-based tool for developing a strategy for the design of sustainable industrial energy systems that can be constrained to reflect the evolution of the design and operation through time. The model determines the best utility system structure, energy mix, and seasonal operation for reducing $CO_2$ emissions while meeting seasonal demand for electricity, heat, and cooling. Furthermore, the framework includes the selection of the steam main operating conditions (pressure and temperature) as a design variable to exploit of the close interrelationship between the site processes and the utility system at multiple temperature levels, ensuring the design of efficient and cost-effective process utility systems.

The resulting multiperiod mixed integer nonlinear model is addressed by an extended version of the decomposition algorithm BEELINE, and a ϵ-constraint approach is included to consider both economic and environmental performance. As a result, provide the decision-maker with several solutions for developing a sustainable pathway from current systems to future ones. The application to a case study from the literature shows that the framework could provide cost-effective guidelines for the energy transition of process utility systems.

**Keywords**: process utility systems, energy systems design, hybrid energy systems, multi-objective optimization, nonconvex mixed integer problem model.

## 1. Introduction

Most industrial facilities meet their heat and power needs with on-site utility systems. On the one hand, process utility systems are the largest consumers of industrial primary energy and the largest source of industrial $CO_2$ emissions, especially when powered by fossil fuels. On the other hand, process utility systems are an efficient solution for energy-efficient generation and distribution, site-wide heat recovery, and increasing energy supply reliability and adaptability. For this reason, both academia and industry are focused on the optimal design and operation of these types of systems. However, achieving a 'optimal' design is not straightforward, particularly for large-scale facilities, as the design is dependent on a number of factors, including the availability of energy conversion technologies, time-dependent energy demand and supply, utility prices (which can vary significantly from industry to industry), and the emission factor of technologies and sources. This has highlighted the need for specific decision-making tools to address this problem.

Many authors in the literature have addressed the optimization of energy system design and operation. Ganschinietz (2021) study provides a comprehensive literature review on this topic. Recent studies have emphasized energy security and environmental impacts, but energy system design and optimization are still driven by techno-economic objectives.

Environmental impacts are often only used as benchmarks or converted into economic terms, penalizing fossil fuel consumption and/or emissions. Although this strategy may lead to lower-carbon technologies, it does not allow the analysis of trade-offs between economic and environmental performance, which may overlook cost-effective options.

Notably, due to the mathematical complexity of maximizing energy supply efficiency by simultaneous consideration of energy integration and switching of fuel and/or technology, previous research has either neglected site-wide heat recovery opportunities or simplified the utility system configuration to the point where only a few utility components with fixed efficiencies have been considered. Moreover, critical practical issues such as equipment part-load performance and steam sensible heat effect are usually overlooked, resulting in misleading targets and thus incorrect analysis of the utility system design and its associated emissions(Jiménez-Romero, Azapagic, & Smith, 2023).

For this reason, the objective of this work is to provide a decision support framework capable of considering a wide range of technology options, its configuration and operation, while ensuring a sustainable energy efficient site. The model, in particular, considers not only the optimal configuration of the utility system but also the heat integration potential, through the optimization of steam mains operating conditions (temperature and pressure) to exploit site wide heat recovery and power generation trade-offs, ensuring that the design is energy efficient.

## 2. Problem statement

An on-site utility system supplies heat and power to several independent plants in the same industrial cluster. The utility system can generate steam from excess heat from one plant to use in another to improve site energy efficiency. Since heat can be recovered/used at a wide temperature range, the best steam distribution system operating conditions (temperature and pressure) must be chosen to balance fuel consumption and power generation.

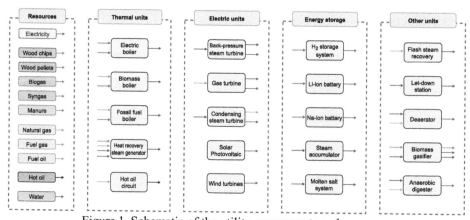

Figure 1. Schematic of the utility components and resources

To meet energy demands, the framework considers a broad technology portfolio (electrode boilers, biomass boilers, gas turbines, wind turbines, steam turbines, solar photovoltaic, among others) as well as electric and thermal energy storage units, as shown in Figure 1. Other utility components include deaerators, let-down stations, furnaces, and flash steam recovery (FSR). Furthermore, the design framework takes operational issues (such as part-load performance and limits, start-up constraints) and practical constraints into account (i.e. steam temperature limitations, steam sensible and latent heat).

The optimal configuration and operation of the process utility system is determined by two criteria: total annualized costs and global warming potential ($CO_2$ equivalent emissions) (Vaskan, Guillén-Gosálbez, Turkay, & Jiménez, 2014).

## 3. Optimization Approach

The resulting optimization problem is a nonconvex mixed integer nonlinear programming (MINLP). The proposed model incorporates three sources of difficulty in terms of:

-   Variable type. Decision variables for equipment selection and operation/activation as well as continuous variables for equipment size and load, steam mass flowrates and enthalpies
-   Constraint type. Nonlinearities result from equipment cost functions (economy of scale), environmental impact qualification, and the selection of steam main operating condition (the integration of steam temperature/enthalpy as a design variable, introducing bilinear terms in the energy balance and some equipment performances as well as the need of functions to estimate the steam properties)
-   Objective function. The economic and environmental performance are conflictive objectives.

Consequently, the problem could be computationally intensive when applied to practical size problems. For this reason, the following solutions have been adopted to approach the problem.

### 3.1. Dealing with non-linearity

Non linearities caused by equipment costs functions and qualification of environmental impact are handled by piecewise affine approximations of the functions. On the other hand, non-linearities introduced by steam temperature as a design variable (and the calculation of steam properties) are addressed by developing a linear approximation for the accurate definition of superheated conditions.

In order to solve this, the BEELINE strategy presented in Jimenez-Romero, Azapagic, and Smith (2022) strategy comprises a bilevel decomposition of the problem, where the master problem is a relaxed version of the mixed-integer linear program (MILP). In the MILP problem the value of the binary variables are defined, to then re-optimize the continuous variables considering the non-linearities in a non-convex linear (NLP) program model.

### 3.2. Dealing with the objective function

#### 3.2.1. Economic objective—minimizing annualized total cost

The economic objective is to minimize the total annual costs (TAC), including the total annualized investment cost($C^{inv}$), maintenance cost ($C^{main}$), operating cost($C^{op}$) and start-up cost ($C^{start}$).

$$\min \text{TAC} = C^{inv} + C^{main} + C^{op} + C^{start} \tag{1}$$

*3.2.2. Environmental objective—minimizing GWP (CO2-eq·y-1)*

The environmental objective is to minimize the total annual greenhouse emissions (TAGWP). The TAGWP comprises the emissions generated by (i) the resources ($E^{re}$), (ii) installation and decommissioning of equipment ($E^{eq}$), and (iii) operation (and waste disposal) of the utility system ($E^{op}$) – including purchased electricity -, as expressed by Eq ( 2 ).

$$\min \text{TAGWP} = E^{re} + E^{eq} + E^{op} \qquad (2)$$

To determine the Pareto-optimal curve and define the trade-off between economic and environmental performance, the ε-constraint approach (Mavrotas, 2009) is employed. The ε-constraint approach begins by establishing minimum and maximum values for the objective functions TAC and TAGWP, which are determined using the lexicographic optimization. Once defined the upper and lower bounds of the objective functions, the rest of Pareto-optimal points are obtained by solving the proposed model with the objective of minimizing TAC, while TAGWP is converted to a parametrized equality constraint as shown in Eq. ( 3 )

$$\min: \text{TAC} + \delta \left( \frac{s_2}{r_2} \right) \qquad (3)$$

$$\text{TAGWP} + s_2 = \varepsilon_2$$

$$r_2 = \text{TAGWP}_{max} - \text{TAGWP}_{min}$$

$\delta$ is a small number (on the order of $[10^{-6}, 10^{-3}]$), $s_2$ is a nonnegative slack variable for the objective function TAGWP. $r_2$ is a parameter, which is equal to the difference between the upper and lower bound of TAGWP. To obtain the set of Pareto solutions the parameter $\varepsilon_2$ is used for asses different interval points between the minimum and maximum emissions.

## 4. Case study and results

The proposed approach was applied to case study of a five-plant petrochemical complex by Sun, Doyle, and Smith (2015). To take into account energy demand variability over time, the production profile across the year is assumed to be similar to that provided for the petrochemical plant in Bungener, Hackl, Van Eetvelde, Harvey, and Marechal (2015) study. A comparison with optimized designs with fixed steam main conditions (noted as reference design) will be performed, to demonstrate the benefit of the methodology. The operating conditions of steam mains described by Sun et al. (2015) are used as reference. Table 1 summarizes the main findings.

Table 1. Main Results of Test Case Optimization

| Parameters | Economic objective | | Environmental objective | |
|---|---|---|---|---|
| | Reference design | Optimized design | Reference design | Optimized design |
| TAC [m€ y$^{-1}$] | 70.89 | 59.17 (-16.5%) | 294.28 | 177.65 (-39.6%) |
| TACWP [kt $CO_2$-eq y$^{-1}$] | 524.58 | 384.68 (-26.7%) | 22.40 | 11.38 (-49.2%) |

As shown in Table 1, optimizing the system configuration while also considering the optimal steam main conditions results in significant reduction not only in terms of TAC but also in terms of GHG emissions (TAGWP). This is because taking advantage of the trade-offs between heat integration and power generation allows for a reduction in overall energy demand. In turn, this can enhance the results of decarbonization when low-carbon technology is implemented.

Figure 2 shows the Pareto curve for the bi-objective optimization problem. Each point corresponds to one sub-problem solved to minimize total costs subject to a certain upper bound of GHG emissions. Figure 3 depicts how the selection and configuration of energy conversion technology varies from the current optimal design (point 0) as GHG emission limits become more restrictive.

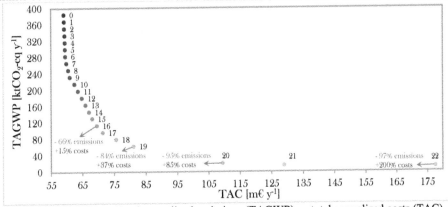

Figure 2 Pareto front: Total annualized emissions (TAGWP) vs total annualized costs (TAC)

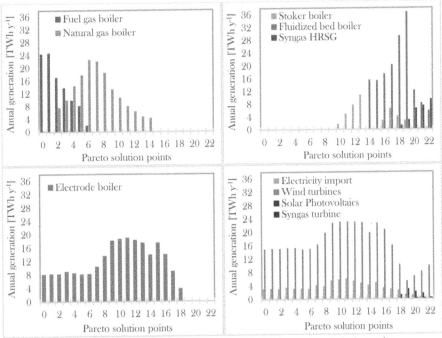

Figure 3 Pareto front: Energy conversion technology at each design point

It is observed that a combination of fossil fuel and low carbon technology can reduce GHG emissions by up to 66%. However, if further decarbonization is required, a complete transition to renewable energy sources is required. It is worth noting that for decarbonization levels above 84%, electricity import is largely avoided, resulting in the remaining demand being met with syngas generated on-site (via gasification), nearly doubling operational costs (in comparison to a conventional fossil fuel-based design) while primarily affecting capital and maintenance costs (due to gasification equipment investment).

## 6. Conclusions

A bi-objective multiperiod optimization model was introduced to consider the environmental impacts of industrial utility systems while providing cost-effective solutions. The model takes into account the selection of the steam main operating conditions in order to take advantage of the close interrelationship between the site processes and the utility system at various temperature levels. The application to the design of a utility system for a petrochemical complex demonstrates that the proposed approach is a highly promising tool for the design of efficient and cost-effective sustainable utility systems. The optimization of steam main conditions can improve the results obtained from decarbonization through a better energy utilization, leading to lower fuel consumption as well as smaller equipment sizes.

Future development of the methodology will address the integration of further energy sources and technologies.

## Acknowledgments

This work has been funded by the Norwegian Research Council through HighEFF (project no. 257632). The authors gratefully acknowledge the financial support from the Research Council of Norway and user partners of HighEFF. Also, a special gratitude to the National Secretariat for Higher Education Science, Technology and Innovation of Ecuador (SENESCYT) for its support.

## References

Bungener, S., Hackl, R., Van Eetvelde, G., Harvey, S., & Marechal, F. (2015). Multi-period analysis of heat integration measures in industrial clusters. *Energy, 93*, 220-234.

Ganschinietz, D. C. (2021). Design of on-site energy conversion systems for manufacturing companies – A concept-centric research framework. *Journal of Cleaner Production, 310*, 127258.

Jimenez-Romero, J., Azapagic, A., & Smith, R. (2022). *BEELINE: BilevEl dEcomposition aLgorithm for synthesis of Industrial eNergy systEms.* Department of Chemical Engineering. University of Manchester. Manchester.

Jiménez-Romero, J., Azapagic, A., & Smith, R. (2023). Style: A new optimization model for Synthesis of uTility sYstems with steam LEvel placement. *Computers & Chemical Engineering, 170*, 108060.

Mavrotas, G. (2009). Effective implementation of the ε-constraint method in Multi-Objective Mathematical Programming problems. *Applied Mathematics and Computation, 213*(2), 455-465.

Sun, L., Doyle, S., & Smith, R. (2015). Heat recovery and power targeting in utility systems. *Energy, 84*, 196-206.

Vaskan, P., Guillén-Gosálbez, G., Turkay, M., & Jiménez, L. (2014). Multiobjective Optimization of Utility Plants under Several Environmental Indicators Using an MILP-Based Dimensionality Reduction Approach. *Industrial & Engineering Chemistry Research, 53*(50), 19559-19572.

Antonis Kokossis, Michael C. Georgiadis, Efstratios N. Pistikopoulos (Eds.)
PROCEEDINGS OF THE 33rd European Symposium on Computer Aided Process Engineering
(ESCAPE33), June 18-21, 2023, Athens, Greece
© 2023 Elsevier B.V. All rights reserved.  http://dx.doi.org/10.1016/B978-0-443-15274-0.50478-9

# Energy and Exergy analysis of Biomass Direct Chemical Looping Combustion for $CO_2$ capture and Utilization

Shailesh Singh Sikarwar, Ramsagar Vooradi, Venkata Suresh Patnaikuni

*National Institute of Technology, Warangal, TG State - 506004, India*
*sarat@nitw.ac.in*

## Abstract

Since a substantial increase in the usage of fossil fuels, particularly in recent past, has resulted in depletion of fossil fuels and the deteriorating state of the environment. Recently, electricity generation from renewable energy sources, such as wind, solar, and biomass, have garnered more attention. To minimize the emissions of $CO_2$, it is crucial to use biomass on a large scale in energy-related applications. In recent years, chemical looping combustion of biomass gained attention as it is a carbon negative technology which can capture $CO_2$ with minimal energy penalty and a potential alternative to the conventional processes. In addition, hydrogen can also be produced using three reactor chemical looping. In this work, a novel cogeneration configuration is proposed for generation of electricity, hydrogen and methane. The proposed integrated system consists of a biomass direct chemical looping unit, organic Rankine cycle, water separation and compression unit, and $CO_2$ & $H_2$ utilization unit. To increase process energy efficiency, a sensitivity analysis is performed to optimize important design parameters such as oxygen carrier flow rate, operating pressure and operating temperature of air, fuel and steam reactors. The performance of the BDCL power plant is compared with conventional and CLC integrated biomass power plants in terms of energy and exergy. Results showed that BDCL plant has higher energy and exergy efficiency compared with the other two.

**Keywords**: Biomass direct chemical looping, $H_2$ production, $CO_2$ utilization, energy and exergy analyses, Organic Rankine cycle.

## 1. Introduction

Renewable energy sources must be adopted by all countries, since fossil fuel usage is a major concern both internationally and domestically. The renewable energy utilization can be further increased by encouraging the use of locally available renewable energy sources in the way as it covers the needs of the customer. With approximately 6% of the world's energy supply and a share of 55% of all renewable energy, modern bioenergy is the most significant source of renewable energy worldwide. Between 2010 and 2021, the use of contemporary bioenergy rose by an average of 7% year and is now on the rise (IEA., 2022). In 2019, 22% of India's total energy supply was derived from renewable sources. Moreover, biomass accounts for approximately 85% of all renewable energy (IEA., 2021). There has been an assessment of the economic, environmental, and energy sustainability of different conventional and non-conventional energy sources in recent years. The power production from biomass is more environmentally sustainable than the coal, while both options score similar exergetic sustainability (Stougie et al., 2018). In the conventional biomass fired power production (BFPP), the biomass burned directly with air in the combustor and the flue gases contain significant amounts of $CO_2$ and $N_2$.

This scheme generally referred as carbon neutral power production. It has become increasingly relevant to integrate $CO_2$ capture technology into BFPP power plants to make this technology a carbon negative. Chemical Looping Combustion (CLC) is one of the technologies being explored on a wide scale. A typical CLC system comprises of air reactor and the fuel reactor in loop as shown in. The metal oxide (oxygen carrier) circulates in between these two reactors and facilitates the transfer of oxygen from air reactor to fuel reactor, which avoids the direct involvement of air in combustion process. The resulting flue gasses contains only $CO_2$ and steam. The studies reported in the literature on CLC integrated biomass-fired power plants (BFPP) mainly focused on integration of CLC technology with steam Rankine cycle for power production with in-situ $CO_2$ capture (Adanez et al., 2018). The integration of CLC with the low capacity BFPP which uses the organic Rankine cycle (ORC) is not widely studied in the literature (Coppola and Scala, 2021). Integration of CLC technology with low capacity BFPP for power production from biomass, makes the process as carbon negative, as well as a sustainable alternative for developing grid-independent plants. Further, by exploring the different cogeneration options along with improving the overall efficiency of the process, the needs of the communities can be met in a sustainable manner. Novel energy systems based on (i) biomass gasification to produce the useful commodities of electricity, heating and hydrogen (Ishaq and Dincer, 2019) (ii) polygenerational system driven by biomass and solar resources to produce useful products of power, hydrogen, hot water for fish farming and cooling (Ishaq et al., 2018) have high energy and exergy efficiencies and shown the distinct advantages of cogeneration in meeting the essential community needs. The Biomass Direct Chemical Looping (BDCL) system is a very efficient option when aiming for co-production of power and hydrogen using CLC technology (Cormos, 2015). This study aims at synthesis of novel BDCL configuration by integrating three reactor CLC unit, ORC unit and $H_2$ & $CO_2$ units for power and hydrogen cogeneration. Furthermore, the produced hydrogen can be utilized for the production of methane. The overall assessment of the developed configurations is carried out on the basis of energy, exergy and environmental parameters and compared with conventional biomass power plant configuration.

## 2. Methodology

In this study a CLC integrated BFPP configuration is developed and validated against the literature model (Sikarwar et al., 2020). The two reactors in the CLC loop of the reference model are replaced with three reactors for electricity and hydrogen cogeneration. Finally, the resulting BDCL configuration is integrated with Methane synthesis unit for deriving multigeneration process configuration. Steady state simulations and thermodynamic analyses of the above mentioned configurations are performed in Aspen Plus V10. All of these plant configurations are simulated for sugarcane bagasse with the following characteristics: carbon 44.48%, ash 2.09%, oxygen 40.69%, hydrogen 6.057%, sulfur 0.047%, nitrogen 0.19% and high heating value 16.45 MJ/kg. $Fe_2O_3$ with 30 wt.% $Al_2O_3$ support is used as oxygen carrier in all cases.

*2.1 Description of CLC integrated BFPP for power production*

In this study, CLC integrated BFPP is considered as a reference case. The plant had already been simulated and detailed analysis of the plant flowsheet can be found in Sikarwar et al., 2020. This plant is mainly composed of two reactors (air and fuel reactors) which act as combustor unit, ORC unit to produce power at small scale, gas turbine and compression unit. Both air and fuel reactors are simulated using RGibbs reactor.

### 2.2 Description of BDCL plant for $H_2$ and power co-production

The proposed BDCL process plant utilizes three reactors (air, fuel and steam reactors) instead of two reactors used in CLC integrated BFPP. In this case, both fuel and steam reactors are simulated as moving bed reactor (multi-stage RGibbs reactor) while air reactor is simulated as single-stage RGibbs reactor. Multi-stage RGibbs reactor is used because it helps in emulating the moving bed conditions. The biomass is combusted in fuel reactor using the oxygen carrier ($Fe_2O_3$ with 30 wt.% $Al_2O_3$ support) where $Fe_2O_3$ is reduced to $FeO/Fe$. Then, reduced $FeO/Fe$ is partially oxidized to $Fe_3O_4/FeO$ using steam in steam reactor. Partially oxidized $Fe_3O_4/FeO$ is fully oxidized to $Fe_2O_3$ in air reactor and sent back to fuel reactor thus forming a loop. The chemical reactions involved in all three reactors are given below (Li et al., 2010).

**Fuel reactor:**

$$Biomass \rightarrow C + CO_2 + H_2O + CO + H_2 + CH_4 \tag{1}$$
$$C + CO_2 \rightarrow 2CO \tag{2}$$
$$C + H_2O \rightarrow CO + H_2 \tag{3}$$
$$CO/H_2 + Fe_2O_3 \rightarrow CO_2/H_2O + 2FeO \tag{4}$$
$$CO/H_2 + FeO \rightarrow CO_2/H_2O + Fe \tag{5}$$
$$CH_4 + 4Fe_2O_3 \rightarrow CO_2 + 2H_2O + 8FeO \tag{6}$$

**Steam reactor:**

$$Fe + H_2O \rightarrow H_2 + FeO \tag{7}$$
$$3FeO + H_2O \rightarrow H_2 + Fe_3O_4 \tag{8}$$

**Air reactor:**

$$4FeO + O_2 \rightarrow 2Fe_2O_3 \tag{9}$$
$$4Fe_3O_4 + O_2 \rightarrow 6Fe_2O_3 \tag{10}$$

Hot gaseous streams of $CO_2$-rich flue gas produced from fuel reactor and $H_2$-rich gas produced from steam rector, are sent directly to evaporator in ORC unit to extract the heat. After extracting the heat from $CO_2$-rich flue gas and $H_2$-rich gas, they are sent to water separation and compression unit where pure $CO_2$ and $H_2$ gases are compressed to sequestration-ready pressures. Water separated from $CO_2$-rich flue gas and $H_2$-rich gas streams, is converted to steam using extra heat available from these two streams. This steam is recycled back to steam reactor for $H_2$ production.

### 2.3 Description of BDCL plant with Methane synthesis

The proposed BDCL plant is further integrated with methanation unit for methane production as shown in Fig.1. In this configuration the $CO_2$ and $H_2$ produced from BDCL plant are sent to methanation reactor. In the reactor, $CO_2$ enters at 30 bar pressure and 68 °C temperature and $H_2$ enters at 30 bar pressure and 121 °C temperature. In the presence of Ni-catalyst, both of them react to produce Methane. Methanation reactor is simulated as single-stage RGibbs reactor where Sabatier reaction (Eq. 11) takes place at 385 °C (Rönsch et al., 2016). Sabatier reaction is exothermic in nature which supplies the heat required to maintain high temperature in methanation reactor. The product stream of methane along with steam is sent to a separator to get pure methane.

$$CO_2 + 4H_2 \rightarrow CH_4 + 2H_2O \quad (\Delta H_{298K} = -164 \text{ kJ/mol}) \tag{11}$$

*2.4 Performance Evaluation*

The overall energy and exergy efficiencies of all plant configurations are calculated using the equations (12) and (13) respectively (Suresh et al., 2010). Here, $m_{biomass}$ is the mass flow rate of biomass (*kg/s*) and *HHV* is the higher heating value of the biomass (*MJ/kg*).

$$\eta_{Gross\ or\ net} = \frac{Gross\ or\ net\ work\ output}{m_{biomass} \times H.H.V.of\ the\ biomass} \tag{12}$$

$$\varepsilon_{Gross\ or\ net} = \frac{Gross\ or\ net\ work\ output}{m_{biomass} \times Specific\ exergy\ of\ the\ biomass} \tag{13}$$

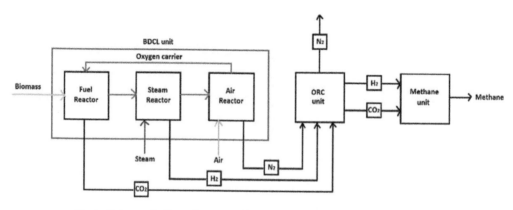

Fig.1: Schematic flow diagram of BDCL plant with Methane synthesis

## 3. Results and discussion

*3.1 BDCL plant for $H_2$ and power co-production*

The BDCL plant configuration is simulated for the biomass flow rate of 0.139 kg/s under steady state condition. The BDCL plant's three main operational parameters: oxygen carrier to biomass ratio, the operating pressure and operating temperatures of the three reactors have been optimized using a sensitivity analysis. The sensitivity analysis results are presented in Figs. 2-5. As operating pressure increases, the energy and exergy efficiencies are exponentially increased up to 15 bar pressure. When the reactor temperature reaches 1150 °C, the maximum energy and exergy efficiencies are observed, but after this extra heat is required to maintain the temperature. Since the reactions in steam and fuel reactors are endothermic, more amount of heat need to be supplied to maintain their temperatures. However, decreasing the temperatures results in low hydrogen production. From the sensitivity analysis, the optimal operating conditions for different units are identified as: loop operating pressure: 15 bar, Air reactor temperature: 1150 °C, Steam reactor temperature: 750 °C and Fuel reactor temperature: 800 °C. Subsequently, the performance of BDCL plant has been compared with conventional and CLC integrated BFPP configurations. In Fig. 6, the exergy

*Energy and Exergy analysis of Biomass Direct Chemical Looping Combustion*
*for CO₂ capture and Utilization*
3005

efficiency of individual units is illustrated for both plants. From the results presented in Table 1, it is observed that the proposed BDCL plant has high energy and exergy efficiencies.

### 3.2 BDCL plant with Methane synthesis

Synthesis of methane results in loss of energy due to utilization of all of the produced hydrogen from BDCL plant. While producing 62.08 kg/hr of methane from the above BDCL plant, the net overall energy and exergy efficiencies are found to be 13.65% and 11.74%, respectively. The stoichiometric ratio of $H_2$ to $CO_2$ is 4:1 for the synthesis of methane. Hence, the methane synthesis plant utilizes 21% of $CO_2$ and 100% of $H_2$ produced from the BDCL plant.

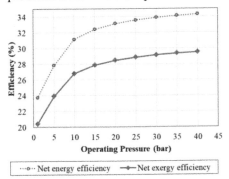

Fig.2. Effect of operating pressure on overall energy and exergy efficiencies.

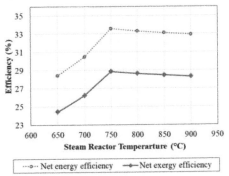

Fig.4. Effect of SR Temperature on overall energy and exergy efficiencies.

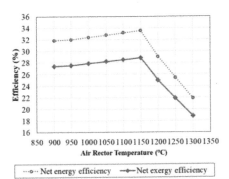

Fig.3. Effect of AR Temperature on overall energy and exergy efficiencies.

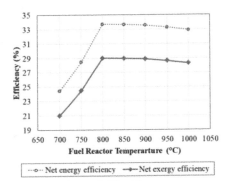

Fig.5. Effect of FR Temperature on overall energy and exergy efficiencies.

Table 1: Performance comparison based on energy and exergy efficiencies.

| Case | Net overall energy efficiency (%) | Net overall exergy efficiency (%) |
|---|---|---|
| Conventional-BFPP | 11.98 | 10.30 |
| CLC integrated BFPP | 21.59 | 18.56 |
| BDCL plant | 33.72 | 28.99 |

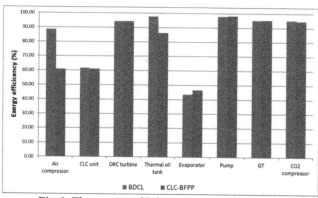

Fig.6: The exergy efficiency of individual units

## 4. Conclusions

In this work, a novel three-reactor BDCL plant is simulated using Aspen Plus V10 for power and hydrogen co-production. The performance of the BDCL plant is compared with the conventional-BFPP and CLC-integrated BFPP energetically and exergetically. The simulation results showed that net overall energy efficiency of the BDCL plant is higher than the conventional-BFPP and CLC-integrated BFPP by 21.74% and 12.13%, respectively. In addition, net overall exergy efficiency of the BDCL plant is higher than the conventional-BFPP and CLC-integrated BFPP by 18.69% and 10.43%, respectively. Furthermore, a $CO_2$ and $H_2$ utilization strategy i.e. methane synthesis is integrated with the BDCL plant. Integration of methane synthesis results in loss of net overall energy efficiency and net overall exergy efficiency by 20.07% and 17.25%, respectively. However, 21% of captured $CO_2$ is effectively utilized in methane synthesis.

## References

- IEA (2022), Bioenergy, IEA, Paris https://www.iea.org/reports/bioenergy, License: CC BY 4.0
- IEA (2021) World Energy Balances and Renewables Information
- L. Stougie, N. Giustozzi, H. Kooi, A. Stoppato, 2018, International journal of energy research, 42, 2916-2926
- J. Adánez, A. Abad, T. Mendiara, P. Gayán, LF. de Diego, F. García-Labiano, 2018, Progress in energy and combustion science, 65,6-66
- Coppola, F. Scala, 2021, Energy & fuels, 35, 23, 19248–19265
- H. Ishaq, I. Dincer, 2019, Energy conversion and management, 196, 395-409
- H. Ishaq, I. Dincer, GF. Naterer, 2018, International journal of hydrogen energy, 43, 52, 23148-23160
- Cormos, 2015, Fuel processing technology, 137, 16-23
- SS. Sikarwar, GD. Surywanshi, VS. Patnaikuni. M. Kakunuri, R. Vooradi, 2020, Renewable energy, 155, 931-949
- F. Li, L. Zeng, LS. Fan, 2010, Fuel, 89, 12, 3773-3784
- S. Rönsch, J. Schneider, S. Matthischke, M. Schlüter, M. Götz, J. Lefebvre, P. Prabhakaran, S. Bajohr, 2016, Fuel, 166, 276-296
- MVJJ. Suresh, KS. Reddy, AK. Kolar, 2010, International journal of energy research, 34, 8, 716-735

Antonis Kokossis, Michael C. Georgiadis, Efstratios N. Pistikopoulos (Eds.)
PROCEEDINGS OF THE 33rd European Symposium on Computer Aided Process Engineering
(ESCAPE33), June 18-21, 2023, Athens, Greece

# End-effect mitigation in multi-period stochastic programming of energy storage operations

Teemu J. Ikonen,[a] Dongho Han,[b] Jay H. Lee,[b] Iiro Harjunkoski,[a,c]

[a]*Aalto University, Department of Chemical and Metallurgical Engineering, PO Box 16100, 00076 Aalto, Finland*
[b]*Korea Advanced Institute of Science and Technology, Department of Chemical and Biomolecular Engineering, 291 Daehak-ro, Yuseong-gu, Daejeon, 34141, Republic of Korea*
[c]*Hitachi Energy Research, Havellandstr. 10-14, 68309 Mannheim, Germany*

## Abstract

Energy storage units offer vital balancing power for energy systems with increasing amount of variable renewable energy sources. The operation of such systems can be optimized by stochastic programming, which anticipates the uncertainty related to the variable energy generation. However, these optimization problems can only be formulated for optimization horizons of a limited length (e.g., 24 or 48 h), due to the rapidly increasing problem size. In this work, we propose the resulting end-effect to be mitigated by valuation of the terminal stored energy level based on an electricity price forecast. We present results on a hybrid energy system, consisting of photovoltaic power generation and an energy storage unit, which trades electricity in the day-ahead market.

**Keywords**: stochastic programming, energy storage, solar energy, electricity market

## 1. Introduction

Energy storage units are essential components of a modern electricity grid, as they can mitigate the undesired variability in many renewable energy sources, such as wind and solar. However, the variable renewable energy sources (VRES) are also inherently uncertain, which needs to be considered in the optimal operation of the energy storage units (Weitzel and Glock, 2018). In the literature, many of the proposed optimization models are based on stochastic programming, i.e., a framework to formulate optimization problems under uncertainty by optimizing the expected outcome (Birge and Louveaux, 2011). Stochastic programming is based on scenarios of realized uncertainty, each of which has dedicated optimization variables. Thus, stochastic programming problems can only be solved for limited horizon lengths, as the optimization problems quickly become intractable due to the increasing number of variables.

The finiteness of the optimization horizon causes a phenomenon, referred to as the end-effect (Grinold, 1983). The end-effect causes the energy storage system to be drained empty at the end of the current optimization horizon if no value is given for the terminal energy level (see, e.g., Singh and Knueven, 2021). Such decisions can be highly sub-optimal over long time horizons. Often used methods to handle the end-effect are i) to enforce the terminal inventory (i.e., in our case, the level of stored energy) to equal the starting inventory or ii) to use a rolling horizon method, such that the current optimization horizon spans beyond the next re-optimization time. Shin et al. (2017) mitigate the end-effect of the energy storage system in wind power-based energy grid systems using a value function learned from reinforcement learning. Han and Lee (2021) propose a method to determine the optimal design and operation strategy of energy grid systems based on stochastic programming while assuming that the terminal level of stored energy is equal to the starting level. Dong and Maravelias (2021) propose multi-material terminal inventory constraints, which are applicable to online production scheduling. In this work, we propose the end-effect to be mitigated by valuating the terminal stored energy level based on an electricity price forecast for the following day.

## 2. Methods

The studied energy system trades electricity in the day-ahead market and consists of a photovoltaic power station and an energy storage unit (Figure 1). In this section, we describe the used stochastic programming model, the methods to mitigate the end-effect on this energy system, and the generation of scenarios.

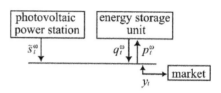

Figure 1: A hybrid energy system.

*2.1. Stochastic programming model*

The objective of the stochastic programming model is to maximize the expected sum of i) the profit during the optimization horizon and ii) the value of stored energy at the end of the horizon. The first stage decision variables, made before the start of each period, are the promised power to be traded, $y_t$, at hour $t \in T$. A positive value of $y_t$ means selling electricity, and a negative value buying electricity. The second stage decision variables, for a given scenario $\omega \in \Omega$, are the amount of stored energy $x_t^\omega$, the power of charging the storage unit $p_t^\omega$, the power of discharging the storage unit $q_t^\omega$, and the photovoltaic power $\tilde{s}_t^\omega$ at hour $t \in T$ (see Figure 1). Further, $\Delta_t^{+,\omega}$ and $\Delta_t^{-,\omega}$ are the positive and negative deviation variables from the promised power at hour $t \in T$ (the former means surplus in the delivered energy). We denote the electricity price by $R_t$, the time interval by $\tau$, the cost of discharging the storage system by $C_\mathrm{d}$ (which represents the aging of the storage system due to cycling), the value of stored energy at the end of the horizon by $V$, and the probability of scenario $\omega$ by $\rho_\omega$. The penalty of deviating from the promised energy is linearly proportional to $R_t$ and $\Delta_t^{+,\omega}$ or $\Delta_t^{-,\omega}$ with coefficients $\gamma^+$ and $\gamma^-$, respectively (Ding et al., 2014). The model is defined as follows:

$$\max \sum_{\omega \in \Omega} \rho_\omega \left\{ \tau \sum_{t \in T} \left[ R_t(\tilde{s}_t^\omega + q_t^\omega - p_t^\omega) - C_\mathrm{d} q_t^\omega - \gamma^+ R_t \Delta_t^{+,\omega} - \gamma^- R_t \Delta_t^{-,\omega} \right] + V x_{|T|+1}^\omega \right\}$$

$$\Delta_t^{+,\omega} \geq \tilde{s}_t^\omega + q_t^\omega - p_t^\omega - y_t, \qquad t \in T, \omega \in \Omega \tag{1}$$

$$\Delta_t^{-,\omega} \geq -(\tilde{s}_t^\omega + q_t^\omega - p_t^\omega - y_t), \qquad t \in T, \omega \in \Omega \tag{2}$$

$$x_{t+1}^\omega = x_t^\omega + \eta_\mathrm{c} \tau p_t^\omega - \frac{\tau}{\eta_\mathrm{d}} q_t^\omega, \qquad t \in T, \omega \in \Omega \tag{3}$$

$$x_1^\omega = x_0 \qquad \omega \in \Omega \tag{4}$$

$$0 \leq p_t^\omega \leq \overline{P}, \qquad t \in T, \omega \in \Omega \tag{5}$$

$$0 \leq q_t^\omega \leq \overline{Q}, \qquad t \in T, \omega \in \Omega \tag{6}$$

$$\underline{X} \leq x_t^\omega \leq \overline{X}, \qquad t \in \{1, \dots, |T|+1\}, \omega \in \Omega \tag{7}$$

$$0 \leq \tilde{s}_t^\omega \leq S_t^\omega, \qquad t \in T, \omega \in \Omega \tag{8}$$

$$\Delta_t^{+,\omega}, \Delta_t^{-,\omega} \geq 0, \qquad t \in T, \omega \in \Omega$$

$$y_t \geq -\overline{P}, \qquad t \in T$$

Constraints 1 and 2 ensure that (at each hour $t \in T$ in scenario $\omega \in \Omega$) the surplus and lack of power is tracked by variables $\Delta_t^{+,\omega}$ and $\Delta_t^{-,\omega}$, respectively. Constraints 3 track the amount of stored energy, where $\eta_c, \eta_d \in [0,1)$ are the efficiencies of charging and discharging, respectively. Constraints 4 define the amount of stored energy $x_0$ at the start of the optimization horizon. Constraints 5 and 6 specify the upper bounds, $\overline{P}$ and $\overline{Q}$, for charging and discharging the energy storage unit, respectively. Accordingly, constraints 7 specify the lower and upper bounds, $\underline{X}$ and $\overline{X}$, for the stored energy. Here, it is worth noticing index $t$ being over set $\{1, \dots, |T| + 1\}$, instead of $T$. Variable $x_{|T|+1}^\omega$ tracks the stored energy level after the last hour of the period (it appears also in the objective function). Constraints 8 facilitate curtailment of the photovoltaic power $\tilde{s}_t^\omega$, where $S_t^\omega$ is the maximum available photovoltaic power at hour $t$ in scenario $\omega$ (see Section 2.3).

*2.2. End-effect mitigation*

The focus of this work is on valuation of stored energy level at the end of an optimization horizon, in order to mitigate the end-effect. In the above-described stochastic programming model, the valuation is controlled via the parameter $V$, which is the multiplier of the terminal storage level $x_{|T|+1}^\omega$ in different scenarios $\omega \in \Omega$. We determine parameter $V$ based on the forecasted electricity price obtained by the Lasso Estimated AutoRegressive (LEAR) model by Lago et al. (2021), which we have modified to also forecast electricity prices beyond the day-ahead. We test setting $V$ to the minimum, mean, and maximum forecasted electricity price on the period following the current optimization horizon of 24 hours (see Table 1). We also test two reference methods. The first is a myopic method that does not mitigate the end-effect at all, referred to as 'no mitigation'. The second is a rolling horizon method, in which the optimization horizon is set to 48 hours.

Table 1: Studied methods to mitigate the end-effect.

| method | horizon length $|T|$ | Valuation of terminal energy level $V$ |
|---|---|---|
| min price-based valuation | 24 | $V$ is the predicted *minimum* electricity price during the next period |
| mean price-based valuation | 24 | $V$ is the predicted *mean* electricity price during the next period |
| max price-based valuation | 24 | $V$ is the predicted *maximum* electricity price during the next period |
| no mitigation | 24 | $V = 0$ |
| rolling horizon | 48 | $V = 0$ |

*2.3. Scenario generation*

The described energy system is highly affected by the uncertainty in the hourly solar irradiance. Solcast is a state-of-the-art model for solar irradiance forecasting (Bright, 2019). Its forecasts are based on satellite images from five geostationary weather satellites, as well as models for aerosol and vapor concentrations. In addition to the mean of the forecast, Solcast also yields estimates of the forecast uncertainty, represented by the 10th and 90th percentiles. Figure 2 shows a seven-day probabilistic forecast of the global horizontal irradiance (GHI) in Bavaria, Germany.

Based on these probabilistic forecasts, we generate the scenarios of the global solar irradiance (GHI) as follows. First, we fit a four-parameter beta distribution to the predicted mean and the 10th and 90th percentiles at each time point $t \in T$. Second, we generate the scenarios of the hourly GHI $S_{GHI,t}^\omega, t \in T$ by the statistical method proposed by Pinson et al. (2009), which takes into account the temporal dependency of the realized solar power generation. The dependency is determined based on historical data of past forecasts and realizations. We further assume that the photovoltaic panels are installed horizontally. The solar power generation scenarios are then

$$S_t^\omega = \eta_s A S_{\text{GHI},t}^\omega \qquad t \in T, \omega \in \Omega \qquad (9)$$

where $S_{\text{GHI},t}^\omega$ is the GHI value obtained by the above-described procedure, $A$ is the total area of the photovoltaic panels, and $\eta_s$ is their efficiency.

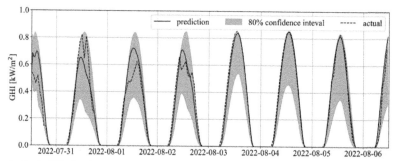

Figure 2: Probabilistic forecast of global horizontal irradiance (GHI) in Bavaria, Germany (49.158°N, 11.433°E) (Solcast, 2019).

## 3. Results

We test the methods, described in the previous section, on a 91-day time window from July 31 to October 29, 2022. The forecasted and actual GHI are obtained from Solcast (Solcast, 2019). The dependency in the realized GHI at the different time points in the forecast horizon (with respect to the forecasts) is modeled from the data recorded from June 20 to July 30, 2022. We use electricity market data from the German Federal Network Agency (https://www.smard.de/en), transmission system operator Tennet (https://netztransparenz.tennet.eu/), and ENTSO-E transparency platform (https://transparency.entsoe.eu/). The results are generated on a laptop with an Intel i5-8365U processing unit. The stochastic programming models are solved by Gurobi 9.1.0.

We investigate the same time window with two configurations of the electricity storage unit (Table 2). The discharge cost of $C_d = 0.04434$ EUR/kWh is calculated for a lithium-ion battery, having an estimated acquisition cost of $132/kWh (Bloomberg, 2021) (we use a currency conversion rate of $1 = 0.96$ EUR), expected lifetime of 3000 cycles, and operation and maintenance costs of 2.1e-3 EUR/kWh (Zakeri and Syri, 2015). We set the number of scenarios $N = 100$, the time interval $\tau = 1$ h, and photovoltaic panels to have an area of $A = 4000$ m$^2$ and efficiency of $\eta_s = 0.25$. We set the deviation penalty coefficients $\gamma^+ = \gamma^- = 10$, aiming to represent a situation where trading at the intraday market is not possible. The charge and discharge efficiencies are $\eta_c = \eta_d = 0.9$. At the beginning of the first 24 h period, the energy storage unit is at the minimum charge level, $x_0 = \underline{X}$. For the sake of a fair comparison, the last period is optimized using the `no mitigation' method.

Table 3 lists the average daily profits, obtained using the five methods to mitigate the end-effect. For a reference, we have also included a method, referred to as *perfect foresight*, which has access to the actual GHI and electricity prices, and uses a horizon length of 72 hours. The value of the stored energy is not considered in the profit. In both configurations, the min price-based valuation yields higher average profits than those based on mean and maximum electricity prices. The result is reasonable because the energy system could also buy energy during the early morning hours when the minimum electricity price often occurs. The min price-based valuation yields 14.2 and 18.3% higher profits than using no end-effect mitigation. Figure 4 visualizes the storage operations during first two days using these methods. In contrast to no mitigation, the energy system optimized with the min price-based valuation avoids buying electricity in the morning of Day 2 (Figure 4b and Figure 4d). The average profits of the min price-based valuation are 2.0 and 5.2% higher than those of the rolling horizon method. Figure 3 shows the cumulative profits of the two configurations when using different end-effect mitigation methods.

Table 2: Parameters of the energy storage system.

| parameter | Configuration 1 | Configuration 2 |
|---|---|---|
| maximum charge power $\bar{P}$ | 500 kW | 1000 kW |
| maximum discharge power $\bar{Q}$ | 500 kW | 1000 kW |
| maximum charge level $\bar{X}$ | 2000 kWh | 4000 kWh |
| minimum charge level $\underline{X}$ | 400 kWh | 800 kWh |

Table 3: Numerical results of the end-effect mitigation methods.

| | average daily profit [EUR] | |
|---|---|---|
| end-effect mitigation | Configuration 1 | Configuration 2 |
| min price-based valuation | 1098.89 | 1268.06 |
| mean price-based valuation | 1096.20 | 1261.50 |
| max price-based valuation | 1066.10 | 1173.45 |
| no mitigation | 961.94 | 1071.84 |
| rolling horizon | 1077.84 | 1205.65 |
| perfect foresight | 1424.82 | 1628.08 |

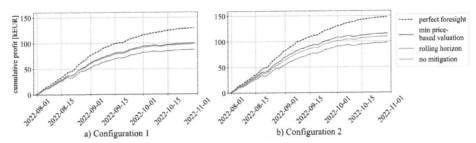

a) Configuration 1　　　　b) Configuration 2

Figure 3: Cumulative profit of the energy system with the two different configurations.

## 4. Conclusions

This paper proposes the end-effect in multi-period stochastic programming of energy storage operations to be mitigated by valuation of the terminal energy storage level. On the two studied energy system configurations, the valuation method based on minimum forecasted price yields 14.2 and 18.3% higher profits than the myopic method, often used in the literature. In comparison to the rolling horizon method, the main benefit is that the proposed method enables the use of shorter optimization horizons without a reduction in the long-term profit.

**Acknowledgment**: Financial support from the Academy of Finland is gratefully acknowledged (project RELOOP, decision number 330388).

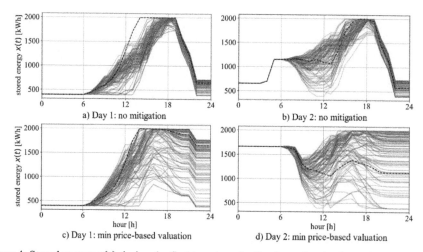

Figure 4: Stored energy $x(t)$ during the first two days for Configuration 1 when using 'no mitigation' or 'min price-based valuation'. Continuous lines are the scenarios. The dashed line is the realized path.

## References

J. R. Birge and F. Louveaux, 2011, Introduction to stochastic programming, Springer Science & Business Media.

J. M. Bright, 2019, Solcast: Validation of a satellite-derived solar irradiance dataset, Solar Energy, 189:435–449.

Solcast, 2019. Global solar irradiance data and PV system power output data. URL https://solcast.com/

H. Ding, Z. Hu, & Y. Song, 2014. Rolling optimization of wind farm and energy storage system in electricity markets. IEEE Transactions on Power Systems, 30(5):2676-2684.

Y. Dong and C. T. Maravelias, 2021, Terminal inventory level constraints for online production scheduling, European Journal of Operational Research, 295(1):102–117.

R. C. Grinold, 1983, Model building techniques for the correction of end effects in multistage convex programs, Operations Research, 31(3):407–431.

D. Han and J. H. Lee, 2021, Two-stage stochastic programming formulation for optimal design and operation of multi-microgrid system using data-based modeling of renewable energy sources, Applied Energy, 291:116830.

J. Lago, G. Marcjasz, B. De Schutter, and R. Weron, 2021, Forecasting day-ahead electricity prices: A review of state-of-the-art algorithms, best practices and an open-access benchmark, Applied Energy, 293:116983.

P. Pinson, H. Madsen, H. A. Nielsen, G. Papaefthymiou, and B. Klöckl, 2009, From probabilistic forecasts to statistical scenarios of short-term wind power production. Wind Energy, 12(1):51–62.

J. Shin, J. H. Lee, and M. J. Realff, 2017. Operational planning and optimal sizing of microgrid considering multi-scale wind uncertainty. Applied energy, 195:616–633.

B. Singh and B. Knueven, 2021. Lagrangian relaxation based heuristics for a chance-constrained optimization model of a hybrid solar-battery storage system. Journal of Global Optimization, 80(4):965–989.

T. Weitzel and C. H. Glock, 2018, Energy management for stationary electric energy storage systems: A systematic literature review. European Journal of Operational Research, 264(2):582–606.

Bloomberg, 2021. https://about.bnef.com/blog/battery-pack-prices-fall-to-an-average-of-132-kwh-but-rising-commodity-prices-start-to-bite/ [accessed on June 15, 2022], 2021.

B. Zakeri and S. Syri, 2015. Electrical energy storage systems: A comparative life cycle cost analysis. Renewable and sustainable energy reviews, 42: 569-596.

Antonis Kokossis, Michael C. Georgiadis, Efstratios N. Pistikopoulos (Eds.)
PROCEEDINGS OF THE 33rd European Symposium on Computer Aided Process Engineering
(ESCAPE33), June 18-21, 2023, Athens, Greece

# How to accurately fast-track sorbent selection for post-combustion $CO_2$ capture? A comparative assessment of data-driven and simplified physical models for screening sorbents

Sai Gokul Subraveti,[a,*] Luca Riboldi,[a] Hao Yang Xu,[b] Yannick Jooss,[a] Simon Roussanaly,[a] Leif Erik Andersson,[a] Rahul Anantharaman[a]

[a]SINTEF Energy Research, 7019 Trondheim, Norway
[b]Department of Chemical and Materials Engineering, University of Alberta, Edmonton, T6G 1H9, Canada
*sai.gokul.subraveti@sintef.no

## Abstract

The recent discovery of a multitude of hypothetical materials for $CO_2$ capture applications necessitated the development of reliable computational models to aid the quest for better-performing sorbents. Given the computational challenges associated with existing detailed adsorption process design and optimization frameworks, two types of screening methodologies based on computationally inexpensive models, namely, data-driven and simplified physical models, have been proposed in the literature. This study compares these two screening methodologies for their effectiveness in identifying best-performing sorbents from a set of 369 metal-organic frameworks (MOFs). The results showed that almost 60% of the MOFs in the top 20 best-performing materials ranked by each of these approaches were found to be common. The validation of these results against detailed process simulation and optimization-based screening approach is currently underway.

Keywords: adsorption; metal-organic frameworks; post-combustion $CO_2$ capture; machine learning; modelling and optimization.

## 1. Introduction

Among several $CO_2$ capture technologies considered for post-combustion $CO_2$ capture, solid adsorbents are seen as a promising alternative to traditional liquid solvents for the separation of $CO_2$ from flue gases. These adsorbents are typically deployed in pressure/vacuum swing adsorption (PVSA) or temperature swing adsorption (TSA) processes. The choice of the adsorbent plays a critical role in determining the separation performance of PVSA or TSA processes [1][2]. Conventionally, better-performing adsorbents are identified through experimentation and testing of a few handfuls of adsorbents as means to understand their performance in the real process [3]. However, this approach is challenged by the recent advent of highly tunable adsorbents, such as metal-organic frameworks (MOFs) for $CO_2$ capture applications, resulting in thousands of potential hypothetical adsorbents [3]. As the experimental evaluation of a multitude of adsorbents is practically impossible, computational screening of the adsorbents has been considered, where process simulations and optimizations based on adsorbent properties are carried out to evaluate the process-scale performance [2][4]. This approach is computationally expensive and time-consuming [2][4][5], which makes it computationally inadequate to handle large databases of adsorbents.

Different approaches have been proposed to reduce the computational costs of existing simulation and optimization tools. One approach is the development of simplified physical models obtained through a simpler description of the process which can be solved in seconds [6][7]. These models proved able to provide reasonable estimations of the process performance. The other approach is the development of surrogate or data-driven models built based on statistical methods that act as faster approximations of process metrics [5]. With groundbreaking advances in machine learning, novel approaches that incorporate physics into surrogate models are also developed to reliably represent physical processes [8].

The goal of this study is to compare the performance of data-driven and simplified physical modeling approaches in rapidly screening databases of adsorbents based on a techno-economic assessment for post-combustion $CO_2$ capture applications. For this analysis, a set of 369 MOFs from the CoREMOF 2014 database provided by Leperi et al. [4] is used and the material performance is assessed using a four-step PVSA cycle with light product pressurization [1].

## 2. Screening methodologies

### 2.1. Data-driven model-based optimization framework

This methodology utilizes data-driven models built based on machine learning principles as a faster approximation for calculating process performance metrics. The data-driven models are coupled with the cost model and the non-dominated sorting genetic algorithm (NSGA – II) to optimize each material for the minimum cost of $CO_2$ avoided. The data-driven models used in this study are artificial neural networks (ANNs) based on the machine-assisted adsorption process learning and emulation (MAPLE) framework [5].

The inputs to the MAPLE model are process features consisting of process operating conditions: adsorption step duration, vacuum pump flow rates, column size, high pressure, intermediate pressure, low pressure, and feed composition; and adsorbent features comprising dual-site Langmuir isotherm parameters of $CO_2$ and $N_2$, and particle morphology. Individual ANN models were trained for each output, namely, step durations, purity, recovery, and energy consumption. These predicted quantities form inputs to the cost model to calculate the cost of the $CO_2$ avoided based on the approach presented in Subraveti et al. [1]. The neural network architecture comprises a feed-forward fully connected network with one input layer including 19 process and adsorbent features, three hidden layers with 10-15 neurons, and an output layer with one output. A tanh activation function was used in the hidden layers and a linear activation was used for the output layer. Around 9000 unique combinations of the input variables generated using the Latin hypercube sampling along with the corresponding outputs were used as samples in the training of the neural networks. Note that the outputs were previously obtained by simulating the detailed adsorption process model until the cyclic-steady state condition [1][9]. The neural networks were trained using Bayesian regularization with the back-propagation algorithm '*trainbr*' in MATLAB 2022a [5][9].

### 2.2. Simplified physical model-based optimization framework

The other approach for the screening of adsorbent materials involves utilizing models that describe the physical phenomena occurring in an adsorption process but introducing simplifications to decrease the computational effort. The larger the simplification level applied, the lower the computational effort. Conversely, the expected accuracy of the

*How to accurately fast-track sorbent selection for post combustion CO$_2$ capture?* 3015
*A comparative assessment of data-driven and simplified physical models for*
*screening sorbents*

models is expected to decrease. For this work, two simplified models are proposed. The first one termed the modified equilibrium model (MEM), relies on the key assumption of local equilibrium, i.e., $CO_2$ gets instantaneously adsorbed onto the adsorbent materials. The model is an extension of an approach presented in the literature [6]. The main modifications with respect to its original formulation include a different routine to solve the adsorption step and the possibility to simulate a 4-step cycle [10]. The second model, termed the reduced-order kinetic model (ROKM), attempts to go beyond the equilibrium assumption by introducing a methodology to implicitly solve the linear driving force (LDF) approximation and, hence, account for mass transfer resistances. The methodology builds on a set of simplifying assumptions, therefore a degree of inaccuracy in capturing the kinetics effects is expected.

The simplified physical models are coupled with the same cost model as in the MAPLE approach and a Bayesian optimization (BO) algorithm to optimize each material for the minimum cost of $CO_2$ avoided. The BO algorithm was developed in-house and tested for the optimization of PSA processes, showing a good balance between computational time and reliability [11]. Simplified physical models might not directly provide all necessary inputs to the cost model owing to the inherent assumptions made while developing these models. For example, the MEM model cannot provide the step durations that are critical for estimating cost. In such cases, relevant and consistent assumptions were made for all the materials to enable the integration of the techno-economic analysis framework for these simplified models. The MEM model needs more assumptions compared to the ROKM model for cost evaluation.

## 3. Results and discussion

The two methodologies are compared in their ability to reliably screen adsorbents for post-combustion $CO_2$ capture. Table 1 briefly summarizes the merits and demerits of each screening model in evaluating the adsorbent performance. In this study, a dry flue gas with $CO_2/N_2$ binary mixture is separated using a four-step PVSA process, a widely studied process that has been demonstrated at the pilot scale [12]. The cycle consists of adsorption (ADS) step, a co-current blowdown (BLO) step, a counter-current evacuation (EVAC), and a light-product pressurization (LPP) step.

Table 1: Merits and demerits of both types of screening models for rapid evaluation of adsorbent performance.

| Screening model type | Strengths | Limitations |
|---|---|---|
| Data-driven models | • Very fast computations<br>• Embeds all physical phenomena from the detailed model<br>• Predictions represent the real process performance | • Requires computational efforts to generate data for training<br>• Black-box model – Applicability within the training range |
| Simplified physical models | • Interpretability through the simplified description of physics<br>• Easy to develop<br>• Entails wider model applicability | • Simulations may not represent the real process performance<br>• May lead to convergence failures and false optima in optimizations |

The performance of each MOF is assessed based on its techno-economic performance in the four-step PVSA cycle. The metric used for ranking the materials was the minimum $CO_2$ avoided cost obtained after optimizing the process operating conditions for each material. It is worth reiterating that both the surrogate and the simplified physical models predict the process performance indicators which are later used as inputs to the cost model within the optimization framework. As mentioned earlier, the cost model employed herein is based on Subraveti et al. [1] for both approaches.

The screening of 369 MOFs was individually carried out for MAPLE, MEM, and ROKM, and the top 20 best-performing materials in terms of cost from each of these methodologies are reported in Fig. 1 for three different $CO_2$ compositions in the flue gas, namely, 7.5%, 13%, and 20%. The top 20 MOFs from the MAPLE-based screening were compared with MEM and ROKM approaches, and the common MOFs are highlighted in green. For the 7.5% $CO_2$ composition case, 8 out of 20 MOFs were featured in both MAPLE and MEM screening methodologies. On the other hand, 12 out of 20 were found

**(a)**

| MOF ID | | |
|---|---|---|
| MAPLE | MEM | ROKM |
| CUGLTM01 | NIKDAM | UBUROY |
| MEHPAQ | CUGLTM01 | QEYWUN |
| CUGLTM02 | CUGLTM02 | MEHPAQ |
| CUGLTM | UBUROY | QUFFED |
| HIDBON | MEHPAQ | QUGNOV |
| NELWIL | FIXFVK | CUGLTM02 |
| QUFFED | PURQEZ | NICJUG |
| RIYDEJ | CUGLTM | ARIBOS |
| UMELUU | QEYWUN | LUMZUO |
| QAVDEW | CAZKRTO1 | NIKDAM |
| WAJHIA | VODPOU | WEPXIA |
| ARIBOS | ZNGLUD | UGEPEB |
| NICJUG | XACZEH | VODPOU |
| TIVFEK | BIUNUKH | WAJHIA |
| BOWQAG | NICJUG | UMELUU |
| NIRDOI | CELKUH01 | PURQEZ |
| TIVFAG | NEZNYU01 | TIVFEK |
| VODPOU | ZNGLUD01 | WUGMAX |
| QEYWUN | IFENOY02 | TIVFAG |
| QUGNOV | RIYDEJ | IFENOY02 |
| *8/20 are common | | *12/20 are common |

**(b)**

| MOF ID | | |
|---|---|---|
| MAPLE | MEM | ROKM |
| CUGLTM01 | NIKDAM | QEYWUN |
| ARIBOS | MEHPAQ | MEHPAQ |
| MEHPAQ | CUGLTM02 | CUGLTM01 |
| NELWIL | CUGLTM | ARIBOS |
| CUGLTM02 | QEYWUN | UBUROY |
| UMELUU | CUGLTM01 | CUGLTM02 |
| HIDBON | UBUROY | LUMZUO |
| NICJUG | LUMZUO | CUGLTM |
| BEPPOD | ARIBOS | QUGNOV |
| QUFFED | FIXFVK | QUFFED |
| CUGLTM | XACZEH | VODPOU |
| RIYDEJ | ZNGLUD | TIVFAG |
| TIVFEK | QUGNOV | NICJUG |
| NINHOH | PURQEZ | WEPXIA |
| QUGNOV | RIYDEJ | UMELUU |
| WAJHIA | QUFFED | TIVFEK |
| BOWQAG | CELKUH01 | XACZEH |
| QEYWUN | VODPOU | WAJHIA |
| IFENOY02 | ZNGLUD01 | NIKDAM |
| CEHWOD | EENHOG | UGEPEB |
| *9/20 are common | | *12/20 are common |

**(c)**

| MOF ID | | |
|---|---|---|
| MAPLE | MEM | ROKM |
| MEHPAQ | QEYWUN | MEHPAQ |
| CUGLTM01 | UBUROY | CUGLTM02 |
| CUGLTM02 | MEHPAQ | QEYWUN |
| BEPPOD | CUGLTM01 | CUGLTM |
| NELWIL | CUGLTM02 | UBUROY |
| TIVFEK | NIKDAM | ARIBOS |
| HIDBON | CUGLTM | FATFUK |
| UMELUU | PURQEZ | UMELUU |
| NAKLIW | WUGMAX | NICJUG |
| LUMZUO | ARIBOS | LUMZUO |
| ARIBOS | RIYDEJ | TIVFAG |
| CUGLTM | ZNGLUD | WUGMAX |
| QUGNOV | XACZEH | QUGNOV |
| NICJUG | LUMZUO | QUFFED |
| VODPOU | QUGNOV | TIVFEK |
| CAYDOX06 | NICJUG | YERJEL |
| OKILEA | VODPOU | IFENOY02 |
| KENJEU | NEPXYU | VODPOU |
| ICEGED | NIKDAM | XACZEH |
| NINHOH | EENHOG | WAJHIA |
| *9/20 are common | | *10/20 are common |

Figure 1: Top 20 best-performing MOFs obtained using MAPLE, MEM, and ROKM screening methodologies for (a) 7.5% (b) 13%, and (c) 20 % $CO_2$ compositions in the flue gas. The common materials found in MAPLE, MEM, and ROKM are highlighted in green. The orange highlighted materials in MEM and ROKM were found in the Top 50 MOFs from MAPLE screening. The red ones were not found in the Top 50. Note that the MOFs are denoted with their index number in the list.

to be common for both MAPLE and ROKM. The MOFs highlighted in orange indicate that they appeared in the top 50 of the MAPLE-based ranking. This indicates that some of the top 20 MOFs from MEM and ROKM methodologies were also good-performing MOFs in the MAPLE-based screening. The red-shaded materials were not found in the top 50 of the MAPLE-based ranking. It is worth mentioning that the percentage differences in the minimum $CO_2$ avoided cost between the top-ranked and the 50th-ranked MOF in the MAPLE-based ranking for 7.5%, 13%, and 20% $CO_2$ composition cases are 94%, 39%, and 31%, respectively. Similarly, the analysis is extended to 13% and 20% $CO_2$ composition cases, and the common materials between MAPLE and ROKM approaches were found to be more than the matched materials between MAPLE and MEM approaches. The addition of simplified mass transfer kinetics in ROKM compared to MEM, which was only based on the equilibrium-based description of physics, could possibly be the reason for the improvement in the number of common materials. Note that the MAPLE model was trained on the data generated by the detailed process model that described the complete physics of adsorption column dynamics.

*How to accurately fast-track sorbent selection for post combustion CO₂ capture?* 3017
*A comparative assessment of data-driven and simplified physical models for*
*screening sorbents*

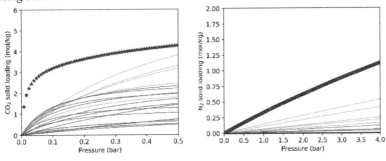

Figure 2: CO$_2$ and N$_2$ isotherms of the materials in the top 20 of the ROKM approach for the case of 13% CO$_2$ composition, out of which 12 were found in the MAPLE-based top 20 (green), 6 MOFs in the MAPLE-based top 50 (orange), and the remaining ones (red). Blue markers represent CO$_2$ and N$_2$ isotherms on zeolite 13X.

The CO$_2$ and N$_2$ isotherms of the top 20 MOFs from the ROKM-based screening approach for the case of 13% CO$_2$ composition are illustrated in Fig. 2. For comparison, CO$_2$ and N$_2$ isotherms of zeolite 13X are also shown as a reference. In Fig. 2, the green lines indicate CO$_2$ and N$_2$ isotherms of those MOFs that were found in the top 20 of both ROKM- and MAPLE-based screening. The orange lines represent the CO$_2$ and N$_2$ isotherms of the MOFs in the top 20 of the ROKM-based ranking that were also found in the top 50 of the MAPLE-based ranking. The red line isotherms are those MOFs in the top 20 of the ROKM-based ranking that were not found in the top 50 of the MAPLE-based ranking. It is interesting to notice that the best-performing materials have fairly linear CO$_2$ isotherms and very low N$_2$ adsorption. This observation remains consistent with several previous studies [1][13][14]. Finally, these common MOFs in the top 20 along with their normalized costs are tabulated in Table 2. It must be stressed that the main objective of the models presented, especially the simplified physical models, is to rank adsorbents rather than provide precise cost figures. Hence, this comparative analysis focused on the relative performances among the adsorbents.

Table 2: List of top-performing MOFs common in all three methodologies with normalized minimum CO$_2$ avoided cost for 13% CO$_2$ composition case. Note that the normalized CO$_2$ avoided cost was obtained by scaling the min. CO$_2$ avoided costs between the CO$_2$ avoided costs of the top-ranked MOF and the 20th-ranked MOF in each category.

| MOF | Normalized minimum CO$_2$ avoided cost (-) | | |
| --- | --- | --- | --- |
| | MAPLE model | MEM model | ROKM model |
| CUGLTM01 | 0.00 | 0.47 | 0.28 |
| ARIBOS | 0.05 | 0.57 | 0.31 |
| MEHPAQ | 0.11 | 0.14 | 0.18 |
| CUGLTM02 | 0.39 | 0.16 | 0.37 |
| QUFFED | 0.73 | 0.81 | 0.53 |
| CUGLTM | 0.74 | 0.17 | 0.49 |
| QUGNOV | 0.79 | 0.71 | 0.53 |
| QEYWUN | 0.88 | 0.40 | 0.00 |

## 4. Conclusions

Two types of computationally inexpensive modelling and optimization frameworks are assessed to enable rapid screening of adsorbents for post-combustion CO$_2$ capture using a four-step PVSA cycle. On the one hand, the data-driven-based MAPLE model was coupled with the cost model and NSGA – II optimizer to minimize the CO$_2$ avoided cost for the set of 369 MOFs to evaluate their techno-economic performance. On the other hand, simplified physical models, MEM and ROKM, both with simpler descriptions of the physics of adsorption columns, were combined with Bayesian optimization to rank the set of MOFs in terms of minimum $CO_2$ avoided cost. The results showed that almost 60% of the MOFs in the top 20 best-performing materials ranked by each of these approaches were found to be common. The validation of these screening approaches against the detailed process simulation and optimization approach is currently ongoing.

## Acknowledgments

The authors are supported by the PrISMa project (No 299659) that is funded through the ACT Programme (Accelerating CCS Technologies, Horizon 2020 Project No 294766), and it receives financial contributions from BEIS, NERC, and EPSRC (UK), RCN (Norway), SFOE (Switzerland) and US-DOE (USA). The authors thank Professor Arvind Rajendran of the University of Alberta for graciously providing us with the data needed for the MAPLE model.

## References

1. S. G. Subraveti, S. Roussanaly, R. Anantharaman, L. Riboldi, A. Rajendran, 2021, Techno-economic assessment of optimised vacuum swing adsorption for post-combustion $CO_2$ capture from steam-methane reformer flue gas, *Sep. Purif. Technol.*, 256, 117832.
2. T. D. Burns, K. N. Pai, S. G. Subraveti, S. P. Collins, M. Krykunov, A. Rajendran, T. K. Woo, 2020, Prediction of MOF performance in vacuum swing adsorption systems for postcombustion $CO_2$ capture based on integrated molecular simulations, process optimizations, and machine learning models, *Environ. Sci. Technol.*, 54 (7), 4536-4544.
3. A. H. Farmahini, S. Krishnamurthy, D. Friedrich, S. Brandani, L. Sarkisov, 2021, Performance-based screening of porous materials for carbon capture, *Chem. Rev.*, 121 (17), 10666-10741.
4. K. T. Leperi, Y. G. Chung, F.You, R. Q. Snurr, 2019, Development of a general evaluation metric for rapid screening of adsorbent materials for postcombustion $CO_2$ capture, *ACS Sustain. Chem. Eng.*, 7 (13), 11529-11539.
5. K. N. Pai, V. Prasad, A. Rajendran, 2020, Generalized, adsorbent-agnostic, artificial neural network framework for rapid simulation, optimization, and adsorbent screening of adsorption processes, *Ind. Eng. Chem. Res.*, 59 (38), 16730-16740.
6. B. Maring, P. Webley, 2013, A new simplified pressure/vacuum swing adsorption model for rapid adsorbent screening for $CO_2$ capture applications. *Int. J. Greenh. Gas Control*, 15, 16–31.
7. V. S. Balashankar, A. K. Rajagopalan, R. de Pauw, A. M. Avila, A. Rajendran, 2019, Analysis of a batch adsorber analogue for rapid screening of adsorbents for postcombustion $CO_2$ capture, *Ind. Eng. Chem. Res.*, 58 (8), 3314-3328.
8. S. G. Subraveti, Z. Li, V. Prasad, A. Rajendran, 2022, Physics-based neural networks for simulation and synthesis of cyclic adsorption processes, *Ind. Eng. Chem. Res.*, 61 (11), 4095-4113.
9. S. G. Subraveti, Z. Li, V. Prasad, A. Rajendran, 2019, Machine learning-based multiobjective optimization of pressure swing adsorption, *Ind. Eng. Chem. Res.*, 58 (44), 20412-20422.
10. L. Riboldi, C. Charalambous, E. Moubarak, R. Anantharaman, S. Roussanaly, C. Fu, B. Smit, J. Young, M. van der Spek, E. Sanchez-Fernandez, D. Ongari, S. Majumdar, E. Garc´ıa-D´ıez, V. Kulakova, S. Garcia, 2020, Advanced methodology for screening of novel adsorption materials for cost-efficient $CO_2$ capture. *SSRN Electronic Journal*.
11. L. E. Andersson, J. Schilling, L. Riboldi, A. Bardow, R. Anatharaman, 2022, Bayesian Optimization for techno-economic analysis of pressure swing adsorption processes. *Comput Aided Chem Eng*, 51:1441–6.
12. S. Krishnamurthy, V. R. Rao, S. Guntuka, P. Sharratt, R. Haghpanah, A. Rajendran, M. Amanullah, I. A. Karimi, S. Farooq, 2014, $CO_2$ capture from dry flue gas by vacuum swing adsorption: A pilot plant study, *AIChE J.*, 60, 1830-1842.
13. A. K. Rajagopalan, A. Rajendran, 2018, The effect of nitrogen adsorption on vacuum swing adsorption based post-combustion $CO_2$ capture, *Int. J. Greenh. Gas Control*, 78, 437-447.
14. S. G. Subraveti, S. Roussanaly, R. Anantharaman, L. Riboldi, A. Rajendran, 2022, How much can novel solid sorbents reduce the cost of post-combustion $CO_2$ capture? A techno-economic investigation on the cost limits of pressure–vacuum swing adsorption, *Appl. Energy*, 306, A, 117955.

Antonis Kokossis, Michael C. Georgiadis, Efstratios N. Pistikopoulos (Eds.)
PROCEEDINGS OF THE 33rd European Symposium on Computer Aided Process Engineering
(ESCAPE33), June 18-21, 2023, Athens, Greece

# A framework for decision-making to encourage utilization of residential distributed energy systems in Brazil

Ana Paula Alves Amorim,[a] Bogdan Dorneanu,[b] Karen Valverde Pontes,[a]
Harvey Arellano-Garcia[b]

[a]*Programa de Pós Graduação em Engenharia Industrial – PEI, Universidade Federal de Bahia, Salvador, 40210-630, Brazil*
[b]*LS Prozess- und Anlagentechnik, Brandenburgische Technische Universität Cottbus-Senftenberg, Cottbus, D-03046, Germany*

arellano@b-tu.de

## Abstract

The Distributed Energy Systems (DES) or microgrid arose from the need to reduce greenhouse gases (GHG) emitted into the atmosphere by burning fossil fuels to generate energy. Reduction of energy losses, reconfiguration of the protection system and reduction of costs, and optimizing the configuration of these systems is recommended. Despite new research in literature, there is still a lack of optimization models that address the Brazilian reality. Therefore, the objective of this work is to introduce a decision-making framework for the design and operation of residential DES that takes into account the particularities of Brazil, based on mixed-integer programming models. The applicability of the framework is tested on a case study of a residential DES of 5 houses, located in Salvador, and used to compare scenarios pre- and post-COVID-19. The results show significant reduction in total annual cost and GHG emissions *versus* the base case without DES. This indicates that, although the country has a mostly "clean" energy matrix due to the use of hydroelectric plants, DES can enable improvement in residential electricity generation.

**Keywords**: Distributed energy systems, Microgrid, Mixed-integer non-linear programming, Net metering.

## 1. Introduction

Currently, energy demand is generally provided by fossil fuels, which release large amounts of suspended particles and greenhouse gas (GHG), leading to global warming and large-scale shifts in climate patterns (Mahmoudan et al., 2022). Distributed energy systems (DES) can improve environmental sustainability and provide an efficient way to achieve the objective of reducing dependence on fossil fuels (Clarke et al., 2021). The adoption of distributed generation from renewable sources is still understated in Brazil, compared to other countries in the world. This can be attributed to regulatory challenges and high acquisition costs of renewable generation technologies. Furthermore, the Brazilian energy matrix is strongly influenced by significant availability of renewable resources (Lima et al., 2020). For the use of this high renewable energy potential that Brazil has, public policies and projects that aim to further encourage the installation of microgrids in the country are needed. Thus, the present work aims to introduce a decision-making framework for the design and operation of residential DES based on mixed-integer programming models that take into consideration the particularities of Brazil. The models optimize the cost of the design and utilization of a microgrid with integrated pipelines to supply hot water and biogas besides electricity. The time horizon for operating the DES is split into time periods based on clustering methods. Furthermore, the efficiency of the various technologies to be installed is considered to vary in time, and several different options are included for the renewable incentive policy, which results in a mixed-integer nonlinear programming (MINLP) model, *versus* the commonly used mixed-integer linear programming (MILP) models in literature (Sidnell et al., 2021).

## 2. Problem definition

The aim of the optimization problem is to scale the system at a lower cost in order to meet the electrical, hot water, air cooling, and gas for cooking demand of a residential network in Salvador (Brazil) using three energy sources: solar, wind and biogas. The technologies that can be installed in each household to meet the electricity demand are photovoltaic (PV) arrays, wind turbines (WT), biogas generators (BG), and batteries (BT). To meet the hot water demand, electric showers (ES), gas heaters (GH), biogas heaters (BH), and thermosolar collectors (SC) are used. To meet the air cooling demand, air conditioners (AC) are used, while a biodigester (BD) will satisfy both the biogas demand for the BH and cooking for the whole network. Furthermore, the electricity generated from renewable resources is used for self-consumption, transferred to another household, fed into the central grid, or stored in electric batteries. To meet demand, in addition to the renewable energy generated, electricity can be purchased from the central grid. Regarding hot water production, this can be used for self-consumption, transferred to another house, or it can be produced in SC, if available. Moreover, the demand for cooking gas can be supplied by natural gas from the grid or by biogas produced in the BD.

To improve on previous work (Sidnell et al., 2021a, Clarke et al., 2021), the time horizon is divided in time periods by means of a systematic clustering method that takes into account the profiles of electrical demand, solar irradiation and wind speed of the site, and the central grid electricity rate that varies during the day. The division is done for each pre- and post-COVID scenarios. Thus, for the pre-COVID scenario three seasons are obtained (*m1*: January, February, March, April, *m2*: May, June, July, August, September, *m3*: October, November, December), with eight periods during the day (*p1*: 12am-3am, *p2*: 3am-6am, *p3*: 6am-8am, *p4*: 8am-4pm, *p5*: 4pm-6pm, *p6*: 6pm-9pm, *p7*: 9pm-10pm, *p8*: 10pm-12am), while for the post-COVID scenario the same three seasons are obtained, but with only five periods (*p1*: 12am-7am, *p2*: 7am-4pm, *p3*: 4pm-6pm, *p4*: 6pm-9pm, *p5*: 9pm-12am). The irradiation and wind speed data used are found in World Bank Group (2022) and DTU (2022). Based on the approximation of the depreciation time of the components of the energy sources used, the useful life of the project is considered to be 20 years. For the interest rate, a value of 0.07 is used, according to the financial cost rate for renewable energy adopted by BNDES (*Banco Nacional do Desenvolvimento Econômico e Social* – The National Bank for Economic and Social Development). The purchase and sale tariff for the central grid is based on the amount adopted by COELBA (*Companhia de Eletricidade do Estado da Bahia* – Electricity Company of Bahia). Because no studies are available on the post-COVID average energy demand, they are estimated in relation to the pre-COVID data. For the electricity demand, this value is 25% higher, on the assumption of continuous behavior during the day, due to the remote work adopted (Macedo, 2021). For the hot water demand, an increase of 15% was considered; for the cooling demand, an increase of 50%, while for cooking gas, an increase of 25% is assumed. In order to determine the best incentive policy to be adopted for distributed generation, the Net Metering (NEM) and Feed in Tariff (FIT) models were considered.

## 3. Mathematical model

The model is implemented as a mixed-integer nonlinear programming (MINLP) problem and solved in the GAMS language. The model is solved on a desktop PC with Intel Core i9-9900K CPU @ 3.60 GHz and 32.0 GB of RAM, using the BARON solver, to full optimality.

### 3.1. Model formulation

The objective function to be minimized is given by the total annual investment and annual operation cost, described by:

$$C_{TOTAL} = C_{INV} + C_{OM} + C_{BUY}^{GRID} + C^{NG} + C^{ENV} - NEM - FIT \tag{1}$$

where $C_{INV}$ is the total investment, $C_{OM}$ is the operating and maintenance cost, $C_{BUY}^{GRID}$ is the total cost of electricity purchased from the grid, $C^{NG}$ is the cost to purchase natural gas from the grid, $C^{ENV}$ is the environmental costs, NEM is the credit revenue obtained by using the Net Metering policy, FIT is the amount received for adopting a Feed in Tariff. All these costs and revenues are measured in Brazilian Reals (R$).

The investment is the sum of all the costs invested to acquire each technology:

$$C_{INV} = C_{OM}^{PV} + C_{OM}^{BG} + C_{OM}^{WT} + C_{OM}^{BT} + C_{OM}^{BD} + C_{OM}^{PPBD} + C_{OM}^{MG} + C_{OM}^{TS} + C_{OM}^{SC} + C_{OM}^{GH} + C_{OM}^{BH} + C_{OM}^{ES} + C_{OM}^{AC} \tag{2}$$

where the superscript OM refers to the maintenance and operation cost. The fixed and variable operating and maintenance costs for each technology are given by the nominal equipment capacity and their operating cost.

The cost of buying power from the central grid is given by:

$$C_{BUY}^{GRID} = \Sigma_{i,m,p}\big(E_{i,m,p}^{GRID} \cdot P_{m,p}^{Elec} \cdot day(m) \cdot hours(p) \cdot season(m)\big) \tag{3}$$

Here, $E_{i,m,p}^{GRID}$ is the power purchased from the central grid [kW], while $P_{m,p}^{Elec}$ is the price of electricity purchased during each time period [R$/kWh], the subscripts $i$ represent the houses, while the season is indicated by the index $m$ and the time period by the index $p$.

The cost of buying natural gas from the grid is determined from:

$$C^{NG} = \frac{P^{NG}}{q^{NG}} \cdot \Sigma_{i,m,p}\big(Use_{i,m,p}^{NG} \cdot day(m) \cdot hours(p) \cdot season(m)\big) + \Sigma_i Y_i^{NG} \cdot C_{Fix}^{NG} \cdot season(m) \tag{4}$$

This cost depends on variable and fixed factors. The variable cost is determined by the volume of gas purchased from the grid, $Use_{i,m,p}^{NG}$ [kW], the price of gas, $P^{NG}$ [R$/m³], the calorific capacity of the natural gas, $q^{NG}$ [kW/m³], and the number of hours that the gas has been used. The fixed costs, $C_{Fix}^{NG}$ [R$] is related to the monthly amount calculated only when natural gas is purchased from the grid. The variable $Y_i^{NG}$ identifies whether natural gas is used or not from the grid.

The environmental costs are calculated from the carbon tax per amount of $CO_2$ emitted for each technology considered:

$$C^{ENV} = CO_2^{GRID} + CO_2^{NG} + CO_2^{WT} + CO_2^{PV} + CO_2^{SC} + CO_2^{BIO} \tag{5}$$

The credits obtained by each incentive policy considered (NEM and FIT, respectively) depend on the total energy sold to the grid and its selling rate. In the case of NEM, it corresponds to the electricity rate adopted by the central grid. For the FIT, the selling rate varies for each technology used, as illustrated in the following equation :

$$FIT = \Sigma_{i,m,p}\big(E_{i,m,p}^{SALE,PV} \cdot P^{FIT,PV} + E_{i,m,p}^{SALE,WT} \cdot P^{FIT,WT} + E_{i,m,p}^{SALE,BG} \cdot P^{FIT,BG}\big) \cdot day(m) \cdot hours(p) \cdot season(m) \cdot Y^{FIT} \tag{6}$$

Where $E_{i,m,p}^{SALE,Tech}$ is the amount of the energy fed into the central grid by the technology *Tech* (kW), $P^{FIT,Tech}$ is the rate of the sale for technology *Tech* ($/kW), with *Tech* = PV, WT, BG, and $Y^{FIT}$ is a binary variable for deciding if the policy is being used or not.

### 3.2. Design and operational constraints

The constraints found in Sidnell et al. (2021a) and Clarke et al. (2021) are adopted for the operation of the microgrid, the pipeline, and the battery, while the operation of the photovoltaic panel and solar collector are described based on Karamov et al. (2021), while for the wind turbines, the constraints are defined as described in Pallabazzer (2003). For the sizing of the biodigester, Araujo (2017) and Otim et al. (2006) are used. Additionally, the model considers that the efficiency of the technologies installed in dwellings is not constant, but varies with the local conditions. For instance, in the case of the PV panels, the efficiency is defined as (Karamov et al., 2021):

$$ne_{m,p}^{PV} = nee^{PV} \cdot \left[(1 - \beta_S) \cdot T_{m,p}^{PV/SC} - 48\right] \tag{7}$$

where $nee^{PV}$ is the nominal energy efficiency of the PV panel, $\beta_S$ is the temperature coefficient for silicon PV panels, and $T_{m,p}^{PV/SC}$ is the operating temperature of the PV converter.

## 4. Case study

The model presented in the previous section is applied to a microgrid of 5 houses located in Salvador da Bahia (Brazil) for two different scenarios: pre- and post-COVID. The results of these scenarios are illustrated in Figure 1 (a) and (b), respectively.

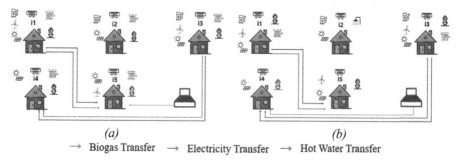

(a)                                                        (b)

→ Biogas Transfer   → Electricity Transfer   → Hot Water Transfer

*Figure 1: DES network for the scenario: (a) pre-COVID-19, (b) post-COVID-19*

For the pre-COVID scenario, PV panels (for electricity generation) and SC (for hot water) are installed in every home, due to the fact that the period of sunlight in the region is distributed over more than one period (*p3* to *p5*), which means the best use of sunlight. In addition, for the electricity generation, WT are considered in houses *i1*, *i3* and *i5*. Thus, house *i1* produces more than what was necessary to meet its own demand, enabling energy sharing with house *i5*. A similar behavior is observed between houses *i3* and *i4*. Batteries are installed in houses *i1*, *i2* and *i3*. It is inferred that it is more efficient to install smaller batteries in *i1* and *i3* that share energy with the houses of higher demand (*i4* and *i5*) than to install a larger battery in these houses. For house *i2*, due to having only PVs to meet the demand, the battery is used at times when energy from the central grid is more expensive (e.g., peak hour periods *p5-p7* in the pre-, or *p3-p5* in the post-COVID scenario, respectively), as illustrated in Figure 2 for both pre- and post-COVID scenarios.

For hot water generation, besides the SC, a BH is installed in house *i5* and a natural GH in houses *i1*, *i2*, *i3* and *i4*, respectively. This is due to the limitation of biogas production, considering it is better to use it in the dwelling with higher demand (*i5*). Since natural gas has a continuous supply, it is used in the other houses to meet the rest of the demand that the SC could not meet. In addition, house *i5* receives hot water from house *i1*, and house *i4*, which has the highest demand, receives hot water from house *i3*. Furthermore, AC is used to meet the cooling demand in all the houses. Finally, a BD is installed in the network and biogas is distributed to house *i5* to meet the gas demand for cooking and hot water generation.

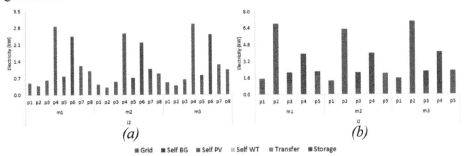

(a)          (b)

■ Grid    ■ Self BG    ■ Self PV    ■ Self WT    ■ Transfer    ■ Storage

*Figure 2 - Profile of resources used to meet the electrical demand in the house i2 for the scenario: (a) pre-COVID-19, (b) post-COVID-19*

The sharing of electricity and hot water is designed to go from the house of lower to the one with higher demand, to ensure the same equipment can serve more than one house. Due to a limitation in the capacity, the opposite direction of sharing is not possible, as this will require equipment above the upper bound of the capacity.

In the post-COVID scenario, PV panels are installed in all residences, but only houses *i1*, *i3* and *i5* adopt the WT. Because houses *i4* and *i5* have a higher electricity demand, the production of houses *i1* and *i3* is shared with these houses, as illustrated in Figure 1. Furthermore, as in the pre-COVID scenario, the battery is installed in houses *i1*, *i2* and *i3*, with lower demand, which share energy with the houses of higher demand (*i4* and *i5*). Although the same type of equipment is installed for electricity generation in both scenarios, their capacity is different due to differences in the distribution of the demand between the pre- and post-COVID scenario. To meet the hot water demand in houses *i1* and *i3*, natural GHs and SCs are installed. Since these houses also share hot water with houses *i5* and *i4*, respectively, and have a lower hot water demand, the model chooses the most economically feasible option. This is to install the two technologies to meet the demands of the 4 houses than to install, for example, a bigger equipment in houses *i4* and *i5*.

Moreover, a BH is installed to supply the rest of the hot water demand in house i4 and the natural GH in house *i5*. In house *i2* the ES is sufficient to meet all its hot water demand. Furthermore, AC is used to meet the cooling demand in all the houses. A BD is installed in the network and connected to house *i4*, to supply part of the gas demand for cooking. This can be explained by the limited biogas production and the lower demand of house *i4* compared to house *i5*, for example.

In terms of renewable incentives policy, for all scenarios, the option selected is net metering. This is the current policy adopted in the country and confirms that, for the current conditions of technology and local electricity prices, it continues to be the most advantageous.

*Table 1: Costs and revenues for all scenarios (all costs are in R$)*

| Scenario | | Total | Invest-ment | O&M | Environ-mental | Grid im-ports | Incen-tives |
|---|---|---|---|---|---|---|---|
| Pre-COVID | Baseline | 160,210.26 | 990.15 | 84,672.04 | 2,015.82 | 72,532.24 | - |
| | 5Houses | 28,956.95 | 24,450.86 | 38,539.39 | 1,428.47 | 3,445.71 | 38,907.48 |
| Post-COVID | Baseline | 249,889.14 | 1,398.02 | 109,351.27 | 3,145.50 | 135,994.34 | - |
| | 5Houses | 31,596.10 | 28,056.46 | 80,756.17 | 2,562.79 | 7,741.56 | 87,520.89 |

Table 1 shows the costs and revenues for all scenarios. In relation to the pre-COVID baseline, there is an 82% reduction in total cost and a 29% reduction in environmental cost. In addition, R$38,907.48 in energy credits are generated. For the post-COVID scenario, a similar reduction is achieved in terms of total cost (87% versus the baseline), while lower savings (19%) are achieved for the environmental cost. However, for this case, higher energy credits (R$87,520.89) are generated due to the higher resource capacity installed compared to the pre-COVID design.

Furthermore, despite a 25% increase in electricity cost, 50% increase in gas cost, and the increase in demand mentioned above, the optimizer is able to find a configuration with an increase of only 9% in total cost for the post-COVID scenario.

## 5. Conclusion

This paper presents the development of a framework to support decisions in terms of residential DES policies applied to Brazil. The proposed framework considers the division of time periods using clustering methods, variable efficiency of the installed technologies, several options for the selection of renewable incentive policies and is able to attest the potential high economic and environmental gains that can be achieved with the adoption of renewable energy resources, for various scenarios considered. The results show that the approach is able to provide information regarding the best incentive policy for the country and the viability of using biogas, solar and wind energy to meet the electrical, hot water, air cooling and gas for cooking demands. Furthermore, significant reduction of economic and environmental costs is achieved, despite the clean energy matrix of Brazil. For future work, a larger set of houses in order to observe the behavior of the microgrid sizing in other configurations, uncertainty in generation or demand, or variable energy pricing will be included.

## References

A.P.C. Araújo, 2017, Produção de biogás a partir de resíduos orgânicos utilizando biodigestor anaeróbico, Universidade Federal de Uberlândia, pp. 42

F. Clarke et al., 2021, Optimal design of heating and cooling pipeline networks for residential distributed energy systems, Energy 235, 121430

DTU Wind Energy, 2022, Global Wind Atlas. Available in: https://globalwindatlas.info/ (Accessed: Mar. 15, 2021)

D.N. Karamov et al, 2021. Optimization of isolated power systems with renewables and storage batteries based on nonlinear Volterra models for the specially protected natural area of lake Baikal, Journal of Physics: Conference Series 1847(1), 012037

M.A. Lima et al., 2020, Renewable energy in reducing greenhouse gas emissions: Reaching the golas of the Paris agreement in Brazil, Environmental Devleopment 33, 100504

A. Mahmoudan et al., 2022, A geothermal and solar-based multigeneration system integrate with a TEG unit: Development, 3E analyses, and multi-objective optimization, Applied Energy 308, 118399

G. Otim et al., 2006, Design of Biogas Plant for Rural Households in Uganda (Case Study Apac District), Second International Conference on Advances in Engineering and Technology, pp. 544-550

R. Pallabazzer, 2003, Parametric analysis of wind siting efficiency, Journal of Wind Engineering and Industrial Aerodynamics 91(11), pp.1329–1352

T. Sidnell et al., 2021, Optimal design and operation of distributed energy resources systems for residential neighbourhoods, Smart Energy 4, 100049

World Bank Group, 2022, Global Solar Atlas, Available in: https://globalsolaratlas.info/map?c=-13.859414,-42.220459,7&s=-12.972442,-38.441162&m=site&pv=small,0,12,1 (Accessed: Mar. 15, 2021)

Antonis Kokossis, Michael C. Georgiadis, Efstratios N. Pistikopoulos (Eds.)
PROCEEDINGS OF THE 33rd European Symposium on Computer Aided Process Engineering
(ESCAPE33), June 18-21, 2023, Athens, Greece

# Hydrogen infrastructure planning for heat decarbonisation in Great Britain

Margarita E. Efthymiadou, Vassilis M. Charitopoulos and Lazaros G. Papageorgiou

*The Sargent Centre for Process Systems Engineering, Department of Chemical Engineering, University College London (UCL), Torrington Place, London WC1E 7JE, UK*
*l.papageorgiou@ucl.ac.uk*

## Abstract

Towards Net-Zero emissions goal in 2050, the UK has set a greenhouse gas emissions target to reduce its environmental footprint. Consequently, the exploitation of alternative low-carbon pathways and energy carriers for the heat sector are required. In this work, we propose a multi-period, spatially-explicit mixed-integer linear programming (MILP) optimisation framework for hydrogen infrastructure to meet hydrogen heating demand in Great Britain. The mathematical model aims to minimise the total cost accounting for investment and operational decisions. The proposed optimisation framework includes dual temporal resolution: 5-year steps 2035- 2050 and typical days with hourly resolution. To enhance the computational performance of the studied model, we developed a hierarchical solution approach that results in near-optimal solutions while reducing the solution time by an order of magnitude.

**Keywords**: Net-Zero; Heat Decarbonisation; Hydrogen Infrastructure; Energy systems modelling; MILP model;

## 1. Introduction

In 2021, UK greenhouse gas emissions reached 447 $MtCO_2e$ (BEIS, 2022), with target reduction of 68% from 2019 to 2035 (BEIS, 2020). The domestic heating sector is responsible for 14% of UK emissions mainly due to the wide use of natural gas boilers (McDowall & Britchfield, 2021). The pathway to energy decarbonisation requires environmentally friendly policies, which support the introduction of low-carbon energy carries and end-use technologies. Regarding the heat sector, the UK government has made several commitments to achieve heat decarbonisation allocating over £1 billion to support them (HM Government, 2021). In this context, BEIS (2021) forecasted that hydrogen demand will increase significantly by early 2030 (suggesting production capacity of 7-20 GW by 2035). Among other alternatives, hydrogen play a key role in the future energy mix either with its direct use or as an efficient storage carrier for renewable electricity production. In both cases, new infrastructure networks connecting supply to demand are required and thus, a novel modelling tool for hydrogen supply chain is essential to investigate design decisions and what-if analysis scenarios for hydrogen infrastructure.

The supply chain optimisation of hydrogen has received considerable attention from the PSE community over the last decade. One of the first infrastructure planning optimisation models was developed by Hugo *et al.* (2005) using a multi-objective optimisation approach. An integrated MILP spatially-explicit framework for hydrogen transportation demand infrastructure design was proposed by Almansoori and Shah (2009). Based on the aforementioned work, Guillen *et al.* (2010) formulated a bi-criterion model for simultaneous minimisation of system cost and environmental impact of the system. Agnolucci *et al.* (2013) introduced SHIPmod, which included Carbon Capture and Storage (CCS) system in the spatially-explicit multi-period MILP model. SHIPmod was extended by Moreno-Benito *et al.* (2016) adding hydrogen pipelines for regional transmission. The role of oxygen as a by-product of hydrogen production for transportation fuel was examined by Ogumerem *et al.* (2018) using a multi-objective approach. Sunny *et al.* (2020) and Samsatli and Samsatli (2019) investigated the role of hydrogen in heat decarbonisation. He *et al.* (2021) proposed a snapshot spatial model which determines the least-cost hydrogen planning for multiple end-uses. Stochastic approaches for hydrogen supply chains have been studied by Camara *et al.* (2019) and Ochoa-Bique *et al.* (2021). This work focuses on the development of an optimisation-based framework for hydrogen infrastructure planning while its applicability is demonstrated through a case study for residential hydrogen heat demand in Great Britain.

## 2. Problem Statement

Overall, the problem investigated in this work can be stated as follows:

**Given:** (i) $H_2$ heating demand and renewables availability in each region, year, cluster and hour, (ii) capital and operating costs for production technologies, storage sites, hydrogen and $CO_2$ pipelines and road transportation modes, (iii) minimum and maximum capacity as well as ramp rates and lifetime of production plants and storage sites, (iv) minimum and maximum flowrate in pipelines, (v) capacity of $H_2$ caverns and $CO_2$ reservoirs, (vi) $H_2$ import price, (vii) carbon tax and capture rates for $CO_2$ emissions as well as $CO_2$ emission targets

**Determine the optimal:** (i) location and capacity of production technologies, storage sites and renewable farms, (ii) $H_2$ production and storage rate in each region, year, cluster and hour, (iii) $H_2$ and $CO_2$ transmission investments between regions, (iv) $H_2$ and $CO_2$ flowrates between regions in year, cluster and hour, (v) electricity generation of renewables, (vi) $H_2$ import rates in each year, cluster and hour

**So as** to minimise the total system cost subject to emission target.

## 3. Mathematical Formulation and Hierarchical Solution Approach

The problem for the cost optimal hydrogen infrastructure design is formulated as a multi-period mixed integer linear programming (MILP) model.

The objective of the model is the minimisation of the total system cost ($TC$) as described by the Eq. (1).

$$\min TC = PCC + SCC + TCC + POC + SOC + TOC + CEC + IIC + ReC \quad (1)$$

The total cost comprised of production capital cost ($PCC$), storage capital cost ($SCC$), transportation capital cost ($TCC$), production operating cost ($POC$), storage operating cost ($SOC$), transportation operating cost ($TOC$), carbon emissions cost ($CEC$), international import cost ($IIC$) and the renewable cost ($ReC$).

The hydrogen energy balance can be described by the Eq. (2).

$$\sum_{p \in P} Pr_{pgtch} + \sum_{l \in \{Road\}} \sum_{g' \in N^r_{gg'}} Q_{lg'gtch} + \sum_{l \in \{Pipe\}} \sum_{g' \in NP_{gg'}} Q_{lg'gtch} + \sum_{s \in GS_{gs}} Q^R_{gstch} + I_{gtch}$$

$$= \sum_{l \in \{Road\}} \sum_{g' \in N^r_{gg'}} Q_{lgg'tch} + \sum_{l \in \{Pipe\}} \sum_{g' \in NP_{gg'}} Q_{lgg'tch} + \sum_{s \in GS_{gs}} Q^I_{gstch} + TD_{gtch} \quad (2)$$

$$\forall g \in G, t \in T, c \in C, h \in H$$

More specifically, in each region $g$, year $t$, cluster $c$ and hour $h$, the total production rate of production technologies $p$ ($Pr_{pgtch}$), the flowrates of all transportation modes $l$ ($Q_{lg'gtch}$) to region $g$, the rejected hydrogen from storage site $s$ ($Q^R_{gstch}$) and the imported hydrogen ($I_{gtch}$) are equal to the flowrates ($Q_{lgg'tch}$) from region $g$, the injected hydrogen to storage sites $s$ ($Q^I_{gstch}$) and the total demand ($TD_{gtch}$). $GS_{gs}$

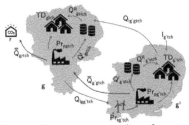

**Figure 1:** Visual representation of energy and mass balance between two regions.

stands for the regions where storage sites can be commissioned and $N^r_{gg'}$ and $N^p_{gg'}$ stand for the neighboring regions for road and pipeline connections respectively.

Due to number of technologies and high spatio-temporal resolution, the resulting optimisation problem is usually computationally intensive. Typical computational times for solving the monolithic model exceed 15h. Reduction of CPU time could be achieved by developing hierarchical solution procedures. In this context, a hierarchical approach has been developed in this work, which includes the steps as presented in Table 1.

**Table 1:** Solution procedure

| | |
|---|---|
| **Step 1** | Solve the model without considering pipeline investment decisions |
| **Step 2** | Fix production and storage investment decisions (integer variables) for all time periods |
| **Step 3** | Solve reduced model |

## 4. Case Study

The investigated case study demonstrates the applicability of the multi-period spatially-explicit MILP for hydrogen infrastructure optimisation for domestic heating in Great Britain (GB) from 2035 to 2050. GB is divided into 13 regions according to local gas distribution zones (LDZ) of the incumbent natural gas network. The temporal resolution of the model is dual considering 5-year time steps for investment decisions and representative days with hourly resolution for operational decisions, such as hydrogen production and storage rates.

This case study includes hydrogen production, storage and transmission technologies and a carbon capture and storage (CCS) system. Moreover, the electricity required for water electrolysis is generated from renewable sources including wind and solar energy.

In the context of model size reduction, the total heat demand and renewable technologies availability hourly data are clustered using clustering techniques. K-Medoids clustering is used for representative days selection according to Charitopoulos *et al.* (2022).

**Figure 2:** Regional representation of Great Britain.

The system-wide hydrogen demand and emission targets for residential heat are obtained from National Grid ESO (2021) System Transformation scenario.

## 5. Results & Discussion

The model is implemented in GAMS 38.2.1 and solved with Gurobi 9.1.2 with optimality gap 5%, using a Dell workstation with Intel® Core™ i9-10980XE CPU @ 3.00 GHz and 128 GB RAM. The multi-period model results provide the optimal cost evolution of hydrogen infrastructure in the UK to meet hydrogen heat demand.

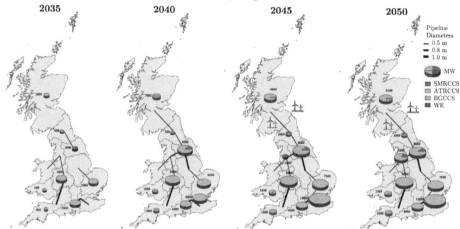

**Figure 3:** Production capacity and hydrogen pipelines expansion maps from 2035 to 2050.

In Fig. 3, the production capacity expansion maps are illustrated from 2035 to 2050. In 2035, a total of 13.5 GW production capacity is commissioned of ATR, SMR and biomass gasification technologies. The total capacity is increased to 33.5 GW in 2040 and 56.6 GW in 2050. Reforming technologies are mostly installed due to their lower production costs in comparison with the other technologies. Moreover, 0.1 GW of water electrolysis for green hydrogen production is commissioned in 2045 in Scotland while the electricity required for electrolysis is generated from wind onshore and offshore farms.

The regional transmission of hydrogen takes place through a pipeline network. As shown in Fig. 3, in 2035 there is a partial installation of the hydrogen transmission network. Over the years, the hydrogen network is expanded connecting most neighboring regions.

Storage is a key element in hydrogen infrastructure strategy to meet peak heat demand. Fig. 4 illustrates the evolution of regional storage capacity from 2035 to 2050. Medium pressure storage vessels are installed for hydrogen storage in the majority of GB regions. In 2050, a total of 247 GW is commissioned with 50GW installed in EA and 32 GW in NE.

Fig. 5 illustrates the production rate, storage inventory and demand in each cluster in 2050. Cluster 1 is the peak day of the year in which

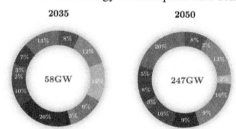

**Figure 4:** Hydrogen storage capacity in GB regions from 2035 to 2050.

hydrogen heating demand reaches 100 GW. As indicated, hydrogen production rate during the day is almost steady as there is a significant installation of gas reforming and biomass gasification units which have low ramp rates.

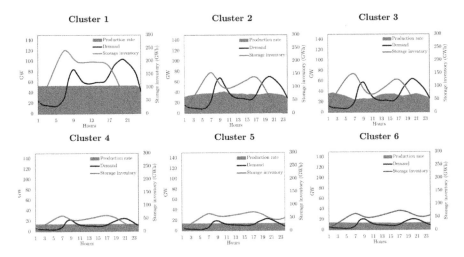

**Figure 5:** Demand, production rate and storage inventory profiles in each cluster in 2050.

The resulting model includes 299,304 equations, 178,162 continuous variables and 776 discrete variables. As it is computationally intensive, the hierarchical approach described in Section 3 is implemented to enhance solution performance. Table 2 summarises the computational statistics for each solution scheme.

**Table 2:** Computational performance of monolithic and hierarchical approaches.

| Approach | Monolithic | Hierarchical | | | |
|---|---|---|---|---|---|
| | | Step 1 | Step 2 | Step 1 | Step 2 |
| **Optimality gap limit (%)** | 5 | 5 | 5 | 1 | 1 |
| **Optimality gap (%)** | 4.74 | 1.00 | 2.04 | 1.00 | 0.88 |
| **CPU time (h)** | 15.48 | 0.83 | 0.20 | 0.87 | 3.55 |
| **Objective value (£b)** | 71.1 | 71.4 | | 71.1 | |

It can be noticed in Table 2 that hierarchical strategy leads to a feasible solution while the computational time is reduced up to 93% without significant compromise of the solution quality. For 1% optimality gap limit, the hierarchical approach can result in the same objective value with the monolithic strategy while it improves CPU time by 72%.

## 6. Concluding Remarks

In this work, an optimisation-based framework has been proposed to facilitate the investigation of design and operating decisions in hydrogen infrastructure in the UK. Reforming technologies with CCS constitute the most cost-effective low carbon alternative for hydrogen production. Hydrogen transmission is based on a pipeline network connecting most neighboring regions in GB. This work also focuses on a hierarchical solution procedure to deal with the combinatorial complexity of the resulting model. A hierarchical approach has been developed to tackle efficiently the large-scale optimisation problem and enables greater model complexity while it provides a near-optimal solution reducing computational time up to 93%.

Future research includes sector coupling of heat and power sector to provide a more holistic approach for heat decarbonisation future decisions. Moreover, the introduction of uncertainty in hydrogen supply chains is a future step for a more risk averse infrastructure strategy in parallel with the exploration of new solution approaches and decomposition techniques to deal with the high computational times.

## Acknowledgements

Authors gratefully acknowledge the financial support from Engineering and Physical Sciences Research Council (EPSRC) under the project EP/T022930/1.

## References

Agnolucci, P., Akgul, O., McDowall, W., Papageorgiou, L. G., 2013, The importance of economies of scale, transport costs and demand patterns in optimising hydrogen fuelling infrastructure: An exploration with SHIPMod (Spatial hydrogen infrastructure planning model), Int. J. Hydrog. Energy, 38, 11189–11201.

Almansoori,A., Shah,N., 2009, Design and operation of a future hydrogen supply chain: multi-period model, Int. J. Hydrog. Energy 34, 7883–7897.

Câmara, D., Pinto-Varela, T., Barbósa-Povoa, A. P., 2019, Multi-objective optimization approach to design and planning hydrogen supply chain under uncertainty: A Portugal study case, Comput. Aided Chem. Eng., 46, 1309–1314.

Charitopoulos, V. M., Fajardy, M., Chyong, C. K., Reiner, D. M., 2022, The case of 100% electrification of domestic heat in Great Britain, Faculty of Economics, University of Cambridge.

Department for Business, Energy & Industrial Strategy (BEIS), 2020, Policies for the Sixth Carbon Budget and Net Zero, www.theccc.org.uk/wp-content/uploads/2020/12/Policies-for-the-Sixth-Carbon-Budget-and-Net-Zero.pdf.

Department for Business, Energy & Industrial Strategy (BEIS), 2021, UK Hydrogen Strategy, www.gov.uk/government/publications/uk-hydrogen-strategy.

Department for Business Energy & Industrial Strategy (BEIS), 2022, Progress in reducing emissions 2022 Report to Parliament, www.theccc.org.uk/publication/2022-progress-report-to-parliament.

Guillén-Gosálbez, G., Mele, F. D., Grossmann, I. E., 2010, A bi-criterion optimization approach for the design and planning of hydrogen supply chains for vehicle use, AIChE J., 56, 650–667.

He, G., Mallapragada, D. S., Bose, A., Heuberger, C. F., Gencer, E., 2021, Hydrogen supply chain planning with flexible transmission and storage scheduling. IEEE Trans. Sustain. Energy, 12, 1730–1740.

HM Government, 2021, Net Zero Strategy: Build Back Greener, www.gov.uk/government/publications/net-zero-strategy.

Hugo, A., Rutter, P., Pistikopoulos, E.N., Amorelli, A., Zoia, G., 2005, Hydrogen infrastructure strategic planning using multi-objective optimization, Int. J. Hydrog. Energy, 30, 1523–1534.

Moreno-Benito, M., Agnolucci, P. Papageorgiou, L. G, 2017, Towards a sustainable hydrogen economy: Optimisation-based framework for hydrogen infrastructure development, Comput. Chem. Eng., 102, 110–127.

National Grid ESO, 2021, Future Energy Scenarios, www.nationalgrideso.com/future-energy/future-energy-scenarios/archive.

Ochoa Bique, A., Maia, L. K. K., Grossmann, I. E., Zondervan, E., 2021, Design of hydrogen supply chains under demand uncertainty - A case study of passenger transport in Germany, Phys. Sci. Rev., 6, 000010151520200052.

Ogumerem, G. S., Kim, C., Kesisoglou, I., Diangelakis, N. A., Pistikopoulos, E. N., 2018, A multi-objective optimization for the design and operation of a hydrogen network for transportation fuel, Chem. Eng. Res. Des., 131, 279–292.

Samsatli, S, Samsatli, N. J., 2019, The role of renewable hydrogen and inter-seasonal storage in decarbonising heat – Comprehensive optimisation of future renewable energy value chains. Appl. Energy, 233–234, 854–893.

Sunny, N., Mac Dowell, N., Shah, N., 2020, What is needed to deliver carbon-neutral heat using hydrogen and CCS?, Energy Environ. Sci., 13, 4204–4224.

W. McDowall, C. Britchfield, 2022, Decarbonising at home, www.instituteforgovernment.org.uk/publications/decarbonising-heating.

Antonis Kokossis, Michael C. Georgiadis, Efstratios N. Pistikopoulos (Eds.)
PROCEEDINGS OF THE 33rd European Symposium on Computer Aided Process Engineering
(ESCAPE33), June 18-21, 2023, Athens, Greece

# Optimal Concentrated Solar Plant (CSP) location accounting for social and environmental impact: A three-location study in Spain

José A. Luceño Sánchez[a], Mariano Martín[b], Sandro Macchietto[a]

[a]*Department of Chemical Engineering, Imperial College London South Kensington Campus, London SW7 2AZ, UK*
[b]*Departamento de Ingeniería Química y Textil. Universidad de Salamanca. Pza. Caídos 1-5, 37008 Salamanca (Spain)*
*j.luceno-sanchez@imperial.ac.uk*

## Abstract

A mathematical framework is presented for sustainable energy production via multiple concentrated solar power (CSP) plants, accounting for geographical, technical, economic, water-energy tradeoff, and social aspects. The model considers variables related to the possible location of facilities (e.g., direct normal irradiance, ambient pressure, humidity, temperature, land, and water availability), technical and economic aspects (e.g., power production, cooling technology, plant and equipment size and costs, or water consumption), and the social impact of a facility (in the form of development, unemployment, and population ratios). The problem is formulated as a multiperiod MILP in which several locations are considered. The location, design, and operation of each facility are chosen to optimize various techno-social-environmental-economic objectives. Results for a representative, three-location case study (Spain) demonstrate the approach flexibility and the importance of social and environmental aspects in the optimal solution.

**Keywords**: Concentrated Solar Plants; energy sustainability tradeoffs; optimal location; mathematical optimization; MILP.

## 1. Introduction

Renewable energy production is essential to the green transition while meeting rising energy consumption related to population growth (Scheffran et al. 2020). Solar thermal energy offers an interesting choice as solar radiation is available in any place. However, various locations present variable amount of radiation, even in the same country, and daily and seasonal variations directly affect power production (Lozano Santamaria et al. 2021). Furthermore, other important variables depend on location, such as water availability for cooling systems (Guerras and Martín 2020), which strongly affects the facility viability and sustainability (Hamiche et al. 2016), and the social impact associated with the construction of the plant (Heras and Martín 2020). Choosing the best locations for Concentrated Solar Power (CSP) plants has an important impact not only on production but also on the society and the environment, for example, on water depletion, as water is lost by evaporation in cooling towers. A detailed procedure has not been presented in the literature for the optimal CSP location selection considering simultaneously costs, technological options, social impacts, and water-energy tradeoffs. In this work, such a mathematical model is developed. Potential locations in various regions are assumed, characterized by monthly average data, to study the combined effect of techno-economic and social aspects with a sustainable scope.

## 2. Problem formulation

This work aims to optimize the location of CSP facilities for renewable energy production, accounting for aspects such as social concerns and energy-water tradeoffs. A mathematical model, divided into 5 modules, considers a number $n_{fac}$ of CSP facilities producing electricity in *Loc* locations over a horizon, *TD* divided into t periods:

-**Facility surrogate model**: the equipment in a CSP plant is grouped into sections (Figure 1). Shared variables such as mass and heat flowrates are calculated using a surrogate model based on energy and material balances as presented in previous work (Martín and Martín 2013). The equipment in each section is costed using correlations from Martín and Grossmann, 2022.

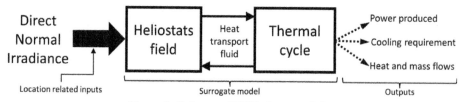

Figure 1. Scheme of CSP plant model.

-**Meeting electricity demand**: each facility produces a net electricity power, $W_{net,t,l}$ [kW], and cumulatively plants must meet an overall demand $W_{Dem,t}$ [kW]. Part of this demand may be supplied by other sources ($W_{add,t}$ [kW]), at an additional cost (Eq. 1).

$$W_{Dem,t} \leq \sum_{l=1}^{Loc}(W_{net,t,l}) + W_{add,t} \qquad \forall t \in TD \qquad (1)$$

-**Location selection**: the selection of facility locations and cooling technology for each is formulated using binary variables (Eqs. 2-3), where $y_{ff,l}$ defines the plant existence, and $y_{DC,l}$ and $y_{WC,l}$ define the choice of dry-cooling or wet-cooling, respectively.

$$\sum_{l=1}^{Loc} y_{ff,l} = n_{fac} \qquad (2)$$

$$y_{DC,l} + y_{WC,l} = y_{ff,l} \qquad \forall l \in Loc \qquad (3)$$

The number of facilities $n_{fac}$ should be lower than a pre-established maximum, while meeting constraints on the total investment and the existence of plants in specific locations (if any). Furthermore, the existence of a facility in a location *l* generating $W_{net,t,l}$ defines the corresponding water consumption (for wet-cooling) or power consumption $W_{consum,t,l}$[kW] (for dry-cooling) and related costs. All these variables are determined applying a BigM formulation in each equation, as shown in Eq. 4 for power consumption as function of the total power produced $W_{gen,t,l}$ [kW] = $W_{net,t,l}$ + $W_{consum,t,l}$:

$$W_{consum,t,l} \geq W_{gen,t,l} \cdot 0.05 - (1 - y_{DC,l}) \cdot BigM \qquad \forall l \in Loc, \forall t \in TD \qquad (4)$$

-**Water index**: water consumption $Water_{consum,t,l}$ [L/kWh], related to the use of wet-cooling technologies, is computed according to literature correlations considering location weather conditions (Guerras and Martín 2020). A relative location water impact $Walp_l$ is defined considering a location water scarcity. A water index $WI$ [€] is calculated as in Eq. 5, where $R_{L \rightarrow \in}$ [€/L] is the water cost and $OP_t$ [h] is the monthly operation time.

$$WI = \sum_{t=1}^{month} \sum_{l=1}^{Loc} [Walp_l \cdot W_{gen,t,l} \cdot OP_t \cdot Water_{consum,t,l} \cdot R_{L \rightarrow \in}] \qquad (5)$$

-**Social indices**: the social impact of a facility in a region *l* is computed considering as inputs the Gross Domestic Product ($GDP_l$), the facility cost ($Cost_{fac,l}$) and design power, the Unemployment Ratio ($UV_l$), the jobs created per MW and salary per job, and the

Relative Population ($RP_l$), as found in the literature (Heras and Martín 2020). GDP, UV and RP are scaled to their maximum values, hence are dimensionless in the range [0-1]. The sum for all regions gives overall economic, unemployment and population indices ($Social_{DR}$, $Social_{UR}$ and $Social_{UR}$), all in [€]. A combined social index (SI) [€] is defined as the sum of these indices, each with suitable weight parameters (P), as seen in Eq. 6:

$$SI = P_{DR} \cdot (Social_{DR}) + P_{UR} \cdot (Social_{UR}) + P_{RP} \cdot (Social_{RP}) \tag{6}$$

## 3. Solution procedure and Case Study

The problem is formulated as a multi-period MILP optimization, where the size and cost of a facility are evaluated at the same time as other important indices (such as social and water indices). Three representative locations in Spain (Cadiz [south], Cuenca [middle], and Bizkaia [north]) are defined as possible CSP plant locations from which the optimal one can be chosen. A year of operation is considered, with a monthly time discretization for the conceptual evaluation of the locations. The specified electricity power demand profile (Table 1) is a small fraction of Spanish non-renewable electricity production. Data for the three locations are shown in Table 2. Their direct normal irradiance (DNI) and sun hours data (as monthly averages) were obtained from an EU database (PVGIS 2022).

**Table 1.** Power demand, as monthly averages [MW] over 1 year ($W_{Dem,t}$ for t=[1,...,12]).

| Month | Jan | Feb | Mar | Apr | May | Jun | Jul | Aug | Sep | Oct | Nov | Dec |
|---|---|---|---|---|---|---|---|---|---|---|---|---|
| $W_{Dem,t}$,MW | 1.18 | 0.95 | 0.86 | 0.86 | 0.96 | 1.21 | 1.44 | 1.36 | 1.30 | 1.26 | 1.28 | 1.18 |

**Table 2.** Location-related parameters. GDP, UV, RP and WaIp are dimensionless.

| | Province [km²] | Land Cost [€/m²] | GDP | UV | RP | WaIp |
|---|---|---|---|---|---|---|
| **Cadiz** | 7,436 | 0.20 | 0.52 | 2.29 | 0.79 | 0.80 |
| **Cuenca** | 17,140 | 0.06 | 0.41 | 0.83 | 0.99 | 0.93 |
| **Bizkaia** | 2,217 | 0.14 | 0.16 | 0.44 | 0.36 | 1.00 |

Two case studies are presented: 1) a stand-alone study for each location, aiming at characterizing the optimal solution if a CSP were built there to maximize the production, using Eq. 7 as objective function, and establishing a benchmark for the results obtained later; and 2) a combined study of possible plants in all locations to meet demand, with 4 different objective functions (Eqs. 7-10). Equations 8-10 represent the minimization of facilities cost, the maximization of social impact, and the combined minimization of all aspects, respectively. In Eq. 10 (scaled to M€), the term in the first square brackets is the cost related to the power surplus and its management, the one in the second brackets is the annualized cost of facilities considering 20 years as the years of operation, and the term in the third brackets is the cost associated to any additional energy purchased to meet the demand of Table 1. A value $AddCost_{kWh \to €}$ (0.10 €/kWh) is attributed to any power surplus, and a cost penalty $Penalty_{kWh \to €}$ (5 €/kWh) for any underproduction ( $W_{add,t}$).

$$min\{-\sum_{t=1}^{month}[\sum_{l=1}^{Loc}(W_{net,t,l}) + W_{add,t}]\} \tag{7}$$

$$min\{\sum_{l=1}^{Loc} Cost_{fac,l}\} \tag{8}$$

$$min\{-SI\} \tag{9}$$

$$min\{-SI + WI - [\sum_{t=1}^{month}(W_{Dem,t} - \sum_{l=1}^{Loc} W_{neat,t,l}) \cdot OP \cdot AddCost_{kWh \to €}] + [(\sum_{l=1}^{Loc} Cost_{fac,l})/20] + [(\sum_{t=1}^{month} W_{add,t} \cdot OP \cdot Penalty_{kWh \to €})]\} \tag{10}$$

The following assumptions are made: 1) no cost or losses for transport of electricity; 2) the maximum plant area per location is 3% of a region area; 3) unless specified, the max total investment is 30M€; 3) the area of a single heliostat is 120 m²; 4) the dry-cooling cost is related to air coolers exchanger area; 5) the value of weight parameter $P_{DR}$ is 1.

## 4. Results

### 4.1. Case study 1: CSP plant in individual locations

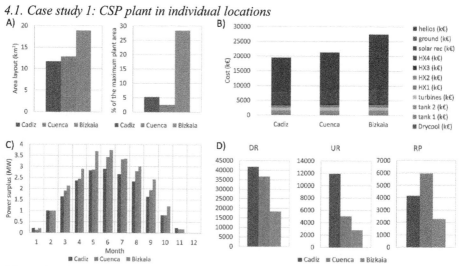

Figure 2.- Main results of Case Study 1: A) land occupation (in km² and as % of region land); B) facility cost; C) power surplus; D) Social impacts (relative to current).

Here, we wish to establish the characteristics and impact of individual CSP plants in the three locations, each built to meet the demand in Table 1. The main results of Case study 1 are collected in Figure 2, with dry-cooling systems selected for comparative purposes. Cadiz requires the lowest surface (~12 km², Figure 2.A), due to its higher values of DNI. Cuenca, with a slightly higher plant area, presents a lower fraction of the occupied surface as it is a larger region. Bizkaia (in the north) needs the largest surface, which would occupy 28% of the surface of the region. The occupied surface is related to the facility cost, which increases with the number of heliostats (Figure 2.B). The results show that, in terms of plant surface and cost alone, the best locations are in the south of the country. Cuenca, the largest province, might be preferred considering possible surface limitations and reduction in costs related to ground and heliostats field.

Regarding power production, in all locations the CSP plant is sized to meet the electricity demand in December, the most demanding month as DNI and solar hours are the lowest. The resulting larger design flowrates (i.e., heat transport and storage, thermal cycle, and cooling systems sizes) lead to substantial excess production in other months (Figure 2.C). As Bizkaia presents lower DNI values than the other regions, and the number of sun hours is also lower, the facility requires larger equipment to overcome the demand in December, giving it the largest power surplus during the rest of the year (28% higher than Cadiz) (Figure 2.C). The CSP facilities of Cuenca and especially Cadiz show reduced overproduction during the majority of the year. Figure 2.D plots the three social indices for plants in each location. Cadiz may be viewed as the best option considering the large impacts on development and employment (i.e., large differences relative to the current state in the DR and UR indices). Cuenca is the most favorable choice in terms of repopulation concerns, due to its lowest RP value. Additionally, Bizkaia seems to be the worst location for social impact as it presents the smallest improvement in all the indices.

### 4.2. Case 2: CSP plants in multiple locations and social-environmental concerns

Here, CSP plants may be built in one or more of the three locations, with combined electricity production to meet the demand in Table 1. Results are collected in Table 3, in which: Scenario 1 is the maximum power production (Eq. 7); Scenario 2 is the minimum cost (Eq. 8); Scenario 3 is the minimum total facility cost if the demand is 10 times the presented in Table 1, an unlimited budget is available, and a minimum investment of 20 M€ must be made in Bizkaia; Scenario 4 is the maximum social impact solution (Eq. 9) with $P_{UR} = P_{RP} = 0.5$; Scenario 5 is again the social impact optimization but considering different social priorities ($P_{UR} = 0.5$ and $P_{RP} = 50$); Scenario 6 is the combined water-energy-social problem (Eq. 10) with the social priorities of Scenario 4; and Scenario 7 is the same problem with the social priorities of Scenario 5.

**Table 3.** Main results - Case Study 2.

| Variable | Location | Scenario | | | | | | |
|---|---|---|---|---|---|---|---|---|
| | | 1 | 2 | 3 | 4 | 5 | 6 | 7 |
| Number of heliostats | Cadiz | 142,761 | 92,495 | 877,085 | 146,075 | 0 | 97,363 | 0 |
| | Cuenca | 0 | 0 | 0 | 0 | 129,106 | 0 | 129,106 |
| | Bizkaia | 0 | 0 | 81,370 | 0 | 0 | 0 | 0 |
| Power Design [MW] | Cadiz | 6.35 | 4.11 | 39.00 | 6.50 | 0 | 4.33 | 0 |
| | Cuenca | 0 | 0 | 0 | 0 | 6.07 | 0 | 6.07 |
| | Bizkaia | 0 | 0 | 2.70 | 0 | 0 | 0 | 0 |
| Facility cost [M$] | Cadiz | 30.00 | 20.34 | 168.86 | 30.00 | 0 | 20.71 | 0 |
| | Cuenca | 0 | 0 | 0 | 0 | 30.00 | 0 | 30.00 |
| | Bizkaia | 0 | 0 | 20.00 | 0 | 0 | 0 | 0 |
| SI | Cadiz | 19.67 | 13.30 | 111.36 | 19.70 | 0 | 13.57 | 0 |
| | Cuenca | 0 | 0 | 0 | 0 | 74.89 | 0 | 74.89 |
| | Bizkaia | 0 | 0 | 3.98 | 0 | 0 | 0 | 0 |
| WI | Cadiz | 0.1515 | 0.0982 | 0.9309 | 0 | 0 | 0 | 0 |
| | Cuenca | 0 | 0 | 0 | 0 | 0 | 0 | 0 |
| | Bizkaia | 0 | 0 | 0 | 0 | 0 | 0 | 0 |

The first two scenarios show the maximum and the minimum design capacities that could meet the demand, respectively; in both scenarios, only one facility is chosen in Cadiz with wet-cooling ($WI > 0$), because it does not have associated power consumption. These results are in line with the analysis in the previous section. In scenario 3 (demand 10 times that in Table 1, infinite budget, and a minimum of 20M€ to be invested in Bizkaia), results show two facilities (Cadiz+Bizkaia) as the optimal (but very expensive) solution, with Cadiz facility larger than Bizkaia one, due to value of DNI. In Scenario 4, Cadiz is again selected, probably related to the large impact of unemployment (UR value). In Scenario 4, increased production always increases the economic development ratio, DR, up to when some other constraint is encountered (here, on max capital cost); this results in a larger facility than in Scenario 1, but with dry-cooling; dry-cooling is chosen instead of wet-cooling because of the higher production required to meet the power consumption, which also affects UR and RP values. With higher social priority assigned to repopulation than unemployment in Scenario 5, a single plant is located in Cuenca; this shows that social policies have an important effect on the optimal decision. In Scenario 6, Eq. 10 is employed with the social priority of Scenario 4 to evaluate the combined effect of all variables. Cadiz is chosen as the optimal location, presenting a solution similar to Scenario 2. This result shows the influence of environmental and social impacts: dry-cooling is chosen to reduce WI and increase design power, which also increases social impact (as seen in Scenarios 4-5) compared to previous ones, balancing with cost reduction and production surplus. Scenario 7, with the same social priority as Scenario 5, presents the same optimal solution as Scenario 6.

## 5. Conclusions

The proposed general model for the optimal location of multiple CSP facilities, to reduce fossil-based energy dependency, incorporates geographical, technical, economic, and social components. The plant model considers technical design variables for sizing key sections and calculating water consumption. The social impact model reflects key social variables in a location. Technical, social, and environmental variables may be used individually or in combination as objective functions or within constraints. The model was addressed by a multiperiod MILP approach, and its generality and flexibility were demonstrated for a small but representative 3-location case study in Spain.

Results suggest that, based on meeting electricity demand or investment cost, the most suitable CSP facility location is Cadiz, due to the high DNI values in the south of Spain. If social indices are also taken into account, in particular, high priority is given to depopulation, the optimal location changes from Cadiz to Cuenca, with dry-cooling used instead of wet-cooling. These results show the promise of the model to be used to improve decisions about future facility distribution across countries, including social aspects.

## Acknowledgments

The authors acknowledge Imperial College London and University of Salamanca for access to scientific sources and databases. The authors acknowledge the Margarita Salas grant, co-funded by the European NextGenerationEU Fund, Spanish "Plan de Recuperación, Transformación y Resiliencia" Fund, Spanish Ministry of Universities, and University of Salamanca ("Ayudas para la recualificación del Sistema Universitario español 2021-2022"), to JA Luceño Sánchez.

## References

Guerras, L. S.; Martín, M. (2020). On the Water Footprint in Power Production: Sustainable Design of Wet Cooling Towers. Appl. Energy, 263, 114620.

Hamiche, A.M.; Stambouli, A.B.; Flazi, S. (2016). A review of the water-energy nexus. Renew. Sust. Energy Rev. 65, 319-331.

Heras, J.; Martín, M. (2020). Social Issues in the Energy Transition: Effect on the Design of the New Power System. Appl. Energy, 278, 115654.

Lozano Santamaria, F.; Luceño, J.A.; Martín, M.; Macchietto, S. (2021). Optimal Operation and Cleaning Scheduling of Air Coolers in Concentrated Solar Power Plants. Computers and Chemical Engineering 150, 107312.

Martín, L.; Martín, M. (2013). Optimal year-round operation of a concentrated solar energy plant in the south of Europe. Appl. Therm. Eng. 59, 627-633.

Martín, M.; Grossmann, I.E. (2022). Mathematical modeling for renewable process design, in: Sustainable Design for Renewable Processes. Elsevier, pp. 35–100.

PVGIS, Photovoltaic Geographical Information System. Interactive tools. Last accessed Oct 2022. https://re.jrc.ec.europa.eu/pvg_tools/en/

Scheffran, J.; Felkers, M.; Froese, R. (2020) Economic Growth and the Global Energy Demand. In Green Energy to Sustainability; Wiley, pp 1–44.

Antonis Kokossis, Michael C. Georgiadis, Efstratios N. Pistikopoulos (Eds.)
PROCEEDINGS OF THE 33rd European Symposium on Computer Aided Process Engineering
(ESCAPE33), June 18-21, 2023, Athens, Greece
© 2023 Elsevier B.V. All rights reserved. http://dx.doi.org/10.1016/B978-0-443-15274-0.50484-4

# Inventory data generation for prospective lifecycle design through process modeling of energy recovery from waste plastics

Shoma Fujii[a], Yuichiro Kanematsu[b], Yasunori Kikuchi[abc]

[a]*Institute for Future Initiatives, The University of Tokyo, 113-8654 7-3-1 Hongo, Bunkyo-ku, Tokyo, Japan*
[b]*Presidential endowed chair for "Platinum society", The University of Tokyo, 113-8656 7-3-1 Hongo, Bunkyo-ku, Tokyo, Japan*
[c]*Department of chemical system engineering, The University of Tokyo, 113-8656 7-3-1 Hongo, Bunkyo-ku, Tokyo, Japan*
*shoma.fujii@ifi.u-tokyo.ac.jp*

## Abstract

A novel energy recovery processes for waste plastics has been proposed, which consists of surface treatment to boilers at waste incineration facilities to increase operating rates and waste heat recovery to generate cold heat. In order to propose the best combination of technologies and to conduct a prospective life cycle assessment that feeds back into technology development, the technologies under development were reflected in a process flow model. Preventing fouling of the boiler tubes leads to less frequent maintenance and longer operating hours. The increase in operating hours results in a slight increase in total annual power generation, but if the annual waste input remains constant, the daily waste throughput will decrease, resulting in lower power output and lower boiler exhaust gas temperatures. Waste heat recovery to generate cold heat in absorption chillers can be done either onsite or offsite, and hot water, steam, and hot air were considered as heat recovery media. The results show that the off-site heat supply is reduced by half to one-fourth compared to the on-site heat supply.

**Keywords**: circular economy, thermal energy storage, cold heat, power generation

## 1. Introduction

Plastics recycling is attracting attention as a way to realize the circular economy (Schwarz *et al.*, 2021). Plastics circulation should be implemented in a cascade of advanced sorting, material recycling, chemical recycling, and finally energy recovery. A computer-aided process engineering that reflects the emerging technical information supports the system design of plastics circulation by optimal combination of these processes from the lifecycle viewpoints (Volk *et al.*, 2022). Each recycling process has various problems, and measures are being considered to solve them. As for the energy recovery process, the operating rate has decreased due to fouling of the boiler tubes and the heat utilization rate has decreased due to the lack of nearby heat demand. A new high-efficient energy recovery process (NEDO, 2022) that combines improvement of operation rate through surface treatment on boiler tubes (Naganuma *et al.*, 2022) and cold heat generation (Isojima *et al.*, 2020) for logistics demands through waste heat recovery was proposed. The objective of this study is to develop a process flow model of above novel energy recovery process for waste plastics circulation, and to generate an inventory for life cycle assessment for designing a best mix of plastics circulation strategy.

## 2. Material and methodology

### 2.1. *Process modeling*

Figure 1 shows the combined process of waste incineration and energy recovery. Water-containing municipal solid waste (MSW) is incinerated in a boiler, the water supplied to the boiler is boiled, and the steam generated is introduced to power turbine to generate electricity. For more efficient energy recovery from waste incineration plant, two measures are being considered: one on the high-temperature side to improve power generation and operating rate, and the other on the low-temperature side to recover waste heat. For high-temperature side, when wastes containing plastics are incinerated, gases containing chlorine and sulfur, as well as ash with low melting points, adhere to the boiler tubes leading decrease in heat transfer coefficient. Thermal spray treatment of boiler tube surfaces can reduce ash adhesion and increase plant operation rate (Naganuma et al., 2022). For low-temperature side, two types of heat recovery methods for boiler exhaust gas are considered in this study: on-site and off-site cold heat recovery (Kimura et al., 2022). In the on-site cold heat generation process (Fig 1 (a)), the heat capacity of the exhaust gas is recovered as water or steam in a heat exchanger and used directly as a heat source in an absorption chiller to generate sub-zero brine, then sub-zero ice slurry is generated under sub cooling condition in an ice generator by heat exchanging with cold brine, and cold ice is produced through a releasing subcooling and a separation process. In the off-site cold heat generation process (Fig 1 (b)), a thermal energy storage and transport system is required. Adsorbent is employed as a heat storage medium, and heat is charged by drying it with air heated by waste heat, transported by truck to a remote cold demand, and supplied to the heat source of an absorption chiller by adsorbing ambient moist air. There are two methods to recover waste heat. Assuming that the heat capacity of the exhaust gas of boiler is recovered by the outside air through a heat exchanger, the hot air generated is directly used to dry the adsorbent (i.e., heat charging). The other method of waste heat recovery is to generate hot water or steam by heat exchange with exhaust gas of boiler as in the on-site heat recovery process. After hot water or steam generation, hot air is generated through a heat exchange process. This process requires two heat exchangers (one to recover waste heat to generate hot water or steam and the other to generate hot air), but the generated hot water or steam can also be used directly as a heat source for an absorption chiller onsite, thus achieving a combination of on-site and off-site heat recovery.

The system is assumed to be retrofitted to a typical waste incineration plant with an energy recovery process. First, to model MSW incineration with only a typical power generation process, without heat recovery process and power generation enhancement measures, the heat exchange process in the boiler is modeled by the specific heat and heating value of the combustion gas and the heat capacity of the feed water. The moisture content of the input waste was assumed to be 45%. The unknown parameters of mass flow of waste input and intake air were adjusted until the target values of 250 °C boiler outlet temperature and 10% oxygen concentration in the final flue gas were reached, and the UA (overall heat transfer coefficient) value of the boiler was calculated. The energy balance of the heat exchanger was divided into the phase change section and other sections, and the phase change section was divided into 10 sections and the UA of each section was calculated using the logarithmic mean temperature difference method.

Next, a case was assumed in which fouling is prevented by surface treatment to the boiler tubes, thereby extending the operating period. Retrofit of the existing boiler was assumed by fixing the calculated UA values. Since the annual waste input to the boiler remains the same before and after the introduction of the energy recovery process, the hourly waste input would decrease if the boiler tubes were surface treated for an extended operating period of one year. The mass flow rate of steam for power generation was recalculated to maintain the UA value under the updated waste input conditions, and the amount of power generation and cold heat recovery were evaluated.

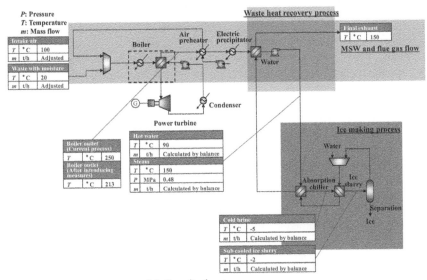

(a) On-site heat recovery process

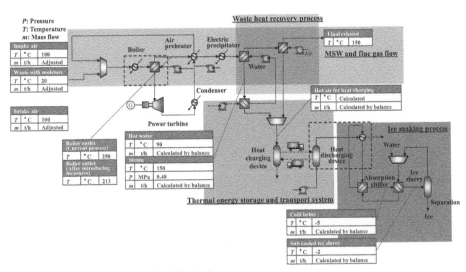

(b) Off-site heat recovery process

Figure 1 Process flow of waste incineration plant with heat recovery process

2.2. *Case study*

As a case study, a case at a steam flow rate of 25 t/h in a boiler was evaluated. It is assumed that the boiler will be operated for 9 months per year, with an extended operating period of 1 month due to surface treatment to prevent fouling of the boiler tubes. The heat transfer coefficient was assumed to be constant during the operation period, but it is possible to simulate the effect of decrease in the heat transfer coefficient by changing the UA.

In the waste heat recovery process, it is assumed that the heat is recovered as saturated steam at 0.48 MPa (saturated temperature of 150 °C) for recovery with steam case, and as hot water at atmospheric pressure of 90 °C for recovery with hot water case. The minimum temperature approach of the heat exchanger for the production of hot air for thermal energy storage system was assumed to be 5 °C. The absorption chiller is a two-stage refrigerator capable of producing sub-zero brine, and it is assumed to produce brine at -5 °C based on the literature, with a COP (Coefficient of performance) of 0.2 considering waste heat input (Kimura et al., 2022). The auxiliary power of the absorption chiller was assumed to be 10% of the cooling capacity. In the ice slurry production, the ice fraction in the ice slurry was assumed to be 30%, and the auxiliary power of the absorption chiller was assumed to be 20% of the cooling capacity. For thermal energy storage system, the equilibrium adsorption water uptake before (4%) and after adsorption (23%) was calculated using adsorption isotherms (Miyahara et al., 2020) and the heat storage density was calculated from the difference between the equilibrium adsorption water uptake and the heat of adsorption (Miyahara et al., 2020). The gas temperature at the outlet of the heat charging device was set to 60 °C, and 80% of the difference from the inlet temperature was assumed to be stored. Heat discharging amount was assumed to be 80% of the heat storage density (Fujii et al., 2022). The pressure drop in both the heat charging and discharging devices was assumed to be 1 kPa, and the efficiency of the blower that injects hot air into the devices was assumed to be 70%. These parameters are subject to sensitivity analysis in the feedback to design based on life cycle thinking in future work.

As evaluation indicators, the increase in power generation, the amount of cold heat generation, the amount of ice slurry produced, and the additional energy input (power for ice slurry production, heat storage, and transportation) are evaluated. These indicators can be incorporated into the next stage of this study, a prospective life cycle assessment for design.

## 3. Result and discussion

The results of power and cold heat generation, auxiliary energy consumption of all processes were shown in Fig. 2. As a result, the boiler air excess ratio was about 1.7. The daily waste input resulted in 250 t/d. The power output was about 2,100 kW, resulting in an annual output of 12,200 MWh. The daily waste input was then reduced to 222 t/d when the operating time was extended by one month by preventing fouling of the boiler tubes. Adjusting the steam flow rate to fix the UA value of the boiler reduced the power output to 1,950 kW, but the extended operation period resulted in a slightly higher annual power output of 12,840 MWh. In addition, the temperature of exhaust gas at the boiler outlet was reduced from 250 °C to 214 °C. Despite the decrease in the daily waste input, the UA value of the boiler was kept at the previous value for retrofit, which resulted in a large heat transfer area relative to the heat exchange rate and lower temperature of boiler outlet. In the heat recovery part, the difference between steam and hot water as a heat source to the absorption chiller was not taken into account in the on-site case, resulting in a cold heat production of approximately 213 kW in both cases. On the other hand, in the off-site case, the heat source that can be input to the absorption chiller at the demand site is smaller than in the on-site case, because the heat capacity of the exhaust gas of the carrier gas cannot be recovered at the heat charging and discharging devices. When the exhaust gas from the waste incineration was directly exchanged for hot air to the heat charging device, the ice-making capacity was 124 kW. If the heat is recovered with steam or hot water, an additional heat exchange process with air for heat storage is required, which further reduces the ice-making capacity compared to the case where the heat is recovered directly from the exhaust gas with hot air. The ice-making capacity is 110 kW when heat is recovered with steam, and in the case of heat recovery with hot water, the amount of heat that can be transported is further reduced because the temperature of hot air obtained through heat exchange is about 60 °C lower than that of steam case, resulting in an ice-making capacity of 64 kW.

These results can be reflected in a prospective life cycle assessment as inventory data to provide feedback for each technology development. Since the UA values of the boiler and heat exchanger are also quantified, the heat transfer area can be calculated by giving the heat transfer coefficient, and the manufacturing and disposal environmental loads of each device can be estimated.

In this case, the measures taken to prevent fouling of the boiler tubes did not result in a significant increase in power generation. However, the heat transfer coefficient decreases with time from the start of operation in the case of the non-surface treatment, so the power output of 2,100 kW in the case of the non-surface treatment gradually decreases until maintenance is performed. The annual power output may be significantly increased by the surface treatment to boiler tubes. Taking into account this change in heat transfer coefficient based on experimental data is the next step.

In order to preemptively evaluate technologies that are still under development, uncertain technology information is reflected in the process modeling, and it is important to be able to make comparisons in each process and to know the approximate contribution of the new process rather than absolute values.

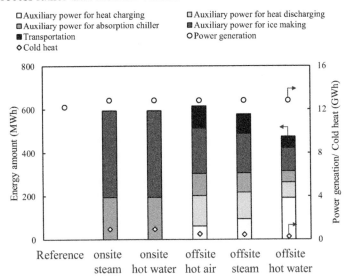

Figure 2 Results of power and cold heat generation, auxiliary energy consumption of each process (Process without any measures, onsite, offsite and hot air)

## 4. Conclusion

This study modeled process flow of waste incineration plant including waste plastics to generate inventory data of novel energy recovery process combined with surface treatment to boiler tubes and waste heat recovery to generate cold heat via absorption chiller, as one of the measures of waste plastics circulation strategy. As a result, total power generation could be slightly increased by extending operation period due to prevention of boiler tubes fouling. Waste heat could produce cold heat for both onsite and offsite demand, but in the offsite case, the amount of cold heat generation is reduced by one-fourth compared to the on-site heat supply.

## Acknowledgement

This work was supported by e New Energy and Industrial Technology Development Organization (NEDO, Grant number JPNP20012), JSPS KAKENHI Grant-in-Aid for Early-Career Scientists (Grant Number 22K18061), JST COI-NEXT (Grant Number JPMJPF2003), JST PRESTO (Grant Number JPMJPR2278) and the Environment Research and Technology Development Fund (Grant Number JPMEERF20213R01) of the Environmental Restoration and Conservation Agency of Japan. The activities of the Presidential Endowed Chair for "Platinum Society" at the University of Tokyo are supported by the KAITEKI Institute Incorporated, Mitsui Fudosan Corporation, Shin-Etsu Chemical Co., ORIX Corporation, Sekisui House, Ltd., East Japan Railway Company, and Toyota Tsusho Corporation.

## References

S. Fujii, T. Nakagaki, Y. Kanematsu, Y. Kikuchi, 2022, Prospective life cycle assessment for designing mobile thermal energy storage system utilizing zeolite, Journal of Cleaner Production, 365, 132592

S. Isojima, H. Noda, M. Taninno, 2020, Crystallization Temperature of the Working Fluid LiBr - H2O - 1-Propanol for Absorption Refrigerator to Generate Below-Zero Brine (in Japanese), Proceedings of the JSRAE Annual Conference, 2020, ROMBUNNO.E213

T. Kimura, H. Hatano, H. Noda, T. Inada, M. Tanino, H. Naganuma, M. Hotta, I. Naruse, 2022, High-efficient energy recovery of waste plastics Part 2- Effective utilization of low temperature waste heat (in Japanese), Kagaku-sochi, 64, 1, 48-54

H. Miyahara, M. Suzuki, S. Matsuda, K. Morimoto, K. Mampuku, Y. Kawakami, H. Nawa, K. Yamauchi, K. Matsunaga, M. Tanino, 2020, Development of Open-type Adsorption Thermal Storage Heat Pump System Applying HAS-Clay Part 2 Hydration Heat Caused by Water Vapor Adsorption on Low-Temperature Regenerative Heat Storage Material (in Japanese), Transactions of the Society of Heating, Air-conditioning and Sanitary Engineers of Japan, 285, 1-8

H. Naganuma, I. Naruse, M. Hotta, H. Hatano, H. Noda, T. Inada, M. Tanino, 2022, High-efficient energy recovery of waste plastics Part 1- Effective utilization of high temperature waste heat (in Japanese), Kagaku-sochi, 64, 1, 43-47

NEDO New Energy and Indsutrial Technology Development Organization, 2022, Innovative Plastic Resource Circulation Process Technology Development, https://www.nedo.go.jp/english/activities/activities_ZZJP_100179.html (Access Sep-27, 2022)

A.E. Schwarz, T.N. Ligthart, D. Godoi Bizarro, P. De Wild, B. Vreugdenhil, T. van Harmelen, 2021, Plastic recycling in a circular economy; determining environmental

R.Volk,C. Stallkamp J. J. Steins, S. P. Yogish, R. C. Müller, D. Stapf, F. Schultmann, 2021, Techno-economicassessmentandcomparisonofdifferentplasticrecyclingpathways, Waste Management, 25, 5, 1318-1337

Antonis Kokossis, Michael C. Georgiadis, Efstratios N. Pistikopoulos (Eds.)
PROCEEDINGS OF THE 33rd European Symposium on Computer Aided Process Engineering
(ESCAPE33), June 18-21, 2023, Athens, Greece

# Process intensification in a fixed bed reactor for a small-scale process in the stranded assets

Adrian R. Irhamna[a] and George M. Bollas[a]

[a] *Department of Chemical and Biomolecular Engineering, UTC Institute for Advanced Systems Engineering, University of Connecticut, 159 Discovery Dr, Storrs, CT, 06269, USA.*

## Abstract

The implementation of small-scale processes on stranded fossil fuel assets could alleviate the loss of valuable energy resources and the environmental damage caused by leaks of greenhouse gases. However, the current state of conventional chemical processes is not economical on a small scale. This study explores intensified fixed-bed reactor designs for small-scale hydrogen production and methane emissions treatment in petroleum-stranded assets. The reactor uses the chemical-looping principle, as it is packed with a metal oxygen carrier capable of performing redox and catalytic reactions. The reactor was designed following a dynamic optimization and a reactor intensification strategy. Performance metrics of each optimally designed reactor were then evaluated at operating conditions that were optimized in terms of manipulated variables and scheduling. The reforming reactor produces hydrogen from stranded natural gas with $H_2/CO$ ratio of 2.15 at the reforming stage, and >98% nitrogen stream at the oxidation stage. On the other hand, the flare emissions treatment reactor converts all the methane emissions in the flare exhaust stream without supply of external heat.

**Keywords**: Small-scale process, fixed-bed reactor, process intensification, dynamic modeling and optimization.

## 1. Background

Stranded assets are small fossil fuel reservoirs that cannot be processed due to their remote location, distribution challenges, small capacity, or the associated regulatory uncertainty. Specifically, stranded natural gas is, typically, flared or vented during oil recovery. Moreover, as the world transitions away from greenhouse gas-emitting energy production, more stranded assets will be generated and could yield losses of up to 1.4 trillion USD (Semieniuk et al., 2022). Abandoned assets can, also, cause environmental damage due to leakages of greenhouse gases, such as methane, generated by an improper shutdown of production and distribution systems. Approximately an average methane emission factor of 6.0 g/h was reported for more than 4 million abandoned oil and gas wells in the U.S. and Canada (Williams et al., 2021). Therefore, stakeholders consider small-scale process alternatives for stranded fossil fuel assets to minimize future financial implications due to greenhouse gas emissions and misuse of resources. The challenge, however, is that the current state of the art in small-scale process systems engineering is not economically viable and lacks efficiency.

This study explores the use of a fixed-bed reactor for small-scale applications in stranded assets utilizing the chemical looping principle and dynamic optimization as a process intensification strategy (Baharudin et al., 2021; Tan et al., 2021). A fixed-bed reactor is selected due to its simplicity, flexibility, and potential modularity. As the oxygen carrier does not circulate, the redox process is determined by switching between alternating fuel and air feed streams. Using a fixed-bed reactor also eliminates the potential for attrition and breakage of oxygen carriers, a common problem in fluidization reactors. As a result, the life cycle of the oxygen carrier is extended, and maintenance costs are reduced. The heart of the proposed process concept lies in the ability of the oxygen carrier to promote gas-solid reactions, assist the catalytic reactions, store the heat generated during the oxidation stage, and release it during the reduction/reforming stages. In this work, two reactor designs are proposed: one to handle methane emissions from oil & gas flaring systems; and one to produce hydrogen and nitrogen for liquid ammonia production from stranded natural gas. We study this concept with high-fidelity dynamic models of the reactors, for which kinetic and transport parameters were validated previously.

## 2. Methodology

### 2.1. Reactor model and process description

A 1D heterogeneous fixed bed reactor model was developed to account for the mass, energy, and momentum balances of the solid and fluid phases. The details of the equations used for reactor modeling are documented in (Han et al., 2013; Han & Bollas, 2016). Kinetic correlations, extensively studied by (Han et al., 2016a, 2016b), were used to predict reactions occurring over Ni-based oxygen carriers. The chemical reactions and kinetic expressions are documented in (Irhamna & Bollas, 2023). The model explores the potential small-scale utilization of stranded gas assets specifically for improving flaring activities and in-situ reforming of stranded natural gas. Fig. 1 shows the process flow diagrams for two applications.

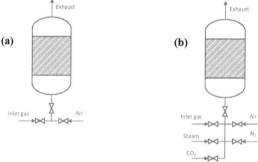

Figure 1: Process diagram of reactor used in this study: (a) flaring; and (b) reforming applications

In flaring applications, the reactor is used as a cleaning unit at the exit of the flare, ensuring no methane is released into the atmosphere. The reactor takes the exhaust gas from the flaring unit as feed and converts the unreacted methane to carbon dioxide to exploit the significant difference in the greenhouse gas potential of these two gases. Based on the process experienced by the oxygen carrier, there are two main stages: reduction and oxidation. The reduction stage occurs as the oxygen carrier reacts with methane and other reducing gases via gas-solid reactions. The reactions occur using the lattice oxygen of the oxygen carrier and heat stored in the bed from the previous stage of exothermic oxidation. As the reduction continues, oxygen in the bed eventually becomes scarce, and the temperature drops, leading to lower methane conversion. A brief period of air flow is introduced to regenerate oxygen and increase the bed temperature, which is coined as the oxidation stage in the reactor. The airflow stops when the bed has sufficient oxygen and heat for methane oxidation. The reactor then switches back to the reduction stage.

In the reforming application, the reactor is designed to convert natural gas from the stranded wellhead to syngas. The reactor takes natural gas from the wellhead as the main feed and operates in three stages: reduction, reforming, and oxidation. Initially, the oxygen carrier is reduced by the feed gas during the reduction stage to provide the catalyst for reforming natural gas. Then reforming commences as the reactor feed switches to steam and $CO_2$. Overall, the proposed scheme accomplishes tri-reforming of methane in one reactor and three stages. Both the reduction and reforming stages leverage the heat stored in the bed from the preceding oxidation cycle. As reforming progresses, the bed temperature drops, resulting in lower fuel conversion. When this happens, the feed gas is replaced by air, commencing the oxidation stage. During the oxidation stage, the bed temperature increases due to heat generated by oxygen carrier oxidation. The stage switches back to reduction when the sufficient heat, required for the following cycle, is stored in the bed.

We used typical flared gas flowrate reported in (Sherrick et al., 2011) and emission factors reported in (E & P Forum, 1994) to estimate flared gas composition for flaring application. Natural gas composition reported in (Kidnay et al., 2020) was used as feedstock for reforming application. Table 1 presents the reactor dimensions and operating conditions used for each flaring and reforming application, which were the result of dynamic optimization discussed in the following section. Dynamic simulation and optimization of each reactor design was conducted in the equation-oriented modeling language gPROMS (Process Systems Enterprise, 2021).

Table 1: Operating conditions of the fixed bed reactor for flaring and reforming applications

| Reactor Parameters | Flaring | | Reforming | | |
|---|---|---|---|---|---|
| Reactor diameter (m) | 10 | | 0.6 | | |
| Reactor length (m) | 1.5 | | 5 | | |
| Operating pressure (bar) | 1 | | 1 | | |
| Inlet gas composition (% mole) | RED | OX | RED | REFORM | OX |
| - $CH_4$ | 0.0030 | 0.0024 | 0.071 | 0.1609 | - |
| - $H_2O$ | 0.1810 | 0.1448 | - | 0.5802 | - |
| - CO | 0.0005 | 0.0004 | - | - | - |
| - $CO_2$ | 0.0910 | 0.0728 | 0.429 | 0.2498 | - |
| - $N_2$ | 0.7237 | 0.7390 | 0.4995 | - | 0.7805 |
| - $O_2$ | - | 0.0401 | - | - | 0.209 |
| - Ar | - | - | - | - | 0.009 |
| Temperature of inlet gas (°C) | 650 | | 600 | | |
| Temperature of inlet air (°C) | 307 | | 600 | | |
| Volumetric flowrate (m^3/s) | 40 | 54 | 0.375 | 0.525 | 0.525 |
| Ni percentage in oxygen carriers (%) | 16 | | 8.0 | | |
| Duration of each stages (s) | 200 | 60 | 210 | 190 | 190 |

## 2.2. Dynamic Reactor Optimization

Reactor intensification is accomplished by simultaneously optimizing reactor admissible inputs and scheduling. The objective function, design variables, and optimization formulation for the flaring and reforming applications are shown in Table 2. The dynamic optimization problem was solved in gPROMS using control vector parametrization and single shooting (Process Systems Enterprise, 2021).

In Table 2, $\mathbf{f}$ is the set of differential-algebraic equations (DAEs) representing the reactor model; $\mathbf{x}$ is the vector of state variables (i.e., mass, temperature, and pressure); $\mathbf{u}$ is the piecewise constant functions of the admissible inputs; $\boldsymbol{\theta}$ is the system parameters including kinetic constants, describing the reactivity of oxygen carrier; $F$ is the molar flowrate of each species; $T$ is the bed temperature in $z$ direction; $P$ is the total pressure of the reactor in $z$ direction.

Table 2: Dynamic optimization problem formulation for the two reactor applications studied.

| Flaring | Reforming |
|---|---|
| Objective function, $\gamma$<br><br>$$\gamma = \int_{t_0}^{t_f} \frac{F_{CO_2,out}}{F_{CH_4,in}} dt$$ | Objective function, $\gamma$<br><br>$$\gamma = \int_{t_f}^{t_f} \frac{F_{H_2,out}}{F_{CH_4,in}} dt$$ |
| Design Variables, $\boldsymbol{\phi}$<br>• Feed air temperature<br>• Air-to-Flared gas Ratio<br>• Reduction & oxidation time interval<br>• Oxygen carrier loading | Design Variables, $\boldsymbol{\phi}$<br>• Temperature of the feed gas<br>• Reduction, reforming, & oxidation interval<br>• Oxygen carrier loading |
| Optimization Problem<br><br>$\max\limits_{\phi \in \boldsymbol{\phi}} \gamma$<br>s.t. $\mathbf{f}(\dot{\mathbf{x}}(t), \mathbf{x}(t), \mathbf{u}(t), \boldsymbol{\theta}, t) = 0,$<br>$\quad \mathbf{f_0}(\dot{\mathbf{x}}(t_0), \mathbf{x}(t_0), \mathbf{u}(t_0), \boldsymbol{\theta}, t_0) = 0,$<br>$\quad T(t_i, z) - 1100\ ^\circ C \leq 0, \forall\, t \in [t_0, t_f],$<br>$\quad 700^\circ C - \frac{1}{L}\int_{z=0}^{z=L} T(t_i, z)\, dz \leq 0, \forall\, t \in$<br>$\quad [t_0, t_f],$<br>$\quad 100\ ^\circ C - T_{air} \leq 0,$<br>$\quad T_{air} - 427\ ^\circ C \leq 0,$<br>$\quad \Delta P(t)/P(t, z=0) - 15\% \leq 0, \forall\, t \in$<br>$\quad [t_0, t_f],$ | Optimization Problem<br><br>$\max\limits_{\phi \in \boldsymbol{\phi}} \gamma$<br>s.t. $\mathbf{f}(\dot{\mathbf{x}}(t), \mathbf{x}(t), \mathbf{u}(t), \boldsymbol{\theta}, t) = 0,$<br>$\quad \mathbf{f_0}(\dot{\mathbf{x}}(t_0), \mathbf{x}(t_0), \mathbf{u}(t_0), \boldsymbol{\theta}, t_0) = 0,$<br>$\quad 95\% - X_{CH_4} \leq 0, \quad \forall\, t \in [t_0, t_f],$<br>$\quad T(t_i, z) - 1100\ ^\circ C \leq 0, \forall\, t \in [t_0, t_f],$<br>$\quad 700^\circ C - \frac{1}{L}\int_{z=0}^{z=L} T(t_i, z)\, dz \leq 0, \forall\, t \in$<br>$\quad [t_0, t_f],$ |

## 3. Result and Analysis

Fig. 2 shows the optimal reactor performance for the flaring applications at a cyclic steady state. Near-complete methane conversion (> 98%) is achieved at the reduction and oxidation stages. Fig. 2(b) confirms that methane is practically undetectable at the reactor exit. The flue gas has a constant exit temperature of 690 °C despite the cyclic steady state. Fig. 2(c) shows that the temperature gradients exist only in the first 20% of the reactor length. The heat front is pushed towards the end of the reactor, creating a relatively uniform temperature distribution near the reactor exit. Fig. 2(d) shows that the NiO form of the oxygen carrier dominates, allowing for sufficient oxygen to oxidize the methane feed. The Ni-NiO reaction occurs at the first 20% of the reactor length, aligned with the temperature gradients.

Fig. 3 shows the optimal performance of the reactor for the reforming application at a cyclic steady state. Fig. 3(a) shows that high methane conversion (> 95%) is achieved at the reduction and reforming stages. At reduction, methane conversion occurs in the first 20-40% of the reactor length, while at reforming, the conversion occurs further down the reactor, between 40-80% of the reactor length. Fig. 3(b) shows that the reactor produces different gases in each stage. Hydrogen produced during the reforming stage accounts for 30% of the exit gas, with a $H_2/CO$ ratio of 2.15. Moreover, during oxidation, the reactor produces an exit stream with a very high nitrogen concentration. The production of nitrogen and hydrogen in each reactor stage provides an opportunity for small-scale ammonia production (Burrows et al., 2021; Burrows & Bollas, 2022). Despite the different types and compositions of the exit gas, the reactor exit temperature is relatively constant, with minor fluctuations around 820 °C. Fig. 3(c) shows that temperature gradients occur in the first 70% of the reactor length. The bed temperature increases during oxidation due to the exothermic reactions of this stage. The heat front is then pushed and stored at about 60% of the reactor length. Afterward, the reactor front undergoes a temperature drop during reduction and reforming, as determined by the endothermic reactions of these stages. Despite these temperature gradients, the temperature bed is relatively uniform near the end of the reactor. Fig. 3(d) shows that Ni-NiO reactions mainly occur at the first 70% of reactor length at the oxidation and reduction stages. Ni form dominates the oxygen carrier bed during reforming, providing sufficient catalytic activity for the reforming reactions.

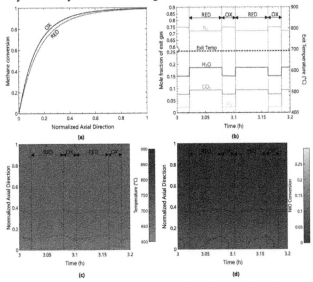

Figure 2: Reactor performance of optimized reactor design and control at cyclic steady state for the flaring application: (a) methane conversion at the end of Reduction and Oxidation stages; (b) exit mole fraction and temperature of the the reactor; (c) temperature contour plot of the reactor bed; and (d) NiO conversion contour of reactor bed – conversion of 0 refers to NiO and conversion of 1 refers to Ni. RED = Reduction stage; OX = Oxidation stage.

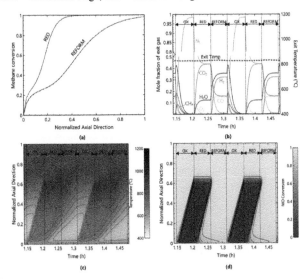

Figure 3: Reactor performance of optimized reactor design and control at cyclic steady state for the reforming application: (a) methane conversion at the end of Reduction and Reforming stages; (b) exit mole fraction and temperature of the reactor; (c) temperature contour plot of reactor bed; and

(d) NiO conversion contour of reactor bed – conversion of 0 refers to NiO and conversion of 1 refers to Ni. RED = Reduction stage; REFORM = Reforming stage; OX = Oxidation stage.

## 4. Conclusions

Conceptual small-scale methane processing options were studied for lean methane from natural gas flaring and hydrogen production from stranded gas. In the flaring application, the intensified reactor converts more than 98% of the methane in the flue gas. In the reforming application, the intensified reactor converts more than 95% methane and produces syngas with a $H_2/CO$ ratio of 2.15. The reactor also produces a stream rich in $N_2$ during oxidation, which could enable small-scale liquid ammonia synthesis.

## References

Baharudin, L., Indera L, A. A., Watson, M. J., & Yip, A. C. K. (2021). Process intensification in multifunctional reactors: A review of multi-functionality by catalytic structures, internals, operating modes, and unit integrations. *Chemical Engineering and Processing - Process Intensification*, *168*(July), 108561. https://doi.org/10.1016/j.cep.2021.108561

Burrows, L., & Bollas, G. M. (2022). Stability Assessment of Small-Scale Distributed Ammonia Production Systems. *Industrial and Engineering Chemistry Research*. https://doi.org/10.1021/acs.iecr.2c00631

Burrows, L., Gao, P. X., & Bollas, G. M. (2021). Thermodynamic feasibility analysis of distributed chemical looping ammonia synthesis. *Chemical Engineering Journal*, *426*(May), 131421. https://doi.org/10.1016/j.cej.2021.131421

E & P Forum. (1994). *Methods for Estimating Atmospheric Emissions from E&P Operations. The Oil Industry International Exploration & Production Forum Report No 2.59/197.*

Han, L., & Bollas, G. M. (2016). Chemical-looping combustion in a reverse-flow fixed bed reactor. *Energy*, *102*, 669–681. https://doi.org/10.1016/j.energy.2016.02.057

Han, L., Zhou, Z., & Bollas, G. M. (2013). Heterogeneous modeling of chemical-looping combustion. Part 1: Reactor model. *Chemical Engineering Science*, *104*, 233–249. https://doi.org/10.1016/j.ces.2013.09.021

Han, L., Zhou, Z., & Bollas, G. M. (2016a). Model-Based Analysis of Chemical-Looping Combustion Experiments. Part I: Structural Identifiability of Kinetic Models for NiO Reduction. *AIChE Journal*, *62*(7), 2419–2431. https://doi.org/10.1002/aic

Han, L., Zhou, Z., & Bollas, G. M. (2016b). Model-Based Analysis of Chemical-Looping Combustion Experiments. Part II: Optimal Design of CH4-NiO Reduction Experiments. *AIChE Journal*, *62*(7), 2432–2446. https://doi.org/10.1002/aic

Irhamna, A. R., & Bollas, G. M. (2023). Intensified reactor for lean methane emissions treatment. *AIChE Journal*, 1–40. https://doi.org/10.1002/aic.18040

Kidnay, A. J. ., Parrish, W. R. ., & McCartney, D. G. (2020). *Fundamentals of Natural Gas Processing*. CRC Press, Taylor & Francis Group. https://www.ptonline.com/articles/how-to-get-better-mfi-results

Process Systems Enterprise. (2021). *gPROMS*. www.psenterprise.com/products/gproms

Semieniuk, G., Holden, P. B., Mercure, J. F., Salas, P., Pollitt, H., Jobson, K., Vercoulen, P., Chewpreecha, U., Edwards, N. R., & Viñuales, J. E. (2022). Stranded fossil-fuel assets translate to major losses for investors in advanced economies. *Nature Climate Change*, *12*(6), 532–538. https://doi.org/10.1038/s41558-022-01356-y

Sherrick, J. J., Mueller, G. R., & Loos, K. R. (2011). *Texas Commission on Environmental Quality Work Assignment 5 Draft Flare Waste Gas Flow Rate and Composition.*

Tan, J., Ji, Y. N., Deng, W. S., & Su, Y. F. (2021). Process intensification in gas/liquid/solid reaction in trickle bed reactors: A review. *Petroleum Science*, *18*(4), 1203–1218. https://doi.org/10.1016/j.petsci.2021.07.007

Williams, J. P., Regehr, A., & Kang, M. (2021). Methane Emissions from Abandoned Oil and Gas Wells in Canada and the United States. *Environmental Science and Technology*, *55*(1), 563–570. https://doi.org/10.1021/acs.est.0c04265

Antonis Kokossis, Michael C. Georgiadis, Efstratios N. Pistikopoulos (Eds.)
PROCEEDINGS OF THE 33rd European Symposium on Computer Aided Process Engineering
(ESCAPE33), June 18-21, 2023, Athens, Greece

# Optimal capacity planning integrating ammonia storage for power and heat decarbonisation

Georgios L. Bounitsis, Vassilis M. Charitopoulos

*The Sargent Centre for Process Systems Engineering, Department of Chemical Engineering, University College London, Torrington Place, London WC1E 7JE, UK*
*v.charitopoulos@ucl.ac.uk*

## Abstract

Deep decarbonisation strategies for achieving the ambitious net-zero target pledged by the UK require thorough investigation of sector coupling dependencies. With heat being the single biggest energy consumer in the UK, pathways including dense energy carriers, which can store the excessive intermittent renewable energy, constitute a focal point of interest. In this work the role of ammonia as an energy vector for long-term storage in Great Britain's (GB) power system planning is evaluated. A linear programming spatially explicit snapshot model is formulated to set a fine-grained temporal resolution and capture seasonality of renewable sources. Decisions on capacity planning and operation of the system for a target year are optimised. Moreover, both power and heat demands are optimised as the heat demand mix is determined. The proposed model is applied on a case study of GB's power system in 2040 and the role of ammonia is investigated.

**Keywords**: Ammonia; Sector coupling; Heat decarbonisation; Energy systems planning; Hydrogen.

## 1. Introduction

### 1.1. Motivation

UK has been one of the leading countries in the race towards Net Zero. The fulfilment of its goals renders the integration of renewable sources in the UK's energy systems imperative. However, increased volatility within the electricity grid and the short-term duration of battery storage do not enable an efficient exploitation of the excessive renewable energy. Resorting to chemical energy storage options, hydrogen ($H_2$), which can be also renewable-based produced, constitutes a challenging dense energy carrier (DEC) for long-term storage due to safety and storage costs aspects. Hence, ammonia ($NH_3$) has emerged as a promising alternative to store the hydrogen-based energy. As Haber-Bosch synthesis allows exclusively renewable-based $NH_3$ production research studies have focused on its role (Valera-Medina & Bañares-Alcantara, 2021).

### 1.2. Literature review

Ammonia's renewable based production constitutes a focal point of research recently, as its benefits for the energy systems can be twofold: (a) its long-term storage and transportation are inexpensive and safe compared to other alternatives, and (b) the stored energy can be efficiently contributed back to energy systems at different time or geographical regions (Valera-Medina & Bañares-Alcantara, 2021). Therefore, critical research studies on power systems scheduling and planning have recently included both renewable-based ammonia production and ammonia-to-power pathways in their considerations (Ikäheimo et al., 2018). Palys & Daoutidis (2020) proposed a capacity planning and scheduling model in order minimise the levelised cost of ammonia in a specific location. Recently, technoeconomic analyses have additionally demonstrated encouraging results on the forecasted levelised cost of electricity from renewable ammonia (Cesaro et al., 2021). Regarding supply chain optimisation, a recent study indicates the impact of renewable ammonia as mean of satisfying demand in the ammonia supply chain (Allman et al., 2017). Finally, ammonia is also considered for energy carriers' supply chain optimisation (Tso et al., 2019).

Here we aim to present a spatially explicit linear programming (LP) model for the strategic planning and operation of GB's power sector including energy carriers' production. The proposed framework aims to assess the role of ammonia as energy vector in GB system's decarbonisation. To this end, a case study focusing on GB's optimal planning and operation in year 2040 is investigated. The remainder of the article is organised as follows: in Section 2 the superstructure of the problem and mathematical developments are outlined. In Section 3, the detailed case study and results are discussed. Finally, future directions are proposed in Section 4.

## 2. Optimisation of integrated production and scheduling of power sector

### 2.1. Superstructure of the problem

Electricity, hydrogen and ammonia systems' planning are integrated in the investigated problem, as sector coupling considerations have been proven beneficial for energy planning (He et al., 2021). The proposed snapshot model is capable to evaluate the mix of technologies and the operation of the sectors in a future year while considering hourly time resolution. Moreover, cases for decarbonisation pathways are investigated while satisfying an optimised region-specific electricity demand. Concurrently the energy mix for the residential heat demand satisfaction is determined. Decisions on the latter are taken into consideration due to its high energy requirements and consequent carbon intensity (Charitopoulos et al., 2022).

In this work, energy planning problem delves into GB's power system using a high-resolution spatial analysis, as this is considered to be imperative on energy planning of whole country's power system (Koltsaklis et al., 2014). Thus, GB is

**Figure 1:** *LDZ of Great Britain.*

divided in 13 regions ($g \in G$) according to the Local Distribution Zones (LDZ) of the gas network (Fig. 1). Regarding decisions on the GB's infrastructure, data on existing technologies' ($j \in J$) generation and storage capacities as well as transmission capacities are considered. Moreover, bidirectional interconnection capacities to third parties ($i \in I$) for electricity supply are set. Regarding operational decisions, the power system is optimised in a certain future time period employing a full year hourly time discretisation ($h \in H$). In this context, energy carriers, i.e., $H_2$ and $NH_3$, are included introducing alternative electricity generation ways, energy storage and transportation alternatives towards decarbonisation. In particular, $NH_3$ pathways can be considered using $H_2$ and electricity as initial flows to Haber-Bosch (HB) process in order to produce $NH_3$. This energy can be stored in liquid $NH_3$ storage tanks and be contributed back to the system for electricity generation in $NH_3$ gas turbines (GT). In this work, HB process is assumed to include the accompanied air separation units (ASU) for the necessary nitrogen ($N_2$) production. In real world, this process can be also exclusively renewable based. The superstructure of the network for the problem is envisaged in Fig. 2. Overall, the resources ($a \in A = \{Elec, H_2, NH_3\}$) are depicted in circles and can be considered as carriers of energy. Storage and interregional transmission/transportation capabilities are also available for them. Finally, region-specific hourly electricity and heat demands profiles are satisfied, while concurrently optimising electricity demand (and its peak) and determining the breakdown of heat demand satisfaction.

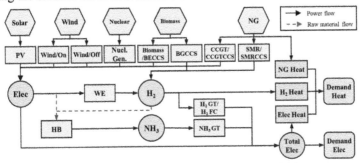

**Figure 2:** *Superstructure of power and heat supply chain.*

## 2.2. Mathematical modelling

An LP spatio-temporal model is developed to address the integrated problem. Power and heat hourly demand profiles for a future year ($DEM_{gh}^{elec}$ and $DEM_{gh}^{heat}$ respectively) are used as input for the model. The breakdown of heat demand is calculated by the model:

$$DEM_{gh}^{heat} = \frac{Q_{gh}^{elec}}{COP_{gh}} + \frac{Q_{gh}^{H2}}{\eta^{H2,boiler}} + \frac{Q_{gh}^{NG}}{\eta^{gas,boiler}} \quad \forall g \in G, h \in H \tag{1}$$

Efficiency of the H$_2$ and natural gas (NG) boilers ($\eta$) is set equal to 90% and the coefficient of performance ($COP_{gh}$) of heat pumps, which consume electricity, is calculated based on the real-world temperatures data (ranges from 1.6 to 3.5). Capturing power requirement from heat electrification ($Q_{gh}^{elec}$) the real electricity demand ($D_{gh}$) is:

$$D_{gh} = (1 + DL) \cdot (DEM_{gh}^{elec} + Q_{gh}^{elec}) \quad \forall \, g \in G, h \in H \tag{2}$$

Accounting for electricity's distribution losses is achieved through factor $DL$, which is set equal to 6.5% according to calculations from historical data (DUKES, 2022). Concerning the resources balances, generation/production or consumption of the resource ($P_{gjh}$), storage charging ($CH_{agjh}$) and discharging ($DC_{agjh}$) and bidirectional transmission/transportation ($TR_{argg'h}$) (among losses) for the satisfaction of demands are taken into consideration. As far as the electricity, bidirectional interconnection to third countries ($PIM_{igh}$), renewables curtailment ($LC_{gh}$) and load shedding ($LS_{gh}$) can be also considered. The spatial explicit mass balance is given by Eq. (3):

$$\sum_{j \in PR_{aj}} P_{gjh} \cdot (1 - PL_j) + \sum_{j \in ST_{aj}} DC_{agjh} + \sum_{i \in IG_{ig}} PIM_{igh} \cdot (1 - L_{ig}^{int}) \bigg|_{a=\{elec\}}$$

$$+ \sum_{(r,g') \in TG_{argg'}} TR_{arg'gh} \cdot (1 - LD_{g'g} \cdot L_{ar}^{tr}) = D_{gh}\big|_{a=\{el.\}} + Q_{gh}^{H2}\big|_{a=\{H2\}} \tag{3}$$

$$+ \sum_{j \in ST_{aj}} CH_{agjh} + \sum_{j \in CON_{aj}} \frac{P_{gjh}}{\eta_j^c} + \sum_{(r,g') \in TG_{argg'}} TR_{argg'h} + (LC_{gh} - LS_{gh})\big|_{a=\{elec\}}$$

$$\forall a \in A, g \in G, h \in H$$

Crucial aspects for the planning are also enforced by capacity constraints. For the sake of stability of the power supply chain, the system-wide electricity peak demand ($D^{peak}$) must be met by the installed capacities ($Cap_{gj}$) (Eq. 5). $D^{peak}$, which is optimised by the model (Eq. 4), is additionally multiplied by a security margin factor ($RM$). Moreover, de-rating factors ($DF_j$) are considered as the technologies are not assumed capable to constantly operate at 100% of their maximum capacity (National Grid ESO, 2022a).

$$D^{peak} \geq \sum_{g \in G} D_{gh} \qquad \forall h \in H \tag{4}$$

$$\sum_{g \in G, j \in (ST_{elec,j} \cup PR_{elec,j})} DF_j \cdot Cap_{gj} \geq D^{peak} \cdot (1 + RM) \tag{5}$$

Decisions on capacity investments are bounded by building ratios and land availability data (Heuberger et al., 2017; Samsatli et al., 2016). For each sector separate carbon budgets are in place which cumulatively are in line with the GB's Climate Change Committee (CCC) net-zero trajectory. In summary, the proposed LP model aims at the minimisation of the total system cost ($TSC$). Terms regarding the capital cost (using capacity recovery factors), variable operational costs (including storage, fuels, curtailment, value of loss load), interconnection costs and carbon taxes are included.

$$minimise \quad TSC = CAPEX + OPEX + CINT + CCT \tag{6}$$

$$subject\ to: \begin{cases} Capacity\ bounds\ and\ expansion\ constraints \\ Energy\ balances\ and\ Technologies\ operation\ constraints \\ Resources\ storage\ and\ transmission\ constraints \\ Carbon\ emission\ constraints \end{cases}$$

## 3. Case study: Power and heat decarbonisation in the UK in 2040

### 3.1. Data preparation

The proposed model is tested for the planning of GB's energy system in 2040 using 2015 data and installed infrastructure as basis. Profiles of electricity demands can be derived by historical data of National Grid (National Grid, 2022). Additional profiles of heat demand are based on hourly natural gas consumption data obtained from the UK gas distribution companies. Both demands are calculated by projecting the data of the base year to the predicted demand values by National Grid Future Energy Scenarios (FES). In particular, "System Transformation" scenario is employed (National Grid ESO, 2022b). Finally, carbon goals for year 2040 are calculated based on data by the UK's Sixth Carbon Budget report (Climate Change Committee, 2020). Predictions on the related fuels' prices and carbon taxes are also reported in FES. Regarding renewables availability we use Renewables.Ninja platform (Pfenninger & Staffell, 2016). The model is calibrated using historical data (of base year 2015) to introduce corrective impact to availability and interconnection prices data (DUKES, 2022; ENTSO-E, 2022). The capacity allocation of the 2015 UK system can be found on DUKES statistics and techno-economic parameters predictions till year 2040 can be retrieved from recent reports (BEIS, 2018; IEA, 2021).

### 3.2. Results and discussion

First of all, electricity demand in 2040 is optimised through the model and heat electrification decisions play a crucial role on this. In Fig. 3 the breakdown of heat demand mix in 2040 is given. The consequent increase on electricity demand is accompanied with decisions on investments on electricity generation technologies and particularly

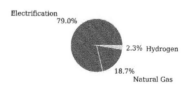

*Figure 3: Heat demand mix in 2040.*

in renewable technologies. The total capacity, load factors and capacity allocation for year 2040 are determined by the model and are visualised in Figs. 4-5. Sizes in Fig. 4 are representative of the relative total generation.

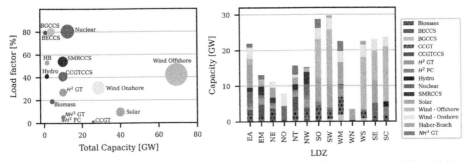

**Figure 4:** *Load factors in 2040.*  **Figure 5:** *Capacity allocation in the UK in 2040.*

Renewable technologies do not achieve high load factors because of their intermittent nature and the seasonality of renewable sources. In contrast, nuclear generation can provide high loads constantly. Furthermore, biomass-fueled technologies (BECCS & BGCCS) display high load factors and also contribute to Net Zero goal via carbon capture and storage (CCS). The remaining

**Table 1:** *Total Storage Capacity [GWh].*

| | |
|---|---|
| Grid-level | 73.7 |
| Hydrogen | 100.6 |
| Ammonia | 4,939 |

thermal technologies operate with lower load factors because of the decarbonisation regulations. However, their installed capacities are vital for system's security considerations. Focusing on renewables and DECs, full year profiles of generation and production are envisaged in Fig. 6 (colors as in Fig. 5). Although during summer small generation rates from thermal or DEC-fueled technologies are observed, during winter months the latter seem to contribute significantly. During summer the higher solar irradiation assist to meet demand. Regarding DEC production, even though hydrogen production displays seasonality, notable production is executed through whole year. This is not true for ammonia, as Haber-Bosch is demonstrated to yield further during summer.

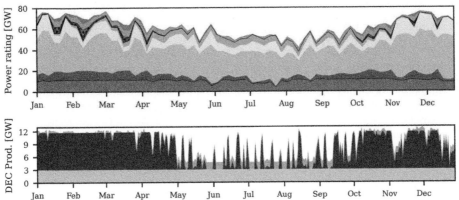

**Figure 6:** *Electricity generation and DEC production profiles in GB in 2040.*

Results from the optimisation model demonstrate the role of ammonia as interseasonal energy carrier. Insights from the installed storage capacities in Table 1 also indicate this. Furthermore, stored ammonia's amount is visualised in Fig. 7. Ammonia storage is consumed during the colder months contributing to power sypply chain.

Finally, the carbon intensity of the system is drastically enhanced as the calculated goal from CCC for 7.87 MtCO$_2$ for the considered system in 2040 is achieved. In parallel, the levelised cost of electricity is calculated to £65.1 per MWh of electricity supplied. This is competitive to third countries' leading to net exports of 6.6 TWh for the whole year.

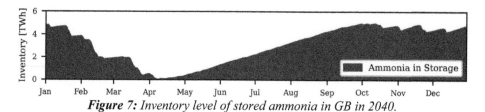

**Figure 7:** *Inventory level of stored ammonia in GB in 2040.*

## 4. Conclusions

The proposed spatially explicit snapshot model's results for the capacity planning and operation of the power system demonstrate the significant role of ammonia as energy vector for UK's decarbonisation. In particular, ammonia offers alternative pathways for power generation and interseasonal energy storage. Future work is directed on the planning and decarbonisation of power systems accounting for stochastic uncertainty.

**Acknowledgements:** Financial support from the EPSRC (under project EP/T022930/1) is gratefully acknowledged.

## References

A. Allman, P. Daoutidis, D. Tiffany, S. Kelley, 2017. A framework for ammonia supply chain optimization incorporating conventional and renewable generation. AIChE J., 63, 4390–4402.

BEIS, 2018. Hydrogen Supply Chain: Evidence base UK. London: Department for Business, Energy & Industrial Strategy.

Z. Cesaro, M. Ives, R. Nayak-Luke, M. Mason, R. Bañares-Alcántara, 2021. Ammonia to power: Forecasting the levelized cost of electricity from green ammonia in large-scale power plants. Appl. Energy, 282, 116009.

V.M. Charitopoulos, M. Fajardy, C.K. Chyong, D.M. Reiner, 2022. Cambridge Working Papers in Economics. The case of 100% electrification of domestic heat in Great Britain

Climate Change Committee, 2020. The Sixth Carbon Budget. The UK's path to Net Zero.

DUKES, 2022. Digest of UK Energy Statistics (DUKES) 2022 – National Statistics.

ENTSO-E, 2022. European Network of Transmission System Operators for Electricity.

G. He, D.S. Mallapragada, A. Bose, C.F. Heuberger, E. Gençer, 2021. Sector coupling via hydrogen to lower the cost of energy system decarbonization. Energy Environ. Sci. 14, 4635–4646.

C.F. Heuberger, E.S. Rubin, I. Staffell, N. Shah, N. Mac Dowell, 2017. Power capacity expansion planning considering endogenous technology cost learning. Appl. Energy 204, 831–845.

IEA, 2021. International Energy Agency. Ammonia Technology Roadmap.

J. Ikäheimo, J. Kiviluoma, R. Weiss, H. Holttinen, 2018. Power-to-ammonia in future North European 100 % renewable power and heat system. Int. J. Hydrog. Energ., 43, 17295–17308.

N.E. Koltsaklis, A.S. Dagoumas, G.M. Kopanos, E.N. Pistikopoulos, M.C. Georgiadis, 2014. A spatial multi-period long-term energy planning model: A case study of the Greek power system. Appl. Energy 115, 456–482.

National Grid, 2022. Historical Data.

National Grid ESO, 2022a. Electricity Market Reform. Capacity Market.

National Grid ESO, 2022b. Future Energy Scenarios.

M. J. Palys, P. Daoutidis, 2020. Using hydrogen and ammonia for renewable energy storage: A geographically comprehensive techno-economic study. Comput. Chem. Eng., 136.

S. Pfenninger, I. Staffell, 2016. Long-term patterns of European PV output using 30 years of validated hourly reanalysis and satellite data. Energy 114, 1251–1265.

Samsatli, S., Staffell, I., Samsatli, N.J., 2016. Optimal design and operation of integrated wind-hydrogen-electricity networks for decarbonising the domestic transport sector in Great Britain. Int. J. Hydrogen Energy 41, 447–475.

W.W. Tso, C.D. Demirhan, S. Lee, H. Song, J.B. Powell, E.N. Pistikopoulos, 2019. Energy Carrier Supply Chain Optimization: A Texas Case Study. Comput. Aided Chem. Eng. 47

A. Valera-Medina, R. Bañares-Alcantara, 2021. Techno-economic challenges of green ammonia as energy vector. Academic Press.

Antonis Kokossis, Michael C. Georgiadis, Efstratios N. Pistikopoulos (Eds.)
PROCEEDINGS OF THE 33rd European Symposium on Computer Aided Process Engineering
(ESCAPE33), June 18-21, 2023, Athens, Greece

# European Union's biomass availability for Sustainable Aviation Fuel production and potential GHG emissions reduction in the aviation sector: An analysis using GIS tools for 2030

Sivaramakrishnan Chandrasekaran,[a] Nora B. Salah,[a] John A. Posada,[a]

[a]*Delft University of Technology, Mekelweg 5, Delft and 2628 CD, the Netherlands*

## Abstract

To be the first carbon-neutral continent by 2050, the European Union (EU) should decarbonize the aviation sector. According to the ReFuel initiative, sustainable aviation fuels (SAFs) are crucial in reducing carbon emissions from the sector. The Clean Sky 2 program by the EU commission, shortlisted four promising technologies - hydro-processed esters and fatty acids (HEFA), Fischer–Tropsch (FT), fast pyrolysis (FP), and alcohol-to-jet (ATJ) for the production of SAFs from bio-based sources. This study addresses the potential of these four technologies to reduce net and total greenhouse gas (GHG) emissions in the aviation sector. With a focus on mapping feedstock availability in 33 European countries for meeting the national demand in 2030. The investigation identified the best pathway combinations for each country, having the highest GHG emissions reduction while satisfying fuel demand when considering different degrees of biomass competition. Without any political and economic barriers to SAF production and biomass competition, we estimated a sufficient biomass supply exists to support the European SAF demand across all forecasted scenarios in 2030.

**Keywords**: Sustainable aviation fuels, GIS tools, Greenhouse gases emission, biomass conversion

## 1. Introduction

Nowadays, there is greater accessibility to air travel, with the majority of flights being used for passenger transport rather than freight. Accordingly, aviation contributes significantly to greenhouse gas (GHG) emissions. By 2050, the GHG emissions from the aviation sector are predicted to be 3.1 billion tons globally. Which is a sharp rise from 0.78 billion tons in 2015 (Doliente et al. 2020). To reduce the impact of these emissions on climate change and also to become the first carbon-neutral continent in the world, the European Union (EU) is taking different initiatives such as the EU Green deal and ReFuelEU aviation initiatives (Soone 2022; Zachmann, Tagliapietra, and Claeys 2019). Aligning with the same goals, CleanSky2 initiated TRANSCEND (Technology Review of Alternative and Novel Sources of Clean Energy with Next-generation Drivetrains). TRANSCEND investigated the potential of drop-in sustainable aviation fuels (SAFs), as a possible means of reducing aviation's influence on the environment. Drop-in SAFs are a new class of aviation fuel blended with regular fossil jet fuel and used in existing aircraft engines without significant changes. It is believed that bio-based drop-in fuels can significantly mitigate the GHG impacts on the aviation sector. TRANSCEND identified four promising technologies for the production of SAFs from bio-based sources. These include the hydro processed esters and fatty acids (HEFA), Fischer–Tropsch (FT), fast pyrolysis (FP), and alcohol-to-jet (ATJ) technologies. This study contributes to this field by addressing the potential of these technologies to reduce net and total GHG emissions in the aviation sector based on biomass availability (type and amount) in different European countries while considering local demand for different forecasted scenarios (Muijden et al. 2021).

The objective of this study is to estimate the total supply of residual biomass available in Europe in 2030. Further, to evaluate potential SAF availability and related net reductions in GHG emission for various SAF conversion pathways. Finally, the results are shown in a comprehensive map indicating the suitable conversion pathway that produces the maximal net GHG emission reduction for each country. The research questions focused in this study are

- Is there enough biomass available to meet European SAF demand in 2030?
- What is the best combination of biomass type and conversion technology leading to the maximum net GHG emission reduction for each country?

## 2. Scope and Boundary

This study uses a mixed-method approach to address the mentioned research questions, where quantitative findings are validated and expanded using data gathered from peer-reviewed articles.

### 2.1. Spatial and temporal Boundary

The geographical scope of this study is limited to 33 European countries. The 33 European countries consist of EU27 + Serbia, Ukraine, Bosnia, Albania, Moldova, and Macedonia. With respect to the temporal scale, this study is limited to the medium-term year of 2030. This was chosen to align with the policy targets in the sector and the maturity of various conversion pathways. "Conversion pathway" refers to a technology and feedstock combination for analysis purposes.

### 2.2. Conversion Pathways

In terms of conversion pathways, technologies considered in this investigation are hydro-processed esters and fatty acids (HEFA), Fischer–Tropsch (FT), fast pyrolysis (FP), and alcohol-to-jet (ATJ) technologies. Likewise, this study focuses on residual biomass as a SAF source because it requires no additional land, consumes lower water and has less commercial value than energy crops. Also, this conform with EU's commitment to using non-food feedstock as biomass sources for SAF. The three types of residual biomass considered in this report are agricultural residues (AR), forestry residues (FR) and municipal solid waste (MSW).

Agriculture residues consists of lignocellulosic by-products, harvesting, logging, and post-harvest operations (e.g. wood processing, crushing, and milling). Examples of agricultural residues include cereal straw, rice straw and corn stover. Similarly, forest residues are by-products of timber-harvesting activities. Examples of forestry leftovers include unprocessed fragments of cut trees (such as stumps and branches), wood pulp, and sawdust and cutter shavings. Lastly, municipal solid waste is defined as waste collected from a municipality and commonly referred to as trash or garbage (e.g. food processing waste and industry and commercial processing waste). In this study, we assesses the biomass availability (in tonnes) of 36 feedstock types in 33 European

*European Union's biomass availability for Sustainable Aviation Fuel production*     3057
*and potential GHG emissions reduction in the aviation sector: An analysis*
*using GIS tools for 2030*

countries. Of the 36 feedstock types, 18 can be categorised as forest residue, 15 as agricultural residue, and 3 as municipal solid waste.

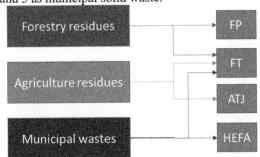

Figure 1: Schematic overview of the combinations of feedstock categories and conversion technologies considered.

The possible conversion pathways are shown in Figure 1. The selection is based on two criteria. The primary criterion is the compatibility between feedstock type and conversion technology. This compatibility depends on the type of biomass sources the technologies can process. The compatibility of feedstock type with certain technologies is obtained from the literature. For example, FT can process almost any carbon-rich material; therefore, it matches all three feedstock categories. The second criterion is whether literature data is readily available on process performance and GHG emissions intensity specific to the aviation sector. For example, the combination of FP and MSW shows promising results for the road sector but was excluded from this study due to missing data on process performance for SAF quality. Thus, only conversion pathways analyzed in previous studies in terms of SAF yield and associated GHG emissions specific to the aviation sector are included. In total, this study examined 85 conversion pathways for the 2030 scenario.

### 2.3. Geographic Information System

Biomass and GHG reduction potentials are mapped using ArcGIS Pro. ArcGIS is a geographic information system (GIS) that captures, stores and displays data related to spatial coordinates. It aids the user in understanding spatial patterns and relationships using layered maps. A demographic feature layer containing all EU countries provided by the ArcGIS database was used as a base map. Data was then added to the base map to illustrate its spatial distribution at a national level. Since this study uses a country-specific approach, the NUTS0 level is the most suitable to illustrate the results.

## 3. Scenario Evaluation

### 3.1. Estimation of potential SAF production

#### 3.1.1. Biomass availability and SAF demand

The data on biomass availability for 2030 by type and country is collected using the S2BIOM tool (Dees et al. 2017). With specification of regional level, year and feedstock type, this tool generate data for the amount of biomass available (in kilo tonnes dry mass) per year and potential type combination as a map. For this study, the technical potential is considered. According to the S2BIOM tool, this potential illustrates the maximum lignocellulosic biomass volume available, without any competing uses and with sustainable constraints. For the SAF demand in 2030, data for each country was provided by the Royal Netherlands Aerospace Centre (NLR). Figure 2 illustrates the spatial distribution of biomass and national SAF demand.

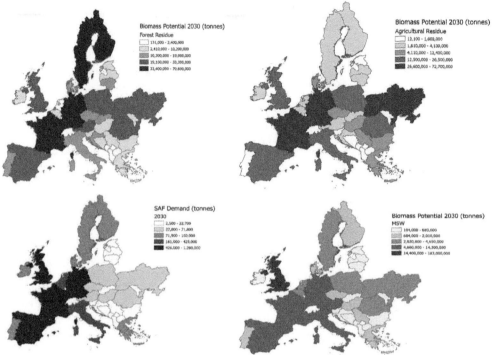

Figure 2: Spatial distribution of forestry residues (top left), Agriculture residues (top right), municipal solid waste (bottom right), and national SAF demand (bottom left).

### 3.1.2. Potential fuel output (PFO)

Potential fuel output can be calculated based on the potential SAF supply and national SAF demand. In order to estimate SAF supply, quantitative conversion yields for certain conversion pathways and biomass availability were taken into account. The conversion yields were obtained from literature data (Capaz et al. 2021; Santos et al. 2018). Due to data limitation for European context, some conversion pathway yields were obtained for the United States and assumed to be the same for the EU. Table 1 shows, example PFO of the most promising conversion pathways for UK in 2030 with 10% SAF blending policy.

$$PFO = \frac{Potential\ SAF\ supply}{National\ SAF\ demand} * 100\% \quad (1)$$

Table 1: PFO for some representative conversion pathways for UK in 2030 with 10% SAF blending

| Technology | Feedstock | Biomass availability (in million tons) | SAF supply (in kilotonnes) | Demand (in kilotonnes) | PFO (in %) |
|---|---|---|---|---|---|
| FT | Thinnings from nonconifer trees | 2,1 | 471 | 1283 | 37 |
| FT | Thinnings from conifer trees | 1,1 | 250 | 1283 | 19 |
| FT | Oil seed rape straw | 2,5 | 508 | 1283 | 40 |
| FT | Sunflower straw | 0,0 | 1 | 1283 | 0 |
| ATJ | Oil seed rape straw | 2,5 | 661 | 1283 | 51 |
| ATJ | Sunflower straw | 0,0 | 2 | 1283 | 0 |
| FP | Thinnings from nonconifer trees | 2,1 | 578 | 1283 | 45 |
| FP | Thinnings from conifer trees | 1,1 | 306 | 1283 | 24 |
| HEFA | UCO | 171,6 | 142445 | 1283 | 11102 |

*European Union's biomass availability for Sustainable Aviation Fuel production*   3059
*and potential GHG emissions reduction in the aviation sector: An analysis*
*using GIS tools for 2030*

### 3.2. Net GHG emissions and biomass competing uses

Based on environmental life cycle analysis, net, and total GHG emissions were calculated for each conversion pathway. A well-to-wake (WtWa) approach was followed in this investigation. We relied on studies that utilized the Greenhouse Gases, Regulated Emissions, and Energy Use in Transportation (GREET) model to assess SAF conversion pathways' medium- and long-term GHG emission performance (Jong 2018). However, GREET uses the US as its geographic coverage of the input data. Therefore, the actual values for GHG emissions in Europe could be different. For the WtWa analysis, the $CO_2$ emissions from SAF combustion are considered part of the biogenic carbon cycle. The average WtWa emission intensity for typical jet fuel used in the United States (87.5 g $CO_2$ eq $MJ^{-1}$) is utilized as the fossil fuel baseline.

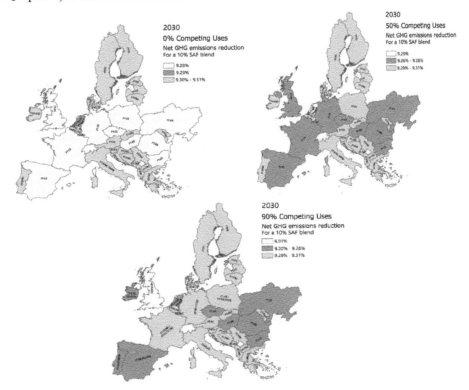

Figure 3: The net GHG emissions reduction potential (in %) based on 10% SAF blend for each European country in 2030 for different biomass availabilities.

Effect of biomass competing sources (0%, 50%, and 90%) was also analyzed as feedstock competition is expected in the future. Figure 3 illustrates the net GHG emissions reduction potential for the considered 33 European countries while accounting for biomass competition. The potential net GHG emissions reduction ranges between 9.25% and 9.31% across all biomass availability levels for most countries. The maximum total GHG emissions reduction potentials collectively for Europe in the 2030 scenario was found to be 21 Mt (0% competing uses), 19 Mt (50% competing uses), 15 Mt (90% competing uses). The difference in values is attributed to the selected feedstock category. For example, FT-AR pathway has slightly higher net GHG emissions (6.3g $CO_2$/MJ SAF) than FT-FR (6g $CO_2$/MJ SAF). The UK is the only country where biomass supply limits potential net GHG emissions reduction. From Figure 3, to cover the UK's SAF demand for 90% competing uses, the conversion pathway is changed to HEFA-UCO, with a significantly lower net GHG emissions reduction potential (6.91%). Overall, the results indicate at least a 9% net reduction in GHG can be achieved for the 33 European countries, even when 90% competing uses are considered.

## 4. Conclusions

In this research, we initially assessed if there is sufficient biomass to supply the SAF demand of Europe; and secondly, identified the best conversion pathways that lead to the highest GHG emissions reductions for each country. For a scenario in 2030 with a 10% blending of SAF with fossil jet fuel, we also investigated the impact of biomass competition with biomass uses varying from 0%, 50%, and 90%. Collectively, the 33 European countries can produce sufficient SAF to meet the total demand in 2030. This was the case for all the competing percentages. One key learning from this study was that conversion pathways with maximum yield need not always perform best in terms of GHG reduction. For example, in the UK, HEFA-UCO offers the highest PFO indicating higher yield, however, FT-FR had the highest GHG emission reduction while satisfying the demand. The conversion pathway that leads to the highest GHG emissions reduction across the EU for 2030 is FT – FR/AR/FR+AR, based on biomass availability. The maximum total GHG emissions reduction potentials collectively for Europe in the 2030 scenario is 21 Mt (0% competing uses), 19 Mt (50% competing uses), and 15 Mt (90% competing uses). Based on the analysis conveyed, it can be concluded that bio-based drop-in fuels can go a long way towards mitigating the impact of the aviation sector. However, there is a lot of room for refinement as a follow-up. Expanding the temporal scale to 2050 and assuming different blending percentages can spotlight some key areas of concern. Therefore, it is believed that the future SAF supply and the associated GHG emission reductions will be strongly impacted by policy incentives, the pace of technology development, and exact biomass supply and demand.

## References

Capaz, Rafael S. et al. 2021. "Mitigating Carbon Emissions through Sustainable Aviation Fuels: Costs and Potential." *Biofuels, Bioproducts and Biorefining* 15(2): 502–24.

Dees, Matthias et al. 2017. "A Spatial Data Base on Sustainable Biomass Cost- Supply of Lignocellulosic Biomass in Europe - Methods & Data Sources. Project Report. S2BIOM – a Project Funded under the European Union 7th Framework Programme for Research. Grant Agreement N°608622." https://zenodo.org/record/1478483.

Doliente, Stephen S. et al. 2020. "Bio-Aviation Fuel: A Comprehensive Review and Analysis of the Supply Chain Components." *Frontiers in Energy Research* 8(July): 1–38.

Jong, Sierk De. 2018. "Green Horizons." Utrecht University.

Muijden, J et al. 2021. "Final Results Alternative Energy and Propulsion Technology Literature Study Deliverable D1.1 of the TRANSCEND Project." (March).

Santos, Catarina I. et al. 2018. "Integrated 1st and 2nd Generation Sugarcane Bio-Refinery for Jet Fuel Production in Brazil: Techno-Economic and Greenhouse Gas Emissions Assessment." *Renewable Energy* 129: 733–47. https://doi.org/10.1016/j.renene.2017.05.011.

Soone, J. 2022. "ReFuelEU Aviation Initiative: Sustainable Aviation Fuels and the Fit for 55 Package ." *Think Tank | European Parliament* (June). https://www.europarl.europa.eu/thinktank/en/document/EPRS_BRI(2022)698900.

Zachmann, Georg, Simone Tagliapietra, and Grégory Claeys. 2019. "How to Make the European Green Deal Work Grégory." *European Commission* 13(9). https://www.jstor.org/stable/resrep28626.

Antonis Kokossis, Michael C. Georgiadis, Efstratios N. Pistikopoulos (Eds.)
PROCEEDINGS OF THE 33rd European Symposium on Computer Aided Process Engineering
(ESCAPE33), June 18-21, 2023, Athens, Greece

# Statistical modeling of electrodes manufacture for $CO_2$ electroreduction to value-added products.

Jose Antonio Abarca, Guillermo Díaz-Sainz, Iván Merino-Garcia, Jonathan Albo, Angel Irabien.

*Departamento de Ingenierías Química y Biomolecular, Universidad de Cantabria, ETSIIT, Avenida de los Castros s/n, 39005, Santander, Spain.*

## Abstract

$CO_2$ electrocatalytic reduction to value-added products stands out as one of the most favorable utilization pathways for captured $CO_2$ to reduce emissions and mitigate climate change. However, current electrode fabrication techniques limit the implementation of the process at an industrial scale, as they are neither reproducible nor automatized. In this work, an automatic spray pyrolysis technique is studied by assessing the effect of different fabrication variables, such as (i) spraying nozzle height, (ii) distance between steps, and (iii) ink flowrate, from a statistical point of view, developing a linear regression model and a neural network-based predictive model that can forecast the behavior of the electrodes fabricated under different conditions. These statistical models are developed to advance from a rudimentary to an automatized electrode fabrication method, considering this as a first step towards establishing an electrode manufacturing protocol based on machine learning.

**Keywords**: $CO_2$ electroreduction, Spray pyrolysis technique, Gas Diffusion Electrode, Statistical modelling, Factorial experimental design.

## 1. Introduction

Climate change and global warming are part of the main challenges that society is facing nowadays. Several strategies have been proposed to minimize carbon dioxide ($CO_2$) emissions in the energy-intensive industrial sectors [1], such as (i) the improvement of energy efficiency in industrial processes, (ii) the development of innovative sources of energy, or (iii) carbon capture, storage, and utilization (CCSU) approaches. The conversion of $CO_2$ to different chemical products is one of the most promising utilization pathways from both economic and environmental points of view [2]. The electrochemical reduction of $CO_2$ ($CO_2ER$) to value-added products emerges as the most suitable for an industrial-level scale-up. Furthermore, this technology allows for storing energy from intermittent and renewable sources in the form of chemical bonds [3]. However, the current technological readiness level of the ER technology is under development stages, between 3 and 5 [4]. Therefore, research efforts are needed to bring ER process closer to industrial scale.

One of the key elements of $CO_2ER$ systems are the electrodes where $CO_2$ reduction reaction occurs. Among the several electrode configurations, gas diffusion electrodes (GDEs), which imply gas phase reagents, promote the contact between the reactive gas, the catalyst, and the electrolyte. The main advantages of these electrodes are that they keep high concentrations of $CO_2$ in the reaction area, and allow the operation at high current densities [7,8]. The GDE is composed of three main layers, (i) carbonaceous support, (ii) a microporous layer (MPL), and (iii) a catalyst layer. The porous structure of the GDE allows a constant flow of gas to the electrocatalyst surface, where contacts the liquid electrolyte to produce the reduction reaction to obtain value-added products. In previous works, electrodes were fabricated by manual airbrushing [5–7], which is a rudimentary technique with high variability in the manufacturing process. The relative standard deviations (RSD) reached for formate rates were as high as 15%, which clearly supports the need to develop reproducible and dedicated GDE fabrication techniques. For this purpose, the spray pyrolysis technique is selected as the most suitable due to its simplicity of operation and automatization. The catalytic inks are atomized into small particles or drops that are deposited onto the support and placed over a heated surface [8]. The automatized operation allows the control of several fabrication variables that may affect electrode morphology [9].

This work aims to analyze, from a statistical point of view, the fabrication of Bi carbon-supported Gas Diffusion Electrodes (Bi/C GDE) for $CO_2$ electroreduction to formate, developing a linear regression and neural network model to predict the influence of the different fabrication variables in process performance.

## 2. Methodology

### 2.1. Spray Pyrolysis Fabrication Technique

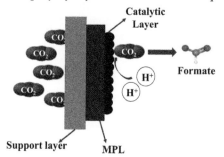

*Figure 1. Scheme of the fabricated Bi/C GDE*

The fabrication of the electrodes has been carried out using an ND-SP Mini Ultrasonic Spray Coater (Nadetech Innovations), whose functioning is based on an automatic spray technique that incorporates an ultrasonic reservoir that keeps the precursor solution dispersed. The GDEs fabricated, as illustrated in Figure 1, are composed of carbonaceous support, (Toray Carbon Paper TGP-H-60), an MPL based on a 3 wt.% dispersion of Carbon Black (Vulcan XC- 72R), and PTFE (60 % wt., Sigma Aldrich) (40/60), and the catalytic ink 3 wt.% in isopropanol (Fischer Chemicals) with Bi carbon-supported nanoparticles as catalysts and Nafion D-521 (5% wt., Alfa Aesar) as a binder (70/30). The geometric area of the electrode is 10 $cm^2$, with an MPL load of 2 mg $cm^{-2}$ and a catalytic loading of 0.75 mg $cm^{-2}$, like previous studies in the research group [6].

### 2.2. Experimental set-up

The electrodes manufactured are tested in a filter-press electrochemical reactor [6] as working electrodes. 0.5 M KCl (PanReac, AppliChem) + 0.45 M $KHCO_3$ (PanReac, AppliChem) and 1 M KOH (85 % pellets, Pan Reac AppliChem), are used as catholyte and anolyte, respectively. The flow rates per geometric surface area for both electrolytes are 0.57 mL $min^{-1}$ $cm^{-2}$ and the pure $CO_2$ stream flow rate is 200 mL $min^{-1}$. The formate concentration obtained in the output stream is measured by Ionic Chromatography (Dionex ICS 1100) [9].

### 2.3. Experimental design

The variables proposed are, spraying nozzle height, $X_1$, the current density applied, $X_2$ as an operational variable, the distance between steps, $X_3$, and ink flowrate, $X_4$. For each different fabrication condition, the performance of the process to produce formate is studied. For this purpose, a factorial experimental design $2^4+8$ is proposed following the approximations reported in our group [10–12].

These four variables have two levels, except for the spraying nozzle height, which has a central point. The value of the different levels of these variables is collected in Table 1.

*Table 1. Variables and different levels were assessed in the factorial experimental design.*

| Variable | | + | - | O |
|---|---|---|---|---|
| Nozzle height (mm) | $X_1$ | 15 | 35 | 25 |
| Current density (mA cm⁻²) | $X_2$ | 200 | 90 | - |
| Step distance (mm) | $X_3$ | 1 | 3 | - |
| Ink flowrate (mL h⁻¹) | $X_4$ | 20 | 10 | - |

The response variables considered are the average formate rate (r) and the energy consumption (CE), shown in Eq. 1 and Eq. 2, respectively.

$$Formate\ rate\ \left(\frac{mol}{m^2\ s}\right) = \frac{C_{Formate}}{A} \tag{1}$$

$$Energy\ Consumption\ \left(\frac{kWh}{kmol}\right) = \frac{Q \cdot V}{C_{Formate}} \tag{2}$$

Where $C_{formate}$ is the molar flowrate of formate obtained in the output stream of the electrochemical reactor (mol s⁻¹), A is the geometric surface area of the electrode (m²), Q is the total charge supplied to the electrochemical cell (A), and V is the absolute cell potential (V).

The approximation to study the influence of the different variables in the electrode performance is to get a linear regression model. Furthermore, to avoid the negative effect of the absolute values in the regression model, the results of the output variables (average formate rate, and energy consumption) are normalized between [-1, 1]. The neural network design is carried out with the software Neural Designer (Artificial Intelligence Techniques, Ltd).

## 3. Results

Table 2 shows the statistical analysis of the factorial design $2^4+8$, only considering the linear interaction of the variables. For this analysis, the results of the factorial design are expressed in a linear regression model, obtaining the coefficients for each variable within a 95 % confidence level.

$$Y = \beta_0 + \beta_1 \cdot X_1 + \beta_2 \cdot X_2 + \beta_3 \cdot X_3 + \beta_4 \cdot X_4 \tag{3}$$

Equation 3 represents the linear regression model taken as the base for the development of the model to predict the behavior of the electrode under different fabrication and operation conditions.

It can be observed that only two variables have a significant effect on formate rates, the spraying nozzle height ($X_1$) and the current density ($X_2$). To determine the significance of a variable, as found before [12-14], the value of the coefficient ($\beta$) must be higher than 0.05, and simultaneously, the probability lower than 0.05. In the case of the nozzle height, the coefficient has a negative value (-0.065), which indicates that larger distances of the nozzle from the substrate surface during the electrode fabrication promote higher formate rate values. This could be attributed to an improved catalyst distribution over the electrode surface, enhancing the surface-active area available for $CO_2$ reduction. In the case of current density, the effect is even more significant, as its coefficient has a higher value (0.769), which indicates that increasing the current supplied to the electrochemical reactor promotes formate rates in the output stream, as expected from previous results [6].

*Table 2. Linear regression analysis of the factorial experimental design.*

| | Interception | $X_1$, Nozzle height (mm) | | | $X_2$, Current density (mA cm$^{-2}$) | | |
|---|---|---|---|---|---|---|---|
| | $\beta_0$ | $\beta_1$ | Error | Probability | $\beta_2$ | Error | Probability |
| $\bar{r}$ | -0.093 ±0.154 | -0.065 ±0.154 | 0.026 | 0.000 | 0.769 ±0.820 | 0.029 | 0.000 |
| $\overline{CE}$ | -0.157 ±0.237 | 0.051 ±0.121 | 0.034 | 0.000 | 0.675 ±0.756 | 0.038 | 0.000 |

| | $X_3$, Step distance (mm) | | | $X_4$, Ink flowrate (mL min$^{-1}$) | | | Adjustment |
|---|---|---|---|---|---|---|---|
| | $\beta_3$ | Error | Probability | $\beta_4$ | Error | Probability | $R^2$ |
| $\bar{r}$ | 0.014 ±0.075 | 0.029 | 0.634 | 0.034 ±0.103 | 0.032 | 0.297 | 0.968 |
| $\overline{CE}$ | 0.001 ±0.081 | 0.038 | 0.988 | -0.026 ±0.117 | 0.043 | 0.546 | 0.929 |

On the other hand, for energy consumption, as it is for formate rates, only the nozzle height ($X_1$) and the current density ($X_2$) applied have a significant effect on the response variable. For both variables, the coefficients are positive, therefore, a smaller distance of the nozzle from the substrate (0.051) and a higher current density supplied to the cell (0.675) increase the energy consumption per molar unit of formate. In the case of the nozzle height, reducing the distances from the substrate causes the non-uniform deposition of the ink. This may induce the formation of agglomerates of the catalyst nanoparticles, worsening the surface conductivity of the electrode. The effect observed with current density makes sense, as for higher current densities it is necessary to supply more energy to reach the set conditions.

Furthermore, the values obtained for the interception indicate that the linear regression model is sensitive to changes produced in the variables assessed. In addition, the adjustment reached for both linear regression models is satisfactory ($R^2$>0.92). However, simplified models can be proposed disregarding the variables that do not have enough significance, resulting in a worse adjustment, but at the same time, facilitating the understanding of the models.

The simplified linear regression models proposed for formate rate and energy consumption are shown below, where only the significant variables (nozzle height and current density) are taken into count:

$$\bar{r} = -0.093 - 0.065 \cdot X_1 + 0.769 \cdot X_2 \tag{4}$$

$$\overline{CE} = -0.157 + 0.051 \cdot X_1 + 0.675 \cdot X_2 \tag{5}$$

The spraying nozzle height curvature is analyzed. For this purpose, formate rate values for the different variable levels [-1 (35 mm), 0 (25 mm), 1 (15 mm)] are depicted in Figure 2.

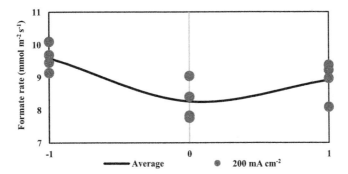

*Figure 2. Spraying nozzle height curvature analysis as a function of formate rate values.*

The data shows a non-linear function with a minimum at the central point (25 mm). This indicates that the optimization of this variable is much more complicated than the simplified linear regression model.

Based on the results obtained in linear regression, it can be seen that the variables in the model are only significant from a mathematical point of view. Thus, a predictive model is proposed using more advanced modeling methods, such as neural networks. In this case, the relevance of the selected input variables is assessed when constructing the neural network, which is formed by different neurons depending on its function: i) the scaling layer to eliminate the influence of the absolute value of the variables, ii) the perceptron layers, in which the model is able to learn the input correlations, iii) the unscaling layers, and iv) the bounding layers, to obtain the predicted output value. As observed in Figure 4, the input variables that have a significant effect in the model for the formate rate (Figure 4a) are the same as the linear regression, while for the energy consumption (Figure 4b), all input variables are considered significant.

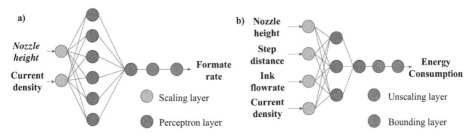

*Figure 3. Neural networks for the predictive models: a) Formate rate, b) Energy consumption.*

The models obtained from the neural networking have adjustment values ($R^2$) of 0.97 and 0.94 for the formate rate and energy consumption, respectively. The information extracted from the first model confirms the linear regression findings: the nozzle height is the manufacturing variable that most influences the performance of the electrode in terms of formate rate. However, this predictive model determines that all manufacturing variables affect the physicochemical structure of the electrodes, and, as this affects their electrical resistance, it impacts on energy consumption.

## 4. Conclusions

A statistical model that relates fabrication and operational variables with electrode performance for $CO_2$ ER to formate has been proposed. A factorial experimental design

$2^4$+8 has been proposed, obtaining two different linear regression models, with a determination coefficient ($R^2$) over 0.9, establishing the effect of each variable and their interactions on the response variables selected: (i) the average formate rate and (ii) energy consumption. Although not all variables and interactions are significant from a statistical point of view, two of them stand up as the most relevant ones, the nozzle height and the current density applied. Additionally, a neural network predictive model is proposed, confirming the information obtained for the formate rate linear regression model. However, for the energy consumption predictive model, all the fabrication variables are considered, in contrast to the linear regression model. These results are relevant to understand the behavior of the electrodes fabricated by the automatized spray pyrolysis technique and are useful as a first step for applying data science to the electrochemical process. As a result, future work will focus on working with neural networking to bring artificial intelligence and machine learning to this process, aiming at further developing a useful tool to predict the performance of electrodes manufactured at any scale, which may save time and experimental efforts.

## References

[1]      C. Hepburn, E. Adlen, J. Beddington, E.A. Carter, S. Fuss, N. Mac Dowell, 2019, The technological and economic prospects for $CO_2$ utilization and removal. Nature. 575, 7781, 87–97.

[2]      R. Chauvy, N. Meunier, D. Thomas, and G. de Weireld, 2019, Selecting emerging $CO_2$ utilization products for short- to mid-term deployment. Applied Energy. 236, 662–680.

[3]      A. Irabien, M. Alvarez-Guerra, J. Albo, and A. Dominguez-Ramos, 2018, C.A. Martínez-Huitle, M.A. Rodrigo, O. Scialdone (eds.) Electrochemical Conversion of $CO_2$ to Value-Added Products., pp. 29–59.

[4]      M. Rumayor, A. Dominguez-Ramos, P. Perez, and A. Irabien, 2019, A techno-economic evaluation approach to the electrochemical reduction of $CO_2$ for formic acid manufacture. Journal of $CO_2$ Utilization. 34, 490–499.

[5]      G. Díaz-Sainz, M. Alvarez-Guerra, and A. Irabien, 2021, Continuous electroreduction of $CO_2$ towards formate in gas-phase operation at high current densities with an anion exchange membrane. Journal of $CO_2$ Utilization. 56, 101822.

[6]      G. Díaz-Sainz, M. Alvarez-Guerra, J. Solla-Gullón, L. García-Cruz, V. Montiel, and A. Irabien, 2019, $CO_2$ electroreduction to formate: Continuous single-pass operation in a filter-press reactor at high current densities using Bi gas diffusion electrodes. Journal of $CO_2$ Utilization. 34, 12–19.

[7]      G. Díaz-Sainz, M. Alvarez-Guerra, B. Ávila-Bolívar, J. Solla-Gullón, V. Montiel, and A. Irabien, 2021, Improving trade-offs in the figures of merit of gas-phase single-pass continuous $CO_2$ electrocatalytic reduction to formate. Chemical Engineering Journal. 405, 126965.

[8]      P.S. Maldar, M.A. Gaikwad, A.A. Mane, S.S. Nikam, S.P. Desai, S.D. Giri, 2017, Fabrication of $Cu_2CoSnS_4$ thin films by a facile spray pyrolysis for photovoltaic application. Solar Energy. 158, 89–99.

[9]      N. Kumari, M.A. Haider, U. Anjum, and S. Basu, 2020, Identifying operating mechanism in the electrochemical reduction of $CO_2$ on thin-film praseodymium-doped ceria electrodes. Ionics. 26, 11, 5673–5684.

[10]      M. Alvarez-Guerra, S. Quintanilla, and A. Irabien, 2012, Conversion of carbon dioxide into formate using a continuous electrochemical reduction process in a lead cathode. Chemical Engineering Journal. 207–208, 278–284.

[11]      M. Alvarez-Guerra, A. del Castillo, and A. Irabien, 2014, Continuous electrochemical reduction of carbon dioxide into formate using a tin cathode: Comparison with lead cathode. Chemical Engineering Research and Design. 92, 4, 692–701.

[12]      A. Del Castillo, M. Alvarez-Guerra, and A. Irabien, 2014, Continuous electroreduction of $CO_2$ to formate using Sn gas diffusion electrodes. AIChE Journal. 60, 10, 3557–3564.

Antonis Kokossis, Michael C. Georgiadis, Efstratios N. Pistikopoulos (Eds.)
PROCEEDINGS OF THE 33rd European Symposium on Computer Aided Process Engineering
(ESCAPE33), June 18-21, 2023, Athens, Greece

# Comparative exergoeconomic analysis of two Organic Rankine Cycle (ORC) configurations

Ladislao E. Méndez-Cruz,[a] Miguel A. Gutiérrez-Limón,[b] Raúl Lugo-Leyte,[c] Mauricio Sales-Cruz,[a,*]

[a]Universidad Autónoma Metropolitana – Cuajimalpa, Av. Vasco de Quiroga No. 4871, Mexico City 05348, Mexico. *asales@cua.uam.mx
[b]Universidad Autónoma Metropolitana – Azcapotzalco, Av. San Pablo No. 180, Mexico City 02200, Mexico.
[c]Universidad Autónoma Metropolitana – Iztapalapa, Av. Ferrocarril San Rafael Atlixco No. 186, Mexico City 09340, Mexico.

## Abstract

Currently, power generation systems that use residual thermal sources are being studied, such as the Organic Rankine Cycle (ORC) technology. This paper presents a comparative exergoeconomic analysis between a simple ORC and one with a preheater. Both configurations work with R134a as refrigerant, under the same waste heat source. The results show a 47.31% reduction in the exergoeconomic cost of residue formation when operating with the ORC with preheater. In addition, the unit production cost is 0.049 USD/kWh with the simple ORC, while it is reduced to 0.046 USD/kWh with the ORC configuration with preheater.

**Keywords**: Organic Rankine Cycle, exergoeconomic analysis, process configurations.

## 1. Introduction

The best use of fossil resources for power generation is through the employment of technologies that require residual gases as a thermal source. In this sense, the Organic Rankine Cycle (ORC) corresponds to this type of power cycles that use low-temperature thermal sources, to generate power from 10 kW to 10 MW (Nondy and Gogoi, 2021). There are various ORC configurations that have been studied from an exergoeconomic point (thermodynamic and economic) that aims to evaluate, diagnose, improve, and optimize this type of energy systems (Torres et al., 2002). Due to this, the exergetic cost theory is a methodology that is widely used and is based on the productive purpose and the formation of the residue (Torres and Valero, 2021).

The main configuration of the ORC consists of a turbine (T), an electric generator (EG), a condenser (COND), a condensate pump (P) and a heat recovery steam generator (HRSG), the latter composed of an economizer (EC), an evaporator (EV) and a superheater (SH). Two configurations are considered to carry out a comparative exergoeconomic study: a simple ORC and an ORC with preheater (PH), as shown in Figure 1. Both configurations operate with R134a as organic working fluid. The purpose of this work is to evaluate the behavior of the exergoeconomic cost of residue formation ($\Pi_R$), and the unit exergoeconomic cost ($c_p$) of power generation, for the same exergoeconomic cost of the external resource ($\Pi_e$). Therefore, it is intended to analyze the contribution of the equipment in the cost for the residue formation generated by a configuration of the given system.

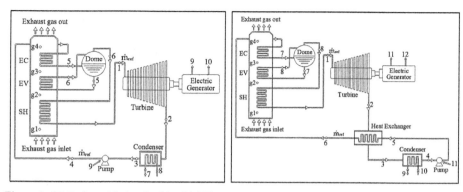

Figure 1. ORC plant: (a) simple, (b) with HE

## 2. Methodology

The framework begins with the construction of a productive structure, which defines which are the productive components that contribute to the formation of the product and the residue of the system. For this, the exergy flows of the resource and the product of the productive components are identified (Lugo-Mendez et al., 2020). From the configurations shown in Figure 1, their productive structures are built, which are shown in Figure 2. Both productive structures describe the product that comes from the environment (0) and is the system resource that corresponds to the exergy change of the exhaust gases ($g_1$ - $g_4$), which is distributed into the HRSG components (SH, EV and EC) through node 1. The union of the products of these components is mainly used for the generation of power in the T and EG, which is distributed both for the generation of the useful product of the system, and in the power supplied to the P, of both configurations. Likewise, the products of the components of SH, EV, EC, P and HE (the latter for the second configuration) that enter node 2, contribute to the formation of the residue in COND in different proportions.

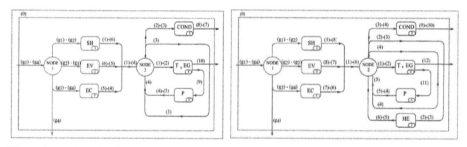

Figure 2. ORC productive structure: (a) simple, (b) with HE

Table 1 presents the exergy fluxes of the resource (fuel, F), product (P) and residue (R) of the ORC components of both configurations, which are based on the definition of the resource product $\dot{F} = \dot{P} + \dot{I}$. Where, the irreversibility flux ($\dot{I}$) generated by each component of the system is determined by the difference between the exergy flux of the resource ($\dot{F}$) and the product ($\dot{P}$).

The exergetic and exergoeconomic cost functions in the ORC economic model are based on the F-P-R representation of the system, where it relates the exergoeconomic variables of the system to external resources (Cuadra and Capilla, 2000). According to this representation, the exergetic fluxes are initially determined and later the exergetic costs of the resource, product and irreversibility of the productive components of the system, as well as the exergetic cost for the formation of the residue, all of them based on the external resource. and the distribution coefficients of the product and the residue. Table 2 presents the matrix expressions that determine the exergetic flows and the exergetic costs of the product, resource and residue of the productive components, which are used for both ORC configurations.

Table 1. Exergy fluxes of fuel, product and residue.

| Components of ORC | $\dot{F}$ (kW) | $\dot{P}$ (kW) | $\dot{R}$ (kW) | Components of ORC with HE | $\dot{F}$ (kW) | $\dot{P}$ (kW) | $\dot{R}$ (kW) |
|---|---|---|---|---|---|---|---|
| HRSG | $\dot{E}_{g1} - \dot{E}_{g4}$ | $\dot{E}_1 - \dot{E}_4$ | - | HRSG | $\dot{E}_{g1} - \dot{E}_{g4}$ | $\dot{E}_1 - \dot{E}_6$ | - |
| T | $\dot{E}_1 - \dot{E}_2$ | $\dot{W}_T$ | - | T | $\dot{E}_1 - \dot{E}_2$ | $\dot{W}_T$ | - |
| COND | $\dot{E}_2 - \dot{E}_3$ | - | $\dot{E}_8 - \dot{E}_7$ | COND | $\dot{E}_3 - \dot{E}_4$ | - | $\dot{E}_9 - \dot{E}_{10}$ |
| P | $\dot{W}_B$ | $\dot{E}_4 - \dot{E}_3$ | - | P | $\dot{W}_B$ | $\dot{E}_5 - \dot{E}_4$ | - |

Table 2. Expressions of the exergetic flows and costs of the productive components for both ORC configurations.

| Exergetic flows | Exergetic cost |
|---|---|
| $P = \langle P\vert F_e \quad$ where $\langle P\vert = \left(K_D - \langle FP\rangle\right)^{-1}$ | $P* = \langle P*\vert F_e \quad$ where $\langle P*\vert = \left(U_D - \langle FP\rangle - \langle RP\rangle\right)^{-1}$ |
| $F = \langle F\vert F_e \quad$ where $\langle F\vert = K_D \langle P\vert$ | $F* = F_e + \langle FP\rangle P*$ |
| $I = \langle I\vert F_e \quad$ where $\langle I\vert = \left(K_D - U_D\right)\langle P\vert$ | $R* = \langle RP\rangle P*$ |
| $R = \langle R\vert F_e \quad$ where $\langle R\vert = \langle RP\rangle\langle P\vert$ | |

The exergoeconomic costs of the product as a function of external resources are determined from the balance of costs

$$\Pi_P = Z + \Pi_F \tag{1}$$

Where, Z represents non-energy factors of production, that is, factors of amortization, maintenance, operation, etc. On the other hand, the exergoeconomic cost of the product ($\Pi_P$) and of the resource ($\Pi_F$), depending on the external resources and the distribution coefficients are

$$\Pi_P = \left(U_D - \langle FP\rangle - \langle RP\rangle\right)^{-1}\Pi_e \quad ; \quad \Pi_F = \Pi_e + \langle FP\rangle\Pi_P \tag{2}$$

The exergoeconomic cost for the residue formation is given by

$$\Pi_R = \langle RP\rangle\Pi_P \tag{3}$$

The exergoeconomic unit cost of the resource and of the product of the ith component exhibits the monetary amount to produce one kWh, and is represented as follows

$$c_{F,i} = \frac{\Pi_{F,i}}{F_i} \quad ; \quad c_{P,i} = \frac{\Pi_{P,i}}{P_i} \tag{4}$$

The exergoeconomic cost of external resources ($\Pi_e$) includes the investment and maintenance costs of the system, $\dot{Z}_i$, and the economic unit cost of fuels, $\dot{E}_{0i}$; where, the cost of the equipment per unit of time ($\dot{Z}_i$) is a function of the cost of the equipment, the annual amortization factor ($a$) the maintenance factor ($\varphi$), and the number of operating hours per year ($N$).

$$\Pi_e = \left[ \dot{Z}_i + c_i \dot{E}_{0i} \right]_{i=1,\ldots,n} \tag{5}$$

$$\dot{Z}_i = \frac{a\varphi}{N} Z_i; \text{ where } a = \frac{i(1+i)^n}{(1+i)^n - 1} \tag{6}$$

Table 3 shows the correlations used to determine the costs of the equipment that make up both the ORC configurations and the economic parameters of the system (Nondy and Gogoi, 2021).

Table 3. Equipment cost and economic parameters of the ORC for both configurations.

| Equipment cost (USD) | Economic parameters | |
|---|---|---|
| $Z_{SH} = 309.143(A_{SH}) + 231.915$ | Annual hours, $N$ (h) | 7446 |
| $Z_{EV} = 309.143(A_{EV}) + 231.915$ | Maintenance factor, $\varphi$ (-) | 1.06 |
| $Z_{EC} = 309.143(A_{EC}) + 231.915$ | Interest rate, $i$ (%) | 12 |
| $Z_T = 6000(\dot{W}_T)^{0.7}$ | Years of life, $n$ (years) | 20 |
| $Z_P = 3540(\dot{W}_P)^{0.71}$ | | |
| $Z_{HE} = 1.3(190 + 310 A_{HE})$ | | |
| $Z_{COND} = 1773(\dot{m}_{ref})$ | | |

The heat exchange areas of each component of the HRSG (this is, SH, EV, EC and HE) are determined as follows

$$A_i = \frac{\dot{Q}_i}{U_i \, DTML} \tag{7}$$

Where the total heat transfer coefficients are obtained from Mohammadi et al. (2018). Finally, Table 4 presents the operating conditions of the ORC for both configurations. The conditions of the residual thermal source correspond to the exhaust gases that come from the hybrid combined cycle plant in the Valley of Mexico (CFE, 2005).

Table 4. ORC operating conditions for both configurations.

| Environment | | Organic fluid | | Waste heat source | |
|---|---|---|---|---|---|
| $P_{atm}$, (bar) | 0.78 | $T_1$, (°C) | 150 | $T_{g1}$, (°C) | 185 |
| $T_{amb}$, (°C) | 10 - 40 | $\Delta T_{cond}$, (°C) | 15 | $T_{g4}$, (°C) | 100 |
| | | $\eta_{sit}$, (-) | 0.90 | $\dot{m}_{eg}$ (kg$_{eg}$/s) | 297.1 |
| | | $\eta_{sib}$, (-) | 0.80 | $c_{peg}$, (kJ/kg K) | 1.13 |

## 3. Results

The simulation of the process was carried out using the Python and Julia software. Figures 3 show the exergoeconomic costs of the turbine product as a function of the total area of the HRSG, for different evaporation and ambient temperatures. It can be seen, an increase in the exergoeconomic cost and the total area in the HRSG with the increase in the evaporation temperature. Figure 3(a) shows an average increase in the area of 20 m² when going from an ambient temperature of 25 to 40°C. In addition, the exergoeconomic cost that oscillates between 224 and 238 USD/h, represents an average increase of 4.77%

when going from an evaporation temperature of 80 to 95°C for the different ambient temperatures. Figure 3(b) shows that the area variation for the same ambient temperature range occurs at temperatures above 90°C, with increments of 13 m². On the other hand, for evaporation temperatures lower than 85°C, there is no significant increase in the area, that is, the area remains almost constant with the variation of the different environmental temperatures. Likewise, the exergoeconomic cost of the turbine product has an increase when adding the HE to the ORC; however, this exergoeconomic cost increases only by 3.81% with respect to the results shown in the ORC configuration when going from an evaporation temperature of 80 to 95°C.

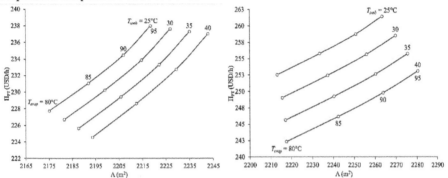

Figure 3. Exergoeconomic cost of the turbine product as a function of heat exchange area for (a) the simple ORC, and (b) the ORC with HE.

Figure 4 shows the exergoeconomic cost of the turbine product and power in both configurations, as a function of evaporation and ambient temperatures. Both configurations show an increase in cost when the evaporation temperature increases from 80 to 95°C; for the simple ORC shown in Figure 4(a), this increase is 4.77%; while in the case of the ORC with HE, it presents an increase of 3.82%. In addition, both configurations also show that, under the condition of the minimum ambient temperature and the highest evaporation temperature, the highest power and the highest cost are presented. The ORC configuration shows the highest power of 4,491.87 kW at a cost of 238 USD/h. On the other hand, the ORC with HE shown in Figure 4(b) shows that the power can be increased by 825.30 kW under the same operating conditions and the cost reflects an increase of 23.44 USD/h.

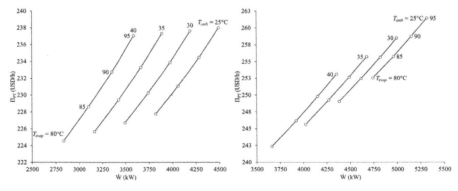

Figure 4. Exergoeconomic cost of the turbine product and power output for (a) the simple ORC, and (b) the ORC with HE.

Finally, Table 5 shows the exergoeconomic cost for the residue formation and the unit exergoeconomic cost of the components of both configurations, for the lowest ambient temperature and the highest evaporation temperature. The cost associated with the external resource (fuel) that enters the HRSG of the two configurations has the same value of 167 USD/h; however, the total cost shows a difference between the simple ORC and ORC with HE due to the increased cost of HE. On the other hand, when adding this component, the total exergoeconomic cost for the residue formation reflects a decrease of 47.31% and, in addition, the unit exergoeconomic cost of the functional product of the system also decreases from 0.049 USD/kWh to 0.046 USD/ kWh.

Table 5. Exergoeconomic costs for the residue formation and unit exergoeconomic cost.

|  | ORC | | | | ORC with HE | | | |
|---|---|---|---|---|---|---|---|---|
|  | $\Pi_F$ (USD/h) | Z (USD/h) | $\Pi_R$ (USD/h) | $c_P$ (USD/kWh) | $\Pi_F$ (USD/h) | Z (USD/h) | $\Pi_R$ (USD/h) | $c_P$ (USD/kWh) |
| (1) SH | 64.22 | 3.54 | 25.79 | 0.031 | 75.20 | 4.21 | 15.64 | 0.027 |
| (2) EV | 40.67 | 2.82 | 16.55 | 0.034 | 46.41 | 3.42 | 9.81 | 0.028 |
| (3) EC | 62.11 | 5.12 | 25.59 | 0.042 | 45.39 | 4.08 | 9.74 | 0.029 |
| (4) T | 0.00 | 38.14 | 0.00 | 0.049 | 0.00 | 54.23 | 0.00 | 0.046 |
| (6) P | 0.00 | 3.85 | 8.14 | 0.102 | 0.00 | 5.50 | 4.88 | 0.087 |
| (7) HE | - |  | - | - | 0.00 | 3.74 | 7.38 | 0.067 |
| Total | 167.00 | 53.47 | 76.06 | - | 167.00 | 71.44 | 40.07 | - |

## 4. Conclusions

Based on the exergoeconomic analysis carried out in the simple ORC and ORC with HE, it is concluded that the unit exergoeconomic cost of the functional product of the system can be reduced by taking advantage of the thermal current that leaves the turbine through a HE. In addition, the exergoeconomic cost for the formation of the residue also reflects a decrease compared to the ORC, both configurations with the same exergoeconomic cost of the fuel associated with the external resource.

## References

CFE - Comisión Federal de Electricidad, 2005, Prontuario de la Central Termoeléctrica de Ciclo Híbrido del Valle de México, Mexico.

C. T. Cuadra, A. V. Capilla, 2000, Termoeconomía, Universidad de Zaragoza, España.

H. Lugo-Méndez, S. Castro-Hernández, M. Salazar-Pereyra, J. Valencia-López, E.V. Torres-González, R. Lugo-Leyte, 2020, Residue Cost Formation of a High Bypass Turbofan Engine, Applied Sciences 10 (24), 9060.

M. Mohammadi, M.H. Ashouri, M. Ahmadi, M. Bidi, M. Sadeghzadeh, T. Ming, 2018, Thermoeconomic analysis and multiobjective optimization of a combined gas turbine, steam, and organic Rankine cycle, Energy Science and Engineering, 6 (5), 506–522.

J. Nondy, T. K. Gogoi, 2021, Exergoeconomic investigation and multi-objective optimization of different ORC configurations or waste heat recovery, Energy Conversion and Management, 245, 114593.

C. Torres, A. Valero, 2021, The exergy cost theory revisited, Energies, 14, 1594.

C. Torres, A. Valero, L. Serra, J. Royo, 2002, Structural theory and thermoeconomic diagnosis: Part I. On malfunction and dysfunction analysis, Energy Conversion and Management, 43 (9–12), 1503–1518.

Antonis Kokossis, Michael C. Georgiadis, Efstratios N. Pistikopoulos (Eds.)
PROCEEDINGS OF THE 33rd European Symposium on Computer Aided Process Engineering
(ESCAPE33), June 18-21, 2023, Athens, Greece
© 2023 Elsevier B.V. All rights reserved.  http://dx.doi.org/10.1016/B978-0-443-15274-0.50490-X

# Hybrid polymeric membrane – chemical absorption system for pre-combustion CO₂ capture

Maytham Alabid[a], Nela Slavu[a,b], Marius Sandru[c], Cristian Dinca[a,b]

[a]Faculty of Energy, University Politehnica of Bucharest, Splaiul Independenței, 060042 Bucharest, Romania
[b]Academy of Romanian Scientists, Ilfov 3, 050044 Bucharest, Romania
[c]SINTEF Materials and Chemistry, Sem Saelands vei 2A, 7465, Trondheim, Norway

## Abstract

The purpose of the article is to develop $CO_2$ capture technologies to face the increasing decarburization requirements of the industrial sector. In this context, air or $O_2$ have been used as oxidizing agents for gasification process with the usage of a hybrid configuration of polymer membranes and chemical absorption process that has been technically and economically analyzed. The role of polymer membranes is to pre-concentrate the $CO_2$ stream in order to separate it in the absorption column. The chemical absorption technology analyzed is based on the use of MEA 30 wt.% solvent. The proposed hybrid solution was integrated pre-combustion in a BIGCC system equipped with a combined cycle. The study modeled energy processes using CHEMCAD version 8.1 software and polymer membranes developed in the $CO_2$ Hybrid research project. The LCOE indicator demonstrated $CO_2$ capture to be remarkably higher when utilizing air at 142.5 €/MWh versus 86 €/MWh for the $O_2$ case.

**Keywords**: Polymeric membrane, Gasification, air separation, chemical absorption.

## 1. Introduction

Energy necessities (particularly electricity energy) are constantly increasing due to the raise in the world population and the evolution of living levels [1]. Presently, a coal-fired power plant is the most energy producer in the world and it is the main $CO_2$ emission that directly influences climate change and causes an increase in the atmosphere temperature [2]. In this context, different solutions have been studied to match energy demands with low/zero carbon dioxide emissions, such as utilizing biomass, considered a $CO_2$-neutral fuel [3,4]. The primary benefit of biomass usage is that it utilizes and absorbs carbon dioxide through its outgrowth, similar to the amount generated during the combustion process [5]. In a combined cycle with integrated gasification, biomass is used efficiently to generate electricity (BIGCC technology). In such a cycle, any type of biomass can be harnessed [6]. Integrating carbon capture systems (CCS) in a combined cycle that used biomass to produce energy can be considered an optimistic technology to achieve carbon mitigation targets and reduce climate change issues [7]. The polymeric membrane is currently used with chemical absorption to capture carbon dioxide emissions with high purity [8-10]. The study aims to evaluate membrane and chemical absorption performance with the gasification process that used either air or oxygen as an oxidizing agent.

## 2. Methodology

In this paper, two cases have been considered as follows:

**Case A**: BIGCC based on air as a gasification agent with hybrid $CO_2$ capture technology using membrane and chemical absorption technology;

**Case B**: BIGCC based on $O_2$ as a gasification agent with $CO_2$ capture technology using membrane technology.

Both technologies will be compared with the variants without $CO_2$ capture technology.

*2.1. Gasification process*

In this study, air and oxygen have been both used as oxidizing agents, where in the case of $O_2$, a compressor was harnessed in the line of $O_2$ inlet with 5 bar to increase the syngas pressure introduced into the membrane technology, the pressure being the maximum accepted for the membrane technology developed in the University Politehnica of Bucharest laboratory. The energy required to separate 1 ton of $O_2$ from $N_2$ is about 540 kJ/kg [11]. The biomass feed was a poplar bark with a LHV (lower heating value) of 18,532.8 kJ/kg, table (1) below demonstrates the elemental composition of the waste in weight concentration (wt.%) [12].

**Table 1.** Biomass waste base characteristics.

| Biomass | Main composition [wt.%] | | | | | | |
|---|---|---|---|---|---|---|---|
| | C | H | S | O | N | A | W |
| Poplar bark | 48.02 | 6.00 | 0.09 | 35.21 | 0.27 | 2.02 | 8.40 |

The gasification process is recognized by the equivalent ratio (ER, in mol/mol) and cold gas ratio (CGR), represented in formulas (1,2). $F_1$, in kg/h, demonstrates the real air/$O_2$ flow inserted into the gasification reactor, while $F_2$ , in kg/h, presents the stoichiometric air/$O_2$ stream needed for the complete combustion of each combustible substance.

$$ER = \frac{F_1}{F_2}, \tag{1}$$

$$CGR = \frac{S_1 \times LHV_1}{S_2 \times LHV_2} \times 100\%, \tag{2}$$

While $S_1$ is the syngas stream rate, in kg/h; $LHV_1$ the syngas lower heating value, in kJ/kg; $S_2$ the biomass stream rate, in kg/h; $LHV_2$ the biomass lower heating value, in kJ/kg.

*2.2. Membrane process*

In the current research, one stage of membrane with 3,000 GPU [10], a vacuum pump and a compressor has been used for capturing $CO_2$ emissions from syngas before its utilization in a combined cycle. Thus, membrane technology has the role of pre-concentrate $CO_2$ in the permeate stream. The membrane consists of 2 layers: a PSF 50 K, the support polymer, and the CA enzyme, the polymer solution [13]. The membrane module used was a spiral wound with a flow style of counter-current, the permeability of $N_2$ was assumed 20 GPU [8]. In case A, a compressor was needed to increase the syngas pressure in order to increase the membrane efficiency for $CO_2$ separation before the chemical absorption unit. However, in Case B, no compressor was used before the membrane unit due to the syngas pressure that comes from gasification process (5 bar). Therefore, the chemical absorption unit is not integrated due to the high purity, more than 99.9%.

*2.3. Chemical absorption process*

In the chemical absorption process (CAP) a chemical solvent is used for capturing the $CO_2$ from different gaseous streams in the absorption column before being regenerated in the stripper column [14,15]. CAP technology is only used in case A due to the low $CO_2$ content in the syngas. The chemical solvent utilized was monoethanolamine in a 30% weight concentration. To reduce the chemical solvent flow and heat required for its regeneration, the syngas stream was treated in the first step by membrane technology.

## 2.4. Combined cycle technology

The syngas obtained after the membrane process (the retentate stream) was compressed at 17 bar and introduced to the combined cycle for electricity generation. The steam obtained from the back-pressure steam turbine (5 bar) was used either to provide heat energy for solvent regeneration (case A) or to cover the WGR (water gas shift reactor) requirements for case B, see figure (1). In case A, the steam required for WGR was generated from HRSG (heat recovery steam generator), where 500 kg/h of natural gas was used.

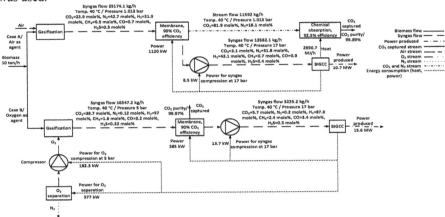

**Figure 1.** Scheme of pre-combustion carbon capture in BIGCC with main results.

## 2.5. Economic assumptions

Table (2) shows the main assumptions considered in the current research.

**Table 2.** Main assumptions for economic assessment [16].

| Indicators | Main data |
|---|---|
| Factor of availability, % | 85 |
| Electricity cost, €/MWh | 200 |
| CO₂ fee, €/t | 82 [17] |
| Working hours, h/year | 75% of 8,760 |
| Membrane module cost, €/m² | 50 |
| Life duration of membrane, years | 5 |
| Vacuum pump / CO₂ pump price, €/kW | 1,300 / 1,350 |
| CO₂ compressor price, €/kW | 1,800 |
| Replacement membrane price, €/m² | 10 |
| Cost of Labor, €/h | 15 |
| Absorber / Stripper part, M€ | 27.7 / 31.4 |
| Pump of rich-lean amine with heat exchanger, M€ | 6.89 |
| Gas / steam turbine cost, M€ | 6 / 3 |
| Condenser / Gasification unit cost, M€ | 39 / 45 [18] |
| Water gas shift / Ash treatment cost, M€ | 21 / 16 [18] |
| Heat recovery steam generator, M€ | 3 [18] |
| CO₂ compression compressor, M€ | 11.7 |
| Compressor inter-stage coolers and separators, M€ | 0.87 |

Equation (3) shows the total CO₂ emissions, while equation (4) presents CO₂ emission factor, $FCO_2$, for cases with and without CO₂ capture (in kg/MWh).

$$CO_{2\,wc} = CO_{2\,CG} - CO_{2\,A} - CO_{2\,BA} + CO_{2\,NG}, \qquad (3)$$

Where $CO_{2\,wc}$ is the total CO₂ emissions; $CO_{2\,CG}$ is the CO₂ generated in the gasification and combustion process; $CO_{2\,A}$ is CO₂ emissions captured by membrane and CAP; $CO_{2\,BA}$ is CO₂ emissions required for biomass growth, ; $CO_{2\,NG}$ is CO₂ produced from natural gas usage (case A), all parameters are in kg/h. When no capture technology integrated, $CO_{2\,woutc}$, $CO_{2\,A}$ is zero. The $CO_{2\,BA}$ is the sum of CO₂ generated in the gasification process and $CO_2$ generated in the combustion process according to CO that exists in syngas. Regarding the value used, $CO_2$ in syngas is 23.9 mole% of the syngas flow, and the $CO_2$ produced from CO exits in the syngas is 276.7 kg/h (as it is in figure 1), therefore, $CO_2$ generated after syngas and combustion process is 6,293.3 kg/h, which represents the amount of $CO_2$ absorbed during biomass growth (photosynthesis process). Considering that the biomass is carbon neutral, all the $CO_2$ emissions generated by the carbon from the biomass composition were considered neutral as well.

The amount of $CO_2$ absorbed by biomass growth is lower compared to the $CO_2$ generated from gasification and combustion process as a result of $CO_2$ emissions from the preparation and transport of biomass to the power plant which have not been considered to simplify the research.

$$FCO_2 = \frac{CO_{2\,wc}\ or\ CO_{2\,woutc}}{Total\ electricity\ generation},$$ (4)

To evaluate the techno-economic effect of $CO_2$ removal process, the coming factors have been suggested [19].

Levelised cost of electricity (LCOE), in €/MWh, can be computed with the relation (5).

$$LCOE = \frac{CAPEX+OPEX}{W_{net}},$$ (5)

$W_{net}$ is the fine electric energy produced (MWh) by each technology with and without $CO_2$ capture; CAPEX represents capital expenditure while OPEX indicates operational expenditure of the project, (in €).

Net present value (NPV) was computed as follows, (in €).

$$NPV = \sum_{i=1}^{n_f} \frac{IN_i - C_i - A_i}{(1+r)^i} - \sum_{i=1}^{n_r} I_i \cdot (1+r)^i,$$ (6)

$IN_i$ is the real bonus (€/year); $C_i$ the price of operation and maintenance (€/year); $A_i$ rate of payback loan (€/year); $I_i$ real investment cost (€/year), r is the rate of discount, which is 8% in energy section.

Discounted payback period (DPP) was computed by formula (7), (in years).

$$NPV = \sum_{i=1}^{DPP} \frac{IN_i - C_i - I_i}{(1+r)^i},$$ (7)

The profitability index (IP) was founded by the next equation, where IA is the deduct investment.

$$IP = \frac{NPV+IA}{IA}$$ (8)

## 3. Results and Discussions

The gasification and capture systems were simulated through CHEMCAD software of 8.1 version while the combined cycle was modeled in excel. In the gasification process, the equivalent ratio was considered 25% for both air and $O_2$. As an example, in figure (2) the variation of the CGE according to ER where $O_2$ was used as an oxidizing agent. Membrane unit either capture most of $CO_2$ content in syngas with lower purity and send the recovered flow (mainly $CO_2$

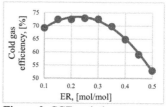

**Figure 2.** CGE variation according to ER for $O_2$ utilization.

and $N_2$) to the chemical absorption (case A) or capture the $CO_2$ stream at 99.97% purity (case B) due to due to the low $N_2$ content in the syngas obtained from gasification process. Chemical absorption usage in case A helps to raise the concentration of $CO_2$ removal from membrane at a specific capture rate. Figures (3, 4) show that $CO_2$ capture efficiency of chemical absorption continually rise with a higher L/G ratio, where an extra chemical solvent is inserted into the process. Taking into account the low $CO_2$ content of the syngas stream, the L/G ratio is greater than 12 kg solvent/kg syngas for a minimum capture efficiency of 90%. The thermal energy consumption required to regenerate the chemical solvent was about 3.9 MJ/kg for a $CO_2$ absorption capacity of 0.36 mole $CO_2$/mole solvent. The $CO_2$ emissions for biomass growth in case A are slightly lower than emissions of case B because of the difference in hydrocarbon concentrations in the syngas of each case. The $CO_2$ emissions generated from natural gas usage were not treated in CCS, therefore, $CO_2$ emission factor for case A is higher than the other case. The global efficiency in case A reduced by CCS utilization, where both electrical and thermal energy was consumed for the membrane and solvent regeneration process. On the other hand, the global efficiency in case B wasn't highly influenced by using CCS due to the low power required for the membrane vacuum pump (385 kW). Table (3) shows the optimum results of each case simulated.

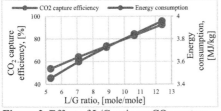

**Figure 3.** Effect of L/G ratio on $CO_2$ capture efficiency and energy consumption.

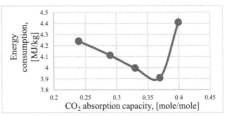

**Figure 4.** $CO_2$ absorption capacity influence on energy consumption.

**Table 3.** The essential results regarding the four cases examined.

| Cases | Case A | | Case B | |
|---|---|---|---|---|
| | No CO₂ capture | With CO₂ capture | No CO₂ capture | With CO₂ capture |
| Biomass flow, ton/h | 10 | 10 | 10 | 10 |
| Heat flow with syngas, kW | 24,979 | 24,979 | 8,698 | 8,698 |
| CO₂ emissions for biomass growth, kg/h | 6,293.3 | | 6,891 | |
| CO₂ emissions from natural gas usage, kg/h | No use | 1,380.3 | No use | No use |
| Total CO₂ emissions, kg/h | 6,293.3 | 2,009.6 | 6,891 | 689.1 |
| Membrane surface area, m² | - | 25,000 | - | 2,500 |
| Compressor pressure, bar | - | 2.2 | - | No use |
| Vacuum pump pressure, bar | - | 0.25 | - | 0.25 |
| L/G ratio for Chemical absorption, mole/mole | - | 12.4 | - | No use |
| Solvent flow, kmol/h | - | 350 | - | No use |
| Energy consumption for chemical absorption, MJ/kg | - | 3.9 | - | No use |
| Gas turbine power, kW | 8,968.2 | 8,968.2 | 12,234.4 | 12,234.4 |
| Steam turbine power, kW | 2,896.2 | 2,896.2 | 4,559.1 | 4,559.1 |
| Global efficiency, % | 42.0 | 38.0 | 42.3 | 41.3 |
| CO₂ factor, kg/MWh | - | -435.5 | - | -877.4 |
| NPV, M€ | 9,152 | 67,411 | 32,470 | 124,830 |
| DPP, years | 17.73 | 8.17 | 8.07 | 4.5 |
| Profitability index | 1.18 | 2.15 | 1.62 | 3.87 |
| LCOE, €/MWh | 157 | 142.5 | 135.3 | 86.1 |

In case A, the gasification process occurred with atmospheric pressure, so no electricity was required to compress the stoichiometric air stream. The syngas produced has a high flow rate, therefore, a compressor was integrated before the membrane stage to raise the efficiency of $CO_2$ removal and that increased the electricity needed. Despite the fact that CAP helped raise the purity of $CO_2$ recovery, it increased CAPEX cost and mitigated the total combined cycle power generation due to the heat energy required. On the other hand, the usage of $O_2$ as an oxidizing agent has the advantage of no CAP utilization in the process due to the high purity (99.9%) achieved after the membrane stage, which enhanced the reduction of CAPEX cost in case B. In contrast to case A, electrical energy was needed for $O_2$ separation which can be considered a power consumption from the combined cycle. However, the integration of a 5-bar compressor in the $O_2$ stream (in gasification) generated the syngas at high pressure where no need to provide high electricity for the membrane stage as in the air case. Consequently, the electricity produced in case B is greater than that produced in case A.

## Acknowledgments

The research has been granted by the UEFISCDI within the International Project NO Grants 2014–2021, under project contract no. 13/2020.

## References

1.  Gaye A , 2007/ 2008, Human development report, fighting climate change: human solidarity in a divided world. Access to Energy and Human Development.
2.  IEA. World energy outlook. Paris: International Energy Agency; 2020.
3.  Slavu, N., Badea, A. and Dinca, C., 2022. Technical and Economical Assessment of $CO_2$ Capture-Based Ammonia Aqueous. Processes, 10(5), p.859.
4.  Slavu, N., Dinca, C. and Banica, C.K., 2021, October. Production of $H_2$-rich Syngas from Biomass Gasification with $CO_2$ Capture Technology. In 2021 10th International Conference on Energy and Environment (CIEM) (pp. 1-5). IEEE.
5.  Dinca, C.R.I.S.T.I.A.N., Badea, A.D.R.I.A.N., Marculescu, C.O.S.M.I.N. and Gheorghe, C.O.R.A., 2009. Environmental analysis of biomass combustion process. In Proceedings of the 3rd WSEAS Int. Conf. on Renewable Energy Sources (pp. 234-238).
6.  Cormos, A.M., Dinca, C., Petrescu, L., Chisalita, D.A., Szima, S. and Cormos, C.C., 2018. Carbon capture and utilisation technologies applied to energy conversion systems and other energy-intensive industrial applications. Fuel, 211, pp.883-890.
7.  Rhodes, J.S. and Keith, D.W., 2005. Engineering economic analysis of biomass IGCC with carbon capture and storage. Biomass and Bioenergy, 29(6), pp.440-450.
8.  Cormos, C.C., Petrescu, L., Cormos, A.M. and Dinca, C., 2021. Assessment of Hybrid Solvent—Membrane Configurations for Post-Combustion $CO_2$ Capture for Super-Critical Power Plants. Energies, 14(16), p.5017.
9.  Alabid, M., Cormos, C.C. and Dinca, C., 2022. Critical Assessment of Membrane Technology Integration in a Coal-Fired Power Plant. Membranes, 12(9), p.904.
10. Sandru, M., Sandru, E.M., Ingram, W.F., Deng, J., Stenstad, P.M., Deng, L. and Spontak, R.J., 2022. An integrated materials approach to ultrapermeable and ultraselective $CO_2$ polymer membranes. Science, 376(6588), pp.90-94.
11. Banaszkiewicz, T., Chorowski, M. and Gizicki, W., 2014. Comparative analysis of oxygen production for oxy-combustion application. Energy Procedia, 51, pp.127-134.
12. Vassilev, S.V., Baxter, D., Andersen, L.K. and Vassileva, C.G., 2010. An overview of the chemical composition of biomass. Fuel, 89(5), pp.913-933.
13. $CO_2$ hybrid project [online website] http://co2hybrid.upb.ro/index_ro.html.
14. Wang, M., Lawal, A., Stephenson, P., Sidders, J. and Ramshaw, C., 2011. Post-combustion $CO_2$ capture with chemical absorption: A state-of-the-art review. Chemical engineering research and design, 89(9), pp.1609-1624.
15. Koronaki, I.P., Prentza, L. and Papaefthimiou, V., 2015. Modeling of $CO_2$ capture via chemical absorption processes– An extensive literature review. Renewable and Sustainable Energy Reviews, 50, pp.547-566.
16. Chemengonline. www.chemengonline.com, 2022. (Accessed 01 June 2022). https://www.chemengonline.com/pci-home
17. Trading economics [online website] https://tradingeconomics.com/commodity/carbon (Accessed 29 November 2022).
18. Kramer, S., 2003. Gasification plant cost and performance optimization. Nexant Inc.(US).
19. Cormos, C.C. and Dinca, C., 2021. Techno-economic and environmental implications of decarbonization process applied for Romanian fossil-based power generation sector. Energy, 220, p.119734.

Antonis Kokossis, Michael C. Georgiadis, Efstratios N. Pistikopoulos (Eds.)
PROCEEDINGS OF THE 33rd European Symposium on Computer Aided Process Engineering
(ESCAPE33), June 18-21, 2023, Athens, Greece

# Electrification of ethylene production: exploring the potential of flexible operation

Julia L. Tiggeloven,[a] André P.C. Faaij,[a,b] Gert Jan Kramer[a] and Matteo
Gazzani*,[a]

[a] *Copernicus Institute of Sustainable Development, Utrecht University, The Netherlands*
[b] *TNO Energy Transition, the Netherlands*
* *Corresponding author*

## Abstract

Electrification of the ethylene production process has potential for reducing hard-to-abate $CO_2$ emissions, however, this comes at the expense of increased electricity consumption. Flexible operation of electric naphtha crackers in response to fluctuating electricity prices can compensate for the increased operating costs, depending on the boundary conditions. However, given the level of technological complexity, it remains uncertain to what extend flexible operation of the ethylene production process is feasible. In this work we use mathematical optimization to investigate the added value of various levels of flexible operation of the process in a low-$CO_2$ energy system. We find that (i) highly variable electricity prices promote flexible operation and (ii) providing flexibility in low-$CO_2$ energy systems by ramping the production or using electricity storage is essential.

**Keywords**: electrification, flexibility, optimization.

## 1. Introduction

Electrification of naphtha steam cracking is a potential alternative to reduce emissions in the ethylene production process. Accordingly, the electricity consumption and operating cost of the process are expected to increase significantly, leading to a new balance between investment and operating costs. Due to the high investment costs and complexity of conventional steam crackers, plants are operated at maximum capacity. However, this prevents exploiting the large variation in electricity price in time, especially when and where undispatchable renewables are substantially installed. Flexible operation of electric crackers in response to electricity prices might be able to compensate for the increased operating costs, opening up new opportunities and challenges in the chemical industry. This study aims at further investigating this topic by optimizing the full-year, hourly operation and system design of a simplified ethylene production process, where either conventional or electric steam cracking of naphtha is used to meet an assumed ethylene demand. More specifically, this work uses optimization to assess the system behavior under multiple scenarios, modifying hourly-resolved electricity price profiles, carbon intensity of electricity, and the extend of operational flexibility of the process. Section 2 describes the modeling framework and the case study input data. Section 3 shows the results.

## 2. Method

### 2.1. Modeling framework

The mathematical problem formulation in this work is derived from an existing optimization framework developed by Gabrielli et al. [1], [2]. The decision variables that are optimized by the framework include design variables (i.e. selection and size of technologies) and operational variables (i.e. energy and material flows and storage levels). The framework uses hourly resolved input data on weather conditions, prices and demand data together with a set of available technologies and the corresponding cost and performance coefficients. The objective function of the problem is the total annualized system cost, $J$, that is the sum of the technology cost, $J_c$, and the operating cost, $J_o$. The annualized technology cost is defined as

$$J_c = \sum_{i \in M} (1 + \psi_i)(\lambda_i S_i + \zeta_i) a_i$$

where $\lambda_i$ and $\zeta_i$ represent the size-dependent and size-independent cost parameters of technology $i$ and the annuity factor $a_i$ is used to compute the annualized capital costs. The maintenance cost of the technology is included as fraction of the annual capital costs $\psi_i$. The operating cost of the system is determined by the annual amount of electricity import, which is expressed as

$$J_o = \sum_{t=1}^{T} \left( u_{e,t} U_{e,t} \right)$$

where $U_{e,t}$ is the electricity import and $u_{e,t}$ the hourly electricity price at hour $t$. The total emissions include indirect emissions from imported electricity and direct emissions from the ethylene production process and are calculated as

$$e_{CO_2} = \sum_{t=1}^{T} \left[ \varepsilon_{elec} U_{elec,t} + \sum_{i \in M} \epsilon_i F_{naphtha,i,t} \right]$$

where $\varepsilon_e$ is the $CO_2$ intensity of the electricity grid and $\epsilon_i$ is the emission factor of the technology per unit of input.

For each hour $t \in T$ and each carrier $j \in N$, the material and energy balances are formulated as:

$$\sum_{i \in M} (U_{j,i,t} + P_{j,i,t} - V_{j,i,t} - F_{j,i,t}) - D_{j,t} = 0$$

where $U_{j,i,t}$ is import, $P_{j,i,t}$ is the production, $V_{j,i,t}$ is export, $F_{j,i,t}$ is consumption and $D_{j,t}$ is the demand. The conversion of the ethylene production plant is described as

$$P_{j',t} = \alpha_{j'} F_{naphtha,t}$$

and

$$F_{j'',t} = \beta_{j''} F_{naphtha,t}$$

where $\alpha_{j'}$ and $\beta_{j''}$ represent the conversion efficiency per kg of naphtha input of the outputs $j' \in J' \subset J$ and the ratio between inputs $j'' \in J'' \subset J$, respectively. Inputs and outputs of the process include naphtha, methane, electricity and steam. The operation range of the plant is expressed as

$$\gamma_{naphta} S_{plant} \le F_{naphtha,t} \le S_{plant}$$

where $\gamma_{naphta}$ is the minimum feasible operating point of the plant as fraction of the installed capacity. For a detailed description of the modeling of storage, PV and offshore wind turbines the reader is referred to Gabrielli et al. [2] and to Weimann et al. [3].

## 2.2. System description

The ethylene production process consist of three main components: pyrolysis (i.e. the cracker), compression and separation. In the cracker furnace, naphtha is preheated and vaporized with superheated steam before it is cracked into light olefins (i.e. ethylene) in the gaseous state. In the conventional cracker the required process heat is supplied by the combustion of a mixture of recovered process gasses, which in this work is assumed to consist of only methane. The exact gas composition depends on the cracker design and on the overall process type; a typical composition is 18% $H_2$, 81% $CH_4$ and 1% residues (i.e. CO and $C_2H_4$) [4]. For electric cracking we assume that indirect resistance heating is used. In both cases the heat in the cracked gas leaving the furnace is recovered by producing high-pressure steam. In the conventional plant design, the high-pressure steam is superheated by hot flue gas in the furnace and used to drive the compressors. As the electric cracker does not produce hot flue gas and therefore no superheated steam, it is assumed that electric compressors are used. After compression and further cooling and drying, the compressed gas enters the separation train where the different products are separated through distillation, refrigeration and extraction.

The modeling framework is used to optimize the design and operation of the ethylene production process for different scenarios. In all scenarios we consider a constant hourly ethylene demand of around 1000 kt ethylene/year, which is typical for ethylene production plants [5]. In the case of the electric cracker, the operation of the plant can be ramped up and down and ethylene can be stored in tanks to maintain the production stable.

*2.3. Input data*

The input and output performance parameters of the conventional and electric ethylene production process are obtained from [5], [6] and shown in Table 1.

*Table 1: Conversion parameters of the conventional and electric ethylene production process.*

| | $\beta_{methane}$ [kWh] | $\beta_{elec}$ [kWh] | $\beta_{steam}$ [kWh] | $\alpha_{ethylene}$ [kg] | $\alpha_{methane}$ [kWh] | $\alpha_{steam}$ [kWh] | $\epsilon_i$ |
|---|---|---|---|---|---|---|---|
| Conventional plant | 1.868 | 0.083 | 0.923 | 0.303 | 2.349 | 0.841 | 0.600 |
| Electric plant | - | 1.942 | 0.492 | 0.303 | 2.349 | 0.542 | - |

The cost parameters $\lambda_i$, $\zeta_i$ and $\psi_i$ of all technologies are shown in Table 2.

*Table 2: Cost data of all technologies.*

| | Type | Unit | $\lambda_i$ [€/unit] | $\zeta_i$ [M€] | $\psi_i$ [%] | Source |
|---|---|---|---|---|---|---|
| Conventional plant | $C_2H_4$ production | $kg_{C2H4}$ | 4531 | 350 | 0.04 | [5] |
| Electric plant | $C_2H_4$ production | $kg_{C2H4}$ | 4433 | 358 | 0.02 | [5] |
| Ethylene tank | Storage | $kg_{C2H4}$ | 18.24 | - | 0.02 | [7] |
| Li-ion battery | Storage | kWh | 128.8 | - | 0.01 | [8] |
| 9.5 MW turbine | Offshore wind | turbine | $17.8 \cdot 10^6$ | - | 0.02 | [9] |
| Ground mounted PV | PV | $m^2$ | 140.9 | - | 0.01 | [9] |

The hourly resolved solar irradiations and wind speeds are obtained from the Dutch meteorology institute (KNMI) and the Dutch Offshore Wind Atlas (DOWA), respectively. It is assumed that the plant is located in the Netherlands near the port of Rotterdam to accommodate a direct connection to offshore wind parks. Hourly resolved spot electricity prices are obtained from ENTSO-E for the year 2019 in the Netherlands.

# 3. Results

In the first analysis we determine the $CO_2$ reduction potential of electrification of the conventional process and analyze the new balance between investment and operating costs that result from electrification. Next, we investigate the potential of flexibility in electric cracking and its sensitivity towards different economic input parameters. Finally, we assess the effect of the minimum feasible operating range on the optimal system design and operation, including when batteries and renewables are adopted along with the electric cracker. An overview of the investigated cases is shown in Table 3.

*Table 3: Available technologies in the four investigated cases.*

|           | Technologies available | Electricity import |
|-----------|------------------------|--------------------|
| Reference | Conventional cracker, Ethylene tank | Yes |
| Case A    | Electric cracker, Ethylene tank | Yes |
| Case B    | Electric cracker, Ethylene tank, Li-ion battery | Yes |
| Case C    | Electric cracker, Ethylene tank, Li-ion battery, offshore wind, PV | No |

### 3.1. Environmental potential of electrification

The performance of the electric cracker in terms of total direct and indirect $CO_2$ emissions is compared to that of the conventional cracker in four scenarios in which electricity is bought from the grid with different projected $CO_2$ intensities (Table 4). In this analysis we only include emissions related to the heat provision of the process, while the $CO_2$ content derived from the product end-of-life is ignored.

*Table 4: Overview of the different projected $CO_2$ intensities and RES production rates of the four scenarios with the corresponding emission reduction potential.*

| Year | Carbon intensity [kg $CO_2$/kWh] | Share of RES production [%] | Reduction potential for electric [%] |
|------|----------------------------------|-----------------------------|--------------------------------------|
| 2019 | 0.369 [10] | 22.0 | 0 |
| 2025 | 0.208 [10] | 54.7 | 36.1 |
| 2030 | 0.094 [10] | 72.0 | 71.1 |
| 2050 | 0 | 100 | 100 |

Not surprisingly, the results show that the emission reduction potential of electrification is strongly determined by the carbon intensity of electricity. For a carbon intensity of 0.369 kgCO$_2$/kWh, which is similar to today's value, there is no $CO_2$ reduction potential of electrification. Based on the projected carbon intensity, a 71% reduction of the total energy related emissions can be achieved in 2030. This potential is relatively small considering the investments, however, it is worth noting that cracker emissions are hard to abate otherwise.

### 3.2. Added value of flexible operation

Based on literature data, the difference in investment costs between a conventional and an electric ethylene production plant is around 2%. However, considering the spot electricity prices of 2019, the import costs of electric cracking account for 73.5% of the total annual costs, compared to 10.5% for the conventional plant. Although the cost parameters are highly uncertain, it is unlikely that the conventional plant would be more expensive than the electric alternative, unless high carbon prices are present. Moreover, the low share of electricity costs of the conventional plant makes flexible operation in response to electricity prices irrelevant.

As opposed to conventional ethylene production, the large share of electricity costs in electric steam cracking can lead to significant cost savings when plants are operated flexibly in response to electricity price. However, adapting the plant to flexible operation requires a more challenging cracker design, ethylene storage and production capacity to shift the production in time, thus increasing the investment costs. We analyze this trade-off under different economic boundary conditions by comparing the steady state operation design with a system design where flexibility in the operation is optimized.

More specifically, we change the value of the (i) size-dependent and (ii) size-independent cost parameters of the plant and the (iii) mean and (iv) standard deviation of the electricity price and evaluate how they affect the value of flexibility (VOF) of the system. The VOF is here defined as

$$VOF = J^{Steady\ state} - J^{Flexible}$$

where $J^{Steady\ state}$ is the total annual cost of the steady state operation design and $J^{Flexible}$ is the total annual cost for the optimal design where flexibility is allowed. The result of this sensitivity analysis is shown in Figure 1 and indicate that an electricity price with a high mean and standard deviation results in a high VOF, as well as a low value of the size dependent investment costs parameter. Furthermore, the slope of the dashed green line, representing the VOF for a high mean (+50%), implies that the effect of variability in the electricity price on the VOF is greater for a high mean.

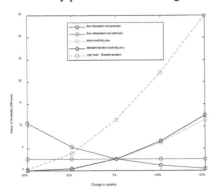 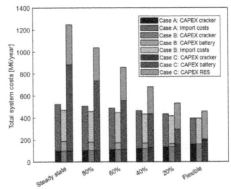

*Figure 1: Result of the sensitivity analysis for the electricity price and investment cost parameters.*

*Figure 2: Total system costs for optimization of Case A, B & C considering different operational ranges.*

### 3.3. Dynamic operation constraints

The previous section shows the optimal system design for a system in which the operational limits of the cracker, such as operational range, are not constrained. This is however unrealistic. As the feasible operational range of electric crackers is uncertain, we assess the effect of the minimum load of the electric steam cracker on the optimal design and operation and the total costs for the three scenarios in Table 4. The aim is to (i) compare different levels of flexible cracker operation with using a battery for flexibility and (ii) analyze how the system performs when grid import is not allowed and the production process is directly integrated with RES. The total system costs of these cases for an electricity price profile with a high mean and variability is shown in Figure 2.

The results show that the investment costs $J_c$ increase and the total system costs $J$ decrease with flexibility, caused by the substantial electricity cost savings in cases A and B. In case C, the savings are a result of the smaller required RES and battery capacity. For example, operating the cracker in case C with a minimum feasible operating point ($\gamma_{naphta}$) of 80% increases the cracker size by 2.21% compared to steady state operation of case C, but decreases the required battery and offshore wind capacity by 19.8% and 16.8%, respectively, leading to an overall cost decrease of 16.8%. Allowing the cracker in case A to operate with a minimum operating point of 20% of the installed capacity can lead to an overall cost reduction of 16.5% compare to steady state operation without battery. Including a battery to a steady state cracker operation (Case A vs. Case B) decreases the costs by 10.3%, however, it requires a battery capacity of around 4 GWh. Steady state cracker operation for case C requires a battery capacity of 10 GWh, which is 40 times larger than the largest current battery installed and has a volume of 85000 $m^3$ [8].

## 4. Conclusion

In this work we used mathematical optimization to investigate the added value of electrification and flexible operation of the ethylene production process in a low-$CO_2$ energy system. We quantified the relation between $CO_2$ reduction potential and the $CO_2$ intensity of the grid, showing that electrification of the ethylene production process only makes sense for a fully decarbonized electricity grid. However, the high share of low-$CO_2$ electricity will lead to a more variable production of electricity, which will be reflected in the price. Our results indicate that operating an electric cracker flexibly in response to these variable prices can lead to significant costs savings compared to steady state operation. Moreover, battery storage shows to be an economically viable alternative or complementary to provide flexibility in the production process. However, the storage capacity that is required in the investigated scenarios result in a significantly large volume, especially when directly integrating the process with offshore wind and PV. We conclude that system optimization to identify the optimal combination and sizes of technologies and flexible operation of the plant is essential to enable the full decarbonization of the ethylene production process.

## References

[1]     P. Gabrielli, M. Gazzani, and M. Mazzotti, "Electrochemical conversion technologies for optimal design of decentralized multi-energy systems: Modeling framework and technology assessment," *Appl Energy*, vol. 221, pp. 557–575, Jul. 2018, doi: 10.1016/J.APENERGY.2018.03.149.

[2]     P. Gabrielli, M. Gazzani, E. Martelli, and M. Mazzotti, "Optimal design of multi-energy systems with seasonal storage," *Appl Energy*, vol. 219, pp. 408–424, Jun. 2018, doi: 10.1016/J.APENERGY.2017.07.142.

[3]     L. Weimann, P. Gabrielli, A. Boldrini, G. J. Kramer, and M. Gazzani, "Optimal hydrogen production in a wind-dominated zero-emission energy system," *Advances in Applied Energy*, vol. 3, p. 100032, Aug. 2021, doi: 10.1016/J.ADAPEN.2021.100032.

[4]     V. Spallina, I. C. Velarde, J. A. M. Jimenez, H. R. Godini, F. Gallucci, and M. van Sint Annaland, "Techno-economic assessment of different routes for olefins production through the oxidative coupling of methane (OCM): Advances in benchmark technologies," *Energy Convers Manag*, vol. 154, pp. 244–261, Dec. 2017, doi: 10.1016/J.ENCONMAN.2017.10.061.

[5]     H. Zimmerman and R. Walzi, "Ullman's Encyclopedia of Industrial Chemistry," *Wiley Online*, vol. 15, pp. 9–17, 2007.

[6]     T. Ren, M. Patel, and K. Blok, "Olefins from conventional and heavy feedstocks: Energy use in steam cracking and alternative processes," *Energy*, vol. 31, no. 4, pp. 425–451, 2006, doi: 10.1016/J.ENERGY.2005.04.001.

[7]     "Analysis Synthesis and Design of Chemical Processes 5th Edition | Richard Turton | West Virginia University." https://richardturton.faculty.wvu.edu/publications/analysis-synthesis-and-design-of-chemical-processes-5th-edition (accessed Jun. 10, 2022).

[8]     DEA, "Technology Data-Energy storage," 2022. Accessed: Nov. 14, 2022. [Online]. Available: http://www.ens.dk/teknologikatalog

[9]     DEA, "Technology Data-Energy Plants for Electricity and District heating generation," 2022. Accessed: Nov. 14, 2022. [Online]. Available: http://www.ens.dk/teknologikatalog

[10]    P. Planbureau voor de Leefomgeving, "Klimaat- en Energieverkenning 2021," 2021. Accessed: Dec. 02, 2022. [Online]. Available: www.pbl.nl/kev

Antonis Kokossis, Michael C. Georgiadis, Efstratios N. Pistikopoulos (Eds.)
PROCEEDINGS OF THE 33rd European Symposium on Computer Aided Process Engineering
(ESCAPE33), June 18-21, 2023, Athens, Greece
© 2023 Elsevier B.V. All rights reserved.  http://dx.doi.org/10.1016/B978-0-443-15274-0.50492-3

# An MINLP model for the optimal design of CO₂ transportation infrastructure in industrial clusters

Jude O. Ejeh,[a] Sergey B. Martynov,[b] and Solomon F. Brown,[a*]

*ᵃDepartment of Chemical & Biological Engineering, The University of Sheffield, Mappin Street, Sheffield, S1 3JD, United Kingdom*
*ᵇDepartment of Chemical Engineering, University College London, London, WC1E 7JE, United Kingdom}*
**s.f.brown@sheffield.ac.uk*

## Abstract

Carbon capture, utilisation and storage (CCUS) is still the most promising decarbonisation route for carbon-intensive sectors. In the context of industrial clusters, although benefits exist from economies of scale and shared transportation infrastructure, challenges remain relating to planning and investing in large-scale implementations. This involves the optimal sizing of the transportation infrastructure to avoid underestimating the transported amounts that could lead to stranded emitters or overestimating the capacity that would translate to financial losses due to unjustified capital expenditures.

In this work, a mixed integer non-linear programming (MINLP) model for the design of carbon dioxide ($CO_2$) transportation infrastructure in industrial clusters is proposed. The optimisation model considers a set of $CO_2$ emitters, available potential $CO_2$ transport and storage/utilisation options, etc. to obtain the detailed infrastructure design. The model assumes a transportation mode solely by pipelines, with steady-state fluid flow throughout the period of consideration. With an overall (capital and operating) cost minimisation objective, globally optimal network design results are obtained for candidate emitters and network routes within industrial clusters subject to constraints relating to storage balances, nominal pipe selection, and pipeline/fluid flow equations.

**Keywords**: CCUS industrial clusters; $CO_2$ transport infrastructure; Optimisation; MINLP.

## 1. Background

Carbon capture, utilisation and storage (CCUS) remains a promising pathway for decarbonising carbon-intensive industrial sectors and bridging the technology gap for a future net-zero society (Bui et al., 2018; Hasan et al., 2022). This technology consists of key elements such as the carbon dioxide ($CO_2$) sources, capture technologies, conditioning and re-conditioning (compression, purification, etc.), transportation, utilisation, and storage technology and infrastructure.

Capture technologies include all chemical and physicochemical processes that take as input flue gases from emitting sources to produce a $CO_2$-rich stream. Examples are all pre-, post- and oxy-fuel combustion processes, the most popular being post-combustion capture using Monoethanolamine (MEA) as a solvent. Conditioning technologies prepare the $CO_2$-rich stream for a suitable mode of transport - via pipelines, ships, motor and/or rail. Amongst available modes of transport, pipelines are still the most popular and widely researched option owing to their cost-effectiveness over long distances, larger scales and a wide range of conditions (Ejeh et al., 2022). $CO_2$ captured from emitting sources, if not utilised on-site, may be transported to other points of utilisation and/or storage sites for sequestration. Each of these CCUS elements has received (and still receives) a considerable amount of research interest, and significant progress has been made over the past years. However, barriers still exist in both small- and large-scale deployments.

One significant barrier to the large-scale deployment of CCUS technologies is cost (Hasan et al., 2022). Although in the context of industrial clusters, benefits may be realised from economies of scale and shared capture and/or transport infrastructure, challenges still exist in the optimal planning and investment decisions for large-scale projects (Ejeh et al., 2022). $CO_2$ transportation has been known to take a significant portion of overall costs in relation to other elements of the CCUS supply chain. Hence, substantial research efforts have focused on the optimal planning and design of $CO_2$ transport infrastructure.

Optimal pipeline transport infrastructure design goes beyond source-sink matching and involves determining the pipeline size (inner/outer diameters), pipeline material, pipeline network route, specifications, target transportation conditions, location, and size of compression/ purification stations (D'Amore et al., 2021). Pipeline diameters are selected from industrial nominal pipe options based on proven correlations available in the literature (Mechleri et al., 2017), with the most popular model objective being the total capital and operating costs for the design. A widely adopted optimisation model for $CO_2$ transportation infrastructure is as described by Zhang et al. (2018) who used the cost model proposed in Serpa et al. (2011). The latter authors adopted a piecewise linear approximation of $CO_2$ cost estimates combined with other publicly available estimates from large natural gas projects. Similar approaches have been adopted by several authors as outlined in Ejeh et al. (2022) but these estimates have been noted to grossly underestimate actual cost values for $CO_2$ transport owing to the difference in fluid properties (Kim et al., 2018). Although it may become more difficult to solve, it then becomes beneficial to adopt more rigorous models that consider unique $CO_2$ flow properties in costing transport infrastructure designs as adopted, for example, by Mechleri et al. (2017).

An optimisation model for $CO_2$ transportation infrastructure design via pipelines is thus proposed that determines the optimal pipeline size and material from industrial nominal sizes for target transportation conditions. It builds on the mixed integer non-linear programming (MINLP) model proposed by Mechleri et al. (2017) that considers rigorous hydraulic equations for $CO_2$ flow in pipelines to minimise the total capital and operating costs of the infrastructure. Our model determines the globally optimal cost for a network of emitters within industrial clusters whilst accounting for utilisation amongst cluster members.

In the rest of the paper, the optimisation problem is clearly described in Section 2, and our proposed MINLP model is presented in Section 3. The model is then applied to a case study is Section 4, with findings discussed and some conclusions drawn in Section 5.

## 2. Problem description

Figure 1 gives a pictorial representation of a typical $CO_2$ transportation network across multiple sources and sinks. The proposed model thus solves the following optimisation problem.

*Given* a set of emitter nodes ($n \in N$) with known locations and $CO_2$ emission ($Q_{nt}^{em}$) and/or utilisation rates ($Q_{nt}^{um}$); a set of transport routes represented by the arcs ($(n, n') \in A$)

between nodes to final storage points, minimum and maximum pipeline operating conditions and $CO_2$ fluid properties.

*Determine* the optimal pipeline diameters (internal and outer) from nominal sizes, pipeline material, and the number of pipeline segments *to* minimise the capital and operating costs for transporting emitted $CO_2$ to pre-specified sequestration sites.

It is assumed that the $CO_2$ transportation network operates at steady state.

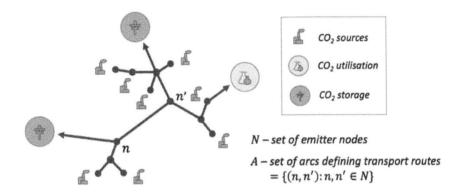

**Figure 1:** Multi-source, multi-sink transportation network

## 3. Mathematical formulation

The objective function (eq. (1)) for the proposed model is the sum of the capital ($TC^C$) and operating ($TC^O$) cost of the transportation infrastructure subject to the constraints outlined in eqs. (2) - (16). The capital cost is as expressed in Mechleri et al. (2017) and the operating cost is taken as 3% of the capital cost (IEA-GHG, 2005).

$$min \quad TC^C + TC^O \tag{1}$$

The mass balance equation in eq. (2) ensures that the flow of $CO_2$ ($Q_{nn'}^{fm}$) to and from a node $n$ balances the amount being emitted ($Q_{nt}^{em}$) and utilised ($Q_{nt}^{um}$) at the node. $N_{nn'}^{p}$ in eq. (3) is an integer variable representing the number of pipeline segments for arc $(n, n') \in A$.

$$\sum_{n':(n',n)\in A} Q_{n'n}^{fm} + Q_{nt}^{em} = \sum_{n':(n,n')\in A} Q_{nn'}^{fm} + Q_{nt}^{um} \quad \forall\, n \in N \tag{2}$$

$$Q_{nn'}^{fm} = N_{nn'}^{p} Q_{nn'}^{fm'} \quad \forall\, (n, n') \in A \tag{3}$$

The Darcy-Weisbach-based hydraulic equation is given in eq. (4), where $D_{nn'}^{pi}$, $f_{nn'}^{D}$, $\rho^0$ and $\Delta P_{nn'}$ represent the internal diameter of the pipe, the Darcy friction factor, the $CO_2$ density and the pressure drop in flow respectively. The pressure drop is defined by eq. (5) as the difference between the desired output pressure ($P_n^o$) from node $n$ and the terminal pressure ($P_{n'}^i$) for flow into node $n'$.

$$D_{nn'}^{pi} = \left( \frac{8 \cdot f_{nn'}^{D} \left( Q_{nn'}^{fm'} \right)^2}{\pi^2 \rho^0 \cdot \frac{\Delta P_{nn'}}{L_{nn'}}} \right)^{\frac{1}{5}} \quad \forall\, (n, n') \in A \tag{4}$$

$$\Delta P_{nn'} = P_n^o - P_{n'}^i, \quad \forall\, (n, n') \in A \qquad (5)$$

The Darcy friction factor is calculated using Swamee–Jain's approximation of the Colebrook–White equation (Mechleri et al., 2017) (eq. (6)). ξ is the pipe roughness and Reynold's number ($Re_{nn'}$) is calculated using eq. (7).

$$f_{nn'}^D = \frac{1}{\left( log_{10}\left( \frac{\xi/D_{nn'}^{pi}}{3.7} + \frac{5.74}{Re_{nn'}} \right) \right)^2} \quad \forall\, (n, n') \in A \qquad (6)$$

$$Re_{nn'} = \frac{4Q_{nn'}^{fm'}}{\mu \pi D_{nn'}^{pi}} \quad \forall\, (n, n') \in A \qquad (7)$$

The required pipe wall thickness ($t_{nn'}^{wc}$) calculation (eq. (8)) considers the longitudinal joint factor ($\kappa^E$), outer diameter ($D_{nn'}^{po}$), specified minimum yield stress ($\underline{\tau}^p$), design factor ($\kappa^{DF}$) of the pipe and its material, as well as the maximum operating pressure ($P^{MOP}$) for the pipe. Internal and outer diameters, as well as the pipe wall thickness, are matched with calculated values and the set of nominal pipe sizes ($d$) according to eqs. (9) - (13). $B_{nn'd}^d$ is a binary variable which takes a value of 1 if the nominal pipe size d is selected for arc $(n, n')$.

$$t_{nn'}^{wc} = \frac{P^{MOP} \cdot D_{nn'}^{po}}{2\underline{\tau}^P \kappa^E \kappa^{DF}} \quad \forall\, (n, n') \in A \qquad (8)$$

$$t_{nn'}^w \geq t_{nn'}^{wc} \quad \forall\, (n, n') \in A \qquad (9)$$

$$D_{nn'}^{po} = D_{nn'}^{pi} + 2 \cdot t_{nn'}^w \quad \forall\, (n, n') \in A \qquad (10)$$

$$D_{nn'}^{po} = \sum_d D_d^{so} B_{nn'd}^d \quad \forall\, (n, n') \in A \qquad (11)$$

$$D_{nn'}^{pi} = \sum_d D_d^{si} B_{nn'd}^d \quad \forall\, (n, n') \in A \qquad (12)$$

$$\sum_d B_{nn'd}^d = 1 \quad \forall\, (n, n') \in A \qquad (13)$$

To prevent problems of erosion within the pipe during flow, the erosional velocity ($v_{nn'}^e$) is calculated using eq. (14) and the $CO_2$ flow velocity ($v_{nn'}^f$) constrained by it (eq. (16)).

$$v_{nn'}^e = \sqrt{\frac{8\tau^w}{\rho^o f_{nn'}^D}} \quad \forall\, (n, n') \in A \qquad (14)$$

$$v_{nn'}^f = \frac{4Q_{nn'}^{fm'}}{\pi \rho^o D_{nn'}^{po.2}} \quad \forall\, (n, n') \in A \qquad (15)$$

$$v_{nn'}^f \leq v_{nn'}^e \quad \forall\, (n, n') \in A \qquad (16)$$

## 4. Case study

The proposed model outlined in section 3 was applied to a case study shown in Figure 2. It consisted of 5 $CO_2$ emitters and 4 arcs defining the transport route between each node. Each of these 5 nodes represents large $CO_2$ emitters in Belgium and The Netherlands and is chosen as part of the investigations of the Horizon 2020 C⁴U project. C⁴U is a holistic interdisciplinary project addressing all the essential elements required for the optimal integration of CO$_2$ capture in the iron and steel industry as part of the CCUS chain. It includes a demonstration of highly efficient CO$_2$ capture technologies for an iron and steel plant and detailed consideration of the safety, environmental, societal, policy and business aspects for successful incorporation into CCUS clusters. For this study, each of nodes 0 - 4 were assumed to have 0.52Mt, 1.23Mt, 1.08Mt, 0.77Mt and 0.48Mt of CO$_2$ being transported per year respectively at a maximum pipeline operating pressure of 110 bar. The model was solved using Pyomo with BARON (Kilinc & Sahinidis, 2018) solver on an Intel Xeon E-2146G with 32GB and 12 threads running on Windows 10.

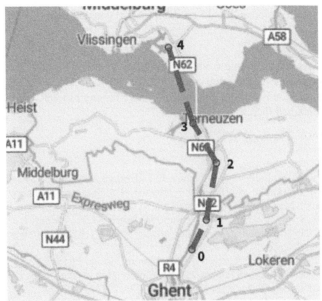

**Figure 2:** Case Study showing emission nodes and transport route

Table 1 shows the results obtained from the solution of the model. The internal and outer diameters of each pipe along the route were determined and matched to standard nominal pipe sizes whilst meeting constraints of the pipe wall thickness (eq. (10)) and the erosional velocity (eq. (16)). The number of parallel pipeline segments was also determined for each arc to meet the material transport requirements at a minimal cost. Model solutions were obtained in 78 seconds with a relative gap of 0%, showing a modest computational performance.

**Table 1:** Optimal pipeline sizes and costs

| $n$ | $n'$ | $L_{nn'}$ (km) | $D^{pi}_{nn'}$ (m) | $D^{po}_{nn'}$ (m) | $N^{p}_{nn'}$ | $TC^{C}$ (M€) | $TC^{O}$ (M€) |
|---|---|---|---|---|---|---|---|
| 0 | 1 | 5.7 | 0.1091 | 0.1143 | 1 | 2.74 | 0.08 |
| 1 | 2 | 10.0 | 0.2091 | 0.2191 | 1 | 3.50 | 0.10 |
| 2 | 3 | 8.1 | 0.2091 | 0.2191 | 1 | 3.25 | 0.10 |
| 3 | 4 | 13.7 | 0.2604 | 0.273 | 1 | 4.33 | 0.13 |

## 5. Conclusion

In this work, an MINLP model for the optimal sizing of infrastructure for CO$_2$ transportation via pipelines is presented. Our proposed model adopted rigorous hydraulic equations to accurately describe $CO_2$ flow within pipelines in an optimisation model, as opposed to using cost estimates based on existing natural gas projects which may underestimate final costs. The resulting model is an extension of the MINLP proposed by Mechleri et al. (2017) and seeks to minimise the total capital and operating costs of pipelines required for a multi-source multi-sink network. It further accounts for $CO_2$ utilisation at nodes, and multiple pipe segments, whilst being solved to global optimality. The proposed model was applied to a case study with 5 nodes and 4 arcs obtaining the optimal internal and outer pipeline diameters, number of segments and associated capital and operating costs in modest computational times. Further work will include extending the model for multi-period and multi-modal transport considerations.

## 6. Acknowledgement

This work has received funding from the European Union's Horizon 2020 research and innovation programme under grant agreement no. 884418. The work reflects only the authors' views and the European Union is not liable for any use that may be made of the information contained therein.

## References

Bui, M., Adjiman, C. S., Bardow, A., Anthony, E. J., Boston, A., Brown, S., Fennell, P. S., Fuss, S., Galindo, A., Hackett, L. A., Hallett, J. P., Herzog, H. J., Jackson, G., Kemper, J., Krevor, S., Maitland, G. C., Matuszewski, M., Metcalfe, I. S., Petit, C., Puxty, G., Reimer, J., Reiner, D. M., Rubin, E. S., Scott, S. A., Shah, N., Smit, B., Trusler, J. P., Webley, P., Wilcox, J., Mac Dowell, N., 2018. Carbon capture and storage (CCS): The way forward. Energy and Environmental Science 11, 1062–1176.

D'Amore, F., Romano, M. C., Bezzo, F., 2021. Optimal design of European supply chains for carbon capture and storage from industrial emission sources including pipe and ship transport. International Journal of Greenhouse Gas Control 109, 103372.

Ejeh, J. O., Yousef, A. Z., Bugryniec, P., Wilkes, M. D., Porter, R. T., Martynov, S., Mahgerefteh, H., Brown, S., 2022. Perspectives on Future CCUS Infrastructure Design. http://dx.doi.org/10.2139/ssrn.4271511.

Hasan, M. F., Zantye, M. S., Kazi, M.-K., 2022. Challenges and opportunities in carbon capture, utilization and storage: A process systems engineering perspective. Computers & Chemical Engineering 166, 107925.

IEA-GHG, 2005. Building the cost curves for $CO_2$ storage: European sector. Tech. rep.

Kilinc, M. and N. V. Sahinidis, 2018. Exploiting integrality in the global optimization of mixed-integer nonlinear programming problems in BARON, Optimization Methods and Software, 33, 540-562.

Kim, C., Kim, K., Kim, J., Ahmed, U., Han, C., 2018. Practical deployment of pipelines for the CCS network in critical conditions using MINLP modelling and optimization: A case study of South Korea. International Journal of Greenhouse Gas Control 73, 79–94.

Mechleri, E., Brown, S., Fennell, P. S., Mac Dowell, N., 2017. $CO_2$ capture and storage (CCS) cost reduction via infrastructure right-sizing. Chemical Engineering Research and Design 119, 130–139.

Serpa, J., Morbee, J., Tzimas, E., 2011. Technical and economic characteristics of a $CO_2$ transmission pipeline infrastructure. Tech. rep., JRC62502.

Zhang, S., Liu, L., Zhang, L., Zhuang, Y., Du, J., 2018. An optimization model for carbon capture utilization and storage supply chain: A case study in Northeastern China. Applied Energy 231, 194–206.

Antonis Kokossis, Michael C. Georgiadis, Efstratios N. Pistikopoulos (Eds.)
PROCEEDINGS OF THE 33rd European Symposium on Computer Aided Process Engineering
(ESCAPE33), June 18-21, 2023, Athens, Greece

# Data Driven Leak Detection in a Real Heat Exchanger in an Oil Refinery

Aslı Yasmal [a,b], Gizem Kuşoğlu Kaya [a], Emirhan Oktay [a], Ceylan Çölmekci [a], Erdal Uzunlar [b]

[a] Turkish Petroleum Refinery, Körfez, Kocaeli, 41780, Türkiye
[b] Department of Chemical Engineering, Izmir Institute of Technology, Urla, Izmir, 35430, Türkiye
erdaluzunlar@iyte.edu.tr

## Abstract

This study focuses on implementation of a data-based leak detection method in a heat exchanger in a petroleum refinery. We have studied on the two real leakage cases in a heat exchanger in Izmit TUPRAS Refinery. Leaks are one of the major problems that occur in operations. The autoencoder (AE) method is implemented for leak detection. Reconstruction error is used as the leak indicator. In case of leakage, the reconstruction value is expected to increase. For both cases examined, the reconstruction error is found to be around 1-5 under normal operating conditions. On the other hand, reconstruction error is observed to change between 10 and 60 under the conditions with leakage. Besides, the AE is able to indicate the start of one leakage case before the process engineers noticed it.

Keywords: Oil and gas industry, leak detection, heat exchanger, data-based, autoencoder

## 1. Introduction

The oil and gas industry converts crude oil into valuable products and plays crucial role in global economy (Asghari and Rakhshanikia, 2013). This industry consists of many complex equipment and pipeline systems which are important to production and transportation of products and by-products (Gossen and Velichkina, 2006). Continuous, safe, efficient and environmentally sustainable production is sought for. However, faults (or anomalies) such as equipment failures, human errors or leaks sometimes disrupt the production process (Ohtani, 2020). Leaks constitute a major portion of faults, making leak detection an important requirement in the production process.

In the literature, leak detection methods are grouped under three main categories. These are direct, indirect and inferential methods(Zaman et al., 2020). Inferential methods generally show the probability of the leak, so generally these methods are not preferred for leak detection. Direct methods involve hardware-based methods, which require the installation of external sensors to detect leaks in pipeline. Indirect methods involve software-based methods that are classified as data-driven and model-based methods. In addition to these methods, there are biological methods that make use of the senses of humans and experienced animals (Mujtaba et al., 2020). These methods are generally used for the detection of leaks in pipelines.

The methods used in the literature to detect leaks in heat exchangers are limited and mostly suitable for offline detection. As an online method optimal exponential moving average (EMA) method was proposed by Panday et al. (2021), who studied leaks at a thermal power plant. The performances of Kalman filter (optimal EMA) and simple EMA filter were compared. It was found that Kalman filter can successfully represent the actual data trend. A long short-term memory (LSTM) method was proposed by Guillen et al. (2020), who studied leaks at a nuclear power plant. They could successfully detect the leaks in the heat exchanger. In another study, Habbi et al. (2009) studied a pilot heat exchanger and proposed A Takegi-Sugeno (TS) fuzzy model-based approach to model heat exchanger. They focused on the residuals that are calculated by using model estimated values and actual measurements. Leaks in the heat exchanger could be detected based on the residuals. In addition, they tested the relationship between leak magnitude and leak detection capability of the model. It was concluded that detectability increased with the increasing leak volume.

In this study, leaks in a heat exchanger which is located in the Integrated Unicracking Unit of İzmit TUPRAS Refinery is studied. The autoencoder method is implemented at two different leakage cases, and detection of leaks are investigated.

## 2. Materials and methods

### 2.1. The Process Unit

Figure 1 shows the simplified process flow diagram of the Integrated Unicracking Unit under study. The feed of the unit consists of Coker Naphtha (CN), Heavy Coker Gas Oil (HCGO), Light Coker Gas Oil (LCGO), Heavy Vacuum Gas Oil (HVGO), Light Vacuum Gas Oil (LVGO). The unit consists of two parts: a reactor part and a separation part. The streams coming from reactor part are collected in a fractionator column and separated into the desired products. Coker Naphtha (CN), Heavy Coker Gas Oil (HCGO), Light Coker Gas Oil (LCGO), Heavy Vacuum Gas Oil (HVGO), Light Vacuum Gas Oil (LVGO) come from different units and compose the feed of Unicracking unit. The main purpose of this unit is to produce kerosene and diesel in accordance with certain specifications. The heat exchanger, at which leakage occurred several times, is located in the part where separation steps take place.

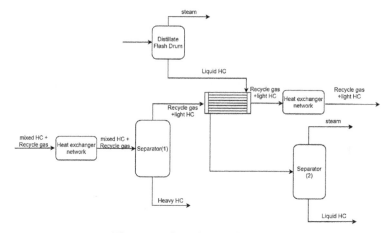

Figure 1: The scheme of the unit

The heat exchanger under study is the shell-and-tube, counter flow-type heat exchanger. Liquid hydrocarbon (HC) passes from the shell side, recycle gas and liquid HC passes from the tube side. If a leak in a heat exchanger is not noticed in time, it causes a sudden and dangerous shutdown of the process unit. Sudden interruption of the unit feed causes coking on the catalyst. At the same time, the sudden increase in temperature during startup of the unit also causes approximately 3-4 month decrease in catalyst lifespan. When the long-term effect is examined, catalyst replacement means an extra 10-day downtime for the unit. Also, the downtime of a particular process unit affects other process units in the refinery. Liquid HC passes from the shell side contains $H_2S$. It causes the deformation on surface of the tubes. Because the pressure of the tube side higher than shell side, leaks occur from tube to the shell. In cooperation with the process engineers of the unit, it is determined that the leaks were detected by the opening of the valve controlling the separator (2). The variables that may be related with the valve opening (%) value are determined. These are inlet and outlet temperatures of the shell and tube parts in the heat exchanger (°C), the flowrate of the unit (kg/h), the pressure of the separator (kg/cm$^2$).

*2.2. Autoencoder (AE)*

The proposed method for leak detection is autoencoder (AE) method. AE is an artificial neural network technique, which is generally used to reduce dimensionality of the dataset, extract features, denoise and recognize images. Five important hyperparameters of AE are encoder, decoder, bottleneck, loss function and epoch number. Figure 2 shows a basic representation of AE. Each block shown in Figure 2 consists of hidden layers. Each layer consists of nodes. In the encoder part, the sent data is compressed and fed to the bottleneck where the data is compressed. Compressed data stored in the bottleneck is then sent to the decoder where the data is reconstructed.

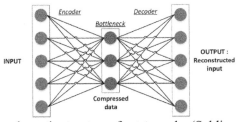

Figure 2. The schematic structure of autoencoder (Sublime *et al.*, 2019).

Encoding and decoding networks are mathematically represented in the Eq. (1-2). Here, W is the weight matrix in the encoder part, $W'$ is the weight matrix in the decoder part, b, and b' are bias vectors in the encoder and decoder parts, respectively, z is the bottleneck dimension, $\sigma$ is the activation function in the encoder part and $\sigma'$ is the activation function in the decoder part, and x' is the output.

$$z = \sigma(Wx + b) \tag{1}$$

$$x' = \sigma'(W'z + b') \tag{2}$$

Reconstruction error (RE) is the metric to evaluate the deviation of the reconstructed data from the actual data. RE is used as the outlier score (An and Cho, 2015). While this error is small for normal data samples, it is expected to be high for data with anomaly. RE is given is Eq. (3) as

$$Reconstruction\ Error = \sqrt{\sum_{i=1}^{n}(x_i - x'_i)^2} \tag{3}$$

where n refers to number of data samples, $x_i$ is the original data sample and $x'_i$ is the reconstructed data sample.

### 2.3. Methodology

The procedure of AE is given below as:

- Data is taken from TUPRAS Historian Database.
- The data is split as training and test dataset (training set: normally operated dataset without anomalies; test set: the dataset which has anomalies).
- Model hyperparameters are determined and the model is trained.
- Test dataset is fed to the model as an input.
- Reconstruction error is calculated using x and x'.

## 3. Results and Discussion

The AE network of this study is based on a literature study where AE was used for clustering of time series data (Tavakoli et al., 2020). In this structure, there are 3 layers in the encoder part with number of nodes descending in the order of 100, 50, 20. The bottleneck contains as many nodes as the number of variables (see Section 2.1). The decoder part is symmetrical to the encoder part with the ascending number of nodes. The AE is implemented in MATLAB using Deep Learning Toolbox. A 2-months dataset is chosen as the training set. The selection of the training set is done in collaboration with process engineers. During training, an MSE (mean square error) value of $3.76 \times 10^{-6}$ is achieved with an epoch number of 37.

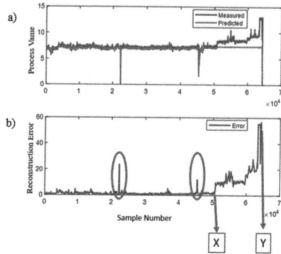

Figure 3. AE results for Case 1, (a) measured and predicted process values, (b) reconstruction error: circle on the left: flowrate changes, circle on the right: pump

replacement, point X: leakage starting point as detected by AE, point Y: the point leak noticed by process engineers.

The results for the test dataset are given in Figure 3. Figure 3a shows the measured and predicted process values and Figure 3b shows the reconstruction error. In the Figure 3b, the red circle on the left is due to a flowrate change in the process (deliberate or due to flowrate changes in upstream processes), and the red circle on the right is due to a pump replacement, point X is the moment at which the leak started as detected by AE, and point Y is the moment at which the leak was noticed by the process engineers and the unit was shut down. As seen in Figure 3b, the reconstruction error is very small, between a value of 1-5, under normal operating conditions without any flowrate changes, equipment replacements, or leaks. Reconstruction error temporarily increases with equipment changes and flowrate variations and diminishes afterwards. However, after some period of time (at point X), the reconstruction error is seen to increase steadily to a higher value than that of temporary changes (reconstruction value of 55-60 versus 20-30). Thus, point X seems to indicate the starting moment of the leakage as detected by AE. With the AE method, the leak could be detected almost 6 days ago before the process engineers took action for shut down the process.

Figure 4 shows the AE results for Case 2, a similar procedure is followed as Case 1. Since the shutdowns occur very frequently in the unit, a 1-month dataset is determined as the training dataset. Since a shorter training set interval is chosen for Case 2 compared to Case 1 and long-term flowrate variations are observed for Case 2, an MSE value of 0.0045 is obtained after 500 epochs in the training step. The obtained results for the test dataset are given in Figure 4. The effect of flowrate changes in the unit is clearly reflected in the predicted values and reconstruction error. No indication of leak is observed before process engineers noticed the leak for Case 2 unlike Case 1. In Case 2, the leak seems to show a non-steady behavior unlike Case 1 where the leak seems to increase steadily over time. This might be due to different leak types occurring in the cases. In both Case 1 and Case 2, leaks are observed to increase the reconstruction error, as expected.

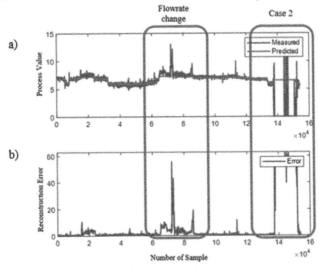

Figure 4. AE results for Case 2, (a) measured and predicted process values, (b) reconstruction error: ellipse on the left: flowrate changes, ellipse on the right: leakage case.

## 4. Conclusion

In this study, we investigate the software-based detection of leaks in heat exchangers using real process data. The cases are located in the kerosene and diesel production unit of the TUPRAS Izmit Refinery. Two different leakage cases occurring in the same heat exchanger are examined. For both cases, AE method enables the detection of leaks in the unit. For one of the cases, it is possible to predict the leak 6 days in advance with the AE method, whereas an early prediction of leak is not possible in the other case. This might be due to different types of leaks, i.e., some leaks may start with small volumetric flowrates and progress slowly enabling early detection by AE, and some leaks may occur instantly at high volumetric flowrate hindering early detection by AE. These results seem to indicate that the AE method can be used as a pre-emptive method for leaks with the low onset volumetric flowrate, and as an alarm for leaks with instant high volumetric flowrate.

## References

A. Habbi, M. Kinnaert, M. Zelmat, 2009, A complete procedure for leak detection and diagnosis in a complex heat exchanger us,ng data-driven fuzzy models', ISA Transaction, 48, 3 , 354-361.

A. Tavakoli, S.S. Namini, M. A. Khanghah, F. M.Soltani, A. S. Namin, 2020, An Autoencoder-Based Deep Learning Approach for Clustering Time Series Data, SN Applied Science 2(5), 1-25.

D. P. Guillen, N. Anderson, C. Krome, R. Boza, L. M. Griffel, J. Zouabe, and A. Y. Al Rashdan, 2020, A RELAP5-3D/LSTM Model for the Analysis of Drywell Cooling Fan Failure, Progress in Nuclear Energy 130, 103540.

D. Zaman, M. K. Tiwari, A. K. Gupta, D. Sen, 2019, A review of leakage detection strategies for pressurised pipeline in steady-state, Engineering Failure Analysis, 109, 104264.

J. An, S. Cho, 2015, Variational Autoencoder based Anomaly Detection using Reconstruction Probability, Signal & Image Processing : An International Journal, 2(4), 13–25

J. Sublime and E. Kalinicheva, 2019, Automatic Post-Disaster Damage Mapping Using Deep-Learning Techniques for Change Detection: Case Study of the Tohoku Tsunami, Remote Sensing, 11(9), 1123

L. P. Gossen, and L.M. Velichkina, 2016, 'Environmental problems of the oil-and-gas industry (review)', Petroleum Chemistry, 46(2), 67–72.

M. Asghari, and M. A. Rakhshanikia, 2013, 'Technology in Oil Industry, Significance and Challenges', Procedia - Social and Behavioral Sciences, 75, 264–271.

M. Mujtaba, T.A. Lemma, S.A.A Taqvi, T.N.Ofei, 2020, 'Leak detection in gas mixture pipelines under transient conditions using hammerstein model and adaptive thresholds', Processes, 8(4).

R. Panday, N. Indrawan, L. J. Shadle, R. W. Vesel, 2021, Leak Detection in a Subcritical Boiler, 185, 116371.

T. Ohtani, 2020, Application of AI to Oil Refineries and Petrochemical Plants', 63(1), 7–10.

Antonis Kokossis, Michael C. Georgiadis, Efstratios N. Pistikopoulos (Eds.)
PROCEEDINGS OF THE 33rd European Symposium on Computer Aided Process Engineering
(ESCAPE33), June 18-21, 2023, Athens, Greece

# Optimization of flash-separation based $CO_2$ purification units

Lorenzo Sala[a], Syed Ali Zaryab[a], Paolo Chiesa[a], Matteo Romano[a], Emanuele Martelli[a*]

[a]*Department of Energy, Politecnico di Milano, via Lambruschini 4, 20156, Milano, Italy*
*emanuele.martelli@polimi.it*

## Abstract

Several $CO_2$ capture and storage technologies, such as oxycombustion systems, membranes, pressure/temperature swing adsorption systems separate a stream of $CO_2$ which does not meet the tight composition specifications required by the storage site. Thus, the captured $CO_2$ must be processed by a $CO_2$ purification unit (CPU). This paper will focus on flash separation-based CPUs where the partial liquification of the pressurized feed gas takes place by temperature reduction at constant pressure. In this paper two schemes of the CPUs are considered, one is a conventional flash separation-based CPUs and the other is a novel design with increased recovery of the CPU. The specific cost (€/ton$_{CO2}$) of these CPUs has been optimized for different levels of carbon tax and captured $CO_2$ purity using SCR, a recently published surrogate-based global-search algorithm.

**Keywords**: CPU, Global Optimization, CCS, process optimization, $CO_2$ purification

## 1. Introduction

CCS ($CO_2$ capture and storage) technologies have been proposed as an attractive method to capture the anthropogenic $CO_2$ released from industrial sources to the atmosphere and mitigating the effect of climate change. This captured $CO_2$ has to be compressed, transported and stored as per guidelines based on environmental regulations, technical, economical and/or safety reasons [1]. All this can be achieved with a CPU ($CO_2$ compression and purification unit) [2] which is used to remove impurities from the feed gas and obtain high purity $CO_2$.

In a CPU the phase separation takes place due to the difference in volatility between $CO_2$ and other non-condensable gases. Based on the method used for separation of $CO_2$ the CPU can be divided into two types:

1- Flash Separation based CPUs: In these CPUs the partial liquification of the pressurized feed gas takes place by temperature reduction at constant pressure. These CPUs do not have any complex separation equipment and are less costly.
2- Stripping/Distillation-based CPUs: In these CPUs a stripper or distillation column (integrated with flash separation) is used to increase the purity of $CO_2$ in the feed gas stream and remove unwanted contaminants. This method provides a high purity $CO_2$.

## 2. CPU Configuration

This paper will focus on two different types of Flash separation-based CPUs. The first CPU configuration (CPU 1) is taken from the IEAGHG report ref. [3]. This configuration includes two cryogenic multi-flow heat exchangers, two flash drums for phase separation and two valves which are used to provide auto refrigeration by throttling the purified $CO_2$.

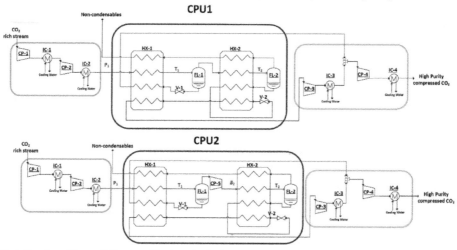

Fig. 1 Flowsheet of the two CPUs selected for the study. On the top there is a conventional flash-based CPU taken from [3] denoted as CPU1. On the bottom there is a novel flash-based CPU, denoted as CPU2.

The flowsheet of CPU1 is shown in Fig. 1, here the $CO_2$ rich feed gas stream is initially cooled and compressed by a multi-stage intercooled compressor. This compressed gas is then sent to the first heat exchanger where it is cooled down to cryogenic temperatures against the evaporating streams, superheating $CO_2$ streams, and the waste stream. This cooled feed is then sent to the first flash where it is separated into liquid and vapor phase. The liquid phase is almost pure $CO_2$ while the vapor phase contains some $CO_2$ along with all the lighter components (waste product) present in the gas stream. This vapor phase is sent to the second heat exchanger where it is cooled to a lower temperature and is then sent to a second flash. The vapor from the second flash is vented: this vent stream contains impurities and a small part of the $CO_2$. This vent stream is sent back through the two heat exchangers where it provides cooling to the $CO_2$ rich streams entering the heat exchangers. This stream is then released into the atmosphere. The liquid phase from the first flash is throttled through a valve, heated, and then sent for compression. While the liquid phase coming from the second flash is heated, throttled through a valve, and then passed through the two heat exchangers. Throttling of the second liquid stream results in a very low temperature (close to the solidification temperature of $CO_2$) so that it can be used as a refrigerator in the second heat exchanger. This second stream is then compressed. The two streams are then mixed and finally compressed for transportation and storage.

The main parameters of this system are the pressure and the temperature of the two flash separators because they influence the composition of the outlet liquid, the gas flows, and the cooling requirement. The pressure of the first flash can be optimized by changing the pressure at the discharge of the first compressor chain. Pressure of the second flash is fixed and equal to that of the first flash minus the pressure drops introduced into the exchanger. Temperatures are determined by the energy balance on the heat exchangers and therefore are determined by the inlet currents, whose flow rates, compositions, pressure, and temperature are functions of the pressure at which the flash separators operate, and the pressure drops introduced by the valves.

Based on these considerations, the scheme of CPU1 can be modified, to improve its performance, by decoupling the pressures of the two flash separators. This can be achieved by adding a compressor between the two flash separators. This modified CPU scheme is shown in Fig. 1 which will be called CPU2 in this paper.

## 3. Modelling Methodology

The models of the CPUs have been developed in Aspen Plus V10, a commercial sequential modular process simulation software using the sequential convergence mode. In order to perform an accurate evaluation of the performance of the CPU, it was crucial to adopt a reliable Equation of State model (EoS) which can predict the vapor-liquid equilibria of multicomponent systems. Therefore, experimental data of multi components systems containing $N_2$ and $CO_2$ at different temperatures and pressures available in refs. [4] [5] [6] were compared with the results of different EoS in Aspen Plus to determine which method best approximates the experimental results. This analysis showed that the Peng-Robinson EoS with Van der Waals mixing rules provides the best approximation as the mean square error between this EoS and the experimental data is the lowest. Thus, Peng-Robinson equation of state has been adopted for the evaluation of the properties of all the streams involved in the simulations.

## 4. Optimization Methodology

In this work the specific cost (€/ton$_{CO2}$) of these CPUs has been optimized using SCR, a recently published optimization algorithm [7]. SCR is a surrogate-based derivative-free global optimization algorithm which works well for process engineering problems and provides the optimum in limited number of functional evaluations compared to other algorithms [7]. SCR uses latin hypercube sampling (LHS) to sample a limited number of points in the design space where the black box function is evaluated. Using the results of these sample points SCR creates a kriging based surrogate model of the objective function and its constraints. SCR then calls CMA-ES to find the global optimum of the constrained surrogate model. Within CMA-ES the surrogate models of the objective function and the constraints are combined using quadratic penalty approach. Once the global optimum of the surrogate model is found, SCR calls the local search algorithm RQLIF [8] which uses a limited number of black box functional evaluation, to find the local minimum of the real function, around the region where the global minimum of the surrogate model was found. After this the surrogate models are updated with the points that RQLIF tested along with some new sample points found by LHS. The SCR algorithm stops when for two subsequent iterations RQLIF finds the same optimum within a certain tolerance range or when the maximum number of black box functional evaluations is reached.

For the optimization, four key performance indicators (KPIs) have been selected for the CPUs. These KPIs include Specific cost (SC), Recovery, Purity, and $O_2$ concentration in compressed $CO_2$. The optimization variables for the CPU1 includes the pressure at the exit of the compression step ($P_1$) and the temperatures of the two flash ($T_1$ & $T_2$) (shown in red in Fig. 1). The CPU2 has the same optimization variables with the addition of the pressure ratio of the new compressor ($B_2$). The optimization activity is repeated considering three different feed streams coming from (i) the Allam cycle [9] (ii) from a combined cycle with a membrane-based $CO_2$ capture plant [10] & (iii) a cement plant with VPSA capture process [11]. The objective function is to minimize the specific cost of the CPU (€/ton$_{CO2}$) at different values of carbon tax (from 100-300 €/ton$_{CO2}$) and different constraint on purity of the captured $CO_2$ (95%-97%). Each optimization run took 2.5 hours corresponding to 500 runs of the flowsheet simulation.

Table 1:Flowrates and molar concentration of the three types of feed gas considered in this analysis

| Source | Pressure [bar] | Flowrate [kg/s] | Molar concentration | | | |
|---|---|---|---|---|---|---|
| | | | $CO_2$ | $N_2$ | $O_2$ | Ar |
| Cement plant with VPSA [11] | 1 | 27.29 | 90.00% | 8.70% | 1.30% | 0.00% |
| Combined cycle with membrane [10] | 1 | 41.15 | 88.32% | 6.66% | 5.02% | 0.00% |
| Allam cycle [9] | 30 | 44.37 | 98.04% | 1.18% | 0.21% | 0.57% |

## 5. Results

The results of the optimization at different tax level and at different constraints of purity and different input feeds are shown in the Table 2 for both CPUs. Furthermore, the graphs in the Fig. 2 show the distribution of costs at different carbon tax level for different input streams for the selected CPUs. The Total annual cost (TAC) is divided into five main categories, (i) the cost of $CO_2$ emissions (Tax Cost), (ii) the electricity cost (El cost), (iii) the cost of the compressors at inlet (CPR in, shown in green in Fig. 1), (iv) the cost of the cryogenic separation unit (Coldbox, shown in blue in Fig. 1 ), and (v) the cost of the final compressor (CPR fin, shown in yellow in Fig. 1).

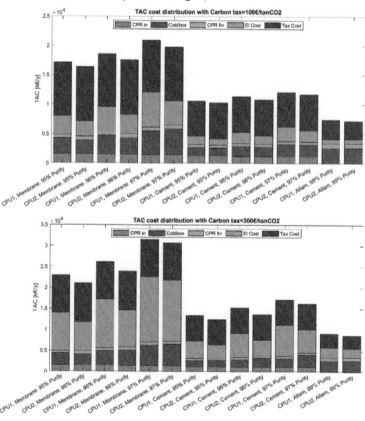

Fig. 2: The distribution of costs for different input streams for the selected CPUs at different carbon tax

The results show that CPU2 has the lowest yearly cost and specific cost in all cases compared to CPU 1. The low cost of the CPU2 is because of its high recovery, which results in a low cost of emissions (Tax cost) as seen in Fig. 2. Thus, it can be stated that the novel design of the CPU2 is generally beneficial for the overall cost reduction of the system.

From the Table 2, it can be seen that the increase in carbon tax does not have any effect on the recovery of the system, this is because for Flash separation-based CPUs the recovery is dependent on the constraint of $CO_2$ purity at the exit of the CPU. In general, the results of the optimization have shown that all the optimal solutions for any carbon tax feature two important elements: 1- the purity of the liquid stream of the two flashes are the same and equal to the constraint 2- the optimal temperature of the second flash is set to the minimum possible value of -50°C. Thus, for CPU1 the pressure of the two flashes is automatically set by the vapor liquid equilibrium of the second flash at -50°C and the target purity level. Similarly, the temperature of the first flash is set by the vapor liquid equilibrium of the feed gas at the pressure required by the second flash and by the target purity. So these values of temperature and pressure of the two flashes determine the recovery and are independent of the carbon tax. This is evident from the results of Table 2. Instead for CPU 2 the presence of the intermediate compressors allows to change the pressures of the two flashes making it possible to vary the recovery independently from the purity although for a very limited range.

Table 2: Key performance indicators along with optimized variables for both CPUs at different feed compositions for different cases

| Membrane | | CPU 1 | | | | | | CPU 2 | | | | | | |
|---|---|---|---|---|---|---|---|---|---|---|---|---|---|---|
| Tax | Cons. Purity | P1 (bar) | T1 (°C) | T2 (°C) | Specific Cost (€/ton$_{co2}$) | Recovery | Purity | P1 (bar) | T1 (°C) | T2 (°C) | B2 | Specific Cost (€/ton$_{co2}$) | Recovery | Purity |
| 100 | >95% | 34.36 | -32.34 | -50.0 | 16.18 | 97.04 | 95.00 | 30.73 | -40.00 | -50.0 | 1.52 | 15.37 | 97.69 | 95.00 |
| 300 | >95% | 37.21 | -25.18 | -50.0 | 21.71 | 97.23 | 95.04 | 32.00 | -34.73 | -50.0 | 1.68 | 19.75 | 97.88 | 95.00 |
| 100 | >96% | 29.21 | -33.79 | -50.0 | 17.79 | 96.07 | 96.00 | 26.46 | -39.10 | -50.0 | 1.45 | 16.63 | 96.95 | 96.00 |
| 300 | >96% | 32.13 | -26.39 | -50.0 | 24.93 | 96.43 | 96.00 | 27.78 | -32.72 | -50.0 | 1.59 | 22.62 | 97.27 | 96.00 |
| 100 | >97% | 24.19 | -34.51 | -50.0 | 20.34 | 94.60 | 97.04 | 23.87 | -34.72 | -50.0 | 1.14 | 18.90 | 96.24 | 96.81 |
| 300 | >97% | 26.88 | -27.06 | -50.0 | 30.43 | 95.23 | 97.00 | 25.15 | -30.35 | -50.0 | 1.14 | 29.57 | 95.55 | 97.00 |
| Cement | | | | | | | | | | | | | | |
| 100 | >95% | 40.67 | -31.26 | -50.0 | 14.77 | 98.08 | 95.00 | 38.57 | -34.76 | -50.0 | 1.71 | 14.31 | 98.55 | 95.00 |
| 300 | >95% | 40.82 | -30.88 | -50.0 | 18.66 | 98.08 | 95.00 | 40.43 | -27.51 | -50.0 | 1.80 | 17.28 | 98.59 | 95.00 |
| 100 | >96% | 34.63 | -32.54 | -50.0 | 15.87 | 97.40 | 96.00 | 33.11 | -34.00 | -50.0 | 1.62 | 15.11 | 98.11 | 96.00 |
| 300 | >96% | 34.31 | -33.45 | -50.0 | 21.34 | 97.38 | 96.00 | 34.09 | -26.05 | -50.0 | 1.92 | 19.10 | 98.27 | 96.00 |
| 100 | >97% | 30.32 | -29.14 | -50.0 | 17.20 | 96.61 | 97.00 | 27.68 | -33.46 | -50.0 | 1.45 | 16.45 | 97.36 | 97.00 |
| 300 | >97% | 30.24 | -29.35 | -50.0 | 24.24 | 96.60 | 97.00 | 29.39 | -25.42 | -50.0 | 1.43 | 22.76 | 97.43 | 97.05 |
| Allam | | | | | | | | | | | | | | |
| 100 | >99% | 20.86 | -25.02 | -50.0 | 5.94 | 99.37 | 99.00 | 22.34 | -21.64 | -50.0 | 1.01 | 5.80 | 99.43 | 99.00 |
| 300 | >99% | 20.83 | -24.92 | -50.0 | 7.25 | 99.36 | 99.01 | 22.14 | -21.44 | -50.0 | 1.07 | 6.95 | 99.46 | 99.00 |

## 6. Conclusions & Future works

In this paper optimization and comparison of a conventional Flash separation-based CPU (CPU1) and its novel modified version (CPU2) was carried out. It was seen that CPU2 always has a higher recovery and a lower specific cost for different feed inputs and different constraints on the output purity of the captured $CO_2$. As shown in Fig. 3, the novel design has a cost that is 3% to 9% lower than the CPU1 in all cases no matter what feed gas is being used.

As mentioned earlier a conventional flash-based CPU is a cost-effective way to compress and purify $CO_2$ rich feed gas. This type of CPU can provide good purity feed gas at a lower cost and can be used in applications where there is not a strict purity requirement. The modified version of this CPU (CPU2) shown in this paper helps in further reducing the yearly cost of the CPU and increasing the recovery that can be achieved.

On the other hand, there are certain applications which require a $CO_2$ stream with $O_2$ concentration below 100 ppm and in such cases flash-based CPUs cannot meet such requirement. In this case, the more expensive distillation-based CPU must be used. In the future, the same optimization methodology of this paper would be applied on distillation-based CPUs.

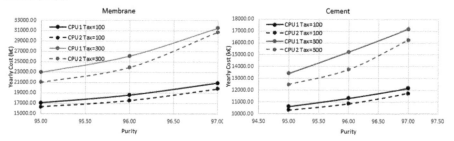

Fig. 3:Yearly cost comparison of CPU1 and CPU2

## References

[1] E. d. Visser, C. Hendriks and et. al., "Dynamis CO2 quality recommendations," *Int J Greenhouse Gas Control,* no. 2, pp. 478-484, 2008.

[2] J. Yan, M. Anheden and et. al., "Conceptual development of flue gas cleaning for CO2 capture from coal-fired oxyfuel combustion power plant," in *8th International Conference on Greenhouse Gas Control Technologies*, Trondheim, 2006.

[3] IEAGHG, "Rotating Equipment for Carbon Dioxide Capture and Storage," 2011.

[4] S. Lasala, P. Chiesa, R. Privat and J. Jaubert, "VLE properties of CO2–based binary systems containing N2, O2 and Ar: experimental measurements and modelling results with advanced cubic equations of state, Fluid Phase Equilibria".

[5] T. A. Al-Sahhaf et. al., "Liquid + Vapor Equilibria in the N2 + CO2 + CH4 System," *Industrial & Engineering Chemistry Fundamentals ,* vol. 22, no. 4, pp. 372-380, 1983.

[6] G. H. Zenner and L. I. Dana, "Liquid-vapor equilibrium compositions of carbon dioxide - oxygen - nitrogen mixtures," in *Chem. Eng. Prog., Symp.*

[7] S. A. Zaryab, A. Manno and E. Martelli, "SCR: A Novel Surrogate-Based Global Optimization Algorithm for Constrained Black-Box Problems," in *32nd European Symposium on Computer Aided Process Engineering*, Toulouse, 2022.

[8] A. Manno, E. Amaldi, F. Casella and E. Martelli., "A local search method for costly black-box problems and its application to CSP plant start-up optimization refinement," Optimization and Engineering, 2020.

[9] S. A. Zaryab, R. Scaccabarozzi and E. Martelli, "Advanced part-load control strategies for the Allam cycle," *Applied Thermal Engineering,* no. 168, 2020.

[10] D. Turi et. al., "CO2 capture from natural gas combined cycles by CO2 selective membranes," in International Journal of Greenhouse Gas Control, 2017.

[11] M. Voldsund et. al., "D4.6 CEMCAP comparative techno-economic analysis of CO2 capture in cement plants," DOI: 10.5281/zenodo.2597090, 2019.

Antonis Kokossis, Michael C. Georgiadis, Efstratios N. Pistikopoulos (Eds.)
PROCEEDINGS OF THE 33rd European Symposium on Computer Aided Process Engineering
(ESCAPE33), June 18-21, 2023, Athens, Greece

# Big data analysis of solar energy fluctuation characteristics and integration of wind-photovoltaic to hydrogen system

Yaoxi Chen, Siyu Yang, Yu Qian*

*School of Chemical Engineering, South China University of Technology, Guangzhou 510640, PR China*
Email address: ceyuqian@scut.edu.cn

## Abstract

Solar energy is a kind of sustainable energy; however, its random and intermittent fluctuation characteristics restrict its large-scale and high permeable applications. In this paper, the frequency spectrum analysis and filtering analysis are applied to reveal that both wind power and photovoltaic power have daily (24 h) and annual (8760 h) fluctuation cycles and the phase differences between their fluctuation period, which establish the scientific basis for energy complementarity to suppress the fluctuation. The data analysis of several regions in north and northwest China shows that the coupling of the wind power and the photovoltaic power alleviates the individual energy fluctuation. Both the unit cost of hydrogen production and the $CO_2$ emission intensity of the large-scale stable wind-photovoltaic power to hydrogen production and supply system are significantly lower than that of the non-complementary coupled solar hydrogen production system.

**Keywords**: solar energy; fluctuation period; wind-photovoltaic energy coupling; hydrogen production.

## 1. Introduction

In the context of the global transition to clean and low-carbon energy, renewable energy sources such as wind and light have great potential to compensate for the decline in coal power (Lu et al., 2009; Kabir et al., 2018). Solar energy is broadly any energy produced by the Sun, including wind energy from the atmosphere and solar energy with radiation and heat from the Sun, with strong randomness and intermittency. This random and intermittent fluctuation limits the large-scale and high-proportion application of wind and solar energy. When conventional grids are connected to a high proportion of wind and solar power, they often have to curtail electricity (Bird et al., 2016), or use large-capacity energy storage devices (Leonard et al., 2020), which have great technical obstacles in terms of safety, reliability and economy (Shaker et al., 2016; Ueckerdt et al., 2015).

In recent years, research on the complementarity of wind and solar energy has attracted attention. Wind energy and solar energy complementarity refers to the joint output of wind energy and solar energy to seek to smooth out the volatility of energy supply, improve the reliability of the system, and reduce the cost of power generation. The better the degree of complementarity between wind and solar, the higher the stability of the system output. From the perspective of data correlation, some researchers proposed to evaluate the degree of complementarity between wind and solar by correlation coefficient (Ren et al., 2019; Tong et al., 2021). The closer the correlation coefficient is to -1, the better the complementarity of the energy in the place. However, no one has proposed a new evaluation method for the degree of complementarity of wind and solar energy from the perspective of the fluctuation law of wind energy and solar energy.

In view of the above problems, this paper explores the scientific laws of fluctuation changes in wind and solar energy. From the perspective of fluctuation periodicity, a new evaluation method for the complementarity of wind and solar energy was proposed, using data analytics to predict the phase difference between the two energies due to intermittence; A wind-solar coupling hydrogen production system to produce a stable and reliable low-carbon hydrogen source was designed; And the reasonable capacity configuration of each unit of wind energy and solar energy electrolysis hydrogen production system was considered. The works were performed in order to form an important technological innovation to promote the complementary utilization of large-scale wind and solar.

## 2. Wind energy and solar energy basic data collection and analysis

### 2.1. Data collection of wind and solar energy

The data in this article was taken from the World Meteorological Organization (WMO) database and the National Aeronautics and Space Administration (NASA) reanalysis database (The Modern-Era Retrospective analysis for Research and Applications Version 2, MERRA2) (Zhang et al., 2018). Studies have shown that these two databases are reliable in terms of wind and solar data. In this paper, the data of solar irradiance intensity and hourly wind speed of 50m from the surface were obtained from the NASA-MERRA2 meteorological database for 11 years from 2010 to 2020. Select the areas where large-scale energy bases in northern China have or are suitable for the construction of large-scale wind power stations and photovoltaic farms, and focus on the areas of Tongliao, Baotou, Gansu Jiuquan and Xinjiang Zhundong in Inner Mongolia.

### 2.2. Analysis of periodic fluctuation characteristics of wind energy and solar energy

In order to analyze the fluctuation characteristics of wind power and photovoltaics, the spectrum analysis of wind power and photovoltaic power data was carried out by fast Fourier transform, and the frequency of each decomposition wave was obtained, and the frequency was converted to the corresponding time in order to reflect the time scale, and the spectrogram is shown in Figure 1. The spectrum analysis results show that the fluctuations of wind energy and solar energy have two cycles: day and night (24 h) and annual (8760 h).

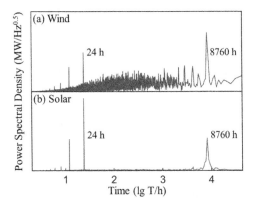

Figure 1: Frequency characteristics of wind speed and solar irradiance intensity fluctuation

Using the filter analysis method, specific frequency waves can be filtered and screened. From Figure 2, the 24 h fluctuation period of wind and solar irradiance intensity can be clearly seen, and it shows the characteristics of complementary strength.

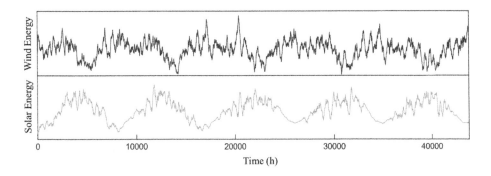

Figure 2: Wind and solar fluctuation curves with 8760 h periodic characteristics after filtering

## 2.3. Feasibility analysis of complementary coupling of wind energy and solar energy

Spectrum analysis shows that the fluctuations of wind energy and solar energy have significant periods of 8760 h and 24 h, but the fluctuation amplitude and phase of wind energy and solar energy may be different. Theoretically, the superposition of two energies can obtain the following different effects: (1) the phase of the solar energy and wind energy fluctuation cycle is the same ( = ), the two fluctuation peaks and peaks are superimposed, and the two cannot cancel each other; (2) The two fluctuations have a certain phase difference (-), partially complementary, and the two-energy coupling output will flatten and complementary, which can partially flatten the volatility. (3) If the annual fluctuation phase difference between wind and solar is 6 months, and the difference between day and night fluctuation phase is 12 hours, then on the annual and daily time scale, the peaks and troughs of wind and solar fluctuations are completely consistent, which can be regarded as the best complementarity between the two on the annual and daily time scales.

Spectrum analysis, fundamental extraction and fitting of wind energy and solar energy data in Tongliao, Baotou, Jiuquan and Zhundong can be analyzed, and the initial phase and phase difference of wind energy and solar energy in various places can be analyzed. The preliminary phase data analysis in Table 1 shows that different places have certain complementarities of scenery and solar, but they are not the same.

Table 1: The initial phases of 8760 h and 24 h cycles of wind energy and solar energy in four locations

| Location | Annual Cycles (8760 h) | | | Daily Cycles (24 h) | | |
|---|---|---|---|---|---|---|
| | Wind Power Initial Phase | Photovoltaic Power Initial Phase | Phase Difference | Wind Power Initial Phase | Photovoltaic Power Initial Phase | Phase Difference |
| Tongliao | December 10 | March 22 | 3 Months 12 Days | 14.25 | 6.21 | 8 Hours 4 Minutes |
| Baotou | December 26 | March 21 | 2 Months 24 Days | 10.24 | 6.09 | 4 Hours 14 Minutes |
| Jiuquan | February 3 | March 23 | 1 Month 18 Days | 6.12 | 6.48 | 36 Minutes |
| Zhundong | October 25 | March 27 | 5 Months 1 Day | 22.51 | 6.33 | 7 Hours 42 Minutes |

## 3. Integration of wind-photovoltaic to hydrogen production system

Based on theoretical analysis and demonstration, this paper selects Zhundong with a more suitable degree of wind-solar energy complementarity for wind-solar complementary coupling, and proposes an integrated system for hydrogen production from wind-solar complementary coupled energy, including wind turbine, photovoltaics, battery, electrolyzer and $H_2$ tank, as shown in Figure 3.

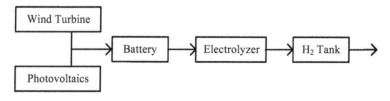

Figure 3: Topological structure of the Wind–PV to Hydrogen System

### 3.1. Specifications for integrated systems

In this paper, the output values and the input values are the power supply or hydrogen flow rate; the average output is the average of output values in T period. Volatility is often used to evaluate the stability of a system or unit output. Volatility within the T period is defined as the average of relative deviations of the output values and the average output. The closer to zero, the less volatility.

From the perspective of the stability and safety of the operation of the integrated system, the power supply fluctuation of the battery should be less than 45%; Alkaline electrolyzers are subjected to input current fluctuations ranging from 15% to 100% of rated power; The hydrogen supply fluctuation rate of hydrogen storage equipment should be less than 10%. In order to achieve this series of key technical indicators, it is necessary to rationally allocate system capacity.

### 3.2. System capacity configuration and hydrogen supply capacity

Based on the wind energy and solar energy coupling of Xinjiang Zhundong, the hydrogen production was set to 7500 t/y, and the capacity configuration of the wind - photovoltaic to hydrogen system was carried out, and the data results are shown in Table 2.

**Table 2: The capacity configuration of wind–photovoltaic to hydrogen production system**

| | PV to $H_2$ | Wind Power to $H_2$ | Wind - PV to $H_2$ |
|---|---|---|---|
| Wind Turbines Capacity (MW) | - | 234 | 130 |
| Photovoltaics Capacity (MW) | 320 | - | 137 |
| Battery Storage Capacity (MWh) | 4225 | 7745 | 1250 |
| Hydrogen Electrolyzer Capacity ($m^3$/h) | 13000 | 13000 | 13000 |
| Hydrogen Storage Tank Volume ($m^3$) | 28790 | 11800 | 4170 |
| Annual Hydrogen Production (t) | 7500 | 7500 | 7500 |

After the capacity of the device was reasonably configured, the fluctuation of hydrogen production and supply of the system is within the specified range, as shown in Figure 4. At this time, the integrated system of hydrogen production from wind-solar complementary coupled energy can stably supply $H_2$ per 7500 t/y. The high-purity hydrogen produced can be used as fuel for hydrogen fuel cell buses. One hydrogen bus travels an average of 200 km per day and consumes 14 kg$H_2$. The largest hydrogen refueling station currently has a daily injection capacity of 4.8 t. The hydrogen supply capacity of the coupled hydrogen production system can be used for at least 4 hydrogen refueling stations to refuel 1368 hydrogen fuel cell buses. According to the latest statistics, in 2019, 4411 buses in Urumqi, Xinjiang Uygur Autonomous Region, that is, hydrogen fuel cell buses supported by hydrogen supply are enough to replace 31% of buses in Urumqi, Xinjiang.

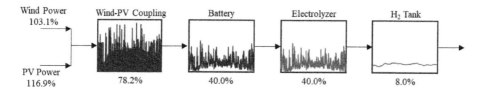

Figure 4: Variation of volatility δof the integrated system

## 4. Techno-economic and environmental performance analysis

In this paper, the life cycle assessment method is used to evaluate and analyze the carbon emission performance of the wind-solar coupled hydrogen production system. Life cycle assessment is an analytical tool that evaluates the environmental impact of a product, process or activity throughout its life cycle, from the collection and processing of raw materials to the production, transportation, sale, use, maintenance, recycling and final disposal of the product (Dennison et al., 1999). The lifecycle boundaries of the system are shown in Figure 5.

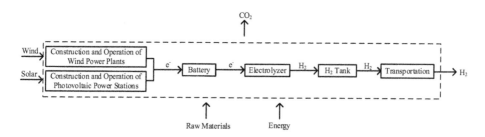

Figure 5: The life cycle boundary of wind–photovoltaic to hydrogen production system

The $CO_2$ emission intensity and unit hydrogen production cost of photovoltaic to hydrogen production system, wind power to hydrogen production system and wind-solar coupling to hydrogen production system are compared. Among the three types of systems, the unit hydrogen production cost of photovoltaic hydrogen production system is the highest, which is 95.6 CNY/kgH$_2$; The unit hydrogen production cost of wind power hydrogen production system is the next second, which is 77.2 CNY/kgH$_2$. The wind-solar coupled hydrogen production system has the lowest unit hydrogen production cost of 25.5 CNY/kgH$_2$, which is significantly lower than the average cost of individual energy hydrogen production systems. This shows that the coupling and complementarity of wind energy and solar energy can smooth out the fluctuation of some power generation, greatly reduce the capacity configuration of batteries and hydrogen storage tanks required by the system, and thus reduce the hydrogen production cost of the wind and solar coupling system. The $CO_2$ emission intensity of photovoltaic hydrogen production and wind power hydrogen production was 3.91 kgCO$_2$/kgH$_2$ and 2.21 kgCO$_2$/kgH$_2$, respectively. The $CO_2$ emission intensity of the wind-solar coupled hydrogen production system was 2.34

$kgCO_2/kgH_2$, which was significantly lower than the average $CO_2$ emission intensity of the separate energy hydrogen production system.

## 5. Conclusions

(1) Wind energy and solar energy have a fluctuation cycle of years and days. There is an optimal complementary phase difference on the complementary time scale, with an annual period of 6 months and a daily period of 12 hours. The analysis of case data from many places in northern China shows that the fluctuation characteristics of wind energy and solar energy in various places are different, but there are certain complementary characteristics.

(2) Design a wind-photovoltaic to hydrogen production system for large-scale hydrogen production, select battery packs and hydrogen storage tanks with appropriate capacity, and reduce the flow fluctuation rate of hydrogen supply to less than 10% to meet the requirements of stable hydrogen supply. The design system delivers enough hydrogen to allow nearly one-third of the public transport capacity of a large and medium-sized city to be replaced with hydrogen fuel cell buses.

(3) Case studies show that the hydrogen production cost of wind-photovoltaic to hydrogen production system in this paper is 25.5 CNY/kg $H_2$, and the emission intensity is 2.34 kg $CO_2$/kg $H_2$, which is basically the same as that of the wind power to hydrogen production system, and the $CO_2$ emission intensity of the wind energy and solar energy coupling system is basically the same, and the obvious decrease is compared with the photovoltaic power to hydrogen production system.

## References

Bird L, Lew D, Milligan M, et al. 2016, Wind and solar energy curtailment: a review of international experience. Renewable and Sustainable Energy Reviews, 65, 577-586.

Dennison F J, Azapagic A, Clift R, et al. 1999, Life cycle assessment: comparing strategic options for the mains infrastructure-Part I. Water Science and Technology, 39, 315-319.

Kabir E, Kumar P, Kumar S, et al. 2018, Solar energy: potential and future prospects. Renewable and Sustainable Energy Reviews,82, 894-900.

Leonard M D, Michaelides E E, Michaelides D N. 2020, Energy storage needs for the substitution of fossil fuel power plants with renewables. Renewable Energy, 145, 951-962.

Lu X, McElroy M B, Kiviluoma J. 2009, Global potential for windgenerated electricity. PNAS, 106, 27, 10933-10938.

Ren G R, Wan J, Liu J F, et al. 2019, Spatial and temporal assessments of complementarity for renewable energy resources in China. Energy, 177, 262-275.

Shaker H, Zareipour H, Wood D. 2016, Impacts of large-scale wind and solar power integration on California's net electrical load.Renewable and Sustainable Energy Reviews, 58, 761-774.

Tong D, Farnham D J, Duan L, et al. 2021, Geophysical constraints on the reliability of solar and wind power worldwide. Nature Communications, 12, 6146.

Ueckerdt F, Brecha R, Luderer G. 2015, Analyzing major challenges of wind and solar variability in power systems. Renewable Energy, 81, 1-10.

Zhang H, Cao Y, Zhang Y, et al. 2018, Quantitative synergy assessment of regional wind-solar energy resources based on MERRA reanalysis data. Applied Energy, 216, 172-182.

Antonis Kokossis, Michael C. Georgiadis, Efstratios N. Pistikopoulos (Eds.)
PROCEEDINGS OF THE 33rd European Symposium on Computer Aided Process Engineering
(ESCAPE33), June 18-21, 2023, Athens, Greece
© 2023 Elsevier B.V. All rights reserved.  http://dx.doi.org/10.1016/B978-0-443-15274-0.50496-0

# Dynamic Modeling and Control of $CO_2$ Capture Systems with a Biphasic Solvent

Panagiotis Kazepidis[a,b], Athanasios I. Papadopoulos[a], Panos Seferlis[a,b]

[a]*Chemical Process & Energy Resources Institute (C.P.E.R.I.), Center for Research and Technology Hellas (CE.R.T.H.), P.O. Box 60361, 57001, Thermi-Thessaloniki, Greece*
[b]*Department of Mechanical Engineering, Aristotle University of Thessaloniki, P.O. Box 484, 54124 Thessaloniki*
*seferlis@auth.gr*

## Abstract

Biphasic solvents are receiving increased attention in post-combustion $CO_2$ capture systems as they reduce the regeneration energy requirements compared to conventional, single-phase solvents. The appearance of a second liquid phase in biphasic solvents results in a complex dynamic behavior of the capture process that has never been investigated. We develop for the first time a dynamic model for the novel biphasic solvent $S_1N$/DMCA (N-Cyclohexyl-1,3-Propanediamine/ N,N -Dimethylcyclohexylamine) to investigate its behavior compared to the conventional MEA (monoethanolamine). The model accounts for both the mass and energy holdup in the liquid phase, whereas a control scheme with two proportional-integral (PI) controllers is used to compare the dynamic performance of the two solvents. For 10% increase in the total flue gas flow, the biphasic solvent is more robust, due to 2.5% and 3% lower change in the reboiler energy demand and solvent replenishing requirement than MEA. The required steam cost is also reduced by 3% compared to MEA.

**Keywords**: $CO_2$ capture, process control, phase-change solvents.

## 1. Introduction

Solvent-based absorption/ desorption processes represent a mature technology for post-combustion $CO_2$ capture, but their wide deployment is prohibited by increased regeneration energy requirements that result in high costs. Such challenges are approached through the development of process schemes that enhance the capture and regeneration driving forces (Bui et al., 2018), of control schemes that enable efficient operation (Pátron and Ricardez-Sandoval, 2022) and of advanced solvents (Papadopoulos et al., 2021). In the latter case, phase-change or biphasic solvents represent a promising technology for the reduction of regeneration energy and capture process economics. Biphasic solvents form a second liquid phase upon reaction with $CO_2$ at the prevailing process conditions. Only the liquid phase with the higher content in $CO_2$ is directed to the stripper for solvent regeneration, enabling up to 51% lower energy requirements and 47% lower cost for the capture process than the conventional MEA (monoethanolamine) solvent (Kazepidis et al., 2021). These findings are important, but they have been attained through steady-state capture process optimization. The variability that is observed in industrial systems has detrimental effects on the capture process operation, hence a systematic assessment of the dynamic behavior and the subsequent design of efficient control schemes are essential (Salvinder et al., 2019). However, such approaches have not yet been implemented in biphasic capture systems.

In the area of $CO_2$ capture, there are several control approaches that have been proposed for conventional (non-phase change) solvents. There are works that consider the reference MEA solvent in approaches such as proportional-integral-derivative (PID) control (Luu et al., 2015), model-predictive control (MPC) (Jung et al., 2021), linear MPC (Jung et al., 2020), non-linear MPC (Pátron and Ricardez-Sandval, 2020), and advanced approaches that combine real-time optimization, non-linear MPC and rolling horizon estimation (Pátron and Ricardez-Sandoval, 2022). Fewer dynamic modeling approaches have been proposed that consider different solvents such as MEA, DEA (Diethanolamine), (Gáspár and Cormos, 2021; Damartzis et al., 2018) MDEA (Methyl-diethanolamine), AMP (2-Amino-2-methyl-1-propanol) (Gáspár and Cormos, 2021) and MPA (3-Amino-1-propanol) (Damartzis et al., 2018). Despite the growing interest in developing optimal control strategies for conventional solvent-based capture systems, the dynamics of $CO_2$ capture processes involving biphasic solvents remain unexplored. The presence of two liquid phases in the absorption column and the subsequent phase separator increase the complexity of the process unit interactions and of the dynamic behavior of the system. The aim of this work is to study the dynamic behavior of a biphasic $CO_2$ capture system and to develop a control strategy for the economic operation of the capture system under variable operating conditions.

## 2. Models and methods

The biphasic solvent mixture of $S_1N$/DMCA (N-Cyclohexyl-1,3-Propanediamine/ N,N - Dimethylcyclohexylamine) proposed by Papadopoulos et al. (2021) is considered in this work with the capture process flowsheet shown in Figure 1. The key difference compared to a conventional capture process is that a liquid-liquid phase separator (decanter) is deployed after the absorber to separate the rich from the lean $CO_2$ liquid phases.

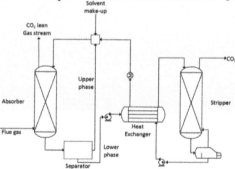

**Figure 1:** Basic Flowsheet diagram of VLLE process for post combustion $CO_2$ capture with the S1N/DMCA mixture.

The developed dynamic model considers vapor-liquid-liquid equilibrium (VLLE) along with material and energy balances for each phase. An orthogonal collocation on finite elements (OCFE) technique is employed to account for the variation of the concentration and temperature profiles along the height of the columns. The OCFE technique enables the formation of a compact in size, dynamic process model which facilitates greatly the numerical solution with good control of the approximation error (Damartzis et al., 2018). The OCFE technique considers the heights of the absorption and desorption columns as continuous variables and uses selected points defined as the roots of orthogonal Legendre polynomials called collocation points, in which mass and energy balances are exactly satisfied. Lagrange interpolation polynomials are used within the finite elements. Dividing the height of the columns into finite elements allows problems with steep profile changes to be accurately represented. This is very important during dynamic transitions where steep fronts in concentration and temperature may move along the columns.

The equations describing the mass balance of the liquid phases in a three-phase dynamic model are the following (Damartzis and Seferlis, 2010):

$$\frac{dm_i^I(s_j)}{dt} = \tilde{L}_i^I(s_j - 1) - \tilde{L}_i^I(s_j) + \varphi_{i,j}^I(s_j) \quad i = 1, \dots, NC, \ j = 1, \dots, n \tag{1}$$

$$\frac{dm_i^{II}(s_j)}{dt} = \tilde{L}_i^{II}(s_j - 1) - \tilde{L}_i^{II}(s_j) + \varphi_{i,j}^{II}(s_j) \quad i = 1, \dots, NC, \ j = 1, \dots, n \tag{2}$$

where $s_j$ is a column position coordinate, $L_i$ is the liquid flow of component $i$ in one of the liquid phases $(I, II)$ and $\varphi$ is the holdup. Similarly, the energy balance is formulated as follows:

$$\frac{dU(s_j)}{dt} = \tilde{L}_t^I(s_j - 1)\widetilde{H^{LI}}(s_j - 1) + \tilde{L}_t^{II}(s_j - 1)\widetilde{H^{LII}}(s_j - 1) - \tilde{L}_t^I(s_j)\widetilde{H^{LI}}(s_j) -$$
$$\tilde{L}_t^{II}(s_j)\widetilde{H^{LII}}(s_j) + \tilde{G}_t(s_j + 1)\widetilde{H^G}(s_j + 1) - \tilde{G}_t(s_j)\widetilde{H^G}(s_j) + Q(s_j) +$$
$$\varphi_{t,j}^I(s_j)\widetilde{H^{LI}}(s_j) + \varphi_{t,j}^{II}(s_j)\widetilde{H^{LII}}(s_j), j = 1, \dots, n \tag{3}$$

where $L_t$ is the total liquid flow in one of the liquid phases $(I, II)$, $G_t$ is the total vapor flow, $H$ is the enthalpy of each phase, $Q$ is the heat loses and $\varphi_t$ is the total holdup. The dynamic behavior is introduced into the three-phase model by the mass holdup term of the two liquid phases and is calculated by the following equation:

$$\frac{dm_i^I(s_j)}{dt} + \frac{dm_i^{II}(s_j)}{dt} = \frac{\rho_{mix}^I(s_j)a^{int}V(s_j)\delta^I}{MW_{mix}^I(s_j)}\frac{\tilde{L}_i^I(s_j)}{\tilde{L}_t^I(s_j)} + \frac{\rho_{mix}^{II}(s_j)a^{int}V(s_j)\delta^{II}}{MW_{mix}^{II}(s_j)}\frac{\tilde{L}_i^{II}(s_j)}{\tilde{L}_t^{II}(s_j)} \tag{4}$$

where $\rho$ is the density of each liquid phase, $a^{int}$ is the liquid phase interphase, $V$ is the control volume in every collocation point, $\delta$ is the film thickness of each liquid phase on the packing and $MW_{mix}$ is the molecular weight of each phase. The control volume is calculated as the volume contained between two collocation points on the separation columns, centered at the location of the collocation points. In the case of the phase separator and reboiler, this volume is equal to the bottom control volume of the absorption and regeneration column, respectively. Note that the vapor phase mass balance of Eq. (1) and (2) remains the same as in the steady-state VLLE model because it is assumed that there is no holdup of the gas phase. Finally, the mass density of each liquid phase is calculated using the composition.

## 3. Implementation

The proposed dynamic model is implemented on the novel biphasic mixture of $S_1N$/DMCA (Papadopoulos et al., 2021). This mixture forms two liquid phases directly upon reaction with $CO_2$, it has high $CO_2$ capture capacity and releases the captured $CO_2$ at lower temperature than MEA. The flue gas stream used in the implementation is based on a quicklime plant and consists of 12 vol.% $CO_2$, has a temperature of 298.15 K and a total flow equal to 320.22 mol/s. To evaluate the performance of the $S_1N$/DMCA mixture a 10% increase in the total flow of the system is imposed in the dynamic simulation. A control scheme is designed for the capture system with MEA and $S_1N$/DMCA under variable operating conditions. It consists of two PI control loops that aim to keep the $CO_2$ capture ratio and the loading (mol $CO_2$ / mol amine) of the $CO_2$-lean stream at their reference values. The $CO_2$ capture ratio is controlled by the manipulation of the reboiler thermal duty, whereas the loading of the $CO_2$-lean stream is controlled by the manipulation of the solvent replenishing (make-up) stream flow. Disturbances are imposed on the system through five successive step changes in the total flue gas flow, each representing a 2 % increase of the nominal operating point. The disturbances begin at 20 s and are repeated every 100 s. The tuning parameters of both controllers for the two cases are calculated by the response curve method using a Ziegler-Nichols correlation. For the $CO_2$ capture ratio control loop we used $K_c = 1.147$, $\tau_I = 0.12$ and $K_c = 1.151$, $\tau_I = 0.22$ for the MEA and $S_1N/DMCA$ cases. For the lean loading control loop we used $K_c = 1.25$, $\tau_I = 1.5$ and $K_c = 0.83$, $\tau_I = 1.1$ for the MEA and $S_1N/DMCA$ cases. The setpoint values for the lean stream loading are 0.20 and 0.43 mol $CO_2$ / mol amine for the MEA and $S_1N/DMCA$ cases, respectively, as obtained from the steady-state optimization. In both cases the $CO_2$ capture ratio is set to 90 %. The values of $a^{int}$ and $\delta$ are considered constant throughout the process ($a^{int} = 250$ $m^2 \cdot m^{-3}$ and $\delta = 0.0005$ m, Rocha et al., 1993). The system of differential-algebraic equations was solved using the solver implemented in DASSL (Petzold, 1982).

## 4. Results and discussion

The dynamic response of the $CO_2$ capture ratio, the reboiler thermal duty, the loading of the $CO_2$-lean stream and the amine replenishing stream flow are shown in Figures 2-4.

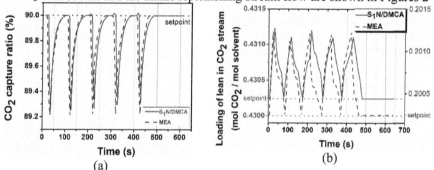

**Figure 2:** Closed loop response of a) the $CO_2$ capture ratio, and b) the $CO_2$-lean stream loading.

According to the results of Figures 2 and 3 for $S_1N/DMCA$, an increase of about 10% in the amine replenishing stream flow and 9% in the reboiler heat duty are sufficient to compensate the effects of the studied disturbance on the controlled variables. $S_1N/DMCA$ has a clear advantage compared to MEA, as it requires less energy to compensate for the effect of the disturbance, as shown in Figure 3 (a). This is mainly attributed to the formation of the second liquid phase in $S_1N/DMCA$, which reduces the solvent flow rate by 70% compared to MEA (Kazepidis et al., 2021). In the case of MEA, the response is faster by 9% (settling time is smaller by 9 s) and the amine replenishing stream flow increases by 13%, while the energy supplied to the reboiler increases by 11.5% (Figure 3). This response is expected as MEA has been reported to have faster kinetics than most biphasic solvents (Zhang, 2013). Also, the system appears to be quite responsive to changes in the reboiler heat duty in both solvent cases, because it has only a 9% change from the optimum state value for the $S_1N/DMCA$ mixture and 11.5% for the MEA case (Figure 3a). In contrast, the amine replenishing stream changes more than 10% to be able to compensate for the disturbance in the case of the $S_1N/DMCA$ mixture and 13% in the case of MEA (Figure 3b).

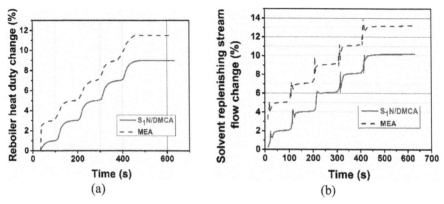

**Figure 3:** Closed loop performance of a) the reboiler heat duty and b) the solvent replenishing stream flow.

An important parameter is the economic effect of the disturbance in the system. Cost calculations in this study were based on Kazepidis et al. (2021). Figure 4 shows the steam costs change with respect to the total flue gas flow change. While energy needs increase by about 2% with each step change, the steam cost has a higher rate of increase. Thus, the total increase of steam cost after all five step changes is 12.2% for $S_1N/DMCA$ which is greater than the change in reboiler energy needs (9%). In the case of MEA, the increase in the steam cost is equal to 15.3%. Regarding the solvent replenishing stream effects on economic performance, $S_1N/DMCA$ has 6 times lower solvent replenishing requirements, i.e., 0.011 mol/s for $S_1N/DMCA$ and 0.066 mol/s for MEA (Kazepidis et al., 2021). This is due to the overall lower flows of $S_1N/DMCA$ to attain the desired capture rate and to its lower volatility compared to MEA. Under disturbance, the percentage change in the flowrate of the replenishing stream of $S_1N/DMCA$ is lower by 3 percentage points than that of MEA. Assuming that the solvent price of $S_1N/DMCA$ is comparable to that of MEA, the latter is greatly outperformed in this indicator.

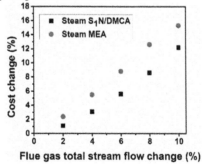

**Figure 4:** Steam cost change with respect to the flue gas total stream flow change.

## 5. Conclusions

The process is controlled efficiently by the proposed scheme, as the CO₂ capture ratio is reduced less than 1% from the nominal point, under the influence of disturbances. MEA has a faster response, but is also more sensitive to the disturbance by having 11.5% and 13% increase in the reboiler demands and solvent replenishing stream. $S_1N/DMCA$ has 9% slower response but is more robust as it has only 9% and 10% increase in the reboiler demands and solvent replenishing stream. The biphasic solvent has a better economic performance than MEA, due to 3% lower steam cost increase and 6 times lower solvent replenishing needs. These new findings suggest that biphasic solvents enhance the reliability and stability of solvent-based $CO_2$ capture systems, making it a feasible option for widespread use. The dynamic performance of such systems is essential as variability in the flue gas conditions is large and the capture targets may vary for optimal operation in most industrial applications.

## Acknowledgements

This research has been financed by the European Union and Greek National Funds through the Operational Program Competitiveness, Entrepreneurship and Innovation, under the call Research – Create – Innovate, Project T2EΔK-01911

## References

M. Bui, C.S. Adjiman, A. Bardow, E.J. Anthony, A. Boston, S. Brown, P.S. Fennell, S. Fuss, A. Galindo, L.A. Hackett, and J.P. Hallett, 2018, Carbon capture and storage (CCS): the way forward, Energy & Environmental Science, 11, 5, pp. 1062-1176.

G.D. Patrón, and L. Ricardez-Sandoval, 2022, An integrated real-time optimization, control, and estimation scheme for post-combustion $CO_2$ capture, Applied Energy, 308, p. 118302.

A.I. Papadopoulos, F.A. Pedromo, F. Tzirakis, G. Shavalieva, I. Tsivintzelis, P. Kazepidis, E. Nessi, S. Papadokonstantakis, P. Seferlis, A. Galindo, G. Jackson, C.S. Adjiman, 2021, Moleculae engineering of sustainnable phase-change solvents: From digital design to scaling-up for $CO_2$ capture, Chemical Engineering Journal, 420, p. 127624.

P. Kazepidis, A.I. Papadopoulos, F. Tzirakis, and P. Seferlis, 2021, Optimum design of industrial post-combustion $CO_2$ capture processes using phase-change solvents, Chemical Engineering Research and Design, 175, pp. 209-222.

K.M.S. Salvinder, H. Zabiri, S.A. Taqvi, M. Ramasamy, F. Isa, N.E.M. Rozali, H. Suleman, A. Maulud and A.M. Shariff, 2019, An overview on control strategies for $CO_2$ capture using absorption/stripping system. Chemical Engineering Research and Design, 147, pp. 319-337.

M.T. Luu, N.A. Manaf, and A. Abbas, 2015, Dynamic modelling and control strategies for flexible operation of amine-based post-combustion $CO_2$ capture systems, International Journal of Greenhouse Gas Control, 39, pp. 377-389.

H. Jung, S. Heo, and J.H. Lee, 2021, Model predictive control for amine-based $CO_2$ capture process with advanced flash stripper, Control Engineering Practice, 114, p. 104885.

H. Jung, D. Im, S. Heo, B. Kim, and J.H. Lee, 2020, Dynamic analysis and linear model predictive control for operational flexibility of post-combustion $CO_2$ capture processes. Computers & Chemical Engineering, 140, p. 106968.

G.D. Patrón, and L. Ricardez-Sandoval, 2020, A robust nonlinear model predictive controller for a post-combustion $CO_2$ capture absorber unit, Fuel, 265, p. 116932.

J. Gáspár, A.-M. Cormos, 2012, Dynamic modeling and absorption capacity assessment of $CO_2$ capture process, International Journal of Greenhouse Gas Control, 8, pp. 45–55.

T. Damartzis, A.I. Papadopoulos and P. Seferlis, 2018, Solvent effects on design with operability considerations in post-combustion $CO_2$ capture plants, Chemical Engineering Research and Design, 131, pp. 414-429.

T. Damartzis and P. Seferlis, 2010, Optimal design of staged three-phase reactive distillation columns using nonequilibrium and orthogonal collocation models, Industrial and Engineering Chemistry Research, 49, 7, pp. 3275-3285.

J.A. Rocha, J.L. Bravo and J.F. Fair, 1993, Distillation columns containing structured packings: A comprehensive model for their performance. 1. hydraulic models, Industrial & Engineering Chemistry Research, 32, pp. 641-651.

L. Petzold, 1982, A description of DASSL: a differential/algebraic equation system solver, Proc. IMACS World Congress, pp. 430-432.

J. Zhang, 2013, Study on $CO_2$ capture using thermomorphic biphasic solvents with energy-efficient regeneration, PhD. Thesis, Techical University Dortmund, Dortmund.

Antonis Kokossis, Michael C. Georgiadis, Efstratios N. Pistikopoulos (Eds.)
PROCEEDINGS OF THE 33rd European Symposium on Computer Aided Process Engineering
(ESCAPE33), June 18-21, 2023, Athens, Greece

# Development of integrated liquid air energy storage systems based on air separation units using waste energy from power plant: A case study of South Korea

Jaerak Ko, Seolji Nam, Soonho Hwangbo[*]

*Department of Chemical Engineering, Gyeongsang National University 501, Jinjudae-ro, Jinju-si, Gyeongsangnam-do, 52828 Korea*
*[*]s.hwangbo@gnu.ac.kr*

## Abstracts

Power consumption has been rising gradually as technology has developed. It is necessary that power generation using renewable energy that does rarely emit carbon. An air separation unit that separates air into nitrogen, oxygen, and argon is used in a variety of industries, including steel mills and chemical plants, which demand pure gas. In order to feed pure gas to the industrial complex utilizing stored air and produce power at the same time, the air separation unit is combined with a liquid air energy storage system. This study used a process simulation program to develop a model aiming to integrate an air separation unit and a liquid air energy storage system using waste energy produced by a liquefied natural gas power plant. According to a Korean case study, the levelized cost of electricity of the integrated process is $320/MWh, which is about $51/MWh less than the levelized cost of electricity of the current liquid air energy storage system. Through this study, it is expected that carbon emissions can be significantly decreased by supplying the Korea petrochemical complex with the pure gas it needs to meet its 5.6% mandated renewable energy supply power need.

**Keywords**: Liquid air energy storage system, Process integration, Techno-economic and environmental assessment, Utilizing waste energy

## 1. Introduction

Power consumption in the industry has been rising rapidly as technology has developed. Fossil fuel-generating systems, such as coal-fired power generation, emit a large amount of carbon dioxide into the air (Chehade and Dincer, 2021). Global carbon emission reductions were discussed during the 2015 Paris Climate Agreement. As a result, the development of a carbon-free power generation system using renewable energy is necessary to replace the current power generating system that emits a small quantity of carbon. Since the production of renewable energy is unpredictable and irregular, it is challenging to consistently produce energy in response to demand (Nam et al., 2020). The excess energy is stored by integrating an energy storage system (ESS), and the stored energy may later be used if it needs to make up for the limitations of the current renewable energy. Typically, the general ESSs take the form of lithium-ion batteries. However, a considerable quantity of energy cannot be stored due to the high cost of system installation and the limited capacity of energy storage (Koohi Fayegh, 2020). As a next-generation ESS to overcome this, liquid air energy storage (LAES) systems are gaining appeal. LAES systems show high energy density regardless of the installation location (Borri et al., 2021). A 20MW LAES system has been substantiated by Highview power, and several similar studies are being conducted (Rarely, 2017; Morgan et al., 2015). The challenge is that setting up LAES system is expensive and difficult to apply in reality. However, some options, such as the use of liquefied natural gas (LNG) cold heat or solar heat, are currently being intensively researched in attempt to address these drawbacks (Qi et al., 2020). This study aims to increase economic feasibility by integrating an air separation unit (ASU) process to separate air into nitrogen, oxygen, and argon, release energy, supply power to petrochemical complex, and supply industrial gas to each customer for overcoming the shortcomings of the recent LAES system. Utilizing waste heat and LNG cold energy from LNG power plants near to petrochemical complex also contributed to improving energy efficiency. Levelized cost of electricity (LCOE) was estimated in a case study of South Korea, and the contribution of Korea's carbon neutral policy was determined through the calculation of the required supply of renewable energy.

## 2. Method

### 2.1. Design of ASES system

Figure 1 shows the power and industrial gas supply network in integration with the LNG power plant, the petrochemical complex, and an air separation energy storage (ASES) system. The ASES system consists of a charging process and discharging process. During charging, power is sourced from low price power grid, and ASU is used to separate and liquefy the air. Charging process combines an air separation step in which gaseous air is liquefied at cryogenic temperature and separated into nitrogen, oxygen, and argon with a LAES system that uses waste heat from power plants to vaporize it before altering it into electricity through turbines. Charging process that uses LNG cold energy to get energy of air separated at an cryogenic temperature includes a compressor, a cold box, a low pressure column, a high pressure column, and an argon column for air separation.

During discharging, liquid air that was stored when power demand was at its peak is vaporized to produce electricity through turbines. Through a waste heat source produced in a power plant, discharging process evaporates liquid air that is separated and stored, and turbines subsequently use the energy to produce electricity. Then, pipelines are used to deliver nitrogen, oxygen, and argon to demand sources located within the petrochemical complex. Discharging process consists of cryogenic storage tanks, heat exchangers for vaporization, and turbines.

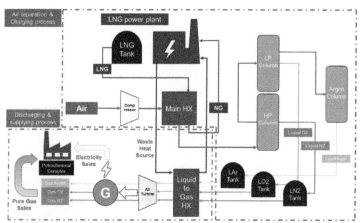

Figure 1. Conceptual design of ASES system for energy charging and discharging via utilizing cold energy and waste heat from LNG power plant.

Table 1. General assumptions which are used in process simulation.

| Parameter | Value | Unit |
|---|---|---|
| Number of stages of HP column | 65 | N/A |
| Number of stages of LP column | 80 | N/A |
| Number of stages of Ar column | 70 | N/A |
| Expansion ratio of the air turbine | 0.3 | N/A |
| Isentropic efficiency of air turbine | 90 | % |
| Isentropic efficiency of compressor | 98 | % |
| Isentropic efficiency of pumps | 70 | % |
| Temperature of dry air | 295.0 | K |
| Temperature of inlet LNG | 110.5 | K |
| Temperature of outlet LNG | 288.8 | K |

Table 1 is presented the important parameters used in simulation. Number of stages of HP, LP and Ar column are 65, 80, 70. The expansion ratio of the air turbine is 0.3 and Isentropic efficiency of the air turbine, compressor, pumps are 90%, 98% and 70%, which were obtained from current studies on LAES systems. Tray by tray modelling was used to replicate the distillation column. Peng Robinson's equation of state was used for simulation of this system.

*2.2. Economic analysis*
Economic analysis method for the ASES system was choose total revenue requirement (TRR) method based on The Electric Power Research Institute (EPRI) used method (Ko et al., 2018). By calculating direct cost (DC), indirect cost (IC), and other outlays (OO) based on purchased equipment cost (PEC), this method determines the total capital investment (TCI). The cost of revenue all outlays and collecting them for system operation is the recovery cost per year. TRR is made up of the total of carrying charges and expenses. According to TCI, carrying charges are estimated as sums that include capital recovery, return on equity, return on debt, income taxes, other taxes and insurance. To evaluate the economy, the following economic indicators were used: 1) The annual inflation rate was 2.5% 2) An 8% discount rate 3) The equity to debt ratio was 50%. 4) The interest rate was 8%. 5) The 30-year lifespan of the plant 6) The system operated for 8,000 hours (Zakeri et al., 2015).

## 3. A case study

*3.1. ASES system in Daesan petrochemical complex*
Daesan petrochemical complex is in Seosan-si, Chungcheongnam-do, Korea, with 10 large petrochemical companies. The ASES system is in Dangjin, Chungcheongnam-do, Korea, and the facility capacity air into the system at a flow rate of 84,375 kg/h. Figure 2(A) shows the site for the construction of the ASES system in integration with the Dangjin LNG power plant. Figure 2(B) shows a pipeline for supplying nitrogen, oxygen, and argon to the Daesan petrochemical complex. The length of the pipeline from the ASES system to the Daesan petrochemical complex is about 15 km.

Figure 2. (A) A land decision of ASES system. (B) A pipeline connected from ASES system to chemical plant in Daesan petrochemical complex.

## 4. Results and discussion

### 4.1. Simulation results of the ASES system

Figure 3 shows the process simulation results of the ASES system in the case study. AVEVA Pro/ii simulation is used for process simulation. The mole fractions for the major streams of three main processes are displayed, and the outputs are as follows. The air was separated into nitrogen, oxygen, and argon through the HP, LP, and Argon columns, respectively. Stream A is an inflow of air from the outside and consists of a general composition of air. Stream B is compressed air from main HX and is similarly the composition of general air. Stream C is the stream where high purity nitrogen flows into the turbine, a 0.9995 mole fraction of $N_2$. Stream D is the result of the Argon column, a 0.99 mole fraction of Ar. Stream E is the result of oxygen flow into the turbine, and a 0.99 mole fraction of $O_2$. Stream F is the result of $N_2$ purge gas and a 0.994 mole fraction of $N_2$.

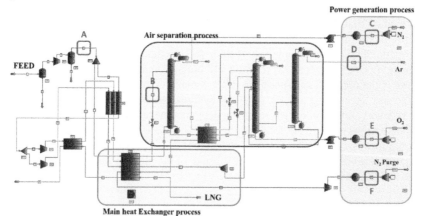

| Mole fraction | A | B | C | D | E | F |
|---|---|---|---|---|---|---|
| $N_2$ | 0.78 | 0.78 | 0.9998 | - | - | 0.994 |
| $O_2$ | 0.21 | 0.21 | - | 0.01 | 0.99 | 0.006 |
| Ar | 0.01 | 0.01 | 0.0002 | 0.99 | 0.01 | - |
| Temperature (°C) | 7 | -176 | 250 | -184 | 250 | 250 |
| Pressure (KPa) | 557 | 539 | 2,200 | 116 | 2,200 | 2,200 |
| Flowrate (kg/h) | 130,927 | 37,792 | 36,221 | 1,251 | 30,693 | 62,760 |

Figure 3. Simulation results of the air separation unit with power generation systems using waste energy.

By simulating ASES system with PRO/II simulation, we can estimate how much electricity is generated during the process of generating power. Through waste heat from power plant, the liquefied air that is stored in the tank heats up to 250°C and generates energy via turbine. 3,224 kW of electricity are produced by using $N_2$ (Figure 3(stream C)). 2,403 kW of electricity is generated by using oxygen as an electricity generator (Figure 3(stream E)). Nitrogen purge gas will be used to generate 5,584 kW of electricity (Figure 3(stream F)). Thus, we assumed the discharging time per day is 8 hours and the total capacity of generated power is 11,211 kW, the total generated power per day is approximately 90 MWh.

### 4.2. Economic analysis

To estimate the TCI of the ASES system, we make several economic assumptions. PEC is used to estimate direct cost, indirect cost, and other costs. TCI is the sum of the three sections. TCI was estimated using parameter values derived from experience and appeared to US$ 167,398,686,952. TRR and LCOE were estimated using this data.

Figure 4 shows the comparison using the results of previous research to compare LCOE with other ESS (Zakeri et al., 2015). The carrying cost ratio determined in this study was used to add capital recovery, return on equity, return on debt, income taxes, other taxes and insurance, which were not taken into account when calculating LCOE in other studies, to other ESS. The results showed that using cold energy and waste heat and selling the by-products resulted in a cheaper LCOE than the current LAES system of US$ 51/MWh.

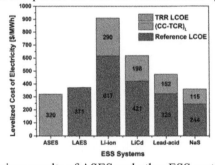

Figure 4. LCOE comparison results of ASES and other ESS systems.

### 4.3. Environment assessment

In this study, we estimated the percentage of overall renewable energy that must be supplied to Daesan petrochemical complex that can be supplied through this process. The Daesan petrochemical complex will require 1,564,035 MWh/yr of renewable energy, and the ASES system has the capacity to provide an additional 88,000 MWh/yr of electricity. 345.96 kg of $CO_2$ are released into the atmosphere for each 1 MWh of electricity produced using sub-bituminous coal (the most of using fuel for generating in Korea) as a fossil fuel. So, this system can significantly reduce 30,444 ton of $CO_2$ of year and equates to 5.6% of the necessary supply of renewable energy. Specific environmental assessment of the proposed energy system will be implemented using life cycle assessment as future perspectives.

## 5. Conclusions

This study aims to 1) develop integrated energy systems that enable generating electrical energy from LAES and producing industiral utilites from ASU and 2) conduct techno-economic assesement to find out the feasibility of the developed model by applying to Daesan petrochemical complex. Waste heat and cold heat generated by LNG power plants were used for air vaporization and liquefaction to boost energy efficiency. To reduce power costs, liquefied air is stored during the late-night hours when energy use are low, and electricity is generated utilizing the air stored during the power peak period to supply power to the petrochemical complex. For the case study in Korea, economic feasibility may be awarded a good rating based on an in-depth economic evaluation that takes into account the carrying cost, and the economic evaluation reveals a reduced equivalent power cost of US$ 51/MWh lower equivalent power generating cost than the present LAES system. It is anticipated that it would be employed as a novel energy storage system for sustainable power generation in Korea.

## References

Borri, E., Tafone, A., Romagnoli, A., & Comodi, G., 2021, A review on liquid air energy storage: History, state of the art and recent developments. *Renewable and Sustainable Energy Reviews*, *137*, 110572.

Chehade, G., & Dincer, I., 2021, Progress in green ammonia production as potential carbon-free fuel. *Fuel*, *299*, 120845.

Ko, A., Park, S., Kim, J. Y., & Cha, J. M., 2018, Development and reliability optimization of economic analysis module for power generation system from industrial waste heat recovery. *Journal of Energy Engineering*, *27*(4), 50-63.

Koohi-Fayegh, S., & Rosen, M. A., 2020, A review of energy storage types, applications and recent developments. *Journal of Energy Storage*, *27*, 101047.

Morgan, R., Nelmes, S., Gibson, E., & Brett, G., 2015, Liquid air energy storage–analysis and first results from a pilot scale demonstration plant. *Applied energy*, *137*, 845-853.

Nam, K., Hwangbo, S., & Yoo, C., 2020, A deep learning-based forecasting model for renewable energy scenarios to guide sustainable energy policy: A case study of Korea. *Renewable and Sustainable Energy Reviews*, *122*, 109725.

Qi, M., Park, J., Kim, J., Lee, I., & Moon, I., 2020, Advanced integration of LNG regasification power plant with liquid air energy storage: Enhancements in flexibility, safety, and power generation. *Applied energy*, *269*, 115049.

Zakeri, B., & Syri, S., 2015, Electrical energy storage systems: A comparative life cycle cost analysis. *Renewable and sustainable energy reviews*, *42*, 569-596.

Antonis Kokossis, Michael C. Georgiadis, Efstratios N. Pistikopoulos (Eds.)
PROCEEDINGS OF THE 33rd European Symposium on Computer Aided Process Engineering
(ESCAPE33), June 18-21, 2023, Athens, Greece

# A systematic method for performing pinch analysis of the Liquid Air Energy Storage (LAES) process

Vuppanapalli Chaitanya[a], S. Narasimhan[a*], G. Venkatarathnam[b]

[a] Department of Chemical Engineering, Indian Institute of Technology Madras, Chennai 600036, India
[b] Department of Mechanical Engineering, Indian Institute of Technology Madras, Chennai 600036, India

*Corresponding author at Department of Chemical Engineering, Indian Institute of Technology Madras, India; E-mail address: naras@iitm.ac.in

**Abstract**

In process design, the insights obtained by applying pinch technology have played an important role in maximizing energy efficiency through energy integration [1]. Pinch technology exclusively addresses temperature variations in process streams resulting from indirect heat exchange. The analysis does not take into account temperature changes in process streams induced by changes in stream pressure.

In this work, a systematic procedure for applying pinch analysis to the Liquid Air Energy Storage (LAES) process is proposed. In this process, air undergoes significant pressure changes, which results in phase changes as well as wide variations in the specific heat capacity. Since the air temperature varies from well above ambient to well below ambient conditions, multiple minimum approach temperature specifications have to be imposed. A parameterized version of the Grand Composite Curves (GCCs) is proposed for pinch analysis that takes into account for all of these special features. The parameterized GCCs are used to identify the feasible design space for a LAES process.

**Keywords**: Pinch analysis, Pressure change, Liquid air energy storage, Grand Composite Curves, Feasible design space.

## 1  INTRODUCTION

The world is rapidly shifting to the use of renewable energy sources to replace fossil fuels for power generation. However, the intermittent nature of renewable energy and the significant difference between its availability and demand time periods are two challenges that need to be tackled. The use of energy storage technologies is one approach to address the above challenges. Liquid Air Energy Storage (LAES) is a thermal energy storage system that has attracted considerable attention recently due to its advantages, such as its high energy density, long life span, no geographical constraints, and environmental friendliness [2]. The main limitation of LAES systems is their low round-trip efficiency (RTE) of around 50–60% for large-scale systems. Several different process designs have been proposed by different researchers to improve the RTE. For example, a part of the cold utility requirements can be provided by cold air or by integrating an LNG regasification process with the LAES process [2]. The proposed designs have to be simulated and optimized to determine the maximum possible RTE gains. In process design, the insights obtained by applying pinch technology have played an important role in maximizing energy efficiency through energy integration [1]. Using pinch technology, it is possible to derive bounds on the minimum utility requirements prior to design. It also provides useful information on the utility design (the quantity and temperature levels at which external utilities can be provided) and how best to integrate compressors and turbines with the thermal process.     However, pinch technology only deals with temperature changes in process streams caused by heat exchange. Temperature change in a process stream induced by a change in the stream pressure is not considered in the analysis. Aspelund et al. [3] proposed an expanded pinch analysis based on exergy analysis for taking into account pressure-induced temperature changes. Such a technique is required to analyze processes such as LAES, air separation, and natural gas liquefaction. The LAES process poses the following additional challenges for pinch analysis:

- Use of a non-global minimum temperature approach in the LAES process.
- A large operating temperature range (100-600 K) results in significant variation in the fluid properties, specifically heat capacity.
- The charging and the discharging sections are thermally coupled with thermal energy storage media, which forces thermal energy storage media to operate in a cyclic mode.

In this work, we propose a systematic approach for applying pinch analysis that deals with all of the above challenges. Based on a parametric version of the Grand Composite Curve (GCC), we quantitatively identify the feasible operating regimes and minimum utility requirements. The GCC can potentially be used for identifying alternative choices of cold storage utilities and the potential for integrating refrigeration cycles with the process.

## 2   PINCH ANALYSIS OF LAES PROCESS

### 2.1 Process description

A typical standalone LAES process is shown in Fig. 1. It includes a charging section (air liquefaction) and discharging section (power recovery). In the charging section, power from a renewable energy source is used to liquefy air and store it in insulated storage tanks. The heat generated from air compression is recovered into a high-temperature energy storage system (thermal oil). When energy is required, liquid air from the storage tank is heated and expanded in the discharging section to generate power. The cold energy of the liquid air is recovered and stored in a low-temperature energy storage system (propane and methanol) to be utilized in the next charging cycle.

### 2.2 Process streams for pinch analysis

In the LAES process, air is compressed and later expanded to produce liquid air. The change in pressure results in phase changes and wide variations in the specific heat capacity. Furthermore, the fraction of liquid air produced depends on the process conditions. Thus, it is not possible to construct a stream table and apply the standard pinch analysis of this process. In order to construct the stream table, the operating pressures ($P_C$ and $P_D$) of the charging and discharging sections have to be chosen. The fraction of air that is liquefied (Y) must also be chosen because this determines the vapor flow rate (stream 7) from the phase separator. The choice of these operating parameters have a significant effect on the utility requirements, and have to be parametrically varied to study their impact. The time periods of operation of the discharge and charging sections are generally specified based on the application requirements, and are assumed to be fixed. Given these specifications, the stream table can be constructed for unit inlet air flow rate chosen as a basis. Any process stream that undergoes pressure changes is treated as multiple segments by considering the segments before and after pressure change as separate streams in the analysis. For example, in Fig. 1, segments from the inlet air between states 1-2, 3-4, and 6-6a (compression and expansion operations) are deleted, and the remaining segments 2-3, 4-5, and 7-8 (heat exchanger operations) are included as distinct streams. For different outlet pressure of compressors, parametric GCC are constructed that are further used in the analysis. The thermal oil that recovers the heat of compression and cold utilities methanol and propane are also included as process streams since they are operated in a cyclic mode. Propane and methanol are assumed to be liquids operating between their normal boiling point and triple point temperatures, while thermal oil is assumed to operate between ambient temperature and its maximum allowable temperature of 603 K. It should be noted that the energy recovered or supplied during the charging cycle by these utilities must match exactly with the energy supplied/recovered during the discharge cycle (to avoid the use of other external utilities). Since the operating time periods for the charging and discharge cycles are assumed to be fixed, the following constraints on the flow rate of methanol and propane can be derived.

$$Y = \frac{\dot{m}_{11}}{\dot{m}_9} = \frac{\dot{m}_{6C1}}{\dot{m}_{3C1}} = \frac{\dot{m}_{6C2}}{\dot{m}_{3C2}} = \frac{t_c}{t_d} \tag{1}$$

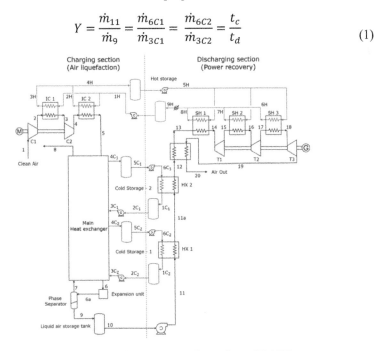

Figure 1: Typical process configuration of LAES

From the above equations, the flow rates of all streams can be determined for the given choice of liquid air yield. The specific enthalpies of the streams depend both on the temperature and pressure. Based on the chosen pressures ($P_c$ and $P_D$), a thermodynamic property estimation package is used to evaluate the specific enthalpy over the entire range of operating range. The GCC for the charging section can now be constructed for every choice of the operating variables $P_C$, $P_D$, and Y. We refer to this GCC curve as a parameterized GCC, since it depends on the chosen values of the operating variables. By analysing the parameterized GCCs over a wide range of the three operating parameters the feasible operating regime and maximum RTE that can be obtained, prior to design. The stream table constructed for the choice of $P_C$ = 100 bar, $P_D$ = 150 bar, and Y = 0.7 is shown in Table 1. All thermodynamic properties are computed using the Peng Robinson equation of state. The specific heat capacities of all streams (air, propane, and methanol) change significantly over the operating temperature range. Therefore, the overall temperature range is divided into differential intervals of $1^0C$ for the purpose of constructing the GCC.

Furthermore, a single minimum temperature approach (MTA) may not be appropriate, since the process streams operate well above and well below ambient conditions. It has been determined that the lower the minimum temperature approach below ambient temperature, the lower the temperature to which air can be cooled before being expanded in the cryo-turbine. This leads to a higher yield of liquid air and improved performance in the process. An assumption has been made that the MTA will be a minimum of 10 degrees above ambient temperature and 5 degrees below ambient temperature. The method presented by Robin Smith [1] is used to deal with the dual MTA specification.

## 3 RESULTS AND DISCUSSION

The stream table for a specific combination of $P_C$, $P_D$, and Y is constructed and shown in Table 1. The GCC plot for this combination of operating parameters is presented in Fig. 2a. From Fig 2a, the pinch temperature is observed to be at 194 K, and the minimum external cold utility ($CU_{min}$) required by the LAES process is 17 kW. The $CU_{min}$ requirement has to be met by external utility below the pinch temperature, which implies that external refrigerants are required. If the utility requirements cannot be met using only ambient air (or water), then we consider the corresponding operating condition to be inadmissible or infeasible (since additional energy has to be spent to generate the external utility). The GCC plot for the same liquid yield, but a different combination of discharge and charging pressures ($P_C$ = 100 bar, $P_D$ = 80 bar) is shown in Fig. 2b. It can be observed from the GCC that the process is self-sufficient and does not require either hot or cold utility. Thus, the process operating condition is feasible. The GCC plot for the process operating at $P_C$ = 100 bar, $P_D$ = 60 bar) is shown in Fig. 2c. It can be observed from Fig. 2c that the process is not pinched and requires a minimum external heating utility ($HU_{min}$) of 7.5 kW. However, from the GCC, it can also be inferred that the entire $HU_{min}$ can be supplied using air available at 300K. Thus, this operating conditions is also called feasible. In order to identify the feasible operating regime, the analysis is performed for different operating conditions. The entire regime of operating conditions is divided into admissible and inadmissible regimes.

The feasible operating regimes identified using pinch analysis for the LAES process described in the preceding section are presented in Fig. 3, for different values of liquid air yield. Corresponding to any given liquid air yield, an operating point in the infeasible region has a GCC similar to the one shown in Fig. 2a, with the pinch temperature being below the ambient temperature. An operating point on the boundary separating the feasible and infeasible regimes has a GCC similar to the one shown in Fig. 2b. Under these operating conditions, the process does not require external utilities and can be considered to be optimum operating points in terms of utility requirements. An operating point within the feasible region has a GCC similar to Fig. 2c, and requires external HU which can be met by ambient air. For these operating points, excess heat is generated during compression in the charging cycle than what can be stored by the thermal oil and utilized during the discharge cycle, and the excess heat is discharged to the ambient leading to sub-optimal efficiencies.

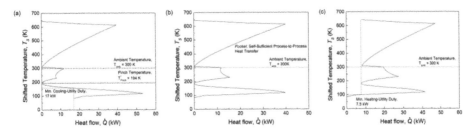

Figure 2: Grand Composite Curve (a) for the data in Table 1 with $P_C$ = 100 bar, $P_D$ = 150 bar and Y = 0.7, (b) $P_C$ = 100 bar, $P_D$ = 80 bar and Y = 0.7 and (c) $P_C$ = 100 bar, $P_D$ = 60 bar and Y = 0.7

Table 1: Process stream data for operating condition $P_C$ = 100 bar, $P_D$ = 150 bar and Y = 0.7

| Stream | $T_i^{Supply}$ | $T_i^{Target}$ | $[\dot{m}C_{P_i}^{Min}, \dot{m}C_{P_i}^{Max}]$ | $\Delta H_i$ |
|---|---|---|---|---|
| i | (K) | (K) | (kW/K) | (kW) |
| $2 \rightarrow 3$ | 621.00 | 302.00 | [1.02, 1.05] | 329.60 |
| $4 \rightarrow 6$ | 626.00 | 104.05 | [1.07, 2.82] | 707.59 |
| $7 \rightarrow 8$ | 79.15 | 295.00 | [0.20, 0.21] | 43.71 |
| $3C_1 \rightarrow 4C_1$ | 225.00 | 295.00 | [1.13, 1.15] | 80.01 |
| $3C_2 \rightarrow 4C_2$ | 93.00 | 225.00 | [1.55, 1.64] | 209.25 |
| $1H \rightarrow 4H$ | 300.00 | 603.72 | [1.69, 2.84] | 684.56 |

It can be observed from Fig. 3c that for the desired liquid air yield of 0.7 and $P_D$ of 120 bar. The minimum required value of charging section operating pressure ($P_C$) is 120 bar to make the process feasible. Similarly, the maximum possible liquid air yield for the process operating with $P_C$ = 120 bar and $P_D$ = 60 bar is 0.8. Any further desired liquid air yield, demands utility that cannot be met with ambient air. The round trip efficiencies corresponding to different operating points on the boundaries separating the feasible and operating regimes for different yields do vary, and can be compared to identify the best operating point that gives the maximum RTE, after which the process design and heat integration for the corresponding operating condition can be carried out.

A study conducted to examine the effect of the minimum temperature approach on the feasible operating region has revealed that a decrease in the MTA leads to an increase in the size of the feasible operating region.

## 4 CONCLUSIONS

A systematic procedure for applying pinch analysis to a LAES process is proposed which considers the impact of temperature and phase changes in process streams induced by pressure change, nonlinear dependence of specific heat on temperature, and multiple minimum approach temperature specifications. The proposed procedure can be used to identify the feasible design space and other options for improving overall energy efficiency. The proposed procedure can potentially be applied to analyze other processes, such as air separation, natural gas liquefaction, and the use of vapor recompression for energy integration in distillation columns, where process streams undergo significant pressure change.

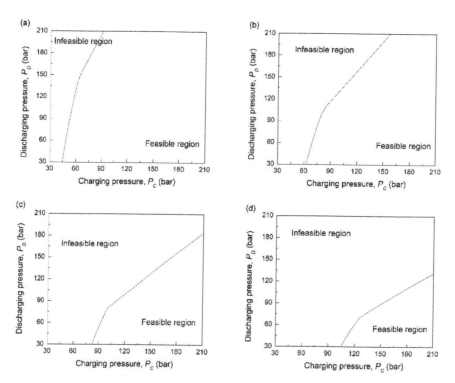

Figure 3: Influence of liquid air yield on the feasible operating region (a) Y = 0.5, (b) Y = 0.6, (c) Y = 0.7, and (d) Y = 0.8.

## 5 REFERENCES

[1]     Smith R. Chemical Process Design and Integration. vol. 83. 2005. https://doi.org/10.1205/cherd.br.0509.

[2]     She X, Zhang T, Cong L, Peng X, Li C, Luo Y, et al. Flexible integration of liquid air energy storage with liquefied natural gas regasification for power generation enhancement. Appl Energy 2019;251:113355. https://doi.org/10.1016/j.apenergy.2019.113355.

[3]     Aspelund A, Berstad DO, Gundersen T. An Extended Pinch Analysis and Design procedure utilizing pressure based exergy for subambient cooling. Appl Therm Eng 2007;27:2633–49. https://doi.org/10.1016/j.applthermaleng.2007.04.017.

Antonis Kokossis, Michael C. Georgiadis, Efstratios N. Pistikopoulos (Eds.)
PROCEEDINGS OF THE 33rd European Symposium on Computer Aided Process Engineering
(ESCAPE33), June 18-21, 2023, Athens, Greece

# Climate-zone-based Techno-Economic Assessment of Different Carbon Capture Technologies for Coal-Fired Power Plants

Mohammadamin Zarei,[a] Ha-Jun Yoon,[a] Chul-Jin Lee,[a,b]

*aSchool of Chemical Engineering and Materials Science, Chung-Ang University, 84 Heukseok-ro, Dongjak-gu, Seoul, Republic of Korea*
*bDepartment of Intelligent Energy and Industry, Chung-Ang University, 84 Heukseokro, Dongjak-gu, Seoul, Republic of Korea*

## Abstract

As fossil fuels are consumed and proven reserves exist, reducing carbon emissions is crucial to ensuring global energy security. It is imperative to reduce $CO_2$ emissions from coal-fired power plants, which can be done most effectively through capturing and storing $CO_2$ (CCS). Contrary to other aspects of power generation, CCS technologies have not been investigated in terms of their sensitivity to climate zones. Having that information helps decision-makers minimize carbon emissions by making long-term plans. Therefore, in this study, a techno-economic assessment (TEA) model was developed for coal-fired power plants using post- and oxy-fuel combustion CCS technologies. A comparison of minimum and maximum values reveals that rising altitude, as reflected in changes in ambient pressure, decreases avoided $CO_2$ costs by 8% for post-combustion technology and 3% for oxy-combustion technology. It also reveals an increase in temperature reduces post-combustion costs by 10.5% and oxy-fuel costs by 5.8%.

**Keywords**: Coal-fired power plant, carbon capture and storage, climate.

## 1. Introduction

The global mean temperature has risen by 1 °C due to anthropogenic greenhouse gas emissions. About 0.3 °C of the global average temperature increase is attributed to $CO_2$ produced by coal combustion. Globally, coal-fired power plants generate 38% of electricity and 30% of carbon dioxide emissions. It is impossible for conventional fossil fuel-fired power plants to achieve environmental goals even after efficiency improvements and process optimization. World power generation continues to be dominated by fossil fuels despite considerable investment and falling renewable energy prices, particularly in developing countries. Consequently, fossil fuels will remain a key source of energy for the foreseeable future. To use a large amount of energy from fossil fuels, efforts are being made to reduce greenhouse gas emissions(Yadav and Mondal, 2022).

Using carbon capture and storage (CCS) technologies has demonstrated great potential in reducing greenhouse gas emissions while utilizing fossil fuels to generate electricity in response to the Paris Agreement, which aims to peak carbon emissions, neutralize carbon emissions, and achieve net zero emissions. The CCS technology combines a variety of integrated technologies to capture huge amounts of $CO_2$ from industrial sources such as power plants(Wei, Manovic and Hanak, 2020). The process can be divided into three stages: capture, transportation, and storage. In the current state of CO2 capture technology, there are primarily three types of systems, which are post-combustion, pre-combustion, and oxy-fuel combustion systems. The pre-combustion capture process involves the separation of fossil fuel carbon before combustion occurs. When oxygen is used instead of regular air as an oxidant in combustion, it is referred to as oxy-fuel combustion. The term "post-combustion capture" refers to capturing and storing CO2 as a result of a conventional power station's exhaust gas(Ye *et al.*, 2019).

Developing a comprehensive understanding of how climate zones affect CCS efficiency is one of the challenges in technical evaluation of these technologies. Consequently, parametric studies in CCS should be performed by changing operating conditions such as temperature, pressure, and relative humidity. There are several studies on the components of power plants. Bataineh and Khaleel investigated the effect of ambient conditions on gas turbines in combined cycle power plants(Bataineh and Khaleel, 2020). Similarly, Zhai and Rubin examined local ambient conditions as a key factor influencing cooling system performance, cost, and water use (Zhai and Rubin, 2010). The influences of the meteorological data, including ambient temperature and DNI on solar power plants, are examined by Wang et al(Wang *et al.*, 2019). However, to the best of our knowledge, there are limited studies that have focused on the effect of ambient parameters on CCS. Rim et al. worked on changes in temperature, humidity, and atmospheric pressure to set optimal process conditions for direct air capture of CO2(Rim *et al.*, 2022). A study on changes in CCS technologies in different climate zones has not been conducted, even though other aspects of power generation have investigated their sensitivity to climate zones. Therefore, this study aims to develop a techno-economic assessment (TEA) model of a coal-fired power plant using two methods of post- and oxy-fuel combustion CCS technology to measure the effect of climate parameters including ambient air pressure, relative humidity, and temperature on CCS technologies.

## 2. Methodology

### 2.1. Description of technical methods

As a result of the above mentioned research gap in CCS-related studies, this work focuses on two main types of CCS technology in coal-fired power plants as Figure 1 shows: 1)post-combustion which is the most cost-effective technology option (Ye *et al.*, 2019) and 2) oxy-fuel combustion: which has the high capacity to absorb CO2 (Alalwan and Alminshid, 2021). The Integrated Environmental Control Model(IECM), developed by Carnegie Mellon University, is used to assess the cost of carbon capture in power plants(CMU, 2021). Through IECM, fossil fuel-fired power systems with CCS can be systematically analyzed in terms of their performance, emissions, and costs. To determine the range of climate-related factors, Köppen climate classification is used to analyze the various climate zones(Cui, Liang and Wang, 2021).

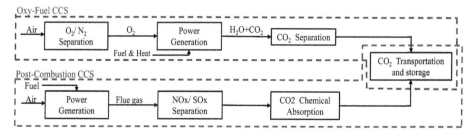

Figure 1. Integrated flow diagram of CCS technologies

## 2.2. The cost analysis framework

650 MW gross power coal-fired subcritical power plant capable of carbon capture is considered for the purpose of comparing costs between CCS options in different climate zones. A schematic of the cost-estimating methodology is presented in Figure 2. The methodology begins with defining the cases. This step determines ambient conditions, combustion process, CCS process, system capacity, and fuel type. In the second part of this analysis, unit prices such as fuel and electricity prices, financial parameters such as interest rates, taxes, and operating schedules such as load factor are used to calculate performance. Finally, cost measures such as Levelised cost of electricity (LCOE), cost of $CO_2$ captured, and cost of $CO_2$ avoided are defined to make the cost evaluation as follows:

$$LCOE = \frac{TCR \cdot FCF + FOM}{MW \cdot CF \cdot 8760} + VOM + HR \cdot FC, \tag{1}$$

$$C_{avoided} = \frac{C_{ccs} - C_{ref}}{E_{ref} - E_{ccs}}, \tag{2}$$

$$C_{captured} = \frac{C_{ccs} - C_{ref}}{E_{captured}}, \tag{3}$$

where TCR is total capital requirement, FCF is fixed charge factor, FOM is fixed operating and maintenance cost(O&M), VOM is variable O&M excluding fuel, HR refers to the heat rate of the powerplant, the cost of fuel per unit of energy is represented by FC, CF refers to capacity factor, and the plant's net power output is represented by MW. Using equations (2) and (3), a comparison is made between the plant using CCS and the reference plant without CCS(Keivani and Gungor, 2022). $C_{ccs}$ and $C_{ref}$ are power generation cost of CCS powerplant and reference powerplant, respectively. $E_{ref}$ and $E_{ccs}$ are carbon emission intensity of the reference and CCS powerplant. Carbon emission intensity of the CCS power plant before the capturing process is represented by $E_{captured}$.

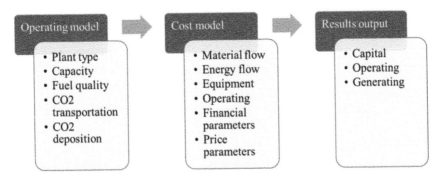

Figure 2. System model. structure of the CCS cost module.

The main parameters of the model include the following four modules: operating parameters of the CCS and reference power plant, parameters of fuel quality, sulfur dioxide treatment system parameters, and CO2 capture system parameters. This study selects a commercial subcritical power plant with an output power of nearly 650 MW. In the case of the absorption-based CO2 capture process, the processes that use MEA for the post-combustion unit(Rubin, Rao and Berkenpas, 2007) and High-sulfur configuration for the oxy-fuel combustion(IECM, 2021). The main design assumptions including main parameters and relevant technical and economic considerations used for design cases are reported in Tables 1 and 2. In this work, reference powerplant is located in Denver.

Table 1. Basic assumption for CCS technologies

|  | Post-combustion control | Oxy-fuel combustion |
|---|---|---|
| **NOx removal** | Hot-Side SCR | |
| **Particulate Removal** | Cold-Side ESP | Fabric filter |
| **SOx removal** | FGD | FGD |
| **CO2 capture** | Amine system(MEA) | High-sulfur (>1.5%) |
| **Storage** | Geological Reservoir | |
| **Transportation** | Pipeline | |

Table 2. Key assumptions for the economic evaluation

| Parameter | Value | Unit |
|---|---|---|
| **Plant capacity** | 650 | MW |
| **Power plant type** | Subcritical | - |
| **Construction period** | 3 | years |
| **Capacity factor** | 75 | % |
| **Economic lifetime** | 30 | years |
| **Method** | Constant money value | |
| **Discount rate** | 7 | % |
| **Inflation** | Constant money value | |
| **Carbon tax** | 0 | $ |
| **Fuel type** | Bituminous | - |
| **Fuel cost** | 49.87 | $/tonne |
| **Electricity cost** | 43.84 | $/MWh |
| **Operating labor rate** | 34.65 | $/hour |
| **Number of Operating Shifts** | 4.75 | shift/day |

## 3. Results and Conclusion

A simulation showing the operating results of a newly constructed power plant that includes CCS and its reference power plant can be seen in figures 3 and 4. Figure 3 presents the effect of three main climate indicators on post-combustion CCS in coal-fired power plant. It shows performance characteristics that distinctly depend on relative humidity. However, as temperature increases, cost of CO2 avoided and added cost of CCS increase by 10.44% and 10.45%, respectively. Likewise, changing ambient pressure by 0.083 bar to 1.01 bar which represents changing 1700 meters in altitude decreases cost of CO2 avoided and added cost of CCS by 8.39% and 8.15%, respectively. Figure 4 represents the effect of same climate indicators on oxy-fuel combustion. Same as Figure 3, it can be seen relative humidity does not affect CCS performances. However, ambient temperature and pressure increase cost by almost 5.8% and 3.5%. In the post-combustion process CO2 is diluted in nitrogen that is existed in air and changing temperature highly effected separation costs. To avoid dilution, in oxy-fuel combustion process pure oxygen is used to yield more concentrated CO2. Therefore, it can be seen these indicators have a greater impact on post-combustion than oxy-fuel combustion. Consequently, it makes changes in LCOE. Increasing temperature and pressure in post-combustion plants increase LCOE by 5% and 3.6%. Moreover, increasing temperature and pressure in oxy-fuel combustion plants increase LCOE by less than 3%. It can be concluded humidity does not affect as much as temperature and pressure. It can be concluded that ambient temperature and pressure have an effect on CCS cost and on the other hand, it is independent of ambient relative humidity.

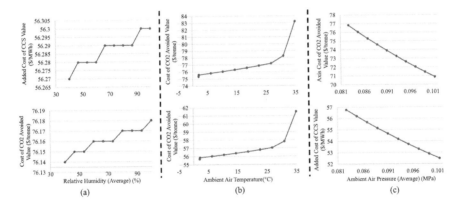

Figure 3 Impact of sensitivity factors on post-combustion performances: (a) relative humidity (b); ambient air; temperature.

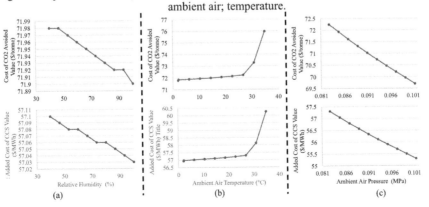

Figure 4 Impact of sensitivity factors on oxy-combustion performances: (a) relative humidity (b); ambient air; temperature.

# References

Alalwan, H.A. and Alminshid, A.H. (2021) 'CO2 capturing methods: Chemical looping combustion (CLC) as a promising technique', *Science of The Total Environment*, 788, p. 147850. Available at: https://doi.org/https://doi.org/10.1016/j.scitotenv.2021.147850.

Bataineh, K. and Khaleel, B.A. (2020) 'Thermodynamic analysis of a combined cycle power plant located in Jordan: A case study', *Archives of Thermodynamics*, 41(1), pp. 95–123.

IECM. (2021). Integrated Environmental Control Model (IECM) Version 11.5 (Carnegie Mellon University). https://www.cmu.edu/epp/iecm/index.html.

Cui, D., Liang, S. and Wang, D. (2021) 'Observed and projected changes in global climate zones based on Köppen climate classification', *WIREs Climate Change*, 12(3), p. e701. Available at: https://doi.org/https://doi.org/10.1002/wcc.701.

IECM (2021) *Amine-based Post-Combustion CO2 Capture*. Pittsburgh. Available at: https://www.cmu.edu/epp/iecm/documentation/2019Jan_IECM Amine-based CO2 Capture.pdf.

Keivani, B. and Gungor, A. (2022) 'Techno-economic assessment of coal and torrefied biomass co-combustion: A case study of oxy-combustion carbon capture power plants in Turkey', *Journal of CO2 Utilization*, 62, p. 102103. Available at: https://doi.org/https://doi.org/10.1016/j.jcou.2022.102103.

Rim, G. *et al.* (2022) 'Sub-Ambient Temperature Direct Air Capture of CO2 using Amine-Impregnated MIL-101(Cr) Enables Ambient Temperature CO2 Recovery', *JACS Au*, 2(2), pp. 380–393. Available at: https://doi.org/10.1021/jacsau.1c00414.

Rubin, E.S., Rao, A.B. and Berkenpas, M.B. (2007) *Development and application of optimal design capability for coal gasification systems*. Carnegie-Mellon University.

Wang, A. *et al.* (2019) 'Thermodynamic and economic analyses of a parabolic trough concentrating solar power plant under off-design conditions', *Applied Thermal Engineering*, 156, pp. 340–350. Available at: https://doi.org/https://doi.org/10.1016/j.applthermaleng.2019.04.062.

Wei, X., Manovic, V. and Hanak, D.P. (2020) 'Techno-economic assessment of coal- or biomass-fired oxy-combustion power plants with supercritical carbon dioxide cycle', *Energy Conversion and Management*, 221, p. 113143. Available at: https://doi.org/https://doi.org/10.1016/j.enconman.2020.113143.

Yadav, S. and Mondal, S.S. (2022) 'A review on the progress and prospects of oxy-fuel carbon capture and sequestration (CCS) technology', *Fuel*, 308, p. 122057. Available at: https://doi.org/https://doi.org/10.1016/j.fuel.2021.122057.

Ye, B. *et al.* (2019) 'Technical and economic analysis of amine-based carbon capture and sequestration at coal-fired power plants', *Journal of Cleaner Production*, 222, pp. 476–487. Available at: https://doi.org/https://doi.org/10.1016/j.jclepro.2019.03.050.

Zhai, H. and Rubin, E.S. (2010) 'Performance and cost of wet and dry cooling systems for pulverized coal power plants with and without carbon capture and storage', *Energy Policy*, 38(10), pp. 5653–5660. Available at: https://doi.org/https://doi.org/10.1016/j.enpol.2010.05.013.

Antonis Kokossis, Michael C. Georgiadis, Efstratios N. Pistikopoulos (Eds.)
PROCEEDINGS OF THE 33rd European Symposium on Computer Aided Process Engineering
(ESCAPE33), June 18-21, 2023, Athens, Greece

# Numerical tool for dynamic simulation of anaerobic digesters including an air-inflated double membrane gasholder

Giberto M. Yuki Junior,[a, b] Sabine Sochard,[a] Elio Dinuccio,[b] Frédéric Marias[a]

*[a]Universite de Pau et des Pays de l'Adour, E2S UPPA, LaTEP, Rue Jules Ferry, Pau 64000, France*
*[b]Department of Agriculture, Forestry and Food Science, University of Turin, Largo Paolo Braccini 2, Grugliasco 10095, Italy*

## Abstract

Air-inflated double membrane gasholders are often used in anaerobic digestion plants to store the biogas produced. In this work, a dynamic model based on conservation equations and the ideal gas law for such type of gas storage was proposed. Simulations during charging and discharging steps of the gas storage led to a stable pressure profile in both cases, but with a higher value through the first period. The model was also used to compare the operation at a full load with one at a medium load, which demonstrates that reducing the gas storage level can avoid overpressure events caused by temperature variations.

**Keywords**: biogas, double membrane, gasholder, model.

## 1. Introduction

In biogas plants, the gas produced is often stored inside the digester's headspace. The air-inflated double membrane gasholder is one of the most used structures to store biogas (Stur et al., 2022). It consists of two polymeric membranes delimiting two compartments over the digester: an outer one filled with air and an inner one filled with biogas. The external membrane is kept inflated by a continuous injection of air using a blower. One benefit of such structure is that the pressure can be controlled regardless of the storage level (Kube, 2018). Moreover, several digesters and post-digesters can have their headspaces interconnected (Kube, 2018). Hence, the flowrate between each unit can be manipulated by controlling the pressure in each reactor (Kube, 2018).

The double membrane is also equipped with a pressure relief valve, which is a safety device to avoid over and underpressure episodes. This equipment works by releasing biogas into the atmosphere in case of overpressure or by injecting air directly into the biogas storage compartment in case of underpressure (Stur et al., 2022). Although such valve is a safety equipment, a monitoring in a biogas plant in Germany showed that biogas release events were common, with $CH_4$ losses reaching up to 1.8% of annual production (Reinelt and Liebetrau, 2020). These events were linked to biogas temperature variations and lack of staff training to operate this kind of gasholder (Reinelt and Liebetrau, 2020). Such losses, however, could have been reduced by automatic gas level control (Reinelt and Liebetrau, 2020) or by operating at a lower storage level (Reinelt and Liebetrau, 2020; Stur et al., 2022).

To the best of authors' knowledge, the double membrane gasholder transient behavior has not yet been modelled despite of its implications on biogas plant operation. Indeed, dynamic modelling approaches in the biogas field have been concentrated on the bioreactions (Emebu et al., 2022) or the digester's thermal behavior (Hreiz et al., 2017; Vilms Pedersen et al., 2020). Thus, in this work an approach to describe the transient operation of a double membrane gasholder is presented. Therefore, the model developed will be useful to improve the simulation of biogas plants and it will be helpful in evaluating control strategies for the gas storage management and to train staff operating such industrial plants. In future work, the digester and the double membrane models will be included in a global model for a multi-energy platform containing methanation, water electrolysis and biogas upgrading units.

## 2. Model description

### 2.1. General digester model

The digester model was developed by integrating different approaches to describe the bioreactions, the reactor thermal behavior and the mass transfer to the gas phase. The digestate phase was supposed well mixed and, thus, a 0-D approach was used. A mass based version of ADM1 was employed to predict the biogas production (Weinrich and Nelles, 2021). However, some small changes were implemented into the biokinetic model. For instance, the $H_2S$ production by sulfate-reducing bacteria were considered (Pokorna-Krayzelova et al., 2017) and the stoichiometry of the cell death reaction was rebalanced so that the atomic balances were fulfilled.

On the other hand, the thermal behavior was estimated by considering the heat losses to the environment through the digester boundaries using empirical correlations for the heat transfer resistances (Hreiz et al., 2017; Incropera et al., 2007; Vilms Pedersen et al., 2020). Finally, the mass transfer between the liquid and the gas phase was evaluated by estimating the mass transfer coefficient from the digestate properties and agitation mobile configuration (Garcia-Ochoa and Gomez, 2004) or using the mass and heat transfer analogy (Incropera et al., 2007).

### 2.2. Double membrane model

The behavior of the air inflated gasholder was described by applying mass and energy balances on the air (A) and the biogas (B) layers as shown in Figure 1 and Eqs. (1)-(4). In Eq. (1), the air molar flowrate through the blower, $F_A^{in}$, was calculated as a function of the relative air pressure, $P_A^g$, using a polynomial function based on the curves used in Kube's work (Kube, 2018), while the outlet flow was estimated using a valve equation, as shown in Eq. (5) and Figure 1 (a). Eq. (2) describes the mass balance on the biogas side, where $F_B^{GL}$ represents the biogas production in the digester and $F_B^{out}$ the current molar flowrate through the valve. Finally, the temperatures of each gas phase were estimated using Eqs. (3) and (4), which were obtained from the energy balances, assuming ideal gas behavior and constant values for the heat capacities. Moreover, the thermal inertia of the walls and the cover in contact with each phase were included in the energy balance in the form of $m_{wall}Cp_{wall}$ in both energy balances. This approach was used to avoid overestimating the internal temperature variations with the external conditions. The heat transfer terms, $Q$, were calculated considering the convection inside and outside the digester, and the radiation exchange with the external environment. The state variables in each gas compartment are summarized in Figure 1 (b).

$$\frac{dn_A}{dt} = F_A^{in}\left(P_A^g\right) - F_A^{out}\left(P_A^g\right) \tag{1}$$

$$\frac{dn_B}{dt} = F_B^{GL} - F_B^{out}\left(P_B^g\right) \tag{2}$$

$$\frac{dT_A}{dt} = \frac{F_A^{in} Cp_A(T_A^{in} - T_A) + RT_A(F_A^{in} - F_A^{out}) + Q_A}{n_A Cv_A + m_{wall,A} Cp_{wall,A}} \tag{3}$$

$$\frac{dT_B}{dt} = \frac{F_B^{GL} Cp_B(T_B^L - T_B) + RT_B(F_B^{GL} - F_B^{out}) + Q_B}{n_B Cv_B + m_{wall,B} Cp_{wall,B}} \tag{4}$$

$$\dot{V} = CV\sqrt{P^g} \tag{5}$$

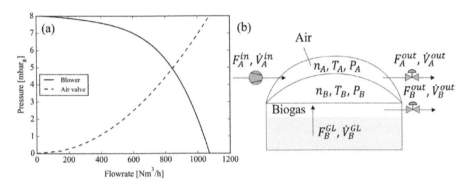

Figure 1 (a) Air blower and valve curves (b) Digester scheme showing the gas flows and state variables in the gas phases

### 2.2.1. Mobile regime

When the air volume was not at its threshold values, it was assumed that the inner membrane could freely move. All forces related to the membrane weight or its displacement were neglected. Thus, the pressures in both sides were supposed to be equal. The outer membrane, nevertheless, was considered as a rigid wall. Therefore, the total volume, delimited by this outer cover and the digester walls, could be considered constant as shown in Eq. (6), where $V_L$ refers to the digestate volume.

$$V_{total} = V_A + V_B + V_L \tag{6}$$

Using Eq. (6), the equality of pressures and the ideal gas law, Eq. (7) could be obtained. Therefore, $V_A$ can be directly evaluated from the molar quantities and temperatures. $V_B$, $P_A$ and $P_B$ were then calculated using Eq. (6) and the ideal gas law.

$$V_A = (V_{total} - V_L)\frac{n_A T_A}{n_A T_A + n_B T_B} \tag{7}$$

### 2.2.2. Isochoric regime

When the biogas compartment is at its maximum level, any further increase in gas stored would lead to an increase in pressure, which would be sustained by the inner membrane and the attachment structure on digester's walls. On the opposite, at minimum air volume, a decrease in pressure would create an overpressure on the air side. In this situation, the pressure difference would be sustained by a central support structure. In both cases, it was assumed that the air compartment becomes an isochoric one. Therefore, $P_A$ was calculated by setting $V_A$ to its minimum or maximum value and employing the ideal gas law.

## 2.3. Biogas valve control

The biogas outlet stream was controlled through the valve constant, $CV_B$, which was evaluated as a function of $\Delta\dot{V}_B$, which represents a material accumulation rate in the biogas storage, as shown in Eq. (8), where the flowrates are in Nm³h⁻¹ and the relative pressure in mbar.

$$\dot{V}_B^{out} = \dot{V}_B^{GL} - \Delta\dot{V}_B = CV_B\sqrt{P_B^g} \tag{8}$$

Although a pressure relief valve has not been considered in the digester model, a maximum pressure event was dealt by manipulating $\Delta\dot{V}_B$. For instance, if $P_B$ reaches its maximum allowed value, $P_{B,max}$, $\Delta\dot{V}_B$ can be set to a negative value until $P_B$ decreases to the same level as $P_A$. Such measure forces an additional flowrate through the biogas valve, which represents the biogas that would be lost through the pressure relief valve.

## 3. Case studies

The simulations were carried out considering a digester with 24 m of diameter. The heights of the cylindrical part and the outer membrane were both set at 8 m. This yielded a total volume, $V_{total}$, of 5697 m³. The thresholds limits applied to the air compartment was of 375 m³ when at full biogas load and of 1965 m³ at minimum load. The biogas volume limits depend also on the liquid volume. During the simulations, $V_L$ was kept approximately at 3400 m³. Therefore, $V_{B,min}$ and $V_{B,max}$ were around 332 and 1922 m³ respectively. The biogas production was computed considering a substrate feeding done once a day and an organic loading rate (OLR) at 2.8 kg VS/m³d.

### 3.1. Double membrane characteristic curve

Stur et al. (2022) proposed a protocol to determine the maximum and minimum capacities of a double membrane gasholder. It consists in filling the gasholder from a technical empty condition until full load and then discharging it until the empty point. The full point is characterized by a biogas pressure surge and the empty one by a sudden pressure reduction (Stur et al., 2022).

To simulate this procedure, $P_{B,max}$ was set at 7 mbar and the filling phase was defined by $\Delta\dot{V}_B$ at 180 Nm³h⁻¹ and at –180 Nm³h⁻¹ during the discharging period. The full load was defined as when $P_B$ reached $P_{B,max}$, from that point forward $\Delta\dot{V}_B$ was set to 0 for a one-hour period before starting the discharging phase. Figure 2 exhibits the simulation results for biogas pressure and volume. Even though a quantitative comparison is not possible, these results follow the same trend as the experimental values obtained by Stur et al. (2022). Indeed, the charging and discharging phases are characterized by two pressure plateaus, with the first one at 6.1 mbar and the latter at 3.7 mbar. Such behavior was previously explained by Kube (2018) and depends on the blower and valve curves. For instance, the pressure is higher when the storage is being filled because, at the air side, the air inlet flow is lower than the outlet when the pressure is above the operating point (Figure 1 (a)).

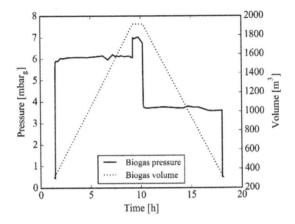

Figure 2 Double membrane's characteristic curve as computed by the model

### 3.2. High and medium load operations

Biogas temperature variations have been linked to overpressure events in double membrane gasholders (Reinelt and Liebetrau, 2020; Stur et al., 2022). Reducing the operating gas storage level has been pointed out as a strategy to mitigate biogas losses through the pressure relief valve (Stur et al., 2022). To test such situation, two simulations were carried out: one at high storage load, with biogas stored volume close to its maximum value, and another one at medium load. In both cases, $\Delta \dot{V}_B$ was set at 0, except in case of overpressure, when $\Delta \dot{V}_B$ was set at -100 Nm³h⁻¹. The simulations were carried out for three days using the weather data (wind speed, solar irradiance and external temperature) from 16th to 18th august 2009 in Pau, France (43°17'N, 24'W) (Huld et al., 2012). The results of such simulations are shown in Figure 3. During the high load operation, pressure peaks were detected during the three days. However, $P_{B,max}$ was reached only on the last two days, when $T_B$ had its highest intraday increase. This also led to additional biogas outlet flow as shown in Figure 3 (b), which represents the losses that would have occurred through a pressure relief valve. On the other hand, operating with a lower storage level completely avoided any pressure surge, as the biogas volume fluctuations were within the threshold limits.

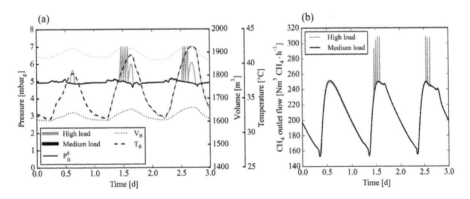

Figure 3 (a) Biogas volume, temperature and relative pressure profiles for the high and the medium load tests (b) Methane flowrate through the outlet valve during high and medium load operations

## 4. Conclusion

A dynamic model for an air inflated double membrane gasholder was developed and integrated to a digester model. The gas storage model was able to simulate the characteristic curve of such kind of gasholder, with results qualitatively comparable to experimental values in the literature. Besides that, a strategy to reduce overpressure events could be tested. The next steps for this work are to validate the full digester model with measures from industrial biogas plants and to integrate it with other units, such as methanation and electrolysis reactors and biogas upgrading units.

## References

S. Emebu, J. Pecha, D. Janáčová, 2022, Review on anaerobic digestion models: Model classification & elaboration of process phenomena, Renewable and Sustainable Energy Reviews 160, 112288.

F. Garcia-Ochoa, E. Gomez, 2004, Theoretical prediction of gas–liquid mass transfer coefficient, specific area and hold-up in sparged stirred tanks, Chemical Engineering Science 59, 2489–2501.

R. Hreiz, N. Adouani, Y. Jannot, M.-N. Pons, 2017, Modeling and simulation of heat transfer phenomena in a semi-buried anaerobic digester, Chemical Engineering Research and Design 119, 101–116.

T. Huld, R. Müller, A. Gambardella, 2012, A new solar radiation database for estimating PV performance in Europe and Africa, Solar Energy 86, 1803–1815.

F.P. Incropera, D.P. DeWitt, T.L. Bergman, A.S. Lavine, 2007, Fundamentals of Heat and Mass Transfer, 6th edition. ed, John Wiley & Sons Ltd, New York.

J. Kube, 2018, Management of Gas Storages in Biogas Plants, Chem. Eng. Technol. 41, 702–710.

L. Pokorna-Krayzelova, K.E. Mampaey, T.P.W. Vannecke, J. Bartacek, P. Jenicek, E.I.P. Volcke, 2017, Model-based optimization of microaeration for biogas desulfurization in UASB reactors, Biochemical Engineering Journal 125, 171–179.

T. Reinelt, J. Liebetrau, 2020, Monitoring and Mitigation of Methane Emissions from Pressure Relief Valves of a Biogas Plant, Chem. Eng. Technol. 43, 7–18.

M. Stur, M. Pohl, C. Krebs, E. Mauky, 2022, Characterisation of biogas storages: influences and comparison of methods, Agricultural Engineering Bd. 77 Nr. 1 (2022).

S. Vilms Pedersen, J. Martí-Herrero, A.K. Singh, S.G. Sommer, S.D. Hafner, 2020, Management and design of biogas digesters: A non-calibrated heat transfer model, Bioresource Technology 296, 122264.

S. Weinrich, M. Nelles, 2021, Systematic simplification of the Anaerobic Digestion Model No. 1 (ADM1) – Model development and stoichiometric analysis, Bioresource Technology 333, 125124.

Antonis Kokossis, Michael C. Georgiadis, Efstratios N. Pistikopoulos (Eds.)
PROCEEDINGS OF THE 33rd European Symposium on Computer Aided Process Engineering
(ESCAPE33), June 18-21, 2023, Athens, Greece

# An iterated double auction model for peer-to-peer electricity trading

Timothy Hutty,[a] Prof Solomon Brown[a]

[a] *Department of Chemical and Biological Engineering, University of Sheffield, Sheffield, S1 3JD, United Kingdom,*
*s.f.brown@sheffield.ac.uk*

## Abstract

Peer-to-peer (P2P) energy trading, whereby customers can trade with one another rather than the energy supplier only, has the potential to save money for consumers whilst also incentivising more efficient and environmentally beneficial behaviour. In this work, an agent-based simulation model for a local P2P market is developed. The market is implemented as an iterative double auction, which resembles wholesale electricity trading and gives participants a high degree of freedom to trade using arbitrary strategies. Strategies are developed to enable flexible devices (EV chargers) to participate profitably in the market. A case study is presented based on future scenarios for a primary substation in the north of England. It is found that the P2P market can achieve significant consumer savings and is also effective in ameliorating the reverse flow of solar power through the substation.

**Keywords**: peer-to-peer, energy, continuous double auction, agent-based, decarbonisation

## 1. Introduction

Peer-to-peer (P2P) energy trading enables energy customers to trade with one another, rather than with the energy supplying company only [1]. A key benefit of P2P is that it provides the incentive for participants to smartly coordinate their devices; for instance, this could involve the timing of electric vehicle (EV) charging to coincide with the solar generation surplus of a peer. This can bring financial savings for energy consumers and generators, greater energy independence for localities, and a reduction in greenhouse gas emissions [2]. It is also possible for P2P trading to relieve the burden on the electricity distribution grid, and here we consider the ability to avoid large reverse flows of energy at substations.

In this work we present a model for P2P energy trading via an iterated double auction. Double auction is chosen as it represents a very simple, generic and adaptable mode of trading [3]. The model is developed in the multi-paradigm simulation software AnyLogic [4], employing the agent-based modelling philosophy; agents participating in the market purely pursue their own self-interest. The model includes the three key demands of heat, power and transportation, which is key to real-world applicability. Strategies are developed to enable flexible devices including EV chargers and heat pumps to participate profitably in the market.

## 2. Method

*2.1 Overview*

In this work a local P2P electricity market is modelled, using AnyLogic simulation software in tandem with MILP optimisation. An iterated double auction is adopted as the market mechanism for P2P electricity trading - this system may be considered comparable to the continuous trading that takes place in wholesale electricity markets. In this work the trading is not envisioned to be truly continuous, but to take place in discrete rounds; this ensures that the speed of information propagation does not unfairly advantage any particular participant [5]. A schematic overview of the market construction and household bidding strategies is given in Figure 1.

In each round of the double auction, bids to buy and sell electricity are collected from auction participants, a clearing price is determined and trades are executed. Each timeslot of the day ahead has its own auction; timeslots do not clear their auctions simultaneously in each round, but in sequence; this enables auction participants to adjust bids in other timeslots as each timeslot is cleared – an ability which is important for flexible devices. Participants gradually acquire their desired energy trades as the rounds proceed. It is assumed that participants do not sell / buy back energy that they have bought / sold in a previous round.

*2.2 Formation of bidding strategy*

The initial price prediction at the start of trading is equal to the mid-market rate midway between retail price $p_{grid\_retail}$ and feed-in price $p_{grid\_FI}$. Subsequent price predictions at each timeslot are the weighted mean of the two most recent clearing prices. Full strategy formation by auction participants occurs at random every few rounds, with MILP optimisation of device schedules carried out in response to latest price predictions. Energy that has already been bought or sold is assigned to devices via an internal double auction at each timeslot, with bids not matched by the internal auction proceeding to the external P2P auction. Bids to (dis)charge the EV battery are first checked to ensure they cannot lead to infringements of state-of-charge limits; any bids that have to be trimmed are restored in future rounds if possible.

*2.3 Truthful limit prices and submitted reserve prices*

Bidders need to assign a value to the energy they are seeking to trade, i.e. limit prices – see Table 1. Generally, these are related to the grid retail price $p_{grid\_retail}$ and feed-in tariff $p_{grid\_FI}$. Bids to charge the EV for essential travel are separated from those for arbitrage. Where an EV battery is used as energy storage, limit prices to charge (discharge) the battery may depend on the prices of any already secured trades to discharge (charge). Note the definitions of variables $c_{V2X}$ (degradation cost per kWh discharged), $\eta_{st}$ (DC round-trip efficiency) and $\eta_{inv}$ (inverter efficiency). Heat pumps use a version of 'bid-as-predicted', never bidding above the predicted price $\tilde{p}_{buy}$ plus a small increment $\delta$.

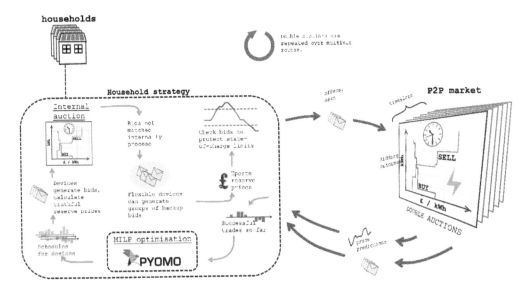

**Figure 1.** Schematic overview of the P2P double auction market for electricity sharing, showing the main steps in strategy formation.

**Table 1.** Truthful reserve prices (i.e. limit prices) assumed for different applications.

| | Category | Truthful reserve price (£/kWh) |
|---|---|---|
| **Offers to buy power** | INFLEXIBLE_LOAD, EV_ESSENTIAL | $p_{grid\_retail}$ |
| | ASHP | $min(\tilde{p}_{buy} + \delta, p_{grid\_retail})$ |
| | EV_ARBITRAGE (EV charging for later discharge to the house or to the grid; or for storage into the next day) | For an amount corresponding to the EV_V2G bids that have been matched (internally or externally) at an average value of $p_{v2x}$: $$(p_{v2x} - c_{v2x}) \cdot \eta_{inv}^2 \cdot \eta_{st}$$ For a further amount not exceeding 10% of battery capacity in each auction round, where $\tilde{p}_{v2x}$ is the *predicted* average value of corresponding EV_V2X. $$(\tilde{p}_{v2x} - c_{v2x}) \cdot \eta_{inv}^2 \cdot \eta_{st}$$ |
| **Asks to sell power** | PV_EXPORT | $p_{grid\_FI}$ |
| | EV_V2G (Sale of EV power to the grid) | For an amount corresponding to the EV_ARBITRAGE bids that have been matched (internally or externally) at an average value of $p_{ARB}$: $$\frac{p_{ARB}}{\eta_{inv}^2 \cdot \eta_{st}} + c_{v2x}$$ For a further amount not exceeding 10% of battery capacity in each auction round, where $\tilde{p}_{ARB}$ is the average predicted price of the EV_ARBITRAGE bids not yet matched. $$\frac{\tilde{p}_{ARB}}{\eta_{inv}^2 \cdot \eta_{st}} + c_{v2x}$$ |

Some auction participants submit their truthful limit prices $p_{tr}$ with their bids, as per Table 1. This is termed an 'aggressive' strategy, since it maximises the chance of making a trade. Other participants are 'zero-intelligence' (Z.I.) bidders. Z.I. bidders submit a reserve price uniformly distributed between their truthful reserve price and an upper or lower bound price, as shown in Equation 1 (for buyers) and Equation 2 (for sellers); this can enable additional value to be extracted, at the cost of decreased probability of trading.

$$p_{res} \sim U\left(p_{grid\_FI}, p_{tr}\right) \qquad\qquad \text{Eqn. 1}$$
$$p_{res} \sim U\left(p_{tr}, p_{grid\_retail}\right) \qquad\qquad \text{Eqn. 2}$$

*2.4  Case study*

For the basis of a case study, we consider a primary substation located in Doncaster, UK at 53.5392°N 1.0443°W. Modelling by Northern Powergrid and Element Energy [6], [7] predicts that this substation will need to support 59 heat pumps, 98 EVs, and 160 kW$_p$ of embedded PV generation per 100 customers by 2050. Avoidance of excessive reverse flow of PV generation is our focus here.

Solar generation is modelled as reported in [8] using climate data from UKECN [9]. EV usage is modelled as in [10] where this model is based on data from the UK National Travel Survey [11]. Inflexible load profiles are taken from [12]. Heat demand is based on building archetypes from the CREST demand model [13]. 50 houses are modelled, since this is generally enough to capture diversity of demand; results can then be scaled to the actual size of the substation demand. The standard grid retail tariff is £0.285 / kWh, with feed-in tariff of £0.075 / kWh [14], [15].

## 3. Results and discussion

We present results from a summer week with relatively high irradiance, which would typically lead to substantial reverse flow of power through the substation. Figure 2 illustrates how the P2P market operates over this week, showing the volumes of successful offers to buy and asks to sell, averaged as a diurnal profile. Also shown for comparison is the average P2P price by time of day. Overall turnover of electricity is 2.40 MWh representing £552 of transactions. Clearly, the main feature is the purchase of PV power in order to charge EVs in the middle of the day. Availability of solar power causes a trough in the price profile, although demand for this generation ensures that the P2P price stays well above the feed-in tariff. It is also interesting to note that small amounts of power for 'essential' EV charging are procured from the V2G power of neighbours' cars.

Figure 3 shows the impact of the P2P trading on the load duration for the substation. Maximum demand at the substation is not significantly reduced. However, reverse power flow is markedly reduced, with the peak reverse flow cut by 48%. Overall imports and exports of grid electricity in energy terms are also reduced, as shown in Table 2. The P2P market also saves £3.29 over the week for the average customer, when compared with grid trade.

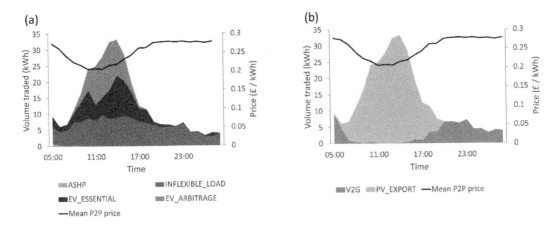

**Figure 2.** P2P electricity trades matched during the summer week with 2050 technology penetrations. (a) offers (b) asks. Shown are the volumes transacted as a daily profile averaged across the week, with the average P2P price for comparison.

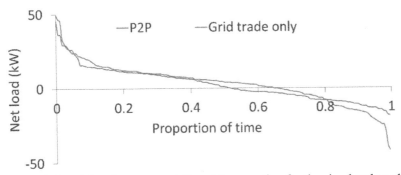

**Figure 3.** Load duration curves at the grid connection for the simulated week.

**Table 2.** Summary metrics for summer week.

| | Grid trade | P2P |
|---|---|---|
| Total exports (kWh) | 713 | 601  (-16%) |
| Total imports (kWh) | 1198 | 995  (-17%) |
| Peak exports (kW) | 35.4 | 18.6  (-48%) |
| Peak imports (kW) | 45.7 | 45.2 (-0.9%) |
| Shared power (kWh) | 754 | 1890  (+ 151%) |
| Average net bill (£) | 14.96 | 11.67  (-22%) |

It is worth noting that around half of the P2P deals for EV charging are for arbitrage, where cheap power imported to the EV battery is discharged later (either to the home 'V2H' or to the grid 'V2G') when power is more expensive. This is clearly an important factor in enabling the P2P to increase PV self-consumption (which we also demonstrated in [10]). The cost of V2H / V2G in terms of battery degradation, represented here by $c_{v2x}$, may be a deciding factor in whether this technology actually becomes widespread. Certain improvements are suggested to augment the applicability and power of the market model in the future:

- Allow trading more than one day in advance
- Incorporate forecasting errors for load and generation
- More trading strategies, e.g. adaptive-aggressive
- Allow non-physical trading
- More sophisticated price prediction

## 4. Conclusions

A double auction model for P2P trading of electricity was developed, along with strategies for the engagement of flexible devices (particularly EV batteries) with this market. The market incentivises efficient behaviour of customers without imposing undue restrictions. Prices across the day respond to market forces, driven by the availability of generation. The P2P market reduces the burden on a substation operating with future penetrations of renewable technologies, with a significant reduction (-48%) in reverse power flow through the substation in sunny weather. Although a corresponding reduction in peak demand was not demonstrated, overall demand for imported electricity was reduced.

## 5. Acknowledgements

This research makes use of data from the UKECN and UK Power Networks.

## References

[1]  Y. Zhou, J. Wu, and C. Long, "Evaluation of peer-to-peer energy sharing mechanisms based on a multiagent simulation framework," *Appl. Energy*, vol. 222, no. November 2017, pp. 993–1022, 2018, doi: 10.1016/j.apenergy.2018.02.089.

[2]  Y. Liu, K. Zuo, X. (Amy) Liu, J. Liu, and J. M. Kennedy, "Dynamic pricing for decentralized energy trading in micro-grids," *Appl. Energy*, vol. 228, no. June, pp. 689–699, 2018, doi: 10.1016/j.apenergy.2018.06.124.

[3]  K. Chen, J. Lin, and Y. Song, "Trading strategy optimization for a prosumer in continuous double auction-based peer-to-peer market: A prediction-integration model," *Appl. Energy*, vol. 242, pp. 1121–1133, May 2019, doi: 10.1016/j.apenergy.2019.03.094.

[4]  The AnyLogic Company, "AnyLogic," 2019. https://www.anylogic.com/.

[5]  W. El-Baz, P. Tzscheutschler, and U. Wagner, "Integration of energy markets in microgrids: A double-sided auction with device-oriented bidding strategies," *Appl. Energy*, vol. 241, no. November 2018, pp. 625–639, 2019, doi: 10.1016/j.apenergy.2019.02.049.

[6]  Northern Powergrid, "Powering network data - Distribution Future Energy Scenarios," *northernpowergrid.com*, 2022. https://www.northernpowergrid.com/network-data.

[7]  Northern Powergrid, "Distribution Future Energy Scenarios," 2021. [Online]. Available: https://www.northernpowergrid.com/asset/1/document/5836.pdf.

[8]  T. D. Hutty, S. Dong, and S. Brown, "Suitability of energy storage with reversible solid oxide cells for microgrid applications," *Energy Convers. Manag.*, vol. 226, p. 113499, Dec. 2020, doi: 10.1016/j.enconman.2020.113499.

[9]  S. Rennie and J. Adamson, "UK Environmental Change Network (ECN) meteorology data: 1991-2015," *Centre for Ecology & Hydrology (Natural Environment Research Council)*, 2017. https://doi.org/10.5285/fc9bcd1c-e3fc-4c5a-b569-2fe62d40f2f5.

[10]  T. D. Hutty, A. Pena-Bello, S. Dong, D. Parra, R. Rothman, and S. Brown, "Peer-to-peer electricity trading as an enabler of increased PV and EV ownership," *Energy Convers. Manag.*, vol. 245, p. 114634, Oct. 2021, doi: 10.1016/j.enconman.2021.114634.

[11]  UK Government, "National Travel Survey ," Jul. 2020. .

[12]  UK Power Networks, "SmartMeter Energy Consumption Data in London Households," 2015. .

[13]  E. McKenna and M. Thomson, "High-resolution stochastic integrated thermal–electrical domestic demand model," *Appl. Energy*, vol. 165, pp. 445–461, Mar. 2016, doi: 10.1016/j.apenergy.2015.12.089.

[14]  Ofgem, "Check if the energy price cap affects you," *ofgem.gov.uk*, 2022. https://www.ofgem.gov.uk/check-if-energy-price-cap-affects-you.

[15]  Solar Energy UK, "Smart Export Guarantee League Table," *solarenergyuk.org*, 2022.

Antonis Kokossis, Michael C. Georgiadis, Efstratios N. Pistikopoulos (Eds.)
PROCEEDINGS OF THE 33rd European Symposium on Computer Aided Process Engineering
(ESCAPE33), June 18-21, 2023, Athens, Greece

# Comparing operational strategies for alkaline electrolysis systems considering a probabilistic wind power distribution

Lucas Cammann,[a] Johannes Jäschke[a]

[a] *Department of Chemical Engineering, Norwegian University of Science and Technology, NTNU, N-7491 Trondheim, Norway*
*johannes.jaschke@ntnu.no*

## Abstract

Coupling alkaline electrolysis processes with renewable energy sources requires rethinking electrolyzer operating practices that today are based on the assumption of constant power supply. Varying wind-power loads give rise to contrasting trade-offs in terms of safe and efficient operation. In this work, we study how keeping the lye flow rate and the pressure in the electrolyzer at their upper and lower bounds, respectively, compares with the policy of always adjusting these values optimally.

To further illustrate the implications of non-constant power supply, the strategies are analyzed considering a uniform, and a non-uniform power probability distribution. We show that currently employed strategies (e.g., high-pressure) may perform poorly when applied to systems subject to power profiles typical for renewable energy systems.

**Keywords**: Hydrogen, Renewable Energies, Optimization, Process Operation

## 1. Introduction

Increasing environmental awareness has led to a renewed interest in using Hydrogen ($H_2$) as an energy vector for renewable electricity through electrolysis of water. Currently, most of the worldwide $H_2$ is produced by steam reforming of methane, with water electrolysis accounting for only 4% of the global production (Kumar and Himabindu, 2019). With rising $CO_2$ taxes and anticipated cost saving potentials for water electrolysis in the range of up to 54% by means of scale-up and R&D (Schmidt et al., 2017), this number is expected to grow considerably in the upcoming years. Nonetheless, the question of how to operate water electrolysis in conjunction with flexible power systems is largely unanswered, which is especially true for alkaline electrolysis according to Brauns and Turek (Brauns and Turek, 2022).

One fundamental consideration for the operation of alkaline electrolysis systems with renewable energy sources is how to safely reconcile the requirements for flexibility and process efficiency. While high pressures and lye flowrates improve the efficiency of the process, they also lead to an increased ratio of Hydrogen-to-Oxygen (*HTO*) in the effluent gas streams. For continuous operation, this metric may not exceed 50% of the lower explosion limit, which becomes particularly difficult in low load scenarios where gas production is reduced (Brauns and Turek, 2020). This work provides more insight into these trade-offs by expanding previous modelling and optimization efforts with further relevant mechanistic effects, such as bubble coverage and pressurization, introduced in

Section 2. The weighted production rate is proposed as comparative metrics and used to analyze the influence of setpoint strategies and power probabilities on the process performance in Section 3. Section 4 lastly discusses implications of the obtained results.

## 2. Model

The model developed in this work is based on previous work of Rizwan et al. (Rizwan et al., 2021), and further adapted to account for effects of pressurization and bubble development on the process operation. This section focuses on the expansion of said model, for a more in-depth description of the unit operations and parameter values the reader is referred to the original publication.

### 2.1. Plant description

Figure 1 shows the process flow diagram of the electrolysis process considered in this work. At the core of the process lies the alkaline water electrolyzer, which is fed by a liquid pump with the required lye (30 wt. % KOH) and which is connected to an AC/DC converter and a renewable power source. In the electrolyzer, the product gases H$_2$ and O$_2$ are formed at the cathode and anode, respectively, and must be separated from the liquid lye in two gravity settlers (separators). The gaseous phase is drawn from the top and compressed to the respective storage tanks, while the liquid lye of both separators is recycled to the buffer tank. Here they are mixed with a water make-up stream which replenishes the H$_2$O expended in the electrolysis reactions. The lye is then pumped through the heat-exchanger before being fed back to the electrolyzer.

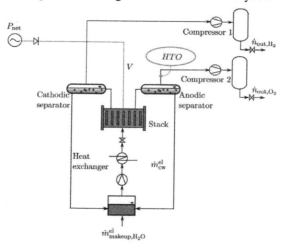

**Figure 1**: Process flowsheet for alkaline water electrolysis.

### 2.2. Electrolyzer model

The electrolyzer model accounts for mass and energy balances as well as the current-voltage relationship. For the latter, the effective current density $I_{eff}$ is introduced which depends on the bubble coverage at the electrode.

#### 2.2.1. Mass and energy balance

The energy balance for the electrolyzer is set up as in Ulleberg, (2003)

$$0 = \dot{m}_{\text{lye,in}}^{\text{el}} Cp_{\text{lye}}\left(T_{\text{in}}^{\text{el}} - T^{\text{el}}\right) + n_c(U_k - U_{\text{tn}}) - A_s\left[h_c\left(T^{\text{el}} - T_a\right) + \sigma\epsilon\left(T^{\text{el}4} - T_a^4\right)\right]. \quad (1)$$

Here, the term $A_s$ denotes the active area w.r.t. radiation and convection, $h_c$ the convective heat transfer coefficient in W m$^{-2}$ K$^{-1}$, $\sigma$ the Stefan-Boltzmann constant in W m$^{-2}$ K$^{-4}$ and $\epsilon$ and $n_c$ the dimensionless emissivity constant and cell number, respectively. Component balances are set up for the components $H_2$ and $O_2$ for the cathode and anode respectively, exemplarily shown below for the cathode

$$0 = \dot{n}_{in,H_2} + \dot{n}_{r,H_2} - \dot{n}_{diff,H_2} - \dot{n}_{out,H_2}^{cat} \tag{2}$$

$$0 = \dot{n}_{in,O_2} + \dot{n}_{diff,O_2} - \dot{n}_{out,O_2}^{cat}. \tag{3}$$

The subscripts *in* and *out* distinguish in- and outgoing flows, while the subscripts *r* and *diff* describe reactive and diffusive fluxes, the latter two being calculated as follows for an arbitrary component *j*:

$$\dot{n}_{r,j} = \frac{I \, A^{el}}{z \, F} \quad \text{and} \quad \dot{n}_{diff,j} = \frac{p_{sys} S_j D_j A^{el}}{L_m}. \tag{4}$$

In Eq. 4, $A^{el}$ and $L_m$ are the electrolytically active surface area and the thickness of the membrane, respectively, which are taken to be 598 $m^2$ and 0.005 m. The calculation of the solubility constant and the diffusion coefficient is further detailed in (Haug et al., 2017). The overall mass balance is closed by enforcing that the sum of in- and outgoing mass be equal.

### 2.2.2. Current-voltage relationship

The current-voltage relationship is assumed to follow the semi-empirical relationship proposed by Ulleberg (2003)

$$U = U_{rev} + \left(r_1 + r_2 T^{el}\right)I + s\log\left(\left(t_1 + \frac{t_2}{T^{el}} + \frac{t_3}{T^{el^2}}\right)I + 1\right). \tag{5}$$

Here, *I* is the current density in A $m^{-2}$, while the terms *r*, *s* and *t* are ohmic resistance and overvoltage parameters that need to be fitted or taken from literature. Eq. 5 does not account for influences of the pressure or the lye flowrate on the current-voltage relationship. The more important effect of the bubble coverage θ on the effective current density can be modelled as follows:

$$I_{eff} = I \times (1 - \theta). \tag{6}$$

The bubble coverage itself is found by calculating the *stagnant bubble coverage* $\theta_0$ (Vogt and Balzer, 2005) according to

$$\theta_0 = \left[\frac{I}{I_{\theta \to 1}}\right]^m, \tag{7}$$

which is corrected for by the lye flowrate (Eigeldinger and Vogt, 2000) through

$$\theta = \frac{\theta_0}{[1 + (K \times v)^2]^2}. \tag{8}$$

In Eq. 7 the exponent *m*, the limiting current density $I_{\theta \to 1}$ and *K* are fitting parameters, while *v* is the superficial velocity of the electrolyte in the electrolyzer. The value of *m* is set to 0.3, while the value of $I_{\theta \to 1}$ is set to 7500 A $m^{-2}$ to indicate a low to medium bubble development. According to (Eigeldinger and Vogt, 2000), a value of *K* of 8 s $m^{-1}$ is representative for most experimental observations and is therefore also used in this work. The electrolyte velocity is calculated by means of continuity as

$$v = \frac{\dot{m}_{lye,in}^{el}}{\rho_{lye} \times A_{lyeflow}}, \tag{9}$$

in which the area through which the lye flows $A_{lyeflow}$ is calculated to be 3.63 $m^2$, based on publicly available data.

### 2.3. Separator model

The molar component balances for the separators are set up similarly to the electrolyzer and shown exemplarily for the cathodic separator

$$0 = \dot{n}_{out,H_2}^{cat} - \dot{n}_{out,H_2}^{sep,cat} - \dot{n}_{in,H_2}^{buffer} = \dot{n}_{out,H_2}^{cat} - \dot{n}_{out,H_2}^{sep,cat} - 0.5\dot{V}_{lye}S_{O_2,lye}p_{sys}/\eta_{sep}$$
$$0 = \dot{n}_{out,O_2}^{cat} - \dot{n}_{out,O_2}^{sep,cat}. \tag{10}$$

It is herein assumed that accumulation in the electrolyte is only relevant for the main gaseous species entering the anodic or cathodic separator. The solubility constants $S_{i,lye}$ are calculated considering the mass fraction of the lye $w_{lye}$ (Haug et al., 2017)

$$S_{i,lye} = \frac{S_{i,H_2O}}{10^{K_i w_{lye}}}, \quad \text{with} \quad S_{i,H_2O} = \frac{\rho_{H_2O}}{M_{H_2O}p_{atm}H_{i,H_2O}}. \tag{11}$$

Here, $K_i$ is the Setchenov constant and $H_{i,H_2O}$ the Henry coefficient of species $i$ in water, the values and correlations for both being taken from Haug et al.

The *HTO* is measured at the outlet of the anodic separator as

$$HTO = \frac{\dot{n}_{out,H_2}^{sep,an}}{\dot{n}_{out,O_2}^{sep,an}}. \tag{12}$$

### 2.4. Power distribution modelling and weighted production rate

We consider two different power availability probability functions. These probability functions account for the uncertainty in the supply of renewable energy for the process, which is assumed to stem exclusively from wind power. In the first case, all power levels are assumed to be equally likely (i.e., a uniform probability distribution). In the second case, the power is assumed to follow the probability density function for the wind velocity, which is commonly modeled as a Weibull distribution:

$$f(\mathbf{x}, \lambda, k) = \begin{cases} \frac{\lambda}{k}\left(\frac{\mathbf{x}}{\lambda}\right)^{k-1} e^{-(x/\lambda)^k}, & \mathbf{x} \geq 0 \\ \mathbf{x}, & \mathbf{x} < 0 \end{cases} \tag{13}$$

in which $k$ is called the shape parameter, $\lambda$ the scale parameter and $\mathbf{x}$ the probabilistic variable. The generated power is calculated from the obtained wind profile according to

$$P_{wind} = \frac{1}{2} \times \rho_{air} \times A_{blade} \times v_{wind}^3, \tag{14}$$

in which $A_{blade}$ is scaled such that the delivered power is equal or less to 2 MW in 95% of cases, based on wind speed data of the month April for the years 1991 to 2000 in Zhuhire, China (Yingni et al., 2006). To gauge how efficiently an operating concept can handle flexible power supplies, a new comparative metrics is proposed, the weighted production rate $\overline{\dot{m}}_{out,H_2}$. This figure convolutes the absolute production rate at a certain power input with the probability of this power occurring,

$$\overline{\dot{m}}_{out,H_2} = \Pr(P_{net}) \times \dot{m}_{out,H_2}. \tag{15}$$

The probability $\Pr(P_{net})$ is computed numerically from the probability density function $f(P_{net})$, herein taken to follow either a uniform, or a Weibull distribution.

### 2.5. Setpoint strategies

In this work, different fixed setpoint strategies for the lye flowrate and the pressure are compared in the face of varying power distributions. Strategy 1 entails to operate both flexibly (optimal), while Strategies 2 and 3 operate both at their upper and lower limit, respectively. Table 1 summarizes the values that are used at the basis of these strategies.

**Table 1:** Overview of setpoint strategies.

|  | Unit | Strategy 1 | Strategy 2 | Strategy 3 |
|---|---|---|---|---|
| $p$ | bar | Flexible | 20 | 10 |
| $\dot{m}_{lye}$ | kg s$^{-1}$ | Flexible | 30 | 15 |

### 2.6. Optimization problem

The model developed in this is work is optimized for values of the available Power input $P_{net}$ in the range of 15 kW to 2 MW according to the following formulation:

$$\max \quad \dot{m}_{out,H_2} \tag{16}$$

$$\text{s.t.} \quad \dot{m}_{lye,min} \leq \dot{m}_{lye,k}^{j} \leq \dot{m}_{lye,max} \qquad \forall\, k \in [\text{in, out}], j \in [\text{el, buff}]$$

$$-20\,°C \leq \Delta T_{in}^{el} \leq 20\,°C$$

$$10\,°C \leq T^{el} \leq 80\,°C$$

$$p_{min} \leq p_{sys} \leq p_{max}$$

$$P_{comp} + P_{el} \leq P_{net}$$

$$\dot{m}_{cw}^{el} \leq 26.6\ \text{kg s}^{-1}$$

$$HTO \leq 2\%$$

For strategies 2 and 3, $p_{min}$ and $p_{max}$ and $\dot{m}_{lye,min}$ and $\dot{m}_{lye,max}$ are set to the respective constant values indicated in Table 1, while these setpoints represent the upper and lower bounds for strategy 1. The optimization problem is solved in the programming language Julia v. 1.7.2. with the NLP solver IPOPT. In scenarios where the outlined constraints cannot be satisfied the plant is assumed to be shut down, and the production rate is equated to zero.

## 3. Results

Figure 2 shows the weighted production rate for strategies 1 to 3 for both considered probability distributions and different values of $P_{net}$. The cumulative monthly production rates are shown in Tab. 2 and used as comparative metric. Generally, these values are lower for the Weibull distribution due to it being right skewed. Fully flexible operation (strategy 1) maximizes Hydrogen production for both probability distributions. Considering a uniform probability distribution, the second most efficient setpoint strategy involves operating lye flow rate and pressure at their upper limit (strategy 2), with the mean production rate being 11% higher than lower limit operation (strategy 3).

**Table 2:** Total monthly production rate for strategies 1 to 3 and both probability distributions.

|  | Distribution | Unit | Strategy 1 | Strategy 2 | Strategy 3 |
|---|---|---|---|---|---|
| $\dot{m}_{out,H_2}$ | Uniform | kg month$^{-1}$ | 11,617 | 10,946 | 9,862 |
| $\dot{m}_{out,H_2}$ | Weibull | kg month$^{-1}$ | 5,715 | 4,362 | 4,977 |

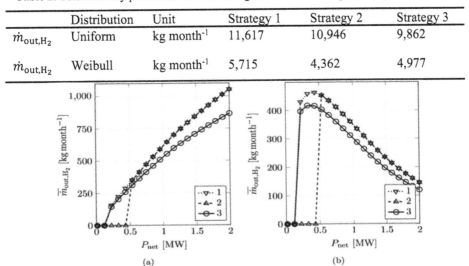

**Figure 2:** Weighted production rate considering (a) uniform, and (b) Weibull power distribution.

This however reverses under consideration of the Weibull power availability distribution, where the operation at the lower limit of the pressure and the lye flowrate achieves a 14% higher mean production rate than the operation at the respective upper limits. The reason for this can be seen in Fig. 2, which shows that strategy 3 is inoperable at lower power inputs due to the violation of the *HTO*-constraint, leading to a production rate of zero up until ~0.5 MW. Operation in this low load region has a higher probability according to the Weibull distribution, leading to it being weighted more strongly than higher power inputs. The loss of Hydrogen production due to plant shutdown at lower power inputs in strategy 3 can therefore not be compensated for by the efficiency gain at high power inputs.

## 4. Conclusion and Outlook

Current paradigm in the field of alkaline electrolysis is to operate with high pressures and lye flowrates in order to reduce both operating and investment costs, as well as to improve the efficiency of the process.

The herein presented results however highlight the need to critically assess the transferability of these design notions to the envisioned flexible operation of alkaline water electrolysis. For example, operating at lower powers and lye flowrates might allow for higher Hydrogen production rates in the face of more frequent low power scenarios as compared to the high setpoint strategy. While the optimal operational strategy remains subject to various other considerations, more detailed modelling and optimization efforts are required to elucidate improved strategies for flexible operation. For instance, different lye recycling strategies, such as separate lye loops with recombination phases, might be used to overcome operational limits in low power scenarios. More importantly, such strategies must be evaluated in a dynamic context to account for the intermittencies occurring on different timescales through the supply of renewable energy.

## References

S. Shiva Kumar; V. Himabindu, 2019, Hydrogen production by PEM water electrolysis – A review, *Materials Science for Energy Technologies* 2.3, pp. 442–454.

J. Brauns and T. Turek, 2022, Experimental evaluation of dynamic operating concepts for alkaline water electrolyzers powered by renewable energy, *Electrochimica Acta,* 404 p. 139715

O. Schmidt et al., 2017, Future cost and performance of water electrolysis: An expert elicitation study, *International Journal of Hydrogen Energy* 42.52, pp. 30470–30492

J. Brauns, T. Turek, 2020, Alkaline Water Electrolysis Powered by Renewable Energy: A Review., *Processes,* Volume 8(2), 248

M. Rizwan, V. Alstad, J. Jäschke, 2021, Design considerations for industrial water electrolyzer plants, *International Jounral of Hydrogen Energy,* 46.75, pp. 37120–37136

H. Vogt, R.J. Balzer, 2005, The bubble coverage of gas-evolving electrodes in stagnant electrolztes, *Electrochimica Acta,* 50.10, pp. 2073-2079

J. Eigeldinger, H. Vogt, 2000, The bubble coverage of gas-evolving electrodes in a flowing electrolyte, *Electrochimica Acta,* 45.27, pp. 4449-4456

Ø. Ulleberg, 2003, Modelling of advanced alkaline electrolyzers: a system simulation approach, *Hydrogen Energy,* 28, pp. 21-33

P. Haug et al., 2017, Process modelling of an alkaline water electrolyzer, *International Journal of Hydrogen Energy,* 42.24, pp. 15689-15707

J. Yingni et al., 2006, Wind Potential Assessment Using the Weibull Model at the Inner Mongolia of China, *Energy Exploration & Exploitation,* 24.3, pp. 211-221

Antonis Kokossis, Michael C. Georgiadis, Efstratios N. Pistikopoulos (Eds.)
PROCEEDINGS OF THE 33rd European Symposium on Computer Aided Process Engineering
(ESCAPE33), June 18-21, 2023, Athens, Greece
© 2023 Elsevier B.V. All rights reserved.  http://dx.doi.org/10.1016/B978-0-443-15274-0.50503-5

# Conceptual design of pre-treatment units for co-electrolysis of $CO_2$ and water

Josephine Vos[a], Andrea Ramirez[a], Mar Pérez-Fortes[a]

*[a]Department of Engineering Systems and Services, Faculty of Technology, Policy and Management, Delft University of Technology, Jaffalaan 5, 2628 BX Delft, The Netherlands.*

## Abstract

Reaching our climate goals will require urgent advancements in the development of fossil-free technologies. Solid-oxide electrolysis (SOE) at high-temperature is a promising candidate for combining $CO_2$ utilization and renewable electricity use. Explorative techno-economic analyses are being performed to understand the full plant design requirements for integrated SOE systems. However, there is still a lack of understanding of the potential impact that the pre-treatment of $CO_2$ will have on the overall design and economics of a SOE-based system. To address this knowledge gap, as a first step, the process model of the pre-treatment units needed to purify $CO_2$ from a bioethanol plant is developed in Aspen Plus in the current work. Based on the preliminary results of this paper, the equipment costs mainly stem from the units related to the removal of sulfur (~65%) and alcohols (~32%). The energy costs are almost entirely related to the cryogenic distillation step required for the removal of non-condensable gases (~96%).

**Keywords**: solid-oxide electrolysis, co-electrolysis, syngas, pre-treatment, ex-ante techno-economic analysis, low carbon technologies

## 1. Introduction

Net-zero $CO_2$ emissions must be reached by 2050 to reduce the disastrous effects of climate change (IEA, 2020). Carbon dioxide electrochemical reduction ($CO_2ER$) has the potential to mitigate $CO_2$ emissions as it combines $CO_2$ utilization and renewable (intermittent) electricity for the synthesis of chemicals. A specific type of $CO_2ER$ technology is the solid-oxide electrolyzer (SOE). Co-electrolysis of $CO_2$ and water in a SOE has a technology readiness level (TRL) between 5-7, and it can be used to generate syngas (Zheng et al., 2017). To reach higher TRLs and eventually large-scale commercial deployment, explorative techno-economic analyses (TEAs) are underway to better understand the full plant design requirements (for example, Gao et al., 2020; Herz et al., 2018).

SOE TEAs assume that future $CO_2$-based plants will be operated using $CO_2$ from industrial point sources or direct air capture (DAC). It is also often assumed that this $CO_2$ stream is pure and available at the gate of the SOE plant. However, this may not be the case. The $CO_2$ purity level of several industrial sources can vary between ~30-96 mol% (Verma et al., 2019). Some SOE TEAs mention that purifying the $CO_2$ will be needed before entering the electrolyzer as experimental studies have indicated that even a slight concentration of impurities (for instance, sulfur or heavy metals) can alter the catalytic performance significantly or deactivate the catalyst entirely (Gao et al., 2020; Kibria et al., 2019). However, neither the target purity levels nor the required types of purification steps have been specified or modeled in SOE TEAs literature.

Therefore, there is currently a lack of understanding of the potential impact of pre-treatment units on the design and economics of SOE plants. To address this knowledge gap, in this study an ex-ante TEA of the pre-treatment units for a $CO_2$ stream from a bioethanol plant for co-electrolysis via SOE to produce syngas is performed. The aim of this paper is therefore twofold: 1) to propose a conceptual design for pre-treatment units of $CO_2$ for future SOE plants, and 2) to evaluate the plant performance. In the upcoming section, the scope, modeling, and evaluation steps are described. In the subsequent sections, the preliminary results are discussed.

## 2. Methodology

### 2.1. Scope
The current techno-economic analysis consists of a 'gate-to-gate' ex-ante assessment. Figure 1a presents an overview of the overall SOE-based plant, and the current system boundaries. The electricity is considered to be continuous and acquired from the grid.

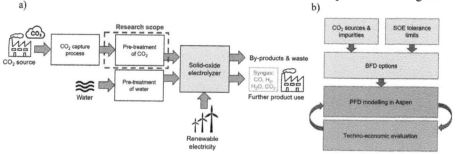

*Figure 1: a) System boundary definition, focus on pre-treatment of $CO_2$. b) Methodological steps for modeling and evaluation (BFD: block flow diagram, PFD: process flow diagram).*

The methodological framework for this research follows the approach for analyzing future "N-of-a-kind" (NOAK) plants (Roussanaly et al., 2021). Since this research involves an ex-ante analysis of a low TRL technology, this means that the entire analysis is based on a "what-if" approach where the SOE is treated as if it was already commercially available today. It is assumed that the performance at industrial scale is the same as currently demonstrated in lab conditions. The model considers a $CO_2$-based plant located in Northwestern Europe and installed in 2019. The scale of the plant corresponds to the production of 1 tonne of pure $CO_2$ per year (8000 hours).

### 2.2. Data collection, modeling & evaluation
The methodology followed for the data collection, modeling and evaluation of the pre-treatment configuration for future SOE plants is illustrated in Figure 1b. A targeted literature review was performed to collect information regarding (i) possible $CO_2$ sources and their compositions, and (ii) the electrolyzer's tolerance levels per contaminant (considering a SOE Ni/YSZ cermet fuel electrode). Assumptions were made based on existing literature for solid-oxide fuel cells and water electrolysis, and information from experts in the field. Next, a screening of potential cleaning technologies for the removal of contaminants was done based on heuristics, temperature and pressure considerations to create a block flow diagram (BFD). For the current bioethanol case, the pilot plant

study from McKaskle et al., the research on purification units from Quevedo et al., and a $CO_2$ purification patent by Gupta et al. served as a starting point (Gupta, 1999; McKaskle, 2018; Quevedo, 2021). The subsequent process flow diagram (PFD) was created in Aspen Plus. The model was validated, unit-by-unit, using data from literature. The Aspen model was used to generate data on the equipment dimensions, mass and energy balances. Finally, key performance indicators (KPIs), i.e. $CO_2$ losses during the process, energy needs, and bare equipment costs, were calculated.

## 3. Results & discussion

The main impurities in the selected bio-based $CO_2$ stream are non-condensable gases (NCDS), such as oxygen and nitrogen, as well as sulfur components, water, alcohols, and other hydrocarbons (see Table 1). The investigation into the target purity levels for SOE revealed that even trace levels of sulfur components are likely to negatively affect the degradation rate of the electrodes (Caliandro, 2018; Rinaldi, 2019). The other identified contaminants from the bioethanol plant are expected to be less problematic for the SOE, but experimental data on the effect of these components is still limited in the current literature, for instance, for alcohols. In the current work, it is considered a conservative goal to reach at least ppb-level of the contaminants that are less known.

*Table 1: Overview composition of the CO₂ stream from a bioethanol plant (i.e., the fermentation off-gas from an ethanol plant using corn as the biomass source) including major and trace impurities alongside tolerance limits for SOE (Caliandro, 2018; McKaskle, 2018; National Academies of Sciences, Engineering, 2022; Rinaldi, 2019; Yokokawa et al., 2008).*

| Composition | Bioethanol plant | Unit used | Degradation type | Tolerable amount | Unit used |
|---|---|---|---|---|---|
| $CO_2$ | 90 | % | C-poisoning | | |
| CO | 1 | ppm | C-poisoning | | |
| $H_2O$ | 5 | ppm | | | |
| $CH_4$ | 3 | ppm | C-poisoning | | |
| $SO_x$ | 1 | ppm | S-poisoning | <2 | ppm |
| $NO_x$ | 1 | ppm | | | |
| $O_2$ | 100 | ppm | | <5 | % |
| $H_2S$ | 1 | ppm | S-poisoning | ~0.05 | ppm |
| $N_2$ | 98768 | ppm | | | |
| Ar | - | ppm | | ~100 | µmol/mol |
| Heavy metals | - | ppm | Metals | - | ppb-level |
| Cl | - | ppm | Cl-poisoning | <5 | ppm |
| Alcohols | 3-950 | ppm | | | |
| Other hydrocarbons | 1 | ppm | C-poisoning | ~2 | µmol/mol |
| Aromatics (benzene, toluene, xylene) | 3 | ppm | | | |
| Carbonyl sulfide | 1 | ppm | S-poisoning | <2 | ppm |
| Dimethylsulfide | 1 | ppm | S-poisoning | <2 | ppm |
| Ethers | 1 | ppm | | | |
| Ketons | 1 | ppm | | | |
| Mercaptans | 1 | ppm | | | |

Figure 2 shows the design of the preliminary $CO_2$ purification train for the removal of the contaminants listed in Table 2. In total, four different purification sections are needed to achieve this level of purity, namely (i) alcohols removal, (ii) sulfur removal, (iii) moisture removal, and (iv) non-condensable gases removal. The global property method Redlich-Kwong-Soave (RKS-BM) was selected in Aspen Plus, which is suitable for gas processes.

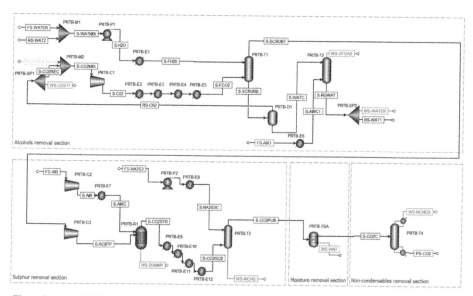

Figure 2: Aspen PFD for the purification of a CO₂ stream from a bioethanol plant to reach SOE purity levels.

The CO₂ from the bio-ethanol plant enters the process at 38°C and 0.9 atm (McKaskle, 2018) and is conditioned to 20°C and 10 bar before being sent to a pressurized water scrubbing tower (RadFrac column –PRTB-T1) for the removal of alcohols (Abu Seman & Harun, 2019). The water scrubbing tower removes the traces of alcohols as well as ~25% of the CO₂, therefore the removed CO₂ is separated from the scrubbing water via a flash drum (Flash2 – PRTB-D1) and is recycled back (RS-CO2). The scrubbing water is regenerated using a counter-current hot air stream in a second tower (RadFrac column – PRTB-T2). Next, the CO₂ stream is mixed with air in a catalytic oxidation unit (REquil – PRTB-R1) operating at 400°C and 22 bar to remove the hydrogen sulfide and COS by converting them into sulfur dioxide and water (Gupta, 1999). The sulfur dioxide is removed by using an aqueous solution of Na₂SO₃ in an absorption tower (RadFrac – PRTB-T3) at 38°C and 22 bar. Then, the remaining moisture is removed using a temperature swing adsorption (TSA) unit consisting of 2-4 columns (Gupta, 1999). The TSA was modeled in Aspen Plus using a separator block (i.e., black-box model for which the energy and economic performance are not yet evaluated in the current work). Finally, the non-condensable gases are removed via cryogenic distillation (RadFrac column – PRTB-T4) at 22 bar.

Table 2 summarizes the preliminary techno-economic results of the CO₂ purification train from Figure 2. The CO₂ from the bioethanol source was purified to 99.9984 wt% with water, carbon monoxide, methane, and argon as trace impurities. The purity level is in agreement with the tolerance limits for SOE (as shown in Table 1) and matches the specifications of food-grade CO₂ (i.e., 99.9% (Parker Hannifin Ltd, 2022)). During the purification process, about ~21% of the CO₂ inlet stream is lost as gaseous emissions despite recycling efforts. Possibilities for further improvement of CO₂ recycling should be investigated to improve the process in the future.

In terms of cost, the total bare equipment costs of the purification train are almost 3M€. The analysis of the different purification sections reveals that the equipment costs related to the removal of sulfur (~65%) and alcohols (~32%) are responsible for most of the total equipment cost. The energy costs are almost entirely related to the removals of non-condensable gases (~96%) due to the cryogenic distillation step.

*Table 2: Energy and economic preliminary results for the purification of the bioethanol $CO_2$ stream. The results are stated per tonne of clean $CO_2$ (VHPS: very high pressure steam at 100 bar, HPS: high pressure steam at 51 bar, MPS; medium pressure steam at 21 bar, LPS: low pressure steam at 5.5 bar, LLPS: low low pressure steam at 3.9 bar, CW: cooling water ~25-40ºC, CHILLED: chilling water ~5-7.5ºC, R50: refrigerant methane ~-162ºC, NA: energy and equipment costs not available for the TSA unit, NCDS refers to non-condensable elements such as nitrogen, argon and oxygen).*

| Section | Energy needs | | | | | | | | | Energy costs | Bare equipment cost |
|---|---|---|---|---|---|---|---|---|---|---|---|
| | VHPS | HPS | MPS | LPS | LLPS | CW | CHILLED | R50 | Electricity | | |
| Unit | GJ/t | GJ/t | GJ/t | GJ/t | GJ/t | GJ/t | GJ/t | GJ/t | kWh/t | €/t | k€ |
| Alcohols | - | - | -0.06 | -0.10 | 0.30 | 0.23 | 0.04 | - | 115.29 | 10.80 | 930 |
| Sulfur | - | 1.00 | -0.31 | -0.31 | 0.75 | 0.76 | | - | 554.29 | 48.95 | 1875 |
| Moisture | NA | NA | NA | NA | NA | NA | NA | NA | NA | NA | NA |
| NCDS | - | - | - | - | 2,80 | - | - | 3.80 | - | 1618.11 | 101 |
| Total | - | 1.00 | -0.38 | -0.41 | 3.86 | 0.99 | 0.04 | 3.80 | 669.58 | 1677.86 | 2907 |

## 4. Conclusion & future work

A preliminary ex-ante techno-economic assessment of the pre-treatment units for purifying $CO_2$ from a bioethanol plant has been performed, as a first step towards the modeling of a complete SOE-based plant for co-electrolysis of $CO_2$ and water to produce syngas. This study aimed to propose an initial PFD and to analyze selected KPIs. Required $CO_2$ purity levels for SOE were identified based mostly on solid oxide fuel cells and water electrolysis literature. Four different purification sections were proposed to purify the $CO_2$ stream resulting in a $CO_2$ purity grade similar to food-grade $CO_2$. The removal of sulfur (~65%) and alcohols (~32%) were the largest contributors to the overall equipment costs. The removal of non-condensable gases via cryogenic distillation was the main contributor to the overall energy costs (~96%). In future work, trade-offs will be further investigated by modeling the TSA unit using RadFrac columns and the possibilities for recycling flows, heat integration, and waste valorization will be further considered. Also, the purification of the water inlets stream will be analyzed.

## Acknowledgements

This research receives funding from the project "Addressing the multiscale challenge of $CO_2$ electrochemical reduction", NWO ECCM tenure track grant (project number ECCM.TT.009), and "Sustainable design of multiscale $CO_2$ electrochemical conversion", MVI grant (ECCM.TT.MVITU.006).

## References

Abu Seman, N., & Harun, N. (2019). Simulation of pressurized water scrubbing process for biogas purification using Aspen Plus. *IOP Conference Series: Materials Science and Engineering*, *702*(1). https://doi.org/10.1088/1757-899X/702/1/012040

Caliandro, P. (2018). *Identification of Solid Oxide Cell Elementary Processes by Electrochemical Impedance Spectroscopy PAR*. PhD thesis number *8389 ÉCOLE POLYTECHNIQUE FÉDÉRALE DE LAUSANNE*.

Gao, N., Quiroz-Arita, C., Diaz, L. A., & Lister, T. E. (2020). Intensified co-electrolysis process for syngas production from captured CO2. *Journal of CO2 Utilization*, *43*(May 2020), 101365. https://doi.org/10.1016/j.jcou.2020.101365

Gupta, H. &. (1999). *Patent CO2 purification system*. *15*(2), 1–23. US patent number: 99108085.4.

Herz, G., Reichelt, E., & Jahn, M. (2018). Techno-economic analysis of a co-electrolysis-based synthesis process for the production of hydrocarbons. *Applied Energy*, *215*(February), 309–320. https://doi.org/10.1016/j.apenergy.2018.02.007

IEA. (2020). Energy Technology Perspectives. *Energy Technology Perspectives*. https://doi.org/10.1787/9789264109834-en

Kibria, G., Edwards, J. P., Gabardo, C. M., Dinh, C., Seifitokaldani, A., Sinton, D., & Sargent, E. H. (2019). *Electrochemical CO 2 Reduction into Chemical Feedstocks : From Mechanistic Electrocatalysis Models to System Design*. *1807166*, 1–24. https://doi.org/10.1002/adma.201807166

McKaskle. (2018). Evaluation of Carbon Dioxide Capture Options from Ethanol Plants. *University of Illinois, Circular 5*, ILLINOIS STATE GEOLOGICAL SURVEY Prairie Research Institute University of Illinois at Urbana-Champaign, http://www.isgs.illinois.edu.

National Academies of Sciences, Engineering, and M. (2022). *Carbon Dioxide Utilization Markets and Infrastructure : Status and Opportunities : A First Report ( 2022 )*. https://doi.org/10.17226/26703

Parker Hannifin Ltd. (2022). *CO2 polishing for the sparkling beverage industry, Accessed via https://www.parker.com/literature/domnick%20hunter%20Industrial%20Division/Static% 20Literature%20Files%20PDFs/Beverage/174004466_EN.PDF*.

Quevedo, 2021. *Techno-economic and environmental comparative assessment of two renewable methanol production routes, TU Delft master thesis, accessible via http://resolver.tudelft.nl/uuid:923d22dd-b711-46ff-9fc3-a3ba695e31bd*.

Rinaldi, G. (2019). *Long-term evolution of solid oxide fuel and electrolysis cell 3-D microstructure*. PhD thesis number 296. *ÉCOLE POLYTECHNIQUE FÉDÉRALE DE LAUSANNE*. http://infoscience.epfl.ch/record/265161

Roussanaly, S., Rubin, E. S., Van Der Spek, M., Booras, G., Berghout, N., Fout, T., Garcia, M., Gardarsdottir, S., Nair Kuncheekanna, V., Matuszewski, M., Mccoy, S., Morgan, J., Mohd Nazir, S., & Ramirez, A. (2021). *Towards improved guidelines for cost evaluation of carbon capture and storage*.

Verma, S., Lu, S., & Kenis, P. J. A. (2019). Co-electrolysis of CO2 and glycerol as a pathway to carbon chemicals with improved technoeconomics due to low electricity consumption. *Nature Energy*, *4*(6), 466–474. https://doi.org/10.1038/s41560-019-0374-6

Yokokawa, H., Tu, H., Iwanschitz, B., & Mai, A. (2008). Fundamental mechanisms limiting solid oxide fuel cell durability. *Journal of Power Sources*, *182*(2), 400–412. https://doi.org/10.1016/j.jpowsour.2008.02.016

Zheng, Y., Wang, J., Yu, B., Zhang, W., Chen, J., Qiao, J., & Zhang, J. (2017). A review of high temperature co-electrolysis of H2O and CO2 to produce sustainable fuels using solid oxide electrolysis cells (SOECs): Advanced materials and technology. *Chemical Society Reviews*, *46*(5), 1427–1463. https://doi.org/10.1039/c6cs00403b

Antonis Kokossis, Michael C. Georgiadis, Efstratios N. Pistikopoulos (Eds.)
PROCEEDINGS OF THE 33rd European Symposium on Computer Aided Process Engineering
(ESCAPE33), June 18-21, 2023, Athens, Greece

# A Process Design, Intensification, and Modularization Approach for Membrane-Assisted Reaction Systems

Yuhe Tian,[a*] Ayooluwa Akintola,[a] Benjamin Akoh[a]

*a Department of Chemical and Biomedical Engineering, West Virginia University, Morgantown, West Virginia, United States*

## Abstract

We present a generalized process modeling and synthesis approach to design optimal modular intensified processes, with particular focus on membrane-assisted reaction systems. The approach is built on the phenomena-based Generalized Modular Representation Framework (GMF), which uses abstract mass/heat exchange modules to model diverse conventional and intensified chemical processes in a bottom-up manner. Gibbs free energy-based driving force constraints are developed to intensify the mass/heat transfer in these modules toward thermodynamic limits, and to dictate the optimal transfer format without pre-postulation of tasks (e.g., liquid-vapor separation, reaction, membrane permeation). Orthogonal Collocation on Finite Elements (OCFE) is applied to model the spatial distribution information within each module. The GMF/OCFE representation also enables the module sizing to be self-adjustable via process synthesis optimization, thus allowing for automatic selection of scaling up or numbering up while retaining computational compactness in the combinatorial space. A case study on hydrogen production via methane steam reforming is presented to showcase the proposed approach.

**Keywords**: Process Synthesis, Modular Process Intensification, Membrane Reactor.

## 1. Introduction

A central research question of modular chemical process intensification (MCPI) lies in how to exploit the synergy of multi-functional physicochemical phenomena at the optimal temporal and spatial scale to substantially improve process efficiency and sustainability (Stankiewicz et al., 2019). As a representative MCPI technology, membrane reactors integrate chemical reaction and membrane separation within a single unit to overcome reaction equilibrium limitation via selective mass transfer (Bernardo and Drioli, 2021). The intrinsic modularity of these systems also opens up the potential for distributed stranded resource utilization and small-scale on-site production (Sjardin et al., 2006).

To rigorously describe the multi-physics interactions in membrane reactors (e.g., reaction, sorption, diffusion, permeation), one-dimensional or two-dimensional first principles models are typically developed for simulation pertaining to pre-postulated reactor configuration and membrane characteristics (Karagöz et al., 2019). The resulting large-scale process-specific partial differential-algebraic equations (PDAE) pose challenges to synthesize optimal membrane reactor designs with structural variations or to incorporate systems-level process integration and intensification. Several recent works have applied phenomena building block-based process representation and synthesis approaches to design membrane-assisted reaction systems (Tula et al., 2019). This offers the potential to rapidly screen and quantitatively evaluate different membrane reactor structures and unit/flowsheet intensification schemes at an early design stage (Monjur et al., 2021; Bishop and Lima, 2021; Babi et al., 2014). However, key open research questions remain on: (i) how to systematically identify the optimal reaction, separation, or hybrid schemes toward ultimate process performance limits, and (ii) how to simultaneously account for the impact of scaling up versus numbering up.

To address these challenges, in this work, we introduce a process intensification synthesis approach for membrane-assisted reaction systems built on the Generalized Modular Representation Framework (GMF) coupled with Orthogonal Collocation on Finite Elements (OCFE). The remainder of this paper is structured as follows. Section 2 presents the physics and mathematics fundamentals for GMF/OCFE modeling of membrane-assisted systems. Section 3 demonstrates the proposed approach on hydrogen production via methane steam reforming. Section 4 discusses ongoing work and future directions.

## 2. Process Intensification Synthesis Approach

### 2.1. An Overview on GMF

As illustrated in Fig. 1, Generalized Modular Representation Framework (Pistikopoulos and Tian, 2022) uses two sets of phenomena modules to capture the vast design space of unit operations and flowsheets from a lower-aggregated level:

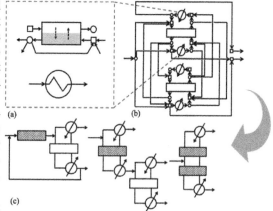

- Mass/Heat exchange module – mass and heat transfer take place between the liquid and/or vapor streams into the module in the form of reaction, separation, reactive separation, etc.
- Heat exchange module – heat transfer takes place between the process and/or utility streams in the form of heating, cooling, heat integration. etc.

Figure 1: A schematic of GMF synthesis approach.

To characterize the mass/heat transfer feasibility in GMF modules (Fig. 1a), a novel driving force constraints formulation has been developed for conventional mass transfer process systems (e.g., reactors, absorption, distillation), based on total Gibbs free energy change $(d(nG)_{T,P}^{tot} = \sum_i \mu_i dn_i \leq 0)$. This enables to: (i) Intensify, and bound, mass transfer in each module against the generalized thermodynamic limits, and (ii) Automatically explore the synergistic or exclusive interactions of separation and reaction phenomena as illustrated in Tian and Pistikopoulos (2018). Physical and computational compactness can thus be attained via a single type of mass/heat exchange module while distilling the multi-functional synergy from thermodynamic fundamentals, instead of enumerating an extensive series of reaction, separation, and reactive separation modules. A superstructure network (Fig. 1b) is then constructed to encapsulate all plausible structural connections of mass/heat exchange modules, heat exchange modules, and process streams. The overall GMF synthesis model is formulated as a mixed-integer nonlinear programming (MINLP) model. Optimal process design solutions, represented using GMF modules (Fig. 1c), can be generated without pre-specifying conventional or intensified unit/flowsheet configurations to innovate the designs with maximal structural flexibility and multi-functional integrity. These designs will be further translated and validated with unit operation-based processes. A number of intensified process systems have been studied with GMF such as dividing wall columns, reactive distillation, solvent selection, etc. (Tian et al., 2022; Tian and Pistikopoulos, 2018)

In what follows, we augment GMF representation and modeling for modular intensified membrane-assisted reaction systems. The novelty of this work is two-fold: (i) Extend the unified Gibbs free energy-based driving force constraints to incorporate the role of membrane selective mass transfer, (ii) Develop a GMF/OCFE modeling strategy for compact, adjustable, and modularized representation of spatially distributed processes.

### 2.2. Representation of Membrane-Assisted Systems

In this work, we focus on gas phase reaction systems modeled with one-dimensional axial distribution. Reaction kinetics and membrane performance data (e.g., permeability) are regarded as given information.

Fig. 2 depicts how pure reaction systems and membrane-assisted systems can be both captured via the generalized GMF mass/heat exchange modules. Two gas-phase inlet streams are considered to enter the module (i.e., $f^{SI}, f^{VI}$) in correspondence to two outlet streams (i.e., $f^{SO}, f^{VO}$). The flow directions can be either co-current or counter-current, as to be showcased in the case study. As per the role of membranes:

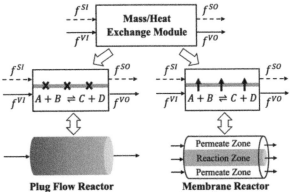

Figure 2: GMF representation for (membrane-assisted) reaction systems.

if transverse flows exist within the module, the mass/heat exchange module represents a membrane reactor with selective mass transfer across the membrane; otherwise, the module represents a plug flow reactor. Auxiliary binary variables (1-0) can be employed to denote the existence (or not) of the membrane. A key research question lies in how to identify when the use of membrane is preferred and vice versa.

### 2.3. Extension of Driving Force Constraints

We address the above question by revisiting the driving force constraints based on total Gibbs free energy change as a function of chemical potentials. Note that mass transfer across membrane is also driven by the difference of chemical potentials between reaction zone and permeate zone. In this regard, we can formulate the driving force constraints for the membrane-assisted systems in a unified from as the systems with conventional mass transfer. More specifically, Eq. 1 defines the driving force constraints which characterize the feasibility of reaction in reaction zone. Eq. 2 are introduced as membrane feasibility constraints to model the process taking place in the mass/heat exchange module. Chemical potential $\mu_i^V$ serves as the joint node to connect the reaction phenomena and membrane permeation phenomena. If membrane is selected in module ($y_{mbr} = 1$), transverse mass flux is activated in Eq. 2 which will impact driving force constraints; if membrane is not selected ($y_{mbr} = 0$), transverse flux is set to 0 and only reaction occurs in module. It is also worth highlighting that, the selection (or not) of the membrane is dictated by thermodynamic rules of the physical process without pre-specification.

$$d(nG)_{T,P}^{tot} = \sum_i \mu_i^V dn_i^V \leq 0 \quad (1) \qquad\qquad 0 \leq J_i = \lambda_i A(\mu_i^S - \mu_i^V) \leq J_{max} y_{mbr} \quad (2)$$

where $\mu_i^V$ ($\mu_i^S$) is chemical potential in reaction (permeate) zone, $\lambda_i$ is permeability, $A$ is membrane area, $J_i$ is transverse mass flux, $y_{mbr}$ is binary variable denoting membrane selection or not.

## 2.4. Spatial Modeling via Orthogonal Collocation on Finite Elements

To model the axial distribution characteristics in (membrane-assisted) reaction systems, one approach is to utilize a number of modules in series as shown in Fig. 3a (Monjur et al., 2021; Bishop and Lima, 2021). However, it is a critical yet open question on how to determine the minimum essential number of phenomena building blocks required for representation, which affects both the combinatorial complexity and solvability of the resulting superstructure network and the mathematical model. Given this, we propose to extract spatial distribution information from intra-module. As shown

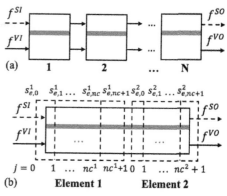

Figure 3: Spatial modeling: (a) Modules-in-series, (b) A single GMF module discretized with OCFE.

in Fig. 3b, each GMF mass/heat exchange module is discretized via Orthogonal Collocation on Finite Elements. The roots of Orthogonal Hahn Polynomials are used to determine the collocation point locations. Component flowrates within the module are approximated using OCFE and major physical modeling constraints are enforced at the collocation points (e.g., mass balances, driving force constraints, reaction kinetics). An indicative list of GMF modeling constraints is provided in Table 1. The following advantages are offered by GMF/OCFE representation: (i) Only continuous variables are introduced to describe the intra-module phenomena, without expanding the combinatorial space using binary variables, (ii) Element partition can be self-adaptive to the underlying faster/slower process changes to enhance modeling accuracy without adding on computational complexity, (iii) The sizing of module can thus be optimized for scaling up or scaling down without compromising modeling accuracy.

Table 1: Mathematical model for GMF/OCFE synthesis – an indicative list

| | |
|---|---|
| Collocation point locations | $s_{e,j}^l - s_j(M_{e,l}) = 0, \qquad e \in E, \, l \in L_e, \, j = 1, \dots, nc_{e,l}$ |
| Weighting functions | $W_j(s) - \prod_{z=0, \, z \neq j'}^{nc_{e,l}} \frac{s - s_{e,j}^l}{s_{e,j}^l - s_{e,z}^l} = 0, e \in E, l \in L_e, j = 0, \dots, nc_{e,l}$ |
| Component mass balances | $fc_c^V(s_{e,j}^l) - \sum_{j'=1}^{nc_{e,l}} W_{j'}(s_{e,j}^l + \Delta M) fc_c^V(s_{e,j'}^l) - J_{e,l,j,c} + \sum_k v_c \, r_{e,l,j,k} \Delta Q_{cat} = 0$ |
| | $fc_c^S(s_{e,j}^l) - \sum_{j'=1}^{nc_{e,l}} W_{j'}(s_{e,j}^l + \Delta M) fc_c^S(s_{e,j'}^l) + J_{e,l,j,c} = 0$ |
| Molar fraction summations | $\sum_{c \in C} fc_c^V(s_{e,j}^l)/f^V(s_{e,j}^l) - 1 = 0, \sum_{c \in C} fc_c^S(s_{e,j}^l)/f^S(s_{e,j}^l) - 1 = 0$ |
| Continuity constraints for adjacent finite elements | $\sum_{c \in C}\left(\sum_{j=0}^{nc_{e,l-1}} W_j(M_{e,l-1}) fc_c^V(s_{e,j}^{l-1})\right) - f^V(s_{e,0}^l) = 0$ |
| | $\sum_{j=0}^{nc_{e,l-1}} W_j(M_{e,l-1}) fc_c^V(s_{e,j}^{l-1}) - fc_c^V(s_{e,0}^l) = 0$ |
| Membrane feasibility constraints: Eq. 4, Driving force constraints: Eq. 5 | |

where subscripts $e$ is index for modules, $l$ is for elements, $j$ is for collocation points, $c$ is for components. Superscripts $V$ and $S$ respectively refer to reaction and permeate side. $s$ is variable for collocation point location, $M$ is element length, $W$ is Lagrange polynomial weighting function, $fc$ is component mass flowrate, $f$ is total mass flowrate.

## 3. Case Study: Hydrogen Production via Steam Reforming

### 3.1. Problem Statement

In this section, we investigate the design of a lab-scale low pressure methane steam reforming (MSR) membrane reactor adapted from Iulianelli et al. (2010). The reactor is 145 mm in length with 20 mm internal diameter, using hydrogen selective Pd-Ag membrane. The reaction utilizes Ni-based catalyst, following the kinetic laws in Xu and Froment (1989). The kinetic efficiency parameters with or without permeation are provided in Iulianelli et al. (2010). The feed gas flowrate is 2.390 mol/h, comprising 0.03 mol/mol $CH_4$, 0.07 mol/mol $H_2O$, and 0.90 mol/mol $N_2$. The sweep gas flowrate is 0.132 mol/h with pure $N_2$. Isothermal operation is considered at 723.15 K.

### 3.2. GMF/OCFE for Membrane Reactor Simulation

Simulation studies are first performed to test the representation efficacy of GMF/OCFE for the above membrane reactor system. Fig. 4a presents the reaction side $H_2$ molar fraction profiles in a co-current flow scheme, respectively simulated with: (i) high-fidelity ordinary differential equations (ODE), (ii) a single GMF/OCFE module decomposed with 2 elements and 4 collocation points per element, (iii) 5 GMF mass/heat exchange modules in series (with equivalent module length), and (iv) 10 GMF modules in series. As can be noted, GMF/OCFE provides better modeling accuracy compared to modules in series, while requiring the use of less simulation points both in the continuous space and the combinatorial space (i.e., 8 collocation points in total vs. 10 GMF modules). The ability to assign different element lengths also contributes to the GMF/OCFE representation enhancement. In this case, Element 1 is 0.050 m in length using 4 collocation points to describe the faster process at membrane reactor entrance. Element 2 is 0.140 m in length using another 4 collocation points to capture the rest slower process. GMF/OCFE is also tested on a counter-current flow scheme using an elevated feed gas flowrate to achieve 60% $CH_4$ conversion and 80% $H_2$ recovery. The $H_2$ molar fraction profiles at permeate side are shown in Fig. 4b, in which GMF/OCFE proves sufficient modeling accuracy compared to simulation using 20 modules in series.

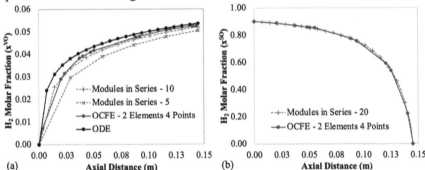

Figure 4: GMF/OCFE simulation for MSR membrane reactor:
(a) Co-current, $H_2$ profiles at reaction side, (b) Counter-current, $H_2$ profiles at permeate side.

### 3.3. Design Optimization of Membrane-Assisted Reaction Systems

The design optimization of a membrane-assisted reaction system is considered with at least 75% $CH_4$ conversion. Two optimization objectives are respectively studied to demonstrate the applicability and versatility of GMF/OCFE synthesis: (i) Maximize $H_2$ recovery, (ii) Minimize membrane area. A maximum of 4 GMF modules are available for use, each discretized using 2 elements and 4 collocation points per element. As a proof-of-concept example, the structural connections of modules are restricted as in series, without opening up the full superstructure network as shown in Fig. 1 (which encapsulates recycle streams, etc.) The selection or not of transverse mass transfer through membrane is to be determined by the process synthesis problem without pre-postulation. Fig. 5a shows the optimal design with maximal $H_2$ recovery, which features a membrane reactor

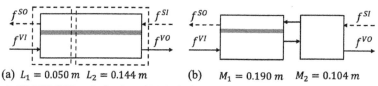

(a) $L_1 = 0.050\,m$   $L_2 = 0.144\,m$    (b)    $M_1 = 0.190\,m$   $M_2 = 0.104\,m$

Figure 5: GMF/OCFE optimization: (a) Maximize $H_2$ recovery, (b) Minimize membrane area.

of 0.195 m in length. Fig. 5b shows the optimal design with minimal membrane area, which features a sequential structure of membrane reactor (0.190 m) followed by a packed bed reactor (0.104 m). By comparing these two design alternatives, the packed bed reactor in Fig. 5b is used to replace the 0.004 m membrane reactor in Fig. 5a to reduce membrane area but attaining the required methane conversion level. For benchmark, a 0.20 meters long packed bed reactor is simulated which reaches only 16% $CH_4$ conversion.

## 4. Conclusion

In this paper, we have presented a process synthesis approach for membrane-assisted reaction systems using Generalized Modular Representation Framework. Ongoing work is addressing: (i) full superstructure-based synthesis to generate better and potentially more innovative design solutions, and (ii) the incorporation of life cycle assessment into optimization formulation to simultaneously account for sustainability considerations.

## 5. Acknowledgement

The authors acknowledge financial support from the Chemical and Biomedical Engineering Department at West Virginia University.

## References

D. K. Babi, P. Lutze, J. M. Woodley, R. Gani. (2014). A process synthesis-intensification framework for the development of sustainable membrane-based operations. Chem. Eng. Process., 86, 173-195.

P. Bernardo, E. Drioli, 2021. Membrane Engineering for a Sustainable Production of Ethylene. Fuel Process. Technol., 212, 106624.

B. A. Bishop, F. V. Lima. (2021). Novel module-based membrane reactor design approach for improved operability performance. Membranes, 11(2), 157.

A. Iulianelli, G. Manzolini, M. De Falco, S. Campanari, T. Longo, S. Liguori, A. Basile, 2010. $H_2$ Production by Low Pressure Methane Steam Reforming in a Pd–Ag Membrane Reactor over a Ni-based Catalyst: Experimental and Modeling. Int. J. Hydrog. Energy, 35(20), 11514-11524.

S. Karagöz, T. T. Tsotsis, V. I. Manousiouthakis. (2019). Multi-Scale Modeling and Simulation of a Novel Membrane Reactor/Adsorptive Reactor Process. Chem. Eng. Process., 137, 148-158.

M. S. Monjur, S. E. Demirel, J. Li, M. M. F. Hasan. (2021). SPICE_MARS: A Process Synthesis Framework for Membrane-Assisted Reactive Separations. Ind. Eng. Chem. Res., 60, 7635-7655.

E. N. Pistikopoulos, Y. Tian. (2022). Synthesis and Operability Strategies for Computer-Aided Modular Process Intensification. Elsevier.

M. Sjardin, K. J. Damen, A. P. Faaij. (2006) Techno-Economic Prospects of Small-Scale Membrane Reactors in a Future Hydrogen-Fuelled Transportation Sector. Energy, 31(14), 2523-2555.

A. Stankiewicz, T. Van Gerven, G. Stefanidis. (2019). The Fundamentals of Process Intensification.

Y. Tian, V. Meduri, R. Bindlish, E. N. Pistikopoulos. (2022). A Process Intensification Synthesis Framework for Design of Dividing Wall Column Systems. Comput. Chem. Eng., 160, 107679.

Y. Tian, E. N. Pistikopoulos. (2018). Synthesis of Operable Process Intensification Systems – Steady-State Design with Safety and Operability Considerations. Ind. Eng. Chem. Res., 58(15), 6049-6068.

A. K. Tula, M. R. Eden, R. Gani. (2019). Computer-Aided Process Intensification: Challenges, Trends and Opportunities. AIChE J., 66(1).

J. Xu, G. F. Froment. (1989). Methane Steam Reforming, Methanation and Water-Gas Shift: I. Intrinsic Kinetics. AIChE J., 35(1), 88-96.

Antonis Kokossis, Michael C. Georgiadis, Efstratios N. Pistikopoulos (Eds.)
PROCEEDINGS OF THE 33rd European Symposium on Computer Aided Process Engineering
(ESCAPE33), June 18-21, 2023, Athens, Greece

# Multiscale design and analysis of templated zeolite for Li-O2 battery with improved discharge capacity

Khizar Hayat[a,b], Daniel Bahamon[a,b], Lourdes F. Vega[a,b], Ahmed AlHajaj[a,b]

[a]Research and Innovation Center on CO2 and Hydrogen (RICH Center), Khalifa University, P.O. Box 127788, United Arab Emirates.
[b]Department of Chemical Engineering, Khalifa University, P.O. Box 127788, Abu Dhabi, United Arab Emirates

## Abstract

The commercialization of practical Li-O2 batteries is restricted by the lower discharge capacity induced by poor mass transport through the cathode structure. In view of that, we have designed four (RHO-, FAU-, MFI-, and BEA-ZTCs) hierarchical zeolite-templated carbon electrodes. We have utilized a multiscale modelling framework to assess the performance of developed structures by integrating cluster and cell-level structural domains. At the cluster level, a reactive forcefield molecular dynamic study is carried out to explore the species (Li+, O2, and DMSO) transport through porous structures. The results revealed that hierarchical structures, particularly RHO-ZTC, have superior mass transport. The subsequent cell level 2-D continuum modelling study resulted in the improved discharge capacities of hierarchical structures. Specifically, hierarchical RHO-ZTC showed nearly three times higher capacity than conventional SP carbon. This improved mass transport is attributed to the mesopores in the systems acting as oxygen transport tunnels and product storage reservoirs.

**Keywords**: ReaxFF-MD, Li-O2 battery, Multiscale modelling, 2-D continuum model

## 1. Introduction

Among the myriad electrochemical storage technologies, the Li-O2 battery is being considered as a promising power source for next-generation electric vehicles. However, its viable commercialization is still the dream due to lower discharge capacity which depends on the mass transport through porous electrode structure (Hayat *et. al.*, 2022). Therefore, improving the discharge capacity of Li-O2 battery (LOB) have become critically acclaimed topic among the scientific community. In that perspective, the designing of novel hierarchical LOB electrode with optimized structural characteristics (porosity, pore size distribution, surface area, and tortuosity) could be crucial in facilitated mass transport which ultimately may leads to high discharge capacity (Hayat *et. al.*, 2021). The mass transfer through porous structures can be, essentially, enhanced through various routes (Schneider *et. al.*, 2016) such as crystal size reduction, incorporating large number of micropores, and introducing mesopores along with micropores as additional storage reservoir and mass transport carriageways. From the Li-O2 storage technology scenario, the third route could be a promising way of developing novel hierarchical structures.

In that sense, our group put significant efforts in developing hierarchical amorphous carbon cathodes (with combined micro- and mesopores) (Elabyouki *et. al.*, 2019 and Hayat *et. al.*, 2022). Despite promising improvement in the storage capacity of Li-O2 battery, the molecular understanding of coupled mass transport and electrochemical reactions inside micro- and mesopores still needs better understanding for prolonged discharge operation and enhanced discharge capacity. Furthermore, the impact of structural properties of hierarchical carbon frameworks on the mass transport (at molecular level) and discharge capacity (at cell level) require comprehensive assessment for designing future generation Li-$O_2$ batteries.

Therefore, in this contribution, we draw attention to the multiscale design of hierarchical zeolite templated (ZTC) carbon cathode structures. Our integrated multiscale study is comprised of two levels including molecular level, and cell level. The molecular level includes reactive forcefield molecular dynamic study (reaxFF-MD) of the screened hierarchical ZTCs. From reaxff-MD, we are intended to get the key performance indicators such as species diffusivities (Li$^+$, $O_2$, and electrolyte), main discharge products, pore volume, pore size distribution, carbon mass loadings, and surface area. The cell level computational work aims at performing process simulations of the main hierarchical ZTC structures considered in this study (using data from molecular simulations) and then evaluate their performance based of discharge capacity and cell voltage.

## 2. Methodology

To obtain physical insight into the transport properties within the hierarchical ZTCs cathodes and their impact on cell discharge capacities, we have constructed an integrated multiscale modelling (MSM) framework, as illustrated in Figure 1. The developed MSM is spanned over cluster and cell scales. The former scale focus on the molecular investigations of transport properties using reactive molecular dynamic simulation. The main key performance indicators that are obtained from reaxFF-MD study include effective-self diffusivities, molecular density number profile, and discharge product clusters formation. While cell scale model (i.e., 2-D continuum model) is developed to screen the hierarchical ZTC electrodes using their corresponding transport characteristics from cluster scale simulation. The cell scale modelling involves the investigation of surface area evolution, electrochemical kinetics, porosity evolution, and discharge capacity and specific energy density calculation during discharging of Li-$O_2$ battery cell. The detail of both modelling studies is explained in following sections.

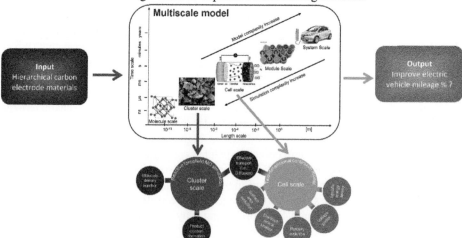

Figure 1. Multiscale modelling framework for Li-$O_2$ batteries

### 2.1. Reactive forcefield molecular dynamic simulation

Molecular dynamic simulation strategy involves the designing and characterizing hierarchical structures and performing reactive forcefield molecular dynamic simulations.

We have employed zeolite-templated carbons (ZTCs) as parent structures for the development of hierarchical electrodes for Li-O₂ battery (Braun *et al.*, 2018). Based on structural analysis of 47 parent ZTCs (using Poreblazer package), we have selected four microporous zeolite templated carbons (RHO-, FAU-, MFI-, and BEA-) which are further utilized for the generation of hierarchical ZTCs having both micro- and mesopores. Moreover, to create hierarchical frameworks from the parent structures, a slit type mesopore with typical size of 25 Å is introduced into the centre of the intrinsic supercells (Elabyouki *et. al.,* 2019). The four generated hierarchical ZTCs composed of slit mesopore sandwiched between microporous walls with different thicknesses such as 17.3, 18.0, 14.0, and 12.8 Å for RHO-, MFI-, FAU-, and BEA-ZTCs, respectively.

For simulation box preparation, firstly we packed the hierarchical ZTC electrodes by randomly placing dimethyl sulfoxide (DMSO i.e., liquid non-aqueous electrolyte solvent) molecules. The number of DMSO molecules in each structure are adjusted to mimic the bulk electrolyte density (i.e., 1.09 g/cm³) (Lebel *et. al.,* 1962). Next, to prepare 1 M electrolyte solution of LiPF₆, we have added Li⁺ and PF₆⁻ salt-ions to the simulation cell. Further, different number of gaseous O₂ (100, 200, 300, and 500) molecules were included into the electrolyte solution to obtain various temporal configurations of hierarchical zeolite-templated carbon electrodes. Here, the main objective of adding different number of oxygen molecules is to demonstrate the discharge mechanism stages Li-O₂ cell, with 100 oxygen molecules being initial stage and 500 oxygen molecules being final step of the discharge process. For molecular interactions calculation, we have utilized reactive forcefield containing the parameter set for the C, H, O, Li, P, F, and S (Islam *et. al.,* 2014) elements. Besides, to accurately predict the formation of Li₂O₂, the forcefield parameter values for Li and O were replaced with the one developed for Li-O₂ systems (Hearn *et. al.,* 2020). Unlike the empirical classical forcefield, the reactive forcefield (reaxFF) is a bond order (BO) based method which permits the bond breakage and formation during the molecular dynamic computations (Raju *et. al.,* 2014). In reaxFF, the total system energy is the sum of individual component energies such as bond, lone pair, torsional, valence, over-coordination, under-coordination, van der Waals, and coulombic energies. During reaxFF-MD simulations, bond order values are calculated at every time step based on interatomic bond distances, consequently acting as a component of prime importance for all types of bonded interactions such as torsional and valence interactions. When the bond breakage happens, all the bonded energy contributions are diminish leaving behind only long-range non-bonded interactions such as van der Waals and coulombic interactions, normally present among the non-bonded pairs of atoms. The reaxff-MD simulations are performed in LAMMPS package involving following steps; simulation cell optimization, equilibration at 10 K (for 10 ps) followed by heating from 10 – 300 K (for 10 ps), equilibration at 300 K (for 10 ps), and production run at target temperature i.e., 300 K (for 1.5 ns). A value of 0.1 fs is used for the time step and Nose Hoover thermoset is taken for simulation temperature control. For post-processing and visualization of data, we have employed OVITO software. For species diffusion calculation, the Einstein's correlation (Islam *et. al.,* 2015) is utilized which computed self-diffusivity values based on the mean square displacement (MSD) of individual molecules as follows.

$$D_x = \frac{1}{2} \lim_{\Delta t \to \infty} \frac{MSD_x(t+\Delta t) - MSD_x(t)}{\Delta t} \quad (D_x, \text{ Diffusivity along preferential direction}) \qquad (1)$$

Here, the self-diffusivity values of Li⁺ and O₂ are based on the total number of respective molecules present in any form such as O₂²⁻, LiO, Li₂O, LiO₂, and Li₂O₂.

2.2. Cell scale 2-D continuum model

To test the cell performance of hierarchical ZTC electrodes, we have developed the two-dimensional continuum model. The detail of the model equations, initial conditions, boundary conditions, and assumptions is given in supplementary material of our previously published work (Hayat *et. al.*, 2021). The reactive forcefield study is integrated with the 2-D model through modifying the effective diffusivity equations which will mimic the molecular transport through hierarchical ZTC cathodes. The curve fitting analysis is utilized to fit the effective diffusivity correlations data with that obtained from reaxFF-MD study. The underlying algorithm for curve fitting involves the generalized reduced gradient method which finds the optimal solution based on the least square error. The mentioned method depends on the initial condition; therefore, we have used the curve fitting method with multi-start in which it automatically finds the most suitable initial condition. After developing 2-D model by including modified effective diffusivity correlations, we have imported the model equations into COMSOL Multiphysics software to perform equation-based simulation of Li-$O_2$ battery cell. During the discharging process, at the airside, oxygen dissolves into the non-aqueous liquid electrolyte (flowing through cathode pores network) and reacts with $Li^+$ subsequently generating the solid $Li_2O_2$ discharge product. The stop condition is applied when the solid cathode potential on the air-side boundary becomes equal to 2.1 V. For all the variables, the convergence criteria are set to $10^{-4}$.

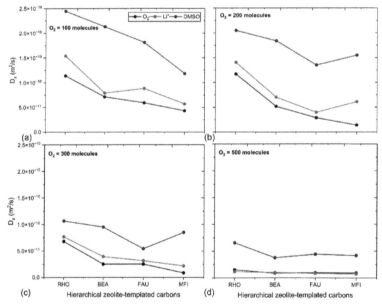

Figure 2. Self-diffusivity (x-direction) trends for oxygen, Lithium-ion, and DMSO electrolyte through hierarchical zeolite-templated carbons at various discharge states (a) 100, (b) 200, (c) 300, and (d) 500.

## 3. Results and discussions

Figure 2 (a-d) is plotting the self-diffusivities curves of oxygen, $Li^+$, and DMSO along the preferential direction through hierarchical zeolite-templated carbon electrodes at various oxygen molecules (100, 200, 300, and 500). The results demonstrate that the self-diffusivities of all the species are decreasing as we move from RHO-ZTC to MFI-ZTC at all oxygen consumption cases. This is because of the reducing micropore size from RHO to MFI. The superior species diffusion through hierarchical RHO-ZTC porous framework (among all the ZTCs) could be induced by the large pore volume ($\sim 1.85$ cm$^3$g$^{-1}$) due to the presence of high density of micro- ($\sim 14.5$ Å), and meso-pores ($\sim 25$ Å). Consequently, RHO-ZTC not only accommodate large fraction of solid discharge product but also it provides enough space for molecules (particularly O$_2$) to transport without pore clogging. Another reason for the facilitated diffusion might be the fast molecular exchange between slit-mesopore and microporous walls of the hierarchical RHO-ZTC. This finding corresponds to the claim reported by one of our group member (Elabyouki *et. al.*, 2019) who stated that the enhanced discharge characteristics of hierarchical electrodes are mainly due to the continuous molecular exchange occurring at meso-micro pores interphase thereby preventing the micropores clogging by solid product. Further, for RHO-ZTC, the attained diffusivity ranges for Li$^+$ and O$_2$ are ($1.54\times10^{-10} - 2.69\times10^{-11}$ m$^2$s$^{-1}$) and ($1.14\times10^{-10} - 1.53\times10^{-11}$ m$^2$s$^{-1}$), respectively. Further, it is evident, that as oxygen consumption increases (from 100 to 500 molecules) the species self-diffusivity coefficients decrease. This is because of the generation of solid discharge product (Li$_2$O$_2$) which not only reduces the free Li$^+$ and reactive O$_2$ but also imposes extra resistance towards their transport. At the lower oxygen consumption (i.e., 100 oxygen molecules), small size discharge intermediates (e.g., LiO, Li$_2$O, LiO$_2$) are the dominant products, however, higher oxygen consumption (i.e., 500 O$_2$ molecules) permits the formation of large size discharge product aggregates (specifically Li$_2$O$_2$) which are strongly adsorbed to the electrode pore surface and fill the entire pore volume resulting in lower diffusivities of Li$^+$, oxygen, and DMSO (electrolyte solvent).

Figure 3 illustrates the comparison of discharge profiles for hierarchical zeolite-templated carbon electrodes and experimental data from Read's work (Read *et. al.*, 2002) at current density value of 0.1 mA/cm$^2$. The discharge capacity trends obtained from 2-D modelling of hierarchical ZTCs are as follows; RHO (2848 mAh/g) > FAU (960 mAh/g) > MFI (740 mAh/g) > BEA (690 mAh/g). These discharge capacities correspond to the self-diffusivity trends obtained from reaxFF-MD simulation for individual hierarchical ZTCs. It is noticed that specifically hierarchical RHO-ZTC have delivered 3 times much higher discharge capacity than that of literature data generated from conventional SP carbon electrode ($\sim 941$ mAh/g). For BEA-ZTC, unlike superior diffusivities, the capacity is lower which is mainly due to the lower porosity, surface area, and cell density of the

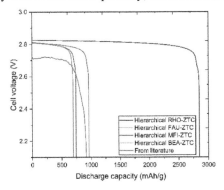

Figure 3. Comparative analysis of discharge profiles of hierarchical-ZTCs and liter. (Read *et. al.*, 2002).

structure. Further, hierarchical electrodes also improved the average discharge voltage which may lead to improved specific energy density of LOB. This finding explains the fact that facilitated mass transport (besides electrochemical kinetics) through hierarchical structures not only improve the storage capacity but also helps to mitigate the effect of voltage loss during galvanostatic discharge resulting in improved energy density. Another reason of improved storage capacities is attributed to the more utilization of pore volume available in the hierarchical structure (particularly RHO-ZTC). Overall hierarchical ZTC based air-electrodes could be promising for the development of future generation Li-O$_2$ power system.

## 4.   Conclusion

Dealing with the challenge of lower capacity due to limited mass transport, here we have proposed novel hierarchical zeolite-templated carbon as potential air-electrodes for high-capacity Li-O$_2$ batteries. An integrated multiscale model is utilized to screen the developed electrodes based on their cell performance, particularly discharge capacity. The reaxFF-MD study revealed that hierarchical structures have facilitated the mass transport characteristics. Specifically, RHO-ZTC showed dominant transport of Li$^+$ and O$_2$ compared to rest of the structures. Subsequently, hierarchal RHO-ZTC generated much higher discharge capacity ($\sim$ 2848 mAh/g) than the rest of the electrode structures. The great improvement in capacity is mainly attributed to the inclusion of mesopores which not only facilitated species diffusion but also improved the accessible free volume to store the solid discharge product i.e., Li$_2$O$_2$. This multiscale study could guide us to design state-of-the-art Li-O$_2$ batteries with ultrahigh capacities.

## References

K. Hayat, L. F. Vega, A. AlHajaj, 2022, What have we learned by multiscale models on improving the cathode storage capacity of Li-air batteries? Recent advances and remaining challenges, Renew Sustain Energy Rev, 154, 111849.

K. Hayat, L. F. Vega, A. AlHajaj, 2021, Modeling of hierarchical cathodes for Li-air batteries with improved discharge capacity, J Electrochem Soc. 168, 120534.

D. Schneider, D. Mehlhorn, P. Zeigermann, J. Kärger, R. Valiullin, 2016, Transport properties of hierarchical micro–mesoporous materials, Chem Soc Rev. 45, 3439–67.

M. Elabyouki, D. Bahamon, M. Khaleel, L. F. Vega, 2019, Insights into the transport properties of electrolyte solutions in a hierarchical carbon electrode by molecular dynamics simulations. J Phys Chem C. 123, 27273–85.

E. Braun, Y. Lee, S. M. Moosavi, S. Barthel, R. Mercado, I. A. Baburin, 2018, Generating carbon schwarzites via zeolite-templating, Mater Cloud Arch. 115, E8116–24.

R. G. LeBel, D. A. I. Goring, 1962, Density, viscosity, refractive index, and hygroscopicity of mixtures of water and dimethyl sulfoxide, J Chem Eng Data, 7, 100–1.

M. M. Islam, V. S. Bryantsev, A. C. T. Van Duin, 2014, ReaxFF reactive force field simulations on the influence of teflon on electrolyte decomposition during Li/SWCNT anode discharge in lithium-sulfur batteries, J Electrochem Soc. 161, E3009.

K. A. O'Hearn, M. W. Swift, J. Liu, I. Magoulas, P. Piecuch, A. C. T. Van Duin, 2020, Optimization of the Reax force field for the lithium–oxygen system using a high fidelity charge model, J Chem Phys. 153, 84107.

M. Raju, P. Ganesh, P. R. C. Kent, A. C. T. Van Duin, 2015, Reactive force field study of Li/C systems for electrical energy storage, J Chem Theory Comput. 11, 2156–66.

M. M. Islam, A. Ostadhossein, O. Borodin, A.T. Yeates, W.W. Tipton, R.G. Hennig, N. Kumar, A.C.T. Van Duin, 2015, ReaxFF molecular dynamics simulations on lithiated sulfur cathode materials, Phys. Chem. Chem. Phys. 17, 3383–3393.

J. Read, 2002, Characterization of the lithium/oxygen organic electrolyte battery, Journal of the Electrochemical Society, 149, A1190.

Antonis Kokossis, Michael C. Georgiadis, Efstratios N. Pistikopoulos (Eds.)
PROCEEDINGS OF THE 33rd European Symposium on Computer Aided Process Engineering
(ESCAPE33), June 18-21, 2023, Athens, Greece

# Numerical Evaluation of Fuel Utilisation Enhancement Strategies in a Solid Oxide Fuel Cell System Fuelled by Hydrocarbons Mixtures

Clyde-Theodore Nguimbous Batista,[a] Amirpiran Amiri,[a] Robert Steinberger-Wilckens,[b]

[a]*European Bioenergy Research Institute (EBRI), School of Engineering and Applied Science, Aston University, Birmingham B4 7ET, UK*
[b]*School of Chemical Engineering, University of Birmingham, Edgbaston, Birmingham B15 2TT, UK*

## Abstract

In this paper an internal reforming SOFC is simulated, including the Balance-of-Plant (BoP) it is embedded in. Various approaches are evaluated to provide data for the trade-off between system efficiency and fuel cell health. The results reveal that controlled single-pass fuel utilisation (~50%) with a maximised system fuel utilisation of 85% is feasible. The operating voltage, current trajectories and detailed patterns of voltage losses and efficiencies are captured. The anode activation loss is observed to be the key contributor to the operating voltage variation when anode-off gas recycling is applied to improve the system's Uf. The BoP modifications are presented to identify the optimal recycling point in the process flowsheet. The simulation results showed that in a comprehensive BoP, optimisation of system fuel utilisation and efficiency through tunning of the anode-off gas recycle needs exploring of both flowsheet and operating parameters enhancement.

**Keywords**: SOFC, fuel utilisation, efficiency, health.

## 1. Introduction

SOFCs are promising devices towards highly efficient electrical power generation from chemical energy. The technology can be used in a wide range of applications for both domestic and industrial sectors, from distributed power/CHP generation to light traction vehicles (O. Sharaf and M. Orhan, 2014). The high operating temperatures make them ideal for combined heat and power systems, utilising high-grade waste heat, wherein, home applications can replace boilers for heating. The SOFCs boast high fuel flexibility, low emission and relatively low operating costs. However, the main drawbacks of this technology are the high costs of manufacture and the rapid deterioration of the fuel cell performance. The performance losses can be associated with the complex degradation process of the SOFC, impacted by both intrinsic and extrinsic factors. Despite the abundant research into the explicit impact of factors such as the presence of impurities, and mechanical deterioration on performance and losses during operation (from an electrochemical standpoint), long-term durability remains a major concern. This, in turn, prevents the development of accurate lifetime predictive models, and so current research focalises on the maximising of the SOFC health, i.e. the performance of the fuel cell over time, until failure. In this consideration, fuel utilisation (Uf), describing the quantity of fuel utilised towards the production of power, is an important aspect to consider particularly at the system level. In this work, two definitions of fuel utilisation will be employed: i. single-pass fuel utilisation (SP Uf) that refers to the stack and ii. Overall system fuel utilisation (System Uf) refers to the system or the BoP. Fuel utilisation maximisation can have both a positive impact (producing more energy with lower fresh fuel input requirements and increased efficiency), and a negative impact correlated to voltage losses and localised degradation by various causes. This impedance on SOFC health, with respect to Uf, can typically be associated with high SP Uf, as such, strategies to maximise the system Uf whilst maintaining moderate SP Uf are important (J. Yi and T. Kim, 2017). Employable strategies include multistaging (MS) and the introduction of anode off-gas recycling (AOGR). In this work, the various methods of implementing the AOGR will be investigated within a single internal reforming SOFC system and the impact on SOFC health explored, with the aim to provide insight into the optimum strategy for improving long-term fuel cell performance. The aim is to investigate the impact of flowsheeting on AOGR effectiveness.

## 2. Simulation

The SOFC and BoP are simulated on Aspen HYSYS® utilising the built-in modules and functions. Three flowsheets are used for the investigation of the effectiveness of the implementation of AOGR on the SOFC performance and health. The base case system depicted in Figure 1, captures the pre-AOGR implementation performance data. Two modifications were implemented in Platform A to create Platform B and C as shown in Figure 2 and Figure 3, respectively.

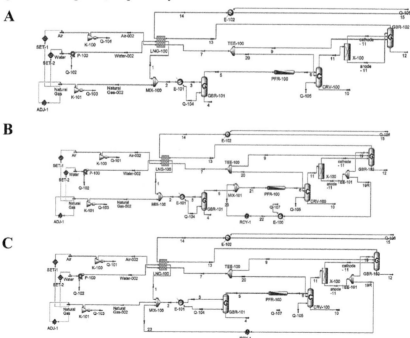

Figure 1: Platform A - base case model of the BoP with no AOGR; Platform B - AOGR connected to the stack inlet point; Platform C - AOGR connected to the external pre-reformer inlet point.

The SOFC electrochemical calculations are carried out within a series of inbuilt SPREADSHEET using the governing equations used by W. Zhang et al., 2005.

### 2.1. Simulation Validation

The model validation is presented in Table 1. To this end, the results of Platform C were compared against the results of similar systems existing in literature where the models' inputs are identical.

Table 1: Simulation results compared to the literature data for power =120kW DC.

| Variable/Parameter | W. Zhang et al., 2005 | W. Doherty et al., 2010 | T. R. Tanim, 2012 | This work |
|---|---|---|---|---|
| Voltage, (V) | 0.70 | 0.68 | 0.69 | 0.69 |
| Current density, (mA/cm$^2$) | 178.0 | 182.9 | 182.0 | 180.7 |
| Pre-reforming temperature, (°C) | 536.0 | 535.1 | 535.0 | 535.1 |
| Cathode inlet temperature, (°C) | 821.3 | 823.7 | 826.0 | 826.0 |
| Stack exhaust temperature, (°C) | 834.0 | 833.7 | 836.0 | 793.9 |
| Anode outlet composition | | | | |
| $H_2O$ | 50.9% | 50.9% | 50.9% | 50.9% |
| $CO_2$ | 24.9% | 24.9% | 24.9% | 24.9% |
| $H_2$ | 11.6% | 11.6% | 11.6% | 11.6% |
| CO | 7.4% | 7.4% | 7.4% | 7.4% |
| $N_2$ | 5.1% | 5.1% | 5.1% | 5.1% |
| Stack exhaust composition | | | | |
| $N_2$ | 77.3% | 77.3% | 77.2% | 77.3% |
| $O_2$ | 15.9% | 15.9% | 15.7% | 15.9% |
| $H_2O$ | 4.5% | 4.5% | 4.7% | 4.5% |
| $CO_2$ | 2.3% | 2.3% | 2.4% | 2.3% |
| Gross electrical efficiency (LHV), (%) | 52.0% | 51.3% | 51.7% | 52.0% |

As shown in Table 1, under the same operating conditions, the simulation is capable of simulating an internal reforming SOFC operating at 85% fuel utilisation and 120kW output power. The data shows the results obtained to be within 5% of that from the literature. Key assumptions made in the work are the inlet fuel composition as CH4 81.3%, C2H6 2.9%, C3H8 0.4%, C4H10 0.2%, N2 14.3% and CO 0.9%, an inlet air temperature of 630°C and fuel feed of 200 °C. A total active area of 96.1m2 over 1152 cells was assumed (W. Zhang et al., 2005).

## 3. Results and discussions

The base case system shown in Platform A is used as a point of reference for the system performance. Figure 2a presents the impact of recycle ratio (RR) on the system Uf and operating voltage captured in Platform B and C for 50kW power output. In Figure 2b variations of voltage and system efficiency, against RR are presented.

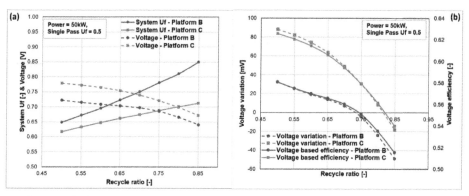

Figure 2: Platform B and C performance comparison at constant power and fueling rate and varying RR; (a) impact on system Uf and SOFC operating voltage, (b) impact on voltage variation $\Delta V = V - V_{ref}$ and voltage efficiency.

From Figure 2a, at RR = 0.85 Platform B and C can reach a system Uf of 0.85 and 0.71 respectively, at a constant fuel rate that is obtained from the base case model of Platform A for 50kW DC power output and SP Uf = 0.5. Despite this, Platform B displays more cause for concern in terms of the SOFC voltage level. As shown in Figure 2a, the SOFC voltage in Platform B is much lower than that of Platform C, ranging from 0.72 to 0.64 compared to 0.78 to 0.67, with a larger difference at lower RRs. The voltage variation against RR (shown in Fig 2b) does not differ significantly comparing these two platforms. The voltage drop can be a health risk for the SOFC by reaching a thermodynamic voltage below which the anode, in this case Ni, will change its oxidation state i.e., conversion from Ni to NiO. This voltage threshold is a function of temperature. So, if higher voltage loss results in dropping the operating voltage below the thermodynamic Nernst voltage limit at that temperature, then anode re-oxidation gets momentum. Subsequently, depending on the voltage drop extent and time, there can be a significant change in the anode microstructure. So even if the voltage drop is temporary and the voltage recovers, the damage can be significant and lead to an increased rate of degradation. To safeguard against this, there is a need to have a control measure for RR to not allow the operating voltage to drop below its temperature-dependent thermodynamic voltage for re-oxidation. Further, the impact of optimising the fueling of the system on the performance is assessed for both Platform B and C, at a constant SP Uf of 0.5. This allows for the determination of the optimum method for the maximisation of system fuel utilisation whilst averting system performance degradation. With this operation mode, both Platforms B and C are seen to be capable of attaining a system Uf of 0.87 at a recycle ratio of 0.85. However, the impact of this on the system varies by platform and with increasing power demand. Figure 3 below shows the fuel input requirements and the associated efficiency for both platforms B and C at a recycle ratio of 0.5, achieving a system Uf of 0.67 each.

As can be seen in Fig 3, at all power values the flowsheet variations presented in Platform B and C show increases in the electrical efficiency of the system when compared to that of the base case (Platform A). For DC power output of 50kW, the base case simulation provided an efficiency of 44% with a SP Uf of 0.5 and consequently a system Uf of 0.5. However, Platforms B and C results showed the efficiency to increase to 47% and 50%, respectively, both showing an increased system Uf of 0.67 achieved through 50% recycling of the anode off-gas. At all DC power values investigated and 50% AOGR,

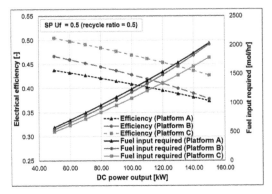

Figure 3: Systems efficiency analysis at different powers, constant SP Uf and RR.

Platform C achieved the greatest overall efficiency, with 47% and 43% efficiencies observed at 100kW and 150kW respectively. This indicated an average of 6% efficiency increase from the base case model. Conversely Platform B achieved 3-5% lower efficiencies when compared to Platform C, while an increase of 1-2% from the base case was observed. As can be seen in Fig 4b, for all platforms the maximum achievable efficiencies occur at higher RR when the drawn power reduces.

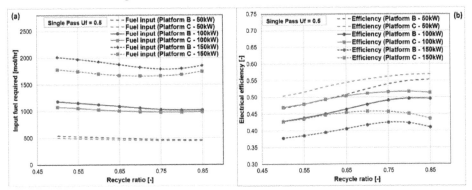

Figure 4: Platforms B and C, efficiency, and fuel input requirement versus RR at different powers.

The incremental increase in DC power output, for all cases, showed to increase in the fuel input required, as shown in Figure 3. As shown in Figure 4a, with increasing RR both Platforms B and C display consistently decreasing fuel input requirements at 50kW, 100kW and 150kW reaches a plateau at a RR about 0.75. for the 150kW case models reaching an optimum recycling ratio at 0.75 followed by an increase in fuel requirement that is because of promoted voltage loss at high RR values. This is consistent with the observations depicted in Figure 4b for efficiency decrease after the optimum RR point.

This is due to greater AOGR ratios reducing the partial pressures of hydrogen and hydrogen carriers within the fuel cell stack inlet, leading to the observed reduction in the electrical efficiency (above 0.75 AOGR). The increasing recycle ratio shows both Platforms B and C to observe changes in efficiency proportional to the changes in the input fuel requirements. For both platforms, operating at 50kW and 100kW shows efficiency to increase to a plateau and 150kW to reach a peak efficiency of 42% and 46% for Platforms B and C respectively, at a recycling ratio of 0.7.

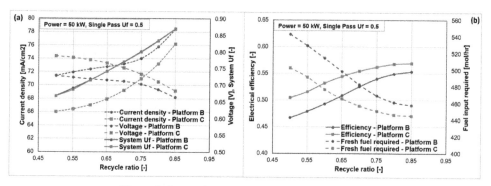

Figure 5: Comparison at 50kW DC power output.

From the results, it can be deduced that AOGR in Platform C is a more desirable method at all simulated system Ufs due to the greater overall increase in efficiency and reduction in fuel input required (Figure 4b and 5b). At 50kW DC power output, the efficiency is shown to increase from 50% to 57%, with Platform B increasing from 47% to 55% for a recycle ratio of 0.5 to 0.85. The maximum system Uf and efficiency reached by both are 0.87 with 55% and 57% efficiency respectively. Furthermore, in the interest of SOFC health, Platform B shows to provide the system with a more stable voltage (decreasing from 0.73V to 0.66V between recycle ratio of 0.5 and 0.85), with a steady increase in current density until a recycle ratio of 0.7, followed by the steep increase (Figure 5a). On the other hand, Platform C shows a more consistent change in both voltage and current density, with the minimum voltage being 0.68V.

## 4. Conclusions

In literature, moderated SP Uf and high system Uf have been recommended for SOFC system operation for sake of SOFC health and overall efficiency, respectively. This result of this work revealed that the system Uf needs to be optimised along with BoP operating conditions due to the concerns associated with high system Uf that should be taken into account in any process optimisation. In this paper, the system level Uf was evaluated for two BoPs with different AOGR points. The results have shown that efficiencies, voltage losses and system Uf can significantly be different influencing the SOFC lifetime and system overall efficiency.

## References

O. Sharaf and M. Orhan, 2014, An overview of fuel cell technology: Fundamentals and application, Renewable and Sustainable Energy Reviews, 32, 810-853

J. Yi and T. Kim, 2017, Effects of fuel utilisation on the performance of SOFC/gas turbine combined power generation systems, Journal of Mechanical Science and Technology, 31, 6, 3091-3100

W. Zhang et al., 2005, Simulation of a tubular solid oxide fuel cell stack using AspenPlusTM unit operation models, Energy Conversion and Management, 46, 2, 181-196

W. Doherty et al., 2010, Computer simulation of a biomass gasification-solid oxide fuel cell power system using Aspen Plus, Energy, 35, 12,4545-4555

T. R. Tanim, 2012, Modelling of a 5kWe Solid Oxide Fuel Cell Based Auxiliary Power Unit Operating on JP-8 Fuel

Antonis Kokossis, Michael C. Georgiadis, Efstratios N. Pistikopoulos (Eds.)
PROCEEDINGS OF THE 33rd European Symposium on Computer Aided Process Engineering
(ESCAPE33), June 18-21, 2023, Athens, Greece

# Heat pumping and renewable energy integration for decarbonizing brewery industry and district heating

Daniel Flórez-Orrego[a,b], Meire Ribeiro Domingos[a], François Maréchal[a]

[a]*IPESE, Federal Polytechnic School of Lausanne, Switzerland,* [b]*School of Mines, National University of Colombia, Colombia, daniel.florezorrego@epfl.ch.*

## Abstract

The energy integration of brewery plants and urban agglomerations has many benefits in terms of rational energy use and reduced environmental impact, especially during scenarios of uncertain supply chain and volatile market prices. In fact, the diversification of the energy inputs along with the waste heat upgrading through the implementation of optimal energy integration systems become crucial for defining the new energy pathways towards a sustainable and robust energy security. The enhanced waste heat recovery and the residues upgrading also increase the revenues of the industrial energy systems, as they can be used to supply the energy demands of urban agglomerations. Yet, the combination of a large number of energy technologies and the time-varying energy demands calls for the application of a systematic approach capable of identifying the operating conditions and arrangements that minimize the energy resources consumption without impairing the financial feasibility. Thus, in this work, a mixed integer linear problem is solved using OSMOSE platform in order to determine the most profitable arrangement that meets supply and demand profiles of the industrial and urban systems when different energy conversion technologies are considered. More precisely, this analysis sheds light on the relevance of relying on a combination of renewable (e.g. solar, anaerobic digestion, heat pumps) and nonrenewable (e.g. natural gas-based) solutions to supply the time-varying electricity and heating demands of a beer factory that settles nearby a city, which also has variable energy demands. In this way, the optimal load distribution between components such as internal combustion engines and high temperature heat pumps can be achieved. The incremental capital cost between the typical and integrated brewery scenarios (5.3 M€/year) is offset by an incremental operating income, leading to an incremental total revenue of about 66.4 M€/year in the integrated scenario. As a result, more stringent environmental and economic scenarios, triggered by a shortage of fossil resources, could be endured thanks to the higher flexibility achieved using a set of renewable, and heat pump and power-to-gas technologies.

**Keywords**: heat pumping, renewable energy, brewery, district heating

## 1. Introduction

Brewing is responsible for a large amount of carbon dioxide emissions, derived not only from the fermentation process, but also from burning natural gas and from the indirect emissions associated to the supply chains of the utilities consumed (e.g. electricity from grid). Fermentation yields approximately three times more $CO_2$ (about 30 g per liter of beer), than what is actually required per each batch of beer, including brewing, canning, and bottling. Some breweries have already implemented $CO_2$ management strategies, although it may become prohibitively expensive, unless efforts to find additional and more profitable uses for $CO_2$ capture are realized. In this regard, brewery, as well as other food and biomass-based industries (e.g. sugar and ethanol mills, pulp and paper plants, etc.) (Domingos 2022, Telini 2022), may benefit from a promotion of net negative $CO_2$

emissions in future scenarios of energy transition. Indeed, biomass-based industries that capture more $CO_2$ than they can use may choose either to sell it, use it in greenhouses to boost plant growth, or trade and inject the biogenic emissions, which directly contributes to a depletion of the $CO_2$ in the atmosphere and increases the plant revenues (Nakashima 2019, Domingos 2021). On the other hand, the increasing integration of renewable, yet intermittent energy technologies, is an option to decarbonize the industrial applications and calls for better carbon management strategies, such as its storage and conversion into synthetic natural (SNG) gas using power-to-gas systems subject to seasonal availability of inexpensive electricity (Flórez-Orrego 2022). Moreover, the surplus power and low-grade waste heat derived from additional energy conversion technologies in the beer industry can be used to supply the energy requirements of an urban agglomeration that settles nearby the brewery process. As a result, synergistic waste heat and mass upgrading processes, along with suitable fuel storage and utilization approaches may help tackling inherent drawbacks of the renewable energy systems and decarbonize the process heating demand, while increasing the process revenues and reducing the cooling duty. Thus, in this work, the integration of more advanced energy technologies, such as supercritical heat pumping and energy storage and conversion systems is compared to the conventional operating scenario of a brewery plant and a city district heating based on natural gas. The cross-cutting challenges to develop and adopt those low carbon industrial heat and power technologies are weighed using thermo-economic and environmental indicators. As a result, despite more equipment and electrification are required, the potential reduction of $CO_2$ emissions and the calculated incremental revenues point towards a promising path for beer industry decarbonization while maintaining high profits.

## 2. Process description and methods

Figure 1 shows the flowsheet of the industrial brewery along with the cogeneration and storage technologies able to be integrated. The brewery process starts when milled barley and corn are mixed with water and heated at 65°C, so that a sugar-rich wort is produced due to saccharification of the mash. In the lautering process, the wort is filtered and the husk can be exported or sent to a biodigestion unit. The filtered mixture is boiled slightly above 100°C (10% wt. evaporation) and then the hops are added. Next, it is stirred and the trub is removed in a centrifuge. The mixture is cooled down to 10°C and goes through the fermentation process, wherein the sugars are converted to alcohols and carbon dioxide using yeasts under anaerobic conditions by releasing heat. Fermented wort is matured at low temperature and then chilled before the yeast is eliminated by filtration. Cold water is mixed up to obtaining the desired alcohol concentration. The pasteurization process occurs hereafter by heating the mixture up to 70°C and cooled to 5°C. The beer is stored and bottled. The bottle cleaning process is also energy consuming and produces waste water. Meanwhile, the utility system options include gas fired boiler, combustion engines with waste heat recovery, sub and supercritical heat pumps, carbon abatement unit, water cooling and refrigerator, biodigestion, electrolysis, methanation, liquefaction, storage and injection compression units. SNG and $CO_2$ are stored in liquid form at -162°C and -50°C, respectively. The district heating relies on a $CO_2$ network system that supplies the domestic hot water, space heating, air conditioning and refrigeration demands (Fig. 2) (Suciu 2019). The waste heat released by the industrial process and the utility systems can be upgraded using surplus electricity and heat pumping systems. In this work, two scenarios are analyzed, i.e. a typical brewery operating using natural gas and electricity from the grid, and other scenario integrating the energy conversion and storage systems shown in Fig. 1, but still allowing for electricity import. Optimal flows have been determined using Osmose Lua platform (Yoo, Lessard et al. 2015), which handles a MILP that identifies the best energy technologies and operating conditions that minimize the operating costs subject to feasibility and minimum energy requirements constraints, shown in Eqs. (1-6).

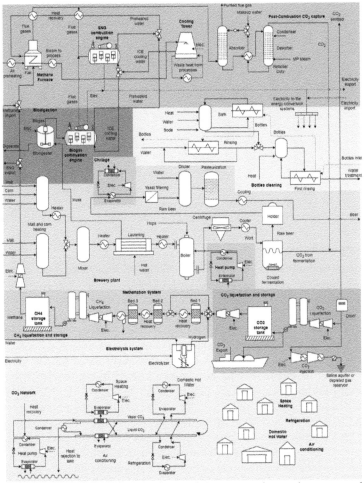

Figure 1. Flowsheet of the brewery and potential cogeneration and storage technologies, and the district heating $CO_2$ network.

The binary $y_w$ and load factor $f_w$ optimization variables are used to define the best size and arrangement based on assumed prices of material and energy inputs and $CO_2$ tax.
$c_{NG}$ *(€/kWh): 1;* $c_{EE}$ *(€/kWh): 0.35 (Jan/Feb/Nov/Dec), 0.001(other months);* $tax_{CO2}$ *(€/t):100:*

$$\underset{\substack{f_\omega,\, y_\omega \\ R_r,\, W}}{\textbf{Min}} \left[ \begin{array}{l} f_{\substack{material \\ inputs,\omega}} \times (c \cdot m)_{\substack{material \\ inputs,\omega}} + f_{EnvEm} \times \left( m_{CO_2} \cdot tax \right) - f_{\substack{material \\ outputs,\omega}} \times (c \cdot m)_{\substack{material \\ output,\omega}} \\ \pm f_{EE} \times (c \cdot W)_{EE} + \dfrac{Z_{equip} \times Ann\_factor}{N_{hours\ per\ year}} \end{array} \right] \quad \text{(Eq.1)}$$

s.t. $\displaystyle\sum_{\omega=1}^{N_\omega} f_\omega q_{\omega,r} + \sum_{i=1}^{N} Q_{i,r} + R_{r+1} - R_r = 0 \quad \forall r = 1..N$      (Eq.2)

$\displaystyle\sum_{\omega=1}^{N_\omega} f_\omega W_\omega + \sum_{\substack{chemical \\ units}} W_{net} + W_{imp} - W_{\exp} = 0$      (Eq.3)

$$f_{\min,\omega}\mathbf{y}_\omega \leq f_\omega \leq f_{\max,\omega}\mathbf{y}_\omega \quad \forall \omega = 1 .. N_\omega \tag{Eq.4}$$

$$W_{imp} \geq 0,\; W_{\exp} \geq 0 \tag{Eq.5}$$

$$R_1 = 0,\; R_{N+1} = 0,\; R_r \geq 0 \tag{Eq.6}$$

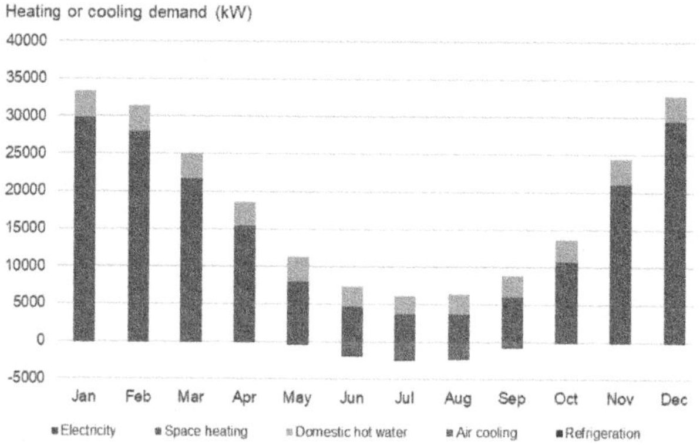

Figure 2. Seasonal variation of the heating and cooling demands of the city.

## 3. Results and discussion

For both typical and integrated beer production scenarios, the total malt, corn, soda and water consumption are 129, 11 and 19 kt/year and 973,263 m³/year, respectively, for a total production of 892,534 m³/year of beer and 38 kt/year of husk with a potential biogas yield of 75 Nm³/t$_{husk}$. Annual direct $CO_2$ emission from natural gas use (64.95 GWh/year) in the typical scenario is 13 kt/year, whereas 24 kt/year are vented from fermentation process and other 6 kt/year are related to indirect emissions of NG/EE supply chains (1.15 kt/year for NG, and 5.14 kt/year for EE), entailing a yearly tax of 4.2 M€. In the typical brewery scenario, the chiller system consumes up to 15 GWh/year of EE, being the second largest EE consumer, after the city (44.6 GWh/year of EE, 12.3 GWh/year for space heating heat pumps). Meanwhile, in the advanced scenario, all husk is biodigested to cut down fossil fuel consumption. Husk-derived biogas falls short to supply the energy demands of the plant, thus requiring to import 133.1 GWh/year of electricity to drive the electrolysis unit (76.6 GWh/year, 12,532 m³$_{water}$/year, 1,39 kt$_{H2}$/year). Electricity import is about 41.25% of the total power consumed in the integrated brewery plant, leading to indirect emissions of 8.34 kt/year. In the integrated scenario, 16 kt/year of $CO_2$ from the fermentation unit are also injected and only 8 kt/year are emitted. Apart from biogas, the SNG produced by methanation (39 GWh/year) is also used in internal combustion engines to cogenerate the heat and power required by the whole system. Other major power consumers are s$CO_2$ heat pump (11.9 GWh/year), while gas liquefaction, recompression and injection compression together only demand about 3 GWh/year of EE. Carbon credits (1.6 M€/year) associated to the injection of $CO_2$ definitely contribute to the increased revenues of the integrated brewery scenario. It is worth noticing that the carbon capture unit becomes prohibitively expensive and is not activated by the optimization routine. Figure 3 shows the integrated curves of the typical (Fig. 3 left) and the integrated (right) brewery scenarios. The blue curve represents the heat cascaded plot of the utility systems, whereas the red curve corresponds to process units (brewery plant). The typical scenario, based on the natural gas combustion, not only has higher associated $CO_2$ emissions, but also entails larger exergy destruction due to the use of high-grade energy resources, such as natural gas, to only generate steam and hot water (Fig. 3 left). In fact, self-sufficient zones indicate a potential to install a temperature-gliding supercritical heat pump to partly deliver the heating demand at temperatures between 50 - 100°C. The heat pumping of the waste heat available at much lower temperatures reduces the need of water cooling, while provides the refrigeration duty. But it also implies a compromise between the utilization of the combustion gases of the engines and the heat pump devices to deliver waste heat to the brewery and the district heating. Anyhow, surplus electricity generated in the integrated brewery scenario allows to simultaneously export electricity to drive the heat pumps of the $CO_2$ network and capitalize on the low-grade waste heat of all the energy technologies to reduce the environmental footprint of the heating processes.

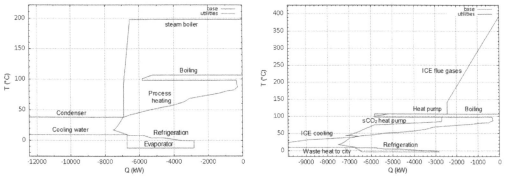

Figure 3. Integrated curves of the typical (left) and the integrated (right) brewery scenarios.

Finally, Figure 4 shows the yearly variation of the storage tanks levels. It is observed that the $CO_2$ tank level increases gradually starting from October till end of February, which coincides with the emptying of the SNG tanks during the period of more expensive electricity price (Nov.-Feb.). Thus, optimal $CO_2$ management implies a higher monthly power consumption during the months with surplus cheap electricity generation (e.g. excess solar, nuclear or hydro power), which in turn can be stored as fuels.

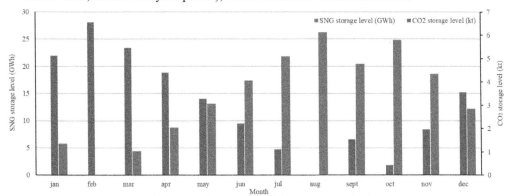

Figure 4. Seasonal variation of the storage tanks levels.

As a result, the operation cost is optimized, because the system uses the most affordable energy resources only when they are available and convert them into other valuable resources that can be used to supply the variable energy demands. In this way, the upgrading of the industrial residues and their ingenious reutilization increases the plant energy security, and contributes to increased revenues of the whole system. Indeed, the incremental capital expenditure between the typical and the integrated brewery scenarios (5.3 M€/year) is completely offset by an incremental operating income (71.7 M€/year), thus leading to an incremental total revenue of about 66.4 M€/year in the second scenario. Naturally, the proposed approach represents a riskier investment, since it depends on the commodities prices, the carbon tax, the emissions trading system, the reliability of the newly integrated energy systems and the space budget of the brewery unit. Nonetheless, the proposed setup sheds light on the thermoeconomic and environmental feasibility of integrating advanced energy technologies for tackling the problem of carbon management and intermittency of renewable energy.

## 4. Conclusions

In this work, the integration of various energy conversion and storage technologies to decarbonize a beer production industry is discussed in the light of thermodynamic and environmental indicators and economic revenues. Future economic and environmental costs of natural gas calls for more electrification to supply heating in a more efficient way (HPs and HTHPs). Meanwhile, the integration of husk biodigestion process, along with the reuse of $CO_2$ from fermentation as a source to store intermittent renewable energy in the form of synthetic natural gas may help to avoid the import of fossil natural gas and still provide half of the power required by the brewery and the heat pumps of the district heating network. The import of electricity is still largely required to balance the capacity of the cogeneration systems, thus, more environmentally friendly and cheaper electricity generation technologies are crucial for the process heat decarbonization in the industry. The carbon trading is an important factor that may boost the deployment of some energy conversion approaches, such as power-to-gas systems, and also promote better $CO_2$ management approaches. As a result, chemical energy storage systems allowed for a cost-beneficial operating condition, in which the incremental capital expenditure seems to be offset by a substantial gain in plant revenues.

## Acknowledgments

The authors thank the Swiss Federal Office of Energy grant no. SI/502336-01. First author also thanks the Colombian Ministry of Science, Technology and Innovation.

## References

Domingos, M. E. G., Flórez-Orrego, D., Teles dos Santos, M., Oliveira Junior, S., Maréchal, F. (2022). "Techno-economic and environmental analysis of methanol and dimethyl ether production from syngas in a kraft pulp process." Computers & Chemical Engineering: 107810.

Domingos, M. E. G., Florez-Orrego, D., Teles, M., Velasquez, H., de Oliveira Jr, S. (2021). "Exergy and environmental analysis of black liquor upgrading gasification in an integrated kraft pulp and ammonia production plant." International Journal of Exergy **35**(1): 35-65.

Flórez-Orrego, D., Domingos, M. E. G., Maréchal, F. (2022). A systematic framework for the multi-time integration of industrial complexes and urban systems. 7th International Conference on Contemporary Problems of Thermal Engineering - CPOTE, 20th-23th September, 2022. Warsaw, Poland.

Nakashima, R. N., Flórez-Orrego, D., de Oliveira Junior, S. (2019). "Integrated anaerobic digestion and gasification processes for upgrade of ethanol biorefinery residues." Journal of Power Technologies **99**(2): 104-114.

Suciu, R., Stadler, P., Kantor, I., Girardin, L., Maréchal, F. (2019). "Systematic Integration of Energy-Optimal Buildings With District Networks." Energies **12**(15): 1-38.

Telini, R., Florez-Orrego, D., Oliveira Jr., S. (2022). "Techno-economic and environmental assessment of ammonia production from residual bagasse gasification: a decarbonization pathway for nitrogen fertilizers." Frontiers in Energy Research **10**(881263).

Yoo, M., L. Lessard, M. Kermani and F. Maréchal (2015). OSMOSE Lua: A Unified Approach to Energy Systems Integration with Life Cycle Assessment. 12th International conference PSE 2015 and 25th International conference ESCAPE 2015., Copenhagen, Denmark.

Antonis Kokossis, Michael C. Georgiadis, Efstratios N. Pistikopoulos (Eds.)
PROCEEDINGS OF THE 33rd European Symposium on Computer Aided Process Engineering
(ESCAPE33), June 18-21, 2023, Athens, Greece

# Dynamic Simulation to Verify Operability of LNG Plants with Post Combustion Carbon Capture

Jaleel Valappil[a]

[a]*Bechtel Energy, 3000 Post Oak Boulevard, Houston, TX - 77407, USA*

## Abstract

Global warming and climate change caused by greenhouse gases have received widespread and growing concern in recent years. The natural gas/LNG industry has seen tremendous over the years. Most of the facilities use gas turbine drivers which emit significant amount of flue gases with $CO_2$. The carbon capture and storage technology (CCS) is one opportunity to capture $CO_2$ emissions from flue gases of combustions processes. The retrofitting of existing natural gas facilities with a carbon dioxide capture offers a promising opportunity to achieve the global target reduction in $CO_2$ emissions. Previous studies have examined the integration of power plants with carbon capture units and the resulting operability challenges and optimization opportunities. Integrating power plant with carbon capture simulation models for analysis has also been performed in the past [1]. To get a full understanding of the transient characteristics of a hydrocarbon facility with post combustion carbon capture (PCC), both the units can be combined in an integrated dynamic model for analysis. A case study is presented where the exhaust from LNG facility is send to carbon capture unit. Several valuable recommendations were derived from the study to ensure the operability of the integrated facility.

**Keywords**: Post combustion carbon capture, Natural gas, Dynamic simulation, Operability, Amine system.

## 1. Introduction

Global warming and climate change caused by greenhouse gases have received widespread and growing concern in recent years. At the United Nations Climate Change Conference in 2015, 196 countries accepted the Paris agreement to reduce their carbon emissions with the goal to keep the global warming below 2 °C. Further, The COP 27 conference held in Sharm-El-Sheikh recognized that limiting global warming to 1.5 °C requires rapid, deep, and sustained reductions in global greenhouse gas emissions of 43% by 2030 relative to the 2019 level. The natural gas/Liquefied Natural Gas (LNG) industry has seen rapid growth over the years with several grassroots plant built around the world to meet the global energy needs. Most of the facilities use gas turbine drivers which emit significant amount of flue gases with $CO_2$. In addition, fired heater used in these facilities also emit $CO_2$. $CO_2$ is also emitted by acid gas removal processes in the pre-treatment of feed gas prior to liquefaction. The carbon capture and storage technology (CCS) is one opportunity to capture $CO_2$ emissions from flue gases of combustions processes. The captured $CO_2$ can be stored in underground formations afterwards. LNG facilities are expected to be designed or retrofitted with CCS in future [4]. However, most of the LNG plants in operation currently are not designed for carbon capture. For this reason, post-combustion $CO_2$ capture (PCC) has an advantage over other alternatives because the technology can simply be implemented as an 'end-of-the-pipe' retrofit without the need for significant changes to existing facilities. The most widely used technology for post combustion $CO_2$ capture is amine solvent-based process.

With the retrofitting of existing natural gas facilities with a carbon dioxide capture, any operational disturbances in the hydrocarbon facility can impact the operation of the carbon capture in an adverse way and vice versa. Accounting for these interactions in the design of carbon capture facility is important in ensuring operation of the integrated facility. This paper discusses the integration of an amine-based post combustion carbon capture unit with an LNG facility and the use of dynamic models to account for resulting effects of the integration on the LNG facility operation.

In order to get a full understanding of the transient characteristics of a hydrocarbon facility with PCC, both the units can be combined in an integrated dynamic model for analysis. Dynamic simulation can play a pivotal role in identifying any operational bottlenecks at transient conditions for the integrated hydrocarbon and $CO_2$ capture plants. The integrated model can also be valuable to establish operational strategies on both sides to account for the various upstream scenarios. As an alternative, individual unit models can be used to establish boundary conditions for each other to get a representative behavior of the entire facility. A case study is presented where the exhaust from LNG facility is send to carbon capture unit. The dynamic model of the Waste Heat Recovery Unit (WHRU), duct work and the associated equipment is used to ensure that the various transient scenarios in LNG facility or in the PCC unit does not adversely impact the LNG plant operation.

## 2. Integration of Post Combustion Carbon Capture Systems with Existing Plants

Post-combustion attractive for new LNG plants or as a retrofit to existing plants is an attractive option as it can be implemented without major modifications to the existing facility. There is also a good amount of experience with post combustion capture in power plants which makes it a less risky option. Also, downtime in carbon capture plant does not have to affect LNG production as the flue gas can be diverted to atmosphere with appropriate design [1]. The use of amine-based solvent for post-combustion $CO_2$ capture (PCC) has attracted considerable interest in $CO_2$ capture. This is a proven technology for $CO_2$ capture to date. Existing PCC pilot plants already demonstrate the feasibility of $CO_2$ removal with amine solvent from flue gas albeit at modest scale. Mono ethanolamine (MEA) is the most commonly used solvent in chemical absorption processes for $CO_2$. A typical PCC process consists of two main columns, an absorber and a regenerator. These may be packed or tray columns, but packed columns are typically used due to their larger contact area. In the absorber, lean amine solvent is counter-currently contacted with flue gas produced from the LNG plant and $CO_2$ is chemically absorbed from the flue gas. The $CO_2$

rich solvent is regenerated in the stripper using heat from either the hot oil, steam or other source as the heating medium.

The integration of post combustion carbon capture with LNG plant is done by directing the flue gas from gas turbines to amine-based carbon capture unit. This will include additional ducting, dampers and possibly a blower to increase flue gas pressure. A Waste Heat Recovery Unit (WHRU) may be used to further recover the heat from flue gas. The heat requirements for the reboiler can be provided by the existing hot oil or steam system in the facility.

The following aspects are important when integrating post combustion carbon capture into an existing facility considered to ensure reliable and safe operation [2].

**Flexibility of operation**: Ability to operate in an acceptable manner over a range of steady-state conditions. For example, this can include operation at turndown rates (Half rate/other) due to changing ambient conditions or other operational reasons. Also, operation with no LNG production (with refrigeration compressors running in recycle with gas turbines partially loaded).

**Controllability:** Ability to recover from process disturbances and move to new set-points in a measured and timely fashion. This is dependent on both the design of process and the underlying process control schemes.

**Start-up and shutdown:** The startup and shutdown of LNG facility/PCC unit is a key operating scenario for the amine system that can induce major changes.

**Reliability/Safety of operation:** Ability to accommodate equipment failures and trips in a safe manner. This includes trips of various equipment, fail closing of valves etc.

The design and integration post combustion carbon capture needs to account for the various operational scenarios and disturbances in the LNG facility and the carbon capture unit. One of the main concerns with integration is the impact of upsets in PCC facility affecting the LNG production. Large variations in gas turbine exhaust pressure can cause the turbine driver to trip, stopping the LNG production with a very significant economic cost.  The key scenarios in LNG plant that impact the integrated system include LNG train trip/facility wide shut down, trip of individual gas turbines and turndown to half rate/standby mode with refrigeration compressors in recycle. Startup of refrigeration compressors/PCC unit is also an important case to consider. The scenarios to consider on the PCC side include trip of flue gas blower, fail closing of flue gas damper and other operational upsets in PCC unit. The operability of the integrated LNG – PCC plant can be studied with high fidelity dynamic simulation tools to ensure the design can handle these scenarios.

*2.1. Application of Dynamic Models in Design and Analysis*

Dynamic simulation utilizing rigorous mathematical models has become an influential tool in the process design, design validation, control system verification, startup support and troubleshooting. Many recent developments in the simulation software and technology have led to the development of large-scale dynamic models and their use in the entire project life. Dynamic simulation can be used to evaluate the operational response and controllability of a plant for a wide range of transient conditions, which may include disturbances due to equipment malfunction or human error, fluctuations in ambient temperature, or changes in feed conditions. Dynamic models can also be used for development of online process optimization strategies is essential to ensure the process operates under optimal conditions.

The scope of the dynamic modeling for the integrated LNG-PCC facility can be divided into three areas as shown in Figure 1. There are different options (model scope/methodology) to study the overall behavior of the integrated LNG plant – PCC facility. This can be selected based on the scope and objectives of the analysis.

For a rigorous understanding of the transient characteristics of an LNG plant with PCC, a combined dynamic model is preferred. The transient responses of the LNG plant are well understood and has been studied over the years. The behavior of integrated LNG-PCC facility is a relatively recent development and can benefit from integrated model-based analysis. The dynamic behavior of amine system is more complicated and less understood compared to that of the LNG plant.

Other option is to have individual models of the three sections of the integrated facility. This way, individual models can be run and used as the boundary condition for the next model. The case study given below is intended to look at upsets in the interconnecting units affecting the LNG facility and vice versa.

The modeling of LNG facilities is normally carried out during the detailed design. This could be a plantwide model developed for engineering studies or an Operator Training simulator (OTS). The use of these models for design and operation of LNG plants have become more widespread in the recent years [4]. The dynamic modeling of interconnecting ductwork, WHRU and flue gas blower can also be performed with available commercial dynamic modeling tools.

Many of the commercially available process simulation software can be used to develop a dynamic model of amine-based $CO_2$ capture processes [3]. The first option to model this is to use equilibrium-based modeling approach. The equilibrium-based modelling assumes that liquid and vapor phases reach equilibrium at theoretical stages and perfect mixing occurs at each stage. The equilibrium-based approach adjusts the performance at each stage with an efficiency correction factor (tray efficiency for tray columns or height equivalent of a theoretical plate (HETP) for packed). The equilibrium approach simplifies the mass transfer process to reduce the complexity of the model, neglecting the limitations of mass and heat transfer.

Equilibrium is rarely acquired in a reactive $CO_2$ absorption process especially during dynamic operation. The rate-based approach is more rigorous and considers the actual rates of mass and heat transfer including chemical reactions. The reaction depends on the kinetics regime and can either be considered instantaneous or kinetically controlled. Rate based approach is preferred for modeling reactive columns as in the PCC process. The disadvantage of this approach is the computational requirements as rigorous rate-based approach results in extended systems of equations to be solved at each integration step.

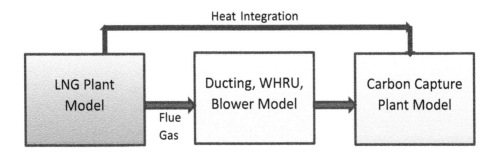

Figure 1: Different section of an Integrated LNG-PCC unit dynamic model

## 3. Case Study – Analysis of Operability of LNG Plant with PCC Unit

This case study evaluates the integration of amine-based PCC unit with an LNG facility utilizing gas turbines to drive refrigeration compressors. The addition of the PCC unit involves introduction of additional ductwork, bypass dampers (to atmosphere and to PCC unit) and a flue gas blower to increase pressure. The flue gas is further cooled a heat exchanger and then routed to the Absorber where it is contacted with amine solvent in the Absorber to remove the $CO_2$ from flue gas. The $CO_2$ depleted flue gas is then released to atmosphere. The main concern with the addition of PCC unit is the possibility of impacting LNG production during various transient upsets in the PCC unit. The gas turbine exhaust outlet must be maintained within a pressure range to avoid a reduction in power output or a total turbine shutdown. Several scenarios were studied to evaluate the transient impact on the gas turbine outlet conditions. A dynamic simulation model of the interconnecting unit (WHRU, flue gas blower, other equipment, and associated piping) was developed to perform this study.

The flue gas blower trip is simulated to verify that the pressure at GT outlet can be maintained within limits so that LNG plant operation is not affected. As soon as the flue gas blower is tripped, the damper to stack is signaled to open to avoid the excessive pressure increase in the system. The blower will coast-down with speed response based on the rotational inertia of the string. The pressure at the GT outlet is shown in Figure 2. As can be seen, the pressure drops rapidly as the damper is opened along with the blower trip. This preemptive action prevented the pressure at gas turbine outlet from increasing due to trip of blower.

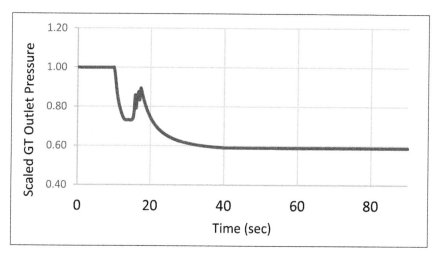

Figure 2: Variation in gas turbine outlet pressure during flue gas blower trip.

The trip of a Gas Turbine (GT) will result in rapid change in temperature and flow rate of flue gas at the inlet of WHRU. The variation of flue gas flowrate and temperature from gas turbine vendor is used. Once the GT is tripped, the flue gas flow reduces, decreasing the pressure at the inlet of flue gas blower. The flue gas blower must be shutdown to prevent significant vacuum formation at suction. Shutting the flue gas bower too early can result in over pressuring the duct as the flue gas flow continues for some time. An alternate option is to shut down the flue gas blower and open the damper to stack as soon as the GT trips. This will prevent over pressuring the duct as the flue gas flow gradually comes down. This operational procedure and timing was tested in the dynamic simulation and the pressure profile at the GT outlet for this scenario is shown in Figure 3.

Several other scenarios were also evaluated with this model to identify any operability concerns. These included dampers fail closing, shutdown of PCC unit, startup of PCC unit and others. The transition from operation without PCC unit to PCC unit was simulated to verify the operating procedure for this transition.

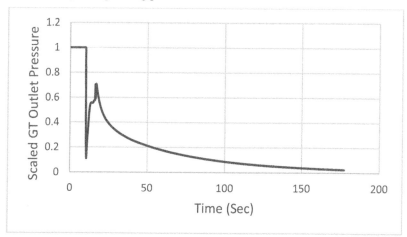

Figure 2: Variation in gas turbine outlet ducting pressure during a gas turbine trip.

## 4. Conclusions and Recommendations

The concerns about global warming have spurred interest in application of carbon capture and storage in the hydrocarbon industry. This paper examined the benefits of using first principle based commercially available dynamic simulation tools to optimize and enhance the design of integrated of PCC - LNG facility. The key operating scenarios that impact the facility operation were selected and simulated.

The insights gained from dynamic simulation was valuable in verifying the operability and identifying design parameters. The key operational recommendations included 1. Shutting down the flue gas blower when damper fail closes and during the GT trip, 2. Opening bypass damper when a damper fail closes or during flue gas blower trip and 3. Sequencing of the blower startup and damper opening during startup. The opening time for the dampers and the sequence of operation of various components were verified using simulation.

Further optimization of the integrated facility is possible using rigorous integrated dynamic models for LNG plant and the PCC unit. This will enable optimizing the entire facility dynamically by selecting the right extent of carbon capture while considering the energy cost (Mainly in the amine regenerator reboilers). This has been studied for power plants in the past and can be extended to LNG facilities.

## References

1.  Bui, M., Gunawan, I., Verheyen, V., Feron, P., Meuleman, E. and Adeloju, S., 2014, Dynamic modelling and optimisation of flexible operation in post-combustion CO2 capture plants—A review, Computers and Chemical Engineering, 61 (2014) 245-265.
2.  Chukukwa, A., Enaasen, N., Kvamsdal, H.M. and Hillestad, M., 2012, Dynamic modeling of post-combustion CO2 capture using amines – A review, Energy Procedia, 23(2012) 82-91.
3.  Mokhatab, S., Mak, J., Valappil, J. and Wood, D., 2014, Handbook of Liquefied Natural Gas, Mokhatab, S., Mak, J., Valappil, J. and Wood, D., Elsevier Publications.
4.  Techno-economic evaluation of CO2 capture in LNG, IEAGHG Technical Report, October 2019.

Antonis Kokossis, Michael C. Georgiadis, Efstratios N. Pistikopoulos (Eds.)
PROCEEDINGS OF THE 33rd European Symposium on Computer Aided Process Engineering
(ESCAPE33), June 18-21, 2023, Athens, Greece

# Optimization of wind farm layout and cable network topology under generalized wake effects

Demian J. Presser,[a,b] M. Josefina Fiorini,[a] Diego C. Cafaro[a,b]

[a]*Fac. de Ing. Química, UNL, Santiago del Estero 2829, Santa Fe (3000), Argentina*
[b]*INTEC, UNL-CONICET, Guemes 3450, Santa Fe (3000), Argentina*

## Abstract

The world is undergoing a significant change of the energy matrix towards a sustainable future. Wind energy has proved to be one of the key players in this transition. A new historical record of installed capacity was achieved in 2021, currently supplying 7% of the world energy demand. The optimal design of wind farms is a still challenging problem for industry, aiming at maximizing power generation while minimizing costs and energy loss, also accounting for uncertain wind speed and direction. We propose a mixed integer linear programming formulation coupled to a wake effect computation algorithm to optimally locate and connect turbines in a wind farm under uncertain conditions. In contrast to previous contributions, the proposed framework accounts for combined wake effects that can significantly compromise turbine efficiency and drastically affect optimal wind farm designs and cable network topologies. An illustrative case shows improvements of 6.8% relative to state-of-the art approaches.

**Keywords**: Wind Farm, Layout, Design, Cable Network, Wake Effect, MILP

## 1. Introduction

The total power produced by a wind farm is directly related to the number of turbines installed. However, the location of these turbines has a considerable impact on their performance due to wind interference interactions known as wake effects. These phenomena occur when upstream turbines reduce the wind speed for downstream turbines. Upstream turbines produce a wake on its back side where the wind speed is reduced, yielding poor performance and eventual damage in downstream turbines. Naturally, interference effects across the farm depend on the wind speed and direction, which vary frequently. Even more, combined wake effects coming from multiple turbine interactions may severely impact the performance and the need for maintenance. Therefore, the optimally design of wind farms over a given region usually seeks to maximize the number of turbines installed while minimizing the impact of interferences. Sparse turbine locations reduce wake effects, but the total energy produced over the same region will be rather poor due to the limited number of turbines installed.

On the other hand, turbines must be connected to collection stations to further deliver power to the grid. Cable networks and stations can represent up to 30% of the cost of a wind farm, since more than one collection hub may be required depending on the spatial dispersion of turbines. In this sense, sparser designs to avoid wake effects, regardless of the wind direction, can significantly impact cable interconnection and stations costs.

One of the earliest contributions to the optimal design of wind farms can be found in Mosetti et al. (1994). The authors use the Jensen (1983) model to find the best arrangement of wind turbines over a region based on genetic algorithms. Herbet-Acero et al. (2009) compare different heuristic approaches based on the Jensen's model. Fischetti et al. (2015) propose a mixed integer linear programming (MILP) model to optimize wind farm layout accounting for wake effects between pairs of turbines. A thorough review of wind farm layout optimization using Jensen's model is later presented by Shakoor et al. (2016). More recently, Mohki et al. (2020) and Bellat et al. (2022) use meta-heuristics to address the cable interconnection problem for a wind farm with a given layout. Finally, Fischetti el al. (2022) extend their approach to address one of the first problems integrating wind farm layout and cable routing. They develop Benders-like cuts and a tailored branch-and-cut strategy to deal with combinatorial complexity. Nevertheless, wake effects are still assessed between every pair of turbines. In this work, we simultaneously address wind farm layout and cable network problems under generalized wake effects. A novel algorithm accurately assesses combined effects prior to solve an MILP model dealing with interferences of higher order.

## 2. The wind farm layout and cable network problem

### 2.1. Problem statement

The wind farm layout and cable network problem aims to optimally place turbines, collection stations and cable interconnections between them. The problem can be stated as follows. Given: (a) a set of potential sites $i \in I$ for the location of wind turbines and $s \in S$ for collection stations; (b) power curves of the turbines; (c) possible wind scenarios ($\pi(u)$ is the probability of scenario $u \in U = D \times V$, with direction $d \in D$ and speed $v \in V$); (d) the loss due to wake effects between potential turbine locations for each wind scenario; and (e) different types of cable and collection stations with capacities $pl \in P$ and $c \in C$, respectively, for conveying and collecting power. We seek to determine: (i) the optimal number and location of wind turbines in the field, (ii) the optimal placement of stations to collect power, and (iii) the optimal cable interconnection between selected turbines and stations, in order to maximize the profit of the project over a long-term time horizon. Since wind behavior is uncertain, the optimal solution does not necessarily correspond to the best arrangement for a particular direction. One must weight all possible wind directions and corresponding speeds.

### 2.2. Assumptions

a. Wind profiles are predicted from statistical data, discretized into directions ($D$), speeds ($V$) and possible scenarios ($U = D \times V$). Figure 1 illustrates an example with $D = \{$N, NE, E, SE, S, SW, W, NW$\}$ and $V = \{$Low, Medium, High$\}$.

b. Jensen (1983) model is used to estimate the impact of wake effects between turbines. However, any other model can be also used in the proposed algorithm.

c. The terrain is assumed to be flat and all turbines have the same height.

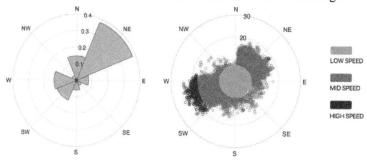

**Figure 1** – Histogram for wind direction probabilities (left) and speed discretization (right)

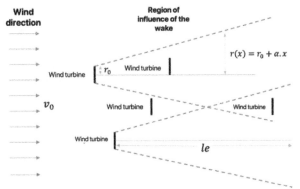

**Figure 2** - Illustration of the area of interference due to wake effects.

# 3. Interferences and wake effect computation

Prior to optimization, an efficient algorithm is required to estimate interferences (i.e., productivity loss due to wake effects) in wind farms. Previous contributions underestimate the impact of interferences by only considering pairs of turbines. Instead, we evaluate impacts of higher order, when multiple turbines combine their wake effects. We address two phenomena: chained and overlapping effects. Chained effects refer to the successive wind energy loss when three or more turbines are placed one behind the other following the wind direction. On the other hand, two wind turbines may affect a third turbine in combination when their wakes overlap. The wake can be visualized as a conical region where the initial air velocity ($v_0$) is reduced (see Figure 2). There is also a distance *le* beyond which the wake effect vanishes. If $r_0$ is the radius of the wind turbine including the blades, $r(x)$ defines the radius of the cone as a function of the distance ($x$).

*3.1. Algorithm for computing interferences*
Let $K$ be the set of wind directions and $WS(k)$ the set of velocities for each direction. Let $INT_{i,j,k}$ be a 0-1 parameter indicating if a turbine placed in $i$ interferes another turbine in $j$ under direction $k$. Let $vr_{i,j,k}$ be the proportion of the original wind speed that can be harvested by the turbine in $j$ due to interference with $i$ in direction $k$. Finally, $C_T$ is the thrust coefficient of the turbines. The algorithm can be outlined as follows.

**Algorithm**
For all $k$, set $i'=i_0$ as the first node to be reached by wind in such direction.
1. Build a line $R_k$ orthogonal to direction $k$, passing through $i'$.
2. Compute the minimum distance $d_{ik}$ from each potential location $i$ to $R_k$.
3. Sort the elements in $I$ by increasing $d_{ik}$.
4. For all $i' \in I$ and $i > i'$:
   4.1. Let $\boldsymbol{\mu}$ be the displacement vector between $i'$ and $i$.
   4.2. Compute the module of the projection of $\boldsymbol{\mu}$ over $k$, $\lambda = |\text{proj}_k(\mu_{i',i})|$
   4.3. If $\lambda > le$, set $INT_{i',i,k}=0$; $vr_{i',i,k}=1$. Go 4.5. Else, go 4.4.
   4.4. Compute the module of the projection of $\boldsymbol{\mu}$ over $R_k$, $\gamma = |\text{proj}_{\perp k}(\mu_{i',i})|$
   4.5. If $\gamma > r(|\boldsymbol{\mu}|)$, set $INT_{i',i,k}=0$; $vr_{i',i,k}=1$. Go 4.7. Else, go 4.6.
   4.6. Node $i$ is interfered by $i'$, $INT_{i',i,k}=1$, $vr_{i',i,k}=1+\left(\sqrt{1-c_T}-1\right)\left(\frac{r0}{r}\right)^2$ (Jensen, 1983).
5. **Direct wake effects** (by-pair). Let $Vf_{i,i',k}$ be the proportion of wind speed in direction $k$ received by $i$, exclusively due to $i'$. Set $Vf_{i,i',k}= vr_{i,i',k}$.

6. **Indirect wake effects** (refinement). For all $i'$ in the ordered set $I$:

6.1. If $\sum_{i=1}^{I} INT_{i,i',k} = 0$, $Vf_{i',k}=1$, $i'$ is not interfered.

6.2. If $\sum_{i=1}^{I} INT_{i,i',k} = 1$, traverse the elements $i$ in $I$ until $INT_{i',i,k}=1$ and update received velocity as $Vf_{i',k}= vr_{i,i',k} \, Vf_{i,k}$ (chain effect).

6.3. If $\sum_{i=1}^{I} INT_{i,i',k} > 1$, add all $i$ such that $INT_{i,i',k}=1$ to set $J$. Then,

$$Vf_{i',k} = 1 - \sqrt{\sum_{j=1}^{J}(1 - Vf_{j,k} \, vr_{j,i',k})^2} \qquad \text{(overlap effect)}$$

The output of this algorithm is used to set input parameters $ip_{i',i}$ (for direct effects) and $is_{i',j,i}$ (for indirect effects) to the optimization model presented in the next section.

## 4. MILP formulation

A mixed integer linear programming (MILP) formulation is proposed to simultaneously address the optimal wind turbines location and cable network interconnection for a wind farm site. The 0-1 variable $x_i$ accounts for the location of a wind turbine in node $i$. Eq. (1) determines when two turbines $i$ and $j$ are installed ($y_{i,j} = 1$) to account for direct wake effects. Notice that minimum distances between turbines are also imposed.

$$x_i + x_j - 1 \leq y_{i,j} \qquad \forall (i,j), \qquad \text{with } y_{i,j} = 0 \text{ if } d(i,j) < D_{min} \qquad (1)$$

Additional constraints are set to address indirect effects. Whenever three or more nearby turbines are selected for placement, indirect effects may have to be assessed. Eq. (2) determines when three interacting turbines are installed, by means of the 0-1 variable $ys_{i,i',j}$. Similar constraints might be added to account for more turbine interactions.

$$x_i + x_{i'} + x_j - 2 \leq ys_{i,i',j} \qquad \forall i,i',j \qquad (2)$$

In Eq. (3), direct and indirect effects are combined into a total wake effect whenever the generator $i$ is installed. Parameters $ip_{i',i}$ and $is_{i',j,i}$ refer to direct and indirect (by-three chained and overlap effects). They are obtained by computing the expected value of inferences coming from calculations provided by the algorithm in Section 3, after reducing the nodes involved to $i$, $i'$ and $j$, instead of the full set. Parameters $wk_{k,ws,i',i}$ and $wk_{k,ws,i',j,i}$ indicate power reduction in turbine $i$ due to $i'$, and due to $i'$ plus $j$ in the latter case. Both of them are derived from the power curve by comparing generation under unrestricted and interfered airstream conditions. Eqs. (4) and (5) show how expected power reduction is obtained by weighing direction and speed probabilities.

$$\sum_{i'} ip_{i',i} \, y_{i,i'} + \sum_{j,i'} is_{i',j,i} \, ys_{i,i',j} \leq W_i + Wmax(1 - x_i) \qquad \forall i \in I \qquad (3)$$

$$ip_{i',i} = \sum_{k} \sum_{ws(k)} \pi_k \, \gamma_{k,ws} \, wk_{k,ws,i',i} \qquad \forall i,i' \in I, i \neq i' \qquad (4)$$

$$is_{i',j,i} = \sum_{k} \sum_{ws(k)} \pi_k \, \gamma_{k,ws} \, wk_{k,ws,i',j,i} - ip_{i',i} \qquad \forall i,i',j \in I, i \neq i' \neq j \qquad (5)$$

On the other hand, binary variable $xs_{i,s,pl}$ indicates if turbine located at position $i$ is connected to a collection station located in $s$ with a cable of type $pl$. Eq. (6) states that a turbine might only be connected to one station while Eq. (7) imposes that the capacity of station $s$ must be unique, if installed ($ys_{s,c} = 1$).

$$\sum_{pl}\sum_{s} xs_{i,s,pl} \leq 1 \ \forall i \in I \tag{6}$$

$$\sum_{c} ys_{s,c} \leq 1 \quad \forall s \in S \tag{7}$$

Furthermore, variable $FP_{i,j}$ assesses the power conveyed from turbine $i$ to station $s$. This flow must not be greater than the power that $s$ is capable of managing (see Eq. 8).

$$FP_{i,s} \leq \sum_{c} pmax_c \ ys_{s,c} \quad \forall i \in I, j \in J \tag{8}$$

Since each location $i$ may serve as a power gathering node, a power balance is required to account for the incoming and outgoing currents. Continuous variable $PE_i$ is the effective power generated by turbine located at $i$ and is computed by discounting wake losses over theoretical power generation capacity (see Eq. 9).

$$\sum_{o \neq i} FP_{o,i} + PE_i = \sum_{j \neq i} FP_{i,j} + \sum_{s} FP_{i,s} \quad \forall i \in I \tag{9}$$

Finally, the objective function accounts for investment costs from wind turbines, stations and cable connections, as well as operating costs of turbines and stations. Benefits from energy production over a time period $\Delta$ are included to determine profit.

$$\max z = \sum_{i} ((pw_i \ x_i - W_i) \ pv \ \Delta - inv \ x_i - opex \ x_i \ \Delta)$$
$$- \sum_{c}\sum_{s} sub_{pl} \ ys_{s,c} + \sum_{i}\sum_{j}\sum_{pl} cc_{pl} \ dist_{i,j} \ xs_{i,j,pl} \tag{10}$$

## 5. Results

An illustrative case study is solved to assess the potential of the optimization tool. The available land size is 1.68 km² with 25 potential sites for turbine placement. Generators involved are Vestas V80 of 2 MW and the wind profile over the region is the same as in Figure 1. The project is evaluated for a 7-year horizon and electricity price is assumed to be constant at $0.06/kWh. Economies of scale are stated for collecting stations and cables. Three capacities are allowed for the installation of stations and 4 types of cable are available. Indirect wake effect calculations are extended up to 4 turbine interactions. The optimization model is implemented in software GAMS 40.2 and solved with GUROBI 9.5.2 in 75 seconds using an Intel Core i7 2.6 Ghz (6 cores) system with 16 GB of RAM. The model involves 21,993 equations and 3,967 variables (with 3,290 of them being 0-1). Solution suggests the installation of 16 turbines (2.5 MUSD each) with a total profit of 3.58 MUSD after 7 years. This implies 6.8% improvement with regards to separate optimization of layout and cable network. Investment costs for stations and cable interconnection amount to 4.02 MUSD. As shown in Figure 3, several turbines are connected with the cheapest cable of 70 mm² section. After collecting power of several turbines, the solution suggests to convey energy to the final station with 180 mm² cable.

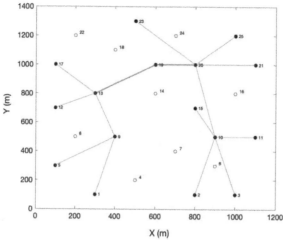

**Figure 3** – Solution suggested by the model for the 25 potential sites illustrative case.

## 6. Conclusions

In this work, we have developed a novel preprocessing algorithm and an MILP model to integrally solve wind turbines layout and cable network design problems for a given wind farm. In contrast to previous contributions, the model involves the evaluation of generalized wake effects comprising direct and indirect interferences. That is, the evaluation of multiple interactions by means of chained and overlapping effects. The model is coupled with an efficient algorithm that allows accurately estimating wind energy loss from interactions of higher order using any surrogate model, even those of maximum complexity. Although the model is effective in solving moderate dimensional cases, combinatorics grows fast when more accuracy is required, leading to refined grids with more potential sites. Future work will be focused on developing solution strategies to address problems with denser grids and continuous modeling approaches, as well as the inclusion of losses in the cabling and decisions over transmission lines.

## References

A. Bellat, I. Tyass, K. Mansouri, A. Raihani, 2022, New approach to optimize the cost and intercon. of wind turbines using the PSO alg. https://doi.org/10.1051/e3sconf/202233600013.

M. Fischetti, J. Leth, A. B. Borchersen, 2015, A MILP approach to wind farm layout and inter-array cable routing. Proc. of Am. Control Conf. https://doi.org/10.1109/ACC.2015.7172266.

M. Fischetti, M. Fischetti, 2022, Integrated Layout and Cable Routing in Wind Farm Optimal Design. Management Science, https://doi.org/10.1287/mnsc.2022.4470.

J. F. Herbert-Acero, J.R. Franco-Acevedo et al., 2009, Linear wind farm layout opt. through comp. inter. Adv. in Artificial Int., 692–703. https://doi.org/10.1007/978-3-642-05258-3_61.

N.O. Jensen, 1983, A Note on Wind Generator Interaction. Risø National Laboratory, No. 2411.

C.E. Mokhi, A. Addaim, 2020, Optimization of Wind Turbine Interconnections in an Offshore Wind Farm Using Metaheuristic Alg., Sustainability, 12. https://doi.org/10.3390/su12145761.

G. Mosetti, C. Poloni, B. Diviacco, 1994, Opt. of wind turbine positioning in large windfarms by means of a genetic algorithm. Journal of Wind Eng. and Ind. Aerodynamics, 51, 105-116.

R. Shakoor, M. Hassan, A. Raheem, Y. Wu, 2016, Wake effect modeling: A review of wind farm layout optimization using Jensen's model. Ren. and Sust. Energy Reviews, 58, 1048-1059.

Antonis Kokossis, Michael C. Georgiadis, Efstratios N. Pistikopoulos (Eds.)
PROCEEDINGS OF THE 33rd European Symposium on Computer Aided Process Engineering
(ESCAPE33), June 18-21, 2023, Athens, Greece

# Mixed-integer recourse in industrial demand response scheduling with interruptible load

Jnana Sai Jagana[a], Satyajith Amaran[b], Qi Zhang*[a]

*a*Department of Chemical Engineering and Material Science, University of Minnesota, Minneapolis, MN 55414, USA
*b*The Dow Chemical Company, Lake Jackson, TX 77566, USA
* qizh@umn.edu

## Abstract

While industrial demand response has become a prominent strategy for power-intensive chemical plants to remain cost-competitive, the financially incentivized provision of load reduction capacities, also called interruptible load, to the power grid is still a less explored topic. Here, a major challenge lies in dealing with the uncertainty that one does not know when load reduction will be requested. In this work, a scheduling model for a continuous industrial process providing interruptible load is developed, where we apply an adjustable robust optimization approach to address the uncertainty. The main difference to previous works is that we incorporate both continuous and binary recourse variables. When applied in our computational case study, the proposed model achieves significant cost savings when compared with a model that only considers continuous recourse.

**Keywords**: Interruptible load, multistage robust optimization, mixed-integer recourse

## 1. Introduction

In recent years, there have been significant advances in industrial demand response (DR) (Zhang and Grossmann, 2016), which has enabled large industrial consumers of electricity, such as power-intensive chemical plants, to reduce their operating costs by altering their power usage in response to varying electricity prices. DR is also beneficial to the power grid as it helps maintain grid stability, and a particularly effective way to do so is through the provision of interruptible load, which constitutes a form of ancillary services (Dowling et al., 2017). Here, economic incentives are offered to electricity consumers for committing load reduction capacities (that is, interruptible load) up to the agreed amount when requested by the grid operator.

The major challenge in providing interruptible load is that load reduction demand is not known in advance, but one must still guarantee dispatch upon request. Disregarding this uncertainty may jeopardize plant safety or lead to situations in which it is no longer possible to satisfy all product demand. Zhang et al. (2015) capture the uncertainty using a tailored uncertainty set and apply robust optimization (Ben-Tal et al., 2009) to this scheduling problem. However, they only model the static case where no recourse is considered, which leads to very conservative solutions. Zhang et al. (2016) address this shortcoming by incorporating continuous recourse decisions using affine decision rules to show significant increases in cost savings enabled by flexible recourse. Yet the proposed approach still cannot realize the full potential of interruptible load since it does not consider discrete recourse and hence does not allow, for example, full plant shutdowns when load reduction is required, which is what is often done in practice. In this work, we extend the previous framework to also include binary recourse decisions.

## 2. Problem statement

Consider a power-intensive continuously operated plant that manufactures a set of products. To satisfy demand, the products can be produced in the plant or purchased at a higher expense. The plant consumes electricity whose varying price is assumed to be known over the scheduling horizon. In addition, the plant can cut costs by providing interruptible load to the grid. To this end, the plant makes a commitment to reduce its electricity consumption at the grid operator's request. Load reduction may not always be requested but the plant earns revenue regardless. We assume that no additional payment is made to the plant when load reduction is requested; this assumption can be tweaked depending on the electricity market with no major changes to the model.

Given the plant model parameters (as discussed in Section 3) and a scheduling horizon, the goal is to determine the production schedule that is feasible for all possible realizations of load reduction while minimizing the total operating cost. Note that recourse variables, e.g., production rates and purchase amounts, depend on the realization of the uncertainty.

## 3. Deterministic model formulation

The model presented here is based on formulations developed in previous works (Mitra et al., 2012; Zhang et al., 2015) and is a direct extension of the model used in Zhang et al. 2016. Hence, only a brief description of the various constraints is provided.

### 3.1. High-level formulation

The structure of the deterministic model can be broadly expressed as follows:

$$\begin{array}{lll} \text{minimize} & \textit{Net operating cost} & \text{(1a)} \\ \text{subject to} & \textit{Feasible regions of operating modes} & \text{(1b)} \\ & \textit{Transition constraints} & \text{(1c)} \\ & \textit{Mass balance constraints} & \text{(1d)} \\ & \textit{Initial conditions} & \text{(1e)} \end{array}$$

The objective function is the cost of electricity plus the cost of additional products purchased minus the revenue from providing interruptible load. We assume that the plant can operate in different operating modes whose *feasible regions* are given in the form of polytopes. One such example of a plant with two products, P1 and P2, is shown in Fig. 1. Here, Region 1 could denote the off mode where no products are produced. *Transition constraints* are used to enforce feasible mode switching. Fig. 2 shows an example of requirements from the transition constraints. For instance, the process shown needs to stay in the off mode for at least 8 h before it can switch to the startup mode. *Mass balance constraints* ensure demand is satisfied through production or purchase; the remaining products are stored. *Initial conditions* are required for the problem to be well-defined.

### 3.2. Interruptible load constraints

As mentioned previously, the grid operator can request load reduction (no greater than the agreed amount) from the IL provider and the plant needs to alter its production schedule to cater to that request. These alterations in production schedule are modeled by introducing variables of the form:

$$\overline{PD}_{mit} = \widehat{PD}_{mit} + \widetilde{PD}_{mit} \quad \forall\, m \in M, i \in I, t \in T, \qquad \text{(2a)}$$
$$\bar{y}_{mt} = \hat{y}_{mt} + \tilde{y}_{mt} \qquad \forall\, m \in M, t \in T, \qquad \text{(2b)}$$

where $T$ denotes the set of time periods and $\overline{PD}_{mit}$ is the production rate of product $i$ in mode $m$ in time period $t$. The nominal production rate is denoted by $\widehat{PD}_{mit}$, and $\widetilde{PD}_{mit}$ is the deviation from the nominal value when load reduction is requested. The binary variable $\bar{y}_{mt}$ equals 1 if the plant operates in mode $m$ in time period $t$; $\hat{y}_{mt}$ is its nominal value while $\tilde{y}_{mt}$ is a discrete recourse variable that can take the values -1, 0, or 1, depending on the amount of load reduction requested. The decrease in power consumption associated with the decrease in production or, in some cases, a process shutdown must be at least as much as the amount of load reduction requested ($LR_t$). This is modeled as the following constraint:

$$\sum_m \delta_m \tilde{y}_{mt} + \sum_m \sum_i \gamma_{mi} \widetilde{PD}_{mit} \leq -LR_t \quad \forall t \in T, \tag{3}$$

where we assume that the electricity consumption is a linear function of production rates with a constant $\delta_m$ and coefficient $\gamma_{mi}$ for the selected operating mode.

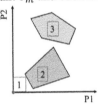

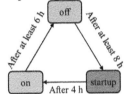

**Fig. 1:** Example for feasible operating regions of a process with three operating modes.

**Fig. 2:** Example for possible transitions between operating modes and corresponding operational constraints.

## 4. Multistage robust formulation with mixed-integer recourse

### 4.1. Uncertainty set

We adopt a "budget of uncertainty" approach (Bertsimas and Sim, 2004; Zhang et al., 2015) to formulate the following uncertainty set $W$ for the load reduction demand:

$$W = \left\{ w \in \mathbb{R}^{|T|} : \left( 0 \leq w_k \leq 1 \; \forall k = 1, \dots, t, \sum_{k=1}^t w_k = \Gamma_t \right) \; \forall t \in T \right\}, \tag{4}$$

where $w_t$ is the normalized requested load reduction, i.e., $LR_t = IL_t w_t$, $IL_t$ is the amount of interruptible load provided, and $\Gamma_t$ is a budget parameter limiting the cumulative load reduction required up to time $t$. The choice of $\Gamma_t$ can be based on historical data or the electricity market rules. Note that $\Gamma_t$ must be a monotonically increasing parameter. We now write Eq. (3) in terms of the normalized load reduction:

$$\sum_m \delta_m \tilde{y}_{mt}(w) + \sum_m \sum_i \gamma_{mi} \widetilde{PD}_{mit}(w) \leq -w_t IL_t \quad \forall t \in T. \tag{5}$$

### 4.2. Adjustable robust formulation with mixed-integer decision rules

The overall adjustable robust optimization problem can be formulated as follows:

minimize   *Net operating cost at $w = 0$ or worst-case net operating cost*

subject to   Eqs. (1b)–(1e), (2), (5) $\forall w \in W$, \hfill (6)

where we either minimize the net operating cost in the nominal or in the worst case. Here, the deviation variables $\widetilde{PD}_{mit}$, $\tilde{y}_{mt}$, etc., serve as the recourse variables and are hence functions of the uncertain parameters $w$. Following the concept of lifted uncertainty (Bertsimas and Georghiou, 2018) and the derivation for multistage problems in Feng et al. 2021, we implement (potentially discontinuous) piecewise linear decisions rules for the continuous variables and piecewise constant decision rules for the binary variables. As an example, the decision rules for $\widetilde{PD}_{mit}$ and $\tilde{y}_{mt}$ have the following form:

$$\widetilde{PD}_{mit} = \sum_{t'=t-\bar\zeta}^{t} \sum_{k=1}^{K_{t'}} \left(\bar{X}^t_{mit'k}\,\bar{W}_{t'k} + \hat{X}^t_{mit'k}\,\hat{W}_{t'k}\right) \quad \forall\, m \in M, i \in I, t \in T, \qquad (7a)$$

$$\tilde{y}_{mt} = \sum_{t'=t-\bar\zeta}^{t} \sum_{k=1}^{K_{t'}} \hat{Y}^t_{mt'k}\,\hat{W}_{t'k} \qquad\qquad\qquad \forall\, m \in M, t \in T, \qquad (7b)$$

where $\bar{w}$ and $\hat{w}$ are the auxiliary lifted uncertain parameters, $K_t$ is the number of breakpoints associated with $w_t$ that define the piecewise structures of the decision rules, and $\bar\zeta$ determines how many uncertain parameters from previous time periods are considered in the decision rules. The coefficients $\bar{X}$, $\hat{X}$, and $\hat{Y}$ define the decision rules and are to be optimized. Problem (6) is a semi-infinite program, which we solve using the reformulation approach that leverages linear programming duality (Yanıkoğlu et al., 2019). For the sake of brevity, we refer the reader to Feng et al., 2021 for more details including the full reformulation, which results in a mixed-integer linear program (MILP).

## 5. Case study

In this section, the proposed robust model with mixed-integer recourse is applied to an illustrative example. All models were implemented in Julia v1.7 using the modeling environment JuMP v0.22.3 and solved to 1% optimality gap using Gurobi v9.5.1 on an Intel Core i7-8700 machine at 3.20 GHz with 8 GB RAM.

In this case study, a single-product plant is considered, and the scheduling problem is solved over a time horizon of 48 hours with hourly time discretization. The plant can operate in three different modes: off, startup, and on. Table 1 shows the details of the polytopes (which here are simple ranges) that characterize the operating modes and the electricity consumption in each operating mode. Table 2 shows the possible mode transitions and the respective minimum stay times. Fig. 3 shows the electricity prices and revenue from providing interruptible load over the time horizon. The plant is operating in the on mode at the start and it is assumed that no mode switching has occurred in the eight time periods prior to the beginning of the scheduling horizon.

The initial inventory is 1,000 kg. The minimum and maximum inventory levels are 0 and 5,000 kg, respectively, for all time points. At the end of the time horizon, the minimum inventory level is set to 1,000 kg. The cost of purchasing additional products is $3/kg. If interruptible load is provided in a time period, then the provided amount must be between 200 and 5,000 kWh. We assume that the budget parameter $\Gamma_t$ increases every 8 time periods by 1, i.e., maximum load reduction can only be requested once during the first 8 h, twice during the first 16 h, etc., and at most six times during all 48 h.

**Table 1:** Polytope equations, fixed ($\delta_m$) and unit ($\gamma_m$) electricity consumption for each operating mode (product indices have been omitted).

| Operating mode | Polytope | $\delta_m$ [kWh] | $\gamma_m$ [kWh/kg] |
|---|---|---|---|
| Off | $0 \le PD_{mt} \le 0$ | 0 | 0 |
| Startup | $5 \le PD_{mt} \le 5$ | 0 | 60 |
| On | $100 \le PD_{mt} \le 160$ | 1,200 | 20 |

### 5.1. Advantages of discrete recourse

We solve the problem for different $\bar\zeta$, which controls the amount of past information used in the decision rules. The flexibility in the solution increases with $\bar\zeta$, but it also increases the model size and hence the computational intensity. Table 3 compares the costs between the continuous recourse only case and the mixed-integer recourse case. The results show significant cost reductions, of up to 14%, for mixed-integer recourse case over continuous recourse case. In Figs. 4 and 5, we see that the nominal electricity consumption profiles in both cases are very similar. This implies that a major factor in the cost reduction is the additional interruptible load provided in the mixed-integer recourse case. Figs. 5 and 7 show that this additional interruptible load is provided in time periods 27 and 48, where process shutdown is a feasible recourse action. This is also reflected in the time period 48 of Fig. 7, where the nominal and recourse production amounts add up to zero, indicating a process shutdown in the worst-case uncertainty realization.

**Table 2:** Possible transitions between operating modes and minimum stay times.

| Transition from mode $m$ to mode $m'$ | Minimum stay time in $m'$ [h] |
|---|---|
| Off → startup | 4 |
| Startup → on | 6 |
| On → off | 8 |

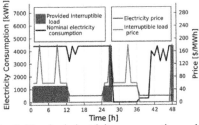

**Fig. 3:** Electricity and interruptible load prices for case study

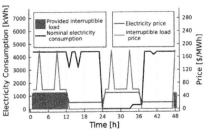

**Fig. 4:** Nominal electricity consumption and interruptible load provided with continuous recourse only and $\bar{\zeta} = 47$.

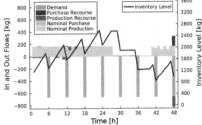

**Fig. 5:** Nominal electricity consumption and interruptible load provided with mixed-integer recourse and $\bar{\zeta} = 47$.

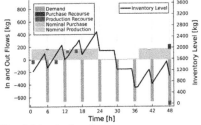

**Fig. 6:** Nominal and worst-case recourse product flows and nominal inventory profile for the case with continuous recourse only and $\bar{\zeta} = 47$.

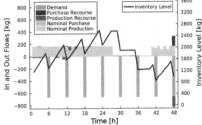

**Fig. 7:** Nominal and worst-case recourse product flows and nominal inventory profile for the case with mixed-integer recourse and $\bar{\zeta} = 47$.

**Table 3:** Net operating cost ($C$) in $ for cases with different $\bar{\zeta}$. Here, $C^{nominal}$ is the cost when no load reduction is requested and $C^{wc}$ is the worst-case cost when load reduction is requested.

| $\bar{\zeta}$ | Continuous recourse only ($C^{nominal}$, $) | Mixed-integer recourse ($C^{nominal}$, $) | Continuous recourse only ($C^{wc}$, $) | Mixed-integer recourse ($C^{wc}$, $) |
|---|---|---|---|---|
| 47 | 3,214.1 | 2,755.3 | 3,266.3 | 2,917.8 |

| 23 | 3,214.1 | 2,755.3 | 3,266.3 | 2,917.8 |
| 11 | 3,214.1 | 2,810.4 | 3,282.7 | 2,999.8 |

### 5.2. Computation time

The computation times required to solve the models are shown in Table 4. As expected, considering mixed-integer recourse is computationally significantly more expensive. Adjusting the parameter $\bar{\zeta}$ can help reduce the solution time but may give a solution with higher objective value. Clearly, a trade-off exists between computational performance and solution quality. In the example considered, setting $\bar{\zeta} = 23$ provides a solution of the same quality as $\bar{\zeta} = 47$ in much shorter time.

**Table 4:** Computation times for cases with different $\bar{\zeta}$.

| $\bar{\zeta}$ | Continuous recourse only | Mixed-integer recourse |
|---|---|---|
| 47 | 90 s | 3,626 s |
| 23 | 32 s | 1,228 s |
| 11 | 10 s | 253 s |

## 6. Conclusion

In this work, we developed a multistage robust optimization model for the scheduling of power-intensive plants that also participate in the interruptible load market. Piecewise linear/constant decision rules are used to determine the recourse actions necessary in both continuous and discrete variables. When applied to an illustrative example, the proposed model achieves significant cost savings compared to the formulation that only considers continuous recourse. The flexibility that mixed-integer recourse provides comes at a substantial computational cost. However, our model provides a way of exploring this trade-off by setting the amount of past information allowed to be considered in the decision rules. By doing so, we find that the problem can often be solved in much less time with little sacrifice on the solution quality.

## 7. Acknowledgements

The authors gratefully acknowledge the financial support from the National Science Foundation under Grant No. 2215526.

## References

Ben-Tal, A., El Ghaoui, L., & Nemirovski, A. (2009). Robust optimization (Vol. 28). *Princeton University Press.*

Bertsimas, D., & Sim, M. (2004). The price of robustness. *Operations Research, 52(1)*, 35-53.

Dowling, A.W., Kumar, R., and Zavala, V. M. 2017. A multi-scale optimization framework for electricity market participation. *Applied Energy, 190*, 147-164.

Feng, W., Feng, Y., and Zhang, Q., 2021. Multistage robust mixed-integer optimization under endogenous uncertainty. *European Journal of Operational Research, 294(2)*, 460-475.

Mitra, S., Grossmann, I.E., Pinto, J.M., & Arora, N. (2012). Optimal production planning under time-sensitive electricity prices for continuous power-intensive processes. *Computers & Chemical Engineering, 38*, 171-184.

Yanıkoğlu, İ., Gorissen, B. L., & den Hertog, D. (2019). A survey of adjustable robust optimization. *European Journal of Operational Research, 277(3)*, 799-813.

Zhang, Q. and Grossmann, I.E., 2016. Enterprise-wide optimization for industrial demand side management: Fundamentals, advances, and perspectives. *Chemical Engineering Research & Design, 116*, 114-131.

Zhang, Q., Grossmann, I.E., Heuberger, C.F., Sundaramoorthy, A. and Pinto, J.M., 2015. Air separation with cryogenic energy storage: optimal scheduling considering electric energy and reserve markets. *AIChE Journal, 61(5)*, 1547-1558.

Zhang, Q., Morari, M.F., Grossmann, I.E., Sundaramoorthy, A., and Pinto, J.M., 2016. An adjustable robust optimization approach to scheduling of continuous industrial processes providing interruptible load. *Computers & Chemical Engineering, 86*, 106-119.

Antonis Kokossis, Michael C. Georgiadis, Efstratios N. Pistikopoulos (Eds.)
PROCEEDINGS OF THE 33rd European Symposium on Computer Aided Process Engineering
(ESCAPE33), June 18-21, 2023, Athens, Greece

# Technoeconomic Assessment of Digestate Valorization for Biogas Plant

Shivom Sharma[a], Rafael Graf[b], Jaroslav Hemrle[b], Adrian Schneider[b], Francois Maréchal[a]

[a]IPESE, EPFL Valais Wallis, 1950 Sion, Switzerland
[b]Hitachi Zosen Inova AG, Zürich, 8005, Switzerland
shivom.sharma@epfl.ch

## Abstract

Anaerobic digestion (i.e., biogas plant) converts organic waste into biogas that can directly be used or upgraded to bio-methane for natural gas grid injection. The digestate (residues) from biogas plant has nutrients and unconverted organic matters. The dry digestate can be used to produce hydrogen and methane *via* thermochemical route. This study has modelled a complete process or value chain for converting digestate into methane and hydrogen. The developed process model includes gasification, water gas shift and methanation as the main conversion units, whereas pressure swing adsorption, membrane separation and amine absorption were used to separate different gaseous mixtures. This study focuses on systematic generation and comparison of digestate valorization options. The formulated optimization problem is a mixed integer linear programming problem, and total annual cost is considered as the performance criterion. Several economic scenarios have been generated based on selling prices of hydrogen and methane, and the optimization problem was solved repeatedly for each scenario. The obtained solutions are divided into three categories: only producing methane, producing methane and hydrogen as main products, and producing hydrogen as main product and methane as side product. As expected, the selection of valorization route and relative production of hydrogen and methane depend upon their selling prices. Finally, use of biogenic carbon dioxide for storing excess renewable electricity has been explored for selected scenario.

**Keywords**: Biogas Plant; Digestate Valorization; Hydrogen Production; Methane Production; Carbon Capture and Utilization.

## 1. Introduction

Anaerobic digestion is a process to convert organic matters (e.g., food waste, sewage sludge, agriculture waste, etc.) into biogas. The composition of biogas varies for different feed-stocks. Typically, 50-80 v/v% methane, 20-50 v/v% carbon dioxide, and small quantities of hydrogen, nitrogen, oxygen and carbon dioxide are present in biogas (Chen et al., 2015). The biogas can be upgraded into bio-methane by separating carbon dioxide and other impurities. The biogas and/or bio-methane can be used as fuel to produce heat and electricity. The residues from biogas plants are called digestate that contain valuable nutrients and unconverted organic matters. The water content of digestate can be as high as 90% (Ehmann et al., 2018), and digestate is dried to achieve 10-20% water content before further usage (Dziedzic et al., 2021). The lower heating value of dry digestate varies between 15 and 20 MJ/kg. The digestate can be used as organic fertilizer, soil conditioner or heat source. In European Union (EU28) about 180 million tonnes of digestate is produced annually (Corden et al., 2019). In literature, several studies have focused on the conventional use of digestate as fertilizer and soil conditioner. However, there are limited number of studies that have focused on the valorization of digestate for producing liquid and gaseous fuels/products (e.g., methane, oil, etc.). Wisniewski et al. (2015) studied pyrolysis and gasification of digestate from agricultural biogas plant. Chen et al. (2017) studied gasification of digestate in a downdraft fixed bed gasifier. Castro-Amoedo et al. (2021) studied biowaste valorization along with $CO_2$ removal from biogas, so that produced bio-methane can be injected into natural gas grid for transportation purpose. Renewable energy requires short- and long-term storage due to its variable or intermittent nature. In case of biogas upgradation and digestate valorization into liquid and gaseous fuels, $CO_2$ is produced as a side product that can be used for storing excess renewable energy. Recently, Wang and Lee (2021) reviewed different valorization options for digestate of different origins (e.g., agriculture waste, food waste, municipal solid waste etc.).

This study focuses on detailed evaluation of high value fuel ($CH_4$, $H_2$) production from digestate. Figure 1 presents a simplified flowchart of digestate conversion into methane and hydrogen. The digestate contains 62 wt.% water and 38 wt.% solid materials. The solid material has 79 wt.% organic matters, and remaining inert. The organic materials are broken down into small gaseous molecules ($CH_4$, $H_2$, $CO$ and $CO_2$) and char inside the gasifier. The product gases from gasifier are processed in different conversion and separation units to produce high quality methane and hydrogen. This study has modelled a complete process or value chain for converting digestate into methane, hydrogen and carbon dioxide. The developed process model includes digestate pre-processing, conversion and gas separation units. The digestate value chain has the possibility to convert the captured $CO_2$ into additional methane, using renewable electricity. The formulated optimization problem is a mixed integer linear programming problem (MILP) that is implemented in AMPL (A Mathematical Programming Language). This study systematically generates and compares different scenarios for digestate valorization, based on the product prices. The obtained solutions are compared based on total annual cost (TAC), and they provide more insights on digestate valorization options.

## 2. Digestate Valorization Model

### 2.1 Process Description

The digestate from biogas plant contains valuable nutrients, unconverted organic matters, and significant amount of water, and so it is dried to about 20% moisture content before gasification. After the gasification, the product gases are cleaned and cooled to remove solid particles, sulphur and other impurities. The clean gases are handled differently for methane (dotted box X, Figure 1) and hydrogen productions (dotted box Y, Figure 1). In case of methane production, water gas shift (WGS) reactor is used to convert part of the carbon mono-oxide into hydrogen. This is required to ensure adequate carbon to hydrogen ratio for the subsequent methane synthesis. The carbon dioxide is removed using pressure swing adsorption (PSA) after WGS reactor. After methanation reactor, product gases are dried and upgraded (*via* membrane unit) for natural gas grid injection. The methane production route has some off-gases that are either recycled to upstream units or burnt in a burner to supply the process heat. In case of hydrogen production, WGS reactor is used to convert most of the carbon mono-oxide into hydrogen. The product gases include mainly methane, hydrogen and carbon dioxide. The carbon dioxide is separated from the gaseous mixture using amine absorption process, followed by methane and hydrogen separation using a membrane unit.

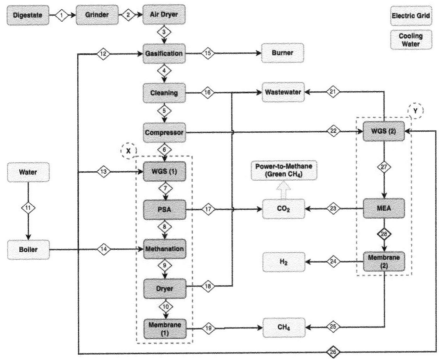

**Figure 1:** Digestate Valorization Chain for Methane and Hydrogen Production

### 2.2 Optimization Problem Formulation

For each conversion and separation unit in the digestate valorization chain, linear models were developed that include mass flow rates, temperature-enthalpy profiles, as well as the use or generation of electricity. Each model also includes fixed and variable capital ($c_i^{inv1}$, $c_i^{inv2}$) and operating ($c_{i,t}^{op1}$, $c_{i,t}^{op2}$) costs. Both binary ($\Psi_{i,t}$, $\Psi_i$) and continuous ($f_{i,t}$, $f_i$) variables are used for each unit/technology. The former accounts for the existence of a unit and the latter for its size. Based on a given objective function, the optimizer defines connections among units, levels of use of units (material flow rates) and heat flow rates. More details on the model development can be found in Castro-Amoedo et al. (2021). The optimization problem can be solved for annual capital cost, annual operating cost or total annual cost ($TAC$). In Equation 1, the first element on the right-hand side presents operating costs, while the second element presents annualized capital expenditures, with $i$ interest rate (0.06) and $n$ assumed lifetime (20 years). Constraints were added to ensure:

- minimum ($f_i^{min}$) and maximum ($f_i^{max}$) capacities of units (Equation 2);
- resource consumption, with $\dot{m}_{r,i,t}^+$ the reference quantity of resource $\forall r \in R$ needed in each unit (Equations 3 and 4);
- mass balances for each unit (Equation 5);
- heat cascade formulation based on Maréchal and Kalitventzeff (1998), where residual heat ($\dot{R}_{t,k}$) is transferred, according to the 2nd law of thermodynamics, from higher ($k + 1$) to lower temperature level ($k$) (Equations 6 and 7).

The mathematical formulation is written in AMPL (v20210220) and solved by CPLEX solver (v12.7.0.0), on a Microsoft Windows v10.0.18363 machine [2.4 GHz Intel(R) Xeon (R), 8 core processor, 16 GB RAM].

$$min\,TAC\,(\$/y) = \sum_{t \in T} \sum_{i \in L} (c_{i,t}^{op1} \cdot \Psi_{i,t} + c_{i,t}^{op2} \cdot f_{i,t}) \cdot t_t^{op} + \frac{i(1+i)^n}{(1+i)^n - 1} \cdot \sum_{i \in Lu} (c_i^{inv1} \cdot \Psi_i + c_i^{inv2} \cdot f_i) \quad (1)$$

$$f_i^{min} \cdot \Psi_{i,t} \leq f_{i,t} \leq f_i^{max} \cdot \Psi_{i,t}, \quad \forall i \in L, \quad \forall t \in T \quad (2)$$

$$\dot{M}_{r,i,t}^+ = f_{i,t} \cdot \dot{m}_{r,i,t}^+, \quad \forall r \in R, \ \forall i \in L, \ \forall t \in T \quad (3)$$

$$\dot{M}_{r,i,t}^- = f_{i,t} \cdot \dot{m}_{r,i,t}^-, \quad \forall r \in R, \ \forall i \in L, \ \forall t \in T \quad (4)$$

$$\sum_{i \in L} \dot{M}_{r,i,t}^- = \sum_{i \in L} \dot{M}_{r,i,t}^+, \quad \forall r \in R, \ \forall t \in T \quad (5)$$

$$\sum_{i \in L} \dot{Q}_{i,t,k} \cdot f_{i,t} + \dot{R}_{t,k+1} - \dot{R}_{t,k} = 0, \quad \forall t \in T, \quad \forall k \in K, with\ T_{k+1} \geq T_k, \quad (6)$$

$$\dot{R}_{t,k} \geq 0, \quad \dot{R}_{t,kmax+1} = \dot{R}_{t,1} = 0, \quad \forall t \in T \quad (7)$$

## 3. Digestate Valorization: A Case Study

For this case study, we considered that 5 t/h digestate is available for valorization. The purchase prices of digestate, water and electricity are 0.01 $/kg, 0.0005 $/kg and 0.15 $/kWh, respectively. The wastewater treatment cost is 0.001 $/kg. The carbon dioxide storage cost is 20 $/t. The relative production of methane and hydrogen depends on their selling prices. The optimization method optimizes distribution of digestate carbon between methane and carbon dioxide. The selling prices of methane (synthetic natural gas, SNG) and hydrogen are 1-1.5 $/kg and 3-5 $/kg, respectively. In order to explore digestate valorization options, we have generated 9 scenarios, by using three different selling prices for methane (1, 1.25 and 1.5 $/kg) and hydrogen (3, 4, and 5 $/kg).

**Table 1:** Digestate Valorization Scenarios based on Selling Prices of $CH_4$ and $H_2$ (Elec: Electricity; WW: Wastewater; S: Solution)

| $H_2$ | $CH_4$ | $H_2O$ | Elec | $H_2$ | $CH_4$ | $CO_2$ | WW | CAPEX | OPEX | S. |
|---|---|---|---|---|---|---|---|---|---|---|
| $/kg | $/kg | kg/h | kWh | kg/h | kg/h | kg/h | kg/h | $10^3.$/y | $10^3.$/y | No |
| 3 | 1 | 876.7 | 602.7 | | | 398 | 1040.6 | 912.8 | 2258 | -1998 | A:1 |
| 3 | 1.25 | 876.7 | 602.7 | | | 398 | 1040.6 | 912.8 | 2258 | -2870 | A:2 |
| 3 | 1.5 | 876.7 | 602.7 | | | 398 | 1040.6 | 912.8 | 2258 | -3741 | A:3 |
| 4 | 1 | 1160.4 | 522.2 | 62.4 | 104.4 | 950.3 | 764.7 | 1666 | -1687 | C:1 |
| 4 | 1.25 | 876.7 | 602.7 | | | 398 | 1040.6 | 912.8 | 2258 | -2870 | A:4 |
| 4 | 1.5 | 876.7 | 602.7 | | | 398 | 1040.6 | 912.8 | 2258 | -3741 | A:5 |
| 5 | 1 | 1160.4 | 522.2 | 62.4 | 104.4 | 950.3 | 764.7 | 1666 | -2233 | C:2 |
| 5 | 1.15 | 1111.3 | 543.7 | 49.8 | 170.5 | 986.5 | 810.3 | 1807 | -2613 | B:1 |
| 5 | 1.5 | 876.7 | 602.7 | | | 398 | 1040.6 | 912.8 | 2258 | -3741 | A:6 |

In Table 1, the obtained solutions are divided into three categories based on the selection of valorization route and relative production of products. Solution A only produces methane, without using technologies in "dotted box Y" (Figure 1). Solution B uses all technologies in Figure 1, and produces both methane and hydrogen. Finally, Solution C does not use technologies in "dotted box X" (Figure 1), and produces hydrogen as the main product and methane as the side product. For Solutions A, B and C, annual capital (CAPEX) and operating (OPEX) costs are shown in Table 1, and all major flows are presented in Table 2. Finally, Figure 2 shows hot and cold composite curves for different solutions. The solid carbon and part of the product gases from gasifier were used in burner to supply the process heat. Solution A produces maximum amount of $CO_2$ (1040.6 kg/h), as it does not produce any hydrogen. Solutions B and C have 986.5 kg/h and 950.3 kg/h $CO_2$, respectively.

**Table 2:** Flow Details (kg/h) for Solutions A, B and C (Stream Numbers are Shown in Figure 1; *solid carbon flow and +product gases flow)

| Stream | Stream Details | Solution A | Solution B | Solution C |
|---|---|---|---|---|
| 1 | Digestate to Grinder | 5000 | 5000 | 5000 |
| 2 | Grinder to Air dryer | 5000 | 5000 | 5000 |
| 3 | Air dryer to Gasification | 2037.5 | 2037.5 | 2037.5 |
| 4 | Gasification to Cleaning | 1882.5 | 1317.8 | 1134.2 |
| 5 | Cleaning to Compressor | 1562.3 | 1093.4 | 941.1 |
| 6 | Compressor to WGS (1) | 1562.3 | 342.2 | |
| 7 | WGS (1) to PSA | 1673.2 | 366.5 | |
| 8 | PSA to Methanation | 632.3 | 138.5 | |
| 9 | Methanation to Dryer | 1027 | 225 | |
| 10 | Dryer to Membrane (1) | 434.7 | 95.2 | |
| 11 | Water to Boiler | 876.7 | 1111.3 | 1160.4 |
| 12 | Boiler to Gasification | 407.5 | 407.5 | 407.5 |
| 13 | Boiler to WGS (1) | 110.9 | 24.3 | |
| 14 | Boiler to Methanation | 358.3 | 78.5 | |
| 15 | Gasification to Burner | 77.3*, 489.7+ | 77.3*, 1054.5+ | 77.3*, 1238.1+ |
| 16 | Cleaning to Wastewater | 320.5 | 224.3 | 193.1 |
| 17 | PSA to $CO_2$ | 1040.6 | 228 | |
| 18 | Dryer to Wastewater | 592.3 | 129.7 | |
| 19 | Membrane (1) to $CH_4$ | 398 | 87.2 | |
| 21 | WGS (2) to Wastewater | | 456.3 | 571.6 |
| 22 | Compressor to WGS (2) | | 751.2 | 941.1 |
| 23 | MEA to $CO_2$ | | 758.6 | 950.3 |
| 24 | Membrane (2) to $H_2$ | | 49.8 | 62.4 |
| 25 | Membrane (2) to $CH_4$ | | 83.3 | 104.4 |
| 26 | Boiler to WGS (2) | | 601 | 752.9 |
| 27 | WGS (2) to MEA | | 896 | 1122.4 |
| 28 | MEA to Membrane (2) | | 142.2 | 178.1 |

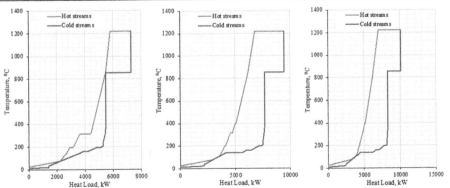

**Figure 2:** Hot and Cold Composite Curves for Solutions A, B and C (Left to Right)

*3.1 Integration of Power to Methane System*

To explore the potential of power to methane concept, three scenarios were selected for further analysis: (1) $H_2 = 3$ \$/kg, $CH_4 = 1.25$ \$/kg (Solution A:2), (2) $H_2 = 5$ \$/kg, $CH_4 = 1.25$ \$/kg (Solution B:1), and (3) $H_2 = 5$ \$/kg, $CH_4 = 1$ \$/kg (Solution C:2). For this analysis, electricity price was reduced to 0.1 \$/kWh, carbon credit (96 \$/t-$CO_2$) was used for converting $CO_2$ into green $CH_4$, and no investment was considered for power to methane system. Table 3 presents important results for integrated system. The integration of power to methane system with digestate valorization provides better heat integration possibilities. For scenarios 2 and 3, flow of gases from gasification to burner has reduced (489.7 and 986.7 kg/h in Table 3 compared to 1054.5 and 1238.1 kg/h in Table 2). This increases $CH_4$ production for scenarios 2 and 3. Further, $O_2$ is also produced from electrolyser that may be used for oxy-combustion (burner) to produce $CO_2$ and $H_2O$.

**Table 3:** Results for Integration of Power to Methane System with Digestate Valorization (EC: Electrolysis, G: Gasifier, B: Burner)

| Scenario No. | CAPEX $10^3$.\$/y | OPEX $10^3$.\$/y | CH$_4$ kg/h | H$_2$ kg/h | Green CH$_4$ kg/h | O$_2$ kg/h | EC Elec, kWh | G to B kg/h |
|---|---|---|---|---|---|---|---|---|
| 1 | 2258 | -2560 | 398 | | 378.4 | 1513.6 | 7881.5 | 489.7 |
| 2 | 2177 | -3314 | **297.1** | 46.5 | 466 | 1864.1 | 9706.2 | **489.7** |
| 3 | 1805 | -1661 | **127.5** | 76.2 | 422.2 | 1688.6 | 8792.8 | **986.7** |

## 4. Conclusions

This study explores digestate valorization that comprises gasification, water gas shift and methanation as the main conversion units. Pressure swing adsorption, amine absorption and membrane separation were considered for separating gaseous mixtures of carbon dioxide, methane and hydrogen. A mixed integer linear programming problem was formulated for digestate value chain, and total annual cost was used as objective function. In total, eight scenarios were generated based on the selling prices of hydrogen and methane. The obtained solutions were categorized into three types, based on the selection of valorization route/technologies and relative production of final products. The power to methane system has good synergies with digestate valorization into methane/hydrogen.

## References

X. Y. Chen, H. Vinh-Thang, A. A. Ramirez, D. Rodrigue, S. Kaliaguine, 2015, Membrane gas separation technologies for biogas upgrading, RSC Adv, 5, pp. 24399-24448.

A. Ehmann, U. Thumm, I. Lewandowski, 2018, Fertilizing potential of separated biogas digestates in annual and perennial biomass production systems, Frontiers in Sustainable Food System, 2 (12), pp. 1-14.

K. Dziedzic, et al., 2021, Solid digestate - Physicochemical and thermal study, Energies, 14, 7224.

C. Corden, et al., Digestate and compost as fertilisers: Risk assessment and risk management options, European Comission, 2019.

D. Wisniewski, J. Gołaszewski, A. Bialowiec, 2015, 3 The pyrolysis and gasification of digestate from agricultural biogas plant, Archives of Environmental Protection, 41 (3), pp. 70-75.

G. Chen, et al., 2017, Air gasification of biogas-derived digestate in a downdraft fixed bed gasifier, Waste Management, 69, pp. 162-169.

R. Castro-Amoedo, J. Morisod, J. Granacher, F. Maréchal F., 2021, The role of biowaste: a multi-objective optimization platform for combined heat, power and fuel, Front. Energy Res. 9:718310.

W. Wang and D. J. Lee, 2021, Valorization of anaerobic digestion digestate: A prospect review, Bioresource Technology 323:124626.

F. Maréchal and Kalitventzeff, B., 1998, Energy integration of industrial sites: tools, methodology and application, Appl. Therm. Eng., 18, pp 921-933.

Antonis Kokossis, Michael C. Georgiadis, Efstratios N. Pistikopoulos (Eds.)
PROCEEDINGS OF THE 33rd European Symposium on Computer Aided Process Engineering
(ESCAPE33), June 18-21, 2023, Athens, Greece
© 2023 Elsevier B.V. All rights reserved.  http://dx.doi.org/10.1016/B978-0-443-15274-0.50512-6

# Optimization of Hydrogen systems for prospective Life Cycle Assessment: Well-to-Tank approach

Rocky Mashi[a], Yohan Vincotte[a], Sofía De-León Almaraz[b], Catherine Azzaro-Pantel [a]*

[a]*Laboratoire de Génie Chimique, Université Toulouse, CNRS, INPT, UPS, Toulouse France*
[b] *Corvinus University of Budapest, Department of Supply Chain Management, 8 Fővám tér. 1093 Budapest, Hungary*
 * *catherine.azzaropantel@toulouse-inp.fr*

## Abstract

The optimization of hydrogen energy systems generally focuses on minimizing total cost and greenhouse gas (GHG) emissions. While climate neutrality by 2050 is the objective set by the European Green Deal, with a target on GHG emissions, other environmental impacts such as resource demand and land use are also of great importance and are mostly not taken into account in these models. This study uses the Life Cycle Assessment (LCA) method to analyze 18 Key Environmental Indicators (KEI). The framework combines a multi-objective design strategy for hydrogen networks with LCA evaluation. The optimization strategy uses a Mixed Integer Linear Programming (MILP) approach with an augmented epsilon-constraint, implemented in the GAMS environment. The Pareto solutions for hydrogen supply chains obtained from optimization were analyzed using the SimaPro Power user package, the Ecoinvent database, and the ReCiPe2016 method with a Well-to-Tank approach. The results showed that considering only GHG emissions leads to poor results for traditional solutions like SMR, and low performance in other KEIs such as water consumption and mineral resource scarcity for the electrolysis process using PV. These findings emphasize the importance of multi-objective optimization that considers multiple environmental criteria, not just GHG emissions.

**Keywords**: Hydrogen Systems, Modelling, Optimization, Prospective Life Cycle Assessment.

## 1. Introduction

Clean hydrogen ($H_2$) from renewable or low-carbon sources is seen as a key solution in achieving net-zero emissions by 2050 and limiting global warming to 1.5 degrees Celsius. This offers a long-term, scalable, and cost-effective option in decarbonizing hard-to-abate sectors (IRENA, 2022). Optimizing hydrogen energy systems thus provides effective support for policy decision-making by prioritizing the minimization of both cost and environmental impact. Although the European Green Deal aims for climate neutrality by 2050, the current optimization of these systems (Li *et al.*, 2019) primarily addresses carbon emissions and does not fully consider other environmental impacts such as resource use and land utilization. This raises various methodological questions, such as expanding the assessment of carbon to a comprehensive, multi-criteria evaluation of environmental impact.

Decision support tools, particularly Life Cycle Assessment (LCA), are essential for guiding stakeholders in their strategic choices and identifying potential ways to reduce environmental impacts. The hydrogen supply chain is here the studied system, covering all stages from resource extraction to production, storage, transportation, and use. LCA, as a widely accepted systemic environmental assessment method, is the best approach for these challenges. Although traditional attributional LCA describes the system and its impacts by assigning a portion of the technosphere's impacts, it is inadequate for capturing the changing emission factors, such as technology advancements over time.

With growing interest in hydrogen, many review papers on hydrogen LCAs have been published, such as (Rinawati *et al.*, 2022). The scientific objective of this paper is to explore the synergies between LCA, energy system optimization, and multi-criteria decision support approaches in selecting a sustainable "hydrogen" system. However, various hydrogen pathways to achieve similar GHG emission reductions may differ in terms of both costs and environmental impacts, which raises several issues such as: which ecological co-benefits and negative side effects can be expected from a climate-friendly hydrogen energy system? How do the various hydrogen supply chains differ in terms of other ecological impacts? The novelty of this work is thus to propose a methodological framework that can aid in selecting a hydrogen supply chain that incorporates a set of environmental criteria.

The paper is organized as follows: the solution approach is developed in Section 2. The main assumptions used for the case study, i.e. the deployment of the hydrogen in Occitanie, are presented in Section 3. Section 4 discusses and highlights some significant results. Finally, some conclusions and perspectives for future work are proposed in Section 5.

## 2. Methods and tools

The hydrogen supply chain for mobility purposes encompasses production, liquefaction, transportation, storage, and delivery at hydrogen refueling stations (HRS). The production methods include two types of electrolysis processes - Alkaline Electrolyser Cell (AEC) and Proton Exchange Membrane (PEM) - utilizing renewable energy sources such as wind, hydro, and solar photovoltaic, as well as grid electricity. Other hydrogen production methods considered are steam methane reforming (SMR) and steam methane reforming with carbon capture, utilization, and storage (CCUS). The possible hydrogen pathways are depicted in Figure 1.

The methodological framework adopts a 3-tier approach.
-   Firstly, the design and operation of a future Hydrogen Supply Chain (HSC) is considered with a geographical and multi-period (6 periods of 5 years each, from 2020 to 2050) approach to meet the hydrogen demand profile of a specific geographic region. The optimization problem is modeled as a Mixed Integer Linear Programming (MILP) using the GAMS® modeling system and CPLEX 12 solver. The comprehensive formulation of the model includes constraints (such as demand satisfaction, mass balance, production, transportation, and storage constraints, primary energy source availability for electricity production) and objective functions (presented in De-León Almaraz et al., 2015). Three optimization objectives are considered: an economic objective based on minimizing the total network cost, an environmental objective related to the global greenhouse gas

(GHG) emissions of the supply chain, and a risk index. The multi-objective optimization is formulated using an augmented epsilon-constraint approach and generates the Pareto front of optimal HSC configurations as outputs.

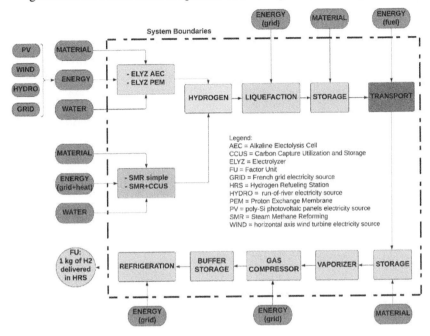

Figure 1 – System study and associated LCA System Boundaries

- Second, the Pareto solutions were evaluated from an environmental perspective using the Life Cycle Assessment (LCA) method. This method was selected for its systemic approach, international standardization, and use of inventory databases such as EcoInvent. The LCA method requires the definition of a functional unit (FU), the implementation of life cycle inventory (LCI), and the life cycle impact assessment (LCIA). The LCA system boundaries for the hydrogen supply chain are shown in Figure 1. The functional unit (FU) was set as 1 kg of hydrogen delivered at the Hydrogen Refueling Station (HRS) using a Well-to-Tank approach. The Life Cycle Inventory (LCI) was supported by the Ecoinvent database in SimaPro Power. Data collection for materials, energy and water use was also been carried out for specific components of the hydrogen supply chain (i.e., electrolyzers). The design of specific modules dedicated to inventory production for the different hydrogen production methods are based on the data provided in (Spath *et al.*, 2000); (Koj *et al.*, 2017); (Bareiß *et al.*, 2019). The ReCiPe2016 midpoint (H) method was used as the LCIA, and 18 Key Environmental Indicators (KEI) were calculated for each configuration of the hydrogen supply chain. A parametric approach was used to automatically generate the LCA of the Pareto solutions using GAMS and SimaPro Power.

- Third, the modified-TOPSIS (m-TOPSIS), a variant of the Technique for Order of Preference by Similarity to Ideal Solution (TOPSIS) is applied to choose the best compromise configuration from the Pareto front.

## 3. Case study

The methodology was applied to study hydrogen deployment in the Occitanie region of France with the aim of decarbonizing the mobility sector (passenger cars, light commercial vehicles, buses, and heavy goods vehicles). The data used was updated from previous studies (REPOS, 2017) and the demand estimation was based on the pluriannual plan of the minister of ecological transition in France. Two scenarios were analyzed: the "Base Scenario" which allows for hydrogen production using all technologies (electrolysis and SMR with and without CCS), and the "e-$H_2$ Scenario" which only allows for hydrogen production through electrolysis technologies (green hydrogen and grid make-up if necessary). The methodology was applied in two variants for each scenario. Variant #1 considered Life Cycle Assessment (LCA) after the multi-criteria decision analysis, while variant #2 considered LCA after the multi-objective optimization, as can be seen in Figure 2 and Figure 3 respectively. The Pareto front consisted of 21 optimal compromise configurations.

Figure 2 – Methodological framework (Variant #1)

Figure 3– Methodological framework (Variant #2)

For the application of the multi-criteria decision method (TOPSIS), an equal weight was assigned to each group of criteria: 1/3 for the cost, risk, and environmental parameters. In variant #1, 1/3 weight was given to the greenhouse gas (GHG) criteria. In variant #2, a weight of 1,852e-2 was given to each Key Environmental Indicator (KEI).

## 4. Results

Table 1 reports the quantitative results of all criteria obtained after conducting a Life Cycle Assessment (LCA) for all variants. The study found that it is feasible to design a hydrogen ecosystem using only renewable energy-powered electrolyzers, with grid support, in line with the region's decarbonization goals. However, the average Levelized Cost of Hydrogen (LCOH) over the study period was 10.22/10.28 €/kg$H_2$, with an average emission of 4.51/4.82 kg$CO_2$eq/kg$H_2$. The optimization of all technologies resulted in the selection of the SMR+CCS version, with a lower LCOH of 5.15/5.34 €/kg$H_2$ and an average GHG emission of 6.92 kg$CO_2$eq/kg$H_2$. The risk index was higher for the SMR version, which is primarily due to its larger plant size. A radar graph (Figure 4) is also provided to analyze the differences between the solutions obtained.

The order of application of the Life Cycle Assessment (LCA) method and the choice of weights in the TOPSIS method did not significantly affect the selected solution. However, these results cannot be generalized at this time.

| Index | Unit | Base Scenario: Variant #1 | Base Scenario: Variant #2 | e-H$_2$ Scenario: Variant #1 | e-H$_2$ Scenario: Variant #2 |
|---|---|---|---|---|---|
| Cost | billion € | 8,85E+00 | 7,63E+00 | 1,60E+01 | 1,65E+01 |
| LCOH | €/ kg H$_2$ | 5,15 | 5,34 | 10,22 | 10,28 |
| Risk | - | 1,03E+03 | 1,26E+03 | 9,57E+02 | 9,18E+02 |
| Global warming | kg CO$_2$ eq / kg H$_2$ | 6,92E+00 | 6,91E+00 | 4,51E+00 | 4,82E+00 |
| Stratospheric ozone depletion | kg CFC11 eq / kg H$_2$ | 5,26E-06 | 5,26E-06 | 3,76E-06 | 4,18E-06 |
| Ionizing radiation | kBq Co-60 eq / kg H$_2$ | 7,53E+00 | 7,53E+00 | 1,61E+01 | 1,87E+01 |
| Ozone formation, Human health | kg NOx eq / kg H$_2$ | 1,36E-02 | 1,36E-02 | 1,19E-02 | 1,25E-02 |
| Fine particulate matter formation | Kg PM2.5 eq / kg H$_2$ | 9,27E-03 | 9,24E-03 | 1,36E-02 | 1,42E-02 |
| Ozone formation, Terrestrial ecosystems | kg NOx eq / kg H$_2$ | 1,42E-02 | 1,42E-02 | 1,22E-02 | 1,29E-02 |
| Terrestrial acidification | kg SO$_2$ eq / kg H$_2$ | 2,62E-02 | 2,62E-02 | 3,69E-02 | 3,88E-02 |
| Freshwater eutrophication | kg P eq / kg H$_2$ | 2,28E-03 | 2,28E-03 | 3,02E-03 | 3,11E-03 |
| Marine eutrophication | kg N eq / kg H$_2$ | 1,84E-04 | 1,83E-04 | 4,89E-04 | 5,39E-04 |
| Terrestrial ecotoxicity | kg 1,4-DCB / kg H$_2$ | 2,15E+01 | 2,12E+01 | 1,15E+02 | 1,18E+02 |
| Freshwater ecotoxicity | kg 1,4-DCB / kg H$_2$ | 1,50E-01 | 1,50E-01 | 1,52E+00 | 1,56E+00 |
| Marine ecotoxicity | kg 1,4-DCB / kg H$_2$ | 2,11E-01 | 2,10E-01 | 1,94E+00 | 1,99E+00 |
| Human carcinogenic toxicity | kg 1,4-DCB / kg H$_2$ | 3,74E-01 | 3,58E-01 | 8,68E-01 | 8,47E-01 |
| Human non-carcinogenic toxicity | kg 1,4-DCB / kg H$_2$ | 3,05E+00 | 3,04E+00 | 1,89E+01 | 1,98E+01 |
| Land use | m$^2$ crop eq / kg H$_2$ | 2,39E-01 | 2,39E-01 | 6,55E-01 | 6,61E-01 |
| Mineral resource scarcity | kg Cu eq / kg H$_2$ | 2,56E-02 | 2,47E-02 | 1,27E-01 | 1,31E-01 |
| Fossil resource scarcity | kg oil eq / kg H$_2$ | 5,47E+00 | 5,47E+00 | 1,20E+00 | 1,28E+00 |
| Water consumption | m$^3$ / kg H$_2$ | 5,17E-02 | 5,17E-02 | 1,74E-01 | 1,89E-01 |

Table 1: Values of cost, risk and environmental indicators for the studied scenarios

The analysis highlights that considering only GHG emissions as an environmental impact criterion, traditional solutions like SMR have the poorest results, while other Key Environmental Indicators (KEIs) such as water consumption or mineral resource scarcity show low performance for the electrolysis process using photovoltaic (PV) technology.

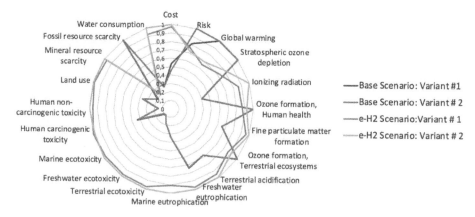

Figure 4 –Radar chart for comparison of all scenarios

## 5. Conclusions

The present paper emphasizes the significance of incorporating LCA into multi-objective optimization analysis as a crucial step in the decision-making process. The proposed framework automates the integration of LCA results with those of the prospective hydrogen energy system model through scenario parameterization. Moreover, this study conducts a thorough well-to-tank analysis, whereas most studies only consider the operational phase impacts. The case study results obtained reinforce the importance of multi-objective optimization approaches that take into account various environmental criteria, not just GHG emissions.

## References

Acar, C., Bicer, Y., Demir, M.E., Dincer, I., 2019. Transition to a new era with light-based hydrogen production for a carbon-free society: An overview. Int. J. Hydrogen Energy 44, 25347–25364. https://doi.org/10.1016/j.ijhydene.2019.08.010

Bareiß, K., de la Rua, C., Möckl, M., & Hamacher, T., 2019. Life cycle assessment of hydrogen from proton exchange membrane water electrolysis in future energy systems. Applied Energy, 237, 862-872.

De-León Almaraz, S., Azzaro-Pantel, C., Montastruc, L., Boix, M., 2015. Deployment of a hydrogen supply chain by multi-objective / multi-period optimisation at regional and national scales. Chem. Eng. Res. Des. 104, 11–31. https://doi.org/10.1016/j.cherd.2015.07.005

Koj, J. C., Wulf, C., Schreiber, A., & Zapp, P. (2017). Site-dependent environmental impacts of industrial hydrogen production by alkaline water electrolysis. Energies, 10(7), 860.

IRENA, 2022, Global hydrogen trade to meet the 1.5°C climate goal: Part III – Green hydrogen cost and potential, International Renewable Energy Agency, Abu Dhabi

Li, L., Manier, H., Manier, M.A., Hydrogen supply chain network design: An optimization-oriented review, Renewable and Sustainable Energy Reviews, Volume 103, 2019, Pages 342-360, ISSN 1364-0321, https://doi.org/10.1016/j.rser.2018.12.060.

REPOS, 2017, Scénario région à énergie positive de la Région Occitanie / Pyrénées-Méditerranée.

Rinawati, D.I., Ryota Keeley, A.,Takeda, S., Managi, S., Life-cycle assessment of hydrogen utilization in power generation: A systematic review of technological and methodological

choices, Front. Sustain., 28 July 2022, Sec. Quantitative Sustainability Assessment, Volume 3 -
2022 | https://doi.org/10.3389/frsus.2022.920876

Spath, P. L., & Mann, M. K. (2000). *Life cycle assessment of hydrogen production via natural gas
steam reforming* (No. NREL/TP-570-27637). National Renewable Energy Lab.(NREL),
Golden, CO (United States).

Antonis Kokossis, Michael C. Georgiadis, Efstratios N. Pistikopoulos (Eds.)
PROCEEDINGS OF THE 33rd European Symposium on Computer Aided Process Engineering
(ESCAPE33), June 18-21, 2023, Athens, Greece

# A techno-economic assessment of biomass combustion with CO$_2$ capture technology

Nela Slavu[ab*], Maytham Alabid[a], Marius Sandru[c], Cristian Dinca[ab]

[a]University POLITEHNICA of Bucharest, Splaiul Independentei, 313, Bucharest, 060042, Romania
[b]Academy of Romanian Scientists, Ilfov 3, 050044 Bucharest, Romania
[c]SINTEF Materials and Chemistry, Sem Saelands vei 2A, 7465, Trondheim, Norway
slavunela@yahoo.com

## Abstract

In this study the technical, economic, and environmental performance of a 50 MW biomass power plant with a post-combustion CO$_2$ capture process by chemical absorption was analysed. The type of biomass used was poplar, with a lower heating value of 18.36 MJ/kg. In the case of CO$_2$ capture process by chemical absorption, three types of amines were analysed in a mass concentration of 30% (monoethanolamine, diethanolamine, methyldiethanolamine). For a capture efficiency of 90%, the specific heat consumption for solvent regeneration is 2.76 for MEA, 2.65 for DEA and 2.48 GJ/tCO$_2$ for MDEA. Thus, after integrating the CO$_2$ capture process, the overall efficiency of the biomass power plant decreases by up to 8.14 percentage points. After integration of the CO$_2$ capture process a negative CO$_2$ emission factor of -746 kg/MWh is obtained. In the case of economic indicators, the levelised cost of electricity increased by up to 129% after the integration of the CO$_2$ capture process.

Keywords: biomass, power plant, CO$_2$ capture, negative CO$_2$ emissions.

## 1. Introduction

Biomass use for power generation is a solution to reduce CO$_2$ emissions from the energy sector. Biomass is considered the renewable energy source with the greatest potential, covering about 10% of global primary energy demand (M.M. Tun, et al., 2019). Biomass accounts for 65% of renewable energy potential in Romania. The energy potential from biomass, estimated at about 7.6 million tonnes/year or 318,000 TJ/year, accounts about 19% of the total primary energy consumption in Romania (R.L. Berevoianu, 2020). There are several methods for using biomass to produce energy, in heat or electricity: thermochemical processes – direct combustion, gasification and pyrolysis, and biochemical processes – anaerobic digestion. The most well-known, verified, and available commercially is direct combustion. Biomass combustion releases about the same amount of CO$_2$ as coal combustion. However, it is considered neutral because it absorbs the CO$_2$ released by combustion during growth (A. Sertolli, et al., 2022). CO$_2$ capture technologies have been developed over the last decades to be integrated into thermal power plants (N.S. Sifat and Y. Haseli, 2019). The CO$_2$ capture technologies can be integrated pre-/post- or oxy-combustion. The most developed method of capturing CO$_2$ from a gas stream is by chemical absorption based on aqueous amines. As biomass is considered CO$_2$ neutral, when a CO$_2$ capture technology is integrated, negative CO$_2$ emissions can be obtained. Therefore, a biomass combustion technology coupled with a

$CO_2$ capture technology can contribute to the decarbonisation of the environment. It is also included in CDR technologies (Carbon Dioxide Removal technologies). This study investigated the integration of the $CO_2$ capture process in a biomass power plant to produce electricity with negative $CO_2$ emissions.

## 2. Biomass power plant with post-combustion $CO_2$ capture

The power plant analysed in this study is based on woody biomass (poplar) with the chemical composition and higher and lower heating value shown in Table 1. The pulverised combustion of biomass was considered for electricity generation. The SST-400 steam turbine was used, with a maximum power of up to 60 MW, and a live steam pressure and temperature of up to 140 bar and 540 °C respectively. The wet and dry flue gas composition resulting from biomass combustion for an excess air coefficient value of 1.4 is shown in Table 2.

Table 1. Biomass characterization

| Content | Value |
|---|---|
| Carbon, wt.% | 50.02 |
| Hydrogen, wt.% | 6.28 |
| Oxygen, wt.% | 42.17 |
| Nitrogen, wt.% | 0.19 |
| Sulphur, wt.% | 0.02 |
| Ash, wt.% | 1.32 |
| Higher heating value, HHV, MJ/kg | 18.95 |
| Lower heating value, LHV, MJ/kg | 18.36 |

Table 2. Flue gas composition

| Component | Wet flue gas | Dry flue gas |
|---|---|---|
| $CO_2$, vol.% | 10.141 | 10.973 |
| $SO_2$, vol.% | 0.002 | 0.002 |
| $N_2$, vol.% | 76.465 | 82.741 |
| $O_2$, vol.% | 5.807 | 6.284 |
| $H_2O$, vol.% | 7.585 | 0 |

The main data of the biomass power plant are presented in Table 3. For an 85% load factor of the biomass power plant, corresponding to an annual operating time of 7500 h/year, the biomass flow rate required for 50 MW power is 6.28 kg/s. The electricity produced annually is 375 GWh. The $CO_2$ emission factor is 829.01 g/kWh. If biomass is considered $CO_2$ neutral, the emission factor is 0 g/kWh.

Table 3. Power plant main data

| Data | Value |
|---|---|
| Net power, MW | 50 |
| Overall efficiency, % | 42 |
| Annual operation, h/year | 7500 |
| Load factor, % | 85 |
| Electric energy, GWh/an | 375 |
| Biomass flow, kg/s | 6.28 |
| Flue gas flow, kg/s | 71.84 |
| $CO_2$ flow, kg/s | 11.51 |
| $CO_2$ emission factor, $gCO_2$/kWh | 829.01 |

The cases analised are:
- Case 1: Biomass power plant without $CO_2$ capture;
- Case 2: Biomass power plant with post-combustion chemical absorption process based on monoethanoamine (MEA 30 wt.%);
- Case 3: Biomass power plant with post-combustion chemical absorption process based on diethanolamine (DEA 30 wt.%);
- Case 4: Biomass power plant with post-combustion chemical absorption process based on metil-diethanolamine (MDEA 30 wt.%).

The conventional amine-based $CO_2$ capture process is shown in Figure 1. The absorption process is characterised by the L/G ratio (ratio of chemical solvent flow rate to flue gas flow rate entering the absorption column). The $CO_2$ capture efficiency depends on the L/G ratio and the type of amine used in the process. In the case of the regeneration process, the lean loading in $CO_2$ of 0.15 was constantly maintained for all types of amines studied. The steam required for solvent regeneration is taken from the biomass power plant. Thus, after post-combustion integration of the $CO_2$ capture process the overall efficiency of the power plant decreases. The $CO_2$ capture process by chemical absorption was modelled in Chemcad. The thermodynamic package Amine was used.

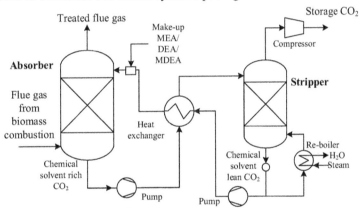

Figure 1. Post-combustion chemical absorption process

Figures 2-4 show the results obtained in terms of $CO_2$ capture efficiency and thermal energy consumption for chemical solvent regeneration. In the case of using MEA in 30 wt.% concentration, the L/G ratio varied between 0.5-2.1 $kmol_{solvent}/kmol_{flue\_gas}$. The $CO_2$ capture efficiency increases with increasing L/G ratio due to the higher amount of chemical solvent introduced into the absorption column. The $CO_2$-rich loading chemical solvent varied in 0.46-0.55 $kmol_{CO2}/kmol_{MEA}$. Heat duty for solvent regeneration increases with increasing L/G ratio, ranging from 31960-135800 MJ/h. For a $CO_2$ capture efficiency of 90%, the L/G ratio is 1.60 $kmol_{solvent}/kmol_{flue\_gas}$, with a specific thermal energy for solvent regeneration of 2.76 GJ/t$CO_2$. Regarding the DEA and MDEA, they have a lower $CO_2$ absorption capacity, resulting in higher amounts of solvent that must be used to achieve $CO_2$ capture efficiencies up to 100%. Thus, in the case of DEA 30 wt.%, for a $CO_2$ capture efficiency of 90%, the L/G ratio is 2.85, respectively 6.54 $kmol_{solvent}/kmol_{flue\_gas}$ for MDEA 30 wt.%. In terms of specific thermal energy consumption, it is 2.65 GJ/t$CO_2$ for DEA and 2.48 GJ/t$CO_2$ for MDEA, lower than for MEA due to lower temperatures in the regeneration process (125 °C for MEA, 118 °C for DEA and 104 °C for MDEA). The specific solvent loss is 0.1 kg/t$CO_2$ for MEA, 0.05 kg/t$CO_2$ for DEA, respectively 0.31 kg/t$CO_2$ for MDEA.

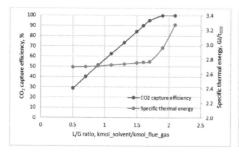

Figure 2. CO₂ capture efficiency and
specific thermal energy according to L/G
ratio for MEA 30%

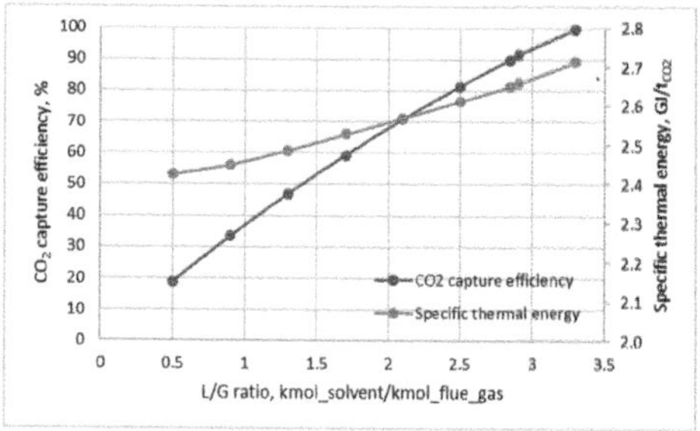

Figure 3. CO₂ capture efficiency and
specific thermal energy according to L/G
ratio for DEA 30%

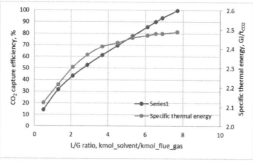

Figure 4. CO₂ capture efficiency and specific thermal energy according to L/G ratio for MDEA
30%

## 3. Techno-economic assessment

The results obtained for the techno-economic indicators are centralised in Table 4. Overall
biomass power plant efficiency decreases by up to 20% after integration of $CO_2$ capture
technology (for a $CO_2$ capture efficiency of 90%). Due to the neutrality of biomass and
the integration of $CO_2$ capture technology, a negative emission factor of 746 g/kWh was
achieved. The methodology used to determine technical and economic indicators is
presented in another article by the authors (N. Slavu, et al., 2022). The update rate
assumed was 8%. The study period is 30 years, during the first 3 years the investment is
made. The specific investment cost increases by 55% with the integration of the chemical
absorption capture process. Due to the lower purchase price and the smaller amount of
solvent used to achieve 90% capture efficiency, the lowest chemical solvent costs were
obtained when using MEA (Case 2). The levelised cost of electricity is 80.69 €/MWh in
Case 1, for Cases 2, 3 and 4 it increases by 109.27%, 113.74% and 128.27% respectively.
The $CO_2$ capture cost ranges from 95-115 €/tCO₂, the lowest being in Case 2 (MEA 30
wt.%), and the $CO_2$ avoided cost ranges from 118-139 €/tCO₂. In the study by B. Yang et
al. (2021), where pulverised biomass combustion with $CO_2$ capture was analysed, the
value obtained for levelised cost of electricity was 168.60 €/MWh, the $CO_2$ capture cost
was 89.21 €/tCO₂, and the $CO_2$ avoided cost was 158.85 €/tCO₂.
Figure 5 shows the influence of the biomass price on the levelised cost of electricity. At
a decrease/increase of the biomass price by 10% compared to the one initially considered
in the analysis, the levelised cost of electricity decreases/increases by 2.8% in Case 1, by
1.66% in Case 2, by 1.61% in Case 3, and by 1.49% in Case 4.

Table 4. Technical and economic indicators

| Technical indicator | Case 1 | Case 2 | Case 3 | Case 4 |
|---|---|---|---|---|
| Specific thermal energy for solvent regeneration, GJ/tCO$_2$ | - | 2.76 | 2.65 | 2.48 |
| $CO_2$ capture efficiency, % | - | 90 | 90 | 90 |
| $CO_2$ amount captured, t/year | - | 279868.2 | 279835.2 | 279823.1 |
| Chemical solvent amount (with losses), t/year | - | 317.6 | 602.6 | 1448.1 |
| $CO_2$ amount (neutral biomass-negative emissions), t/year | 0.00 | -279868.2 | -279835.2 | -279823.1 |
| Electric energy, MWh/year | 375000 | 302343.7 | 304662.0 | 308448.3 |
| Overall efficiency, % | 42 | 33.86 | 34.12 | 34.55 |
| Overall efficiency penalty, percentage points | - | 8.14 | 7.88 | 7.45 |
| $CO_2$ emission factor, g/kWh | 829.01 | 102.57 | 101.90 | 100.69 |
| $CO_2$ emission factor (neutral biomass - negative emissions), g/kWh | 0 | -746.32 | -746.23 | -746.20 |
| **Economic indicator** | **Case 1** | **Case 2** | **Case 3** | **Case 4** |
| Update rate, % | 0.08 | 0.08 | 0.08 | 0.08 |
| Operating time, year | 30 | 30 | 30 | 30 |
| Investment completion time, year | 3 | 3 | 3 | 3 |
| Specific investment cost, €/kW | 3917.68 | 6111.04 | 6111.04 | 6111.04 |
| Specific fixed costs O&M, €/kW | 42.20 | 61.92 | 61.92 | 61.92 |
| Specific variable costs O&M, €/MWh | 4.68 | 11.42 | 11.42 | 11.42 |
| Fuel price, €/kg | 0.05 | 0.05 | 0.05 | 0.05 |
| Chemical solvent price, €/kg | - | 2.6 | 3.8 | 4.5 |
| Investment cost, M€ | 195.8 | 305.5 | 3055.5 | 305.5 |
| Fixed costs O&M, M€/year | 2.11 | 3.09 | 3.09 | 3.09 |
| Variable costs O&M, M€/year | 1.75 | 3.45 | 3.47 | 3.52 |
| Fuel cost, M€/year | 8.48 | 8.48 | 8.48 | 8.48 |
| Chemical solvent cost, M€/year | - | 0.82 | 2.29 | 6.51 |
| Levelised cost of electricity, €/MWh | 80.69 | 168.86 | 172.47 | 184.19 |
| $CO_2$ capture cost, €/tCO$_2$ | - | 95.25 | 99.92 | 114.09 |
| $CO_2$ avoidance cost, €/tCO$_2$ | - | 118.14 | 122.09 | 138.71 |

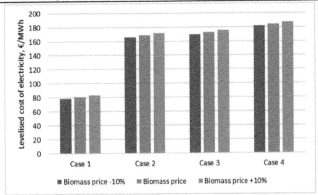

Figure 5. Levelised cost of electricity variation with –/+ 10% of biomass price

The financial-economic indicators are presented in Table 5. The price of electricity on sale was 250 €/MWh. In all the cases studied, the values of the indicators indicate that the proposed solution is economically feasible (NPV is greater than 0, IRR is greater than the update rate considered, and UPP is less than the operating life). Figures 6 and 7 show the variation of the NPV and the UPP as a function of the update rate. An update rate of 8,

10 and 12% was considered. The best values are obtained at the lowest update rate of 8%. As the update rate increases the NPV decreases and the UPP period increases. In Case 3 and Case 4, for an update rate of 12% the project is no longer feasible.

Table 5. Financial-economic indicators

| Indicator | Case 1 | Case 2 | Case 3 | Case 4 |
|---|---|---|---|---|
| Net present value, NPV, M€ | 668 | 182 | 174 | 146 |
| Internal rate of return, IRR, % | 30.96 | 16.39 | 16.16 | 15.31 |
| Updated payback period, UPP, year | 7.04 | 14.61 | 14.87 | 15.92 |

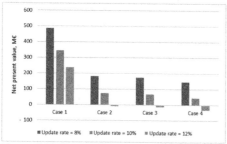

Figure 6. NPV according to update rate      Figure 7. UPP according to update rate

## 4. Conclusions

Biomass combustion coupled with $CO_2$ capture technology can significantly contribute to $CO_2$ emission reductions, as both the electricity generation process and the post-combustion capture by chemical absorption process are mature and can be implemented on industrial scale. In this study, for a 50 MW biomass power plant, a negative $CO_2$ emission factor of 746 g/kWh was obtained after integration of $CO_2$ capture technology. Therefore, over a year, this technology can absorb about 279.8 $ktCO_2$ from the environment. The levelized cost of electricity for the biomass power plant without $CO_2$ capture process is 80.69 €/MWh. In the case of integrating the $CO_2$ capture process by chemical absorption, the cost obtained is between 168-185 €/MWh, depending on the type of amine used.

## Acknowledgments

The study was funded by the UEFISCDI within the National Project number 106PTE/2022. The research leading to these results received funding from the NO Grants 2014–2021, under project contract No. 13/2020.

## References

M.M. Tun, et al., 2019, Biomass energy: An overview of biomass sources, energy potential, and management in Southeast Asian countries, Resources, 8(2), 81.

R.L. Berevoianu, 2020, Main directions for energy use of biomass in Romania, International Symposium, 11th Edition (pp. 333-339).

A. Sertolli, et al., 2022, Biomass Potential and Utilization in Worldwide Research Trends—A Bibliometric Analysis. Sustainability, 14(9), 5515.

N.S. Sifat and Y. Haseli, 2019, A critical review of $CO_2$ capture technologies and prospects for clean power generation. Energies, 12(21), 4143.

N. Slavu, et al., 2022, Technical and Economical Assessment of $CO_2$ Capture-Based Ammonia Aqueous. Processes, 10(5), 859.

B. Yang, et al., 2021, Life cycle cost assessment of biomass co-firing power plants with $CO_2$ capture and storage considering multiple incentives. Energy Economics, 96, 105173.

### Reviewers' answers

First, we would like to thank you for your recommendations and remarks.

1. The novelty is not clear. Amine based $CO_2$ capture has been studied for long. So the specific objective of this new study is not clear.

As you said, the $CO_2$ capture process by chemical absorption-based amine has been studied over the years and is a mature process. The aim of this study was to integrate this process in a biomass power plant, and to analyze economically the use of different amines. Considering that we have a biomass power plant with $CO_2$ capture, this technology is included in the CDR technologies (carbon dioxide removal technologies).

2. How are data reported in table 3 obtained, particularly numbers for $CO_2$ emission factor?

Table 3 reports the data obtained from the thermodynamic cycle calculation. The $CO_2$ emission factor was determined based on the flue gas composition, the flue gas flow rate and the amount of electricity produced.

3. What do you mean by lean loading of $CO_2$ in the regeneration system?

The lean loading solvent is the molar ratio of $CO_2$ to the used amine (MEA, DEA, MDEA) in the stream leaving the regeneration column.

4. Please add some information regarding Chemcad simulation (thermodynamic models, source of kinetic data etc.)

The thermodynamic package Amine was used to simulate the $CO_2$ capture process by chemical absorption in Chemcad. We have added this information in the text.

5. The negative emission factor seems to be calculated based on 90% capture efficiency. I do not think it is from life cycle perspective where the emissions related to amine production as well as recycling will be considered. Please clarify.

Yes, you are right. In this study no life cycle analysis was done for either the biomass or the amines used.

6. The difference between $CO_2$ capture cost and $CO_2$ avoidance cost is not clear.

The difference between the two calculated costs can be seen from the relationships applied. I did not add them in this article because a reference (another article by the authors) has been placed where the methodology for calculating all economic indicators is described. In the case of $CO_2$ capture cost, the difference between levelized cost of electricity with capture and without capture is reported to the amount of $CO_2$ captured. In the case of the $CO_2$ avoidance cost, the same difference is reported to the difference between the $CO_2$ emission factor with capture and without capture.

7. Comparison of results with prior literature will be helpful.

We compared with the literature on economic indicators. Thus, in the study by B. Yang et al. (2021), where pulverized biomass combustion with $CO_2$ capture was analyzed, the value obtained for levelized cost of electricity was 168.60 €/MWh, the $CO_2$ capture cost was 89.21 €/t$CO_2$, and the $CO_2$ avoided cost was 158.85 €/t$CO_2$. In our study the levelized cost of electricity with $CO_2$ capture is between 168-185 €/MWh, the $CO_2$ capture cost is between 95-115 €/t$CO_2$, and the $CO_2$ avoided cost is between 118-139 €/t$CO_2$.

Antonis Kokossis, Michael C. Georgiadis, Efstratios N. Pistikopoulos (Eds.)
PROCEEDINGS OF THE 33rd European Symposium on Computer Aided Process Engineering
(ESCAPE33), June 18-21, 2023, Athens, Greece

# Process Modelling and Pinch Analysis for an Integrated System of Anaerobic Digestion with Digestate Recycling via Hydrothermal Gasification

Fadilla Noor Rahma[a], Khanh-Quang Tran[a], Roger Khalil[b]

[a]*Norwegian University of Science and Technology, Høgskoleringen 1, Trondheim 7034, Norway*
[b]*SINTEF Energy Research, Sem Sælands vei 11, Trondheim 7034, Norway*

## Abstract

Anaerobic digestion (AD) of low-grade biomass materials is one of the strategical technologies to achieve the climate-neutral target. Its implementation is however limited due to problems related to digestate management and feedstock scarcity. Digestate recycling to the AD process via hydrothermal gasification (HTG) may be an answer to the problems. This work develops and analyzes thermodynamically a novel integrated process including among others AD, HTG, and power generation unit for energy recovery from the HTG, using Aspen Plus software, with a focus on the HTG block. Effects of HTG process parameters on biogas production and energy recovery are investigated. In addition to that, a Pinch analysis was performed. The result shows that higher energy efficiency is obtained at higher temperature and higher D/W ratio. The syngas recycling to the AD increases biomethane production by 26.10%, power production by 21.42%, and total energy efficiency by 20.05%, compared to the process without syngas recycle.

Keywords: Anaerobic digestion; hydrothermal gasification, Aspen Plus; process integration; Pinch analysis.

## 1. Background

Biogas production from low-grade biomass via anaerobic digestion (AD) is essential in the transition towards sustainable and renewable energy. However, AD implementation has been hindered by challenges related to the digestate management [1] and the limited sustainable feedstocks [2]. Integration of AD and hydrothermal gasification (HTG) is a potential answer to solve both the digestate management and feedstock scarcity issues.

Indeed, the AD-HTG integration allows valorization of AD digestate through HTG, facilitating the digestate management [3]. Another key benefit of the AD-HTG integration is the potential to recycle HTG-generated syngas to the AD system [4].

Previous studies have confirmed that addition of syngas produced from the digestate via HTG into the AD accelerates the digestion process and enhances $CH_4$ production [5, 6]. Prior to syngas recycle, the energy associated with HTG product fluid streams at high pressures and temperatures can be recovered for electricity generation through a series of turbines and heat exchangers. A number of process configurations integrating HTG with power production has been proven to be more efficient than the stand-alone processes [7].

In this paper, a conceptual process design of AD-HTG integration with syngas recycling and power production is proposed. To the best of the authors' knowledge, such system has not been previously studied in the literature. This research aims to predict the performance of the integrated system under various operating conditions, focusing on the HTG block. The process performance is indicated by biomethane and power production capacity, as well as the process energy efficiency. In addition, the heat recovery potentials of the integrated process are evaluated using Pinch analysis.

## 2. Methods

### 2.1. Description of the Process Simulation

The conceptual design of the integrated system under study and its model in Aspen Plus are presented in Figure 1 and Figure 2, respectively.

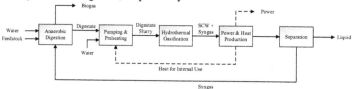

Figure 1. Process Design of the Integrated System under Investigation

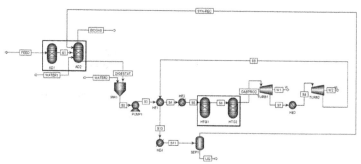

Figure 2. Process Flow Diagram of the Integrated System in Aspen Plus

### 2.1.1. Anaerobic Digestion (AD)

In Aspen Plus, AD process is modelled using a kinetic-free equilibrium model based on Buswell equation [8]. This equation uses theoretical stoichiometric method to estimate the products of the AD process, including biogas and digestate. The method was widely applied in earlier studies [9-11] and adopted for the present work to reduce the model complexity. According to this method, the volatile matter in the biomass feedstock is converted into $CH_4$, $CO_2$, and smaller amounts of $NH_3$ and $H_2S$, according to Equation (1) below:

$$C_aH_bO_cN_dS_e + \left(a - \frac{b}{4} - \frac{c}{2} + \frac{3d}{4} + \frac{e}{2}\right)H_2O \tag{1}$$
$$\rightarrow \left(a + \frac{b}{8} - \frac{c}{4} - \frac{3d}{8} - \frac{e}{4}\right)CH_4 + \left(\frac{a}{2} - \frac{b}{8} + \frac{c}{4} + \frac{3d}{8} + \frac{e}{4}\right)CO_2$$
$$+ dNH_3 + eH_2S$$

For the Aspen Plus modelling, two blocks of RYIELD reactor, each incorporated with a calculator block, are employed to represent AD. Biomass feedstock (*FEED*) is defined in Aspen Plus as a non-conventional compound consisting of volatile matter, fixed carbon, moisture, and ash content. The first RYIELD reactor (*AD1*) is used to breakdown the volatile matter in the feedstock into its components, consisting of carbon, hydrogen, oxygen, nitrogen, and sulfur. The output of *AD1* is the fictitious stream *S1*, which does not represent a physical stream in the real condition. The *S1* stream flows into another RYIELD reactor (*AD2*) which calculates the biogas and digestate production based on Equation (1). In the simulation, the recycle stream (*SYN-REC*) and water stream (*WATER1*) also enter the AD system through this reactor. During the AD process, the fixed carbon and ash contents are assumed to remain undigested [10]. The AD system produces two product streams, i.e., the biogas (*BIOGAS*) and digestate (*DIGESTAT*), which is further processed in the HTG section.

### 2.1.2. Hydrothermal Gasification (HTG)

The HTG reactor model is based on the Gibbs free energy minimization principle. This approach is considered suitable to evaluate the performance and predict the equilibrium composition of HTG products [7]. Similar approach has been widely adopted in numerous

HTG modelling works utilizing Aspen Plus [12, 13], where the modelling results have been verified to accurately represent the experimental data from previous HTG studies.

Prior to entering the reactor, the digestate from the AD reactor (*DIGESTAT*) is mixed with water (*WATER2*) in a mixer (*MIX1*) and pumped to the reactor pressure in *PUMP1*. Subsequently, the stream *S3* is preheated in heat exchanger HE1, which utilizes heat from the turbine's exhaust stream, and sent to heat exchanger *HE2* for further heating to its supercritical state. Since the *DIGESTAT* stream still contains the non-conventional fixed carbon compound from the undigested AD product, an RYIELD reactor block (*HTG1*) is employed to breakdown the compound into its elements. The output of *HTG1* is a fictitious stream *S6*, which flows to the RGIBBS reactor (*HTG2*), where the Gibbs free energy minimization takes place. The reaction produces gaseous product (*GASPROD*) consisting of supercritical water and syngas, which is mainly composed of $H_2$, CO, $CO_2$, and $CH_4$.

*2.1.3. Power generation for energy recovery from HTG*

The hot-pressurized gaseous product from the HTG (*GASPROD*) contains a high amount of energy which can be recovered via power generation. For this purpose, it is important to consider a key requirement of the system that the syngas can be recycled to the AD reactor. Therefore, the power generation in this integrated system is designed to utilize the sensible heat in the *GASPROD* stream without chemical conversion. This is achieved by employing two turbines (*TURB1* and *TURB2*) for power generation with a reheater (*HE3*) between the turbine stages. Two-stage turbines with reheater are employed to obtain a higher energy recovery. A number of previous studies have also reported using turbine for direct expansion and energy recovery of HTG gaseous product [14, 15]. The heat remaining in the turbine exhaust stream (*S9*) undergoes cooling in *HE1* and *HE4* before the stream is sent to *SEP1* for the separation of syngas and water phase.

*2.2. Performance Evaluation of the Process*

The performance of the proposed integrated system is evaluated by investigating the effect of important process parameters, i.e., HTG temperature and digestate-to-water (D/W) ratio, on biomethane and power production. As the proposed system requires additional heat supply from the utility, the total heat requirement is also assessed. In addition, the overall energy efficiency, $\eta$, of the process is calculated using Equation (2) [16], where the *total energy recovered* is the sum of recovered energy in the form of electricity and lower heating value (LHV) of the produced biogas; and the *total energy input* is the sum of input energy from available sources, including heating value (LHV) of the feedstock.

$$\eta = \frac{Total\ energy\ recovered}{Total\ energy\ input} \tag{2}$$

*2.3. Pinch Analysis*

Pinch analysis is performed in this study to identify the possibility for reducing the energy consumption (heating and cooling duties) of the system by heat integration. The first step is analyzing the available heat sinks and sources in the processes. A grand composite curve is developed based on the heat sinks and sources data obtained from the simulation [17].

# 3. Results

To evaluate the effect of syngas recycling, a comparison of the proposed process with and without syngas recycle was carried out. The comparison was performed under the base-case condition (Table 1).

*Table 1. Process Condition for the Aspen Plus Simulation*

| Process parameter | Value |
|---|---|
| HTG Temperature | 600 °C |
| HTG Pressure | 250 bar |
| Feedstock mass flow | 10000 kg/hr |

Figure 3 (a) and (b) show a clear correlation between the amount of recycled syngas from the HTG and total biomethane production from the AD, indicating that the amount of recycled syngas directly affects biomethane production. According to the figures, both syngas and biomethane production increase at higher HTG temperature and lower D/W ratio. The HTG temperature positively affects syngas production by enhancing the highly endothermic stream reforming reaction within the HTG [12, 18]. On the other hand, a lower D/W ratio means providing more water into the system, making the HTG feed more dilute. Water played a significant role in HTG as a reactant for the steam-reforming reaction and water-gas shift reaction, both are enhanced with an increase in water concentration [19]. Previous studies have confirmed that a lower feedstock concentration leads to higher gasification efficiency and increasing gas yield [20]. Furthermore, both figures indicate that the influence of temperature is more prominent at lower D/W ratio. A possible reason is that the lower feedstock concentration minimizes competing reaction pathways [21]. Therefore, the positive effect of temperature towards the main reactions in HTG are more significant at lower D/W ratio.

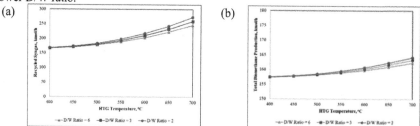

*Figure 3. Effect of HTG Temperature and D/W Ratio on (a) Syngas Production; and (b) Biomethane Production (P = 250 bar)*

The influence of temperature and D/W ratio on the energy performance of the process is shown on Figure 4. Operating the HTG reactor at a higher temperature requires higher heat input prior to the HTG reactor (HE 1 and HE 2). Accordingly, the total heat requirement increases as the temperature rises. However, higher HTG temperature also leads to an increase in the total power recovery. This is due to the higher syngas production, as previously indicated in Figure 3 (a), which leads to pressure increase in the steam-syngas mixture entering the steam turbines. Consequently, higher HTG temperature results in an increased overall energy efficiency of the process (Figure 4 (b)). On the other hand, lowering D/W ratio, which means providing more water into the system, also increases both the power production and heat requirement. Operating at a lower D/W ratio increases the heat requirement substantially, whereas the increase in power recovery is less prominent, as suggested by Figure 4 (a). Consequently, as shown in Figure 4 (b), the overall energy efficiency of the process decreases at lower D/W ratios.

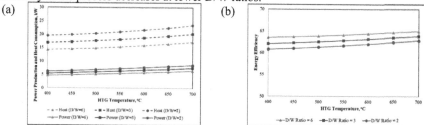

*Figure 4. Effect of HTG Temperature and D/W Ratio on (a) Total Produced Power and Total Required Heat; and (b) Energy Efficiency (P = 250 bar)*

Figure 5 displays the grand composite curve obtained from pinch analysis of the system. The curve was obtained using $\Delta T_{min}$ of 10 °C. The analysis found that the system does not have further potential for heat integration, as the availability of heat sinks are significantly larger than those of heat sources. The utilization of the turbine exhaust stream (*S9*) for the preheating of the stream entering HTG reactor (*S3*) reduces 1.1 MW of both the hot and cold utility requirement. However, 14.08 MW of heating duty and 0.22 MW of cooling duty should be provided by the utility.

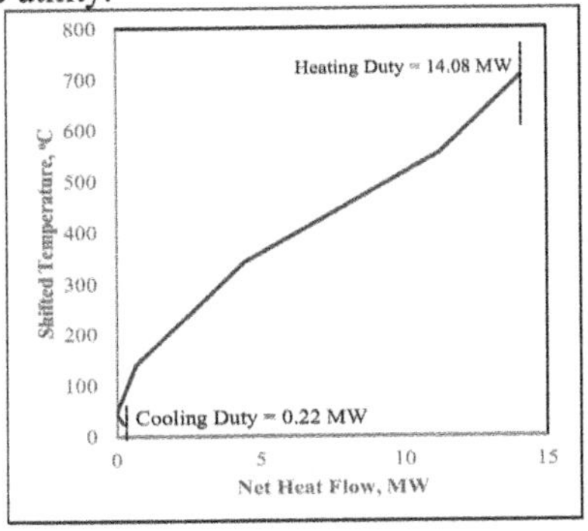

*Figure 5. Grand Composite Curve from Pinch Analysis*

## 4. Discussion

The present study confirms the potential to improve biomethane production in AD through an integrated AD-HTG system with syngas recycle. The developed process model has been able to investigate the effect of key process parameters with a focus on the HTG block, without modifying process parameters in the other parts of the process. Overall, the result shows a substantial increase of 26.10% in total biomethane production when syngas is recycled to the AD. In addition, power production increases by 21.42% and total energy efficiency is 20.05% higher compared to the process without syngas recycle. However, evaluation of other process parameters as such of the AD block would be of interest. Future works might benefit from utilizing a more complex model that can better represent the complex biochemical reactions in the AD system.

On the other hand, the Pinch analysis was performed in this study with a $\Delta T_{min}$ of 10 °C. The consequence of using a low $\Delta T_{min}$ is that a large heat transfer area might be required, leading to higher heat exchanger capital cost. A more comprehensive evaluation with techno-economic analysis should be performed in the future work. It also suggests that the process design requires further modification to obtain a higher heat integration. A possible option for example is integrating a gas turbine combusting a fraction of the syngas.

## 5. Conclusion

A process integration of AD, HTG, and power production is proposed in this paper to improve the efficiency of the AD. A process model is developed using Aspen Plus to assess the performance of the integrated process. The effect of temperature (400-700 °C) and digestate-to-water ratio (2, 3, and 6) is investigated. The result shows that higher energy efficiency is obtained at higher temperature and higher D/W ratio. The syngas recycling to the AD increases biomethane production by 26.10%, power production by 21.42%, and total energy efficiency by 20.05%, compared to the process without syngas recycle. The proposed process design provides an innovative solution for digestate management and feedstock scarcity, as well as enhancing biomethane production via AD, with an additional benefit of producing power from the integrated process.

## Acknowledgements

This work was supported by the BioSynGas project partly funded by the Research Council of Norway (Project Number: 319723).

# References

1. R. Nkoa, 2014, Agricultural benefits and environmental risks of soil fertilization with anaerobic digestates: a review, Agronomy for Sustainable Development, 34(2), 473-492.
2. D. Divya, L. Gopinath, and P.M. Christy, 2015, A review on current aspects and diverse prospects for enhancing biogas production in sustainable means, Renewable and sustainable energy reviews, 42, 690-699.
3. R. Kumar, S. Singh, and O.V. Singh, 2008, Bioconversion of lignocellulosic biomass: biochemical and molecular perspectives, Journal of industrial microbiology and biotechnology, 35(5), 377-391.
4. A. Molino, et al., 2019, Experimental and theoretical investigation on the recovery of green chemicals and energy from mixed agricultural wastes by coupling anaerobic digestion and supercritical water gasification, Chemical Engineering Journal, 370, 1101-1110.
5. Z. Yang, et al., 2020, Improvement of biofuel recovery from food waste by integration of anaerobic digestion, digestate pyrolysis and syngas biomethanation under mesophilic and thermophilic conditions, Journal of Cleaner Production, 256, 120594.
6. Y. Li, Y. Chen, and J. Wu, 2019, Enhancement of methane production in anaerobic digestion process: A review, Applied energy, 240, 120-137.
7. D. Hantoko, et al., 2019, Supercritical water gasification of sewage sludge and combined cycle for H2 and power production–a thermodynamic study, International Journal of Hydrogen Energy, 44(45), 24459-24470.
8. G. Symons and A. Buswell, 1933, The methane fermentation of carbohydrates, Journal of the american chemical society, 55(5), 2028-2036.
9. H. Nguyen, S. Heaven, and C. Banks, 2014, Energy potential from the anaerobic digestion of food waste in municipal solid waste stream of urban areas in Vietnam, International Journal of Energy and Environmental Engineering, 5(4), 365-374.
10. A. Naqi, J.N. Kuhn, and B. Joseph, 2019, Techno-economic analysis of producing liquid fuels from biomass via anaerobic digestion and thermochemical conversion, Biomass and Bioenergy, 130, 105395.
11. A. Skorek-Osikowska, et al., 2020, Thermodynamic, economic and environmental assessment of energy systems including the use of gas from manure fermentation in the context of the Spanish potential, Energy, 200, 117452.
12. D. Hantoko, et al., 2018, Thermodynamic study on the integrated supercritical water gasification with reforming process for hydrogen production: Effects of operating parameters, International Journal of Hydrogen Energy, 43(37), 17620-17632.
13. J.A. Okolie, et al., 2020, Hydrothermal gasification of soybean straw and flax straw for hydrogen-rich syngas production: Experimental and thermodynamic modelling, Energy Conversion and Management, 208, 112545.
14. A. Molino, et al., 2016, Process innovation via supercritical water gasification to improve the conventional plants performance in treating highly humid biomass, Waste and biomass valorization, 7(5), 1289-1295.
15. C. Cao, 2017, et al., System analysis of pulping process coupled with supercritical water gasification of black liquor for combined hydrogen, heat and power production, Energy, 132, 238-247.
16. M. Luqman and T. Al-Ansari, 2021, A novel solution towards zero waste in dairy farms: A thermodynamic study of an integrated polygeneration approach, Energy Conversion and Management, 230, 113753.
17. I.C. Kemp, 2011, Pinch analysis and process integration: a user guide on process integration for the efficient use of energy, Elsevier.
18. D. Macrì, et al., 2020, Supercritical water gasification of biomass and agro-food residues: Energy assessment from modelling approach, Renewable Energy, 150, 624-636.
19. M. Yan, et al., 2019, Experimental study on the energy conversion of food waste via supercritical water gasification: improvement of hydrogen production, International Journal of Hydrogen Energy, 44(10), 4664-4673.
20. Y. Matsumura, et al., 2005, Biomass gasification in near-and super-critical water: status and prospects, Biomass and Bioenergy, 29(4), 269-292.
21. J.A. Onwudili and P.T. Williams, 2014, Production of hydrogen from biomass via supercritical water gasification, in Near-critical and supercritical water and their applications for biorefineries, Springer, 299-322.

Antonis Kokossis, Michael C. Georgiadis, Efstratios N. Pistikopoulos (Eds.)
PROCEEDINGS OF THE 33rd European Symposium on Computer Aided Process Engineering
(ESCAPE33), June 18-21, 2023, Athens, Greece

# Optimization of a continuous multi-stage fluidized bed system for CO2 capture utilizing temperature swing adsorption

Yuri Souza Beleli,[a] José Luis de Paiva,[a] Marcelo Martins Seckler,[a] Galo Antonio Carrillo Le Roux[a]

[a]*Department of Chemical Engineering, Polytechnic School, University of São Paulo, Av. Prof. Luciano Gualberto, trav. 3, 380, São Paulo 05508-010, Brazil.*

## Abstract

In this work we study a system to capture the $CO_2$ resulting from processes of power generation combustion by capturing it with a solid adsorbent in a fluidized bed, thus obtaining a process with low carbon emission. The flue gas firstly goes through the adsorption column in an upward flow, contacting an adsorbent fluidized at each stage, which captures the $CO_2$. The adsorbent flows downward, from a stage to the next right below. The resulting bottom solid flow containing the loaded adsorbent is transported to the desorption column so that a stripping gas removes the $CO_2$ from the adsorbent. The simulation is carried out in GAMS so that the conditions necessary to achieve the adsorption and the desorption processes could be analyzed and optimized to best synthesize the full system.

**Keywords**: CO2 adsorption; fluidized bed; CO2 capture; Temperature Swing Adsorption.

## 1. Introduction

For the mitigation of the effects of greenhouse gases (GHG) concentration in the atmosphere, $CO_2$ capture is a possible solution because the captured $CO_2$ can be concentrated and stored or used as a chemical product.

Recently, the use of solid adsorbents has been studied due to their economic and energetic advantages[1]. In trying to progress this technology further, it is possible to use solid fluidized bed adsorbents, which have even better thermal and material exchange conditions[2]. Adsorption is an exothermic process, while desorption is an endothermic process. To capture $CO_2$, both adsorption and desorption steps are necessary, which makes the temperature swing adsorption process studied in this paper a possibility. The temperature swing adsorption defines that the continuous system composed of the two parts (adsorption and desorption) should be operated at temperatures that favor the respective mechanics, thus modulating the temperatures between them.

The reduction of $CO_2$ emissions has become of great interest worldwide in order to reduce the effects of this gas in the atmosphere. An issue of great interest is controlling the rate of global warming, discussed in the treaty of Paris, which proposes to keep it between 1.5 and 2.0°C on average[3]. Among the alternatives for reducing the emission of greenhouse gases, carbon capture technologies stand out. Post-combustion capture technologies have been considered the most viable because they can be implemented directly in the effluent gases of the combustion energy production process[4]. The $CO_2$ resulting from capture technologies can be transported for storage or used as feed for industrial processes.

For the adsorption process to be used continuously, it is necessary that there be recovery of the adsorbent (desorption of the adsorbate), which can be done through a cyclic chain where the situations occur one after the other.

The adsorption process is favored at high pressures and low temperatures while the adsorbent recovery process (desorption) is favored at low pressures and high temperatures. In cyclic adsorption processes there are the options of pressure modulation (PSA), temperature modulation (TSA) and a combination of these processes (PTSA).

In pressure modulation, the adsorbed gases in the adsorption step are desorbed by reducing the pressure in the bed, while in temperature modulation the desorption occurs by heating the adsorbent[5].

The system studied is composed of two columns, in which the first one is the adsorption column and the second one is the desorption column. In both columns the solid flows downwards while the gas flows upwards. The columns are connected by the solid flow, which after coming out of the adsorption column at its base, is transported to the desorption column at its top so the $CO_2$ adsorbed can be stripped and captured for stocking or posterior usage.

## 2. Methodology

For multi-stage adsorption and desorption columns, stage modeling is used, where the balances of each stage are described in a general way so that the set of stages can be used in the optimization step. The stage has two countercurrent flows, the gas flows upwards and the solid flows downwards. The stages are designed so the gas flow is able to fluidize the solid flow, resulting in a downward fluidized bed. A representation of a generic adsorption and desorption column stage can be found in Figure 1. The mass balance is represented in Equation (1).

$$F_{j-1}y_{i,j-1} - ms(q_{i,j} - q_{i,j+1}) - F_j y_{i,j} = 0 \tag{1}$$

The adsorbed amount is simulated using Toth's equilibrium, represented in Equation (2), which relates the partial pressures of the components to the equilibrium variables.

$$q_i^*[mol/kg] = \frac{q_{mi}(b_i P_i)^{n_i}}{(1+\sum_i (b_i P_i)^{n_i})^{\frac{1}{n_i}}} \tag{2}$$

In the energy balance, the total enthalpies of the inlet and outlet currents are evaluated, as well as the energy added to or removed from the system. It is represented by Equation (3).

$$F_{j-1}h_{j-1} + ms(H_{j+1} - H_j) - F_j h_j + Q_j = 0 \tag{3}$$

The enthalpies of the gas and solid streams are evaluated, with the enthalpies of the components present, the enthalpy of the solid and the enthalpy of the adsorption process, they are presents in Equation (4) and Equation (5).

$$h_j[J/mol] = \sum_i y_{i,j} \int_{Tr}^{T_j} cp_i dT \tag{4}$$

$$H_j[J/kg] = \int_{Tr}^{T_j} cp_s dT + \sum_i q_{i,j} \int_{Tr}^{T_j} cp_i dT - 1000 \sum_i \Lambda(q_{i,j}) \tag{5}$$

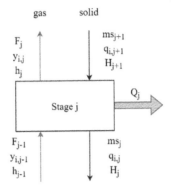

Figure 1: Stage representation with its gas and solid flows.

The parameters of the equilibrium model were previously validated[6] and used to simulate the stages. This model was then simulated in GAMS so the conditions necessary to achieve the adsorption and the desorption processes could be studied.

## 3. Results and discussion

### 3.1. Adiabatic Simulation

#### 3.1.1. Adsorption column

For the adsorption simulations, a gas stream with 15% $CO_2$ and 85% $N_2$ was considered. The solid inlet stream is composed of pure adsorbent (zeolite 13x BF). The column inlet streams are at 323 K[7]. The simulation was done by varying the ratio between the gas-solid mass flow rates, fixing the gas flow rate and varying the pure adsorbent flow rate at the column inlet (S/G ratio). The results of the solid stream outlet temperature as a function of the S/G ratio of the column feed (with a different number of stages) are shown in Figure 2.

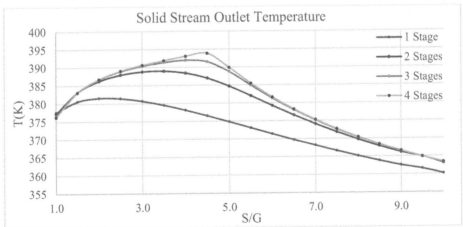

Figure 2: Bottom solid stream temperature related to column feed S/G ratio.

By increasing the amount adsorbed (increasing S/G), more adsorption heat is released and then the temperature increases. However, by increasing S/G, more sensible heat will be required for the temperature of the currents to increase. In each simulation there is a maximum temperature point, and from this point on, the column temperature decreases as S/G increases, because the amount of solid becomes more prominent than the amount adsorbed, in terms of energy distribution.

The results of the total percentage adsorbed (of the amount of $CO_2$ available in the gas) function of the S/G ratio of the column feed are shown in Figure 3.

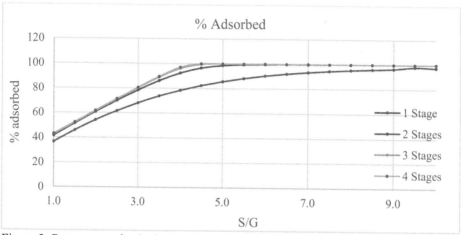

Figure 3: Percentage adsorbed related to column feed S/G ratio.

By increasing the number of stages, a lower S/G ratio is required for the adsorbed percentage to reach significant numbers, as well as the solid flow rate. As stated before, the relationship between number of stages and solid flow rate will be an essential part of the optimization, since their costs will be of extreme importance when calculating the total cost of the project.

To confirm how adsorption is influenced by column temperature, a one (1) stage simulation was performed, with S/G ratio equal to five (5), varying the temperature between 313 K and 413 K. The results are shown in Figure 4.

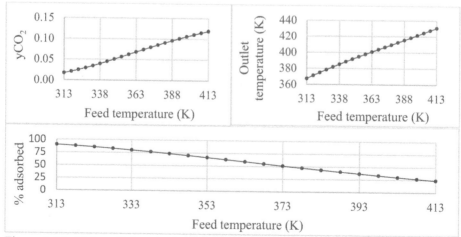

Figure 4: Variables of interest related to the feed temperature in 1 stage.

Since the adsorption reaction is exothermic, increasing the temperature will disfavor it. By increasing the temperature in the column, the percentage of $CO_2$ adsorbed will be lower, causing its mole fraction in the outlet gas to be higher. As less adsorption occurs, causing less heat to be released into the column, the difference between the column inlet and column outlet temperatures decreases.

### 3.1.2. Desorption Column

For the recovery simulations a gaseous stream of pure $CO_2$ was considered so that the driving forces relating to the gas composition and temperatures can be studied. The solid inlet stream is composed of adsorbent (zeolite 13x BF) and adsorbed $CO_2$. The column inlet streams are at 513 K[7]. Simulations of the desorption column with different inlet temperatures were made to evaluate the temperature influence in the process. The results of the percentage recovered and outlet temperatures of the solid outlet stream are shown in Figure 5.

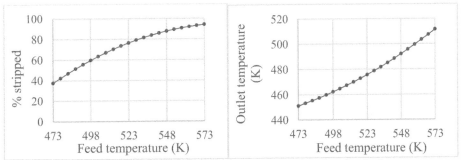

*Figure 5: Percentage stripped and outlet temperature related to the feed temperature.*

As expected, when increasing the inlet temperature of the currents, the recovery is favored and the percentage recovered is higher. Like adsorption, when the desorption mechanism is favored the difference between the temperatures of the inlet and outlet column currents increases.

### 3.2. Isothermal simulation

For the isothermal simulation of the adsorption column, a gas with 15% $CO_2$ and 85% $N_2$ was again considered. The solid inlet stream is composed of pure adsorbent (zeolite 13x BF). The column inlet and outlet streams are at 323 K[7].

Simulations were done by varying the ratio between the S/G ratio. One (1) stage results of the gas mole fraction at the outlet, percentage adsorbed are shown in Figure 6.

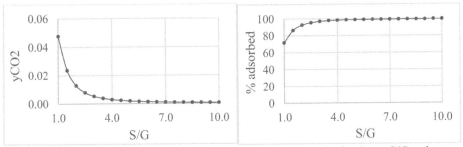

Figure 6: Outlet gas molar fraction and percentage related to feed column S/G ratio.

Later simulations with more than 1 stage showed that there is no significant increase in the adsorption process in this specific temperature when compared to 1 stage, due to the saturation of the adsorbent (lower S/G) or adsorption near 100% of equilibrium (higher S/G).

## 4. Conclusion

A mathematical model for stage adsorption has been developed so that it can be extended to multi-stage configurations and to the desorption process. The model consists of mass and energy balances coupled to the thermodynamics of adsorption of the mixture of carbon dioxide and nitrogen on solid adsorbents. The Toth equilibrium isotherm was considered, employing experimentally determined parameters. Initial studies indicate that less than four stages are sufficient for effective $CO_2$ removal. The mass ratio of solid to gas proved to be important for the adsorption process because the amount of pure solid present in the inlet stream favors the adsorption mechanics. In the future, a cost analysis will be performed, and it is expected that there should be a trade-off between the energy cost of heat exchanger and the cost of the adsorbent that will be used in the column. This happens because these factors will directly influence the percentage adsorbed, since in adsorption both the temperature of the stages and the S/G ratio are key factors in obtaining a high percentage adsorbed, while in desorption the energy cost will be the main factor to consider. This study was financed in part by the Coordenação de Aperfeiçoamento de Pessoal de Nível Superior – Brasil (CAPES) – Finance Code 001. We gratefully acknowledge support of the RCGI – Research Centre for Greenhouse Gas Innovation, hosted by the University of São Paulo (USP) and sponsored by FAPESP – São Paulo Research Foundation (2014/50279-4 and 2020/15230-5) and Shell Brasil, and the strategic importance of the support given by ANP (Brazil's National Oil, Natural Gas and Biofuels Agency) through the R&D levy regulation.

## References

1. R. Morales-Ospino, et al., 2018, Assessment of temperature swing adsorption configurations for CO2 capture on zeolite 13X, Dissertation (Masters), Universidade Federal do Ceará.
2. S.E. Zanco et al., 2018, Modeling of circulating fluidized beds systems for post-combustion CO2 capture via temperature swing adsorption, AIChE Journal, , v. 64, n. 5, p. 1744–175.
3. S. Neto et al., 2021, Calcium looping post-combustion CO2 capture in sugarcane bagasse fuelled power plants. International Journal of Greenhouse Gas Control, v. 110, p. 103401.
4. Y. Wang et al., 2017, A Review of Post-combustion CO2 Capture Technologies from Coal-fired Power Plants. Energy Procedia, v. 114, p. 650–665.
5. F. Dietrich et al., 2018, Experimental study of the adsorber performance in a multi-stage fluidized bed system for continuous CO2 capture by means of temperature swing adsorption. Fuel Processing Technology, v. 173, p. 103–111.
6. R. Morales-Ospino et al., 2020, Assessment of CO2 desorption from 13X zeolite for a prospective TSA process. Adsorption 26, 813–824.
7. R. Morales-Ospino et al., 2021, Parametric Analysis of a Moving Bed Temperature Swing Adsorption (MBTSA) Process for Postcombustion CO2 Capture. Industrial & Engineering Chemistry Research, v. 60, n. 29, p. 10736–10752.

Antonis Kokossis, Michael C. Georgiadis, Efstratios N. Pistikopoulos (Eds.)
PROCEEDINGS OF THE 33rd European Symposium on Computer Aided Process Engineering
(ESCAPE33), June 18-21, 2023, Athens, Greece

# Regional sustainability of food-energy-water nexus considering water stress using multi-objective modeling and optimization

Anupam Satyakam,[a] Rashi Dhanraj,[a] Yogendra Shastri,[a]

[a]*Indian Institute of Technology Bombay, Mumbai 400076, India*
*yshastri@iitb.ac.in*

## Abstract

In this work, we developed a regional optimization model to achieve food-energy-water nexus sustainability in the context of water stress. An ethanol-based bioenergy system is developed. The model considers district-level water and land availability. The critical decision variables are the allocation of land area to chosen crops and the residue selection for ethanol production. The primary goals are to maximize farmers' profit and minimize water withdrawals while meeting the ethanol production targets. The resulting multi-objective mixed-integer linear programming problem was applied to a case study of 33 districts in Maharashtra, India. Results are compared for two cases, the land practices suggested by the optimization model and the existing practices. Upon reducing water consumption by 40.7% compared to the base case, only a 2.2% reduction in profits was observed from 229 $/ha to 224 $/ha. For ethanol water footprint minimization, 60% of available water consumption is found to be optimal where profits stand at 117.4 $/ha.

**Keywords**: Water stress, food-energy-water nexus, regional sustainability, optimization.

## 1. Introduction

The security of food, energy, and water has been a subject of serious concern for the last few decades. These resources are being depleted at an alarming rate. The food, energy, and water nexus provides a strategy for achieving their security. According to United Nations projections, India's population will reach 1.5 billion people in 2030. This demand growth causes more than 60% of energy consumption (UN,2014). Water stress is present in 45% of the regions globally, with 18% of them experiencing high water stress and 9% experiencing severe water stress. In India, 600 million people face high to extreme water stress (UN-Water,2021). Additionally, the area under the crops will grow by 6% between 2015 and 2050, while the water withdrawn for the same will grow by 42% (IPCC, 2018). Particularly, in the semi-arid and arid regions like India, the competition for water resources between the production of food and energy can result from the unsustainable use and management of water resources. Therefore, water resources should be handled sustainably. In this study, we introduced a water stress constraint that would limit the consumption of water for irrigational purposes to a much lower value compared to the existing practices and simultaneously maintain the economic benefits. The bio-refinery model considered in this work was developed earlier in the literature (Dhanraj et al., 2021). Their work didn't take surface water as one of the sources for irrigation. Also, the rainfall recharge was neglected. This is not desirable as some crops rely on surface water for irrigation and rainfall recharge availability relaxes the stress on groundwater. To overcome these shortcomings, changes have been made to this model to obtain optimal land patterns in the context of water stress.

## 2. Model description

A multi-objective optimization approach is used to build an ethanol-based bioenergy system. The objective of this study is to develop a bioenergy system that is limited by the availability of district-level land, regional water, and conflicting water demands. The choice of residues for ethanol production and the allocation of land areas to the chosen crops are the crucial choices. There are four objectives: minimization of ethanol cost, ethanol's water footprint, irrigation water, and farmers' profit maximization. The resulting problem was formulated as a mixed integer linear problem (MILP) and solved using the epsilon constraint method (EPCM). The optimization model, constraints, parameters, key variables, and objectives are represented in Figure 1.

The model considers the amount of water used by agricultural crops as well as the economic rewards to those involved in agriculture and ethanol production. For water balance modeling, the model uses the district as the base unit. The consumption and groundwater recharge for each district are then estimated based on the agricultural land use pattern. The water stress constraint is applied in each district for each season separately. The time frame of the model is one year, and is divided into three seasons: Kharif, Rabi, and Summer.

Important assumptions of this model:
- Inter-district groundwater recharge flow is ignored, which implies that the recharge occurring in a district is used in the same district.
- Ethanol production was based on the total transport fuel consumption and a particular petrol blending rate.
- Groundwater recharge during Kharif season was available for utilization during Rabi season and groundwater recharge during Rabi season was available for utilization during the summer.

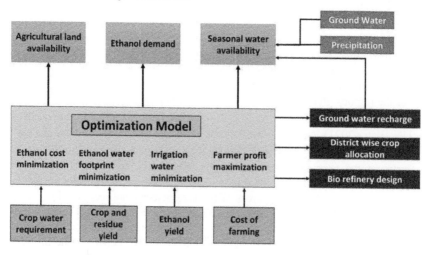

Figure 1: Schematics representing the scope of the model: orange, green, yellow, and grey boxes represent constraints, parameters, optimization model and the key variables, including final decisions, respectively (Adapted from Dhanraj et al. (2021)).

### 2.1. Optimization model formulation

The mixed-integer linear programming problem was formulated to solve the multi-objective optimization problem in General Algebraic Modeling System (GAMS) version 24.9.2 and solved using the CPLEX® MILP solver (Robichaud, 2010). This section discusses the constraints, decision variable and the objective functions of the model.

### 2.1.1. Constraints

The amount of land allotted $x(i,j,t)$ to various crops is the key decision variable in this model. This cannot exceed the amount of agricultural land available $AL(i,t)$ in each district. Here index $i$, $j$, and $t$ denotes the location of farm, crops and season, respectively. Agricultural land is often used for other purposes, such as cultivating fruits and vegetables. Therefore, a fraction of the land $F_{AL}(i,t)$ is used for specific crops.

$$\sum_j x(i,j,t) \leq AL(i,t) \times F_{AL}(i,t) \qquad \forall i,t \qquad (1)$$

Rainwater or irrigation can be used to meet the crop's water needs. The rainfall absorbed by plants to account for crop water requirement is termed green water requirement or effective rainfall (ER), and the irrigation water (IR) used to meet the crop water requirement (CWR) is termed blue water. Irrigation water requirement is calculated as:

$$IR(i,j,t) = CWR(i,j,t) - ER(i,j,t) \qquad \forall i,j,t \qquad (2)$$

In the constraints related to water, the water balance for Kharif season is discussed first. Equation 3 represents the constraint on effective rainfall (green water)

$$\sum_j ER(i,j,t_k) \times x(i,j,t_k) \leq \quad R(i,t_k) \times (1-\zeta) \times AL(i,t_k) \times F_{AL}(i,t_k) - $$
$$\sum_j GWR(i,j,t_k) \times x(i,j,t_k) \qquad \forall i \qquad (3)$$

Here, the LHS term represents the rainwater consumed by crop $j$, in the district $i$ during the Kharif season $t_k$. On the righthand side, the first term is the total rainfall available after run-off consideration. The land fraction in this term ensures the rainfall is considered only within the area covered by the crops of interest. $\zeta$ is the run-off fraction, assumed to be the same for all the districts. The second term indicates the groundwater recharge that is not utilized as rainwater source for crop utilization.

Irrigation water requirements for the crops can be met in two ways, the crops that use groundwater for irrigation and the others that use surface water. The resulting constraints are then modeled using equations 4 and 5.

$$\sum_j IR(i,j,t_k) \times x(i,j,t_k) \leq GW(i,t_k) \times F_{AL}(i,t_k) + \sum_j GWR(i,j,t_k) \times x(i,j,t_k) + $$
$$GRO(i,t_k) \qquad \forall i \qquad (4)$$
$$\sum_j IRS(i,j,t_k) \times x(i,j,t_k) \leq SW(i,t_k) \times F_{AL}(i,t_k) \qquad \forall i \qquad (5)$$

Here, $IR(i,j,t_k)$ denotes the groundwater needed by crop $j$ in the district $i$ during the Kharif season and $IRS(i,j,t_k)$ denotes the surface water needed by crop $j$ in the district $i$ during the Kharif season. The RHS term in equation 4 is the sum of three terms, a fraction of total groundwater that is available for utilization of selected crops, groundwater getting recharged within the same season, and recharge through the land other than the selected crops. Similarly, in equation 5, the RHS term indicates the fraction of surface water available for the consumption of selected crops. After green water and blue water requirements are met, the net groundwater left in the Kharif season is represented through equation 6.

$$N_{GW}^{K}(i) = [R(i,t_k) \times (1-\zeta) \times AL(i,t_k) \times F_{AL}(i,t_k) - \sum_j ER(i,j,t_k) \times x(i,j,t_k)]$$

$$+ [(GW(i,t_k) \times F_{AL}(i,t_k) + GRO(i,t_k) \times F_{AL}(i,t_k))$$
$$- \sum_j IR(i,j,t_k) \times x(i,j,t_k)] \qquad \forall i \qquad (6)$$

Here, the RHS denotes the difference between the sum of water available in the form of rainwater, groundwater, and surface water minus the total crop water requirement. Water balances for Rabi and summer seasons are modeled in a similar manner as that of Kharif. In the equations 4 and 6, for the Rabi season, the net groundwater left after the Kharif season is available for irrigation usage. Similarly, for the Summer season, the net groundwater left after the Rabi season is available for irrigation usage.

To reduce this over-dependence on groundwater, a groundwater stress constraint that puts a limitation on the total available water for agricultural purposes is included in the model. This constraint is imposed seasonally and for each individual district. Groundwater stress is defined as the ratio of demand for water to the available water, and it is an indicator of competition for water resources (Luck M. et al., 2015). Its value ranges from '0' to '1' where 0 indicates no availability of water for irrigation and 1 indicates entire water availability. The groundwater stress factor accounts for the groundwater stress level across each individual district. This can be mathematically written as:

$$g_k =$$

$$\frac{\sum_j IR(i,j,t_k) \times x(i,j,t_k) + DIW(i,t_k)}{[GW(i,t_k) \times F_{AL}(i,t_k) + \sum_j GWR(i,j,t_k) \times x(i,j,t_k) + GRO(i,t_k) + SW(i,t_k) \times F_{AL}(i,t_k)]} \quad \forall i \quad (7)$$

The total available water for irrigational purposes is modeled from equation 10 as:

$$\sum_j IR(i,j,t_k) \times x(i,j,t_k) \leq g_k \times [GW(i,t_k) \times F_{AL}(i,t_k) + \sum_j GWR(i,j,t_k) \times$$
$$x(i,j,t_k) + GRO(i,t_k) + SW(i,t_k) \times$$
$$F_{AL}(i,t_k)] - DIW(i,t_k) \qquad \forall i \qquad (8)$$

This puts a constraint on the sum of blue water for the Kharif season. In the equation 7, numerator represents the sum of blue water requirement and water consumed by domestic and industrial sectors $DIW(i,t_k)$ and the denominator represents the total available water. In the stress equations for the Rabi and Summer, water left after Kharif and Rabi will be added to the total available water.

*2.1.2. Objective functions*
There are four objectives in this multi-objective optimization model. The first objective is minimization of ethanol cost, and is formulated as follows:

$$\text{Min } J_c = \sum_{i,j,t} C_E(i,j,t)$$

$$(9)$$

Here, $C_E(i,j,t)$ is the cost of ethanol production. Cost of ethanol includes the cost of residue, cost of transport, cost of ethanol production process and storage cost. The objective of maximization of profit earned by farmers is formulated as follows.

$$\text{Max } J_P = \sum_{i,j,t} P_F(i,j,t)$$

$$(10)$$

The profit earned by farmers $P_F(i, j, t)$ is the difference between the price of agricultural product and residue to the cost of cultivation. The third objective, minimization of water footprint of ethanol, is formulated as follows:

$$\text{Min } J_{WF} = \sum_{i,j,t} W_{FR}(i, j, t) \tag{11}$$

Here, $W_{FR}(i, j, t)$ is the water footprint of ethanol produced from different agricultural residue. The fourth objective, minimization of irrigation water consumption is formulated as follows:

$$\text{Min } J_{IR} = \sum_{i,j,t} IR(i, j, t) \times x(i, j, t) \tag{12}$$

Here, $IR(i, j, t)$ is the irrigation water required by the crop $j$ in m³/ha, which is multiplied by land allocated to the crop. This single objective optimization problem is solved for various combinations of groundwater stress to obtain the trade-offs between different objective functions and find out the optimal water practices.

## 3. Case study of Maharashtra, India

The model has been applied to a case study of 33 districts covered under 12 river basins. Cotton, sorghum (both Kharif and Rabi varieties), wheat, rice, and sugarcane are the five crops considered in the case study. The area allocated to crops other than the five crops of interest is assumed to be constant. The groundwater recharge data for the Solapur district was calibrated for different crops. Based on the data for the Solapur district, the correlation between rainfall and groundwater recharge was obtained using the linear regression method. This correlation was used for all districts.

## 4. Results and discussion

Based on historical water use from the years 2004 to 2020, the degree of groundwater stress in various districts was computed. It was observed that the number of districts moving towards high water stress has increased from 17 districts (58.6%) in 2004 to 23 districts (67.6%) in 2020.

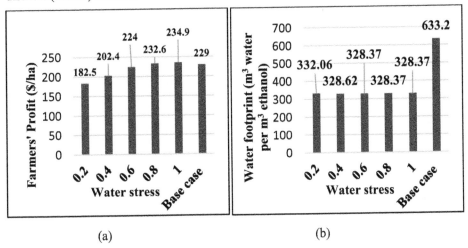

(a)                                              (b)

Figure 2: Effect of groundwater stress factor on two objectives (a) Maximum farmers' profit and (b) Minimum ethanol water footprint.

Profit increased with the rising groundwater stress factor, or higher water availability, as shown in figure 2(a). This can be explained by the rise in the amount of land allocated for rice and wheat, as well as the overall acreage. The stress factor was also calculated for the current land use practices and its value was found to be 1.07. As compared with the base case, for a stress factor of 0.6, a reduction in 40.7% of water consumption, profit only reduced by 2.2% and ethanol cost had a least value of 0.71 $/lit. ethanol. From figure 2(b), water footprint value for 0.6 stress factor is almost half (328.3) that of the base case (633.2). Also, farmers' profit has a value of 117.4 $/ha and ethanol cost has a value of 0.69 $/lit. ethanol.

## 5. Conclusion

In this work, we tried to reduce the water consumption for irrigation and simultaneously maintain economic benefits. We quantified the trade-offs between profits and water withdrawals. In the future, the model can be used to capture the food production aspects and also consider the impacts of climate change on decision-making. Important observations from this study are as follows:

- In case of reduction in water consumption, more land should be allocated to sorghum and less land should be allocated to rice, cotton, and sugarcane.
- On comparing the current land use practices and the land allocation suggested by the model for reduced water consumption, it is evident that there is a need to change the cropping pattern.
- As the change in cropping pattern is farmers choice, government should provide incentives for farmers to shift to less profitable crops.
- Decision makers should make a choice on the water stress factor as increase in profit comes at an expense of increased water consumption.

## References

The United Nations World Water Development Report. 2014. Water and Energy, Paris, UNESCO, Volume 1, ISBN: 978-92-3-104259-1.

The United Nations World Water Development Report, 2021 SDG 6 Water and sanitation for all, Geneva, Switzerland.

IPCC, Global Warming of 1.5 °C. Special Report, Intergovernmental Panel on Climate Change, Geneva, 2018

Dhanraj, R., Punnathanam, V., Shastri, Y. 2021. "Multi objective optimization of ethanol production based on regional resource availability". *Sustainable Production and Consumption*, **27**, 1124-1137.

Robichaud, V., 2010. An Introduction to GAMS 1. Matrix 1–14.

Luck, M., M. Landis, F. Gassert. 2015. "Aqueduct Water Stress Projections: Decadal Projections of Water Supply and Demand Using CMIP5 GCMs." Technical Note. Washington, D.C.: World Resources Institute. Available online at: wri.org/publication/aqueduct-water-stress-projections

Antonis Kokossis, Michael C. Georgiadis, Efstratios N. Pistikopoulos (Eds.)
PROCEEDINGS OF THE 33rd European Symposium on Computer Aided Process Engineering
(ESCAPE33), June 18-21, 2023, Athens, Greece

# Toluene as effective LOHC: detailed techno-economic assessment to identify challenges and opportunities

Elvira Spatolisano[a], Angelo Matichecchia[a], Laura A. Pellegrini[a]
Alberto R. de Angelis[b], Simone Cattaneo[b], Ernesto Roccaro[b]

*[a]GASP - Group on Advanced Separation Processes & GAS Processing, Dipartimento di Chimica, Materiali e Ingegneria Chimica "G. Natta", Politecnico di Milano, Piazza Leonardo da Vinci 32, 20133 Milano, Italy*
*[b]Eni S.p.A. Research and Technological Innovation Department, via F. Maritano 26, 20097 San Donato Milanese, Italy*
elvira.spatolisano@polimi.it

## Abstract

Liquid Organic Hydrogen Carriers (LOHC) are organic molecules that can be reversibly hydrogenated and dehydrogenated to release $H_2$. Due to their easy transport and adaptability to the existing infrastructures, they are gaining attention in research panorama. However, despite their flexibility, LOHC are not yet exploited as large-scale energy storage/transport medium due to the too high costs. In this respect, this work is aimed at performing a detailed techno-economic assessment of $H_2$ distribution through toluene as LOHC. Several scenarios are discussed, at variable distance covered via ship transport together with utilities and raw materials costs, to identify the weaknesses of the overall value-chain and know where to focus research efforts to improve the existing technologies.

**Keywords**: LOHC, hydrogen distribution, hydrogen storage, techno-economic assessment.

## 1. Introduction

To address climate change and achieve the decarbonization target, power generation from fossil fuels has to be limited in favor of an increase in the shares of renewable energies (Pellegrini et al., 2018). The intermittent and seasonal nature of these sources has raised issues on their effective application, also considering that they are often produced in remote sites. In this panorama, where energy storage and transport solutions are needed, hydrogen is a key player supporting the indirect electrification (Hurskainen, 2019). For large-scale distribution and utilization of hydrogen as an energy vector, its safe, efficient and economical storage and transportation is needed (Aakko-Saksa et al., 2018). Among the various alternatives for $H_2$ transportation and storage, a promising one, which has gained increased attention in the last years, is the one based on the so-called liquid organic hydrogen carriers (LOHC), which can be reversibly hydrogenated and dehydrogenated. The hydrogenation involves the chemical bonding of hydrogen to the organic liquid. In this way, the hydrogenated compound can be transported at atmospheric pressure like many other oil-like substances. At the destination, the hydrogen is released via an endothermic dehydrogenation reaction (Roland Berger, 2021). In most of the proposed supply chains, the dehydrogenated LOHC is intended to be transported back to the hydrogen source for reuse. Examples of LOHCs include toluene, dibenzyltoluene or other N-substitute heterocycles. Among them, toluene is the most mature option, used in a demonstration project by Chiyoda Corporation (Naruke, 2017).

Despite the high technology readiness level, no detailed analysis of the overall value-chain of hydrogen transport through toluene is available in literature. To fill this gap and to understand the opportunities and challenges of the LOHCs, this work focuses on an in-depth techno-economic assessment of hydrogen transport considering toluene as LOHC medium. When possible, a detailed Aspen Plus® simulation is carried out for evaluating process performances. For each section of the value-chain (i.e., storage at the loading terminal, hydrogenation, transportation, dehydrogenation, storage at the unloading terminal, distribution to the end-users), drawbacks and weaknesses are pointed out for the identification of future research developments. Several scenarios are discussed, depending on utilities, raw materials and carbon tax costs. A sensitivity analysis as a function of the harbor-to-harbor distance is performed, to cover different situations. Due to the encouraging outcomes of the technology assessment and the easy adaptability to the existing infrastructures, the potential of LOHC is demonstrated, proving that they can become a feasible hydrogen distribution choice.

## 2. Toluene value-chain

$H_2$ distribution through LOHC is typically based on a reversible hydrogenation and dehydrogenation of carbon double bonds. The system boundaries for toluene value-chain are reported in Figure 1. In our study, 43 t/d of $H_2$ from alkaline electrolyzers at 20 bar and 50 °C enter the process battery limits at the departure site. Hydrogen is reacted together with toluene into the hydrogenation stage, to produce methylcyclohexane (MCH). The process is exothermic and takes place at elevated temperatures and pressures. After being produced, MCH is stored in tanks and shipped from the loading terminal to its final destination (unloading terminal), through cargo powered with traditional fossil fuels. A sensitivity analysis as a function of the distance covered via ship in the range 2500 – 10000 km has been performed.

When arrived at the unloading terminal, MCH is routed via truck to the $H_2$ valley, far 100 km from the unloading terminal. Here, MCH undergoes a catalytic endothermic dehydrogenation reaction, operated at high temperatures and low pressures, and $H_2$ is released, with a purity of 99.97% (ISO 14687:2019) and a pressure of 30 bar, to be collected into the $H_2$ valley. For the dehydrogenation process, heat is provided through the combustion of part of the $H_2$ produced.

The hydrogenation and dehydrogenation stages have been simulated through Aspen Plus V11® simulation software, to retrieve heat and material balances and, thus, evaluate the associated fixed and operating costs.

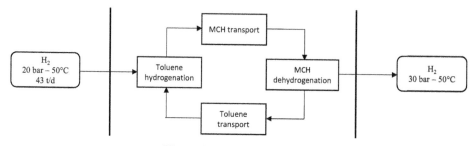

**Figure 1.** Toluene value-chain.

## 2.1 Toluene hydrogenation

The developed process scheme for toluene hydrogenation, together with the specifications of inlet and outlet streams from the process battery limits, is reported in Figure 2. Toluene from the unloading terminal, *TOL* in Figure 2, which contains benzene impurities from the dehydrogenation section, is mixed with the make-up toluene, *MAKEUP* in Figure 2, to recover unavoidable losses in the overall value-chain. The mixed stream *TOL-MIX* is pumped up to 20 bar and, after preheating, is routed to *REACTOR,* together with $H_2$ and $N_2$. The inlet nitrogen acts as thermal diluent, being the hydrogenation reaction exothermic. The *REACTOR* operates at $P = 20$ bar and $T = 210$ °C in the presence of a Pt-based catalyst. Due to the lack of experimental data and a well-established kinetic expression, the reactor has been simulated through the RGibbs module of Aspen Plus. Thus, the toluene conversion is the thermodynamic equilibrium one at the fixed $T$ and $P$. Steam is generated to benefit from the reaction exothermicity. Downstream the reactor, methylcyclohexane is purified from the heavy byproducts eventually produced from side reactions. Unconverted hydrogen, fed in excess of the stoichiometric, is recycled back to the reactor, after compression up to 20 bar, while the MCH produced is collected for storage and transport to the unloading terminal.

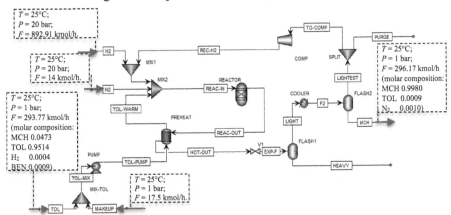

**Figure 2.** Toluene hydrogenation. Simulation in Aspen Plus® V11.

## 2.2 MCH dehydrogenation

Figure 3 reports the flowsheet of the toluene dehydrogenation. Methylcyclohexane from the hydrogenation section is pumped, preheated and routed to the dehydrogenation reactor (*REACTOR* in Figure 3). The dehydrogenation reaction, strongly endothermic, is performed at $P = 3$ bar and $T = 350$°C in the presence of a Pt-based catalyst. The dehydrogenation reactor is simulated as a black box with fixed conversion, whose value is in line with the literature one. The reaction products, toluene and hydrogen, are separated in a series of flash units downstream the reaction section. $H_2$ is compressed up to 30 bar, the pressure needed for its destination to $H_2$ valley, and is recovered with a purity suitable for its commercialization, while toluene can be sent back to the hydrogenation section. Part of the produced hydrogen (297.60 kmol/h of the 843.39 kmol/h shown in Figure 3) is burned to cope the reaction endothermicity

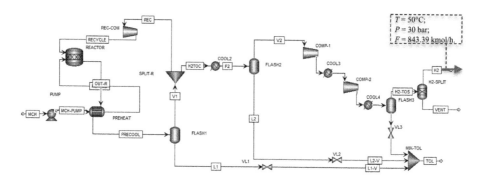

**Figure 3.** Methylcyclohexane dehydrogenation. Simulation in Aspen Plus V11®.

## 3. Methodology

The toluene pathway described in section 2 has been analysed through a techno-economic assessment, to identify the cost-drivers of the whole value-chain.

Fixed and operating costs for the hydrogenation and dehydrogenation sections have been evaluated according to the Turton methodology (Turton et al., 2008).

For fixed costs, the purchased base cost ($C_{P,i}^0$) is calculated for each piece of equipment of Figure 2 and Figure 3, through equation (1), where $K_{1,i}$, $K_{2,i}$ and $K_{3,i}$ are specific constants available for each equipment type and $A_i$ represents the equipment capacity.

$$\log_{10}\left(C_{p,i}^0\left(2001\right)\right) = K_{1,i} + K_{2,i}\log_{10}\left(A_i\right) + K_{3,i}\left[\log_{10}\left(A_i\right)\right]^2 \tag{1}$$

The purchased base cost, referred to 2001 year, is actualized through the 2022 Chemical Engineering Plant Cost Index (CEPCI), which is CEPCI (2022) = 825 ( https://chemengonline.com/). Equation (2) allows the calculation of the bare module cost ($C_{BM,i}$), to account for the equipment material of construction and operating pressure. $B_{1,i}$, $B_{2,i}$, $F_{M,i}$ and $F_{P,i}$ are pressure and material dependent constants.

$$C_{BM,i} = C_{p,i}^0 F_{BM,i} = C_{p,i}^0\left(B_{1,i} + B_{2,i}F_{M,i}F_{P,i}\right) \tag{2}$$

The total module cost ($C_{TM}$) is evaluated from the bare module cost according to equation (3) and the grassroots cost according to equation (4), where $C_{BM,i}^0$ is the bare module cost of each equipment evaluated at atmospheric pressure and with carbon steel as the material of construction. The Fixed Capital Investment (*FCI*) is retrieved as equation (5).

$$C_{TM} = 1.18\sum_{i=1}^{n} C_{BM,i} \tag{3}$$

$$C_{GR} = 0.5\sum_{i=1}^{n} C_{BM,i}^0 \tag{4}$$

$$FCI = C_{TM} + C_{GR} \tag{5}$$

As regards the operating costs, they include the Direct Manufacturing Costs (*DMC*), the Fixed Manufacturing Costs (*FMC*) and the General Expenses (*GE*), all evaluated as in Turton (2008). The cost of waste treatment ($C_{WT}$), as well as the depreciation, has been neglected in the present analysis, while all the assumptions introduced in the economic evaluations are listed in Table 1.

Two different scenarios (actual and future) have been considered, at variable cost of utilities, raw materials and $CO_2$ emissions. In the future scenario (in 5 years) a cost reduction is foreseen, after the huge 2022 inflation. When possible, the hourly utility consumption has been calculated through the energy balance retrieved from process simulations.

**Table 1.** Assumptions introduced in the economic assessment.

| Assumption | value | |
|---|---|---|
| payback time | 10 years | |
| operator yearly wage | 40000 €/y | |
| plant operability | 8000 h/y | |
| exchange rate (2022) | 0.915 €/$ | |
| *Utilities cost* | | |
| | *actual* | *future* |
| cooling water (30 to 40°C) | 0.015 €/t | 0.015 €/t |
| MP steam (200°C, 15 bara) | 130 €/t | 50 €/t |
| boiler feed water | 1.15 €/t | 1.20 €/t |
| electric energy | 500 €/MWh | 220 €/MWh |
| *Raw materials cost* | | |
| | *actual* | *future* |
| toluene | 1300 €/t | 850 €/t |
| nitrogen | 0.2 €/Nm³ | 0.15 €/Nm³ |

Costs of harbor infrastructures at both the loading and unloading terminals have been neglected, as well as catalysts costs, spare units and indirect $CO_2$ emissions.
The *FCI* has been divided for the payback time and added to the operating expenses. Their sum was then divided for the $H_2$ production to retrieve the $H_2$ transport cost [€/kg$_{H2}$].
As regards ship transport (https://compassmar.com), storage (IEA, 2019) and distribution (Teichmann et al., 2012), costs are retrieved from typical oil products applications.

## 4. Results and discussion

Results for the economic assessment performed are reported in Figure 4 considering the different distances covered through ship transport (2500-5000-10000 km) and the actual and future scenarios. $H_2$ transport costs increase as the distance covered via ship increases: in this case, a higher fuel consumption and a higher fixed cost of the tanker is observed. As expected, the cost-driver of the overall value-chain is the dehydrogenation.

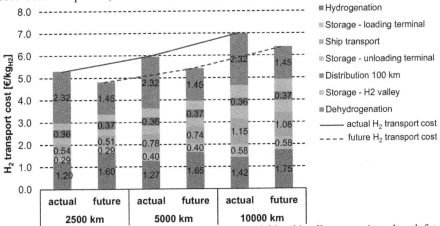

**Figure 4.** Results of the economic assessment at variable ship distances. Actual and future scenarios.

Figure 5 reports the CAPEX and OPEX for the value-chain cost driver (MCH dehydrogenation). Costs are almost entirely due to operating expenses, whose most-significant cost-item is utilities consumption. Future research has to be focused for sure on the reaction section, to identify active catalysts such that the reaction can be efficiently performed at lower temperatures.

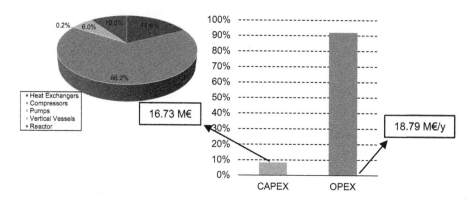

**Figure 5.** CAPEX and OPEX for MCH dehydrogenation stage.

## 5. Conclusions

Nowadays, exploiting the existing installations, only a small amount of the $H_2$ produced in Europe is transported: it is rather produced onsite from natural gas via steam reforming. The techno-economic assessment presented in this work shows that $H_2$ transport via LOHC can be economically more attractive in the near future, considering the increasing cost associated to $CO_2$ emissions together with the expected higher $H_2$ demand.

## References

A. Ajanovic, M. Sayer, R. Haas, 2022, The economics and the environmental benignity of different colors of hydrogen. Inernational Journal of Hydrogen Energy 47, 24136-24154.

https://chemengonline.com/. Accessed: October 2022.

https://compassmar.com. Accessed: October 2022.

IEA G20 Hydrogen report: Assumptions. 2019.

ISO 14687:2019. Hydrogen fuel quality — Product specification.

Naruke, 2017, The world's first global hydrogen supply chain demonstration project. https://www.chiyodacorp.com/meida/170727_e.pdf.

P. T. Aakko-Saksa, C. Cook, J. Kiviaho, T. Repo, 2018, Liquid organic hydrogen carriers for transportation and storing of renewable energy – Review and discussion. Journal of Power Sources 396, 803-823.

M. Hurskainen, 2019, Liquid organic hydrogen carriers (LOHC): Concept evaluation and techno-economics. VTT Technical Research Centre of Finland. Research Report No. VTT-R-00057-19Y.

Roland Berger, 2021, Hydrogen transportation | The key to unlocking the clean hydrogen economy. ROLAND BERGER GMBH, Sederanger 1, 80538 Munich, Germany.

R. Turton, R.C.Bailie, W.B.Whiting, J.A. Shaeiwitz, 2008, Analysis, Synthesis and Design of Chemical Processes. Pearson Education.

L. A. Pellegrini, G. De Guido, S. Langé, 2018, Biogas to liquefied biomethane via cryogenic upgrading technologies. Renewable Energy, 124, 75-83.

D.Teichmann, W.Arlt, P. Wasserscheid, 2012, Liquid Organic Hydrogen Carriers as an efficient vector for the transport and storage of renewable energy. International Journal of Hydrogen Energy, 37, 18118-18132.

Antonis Kokossis, Michael C. Georgiadis, Efstratios N. Pistikopoulos (Eds.)
PROCEEDINGS OF THE 33rd European Symposium on Computer Aided Process Engineering
(ESCAPE33), June 18-21, 2023, Athens, Greece

# Evaluation of Methane Mitigation Technologies in the Upstream Oil and Gas Sector using the TEAM Digital Platform

Marcelo Mathias, Ahad Sarraf Shirazi, Jairo Duran, Alberto Alva-Argaez [a]

[a] *Process Ecology Inc., 401 – 301 14 St. NW, Calgary, AB T2N 2A1, Canada*
*alberto@processecology.com*

## Abstract

Greenhouse gas emissions from upstream operations account for most of the methane emitted in the oil and gas industry in Canada. To achieve its national emissions reduction target, Canada intends to make significant investments, however there is a need to design specific mitigation strategies at a regional level to implement cost-effective mitigation technologies. In this work, a detailed mitigation techno-economic analysis for a subset of oil and gas facilities in Alberta was performed using the TEAM digital platform. The inputs of the model include production levels and vented and flared volumes for each facility obtained from publicly available data. The analysis shows that 14.8 Mtpa $CO_2e$ of carbon emissions can be removed from the atmosphere per year at marginal abatement costs of \$50/t$CO_2e$ or below. Regional differences in production and facility types suggest that gas conservation technologies such as tie-in to gathering systems or onsite power generation are well suited for facilities with large reported vented emissions, whereas sites in eastern Alberta that predominantly report fugitive emissions can benefit more from facility upgrades and leak detection and repair programs (LDAR). About 70% of methane emissions in the selected facilities can be mitigated at nearly zero abatement cost.

**Keywords**: methane mitigation, carbon abatement, marginal abatement cost curve, upstream emission mitigation, carbon credits.

## 1. Introduction

Methane is responsible for approximately 30% of the global rise in temperatures to date and accounts for approximately 13% total greenhouse gas emissions in Canada (UNEP, 2021; ECCC, 2021). The Canadian government is committed to ambitious climate action, including a new target to reduce methane emissions in the oil and gas sector by at least 75% by 2030 and capping and reducing emissions from the oil and gas sector (O&G). Cutting methane emissions is one of the fastest and lowest-cost ways to fight climate change and is one of the top recommendations made by climate scientists (IPCC, 2022).

Several publications have assessed the technical and economic feasibility of implementing mitigation technologies in the sector, especially in the upstream segment which contributes most of the emissions. Proven technologies to tackle this problem tend to concentrate on gas conservation or destruction via combustion. For example, some studies have shown the impact and costs of flaring stranded gas, leak detection and repair

(LDAR) programs, replacing pneumatic pumps, and increased frequency for replacing rod packing seals in reciprocating compressors. The cost of these technologies is usually assessed over a certain time duration and is expressed as a marginal abatement cost (MAC), typically in dollars per $tCO_2e$ abated. The viability of these mitigation projects usually depends on site-specific factors, technologies, commodities, labor prices, among others. The most viable projects have MAC close to zero or even return profit over its duration (negative MAC). For the thousands of facilities that comprise the upstream O&G in Alberta (oil batteries, wells, etc.), the evaluation of baseline GHG emissions, the potential mitigated emissions achieved with a set of technologies, and the economic evaluation of each of these is time consuming. In this work, we used the TEAM (Techno-Economic Analysis Model) digital platform developed by Process Ecology Inc. to automate all calculations and perform sensitivity analysis of key technical and economic parameters for a collection of oil and gas facilities in Alberta.

In this study, a total of 7,177 installations were selected, including oil batteries, gas gathering systems, and gas plants. This selection of sites generated nearly 60% of reported provincial GHG emissions in the sector in 2020 (the year of the data selected). Volumetric emissions data from publicly available sources and engineering assumptions were used to generate a detailed inventory of emission sources, estimate the emissions profile of each facility, and then perform a detailed feasibility and economic assessment of selected methane mitigation technologies.

## 2. Methodology

### 2.1. Oil and Gas Facility Data

Volumetric production and flaring data for 2020 were retrieved from Petrinex (Petrinex, 2022) database. Of the total 7,177 facilities, 5,955 are oil batteries (BT), 861 gas gathering stations (GS), and 361 gas plants (GP). To avoid including non-routine large flaring events, median values for the reported vented and flared volumes were considered. The facilities were organized into subregions, as geographical location provides indications of fluid properties, facility type and number of equipment or emissions control methods used in each site. The PSAC (PSAC, 2022) and heavy oil migration classifications (AER, 2020) were applied here and the Montney region was added separately due to the large number of hydraulic fracturing projects in the area. Figure 1 shows the regional distribution considered. It is worth noting that the AB4 (Lloydminster area) is characterized by heavy oil production, whereas the AB6 region has the largest portion of oil sands production in the province. Based on location, a fluid characterization (heavy or light/medium oil) was derived for each facility. The PetroNinja database (Stack Technologies, 2022) was used to sample "typical" oil and gas compositions in each region. The fluid type impacts how the facility is designed and operated and ultimately determines the type of equipment and emissions sources that are likely to be found.

### 2.2. Distance to Critical Infrastructure

In this study, critical infrastructure refers to gas gathering pipelines, electricity grid, and qualified labor pools. This information is required to determine the feasibility and costs of implementation of some key mitigation technologies. Geospatial pipeline data from The Alberta Energy Regulator was loaded into TEAM to calculate distances for all facilities. A total of 120,226 pipelines were considered as part of the existing gas gathering network (AER, 2020). Each pipeline was discretized into segments which represent potential tie-in options for each facility. For each site, the shortest distance to a tie-in point was determined applying the KD-Tree search algorithm (Skrodzki, 2019). The cost of tie-in depends on distance and compression needed to bring the recovered gas to the necessary tie-in pressure. The search algorithm was expanded to allow the identification of the closest pipeline with low pressure. Information for the electricity grid distribution in Alberta is sparse, therefore it was assumed that distances from facilities to a grid connection follow a Poisson distribution. For the distance to labor, the previously mentioned KD-Tree search algorithm was applied considering only population centers of more than 12,000 inhabitants in Alberta.

### 2.3. Facility Configuration

TEAM relies on a detailed bottom-up model of the emissions sources present at each facility. Since this information is usually not publicly available, TEAM was equipped with "autoconfigure" rules that help to fill the gaps in information and determine the number and type of equipment present at each facility. The resulting process configuration depends on the type of fluid and production rates of each facility and was validated through conversations with SMEs, operators, and after inspection of process flow diagrams of representative facilities. For example, heavy oil batteries were assumed to contain a line heater, a flare stack (if the facility reported flare emissions), production tanks for 7 days of production, and a glycol dehydrator if gas throughput exceeded 0.5 MMSCFD. A set of process design rules were derived for each facility subtype and the selected equipment counts depend on the production rates. Pneumatic devices and fugitive component counts depend on the types of equipment assigned to each facility and were obtained from industry literature (Clearstone, 2018). Additional details and assumptions for other facility types can be found elsewhere (Process Ecology, 2020).

### 2.4. Other Considerations

Fugitive emissions from each main equipment type (*i.e.,* reciprocating compressors, centrifugal compressors, glycol dehydrators, etc.) are calculated in TEAM using the equipment inventory determined in the autoconfiguration step, and fugitive components and associated emission factors as reported in the literature (IPCC, 2006; Clearstone, 2018). To reflect recent efforts in replacing high-bleed pneumatic controllers, it was assumed that 75% of the devices were low-bleed. The selected sites capture approximately 60% and 70% of total reported volumes for flaring and venting, respectively. From the collection of facilities studied here, the region identified as AB4 contains most of the heavy oil batteries (1,566) and the Montney region has the largest number of gas plants (120). This is expected to impact the most economical mitigation strategies by region.

### 2.5. The TEAM Digital Platform

The digital platform allows for easy upload of the input data and automates the calculation of GHG emissions and mitigation strategies. TEAM calculates emissions profiles for each facility (vented, flared, fugitive, and combustion), as well as a marginal abatement cost curves (MACC) for single sites and for any subset of facilities. For each technology assessed, the program estimates the anticipated emission reductions and the marginal abatement cost (*i.e.,* $/tCO2e). For each mitigation project (*i.e.,* the implementation of a given technology at a given site), the tool produces an estimated cash flow for the lifetime of the project (assumed to be 10 years). Net present value (NPV), return of investment (ROI), and payback period (PB) are reported as quantitative indicators of the performance of each project.

## 3. Results and Discussion

A techno-economic analysis model was configured with over 7,000 facilities that include oil batteries, gas plants, and gas gathering systems. The model was then solved to calculate emission profiles and mitigation strategies for each facility. It is worth noting that the reported volumetric venting and flaring data were used to configure the facilities but are different to the calculated values. The model estimates 14.8 Mtpa $CO_2$e including carbon dioxide and methane, and 233,906 ton/year of methane emissions (GWP of 25 was applied for methane). Total venting emissions were estimated at 1.04 Mtpa $CO_2$e and 1.3 Mtpa of flaring emissions. Pneumatic devices represent 1.8 Mtpa $CO_2$e while fugitive emissions contribute and additional 1.82 Mtpa $CO_2$e. The remaining 8.79 Mtpa $CO_2$e corresponds to fuel gas combustion.

Oil batteries represented 40% of the total GHG emissions, gas plants and gas gathering stations contributed 34% and 26%, respectively. About 60% of total GHG emissions originate from fuel gas combustion. Pneumatic devices and fugitives contribute about 30% each to methane emissions.

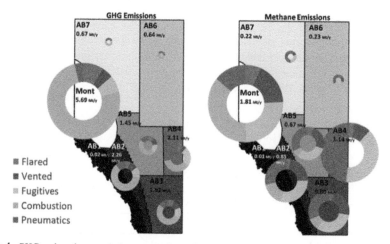

Figure 1. GHG and methane emissions per region calculated in TEAM for a subset of facilities in Alberta.

The Montney region represented the largest emitting area having almost double the emissions of the next largest region AB2 (5.7 vs 2.3 Mtpa $CO_2$e). Most of the emissions from Montney originate from combustion sources, which is related to the large number of gas plants present in the region. In contrast, pneumatic and fugitive emissions in region AB4 have the largest contribution. A reasonable agreement between the model results and Petrinex data was found for flaring emissions. The greater deviations occurred for venting emissions, further investigation would be required to explain these differences, however it is likely that vented volumes have not been consistently reported by all operators.

TEAM provides economic indicators for each potential project and for all facilities. Conventional MAC curves display all possible technologies and their potential for emissions reductions, in general several mitigation technologies would act to conserve the same emissions source, *i.e.,* mitigation projects that are mutually exclusive. A function was implemented to eliminate these competing projects by selecting the lowest MAC project at each facility. After this selection, a total of 19,559 mitigation projects were assessed by TEAM, resulting in potential for total emissions reduction of 4,6 $MtCO_2e/y$ for an estimated capital investment of $222 million (USD). This represents a 75.4% emissions reduction compared to the business-as-usual scenario (BAU). Figure 2 presents the MACC for the maximum reduction scenario (after screening out mutually exclusive technologies). About 72.5% of potential mitigation can be achieved at zero or negative marginal cost making most of these projects profitable. Around 66% of projects were projected to cost $0 USD/tCO_2e or cheaper. It is worth noting that in our analysis the abatement cost considers the NPV of the projects and the carbon tax $15 CAD/tCO_2e is assumed to be a revenue stream for the project (tax credit or trading of carbon credits in the market). Subject matter experts advised that projects under $50 USD/tCO2e are worth pursuing given current conditions. For this MAC threshold, 14% of the assessed mitigation projects are left out and the remaining projects provide an emissions reduction potential of 4.53 $MtCO_2e$ with a capital investment of $129.1 MMUSD. The largest opportunities are the replacement of chemical pumps with solar or electric pumps (27% of total reductions) and installing vapor recovery units (23%).

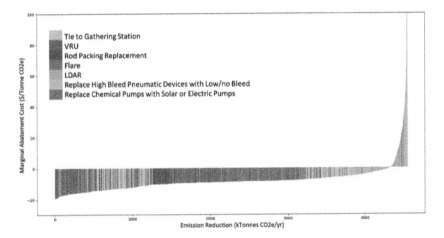

Figure 2. Maximum reduction MACC analysis for individual mitigation projects.

Figure 2 shows the distribution of ranked emission reduction projects. Replacing chemical pumps with solar or electric pumps accounts for 27% of total emissions reduction below $50/tCO_2e. This technology displays a negative average marginal abatement cost, meaning the installation of these is profitable. Chemical pump replacement and VRU installations represent the majority of the selected projects, several of which are economical to implement (MAC below $0 USD/tCO_2e). The option of tying in facilities to nearby gas gathering systems also appears promising with fewer projects delivering significant emissions reductions. The average tie-in to gathering station project reduces 1.09 $ktCO_2e$ while chemical pump replacement and VRUs have an average emission reduction of 0.27 and 0.67 $ktCO_2e$ per facility, respectively.

The Montney region contains the largest reduction potential (1.13 $MtCO_2e$). Region AB4 has a similar reduction potential of 0.94 $MtCO_2e$. However, these two regions present different mitigation strategies. While the Montney region would derive most reductions from installing VRUs, the AB4 region obtains its reductions from replacing chemical pumps. This aligns with the type of operations found in each region. Interestingly, only about a third of the emissions reduction potential are attained with technologies currently addressed by regulations (LDAR programs, replacement of high-bleed devices, and rod packing replacement). Initially, the analysis did not consider onsite power generation as literature usually reports that this technology is not economical. With the limited data set and high uncertainty, it should be noted that power generation projects displace both VRU and tie-in to gathering projects in multiple sites, as this is a more economic option in some circumstances given the additional revenue from selling power to the grid or to neighbouring facilities. Power generation is most promising for larger facilities with large volumes of vented gas and in proximity to connection points to the grid.

## 4. Conclusions

The results of the techno-economic assessment performed in the TEAM digital platform indicate that there are significant benefits in applying differentiated mitigation strategies on a regional basis as opposed to a province-wide approach. Fugitive emissions and pneumatic devices remain a significant source of emissions from the sector as well as un-combusted methane from natural gas engines. There are regulations in place for these sources, however there may be still a significant potential for further emissions reduction by increasing the adoption of gas conservation technologies (VRU, tie-in to gathering, onsite power generation, etc.). Similarly, the application of mitigation technologies to small and remote facilities with low gas venting volumes resulted in the most expensive abatement costs. Most emissions reductions can be achieved with projects below $50 CAD/tCO$_2$e, with about two thirds of this potential achieved at a profit. It must be noted that the mitigation technology costing information used in this study does not consider sub regional differences and would need further refinements. As such these results should be construed as preliminary indications of the total cost of mitigation from the sector. Even though a rigorous uncertainty analysis is still necessary to further validate these results, the regional analysis still suggest that a single mitigation strategy province-wide may not be optimal, but rather certain regions would have better mitigation results per dollar invested using a particular set of technologies.

## Acknowledgments

The authors would like to acknowledge the support provided by Natural Resources Canada and Clearstone Engineering in providing financial support and costing information.

## References

United Nations Environment Programme and Climate and Clean Air Coalition, 2021, Global Methane Assessment: Benefits and Costs of Mitigating Methane Emissions, Nairobi, UNEP.
Environment and Climate Change Canada (ECCC), 2021, Review of Canada's Methane Regulations for the Upstream Oil and Gas Sector, Gatineau, QC.
Intergovernmental Panel on Climate Change (IPCC), 2022, Summary for Policy Makers, In: Climate Change 2022: Mitigation of Climate Change. Contribution of Working Group III to the Sixth Assesment Report of IPCC, Cambridge University Press, UK.
Petrinex, Canada Petroleum Information Networks, 2022. Available at https://www.petrinex.ca/.
Petroleum Services Association of Canada (PSAC), 2022, PSAC Resources. Retrieved April 25, 2022, from https://www.psac.ca/resources/
Alberta Energy Regulator (AER), 2020, Atlas of the Western Canada Sedimentary Basin, Chapter 31: Petroleum Generation and Migration in the Western Canada Sedimentary Basin, Edmonton, AB.
Stack Technologies Ltd., PetroNinja, 2022, Retrieved May 20, 2022, from https://petroninja.com/

Skrodzki, M.,2019, The K-D Tree Data Structure and a Proof for Neighborhood Computation in Expected Logarithmic Time, Cornell University, https://doi.org/10.48550/arXiv.1903.04936

Clearstone Engineering, 2018. Update of Equipment, Component, and Fugitive Emission Factors for Alberta Upstream Oil and Gas, Calgary, AB.

Process Ecology Inc., 2020, Techno-Economic Assestment Model: Product Documentation, Calgary, AB.

Delphi Program, 2017, Methane Abatement Costs: Alberta. Report for the Alberta Energy Regulator, Ottawa, ON.

Antonis Kokossis, Michael C. Georgiadis, Efstratios N. Pistikopoulos (Eds.)
PROCEEDINGS OF THE 33rd European Symposium on Computer Aided Process Engineering
(ESCAPE33), June 18-21, 2023, Athens, Greece

# Thermodynamic description of the $CO_2$-AMP-$H_2O$ system by ENRTL-RK model

Stefania Moioli[a,*], Laura A. Pellegrini[a], Ricardo R. Wanderley[b], Hanna K. Knuutila[b]

[a]GASP, Group on Advanced Separation Processes & GAS Processing, Dipartimento di Chimica, Materiali e Ingegneria Chimica "Giulio Natta", Politecnico di Milano, Piazza Leonardo da Vinci 32, I-20133 Milano, Italy
[b]Department of Chemical Engineering, Norwegian University of Science and Technology (NTNU), NO-7491 Trondheim, Norway
stefania.moioli@polimi.it

## Abstract

Aqueous MonoEthanolAmine (MEA) solution is a well-established benchmark solvent for capturing $CO_2$, however it is characterized by some relevant drawbacks that make its substitution with other solvents an important target to be achieved for Carbon Capture, Storage and Utilization.

2-Amino-2-Methyl-1-Propanol (AMP) is a sterically hindered primary amine which is being under consideration because of some advantages as those related to its high loading capacity and high thermal stability.

This work focuses on studying of the $CO_2$ chemical absorption in an aqueous solvent containing AMP. ASPEN Plus® process simulator has been used. After determining the thermodynamic method and the reaction set to be employed, the obtained model has been used for the simulation of a pilot plant for validation and has been employed for the study of possible application of the AMP solvent to the upstream $CO_2$ removal of an Integrated Biomass Gasification Combined Cycle (IBGCC).

Keywords: CCUS, AMP, IBGCC, chemical absorption.

## 1. Introduction

Aqueous MonoEthanolAmine (MEA) solution is a well-established benchmark solvent for capturing $CO_2$. However it has some drawbacks that make research focusing on alternative solvents for Carbon Capture, Utilization and Storage (CCUS) necessary.

2-Amino-2-Methyl-1-Propanol (AMP) is being considered one possible substitute to the already industrially employed MEA, despite its lower kinetics, because of some advantages such as those related to its high loading capacity and high thermal stability (Barzagli et al., 2019) and low heat of absorption of $CO_2$. AMP is a sterically hindered amine, a primary amine with the amino group attached to a tertiary carbon atom, and is not expected to form a stable carbamate, as primary and secondary amines do. Because of the different stoichiometry of the reaction, the maximum loading of $CO_2$ in AMP solvent is higher when compared to MEA (Gabrielsen et al., 2006). It has been studied in aqueous solution (Barzagli et al., 2013; da Silva and Svendsen, 2006), in mixtures with other amines in aqueous solutions, such as AMP+PZ (Artanto et al., 2014; Nwaoha et al., 2018) and also as a component of water-lean or water-free solvents. Water-lean solvents could reduce the energy demand due to lower heat capacity, thus reducing the heat demand and potentially lowering the cost of carbon capture (Sanku and Svensson, 2019).

This work focuses on the thermodynamics of the system of $CO_2$+AMP+water intending to provide a vapor-liquid equilibrium model suitable for process simulations.

The proposed model, after validation on experimental data of a pilot plant (Gabrielsen, 2007), is employed for the study of possible application of the AMP solvent to the upstream $CO_2$ removal of an Integrated Biomass Gasification Combined Cycle (IBGCC) (Carpentieri et al., 2005), with optimization of the main process characteristics.

## 2. Thermodynamic modeling with chemical reaction

A rigorous thermodynamic model must take into account the Vapor-Liquid-Equilibrium (VLE), physical solubility of gases in the solvent, and the chemical reactions occurring in the liquid phase.

In this work, the set of chemical reactions often employed to describe AMP reacting with $CO_2$ in aqueous systems (AspenTech, 2021) has been modified to take into account the reactions required to describe water-lean or water-free AMP-based solvents. In particular, in order to consider only linear independent reactions on the basis of the rank of the matrix species-elements, the considered set is:

$$2H_2O \rightleftharpoons H_3O^+ + OH^- \tag{1}$$

$$CO_2 + 2H_2O \rightleftharpoons H_3CO^- + H_3O^+ \tag{2}$$

$$HCO_3^- + H_2O \rightleftharpoons CO_3^{2-} + H_3O^+ \tag{3}$$

$$AMPH^+ + H_2O \rightleftharpoons AMP + H_3O^+ \tag{4}$$

$$2AMP + CO_2 \rightleftharpoons AMPH^+ + AMPCOO^- \tag{5}$$

The set includes the formation of carbamate by a reaction between AMP and $CO_2$ as considered in Sanku and Svensson (2019), not including water.

The ENRTL-RK method in ASPEN Plus® was used. This method is based on the Electrolyte-NRTL theory developed by Chen et al. (Chen et al., 1979; Chen et al., 1982; Chen and Evans, 1986; Mock et al., 1986), though with some modifications. In particular, for mixed electrolyte systems, the ENRTL-RK method uses the mixing rules only to calculate interaction parameters, instead of calculating both interaction parameters and Gibbs free energy from mixing rules. Moreover, the ENRTL-RK uses a single thermodynamics framework to calculate the activity coefficients, Gibbs free energy and enthalpy, instead of using separate models. The two methods (ENTRL-RK and Chen et al.) are identical for systems containing a single electrolyte.

Binary interaction parameters, without default values for ENRTL-RK in the software, have been obtained by using Data Regression System. Both in-house experimental data and literature data (Montalbano, 2022) of solubility of $CO_2$ in the aqueous AMP solution, and heat of absorption data (Arcis et al., 2007; Kim, 2009) were used. A non-randomness factor of 0.2 resulted to best represent the experimental values together with the determined values for $a_{ij}$ and $a_{ji}$, $b_{ij}$ and $b_{ji}$ determining the $\tau$ parameter of $H_2O$-(AMPH$^+$, HCO$_3^-$), of AMP-(AMPH$^+$, HCO$_3^-$) and of $CO_2$-(AMPH$^+$, HCO$_3^-$). The % Absolute Average Deviations (AAD%) on the partial pressure of $CO_2$ of all the considered sources of experimental data is 13.86%, with a minimum of 1.63% for one source and a maximum of 43.97% for another source. Results are presented in Figure 1 for one set of experimental data as example, for which the AAD% resulted to be equal to 35.9% for data at 313 K, equal to 3.79% for data at 353 K and 12.15% for data at 393 K, considering all the available data. The AAD% for 313 K resulted high because of five points not well represented at low loadings, with a % error > 30%. Without these points the resulting AAD% would be equal to 7.83%. The obtained AAD% for the heat of absorption data is 0.41% for all the considered data.

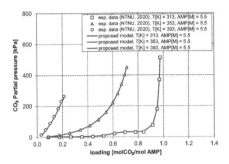

Figure 1. Comparison between the experimental points from NTNU and the calculated values of $CO_2$ partial pressure for varying loading and temperatures obtained in this work.

## 3. Simulation of the process

### 3.1. Validation on pilot plant data

The experimental points obtained in runs of a pilot plant providing data for both the absorption section (with diameter equal to 0.15 m and packing height of 4.36 m) and the regeneration section (with diameter equal to 0.10 m and packing height of 3.89 m) by Gabrielsen (2007) have been used for model validation. Rate-based simulations have been performed, using reaction kinetics as reported in ASPEN Plus® (AspenTech, 2021). On the basis of the experimental data, the absorber and the regeneration column have been simulated separately. The input streams for absorber simulations were the lean solvent flow rate, temperature and loading, column specifications (packing type, height and diameter) and flowrate, temperature and pressure of the inlet gas stream. In the stripper simulation, the rich solvent composition, temperature and pressure, column specifications, condenser temperature and reboiler duty were used as input.

The temperature profile of the absorber for one run (RUN4) is reported in Figure 2a) and the obtained lean loadings for a fixed duty required at the reboiler are shown in Figure 2b), showing a good representation of the main characteristics of the process, including the position and the extension of the temperature bulge in the absorber, due to the liquid to gas ratio and to the exothermicity of the reactions (Kohl and Nielsen, 1997).

### 3.2. Application to a IBGCC plant

The developed model has been used to study the application of the AMP aqueous solvent for removing $CO_2$ from a gaseous stream at atmospheric pressure in an IBGCC plant previously reported in the literature (Carpentieri et al., 2005). In the plant biomass is used to reduce greenhouse gas emissions and natural reserve depletion. $CO_2$ removal is applied to obtain a gas with high hydrogen and low carbon dioxide contents to have a fuel with high lower heating value suitable for utilization in a gas turbine for power production. The considered scheme is the base one, composed of one absorber and one regeneration column, with a lean-rich heat exchanger for heat recovery between the hot lean solvent and the cold rich solvent entering the regeneration section. The internals for both columns is Mellapak 250Y, which has an increased contact area and higher mass transfer than Mellapak 250X (Wang et al., 2013).

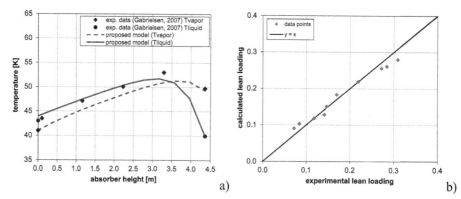

a)                                                                                          b)

Figure 2. a) Profiles of temperature for the vapor and the liquid phase in the absorption column for RUN 4 and b) parity plot of $CO_2$ lean loading in the lean solvent exiting the regeneration section for the different runs of the pilot plant obtained with the model proposed in this work.

A parametric study aimed at optimizing the capture process for lowest thermal energy requirement, by analyzing the influence of lean $CO_2$ loading, absorber height and AMP concentration in the lean solvent has been carried out.

The obtained results are reported in Figure 3 and Figure 4. The lean solvent flow rate increases as the lean loading increases, and the energy requirement is characterized by a minimum (detailed in Figure 3b)), that decreases for higher heights of the absorption column. An absorber height of 40 m has been selected in order to reduce the energy consumptions and the operating costs in line with the recent trends in process design and, on the basis of the obtained results at different AMP concentrations reported in Table 1, the 46.3% wt. AMP solution gives the lowest energy requirement. However, the impact of the concentration on the energy consumption is minor. The reboiler duty is quite high and similar to that of 30 wt% MEA. This is due to low kinetics (the $k$ value for the direct reaction of AMP with $CO_2$ is more than one order of magnitude lower than the reaction of MEA), reducing the rich loading that can be reached and also increasing the required liquid flow rate. The results here illustrate why AMP should always be combined with an amine, like Piperazine in CESAR1 blend, able to promote the absorption kinetics.

Table 1. Optimal lean loading and minimum energy requirement for different AMP concentrations in the lean solvent with an absorber height of 40 m.

| AMP mass fraction | Optimal lean loading [mol $CO_2$/mol AMP] | Minimum energy requirement [MJ/kg$CO_2$] |
|---|---|---|
| 26.3 wt% | 0.125 | 4.274 |
| 30.0 wt% | 0.136 | 4.269 |
| 36.7 wt% | 0.138 | 4.241 |
| 46.3 wt% | 0.130 | 4.193 |

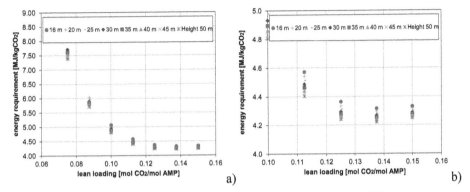

Figure 3. a) Full profile and b) detail of the profiles of energy requirement for different lean loadings and absorber heights for 90% CO₂ removal with an aqueous solution of AMP 36.3% wt.

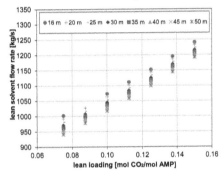

Figure 4. Profile of the needed solvent flowrate of an aqueous solution of AMP 36.3% wt. for different lean loadings and absorber heights to remove 90% of CO₂ present in the raw gas to be treated.

In this work, the $\Delta T$ of approach in the lean-rich heat exchanger has been fixed to be 10 K and the regeneration pressure has been fixed to 2 bar. An analysis of the influence of the regeneration pressure is of interest in future development, considering that, as reported by Osagie (Osagie et al., 2018), the AMP solvent can be regenerated at higher temperatures (140°C) and higher pressures (3.5 bar) than MEA, potentially reducing the reboiler duty.

## 4. Conclusions

This work has focused on studying the CO₂ chemical absorption with aqueous AMP, by employing ASPEN Plus® process simulator. The binary interaction parameters for the description of the thermodynamics of the system AMP-H₂O-CO₂ with the ENRTL-RK method have been obtained by regression using experimental data for the solubility of CO₂ in the solvent at different conditions and using data for the heat of absorption of CO₂. In addition, a new set of chemical reactions has been proposed to consider the contribution of a chemical reaction between AMP and CO₂ without water with the aim of also describing water-lean systems in the future.

The obtained model has been used for the simulation of a pilot plant for validation and has been employed for the study of possible application of the AMP solvent to the upstream CO₂ removal of an Integrated Biomass Gasification Combined Cycle to evaluate its substitution to the already considered MEA.

# References

H. Arcis, L. Rodier, J.-Y. Coxam, 2007, Enthalpy of solution of $CO_2$ in aqueous solutions of 2-amino-2-methyl-1-propanol, J. Chem. Thermodyn., 39, 878-887.

Y. Artanto, J. Jansen, P. Pearson, G. Puxty, A. Cottrell, E. Meuleman, P. Feron, 2014, Pilot-scale evaluation of AMP/PZ to capture $CO_2$ from flue gas of an Australian brown coal–fired power station, Int. J. Greenh. Gas Control, 20, 189-195.

AspenTech, 2021, Rate-Based Model of the $CO_2$ Capture Process by AMP using Aspen Plus. AspenTech, Burlington, MA.

F. Barzagli, C. Giorgi, F. Mani, M. Peruzzini, 2019, Comparative Study of $CO_2$ Capture by Aqueous and Nonaqueous 2-Amino-2-methyl-1-propanol Based Absorbents Carried Out by 13C NMR and Enthalpy Analysis, Ind. Eng. Chem. Res., 58, 4364-4373.

F. Barzagli, F. Mani, M. Peruzzini, 2013, Efficient $CO_2$ absorption and low temperature desorption with non-aqueous solvents based on 2-amino-2-methyl-1-propanol (AMP), Int. J. Greenh. Gas Control, 16, 217-223.

M. Carpentieri, A. Corti, L. Lombardi, 2005, Life cycle assessment (LCA) of an integrated biomass gasification combined cycle (IBGCC) with $CO_2$ removal, Energy Conversion and Management, 46, 1790-1808.

C.C. Chen, H.I. Britt, J.F. Boston, L.B. Evans, 1979, Extension and application of the Pitzer equation for vapor-liquid equilibrium of aqueous electrolyte systems with molecular solutes, AIChE J., 25, 820-831.

C.C. Chen, H.I. Britt, J.F. Boston, L.B. Evans, 1982, Local composition model for excess Gibbs energy of electrolyte systems. Part I: single solvent, single completely dissociated electrolyte systems, AIChE J., 28, 588-596.

C.C. Chen, L.B. Evans, 1986, A local composition model for the excess Gibbs energy of aqueous electrolyte systems, AIChE J., 32, 444-454.

E.F. da Silva, H.F. Svendsen, 2006, Study of the Carbamate Stability of Amines Using ab Initio Methods and Free-Energy Perturbations, Ind. Eng. Chem. Res., 45, 2497-2504.

J. Gabrielsen, 2007, $CO_2$ Capture from Coal Fired Power Plants. Technical University of Denmark.

J. Gabrielsen, M.L. Michelsen, E.H. Stenby, G.M. Kontogeorgis, 2006, Modeling of $CO_2$ absorber using an AMP solution, AIChE J., 52, 3443-3451.

I. Kim, 2009, Heat of reaction and VLE of post combustion $CO_2$ absorbents. Norwegian University of Science and Technology (NTNU).

A.L. Kohl, R. Nielsen, 1997, Gas Purification, 5th ed. Gulf Publishing Company, Book Division, Houston, Texas, USA.

B. Mock, L.B. Evans, C.C. Chen, 1986, Thermodynamic Representation of Phase Equilibria of Mixed-Solvent Electrolyte Systems, AIChE J., 32, 1655-1664.

D. Montalbano, 2022, Improved Thermodynamic Model and Simulation of the Absorption Process by Aqueous AMP Solvent for $CO_2$ Removal. Politecnico di Milano, Milano, Italy.

C. Nwaoha, M. Beaulieu, P. Tontiwachwuthikul, M.D. Gibson, 2018, Techno-economic analysis of $CO_2$ capture from a 1.2 million MTPA cement plant using AMP-PZ-MEA blend, Int. J. Greenh. Gas Control, 78, 400-412.

E. Osagie, C. Biliyok, G. Di Lorenzo, D.P. Hanak, V. Manovic, 2018, Techno-economic evaluation of the 2-amino-2-methyl-1-propanol (AMP) process for $CO_2$ capture from natural gas combined cycle power plant, Int. J. Greenh. Gas Control, 70, 45-56.

M.G. Sanku, H. Svensson, 2019, Modelling the precipitating non-aqueous $CO_2$ capture system AMP-NMP, using the unsymmetric electrolyte NRTL, Int. J. Greenh. Gas Control, 89, 20-32.

C. Wang, M. Perry, F. Seibert, G.T. Rochelle, 2013, Characterization of Novel Structured Packings for $CO_2$ Capture, Energy Procedia, 37, 2145-2153.

Antonis Kokossis, Michael C. Georgiadis, Efstratios N. Pistikopoulos (Eds.)
PROCEEDINGS OF THE 33rd European Symposium on Computer Aided Process Engineering
(ESCAPE33), June 18-21, 2023, Athens, Greece

# An Automated Approach for Emission Reduction Cost Calculation

Maria Victoria Migo-Sumagang,[a,b] Raymond R. Tan,[a] Kathleen B. Aviso,[b]
Dominic C. Y. Foo,[c*]

[a] *Department of Chemical Engineering, De La Salle University, 2401 Taft Avenue, 0922 Manila, Philippines*
[b] *Department of Chemical Engineering, College of Engineering and Agro-Industrial Technology, University of the Philippines Los Baños, College, Los Baños, Laguna, 4031, Philippines*
[c] *Department Chemical and Environmental Engineering/Centre of Excellence for Green Technologies, University of Nottingham Malaysia, Broga Road, 43500 Semenyih, Selangor, Malaysia*

## Abstract

The marginal abatement cost (MAC) curve is a popular visual tool in emissions reduction planning. The curve is generated by plotting the emission reduction measures by increasing MAC or specific cost on the vertical axis vs. their cumulative emissions reduction potential on the horizontal axis. The resulting graph shows the different measures arranged by cost-effectiveness, which can be easily communicated to stakeholders. The practicality of the tool makes it useful in evaluating the tradeoffs between emissions reduction and cost. However, the main limitation of the tool is the indirect determination of the total cost, which requires tedious steps in calculating the areas under the curve. This work addresses this limitation by an automated-MAC (AMAC) approach. The latter performs the calculations on the total emission reduction cost. A case study on emissions reduction planning with negative emission technologies illustrates the proposed method. This new approach removes the tediousness of calculating the total cost for emission reduction.

**Keywords**: negative emission technologies, process integration, targeting, net-zero emissions planning

## 1. Introduction

The latest IPCC reports show that achieving net-zero emissions by 2050 is critical to limiting global warming to 2 °C and even 1.5 °C (IPCC, 2022). Net-zero emissions are being targeted by firms (Chrobak, 2021) and countries worldwide (Iyer et al., 2021). Aside from the conventional approaches like turning to renewable energy and increasing energy efficiency, negative emission technologies (NETs) are now part of the solution portfolio to address the residual emissions from the hard-to-abate sectors (IPCC, 2022). These technologies remove carbon dioxide from the atmosphere resulting in a net decrease in its atmospheric concentration (The Royal Society, 2018). Examples of NETs include the ones utilizing the biological pathway: afforestation/reforestation, bioenergy with carbon capture and storage (BECCS), biochar (BC), and soil carbon sequestration (The Royal Society, 2018). The advantages of BECCS and BC over the other NETs are the generation of energy on top of their carbon sequestration function and the increased permanence of their carbon storage (The Royal Society, 2018).

Several studies have investigated the integration of NETs into energy systems to achieve net-zero emissions, particularly energy systems models involving BECCS (Köberle, 2019). A linear program was used to transition the global energy mix to net-zero emissions using BECCS (Selosse and Ricci, 2014). The same approach was done in a country-scale energy mix (Kato and Kurosawa, 2019). BECCS supply chain optimization using process systems engineering has also been investigated (Fajardy and Mac Dowell, 2017). Optimization techniques using process integration also play a part in implementing cost-effective decarbonization strategies while simultaneously considering energy and resource use efficiencies (Klemeš, 2022). For instance, a NET portfolio was optimized under multi-footprint resource constraints (Migo-Sumagang et al., 2021).

The mentioned studies utilize mathematical programming, which can handle complex problems in planning/integrating NETs. However, mathematical programming has less interactivity compared to graphical techniques. On the other hand, graphical approaches provide immediate visualization of the solutions, which can support the first steps of decision-making (Klemeš et al., 2013). Graphical approaches in carbon footprint planning have also been developed to include algebraic targeting techniques such as cascade analysis to improve their targeting features (Foo et al., 2008). Graphical approach studies that integrate NETs in energy mixes and decarbonization strategies include pinch analysis (Nair et al., 2020) and marginal abatement cost (MAC) curves (Lameh et al., 2022).

MAC curves were derived from the energy conservation supply curves in the 1980s (Meier et al., 1982). They involve plotting the specific cost (or MAC) vs. the cumulative abatement potential of mitigation options in rectangular coordinates. The mitigation options are arranged in increasing specific costs to enable the easy determination of the most cost-effective options visually. MAC curves gained attention when they were used to rank global decarbonization options (Enkvist et al., 2007). The main limitation of the tool is the indirect determination of the total cost, which requires tedious steps in calculating the areas under the curve. So far, only two studies have been found utilizing MAC curves for decarbonization planning with NETs (Lameh et al., 2022) and net-zero planning (Migo-sumagang et al., 2022).

There is an overall lack of studies in graphical approaches to net-zero planning with NETs. Although MAC curves are a practical tool in decarbonization planning, the calculation of the total cost using this method is tedious. To address the research gap and to remove the tediousness in the cost calculation of MAC curves, this work develops an automated-MAC (AMAC) approach to calculate the total cost in MAC curves. Additionally, the developed technique enables the targeting of net-zero emission. The rest of the paper is organized as follows. The problem statement is given in the next section, followed by the proposed methodology. Next, an illustrative case study on net-zero planning with NETs is presented. Lastly, the conclusions and future work are given.

## 2. Problem Statement

The net-zero planning problem is stated as follows. Given a set of NETs ($N_1, N_2, ... N_i$), with their specific costs and their negative emission capacities ($A_i$). Given a set of $CO_2$-emitting sources ($P_1, P_2, ... P_j$), with their specific costs and emissions ($G_j$). The objective of the current work is to determine the total cost in the MAC curve using an automated approach. The work also enables the determination of the negative emissions deficit to achieve net-zero emission, as well as the total cost to reach such target.

## 3. Proposed methodology

This section describes the newly proposed automated-MAC (AMAC) technique, with its basic structure shown in Table 1. Procedure for the AMAC is given as follows.

i. Arrange the specific costs ($C_k$) of the NETs and the $CO_2$-emitting sources in descending order in column 1. The last value in column 1 should be zero.

ii. Get the difference between the adjacent rows of the specific cost ($\Delta C_k$) using Eq. (1), placing the results in the intervals as shown in column 2.
$$\Delta C_k = C_{k+1} - C_k \tag{1}$$

iii. Place the total negative emission capacity of each NET ($\sum_i A_i$) in column 3 and the total emission of each $CO_2$-emitting source ($\sum_j G_j$) in column 4 at their respective specific cost level $k$.

Table 1 Basic structure of the AMAC technique.

| $C_k$ | $\Delta C_k$ | $\sum_i A_i$ | $\sum_j G_j$ | $E_k$ | Cum. $E_k$ | Cum. $\sum_i A_i$ | Cum. $\sum_j G_j$ | $TC_k$ | Cum. $TC_k$ |
|---|---|---|---|---|---|---|---|---|---|
| $C_1$ | | $\sum_i A_i$ | $\sum_j G_j$ | $E_1$ | | | | | |
| | $\Delta C_1$ | | | | Cum. $E_1$ | Cum. $\sum_i A_i$ | Cum. $\sum_j G_j$ | $TC_1$ | |
| $C_2$ | | | | $E_2$ | | | | | Cum. $TC_1$ |
| | $\Delta C_2$ | | | | Cum. $E_2$ | | | $TC_2$ | |
| $\vdots$ | | $\vdots$ | $\vdots$ | $\vdots$ | | | | | Cum. $TC_2$ |
| | $\vdots$ | | | | $\vdots$ | $\vdots$ | $\vdots$ | $\vdots$ | |
| $C_{n-1}$ | | $\vdots$ | $\vdots$ | $E_{n-1}$ | | | | | $\vdots$ |
| | $\Delta C_{n-1}$ | | | | Cum. $E_{n-1}$ | $\vdots$ | $\vdots$ | $TC_{n-1}$ | |
| $C_n$ | | $\sum_i A_i$ | $\sum_j G_j$ | $E_n$ | | | | | Cum. $TC_{n-1}$ |
| | $\Delta C_n$ | | | | Cum. $E_n$ | Cum. $\sum_i A_i$ | Cum. $\sum_j G_j$ | $TC_n$ | |
| 0 | | | | | | | | | Cum. $TC_n$ |

iv. Subtract the negative emission capacity ($\sum_i A_i$) from the total emission ($\sum_j G_j$) at each specific cost level $k$ and assign it as $E_k$ in column 5 and is calculated using Eq. (2). A positive value indicates a positive emission or $CO_2$ released while a negative value indicates a negative emission or $CO_2$ removed from the atmosphere. The last value in column 6 (Cum. $E_n$) represents the negative emissions deficit; the latter refers to the amount of negative emissions required to reach net zero.
$$E_k = \sum_j G_j - \sum_i A_i \tag{2}$$

v. Get the cumulative values of $E_k$ (column 6), $\sum_i A_i$ (column 7), and $\sum_j G_j$ (column 8) using Eqs. (3) to (5).
$$\text{Cum.}\, E_k = \text{Cum.}\, E_{k-1} + E_k \tag{3}$$
$$\text{Cum.}\, \sum_i A_i = \text{Cum.}\, \sum_{i-1} A_{i-1} + \sum_i A_i \tag{4}$$
$$\text{Cum.}\, \sum_j G_j = \text{Cum.}\, \sum_{j-1} G_{j-1} + \sum_j G_j \tag{5}$$

vi. Calculate the total cost ($TC_k$) in column 9 using Eq. (6). This value represents the area of a rectangle formed by the cumulative specific cost and emissions in the MAC curve.
$$TC_k = \left(\text{Cum.}\, \sum_i A_i + \text{Cum.}\, \sum_j G_j\right)\Delta C_k \tag{6}$$

vii. Get the cumulative total cost (Cum. $TC_k$) using Eq. (7) in the last column. The last value in column 10 (Cum. $TC_n$) represents the total cost of the system.
$$\text{Cum.}\, TC_k = \text{Cum.}\, TC_{k-1} + TC_k \tag{7}$$

viii. Formulate the objective function and constraints. The former is set to minimize the total cost of the system as found in Eq. (8), subject to all constraints in Eqs. (1) – (7), as well as a target net-zero emissions in Eq. (9). The optimization model is a linear programming (LP), which can be solved using any LP optimization tool such as Matlab, Lingo, MS Excel, etc.

$$\min \text{Cum.} TC_n \qquad (8)$$
$$\text{Cum.} E_n \leq 0 \qquad (9)$$

## 4. Illustrative Case Study

The following case study is adapted from the work of Migo-sumagang et al. (2022). The net-zero emissions targeting of a power industry using coal and natural gas as energy sources and BC and BECCS as NETs is investigated. Table 2 shows the specific costs, emissions, and NET capacities of the said system.

Table 2 Data of the NETs and $CO_2$-emitting sources

| Entity | Power Rating (MW) | Specific Cost ($/t CO_2) | Emissions (Mt CO_2/y) | Reference |
|---|---|---|---|---|
| Coal power plant | 500 | 9.91 | 4.14 | (Lameh et al., 2022) |
| Natural Gas power plant | 500 | 12.21 | 1.69 | (Lameh et al., 2022) |
| BC | 0 | 30 | To be determined | (Fuss et al., 2018) |
| BECCS | 500 | 100* | | (Donnison et al., 2020) |

*(Fuss et al., 2018)

Implementing the AMAC procedure in MS Excel by solving Eq. (8), subject to the constraint in Eqs. (1) – (7) and (9), with results shown in Table 3 (scenario 1). Based on the results, the system now achieves net-zero emissions (see column 6, last row) with a total cost of 236.56 M $/y (see column 10, last row).

Table 3 Results of Scenario 1.

| $C_k$ $/t CO_2$ | $\Delta C_k$ $/t CO_2$ | $\Sigma A_i$ Mt CO_2/y | $\Sigma G_j$ Mt CO_2/y | $E_k$ Mt CO_2/y | Cum. $E_k$ Mt CO_2/y | Cum. $\Sigma A$ Mt CO_2/y | Cum. $\Sigma G$ Mt CO_2/y | $TC_k$ M $/y | Cum. $TC_k$ M $/y |
|---|---|---|---|---|---|---|---|---|---|
| 100 | | 0 | | 0 | | | | | |
| | 70 | | | | 0 | 0 | 0 | 0 | |
| 30 | | 5.83 | | -5.83 | | | | | 0 |
| | 17.79 | | | | -5.83 | 5.83 | 0 | 103.72 | |
| 12.21 | | | 1.69 | 1.69 | | | | | 103.72 |
| | 2.3 | | | | -4.14 | 5.83 | 1.69 | 17.30 | |
| 9.91 | | | 4.14 | 4.14 | | | | | 121.01 |
| | 9.91 | | | | 0 | 5.83 | 5.83 | 115.55 | |
| 0 | | | | | | | | | 236.56 |

In scenario 2, the model is set to minimize cost, subject to the maximum BC capacity of 1.25 Mt $CO_2$/y (Migo-sumagang et al. (2022), with a new constraint in Eq (10).

$$\Sigma A_{BC} \leq 1.25 \qquad (10)$$

Solving the AMAC with objective in Eq. (8), subject to the constraints in Eqs. (1) – (7) and (9) – (10), with results given in Table 4. As shown, the system has an increased BECCS capacity of 4.58 Mt $CO_2$/y, while BC is kept to the maximum of 1.25 Mt $CO_2$/y. The new system has a higher total cost of 557.16 M $/y (column 10, last row). Note that these results were identical to those reported by Migo-sumagang et al. (2022) using graphical method.

Comparison of the two scenarios is shown in the MAC curves in Figure 1. Note that in the original graphical procedure, the total cost has to be calculated by manually summing the areas below the MAC curves (see details in Figure 1; Migo-sumagang et al. (2022)). With the AMAC, the total cost values can be easily determined. Besides, changes due to process system improvement can also be updated easily with the AMAC model.

Table 4 Results of Scenario 2.

| $C_k$ $/t CO_2$ | $\Delta C_k$ $/t CO_2$ | $\Sigma A_i$ Mt $CO_2$/y | $\Sigma G_j$ Mt $CO_2$/y | $E_k$ Mt $CO_2$/y | Cum. $E_k$ Mt $CO_2$/y | Cum. $\Sigma A$ Mt $CO_2$/y | Cum. $\Sigma G$ Mt $CO_2$/y | $TC_k$ M $/y | Cum. $TC_k$ M $/y |
|---|---|---|---|---|---|---|---|---|---|
| 100 | | 4.58 | | -4.58 | | | | | |
| | 70 | | | | -4.58 | 4.58 | 0 | 320.6 | |
| 30 | | 1.25 | | -1.25 | | | | | 320.6 |
| | 17.79 | | | | -5.83 | 5.83 | 0 | 103.72 | |
| 12.21 | | | 1.69 | 1.69 | | | | | 424.32 |
| | 2.3 | | | | -4.14 | 5.83 | 1.69 | 17.30 | |
| 9.91 | | | 4.14 | 4.14 | | | | | 441.61 |
| | 9.91 | | | | 0 | 5.83 | 5.83 | 115.55 | |
| 0 | | | | | | | | | 557.16 |

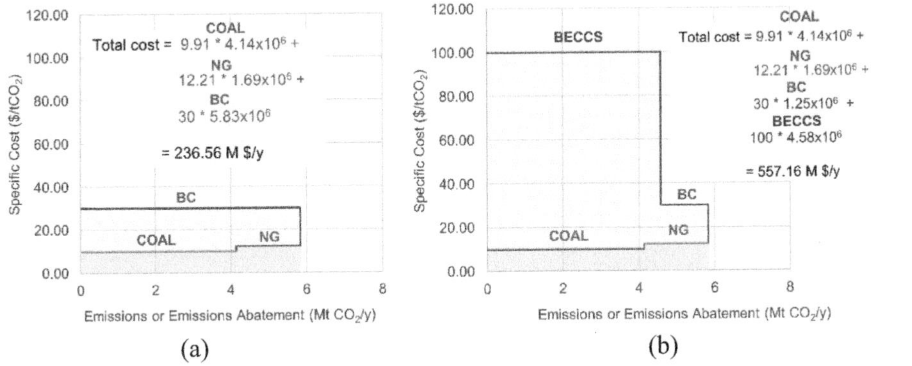

Figure 1 MAC curves for (a) scenario 1 and (b) scenario 2 (with a capacity constraint on BC)

## 5. Conclusions

An automated MAC (AMAC) technique for targeting net-zero emissions was developed. The technique enables the automated calculation of the total cost for net-zero scenarios. A case study on emissions reduction planning with NETs was used to illustrate the method. The results of the automated method match those from graphical approach, and removes the tediousness of calculating the total cost in emission reduction planning. Future work can include the calculation of the cost of the alternative energy, as well as the consideration of other environmental footprints of NETs aside from cost.

# References

Chrobak, U., 2021. Corporate Climate Pledges Pile Up—Will It Matter? Engineering 7, 1044–1046.

Donnison, C., Holland, R.A., Hastings, A., Armstrong, L.M., Eigenbrod, F., Taylor, G., 2020. Bioenergy with Carbon Capture and Storage (BECCS): Finding the win–wins for energy, negative emissions and ecosystem services—size matters. GCB Bioenergy 12, 586–604.

Enkvist, P.-A., Nauclér, T., Rosander, J., 2007. A cost curve for greenhouse gas reduction [WWW Document]. Mckinsey. URL https://www.mckinsey.com/business-functions/sustainability/our-insights/a-cost-curve-for-greenhouse-gas-reduction (accessed 3.21.22).

Fajardy, M., Mac Dowell, N., 2017. Can BECCS deliver sustainable and resource efficient negative emissions? Energy and Environmental Science 10, 1389–1426.

Foo, D.C.Y., Tan, R.R., Ng, D.K.S., 2008. Carbon and footprint-constrained energy planning using cascade analysis technique. Energy 33, 1480–1488.

Fuss, S., Lamb, W.F., Callaghan, M.W., Hilaire, J., Creutzig, F., Amann, T., Beringer, T., De Oliveira Garcia, W., Hartmann, J., Khanna, T., Luderer, G., Nemet, G.F., Rogelj, J., Smith, P., Vicente, J.V., Wilcox, J., Del Mar Zamora Dominguez, M., Minx, J.C., 2018. Negative emissions - Part 2: Costs, potentials and side effects. Environmental Research Letters 13, 063002.

IPCC, 2022. Summary for Policymakers. Climate Change 2022: Mitigation of Climate Change. Contribution of Working Group III to the Sixth Assessment Report of the Intergovernmental Panel on Climate Change. Cambridge University Press, Cambridge, UK and New York, NY, USA.

Iyer, G., Clarke, L., Edmonds, J., Fawcett, A., Fuhrman, J., McJeon, H., Waldhoff, S., 2021. The role of carbon dioxide removal in net-zero emissions pledges. Energy and Climate Change 2, 100043.

Kato, E., Kurosawa, A., 2019. Evaluation of Japanese energy system toward 2050 with TIMES-Japan – deep decarbonization pathways. Energy Procedia 158, 4141–4146.

Klemeš, J.J., 2022. Process Integration (PI): An Introduction. In: Klemeš, J.J. (Ed.), Handbook of Process Integration (PI): Minimisation of Energy and Water Use, Waste and Emissions. Woodhead Publishing, Cambridge, UK, pp. 3–27.

Klemeš, J.J., Varbanov, P.S., Kravanja, Z., 2013. Recent developments in Process Integration. Chemical Engineering Research and Design 91, 2037–2053.

Köberle, A.C., 2019. The Value of BECCS in IAMs: a Review. Current Sustainable/Renewable Energy Reports 6, 107–115.

Lameh, M., Al-Mohannadi, D.M., Linke, P., 2022. Minimum marginal abatement cost curves (Mini-MAC) for CO2 emissions reduction planning. Clean Technologies and Environmental Policy 24, 143–159.

Meier, A., Rosenfeld, A.H., Wright, J., 1982. Supply curves of conserved energy for California's residential sector. Energy 7, 347–358.

Migo-Sumagang, M.V., Aviso, K., Tapia, J.F., Tan, R.R., 2021. A Superstructure Model for Integrated Deployment of Negative Emissions Technologies under Resource Constraints. Chemical Engineering Transactions 88, 31–36.

Migo-sumagang, M.V., Aviso, K.B., Bhasker, P.N.S., Short, M., Tan, R.R., Foo, D.C.Y., 2022. A Graphical Technique for Net-Zero Emissions Planning Based on Marginal Abatement Cost ( MAC ) Curves. Chemical Engineering Transactions 96.

Nair, P.N.S.B., Tan, R.R., Foo, D.C.Y., 2020. Extended Graphical Approach for the Deployment of Negative Emission Technologies. Industrial and Engineering Chemistry Research 59, 18977–18990.

Selosse, S., Ricci, O., 2014. Achieving negative emissions with BECCS (bioenergy with carbon capture and storage) in the power sector: New insights from the TIAM-FR (TIMES Integrated Assessment Model France) model. Energy 76, 967–975.

The Royal Society, 2018. Greenhouse Gas Removal, The Royal Society. London, UK.

Antonis Kokossis, Michael C. Georgiadis, Efstratios N. Pistikopoulos (Eds.)
PROCEEDINGS OF THE 33rd European Symposium on Computer Aided Process Engineering
(ESCAPE33), June 18-21, 2023, Athens, Greece
© 2023 Elsevier B.V. All rights reserved.  http://dx.doi.org/10.1016/B978-0-443-15274-0.50521-7

# Lumped-Parameter Heat Exchanger Models for the Robust Dynamic Modelling of Power Generation Cycles

Oliver Ward[a], Federico Galvanin[a], Nelia Jurado[b], Chris Clements[c], Mohamad Abdallah[d], Daniel Blackburn[c], Eric Fraga[a]

[a]Department of Chemical Engineering, University College London, Torrington Place, London, WC1E 7JE, UK
[b]Department of Mechanical Engineering, University College London, Torrington Place, London, WC1E 7JE, UK
[c]United Kingdom Atomic Energy Authority, Culham Science Centre, Abingdon, OX14 3DB, UK
[d]Formerly at United Kingdom Atomic Energy Authority, Culham Science Centre, Abingdon, OX14 3DB, UK

## Abstract

In this work, novel lumped-parameter dynamic models are presented for one-phase and two-phase heat exchangers, based on the logarithmic mean temperature difference. These models allow for the more robust and computationally efficient simulation of thermal power plants than traditional discretized finite volume models. Comparison of the one-phase lumped model and the finite volume model shows good agreement in the computed outlet temperatures under transient inlet conditions, with steady state differences of <0.15°C. The dynamic responses of outlet temperatures from the models show good agreement, besides a response delay that the lumped model cannot replicate. The lumped models are then implemented in a model of a steam Rankine cycle driven by a source of hot molten salt. The behavior of the system is investigated under a 10% drop in the molten salt mass flow rate, with comparable drops in the main steam pressure, mass flow rate and net power output but a negligible impact on the main steam temperature. The future use of the models is in the design and control optimization of the power conversion system for the STEP fusion power plant being designed by UKAEA.

**Keywords**: Heat exchanger modelling; Dynamic simulation; Steam Rankine cycle; Fusion power; Modelica.

## 1. Introduction

The Spherical Tokamak for Energy Production (STEP) is a project run by the United Kingdom Atomic Energy Authority (UKAEA) to demonstrate the commercial viability of fusion power generation [UKAEA (2022)]. Nuclear fusion is an attractive prospect to meet growing energy demands, using a fusion reactor as the thermal energy source for a thermal power plant. Fusion energy has the potential for an abundant fuel supply that can be extracted from water or bred within the reactor, low environmental impact (emissions and radioactive by-products) and safe operation. It also poses unique design challenges relative to current thermal power plants, such as transient reactor energy output and multiple heat sources. These need to be accounted for in the design of the power conversion system, which converts the thermal energy into electrical energy. Hence, dynamic models are required for the designs to evaluate their transient performance; these evaluations will be performed within an optimization algorithm that aims to search for promising designs.

Robust and computationally inexpensive models that still capture the main system dynamics are a key requirement; effectively exploring the design space during optimization will need a sizeable number of simulations. Novel lumped-parameter dynamic models of one-phase and two-phase heat exchangers are developed to meet these requirements, with their use demonstrated in the simulation of a steam Rankine cycle.

## 2. Heat Exchanger Modeling

The modelling of heat exchangers varies in complexity depending on the specific component and the intended application of the model. For example, an evaporator model will need to be able to handle phase-change in the fluid whereas a preheater model can ignore this for normal operation. The finite volume method is a common approach [Desideri (2016)], which discretizes a one-dimensional thermofluid flow into several lumped storage volumes, each with dynamic balance equations.

Lumped-parameter models may be preferable for computer aided design and optimization. Their simplicity means that a minimal amount of geometric parameterization is required, useful at the conceptual design stage when no fixed details are known. Lumped models also improve initialization and reduce the required simulation time. Both aspects will be advantageous when optimizing the power plant design as each design will need to be simulated without user intervention to evaluate its effectiveness.

The development of distinct one-phase and two-phase heat exchanger models avoids an issue known as chattering that occurs in finite volume models. Chattering occurs when there are discontinuities in the model variables occur for the density on the saturated liquid curve. Chattering can lead to simulation failure unless numerical methods are employed to improve the robustness [Quoilin (2014)].

The models presented below have been implemented in the open-source OpenModelica [Open Source Modelica Consortium (2022)]. Modelica has been chosen as it is an acausal and object-oriented language [Modelica Association (2021)].

2.1. One-Phase Heat Exchangers

A counter-current one-phase heat exchanger model may be used to model preheaters, superheaters and reheaters in a thermal power plant. Each fluid side is modelled as a lumped thermal mass [Kannaiyan (2019)]. With the assertion that only one phase is present on each side of the heat exchanger, the assumption is made that density time derivatives are negligibly small in both fluids (see equation 1). This simplifies the resulting mass and energy balance equations of the fluids. The mass balance equation is static, with no mass storage of the fluids and hence equal inlet and outlet mass flow rates for both fluids. Equal inlet and outlet pressures are assumed here.

The energy balances are dynamic with one state variable, the outlet specific enthalpy, which is taken to be the specific enthalpy in the lumped fluid mass:

$$\frac{d}{dt} h_{f,\text{out}} = \frac{\dot{m}_f \cdot (h_{f,\text{in}} - h_{f,\text{out}}) + \dot{Q}_f}{\rho_{f,\text{out}} \cdot V_f} \tag{1}$$

Subscript $f$ denotes either the hot or cold fluid. $h_{f,\text{in}}, h_{f,\text{out}}$ are the fluid's inlet and outlet specific enthalpy [J·kg$^{-1}$], $\dot{m}_f$ is the fluid's mass flow rate [kg·s$^{-1}$], $\dot{Q}_f$ is the heat flow rate into the fluid [W], $\rho_{f,out}$ is the fluid's outlet density [kg·m$^{-3}$] and $V_f$ is the volume of the fluid's heat exchanger side [m$^3$].

Thermal storage in the heat exchanger walls is modelled assuming a linear temperature profile via two temperature state variables [Altés-Buch (2015)]. Both fluids exchange heat with the wall only. The heat transfer on each fluid side is modelled using a robust logarithmic mean temperature difference proposed for dynamic simulations [Altés-Buch (2015)]:

$$\Delta T_{RLMTD} = \begin{cases} \dfrac{\Delta T_1 - \Delta T_2}{\ln(\Delta T_1) - \ln(\Delta T_2)} & \begin{array}{l} \text{if } \Delta T_1 \neq \Delta T_2, \\ \Delta T_1 \geq \varepsilon, \Delta T_2 \geq \varepsilon \end{array} \quad (2) \\[2em] \dfrac{\Delta T_1 + \Delta T_2}{2} & \begin{array}{l} \text{if } \Delta T_1 = \Delta T_2, \\ \Delta T_1 \geq \varepsilon, \Delta T_2 \geq \varepsilon \end{array} \quad (3) \\[2em] \dfrac{\Delta T_1 - \varepsilon}{\ln\left(\frac{\Delta T_1}{\varepsilon}\right) \cdot \left(1 - \xi \cdot (\Delta T_2 - \varepsilon)\right)} & \begin{array}{l} \text{if } \Delta T_1 \geq \varepsilon, \\ \Delta T_2 < \varepsilon \end{array} \quad (4) \\[2em] \dfrac{\Delta T_2 - \varepsilon}{\ln\left(\frac{\Delta T_2}{\varepsilon}\right) \cdot \left(1 - \xi \cdot (\Delta T_1 - \varepsilon)\right)} & \begin{array}{l} \text{if } \Delta T_2 \geq \varepsilon, \\ \Delta T_1 < \varepsilon \end{array} \quad (5) \\[2em] \dfrac{\varepsilon}{\left(1 - \xi \cdot (\Delta T_1 - \varepsilon)\right) \cdot \left(1 - \xi \cdot (\Delta T_2 - \varepsilon)\right)} & \begin{array}{l} \text{if } \Delta T_1 < \varepsilon, \\ \Delta T_2 < \varepsilon \end{array} \quad (6) \end{cases}$$

$\Delta T_1$, $\Delta T_2$ are the temperature differences at each heat exchanger end [K], $\varepsilon$ is the threshold temperature difference for the alternative equations [K] and $\xi$ is a parameter that controls how fast the function goes to zero [K$^{-1}$]. More detailed discussion of the parameters can be found in [Altés-Buch (2015)]. The formulation avoids simulation failures by allowing for all possible temperature differences as inputs, which is useful for initialization when large transients are common. The function is also continuous to help with solver convergence. Note that equations 4-6 are non-physical and normal model operation should not be within these regions.

The lumped one-phase heat exchanger model can be compared with the finite volume model, using the upwind discretization scheme and 100 cells [Desideri (2016)], considering transient inlet conditions. Parameters are taken from [Altés-Buch (2015)] with steel walls, and are subjected to the same transient inlet conditions, with both fluids being water at 1bar. The initial inlet conditions are 3kg·s$^{-1}$ at 20°C and 2kg·s$^{-1}$ at 80°C. A sigmoidal ramp in the cold fluid inlet temperature from 20°C to 10°C between t=25s and t=50s is considered. The results are shown in figure 2.

Model agreement in the outlet temperatures can be seen to be within 0.15°C for both steady states, with the lumped model over-estimating the total heat transferred relative to the finite volume model. The dynamic behavior of the lumped model closely follows the finite volume model, with a maximum difference of 1.4°C in the outlet temperatures. This is caused by a delayed response in the finite volume model due to the temperature front propagation. Only the spatially discretized finite volume model can capture this effect. Otherwise, the lumped model reflects the key behavior of the heat exchanger. The finite volume simulation required ~1000x the time of the lumped-parameter simulation.

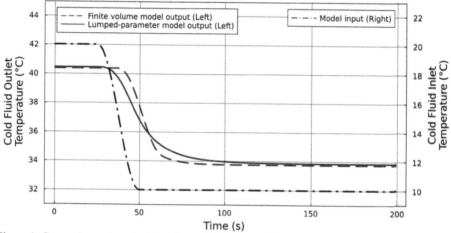

Figure 1: Comparison of results from the one-phase lumped-parameter (LP) heat exchanger model (solid blue line) with a discretized finite volume (FV) model (dashed purple line) under a 10°C decrease in the cold fluid's inlet temperature over 25s (dash-dot black line). Both models are initially at steady state. A ~10s delay is seen in the response of the FV model that is not seen in the LP model.

## 2.2. Two-Phase Heat Exchangers

The model introduced in the previous section is extended for two-phase heat exchangers such as evaporators and condensers. The model structure of the side undergoing phase-change, the working fluid, is modified: the working fluid is modelled as a storage volume at the saturation condition; all fluid is either saturated liquid or saturated vapor. The secondary fluid, wall and heat transfer are modelled as in the one-phase model.

The working fluid side is governed by dynamic mass and energy balance equations [Zhang (2021)]. For an evaporator, the outlet working fluid is saturated vapor, while in a condenser, it is saturated liquid. As the phases share the same physical space of volume in the heat exchanger, there is an additional constraint: the volumes occupied by each phase must add up to the total working fluid side's volume.

Both phases are in pressure equilibrium and, hence, also thermal equilibrium. The model accounts for phase-change by allowing for the phase volumes to change dynamically, dependent on the heat flow from the wall, without encountering any numerical issues from discontinuities in the density model at the saturated liquid curve.

## 3.  Example: Steam Rankine Cycle Modeling

The case study is the modelling of a 45MW steam Rankine cycle, shown in figure 3. The cycle fed by a 350kg·s⁻¹ molten salt stream at 550°C, as in a power plant with direct thermal energy storage [Zhang (2021)].

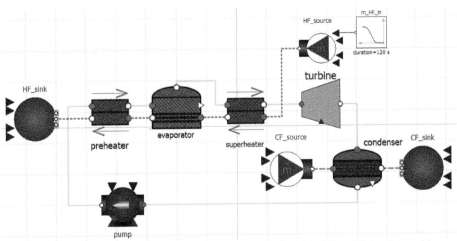

Figure 2: Diagram of the modelled steam Rankine cycle in OpenModelica. Water, the working fluid (solid green line), is heated by a source of hot molten salt at constant temperature (dotted red line) and cooled by a constant source of cooling water (dashed blue line).

The preheater and superheater are one-phase exchangers, and the evaporator and condenser are two-phase. The turbine and pump are both modelled as static components, each assuming a constant isentropic efficiency. The mass flow rate and pressure drop through the turbine is modelled using the Stodola equation [Hefni (2019)]. The pump is modelled using the Modelica Fluid library, producing an ideally constant mass flow rate [Modelica Association (2021)]. The molten salt is modelled assuming constant specific heat capacity and density, while water is modelled using the IF97 standard implemented in the Modelica Media library. Parameter values are extrapolated from [Zhang (2021)].

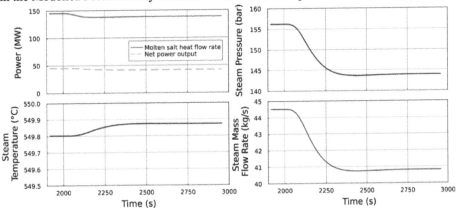

Figure 3: Dynamic response of the steam Rankine cycle to a 10% drop in the molten salt mass flow rate, between t=2000s and t=2120s, from 350kg·s⁻¹ to 315kg·s⁻¹. Comparable drops in steady state values can be seen in the main steam mass flow rate, pressure, and the net power output, while the main steam temperature remains relatively unchanged. The heat flow rate delivered by the molten salt to the cycle undergoes a smaller relative drop.

The cycle is simulated undergoing a 10% sigmoidal drop over 120s in the molten salt mass flow rate, from 350kg·s⁻¹ to 315kg·s⁻¹. The results are shown in figure 4. The 10% drop in molten salt mass flow rate results in comparable drops in the steady state values of the net power output, main steam (at the turbine inlet) pressure and main steam mass flow rate, with percentage changes of 7.9%, 7.9% and 8.3% respectively. The heat flow rate from the molten salt to the cycle drops by 4.5%, which differs from the net power output drop due to a simultaneous drop in cycle efficiency. The main steam temperature increases, but to a much smaller degree than the other variables. This is because the superheater, as specified, is sufficiently sized to heat the steam to near the constant molten salt inlet temperature. The 0.1°C temperature increase of the steam temperature is due to the reduced steam mass flow rate through the superheater, reducing the heat capacity of the steam flow and allowing for a greater temperature change.

Each of the four decreasing variables shows a similar dynamic profile, with a slight overshoot of the new steady state value due to the lower inlet temperature of the molten salt to the evaporator while the superheater's steam outlet temperature is still increasing.

## 4. Conclusion

In this work, robust lumped-parameter models were developed for one-phase and two-phase heat exchangers that make use of the logarithmic mean temperature difference. This robustness is desirable for the simulation of thermal power plants in the context of the early design and control optimization of the STEP fusion power plant being designed by UKAEA. Comparison of the one-phase heat exchanger model with a finite volume model showed good agreement in both the dynamic and steady-state outlet temperatures for changes in the inlet temperature, except for the temperature front propagation through the heat exchanger which the lumped model could not capture.

The new lumped heat exchanger models were then used in a steam Rankine cycle model, driven by a source of molten salt, as an example of their use. The system dynamics under a 10% drop in the molten salt mass flow rate showed comparable drops in the net power output, main steam pressure and main steam mass flow rate. The main steam temperature increased by only 0.1°C due to the sufficient sizing of the superheater. These results demonstrate the potential of using lumped heat exchanger dynamic models in a computer aided design environment aiming to identify not only the design of the power conversion system for STEP but also the control structure that may be necessary. The next steps include extending the Rankine cycle model with a thermal energy storage system, implementing, and comparing alternative control strategies, including energy input from the reactor, and modelling reheat and regeneration cycles.

## References

Q. Altés-Buch et al., 2015, *Dynamic modeling of thermal systems using a semi-empirical approach and the ThermoCycle Modelica library.*

A. Desideri et al., 2016, *Comparison of moving boundary and finite-volume heat exchanger models in the Modelica language*, Energies, 9, 5

B. E. Hefni and D. Bouskela, 2019, *Modeling and Simulation of Thermal Power Plants with ThermoSysPro*, Springer Cham.

S. Kannaiyan et al., 2019, *Dynamic modeling and simulation of a hybrid solar thermal power plant*, Industrial Engineering Chemistry Research, 58, 18

Modelica Association, 2021, *Modelica Language.*

Open Source Modelica Consortium. 2022, *OpenModelica.*

S. Quoilin et al., 2014, *Methods to increase the robustness of finite-volume flow models in thermodynamic systems*, Energies, 7, 3

UKAEA, 2022, *Spherical Tokamak for Energy Production.*

S. Zhang et al., 2021, *Dynamic simulation and performance analysis of a parabolic trough concentrated solar power plant using molten salt during the start-up process*

Antonis Kokossis, Michael C. Georgiadis, Efstratios N. Pistikopoulos (Eds.)
PROCEEDINGS OF THE 33rd European Symposium on Computer Aided Process Engineering
(ESCAPE33), June 18-21, 2023, Athens, Greece

# Energy and economic analysis of integration of water electrolysis with an oxygen-enriched combustion power plant

Yuxing Peng,[a] Pei Liu,[*] Zheng Li

[a]*State Key Lab of Power Systems, Department of Energy and Power Engineering,
Tsinghua-BP Clean Energy Center, Tsinghua University, Beijing 100084, China
liu_pei@tsinghua.edu.cn*

## Abstract

Hydrogen is an ideal energy carrier to promote clean utilization of fossil energy and support large-scale development of renewable energy. Green hydrogen production has no carbon emissions therefore is an ideal hydrogen source, albeit its relatively high cost. One way to reduce the cost of green hydrogen is to effectively utilize the oxygen by-product in a water electrolysis process, for instance, in a transformation of oxygen-enriched combustion coal-fired power plant. This paper discusses potential of integrating a coal-fired power plant with a water electrolysis process via oxygen production and utilization. This provides opportunities for more cost-effective utilization of oxygen produced in a water electrolysis process, and opportunities for reduction in cost of supplying oxygen to an oxygen-enriched combustion coal-fired power plant. Analysis results indicate that the oxygen supply using green hydrogen system can save 8.08 million euros compared to the oxygen supply using air separation device, which lowers the price per kilogram of green hydrogen generation by 0.07 euros, for a 2×300MW oxygen enhanced burning coal-fired power plant with 4000 hours of operation per year.

**Keywords**: green hydrogen, water electrolysis by-product oxygen, coal-fired power plants, oxygen-enriched combustion

## 1. Introduction

Hydrogen is regarded as a promising alternative energy carrier in a low/zero carbon emission energy system, especially for sectors that have difficulties with carbon emissions reduction using existing technologies, for instance, transportation and steel industry (IRENA, 2022). Water electrolysis using renewable energy, typically solar and wind, appears to be a technically viable way to produce hydrogen with low carbon emissions, namely green hydrogen (Ge, 2022). Production of green hydrogen is now significantly more expensive than that of gray hydrogen.

As a result, the most pressing issue is lowering the cost of green hydrogen generation (Wang, 2022). Utilizing the by-product oxygen from the water electrolysis process is an excellent cost-cutting method. When hydrogen is produced in a water electrolysis process, half a mole of oxygen is produced as a byproduct, and this oxygen is currently vented straight into the atmosphere. If the scale of green hydrogen production is considerably enlarged in the future, the byproduct oxygen would also be mass produced. If oxygen is completely used, the resulting economic benefits could lower the cost of hydrogen generation.

An effective and energy-saving combustion method called oxygen-fuel combustion uses pure oxygen or oxygen-enriched air with a higher oxygen concentration than regular air as the combustion gas. Horn and Steinburg first put up the idea of oxy-fuel combustion in 1981 (Horn, 1982), and Argonne National Laboratory confirmed it later (Abraham, 1982). Oxygen-enriched combustion can effectively minimize the emissions of various pollutants after combustion, which has a significant application potential for carbon neutralization. It can also increase the efficiency of fuel consumption.

However, when the coal-fired power plant is transformed by oxygen-enriched combustion, which will significantly increase the power plant's energy consumption, the additional air separation oxygen system is required. If the oxygen-enriched combustion is changed, the entire plant's net efficiency will be decreased by at least 10% (Pikkarainen, 2014). Therefore, one significant drawback of this technology is its enormous energy usage. The air separation unit (ASU) is completely removed if the oxygen generated by electrolyzed water is used for oxy-fuel combustion in coal-fired power plants. This not only reduces the initial cost of the air separation unit but also reduces the significant energy consumption of the air separation system.

Although some coal-fired power plants will be replaced by renewable energy in the future, due to the intermittent nature of renewable energy, coal-fired power plants will still be required to perform peak shaving. As a result, it is important to investigate the oxygen-enriched combustion of coal-fired power plants for low carbon emissions. Simultaneously, an energy system comprised of renewable energy units and coal-fired power plants not only realizes renewable power absorption, but also ensures the safety and stability of power supply. As a result, using the oxygen produced by the electrolytic cell for oxygen-enriched combustion power stations is a good choice.

This paper proposed an energy system consisting of a wind turbine, an electrolyzer, and an oxy-fuel combustion coal-fired power station in order to effectively use the oxygen produced by water electrolysis from renewable energy sources. It also compared the costs of the new energy system's oxygen supply transformation to the costs of the traditional air separation oxygen supply transformation.

## 2. Methodology

### 2.1. System description

This new energy system is depicted in Figure.1. The electrolytic cell uses power from the wind farm to operate normally and generate hydrogen and oxygen. High-purity hydrogen can be used in many fields such as energy and chemical industry, while oxygen is transported to the compressor. The alkaline electrolytic cell used in the electrolytic cell is now the most developed. The compressor increases the by-product oxygen's pressure to an appropriate level before transferring it via the oxygen pipeline to the liquefaction equipment. The oxygen storage tank holds the liquid oxygen. Designers usually select the liquid form for long-term storage of huge amounts of oxygen due to the volatility of wind turbines, which may cross seasons. ASU also employs a liquid oxygen storage tank since it often has a low-capacity standby oxygen storage tank that needs to be kept for a long time. Before delivering appropriate oxygen for the power plant, the high-pressure pump and vaporizer are the necessary treatment devices. It will be present in the conventional air separation system as well, so it won't be taken into account in the following cost analysis.

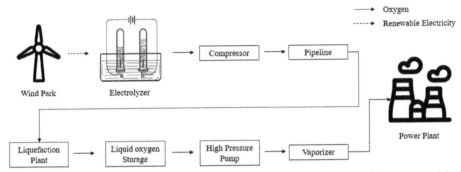

Figure 1. Composition of Energy System integrated by Electrolyzed Water and Oxygen - enriched Combustion Power Plant

Before determining the system's overall cost, make the following assumptions: assume that every equipment has a 25-year service life and that the capital investment cost depreciates linearly. Annual calculations are made for operational costs (OPEX). Some operational costs are computed as a percentage of CAPEX, while others are computed based on a specific energy use. 72 €/MWh is the projected electricity cost for operating compressors, the ASU, the liquefaction plant, etc. (Gonzá, 2021). This is the transaction price for major electricity users which is greater than 150,000 MWh in 2019, including energy taxes but excluding VAT.

## 2.2. Components description

The energy system requires a number of components that are important to our study. The conventional 2×300 MW unit of oxy-fuel coal-fired power plants is used. ASU is a widely used technology and the industry standard for producing huge volumes of oxygen; in this study, the ASU parameters are chosen based on the oxygen requirements of coal-fired power plants. When oxygen is transferred from an electrolytic tank to a coal-fired power plant, compressors are needed. This complies with applicable industry standards. Carbon steel pipelines can be utilized to transmit oxygen because no particular restrictions exist. There are some study models on gas pipeline costs that relate to the pipeline's diameter, length, gas pressure, and other elements. Tanks for liquid oxygen (LOX) are typically used in the ASU design. The LOX tanks of an ASU can be built to have a minimal capacity, while the LOX tanks of a green hydrogen module must be greatly expanded due to the erratic nature of renewable electricity. Assuming a particular energy consumption of 17% of the ASU, the liquefaction plant can be regarded as a component of the ASU. Table 1 displays the parameters for these components (Berenschot. 2019)(Cai, 2014).

Table 1. Components' parameters of the new energy system and ASU

| Component | Unit | Parameter |
|---|---|---|
| **Electrolyzer** | Nominal power | 1680MW |
| | Oxygen production rate | 480t/h |
| | Yearly working hours | 2000h |
| **Power plants** | Nominal power | 2x300 MW |
| | Coal consumption per unit power | 300 t/MWh |

| | | |
|---|---|---|
| | Coal consumption per unit time | 180 t/h |
| | Yearly working hours | 4000 h |
| **ASU** | CAPEX | 200 M€ |
| | Oxygen feeding rate | 240 t/h |
| | Specific energy consumption | 210 kWh /t $O_2$ |
| | LOX capacity | 1200 t |
| **Compressor** | CAPEX | 11.6 M€ |
| | Specific energy consumption | 33 kWh /t $O_2$ |
| **Pipeline** | Investment cost per unit length | 1.08 M€/km |
| | Pipeline length | 5 km |
| **LOX storage tank** | Unit volume investment cost | 1500€/m$^{-3}$ |
| | Liquid oxygen density | 1.413 t/m$^3$ |
| | LOX capacity | 144000 t |
| **Liquefaction plant** | CAPEX | 100 M€ |
| | Specific energy consumption | 40.8 kWh /t $O_2$ |

## 3. Results and discussion

### 3.1. Cost comparison

The cost comparison results are shown in Figure 2: the yearly total savings is 8.08 million euros. The main reason of this saving is the complete removal of the ASU, which saves 18.59 million euros in OPEX and 8.00 million euros in CAPEX.

In the new energy system, since the wind park is intermittent, the gaseous oxygen from the electrolyzer needs to be stored in the oxygen tank. If oxygen is overproduced, gaseous oxygen needs to be liquefied. The liquefaction process increases OPEX by about 3.92 million euros and increases CAPEX by about 4.00 million euros The capacity of oxygen storage tank is obviously increased, the CAPEX of oxygen tank reaches 7.56 million euros, while the CAPEX of oxygen tank in BAU is 0.50 million euros. The remaining costs include compressors and oxygen pipelines, these costs are 3.13 million euros.

The annual saving of 8.08 million euros is used to produce green hydrogen. Divided by the amount of green hydrogen produced (120 million kilogram), 0.07 euros can be saved per kilogram of $H_2$.

### 3.2. Sensitivity analysis

The results of this analysis will be somewhat impacted by the actual adjustments made to the LOX tank capacity and pipeline length based on the particular project. Therefore, the

*Energy and economic analysis of integration of water electrolysis with an*                    3281
*oxygen-enriched combustion power plant*

length of the pipeline and the oxygen storage tank's capacity received a sensitivity analysis in this study.

It is obvious that a significant share of the costs of new energy systems are accounted for by LOX tank CAPEX. The cost can be further decreased if we can reduce the capacity of the LOX storage tanks. The following expression is used to define the storage factor: LOX tank capacity/total LOX volume passing through the tank. The conclusion we previously described has a storage factor of 15%, and the tank can hold 144000 tonnes of liquid oxygen. Table 2 shows the influence of tank capacity on savings: savings decrease when tank capacity increases. When the storage factor is more than 0.31, the savings become negative. In order to save more costs for new energy systems, we need to minimize tank capacity while ensuring the normal operation of the system, This can be done by adjusting the rated power of the wind park and the rated power of the electrolyzer.

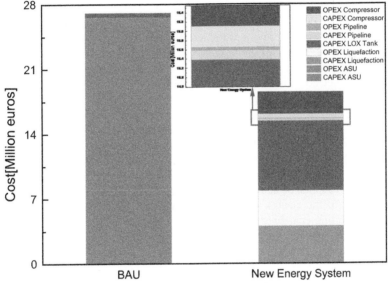

Figure 2. Yearly CAPEX and OPEX for BAU and New Energy System (Million Euros)

Table 2. Sensitivity Analysis of LOX Tank Capacity

| The storage factor | Tank capacity/t | Savings/M€ |
|---|---|---|
| 0.05 | 48000 | 13.12 |
| 0.10 | 96000 | 10.06 |
| 0.15 | 144000 | 8.08 |
| 0.20 | 192000 | 5.56 |
| 0.25 | 240000 | 3.04 |

In this analysis, the pipeline's length is fixed at 5 km, which is the optimal circumstance. The length of the pipeline will actually be significantly extended in several nations with greater landmasses. Savings are impacted by pipeline length in Table 3 and decline as pipeline length rises. If the pipeline is longer than 155 kilometers, the savings are zero. As a result, we must minimize the distance between the green hydrogen system and the power plant in order to save expenditures. Therefore, it is more cost-effective to convert coal-fired power plants to oxy-fuel combustion in regions with a wealth of renewable energy supplies.

Table 3. Sensitivity Analysis of pipeline length

| The pipeline length/km | Pipeline cost/M€ | Savings/M€ |
|---|---|---|
| 5 | 0.27 | 8.08 |
| 25 | 1.35 | 7.00 |
| 50 | 2.7 | 5.65 |
| 100 | 5.4 | 2.95 |

## 4. Conclusion

The integration of wind energy, a water electrolysis system, and an oxygen-enriched combustion power plant creates the suggested new energy system as a whole. In order to achieve a low-carbon, economic goal, the electrolytic water system by-product of oxygen for oxygen-enriched combustion power plants thoroughly remove the air separation plant. This increases coal-fired power plants' efficiency, lowers carbon dioxide emissions, and lowers the cost of retrofitting coal-fired power plants for oxygen-enriched combustion.

From the results of cost comparison, when the tank capacity is 144,000 tonnes, the new energy system can save 8.08 million euros annually compared to BAU. Green hydrogen generation can be produced for 0.07 euros less per kilogram if cost savings are computed to do so. Larger cost savings are possible with smaller tank capacities and shorter pipeline length. The goal can then be achieved by optimizing the rated power of the wind park and the rated power of the electrolyzer in accordance with the 1-year wind turbine output curve and converting coal-fired power plants to oxy-fuel combustion in regions with a wealth of renewable energy supplies.

## References

IRENA. 2022. GLOBAL HYDROGEN TRADE TO MEET THE 1.5°C CLIMATE GOAL.

L. Ge, Q, Cui, M. Li, et al. 2022. Review on water electrolysis for hydrogen production powered by fluctuating wind power and PV. Integrated Intelligent Energy, 2022,44(05):1-14.

H. Wang, W. Xu, Z. Zhang. Development status and suggestions of green hydrogen energy produced by water electrolysis from renewable energy. Chemical Industry and Engineering Progress, 2022,41(S1):118-131.

J. Deng. Study on carbon content per unit calorific value of coals in China. Coal Processing & Comprehensive Utilization, 2022,(01):58-62.

Horn F L, Steinberg M. Control of carbon dioxide emissions from a power plant (and use in enhanced oil recovery). Fuel, 1982, 61(5)415-422.

B. M. Abraham, J. G. Asbury, E. P. Lynch, et al. Coal-oxygen process provides CO2 for enhanced recovery. Oil Gas J, 1982, 80(11).

Pikkarainen T, Saastamoinen J, Saastamoinen H, et al. Development of 2nd generation oxyfuel CFB technology-Small scale combustion experiments and model development under high oxygen concentrations. Energy Procedia, 2014, 63: 372-385.

Berenschot. 2019. Oxygen synergy for hydrogen production.

G. Cai. 2022. Analysis on the influence of changing operation conditions on energy consumption of air separation plant. Copper Engineering 2022(02):81-83.

Javier Serrano Gonzá,lez,Cé,sar Á,lvarez Alonso. Industrial electricity prices in Spain: A discussion in the context of the European internal energy market. Energy Policy,2021,148.

Antonis Kokossis, Michael C. Georgiadis, Efstratios N. Pistikopoulos (Eds.)
PROCEEDINGS OF THE 33rd European Symposium on Computer Aided Process Engineering
(ESCAPE33), June 18-21, 2023, Athens, Greece

# CO₂ water-lean capture: Mathematical modelling and analysis of the industrial process

Ulderico Di Caprio[a], Emine Kayahan[a], Min Wu[a], Peter Hellinckx[b], Tom Van Gerven[c], Steffen Waldherr[d,e] and M. Enis Leblebici[a,*]

[a]*Center for Industrial Process Technology, Department of Chemical Engineering, KU Leuven, Agoralaan Building B, 3590 Diepenbeek, Belgium*
[b]*Faculty of Applied Engineering, University of Antwerp, Groenenborgerlaan 171, 2020 Antwerpen , Belgium*
[c]*Process Engineering for Sustainable Systems, Department of Chemical Engineering, KU Leuven, Celestijnenlaan 200F, B-3001 Heverlee, Belgium*
[d]*KU Leuven, Department of Chemical Engineering, Celestijnenlaan 200F-bus 2424, 3001 Leuven, Belgium*
[e]*University of Vienna, Molecular Systems Biology (MOSYS), Department of Functional and Evolutionary Ecology, Faculty of Life Sciences, 1030 Vienna, Austria*
*\*muminenis.leblebici@kuleuven.be*

## Abstract

The most mature post-combustion capture technology is absorption of $CO_2$ into monoethanolamine (MEA). Typically, this process utilizes a solution of 30wt.% aqueous MEA as absorbent liquid; however, recent studies showed how increasing MEA concentration enhances mass-transfer coefficient in absorption columns. This work investigates effect of MEA concentration on the overall process. The main focus is given to regeneration heat. Heat duty at the reboiler per unit of recovered $CO_2$ (HDUC) is utilized as the primary performance indicator. The analysis employs an Aspen HYSYS® model. Increasing MEA concentration reduces HDUC by 74% when MEA concentration goes from 30wt.% to 90wt.%. Another parameter affecting HDUC is stoichiometric ratio between moles of MEA and $CO_2$. Halving molar ratio between MEA and $CO_2$, at 30 wt.% MEA concentration returns a reduction in HDUC of 48%, while at 90wt.% MEA concentration, the observed reduction is 9%. Overall, increasing MEA concentration improves process efficiency.

**Keywords**: $CO_2$ capture, monoethanolamine, water-lean solvent, HYSYS, heat duty

## 1. Introduction

The anthropogenic $CO_2$ emission reinforces the global warming phenomena. The International Panel on Climate Change recently highlighted how humanity is urged to reduce $CO_2$ emission to prevent the global average temperature from rising and hitting 1.5°C. Besides alternative energy sources, several technologies are available to reduce anthropogenic $CO_2$ emissions, such as oxyfuel technologies, precombustion capture and post-combustion capture. Among these technologies, post-combustion capture is the most mature solution and requires a minor modification to the currently available production processes (Luis, 2016). This process is executed in a cycling system. $CO_2$ in a flue gas is captured within absorption column using monoethanolamine (MEA) aqueous solutions. $CO_2$-rich amine solution is then processed in stripping column. Here, $CO_2$ is removed from the amine solution at a high temperature and collected from the head of the column.

The $CO_2$-lean amine solution is then conveyed to absorption column to serve as absorbent liquid. Typically, this process utilizes a solution of 30wt.% aqueous MEA. Despite this being the most mature technology, its widespread usage is limited by high regeneration costs, as highlighted by Sreedhar et al. (2017). To reduce the required regeneration heat and increase mass-transfer coefficients within absorption columns, Kayahan et al. (2022) proved the benefits of the $CO_2$ post-combustion process when employing an MEA solution with low water concentration. The increased transfer coefficients allow lower dimensions of the absorption columns or a higher flue gas flow rate processable by the plant. It has been shown that reducing water amount in the MEA solution can lead to 3-10 fold decrease in the reboiler heat duty. However, this calculation did not consider the kinetics of the reaction. In the paper, it has been shown by NMR analysis that using 90wt.% MEA leads to a significant increase in the carbamate formation compared to other aqueous MEA concentrations. This suggests change in the reaction mechanism of $CO_2$ absorption into MEA at and above 90wt.% MEA. In this work, we are still not accounting for this change. However, by using a commonly accepted rate-based model of $CO_2$ absorption into MEA, we aim to calculate the heat of desorption more accurately with increasing MEA concentrations. The analysis employs a mathematical model of the post-combustion $CO_2$ capture process. More specifically, the analysis will be executed in Aspen HYSYS®. Despite the advanced optimisation techniques deployed in the simulation software, this study will not employ them since it does not aim to obtain the optimal process condition. On the contrary, this study focuses on the effect of the MEA concentration on process efficiency. In addition, such behaviour will be correlated to, and explained with, the physical and chemical phenomena underlying the capture process.

## 2. Methodology

This work investigates effect of MEA concentration using a mathematical model of the process. The model is executed using Aspen HYSYS® as simulation software, and its property package "Acid Gas – Chemical Solvents" has been employed to predict physicochemical behaviour of the mixture. It considers the rate-based model proposed by Zhang et al. (2009). In this work we assume that the $CO_2$ absorption into MEA follows the same kinetic within the entire MEA concentration range. The plant scheme implemented in the simulation was reported in the literature by Øi (2007). The absorber column comprises 10 equilibrium stages, and the desorption column comprises 6 equilibrium steps. The stripper worked at 120°C with an overall recovery efficiency of 85%. The representation of the simulation model is reported in *Figure 1*.

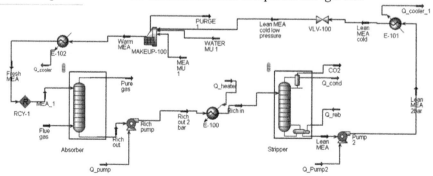

*Figure 1. Overall representation of the HYSYS model employed in this work. The system comprises an absorber, reported in the left-hand of the picture, and a stripper, reported in the right-hand of the picture.*

The gas composition was obtained from the paper of Arachchige et al. (2012). It considers the typical flue gas obtained by a gas-fired plant. Namely, the gas composition is the following: 4% $CO_2$, 8% $H_2O$, 76% $N_2$, and 12% $O_2$. The inlet temperature of the gas is 40°C.

The absorbent liquid was composed of MEA and water. The model also includes make-up for absorbent solution, which tackles absorbent liquid losses because of evaporation in the reboiler. Fresh absorbent mixture is fed at this point and is mixed with the $CO_2$-lean absorbent solution leaving the stripper. The latter contains a load of not-stripped $CO_2$; therefore, the absorber is fed with an absorbent solution containing a certain amount of $CO_2$.

MEA concentration was varied in the study to investigate their effects on the energy efficiency of the reboiler. More specifically, the evaluation was executed on stripper column reboiler heat duty. Together with the reboiler duty, the metric utilized to evaluate the system performance is heat duty at reboiler per unit of recovered $CO_2$ (HDUC). In this work we assume that the pumping cost of the liquid does not change with the MEA concentration. Therefore, lower values of HDUC indicate more energy-efficient process. The following MEA concentrations were utilized in this study: 20wt.%, 30wt.%, 50wt.%, 70wt.%, and 90wt.%. Effect of absorbent liquid inlet temperature on the absorber column on the HDUC was also investigated in this study. The absorber inlet liquid temperature was set to 30°C, 40°C and 50°C. All the experiments mentioned above were carried out with a molar ratio between MEA in absorbent liquid and $CO_2$ in flue gas (nMEA/nCO₂) of 10. The effect of nMEA/nCO₂ was investigated. In addition, nMEA/nCO₂ of 6 was tested to investigate the effect of this parameter. The molar ratio was tuned by changing liquid flow rate going to absorption column.

## 3. Results and discussion

### 3.1. Effect of the MEA concentration

In *Figure 2*, profile of HDUC and reboiler duty are reported with changing MEA mass fraction at the make-up outlet. The curves within the plot are reported at different liquid inlet temperature to the absorber. Increasing MEA mass fraction, HDUC slightly increases from 20wt.% to 30wt.% and steadily decreases when moving MEA fraction from 30wt.% to 90wt.%. On the contrary, overall heat duty at reboiler steadily increases with mass fraction of MEA. The presence of the peak is investigated in Section 3.2. Changing MEA mass fraction from 30wt.% to 90wt.%, decreased HDUC by 74% while it increased reboiler heat duty by 60%. We hypothesize it is related to the absorption heat and evaporation capacity of the absorbent liquid. Energy given by the reboiler of the stripping column is employed to 1) evaporate water and MEA, and 2) strip the $CO_2$ molecules from the liquid. At 120°C, the latent heat of the MEA is 54.7kJ/mol MEA (McDonald et al. (1959)), while for water, it is 36.71kJ/mol $H_2O$. The absorption heat of $CO_2$ into aqueous MEA solution at 120°C is around 105 kJ/mol $CO_2$; this value is almost independent of MEA concentration in the range 10wt.% to 70wt% MEA (Kim et al. (2014)). Therefore, moving from 30wt.% to 70wt.% MEA concentration, absorption heat does change its value. Consequently, in this range, the increasing of the heat duty is only related to the change in the absorption liquid composition. Using the value reported above and assuming the mixture enthalpy to be negligible, latent heat of an aqueous MEA solution at 30wt.% is 30.72kJ/mol while a solution with 70wt.% MEA has a latent heat of 44.04kJ/mol. Thus, the latent heat increases by 43% when the MEA mass fraction increases, which explains the reboiler heat duty increase. However, the value increases when energy is normalized with the amount of released $CO_2$ (i.e., HDUC). Increasing

MEA concentration increases absorbent amount faster than the latent heat. The result is in line with our previous findings. Kayahan et al. (2022) proved that increasing MEA concentration increased overall mass transfer coefficients and overall capture efficiencies. In addition, in *Figure 2*, the curves are parametric with the inlet temperature of the absorbent liquid within the absorption column ($T_{in,abs}$). Even if the effect is negligible, when increasing $T_{in,abs}$ both reboiler duty and HDUC decrease. In other words, increasing the temperature at the absorber decreases the amount of energy required in the stripping step. We hypothesize this is related to the temperature profiles established within the loop at the steady state. Increasing the inlet temperature increases the temperatures of the various streams in the system. Therefore, increasing $T_{in,abs}$ also increases the liquid inlet temperature at the stripper. Therefore, the reboiler must supply less sensible heat to let the stream arrive at boiling.

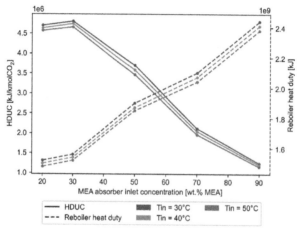

*Figure 2. Profile of reboiler heat duty per unit of recovered $CO_2$ (HDUC) and reboiler duty. The HDUC is reported on the left-hand y-axis. The reboiler heat duty is reported on the right-hand y-axis. The HDUC decreases by 74% when the concentration of MEA is increased from 30wt.% to 90wt.% within the absorbent liquid. On the contrary, the reboiler duty increases by 60% in the same MEA mass fraction range.*

### 3.2. Effect of the molar ratio between MEA and $CO_2$

*Figure 3* shows the behavior of the HDUC parametric in nMEA/nCO$_2$. Namely, two cases are analyzed in this study with an nMEA/nCO$_2$ of 6 and 10. For both the molar ratios, the HDUC decreases when increasing the MEA mass fraction from 20wt.% to 90wt.%. However, as also previously mentioned, the curves present a local maximum. The local maximum is located around 30wt.% MEA when the molar ratio is 10, while it is around 50wt.% MEA when the molar ratio is 6. In other words, the peak shifts to higher values of MEA mass fraction when decreasing the nMEA/nCO$_2$. We hypothesize that the existence of the peak and its shifting toward higher MEA mass fractions with decreasing nMEA/nCO$_2$ is related to the amount of the absorbed $CO_2$ in the absorption column. In the left-hand of the peak, increasing the MEA mass fraction increases the HDUC; therefore, the energy required for the stripping increases faster than the released $CO_2$ at the stripper. On the right side of the peak, the released $CO_2$ increases faster than the energy required for the stripping; this is related to the absorbed amount of $CO_2$ within the absorbent liquid. Here, increasing the MEA mass fraction increases the amount of absorbed $CO_2$; however, as previously highlighted, the desorption heat increase is negligible with the MEA mass fraction in the liquid. Therefore, since the required heat is

mainly given by the latent heat of the absorbent liquids, the reboiler duty is spread over a
higher amount of $CO_2$ at high MEA mass fractions. Thus, the energy spent to strip one
mole of $CO_2$ decreases by increasing the MEA mass fraction within the absorbent liquid.
The peak shift to higher MEA mass fractions when decreasing the molar ratio means that
the trade-off between the energies is reached for higher MEA mass fractions when the
molar ratio is lower. This effect is related to the relative presence of MEA. The MEA is
the main component driving the $CO_2$ capture into the absorbent liquid; thus, increasing
the concentration of MEA increases the number of molecules absorbed by the liquid.
Decreasing nMEA/nCO₂ decreases the amount of MEA molecules available to run the
capture. Therefore, a higher MEA mass fraction in the absorbent liquid is needed to reach
the absorption energy trade-off. We hypothesize this is the main reason driving the peak
shift toward higher MEA mass fraction when decreasing the nMEA/nCO₂ ratio.

*Figure 3* shows a different decrease in the HDUC with the nMEA/nCO₂ at 20wt.% and
90wt.%. At 20wt.%, the HDUC decreases by 48% when moving the nMEA/nCO₂ ratio
from 10 to 6. On the contrary, the decrease is only 9% when the MEA mass fraction is
90wt.%. This effect is connected to the amount of water utilized in the system. Increasing
the nMEA/nCO₂ ratio causes an increase in the ratio between the water in the absorbent
liquid and the $CO_2$ in the flue gas (nH₂O/nCO₂). For low MEA mass fractions,
nH₂O/nCO₂ increases faster than nMEA/nCO₂ because of the higher presence of water
within the liquid. However, the water weakens the absorption of the $CO_2$ molecules, but
it still requires energy from the reboiler duty to arrive at the stripping temperature.
Therefore, it behaves as an inert specie that still requires energy. Consequently, by
reducing the ratio nMEA/nCO₂, the HDUC decreases more than having a solution with a
higher MEA mass fraction. The effects of the water as inert are mitigated at high MEA
mass fractions. The substantial increase in the HDUC at higher nMEA/nCO₂ ratios does
not occur since nMEA/nCO₂ changes faster than nH₂O/nCO₂. Therefore, the increase in
the reboiler duty when increasing the ratio nMEA/nCO₂ is compensated by more $CO_2$
molecules absorbed within the liquid.

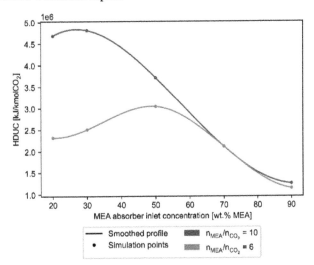

*Figure 3. Heat reboiler duty per unit of recovered CO₂ as a function of the MEA wt.% in the
absorbent liquid. The curves are parametric with the molar ratio between CO₂ and MEA. By
decreasing the molar ratio from 10 to 6, the HDUC decreases. At 20wt.% MEA, the HDUC
decreases 48%, while at 90wt.% MEA the HDUC decreases 9%.*

## 4. Conclusion

In this work, we analysed the effect of the monoethanolamine (MEA) concentration on the reboiler energy efficiency of the $CO_2$ capture process. The heat duty per mole of recovered $CO_2$ (HDUC) has been utilized as the main key performance indicator. Increasing the MEA mass fraction in the absorbent liquid increases the heat duty at the stripper by 60%, but it decreases the HDUC by 72%. This effect is mainly related to the latent heat of the absorbent liquid and the independency of the $CO_2$ desorption heat with the MEA mass fraction in the absorbent liquid. In addition, we showed how the HDUC is affected by the molar ratio between MEA in the absorbent liquid and $CO_2$ in the flue gas. Increasing the ratio at a fixed MEA mass fraction generally corresponds to an increase in the HDUC. However, this effect is not constant toward the entire MEA mass fraction range. At 20wt.%, the HDUC decreases by 48% when moving the ratio nMEA/nCO2 from 10 to 6, while at 90wt.%, the HDUC decreases by only 9%.

Overall, this work showed how increasing the MEA mass fraction within the absorbent liquid increase the energy efficiency of the reboiler. However, for this study, only the energy of the reboiler has been considered. Further investigations are required to investigate the impact of the higher MEA concentration on the pumping cost and evaporation losses.

## Acknowledgements

The authors acknowledge funding from VLAIO Moonshot HBC.2019.0109　and HBC.2021.0255 "Intensification of $CO_2$ capture processes (CAPTIN)".

## References

U.S.P.R. Arachchige , M.C. Melaaen, 2012, Aspen Plus Simulation of CO2 Removal from Coal and Gas Fired Power Plants, Energy Procedia, 23, 391-399

E. Kayahan, U. Di Caprio, A. Van den Bogaert, M.N. Khan, M. Bulut, L. Braeken, T. Van Gerven, M.E. Leblebici, 2023, A new look to the old solvent: Mass transfer performance and mechanism of CO2 absorption into pure monoethanolamine in a spray column, Chemical Engineering and Processing - Process Intensification, 184, 109285

I. Kim, K.A. Hoff, T. Mejdell, 2014, Heat of absorption of CO2 with aqueous solutions of MEA: new experimental data, Energy procedia, 63, 1446-1455

P. Luis, 2016, Use of monoethanolamine (MEA) for CO2 capture in a global scenario: Consequences and alternatives, Desalination, 380, 93–99

R.A. McDonald, S.A. Shrader, D.R. Stull, 1959, Vapor Pressures and Freezing Points of Thirty Pure Organic Compounds, Journal of Chemical and Engineering Data, 4, 4, 311-313

L. E. Øi, 2007, Aspen HYSYS simulation of CO2 removal by amine absorption from a gas based power plant, SIMS2007, 73-81

I. Sreedhar, T. Nahar, A. Venugopal, B.Srinivas, 2017, Carbon capture by absorption–Path covered and ahead, Renewable and Sustainable Energy Reviews, 76, 1080-1107

Y. Zhang, H. Chen, C. Chen, J.M. Plaza, R. Dugas, G.T. Rochelle, 2009, Rate-Based Process Modeling study of CO2 Capture with Aqueous Monoethanolamine Solution, Industrial & Engineering Chemistry Research, 48, 20, 9233-9246

Antonis Kokossis, Michael C. Georgiadis, Efstratios N. Pistikopoulos (Eds.)
PROCEEDINGS OF THE 33rd European Symposium on Computer Aided Process Engineering
(ESCAPE33), June 18-21, 2023, Athens, Greece

# Stochastic pinch analysis to target for resources in batch processes

Md Alquma Haider, Nitin Dutt Chaturvedi*

*Process Systems Engineering Laboratory, Department of Chemical and Biochemical Engineering, Indian Institute of Technology Patna, Bihta, Patna, 801106, Bihar, India*

*nitind@iitp.ac.in*

## Abstract

Resource conservation in batch processes is critical for process industries. For minimizing resource consumption in batch and continuous processes, Pinch Analysis is one of the best insight-based optimization techniques. Variation in operational conditions and/or environmental changes may cause changes in quality and flow. Uncertain quality and flow can be addressed using distinct probability distributions with known mean and standard deviations. The objective of this work is to minimize the resource in a batch process with uncertain flow. In order to transform the probabilistic flow constraints associated with the sources into deterministic ones, a chance-constraint programming approach is used. An illustrative example is given to show how the suggested method works, with analysis based on three distinct distributions (the normal distribution, the lognormal distribution, and Chebyshev's one-sided inequality).

**Keywords**: Stochastic Pinch Analysis, Batch process, Resource

## 1. Introduction

. Process Systems Engineering's contributions in the area of optimization under uncertainty can enhance numerous fields, including synthesis, design, planning, scheduling, control, and supply chain management. Studying optimization under uncertainty has been prompted by the prevalence of uncertain parameters in optimization models for synthesis, design, planning, scheduling, and supply chains. Stochastic programming is an approach to the problem of uncertainty in which a subset of decisions is made in the belief that corrective actions will be available over a specified scenario tree with discrete probabilities of the uncertainties[1].

Batch processes make it possible to make many different kinds of products and share resources [2]. The pharmaceutical, polymer, food, and specialty chemical industries have all made extensive use of batch processing.[3] The most important area for enhancement in batch processes is resource conservation or the efficient use of resources. Haider and Chaturevedi[4] have created a Pinch Analysis(PA)-based methodology for specialising in the conservation of resources through the use of dedicated sources in segregated targeting problem for batch processes.The addition of time makes the design and synthesis of resource allocation networks for a batch process more difficult. However, as product-oriented industrialization has become increasingly emphasized, more systematic integration and design methodologies have been developed for batch processes considering uncertain parameters.

This paper focuses on the water allocation problem (WAN) and how to handle it when there are unknown parameters. Parametric uncertainty associated with source flows is incorporated into resource allocation networks using the chance-constrained approach[5]

and the PA framework. Modeling these parameters' unknown values requires the use of probability distribution functions whose mean and standard deviation are already known. Through the use of a chance-constraint programming strategy, the probabilistic flow constraints related to the sources can be converted into deterministic ones. The proposed method is explained with the help of an example, which employs analysis based on three different distributions (the normal distribution, the lognormal distribution, and Chebyshev's one-sided inequality).

## 2. Problem statement and mathematical formulation

The following mathematical expression describes the general stochastic Pinch problem, which seeks to optimise the resource in a batch network subject to uncertainties in source parameters.

There is a set of $N_s$ internal sources available. Each internal source generates a uncertain flow $F_{is}$ (with a mean and standard deviation) at a certain quality $q_{is}$ at a definite time interval. It is also known that there is a set of $N_d$ internal demands that must be met, and that each of these demands is willing to accept a flow of some quality that is below some maximum quality limit $F_{dj}$. Each demand is also bound with definite time interval. To meet the unmet needs, there is also access to an external source called resource ,which has an known quality $q_r$ and no flow restriction. Resource is available all the time. Unused flows from internal sources are routed to an external demand known as waste, with no caps on quality or quantity.

Let $f_{ij,t}$ denote the flow from $i^{th}$ source to $j^{th}$ demand at a given time interval (t). For a given time interval (t), $f_{iw,t}$ denote flow from $i^{th}$ source to the waste (w) while $f_{oj,t}$ represent flow from fresh water (resource) to the $j^{th}$ demand. In accordance with the flow conservation principle, the following expressions can be used to express the flow balance for all internal sources and sinks for batch processes. $\sum_{j=1}^{N_d} f_{ij,t} + f_{iw,t} = F_{si,t}$          $\forall\ i$
(1)

$$\sum_{i=1}^{N_s} f_{ij,t} + f_{oj,t} = F_{dj,t} \qquad \forall\ j \tag{2}$$

Where

$F_{si,t}$ : total flow from $i^{th}$ source at a particular time interval (t).

$F_{dj,t}$ : total flow in $j^{th}$ demand at a particular time interval (t).

$C_{si,t}$ : contaminant concentration of $i^{th}$ source at a particular time interval (t).

$C_{so,t}$ : contaminant concentration of fresh source at a particular time interval (t).

$C_{dj,t}$ : contaminant concentration of $j^{th}$ demand at a particular time interval (t).

The contaminant constraint can be mathematically expressed for any internal demand as

$$\sum_{i=1}^{N_s} f_{ij,t}\, C_{si,t} + f_{oj,t} C_{so,t} \le F_{dj,t}\, C_{dj,t} \qquad \forall j \tag{3}$$

A WAN's primary goal is to decrease the demand for fresh water, and this can be expressed mathematically as follows:

$$Minimize\ R(t) = \sum_{j=1}^{N_d} f_{oj,t} \tag{4}$$

Since it is not possible to guarantee that the constraints in eqs. 1 and 3 will be met in the presence of uncertainty in the source flow ,these constraints are treated as probabilistic in order to account for the parametric uncertainty.The source flow constraints in eq. 1 has reliability parameter, and denote them by $\beta(t)$.The probabilistic constraints in Equations 2 is rewritten as follows.

$$Prob\left(\sum_{j=1}^{Nd} f_{ij,t} \leq F_{si,t}\right) \geq \beta(t) \quad \forall\ i \tag{5}$$

A stochastic technique called chance-constrained programming uses the probability distribution of the random variables to transform a probabilistic constraint into a deterministic constraint. It can therefore be utilised to resolve an optimization issue with parametric uncertainty. The probabilistic restrictions in equations 5 is transformed into deterministic equivalents in this study using the chance-constrained programming methodology.It should be noted that uncertainity is source quality is not considered here.

Because $f_{iw,t}$ in equation (1) is a slack variable, the probabilistic constraint (eq. (5)) can be rewritten as

$$Prob\left(\sum_{j=1}^{Nd} f_{ij,t} \leq F_{si,t}\right) \leq (1 - \beta(t)) \quad \forall\ i \tag{6}$$

It is possible to write a deterministic form of eq. (7) using chance-constrained programming as follow:

$$\sum_{j=1}^{Nd} f_{ij,t} \leq P_{F_{si,t}}^{-1}\ (1 - \beta(t)) \quad \forall\ i \tag{7}$$

Where $P_{F_{si,t}}$ represent source flow probability distribution time function

For the purpose of determining effective flow, the following equations[6] are used:
$$Effective\ flow = \mu_{i,t} - z_{\beta,t}\ \sigma_{i,t}\ \forall\ i \tag{8}$$
$$Effective\ flow = e^{m_{i,t} - z_{\beta(t)}s_{i,t}} \tag{9}$$
Where

$$s_{i,t} = \sqrt{ln\left(1 + \left(\frac{\sigma_{i,t}}{\mu_{i,t}}\right)^2\right)} \quad \text{and}\quad m_{i,t} = ln(\mu_{i,t}) - \frac{s_{i,t}^2}{2}$$

$\mu_{i,t}$:      mean of $i^{th}$ source for a given time interval (t)
$z_{\beta,t}$:      inverse cumulative probability distribution function of a standard normal distribution for a given time interval (t)
$\sigma_{i,t}$:      standard deviation of $i^{th}$ source for a given time interval (t)
$s_{i,t}\ and\ m_{i,t}$:      two parameters to characterize the log-normal distribution for a given time interval (t)

$$Effective\ flow = \mu_{i,t} - \sqrt{\frac{\beta(t)}{1-\beta(t)}}\ \sigma_{i,t}\ \forall\ i$$
$$\tag{10}$$

Eq. 8 is used for calculation of effective flow for normal distribution . Eq. 9 is used for calculation of effective flow for lognormal distribution. Eq. 10 is used for calculation of effective flow for Chebyshev's one-sided inequality.

The overall goal of stochastic optimization problem is to reduce the amount of resources needed (eq. 4) in a batch resource allocation network while maintaining the required reliability of all sources and demands.

## 3. Proposed Algorithm

To reduce the amount of resources needed for a batch process, the following algorithm has been proposed:

1. First, the entire time horizon of the batch process is divided into several time intervals (say $(I_1, I_2, I_3.., I_m)$ such that all sources and/or demands must start or end at the end points of these intervals.

2. Determine the bare minimum of resources needed for each time interval without taking uncertainty into account using any PA technique like source composite curve [7] (i.e., first solve for the deterministic case).

3. The waste profile is transferred in a sequential manner for all upcoming time periods [8].

4. Using any PA technique, calculate the minimum resource requirements for each interval while taking into account uncertainty in one parameter, say source flow. Make an effective flow calculation for each of the three possible distributions. For the purpose of determining effective flow eqs. (8),(9),and (10) are used.

5. Create a comparison plot for each interval for all three distributions.

6. Develop a network for allocating resources, making sure to account for efficient flows and specific time periods.

## 4. Illustrative example

In order to demonstrate how the proposed algorithm operates, an example will be used. There are six different sources of water, but only one freshwater resource, so the water conservation problem has six different need demands. The fact that the source flow is uncertain by 10% is taken into consideration here. The data for the source and the demand are shown in Table 1, with the only uncertain variable being the source flow.Table 1. Source and demand data

| Source | Concentration(ppm) | Flow(t) | | Duration(h) |
|--------|--------------------|---------|------|-------------|
|        |                    | Mean | S.D |             |
| S1 | 330 | 40 | 4 | 1-3 |
| S2 | 300 | 45 | 4.5 | 1-3 |
| S3 | 255 | 42 | 4.2 | 0-3 |
| S4 | 200 | 32 | 3.2 | 0-2 |
| S5 | 150 | 15 | 1.5 | 0-1 |
| S6 | 100 | 50 | 5 | 2-3 |
| FW | 10 | | | 0-3 |
| Demand |  | Flow(t) | | |
| D1 | 110 | 40 | | 0-3 |
| D2 | 100 | 45 | | 0-2 |
| D3 | 125 | 42 | | 2-3 |
| D4 | 50 | 32 | | 2-3 |
| D5 | 20 | 15 | | 0-3 |
| D6 | 15 | 50 | | 0-2 |

In accordance with Step 1, the entire batch process is broken up into three distinct intervals, which are referred to as 0-1, 1-2, and 2-3 h. The next step, which is called Step

2, is to calculate the minimum resource requirements. For the first interval, the minimum resource requirements are calculated to be 43.288 t/h without taking into consideration any uncertainty. In accordance with step 3, the waste that was produced during the initial interval will be transported to the subsequent interval in order for it to be incorporated between the intervals. In the source flow with interval integration, the minimal resource requirements for upcoming intervals are 47.235 and 30.692 t/h, respectively. Equations 8, 9, and 10 are used to figure out the effective flow for the normal distribution, the lognormal distribution, and Chebyshev's one-sided inequality, as demonstrated in Step 4. These effective flows are computed for a range of source reliabilities, including 90%, 80%, 70%, 60%, and 50% respectively. It is highly likely that the freshwater requirement ought to be increased in order to make source flows more dependable. Figure 1 illustrates how the freshwater requirements of various distributions shift in response to increasing levels of source reliability. Chebyshev's distribution requires more fresh water than a normal distribution does, and the log-normal case requires a significantly greater quantity of fresh water at each interval.

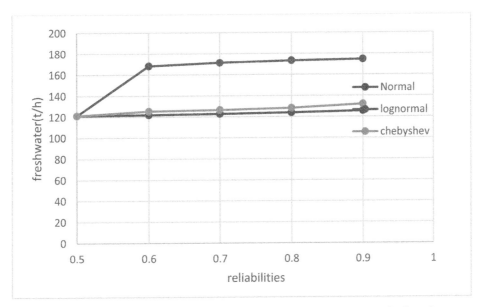

Figure 1: Variation of freshwater with reliability of sources with uncertain flow for different distributions

## 5. Conclusion

This study presents a conceptual methodology for resource targeting in batch processes utilising the idea of stochastic optimization. The methodology is based on pinch analysis, and it uses the idea. The constraints are probabilistic because of the presence of source flow uncertainty; however, they can be transformed into a deterministic form by utilising chance-constrained programming with the normal distribution or Chebyshev's one-sided inequality. The waste profile is transferred sequentially for all future time periods in order to reduce the amount of waste produced. It should be noted that the normal distribution is a natural choice for such investigations; Chebyshev's one-sided inequality, which produces very conservative results, can be used for any unknown distribution. Pinch analysis techniques that have been tried and tested have developed the concepts of effective flow in order to solve the resulting problem in a manner that can be anticipated. The mean and standard deviation of flow metrics, in addition to the desired level of constraint reliability, are used to calculate these effective values. The concept of effective flow was first presented as part of the standard pinch analysis methods in order to deterministically address this issue.

## References

1.  I.E.Grossmann,R.M.Apap,B.A.Calfa,P.García-Herreros,Q. Zhang,2016. Recent advances in mathematical programming techniques for the optimization of process systems under uncertainty. Computers & Chemical Engineering,91,3-14.
2.  N.D.Chaturvedi,Z.A.Manan,2021. Batch process integration for resource conservation toward cleaner production–A state-of-the-art review. Journal of Cleaner Production,318, .128609.
3.  G.Shukla,N.D.Chaturvedi,2021.Targeting compression energy in batch process. Cleaner Engineering and Technology, 5, 100315.
4.  M.A.Haider,N.D.Chaturvedi,2021.Segregated    targeting    for    resource conservation with dedicated sources for batch process. Chem. Eng. Trans. 88, 175–180.
5.  A.Charnes,W.W. Cooper,1959.Chance-constrained programming. Management Science. 6, 73–79.
6.  D.Arya,K. Shah,A.Gupta,S.Bandyopadhyay, 2018. Stochastic pinch analysis to optimize resource allocation networks. Industrial & Engineering Chemistry Research,57(48), 16423-16432.
7.  S.Bandyopadhyay,2006. Source composite curve for waste reduction. Chemical Engineering Journal, 125(2), 99-110.
8.  N.D.Chaturvedi,S.Bandyopadhyay,2013 Targeting for multiple resources in batch processes, Chem. Eng. Sci. 104 ,1081–1089.

Antonis Kokossis, Michael C. Georgiadis, Efstratios N. Pistikopoulos (Eds.)
PROCEEDINGS OF THE 33rd European Symposium on Computer Aided Process Engineering
(ESCAPE33), June 18-21, 2023, Athens, Greece
© 2023 Elsevier B.V. All rights reserved.  http://dx.doi.org/10.1016/B978-0-443-15274-0.50525-4

# MINLP modelling and optimization of the supply chain for the renewable production of methanol in Mexico

Nereyda Vanessa Hernández-Camacho,[a] Fernando Israel Gómez-Castro,[a,*] José María Ponce-Ortega,[b] Mariano Martín [c]

[a] *Universidad de Guanajuato, Campus Guanajuato, División de Ciencias Naturales y Exactas, Departamento de Ingeniería Química, Noria Alta S/N, Guanajuato, Guanajuato 36050, Mexico*
[b] *Universidad Michoacana de San Nicolás de Hidalgo, Departamento de Ingeniería Química, Francisco J. Múgica S/N, Morelia, Michoacán 58060, Mexico*
[c] *Universidad de Salamanca, Departamento de Ingeniería Química, Pza. Caídos 1-5, Salamanca 37008, Spain*
*fgomez@ugto.mx*

## Abstract

Methanol production in Mexico is limited since it is produced from natural gas and only in a few facilities, causing a lack of supply and the need for import from other countries. Due to this, finding production alternatives such as biomass is necessary to satisfy the national demand. In this work, a supply chain to produce methanol from renewable and waste materials available in Mexico is proposed. The supply chain has been modelled following a generalized disjunctive programming approach, including as elements of the supply chain the election of the type and source of raw materials, the selection of the location of the facilities, the type of technology to be used, and the election of the market to be satisfied. The optimal route involves using 8 raw materials, 19 processing plants and the use of three different process technologies to help satisfying national demand with a profit of 7.34 MUSD/y.

Keywords: methanol, renewable sources, industrial waste, supply chain, optimization.

## 1. Introduction

Methanol is a highly relevant product. It is used as raw material to produce a diversity of derivates, such as dimethyl ether, formaldehyde, among others. It is commonly obtained from sources such as natural gas and coal. Global methanol demand has grown over the last years, from 80 Mt in 2016 to 91.55 Mt by 2018 (Alvarado, 2016; Maddren, 2019). The only methanol production facility in Mexico is managed by the national enterprise PEMEX. Unfortunately, difficulties have been identified to satisfy the methanol demand, due to the uncertainties regarding the availability of natural gas. This opens an area of opportunity to search for alternative raw materials for methanol production. Such alternative routes must have the potential to reduce the environmental impact associated with the production of methanol, while efficiently satisfying the demand. However, it is important to evaluate the economic potential of such production schemes from a macroscopic point of view. The use of renewable sources is an interesting approach, where biomass is one of the renewable sources that has presented the greatest potential for use as carbon source. It is used from 10 to 14% in the world (Shen y Yoshikawa, 2013), and methanol can be obtained from biomass or industrial residues. The use of biomass in the world is lower than fossil fuels. However, within clean energy sources, biomass presents a greater advance because it includes any biological material such as wood, energy crops, agricultural residues, food waste, etc. (Valdez-Vazquez et al., 2010). Biomass can be used as a renewable source to produce various fuels and chemical products. Products as biomethanol can be produced from non-food biomass (inedible lignocellulosic biomass residues) (Adelabu et al., 2017). Currently, the development of products from second-generation biomasses is receiving more attention to avoid competition between food and fuels. In countries like Mexico, the use of food-grade biomass is not allowed since it could generate shortages. Moreover, due to population expansion, it is probable that in the future farmland will be more limited. This shows that second-generation raw materials have an advantage as they do not require additional farmland that is already available for other purposes.

The conversion of biomass into products can take place by various routes, such as thermochemical or biological processes. Biochemical processes follow microbial/enzymatic pathways, such as anaerobic digestion. In the case of thermochemical processes, these include three basic subcategories: combustion, pyrolysis, and gasification (Demirbas, 2009). It is important to know what type of biomass will enter the system, since residues with high water content are more favorable to be processed by anaerobic digestion, and biomass residues with low water content are more favored by thermochemical processes.

Decision-making surrounding the supply chain for methanol production from biomass involves different aspects to consider. All these potential decisions and their interactions can be represented in terms of superstructures. This allows decision-making based on technical judgment and established rules. Generalized Disjunctive Programming (GDP) offers an intuitive way of representing the relationship between the different process alternatives represented in the superstructure, while capturing the connection between logical clauses and algebraic logic (Mercarelli et al., 2020). In this work, the supply chain to produce methanol from renewable and waste materials available in Mexico is modelled and optimized. The model follows a GDP approach, including as elements of the supply chain the election of the type and source of raw materials, the election of the location of the facilities and the kind of technology to be used, and the election of the market to be satisfied.

## 2. Methodology

### 2.1. Raw material selection

For the selection of the types of biomasses that have been considered for this study, the National Atlas of Biomass (ANBIO, 2012) is used. Within this Atlas, the availability of biomass residues in Mexico for the entire country is reported. The selected residues with the highest annual availability are shown in Table 1. These values are limiting for each type of residue.

### 2.2. Processing technologies

Within the raw materials, there are three subdivisions: lignocellulosic waste with low water content, waste with high water levels, and materials with specific treatments, such as $CO_2$. Due to this, 4 different technologies are defined as potential conversion routes: gasification, pyrolysis, anaerobic digestion, and $CO_2$-based synthesis. Depending on the type of waste, one technology or another is selected according to the properties of this waste. In addition, there is the condition of selecting only one type or thermochemical technology, either gasification or pyrolysis, but never both together. Table 2 shows the yields considered for each of the processing technologies.

Table 1. Availability of biomass residues (ANBIO, 2012).

| Biomass | Availability [t/y] |
|---|---|
| Solid urban waste | 17,586,209.83 |
| Cane bagasse | 17,689,266.38 |
| Agave bagasse | 2,026,575.00 |
| Vegetable oil production waste | 1,494,257.00 |
| Beer production waste | 1,430,959.00 |
| Coffee bagasse | 977,261.00 |
| Sawmill waste | 728,846.00 |
| Pig manure | 55,328.32 |
| Corn bagasse | 442,335.00 |
| Chicken manure | 217,407.00 |
| Sorghum bagasse | 139,689.00 |
| Bovine manure | 125,241.40 |
| Wheat bagasse | 65,527.00 |
| $CO_2$ | 755,000,000.00 |

Table 2. Process yields.

| Process | Yield [t MeOH/ t raw material] | Source |
|---|---|---|
| Gasification | 50.35 | Yang et al. (2018) |
| Pyrolysis | 51.20 | Kasmuri et al. (2017) |
| Anaerobic Digestion | 46.8 | Patel et al. (2021) |
| Syntesis from $CO_2$ | 50.00 | Martín and Grossmann (2017) |

### 2.3. Selected markets

The studies carried out by the Ministry of Economy through Data Mexico regarding the purchase and sale of methanol in Mexico were taken into consideration. It was detected that the states that require purchasing methanol from abroad due to lack of supply are Baja California, Nuevo León, Chihuahua, the state of Mexico and Mexico City, with methanol requirements in 2021 equivalent to 162,442.4 tons (Harris, et al., 2021; Secretaría de Economía, 2021). The superstructure that includes the aspects raised is shown in Figure 1. 12 types of waste, 29 states for obtaining raw materials, 32 states for the analysis of the location of processing plants and 5 sales markets are included in the superstructure.

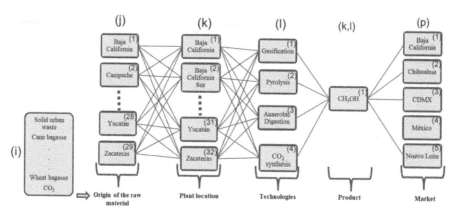

Figure 1. Superstructure for the wastes-to-methanol supply chain.

## 2.4. Mathematical model

Nested disjunctions are used for the location of the plants and the technology used in each of these facilities, recalling that for each location there may be one or more of the four available technologies. The nested disjunction system is shown in equation 1, while equation 2 represents the objective function for a maximum profit given in USD/y.

$$
\begin{bmatrix}
\begin{array}{c}
Y_k \\
CBT_k = \sum_j \sum_i CB_i \cdot F_{i,j,k} \\
CTOP_{j,k} = \sum_j \sum_i F_{i,j,k} \cdot D_{j,k} \cdot C_{comb} \\
CTPM_{k,p} = \sum_k \sum_p F_{MeOH,k,p} \cdot D_{k,p} \cdot C_{comb} \\
CV_{MeOH,k} = \sum_k \sum_p F_{MeOH,k,p} \cdot PV_{MeOH} \\
\left[\begin{array}{c} Y_{k,l} \\ \sum_j \sum_i F_{i,j,k} \cdot n_G = FME_{1,k} \\ CPr_{1,k} = FME_{1,k} \cdot C_{prod1,k} \\ COpe_{1,k} = FME_{1,k} \cdot C_{oper1,k} \end{array}\right] \vee
\left[\begin{array}{c} Y_{k,l} \\ \sum_j \sum_i F_{i,j,k} \cdot n_P = FME_{2,k} \\ CPr_{2,k} = F_{Me2,k} \cdot C_{prod2,k} \\ COpe_{2,k} = FME_{2,k} \cdot C_{oper2,k} \end{array}\right] \vee
\left[\begin{array}{c} Y_{k,l} \\ \sum_j \sum_i F_{i,j,k} \cdot n_{DA} = FME_{3,k} \\ CPr_{3,k} = FME_{3,k} \cdot C_{prod3,k} \\ COpe_{3,k} = FME_{3,k} \cdot C_{oper3,k} \end{array}\right] \vee
\left[\begin{array}{c} Y_{k,l} \\ \sum_j \sum_i F_{i,j,k} \cdot n_C = FME_{4,k} \\ CPr_k = FME_{4,k} \cdot C_{prod4,k} \\ COpe_{4,k} = FME_{4,k} \cdot C_{oper4,k} \end{array}\right]
\end{array}
\end{bmatrix}
\vee
\begin{bmatrix}
\neg Y_k \\
CBT_k = 0 \\
CTOP_{j,k} = 0 \\
CTPM_{k,p} = 0 \\
CV_{MeOH,k} = 0
\end{bmatrix}
\forall k \quad (1)
$$

$$
Profit = \sum_k (CV_{MeOH})_k - \sum_k (C_{Pr} * F_{MeOH})_k - \sum_k (C_{Ope} * F_{MeOH})_k - \sum_k (C_{BT})_k - \sum_k (C_{TOP,jk}) - \sum_k (CTPM_{,km}) \quad (2)
$$

Where $i$ represents the raw material, $j$ is the origin of raw material, $k$ is location of plants and $l$ is the kind of technology. $Y_k$, $Y_{k,l}$ are logical variables for plant location and type of technology. $CBT_k$ is the total cost of raw material and $CB_i$ is the cost for each raw material [USD/t], $F_{i,j,k}$ is the biomass rate sent to $k$ [t/y], $CTOP_{j,k}$ and $CTPM_{k,p}$ represent the cost of transportation from origin to facility and facility to market, respectively [USD/y]. $D_{j,k}$, $D_{k,p}$ are transport distances [km], $C_{comb}$ is transport cost [USD/km· t] $CV_{MeOH,k}$ are the total sales of methanol [USD/t], $F_{MeOH,k}$ is produced methanol [t/y], $PV_{MeOH}$ is unitary methanol sales price [USD/t]. $n_G, n_P, n_{DA}, n_C$ are technologies yields [t MeOH/ t raw material], $FME_{1,k}$ is the methanol produced by the technology $l$ [t MeOh/ t raw material], $CPr_{l,k}$ represent the cost of production for each technology and $COpe_{l,k}$ represents the operating cost for each technology. $C_{prod1,k}$, $C_{oper1,k}$ are the unitary cost of production and cost of operation [USD/y]. Model is reformulated into an MINLP using the convex hull method and solved in the software GAMS to maximize the profit. The purpose of the model is to satisfy a production of 162,442.4 t/y.

## 3. Results

The relaxed model using the convex hull reformulation was coded in the GAMS software, obtaining a nonlinear mixed integer programming (MINLP) model, which was solved using the BARON solver. The model has 3,509 equations and 9,641 variables. The solution results in a profit of 7,336,700.00 USD/y, this profit is obtained with the route shown in Figure 2.

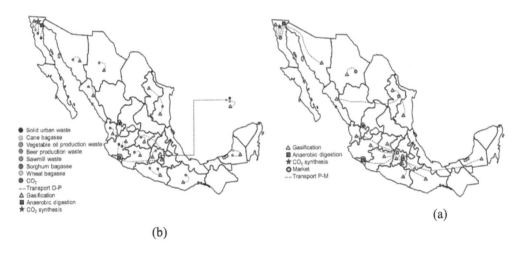

(b)

(a)

Figure 2. Transportation route, (a) from origin to facility, (b) from facility to market.

According to Figure 2.a, the solution implies the use of eight raw materials: urban solid wastes, cane bagasse, vegetable oil production waste, beer production waste, sawmill waste, sorghum waste, wheat bagasse and $CO_2$. These raw materials are obtained from 14 states: Baja California, Sonora, Chihuahua, Sinaloa, Tamaulipas, Nayarit, Jalisco, Guanajuato, Michoacan, Guerrero, México, CDMX, Oaxaca and Campeche. The predominant biomass is sorghum bagasse and sawmill waste because its sale price is low. The facilities are placed in 17 states, which are the same from where waste is obtained, plus Nuevo León, Colima, and Morelos. It is important to mention that in Baja California there will be 3 different processing routes: gasification, anaerobic digestion, and $CO_2$-based synthesis. This is the only state that has all 3 types of technology, because it handles 3 different types of waste. Colima is the other state that has an anaerobic digestion plant installed. The rest of the installed plants use gasification. The pyrolysis process was not selected for any state, because of the high cost of this technology, which is not compensated by its slightly higher yield. Figure 2.b shows the methanol transportation route from the production plant to the markets. It is observed that the production of the Baja California plants, and the production of Sonora are sent to the Baja California market. Chihuahua is supplied with methanol from its own facility. Nuevo León market is supplied by its own plant, receiving additional product from the plants in Tamaulipas and Sinaloa. The State of Mexico market is supplied by six different plants located in Colima, Nayarit, Jalisco, Michoacan, Guanajuato and State of Mexico. Finally, the

Mexico City market is supplied by four plants located in Guerrero, Oaxaca, Morelos, Campeche and Mexico City. This distribution shows that methanol plants in the north supply the northern markets and the plants in the center and south of the country satisfy the markets in that area. The installed plants vary according to the location in terms of capacity to produce methanol, the minimum is 5.88 kg/h and the maximum is 1,910.85 kg/h.

## 4. Conclusions

In this work, a mathematical model to represent the methanol supply chain in Mexico has been developed. The supply chain has been optimized through the software GAMS, obtaining the maximum-profit route from the origin of the raw materials to their delivery to the market. The solution allows a profit of 7.34 MUSD/y, making use of 8 raw materials from 14 different states of obtaining, with 19 facilities installed in 17 different states, supplying 5 different markets. It has been possible to observe the versatility of the route, which transforms several raw materials using 3 different processing technologies, demonstrating that, regardless of the type of waste to be treated, there is a processing option available for its use. Finally, it is important to mention that this model was constrained to a maximum methanol production, which is satisfied, but there are still available wastes in the country. Thus, the potential for exporting renewable methanol could be explored in future works.

## References

Atlas Nacional de Biomasa (ANBIO), 2012, https://www.gob.mx/sener/articulos/atlas-nacional-de-biomasa

B. A . Adelabu, S. O. Kareem, F. Oluwafemi, I.A. Adeogun, 2017, Bioconversion of corn straw to ethanol by celluotyc yeasts immobilized in Mucuna urens matrix, Journal of King Saud University-Science, 1-6.

M. Alvarado, 2016, The changing face of the global methanol industry, HIS Chemical, 10-11.

A. Demirbas, 2009, Biofuels securing the planet´s future energy needs, Energy Conversion and Management, 50, 2239-2249.

K. Harris, R. G. Grim, Z. Huang, L. Tao, 2021, A comparative techno-economic analysis of renewable methanol synthesis from biomasss and $CO_2$: Opportunities and barriers to commercialization, Applied Energy, 303, 117637.

S. Maddren, 2019, Asia methanol – China and the rest, 22$^{nd}$ IMPCA Asian Methanol Conference, Singapore, November 5-7.

M. Martín, I.E. Grossmann, 2017, Towards zero $CO_2$ emissions in the production of methanol from switchgrass. $CO_2$ to methanol, Computers and Chemical Engineering, 105, 308-316.

L. Mercarelli, Q. Chen, A. Pagot, I. Grossmann, 2020, A review on superstructure optimization approaches in process system engineering, Computers and Chemical Engineering, 1-15.

S.K.S. Patel, R.K. Gupta, V.C. Kalia, J.K. Lee, 2021, Integrating anaerobic digestion of potato peels to methanol production by methanotrophs immobilized on banana leaves, Bioresources Technology, 323, 124550.

Secretaría de Economía, 2021, Metanol: alcohol metílico, Data Mexico, https://datamexico.org

Y. Shen, K. Yoshikawa, 2013. Recent progress in catalytic tar elimination during biomass gasification or pyrolysis- A review, Renewable and Sustainable Energy Reviews, 21, 371-392.

I. Valdez- Vazquez, I., J. A. Acevedo-Benitez, & C. Hernández-Santiago, 2010, Distribution and potential of bioenergy resources from agricultural activities in México, Renewable and Sustainable Energy Reviews, 14, 2147-2153.

S. Yang, B. Li, J. Zheng, R.K. Kankala, 2018, Biomass-to-Methanol by dual-stage entrained flow gasification: Design and techno-economic analysis based on system modeling, Journal of Cleaner Production, 205, 364-374.

Antonis Kokossis, Michael C. Georgiadis, Efstratios N. Pistikopoulos (Eds.)
PROCEEDINGS OF THE 33rd European Symposium on Computer Aided Process Engineering
(ESCAPE33), June 18-21, 2023, Athens, Greece

# Supply chain optimal planning for revalorization of empty plastic pesticide and fertilizer containers

Sergio Iván Martínez-Guido [a], Rubén Bernabé-Martínez [b], Claudia Gutiérrez-Antonio [a*], Salvador Hernandéz [c]

[a]Universidad Autónoma de Querétaro, El Marqués, Querétaro, 76265, Mexico
[b]PRANA Proyectos de Reciclaje y Acciones por la Naturaleza, Tuxtla Gutiérrez-Chiapas, 29000, Mexico
[c]Universidad de Guanajuato, Guanajuato, 36050, Mexico
claudia.gutierrez@uaq.mx

## Abstract

Particularly, in agro-industry most of the plastic products are single-use and can persist in the environment long after their intended use, threatening food security and safety (FAO, 2021). Then, in this work is proposed the optimal planning of the supply chain for the revalorization of empty plastic pesticide and fertilizer containers (bottles) generated during the production period. In this way, a mathematical model was proposed to represent all the supply chain steps, and codified in GAMS®. As a case of study, three states in Mexico were selected, taking into consideration some of the higher agricultural sites. Main results show that is possible to obtain 715 tonnes of pellets as products from pesticide and fertilizer containers. Moreover, it is possible to forecast an economic benefit of USD$164,480 per year, and an annual reduction of 1,136 tonnes of $CO_2$, in comparison with the current situation.

**Keywords**: waste management, circular economy, supply chain, optimization, mathematical model.

## 1. Introduction

According to Pohjakallio (2020), if we continue producing plastics as we do now, the plastic industry would consume 20% of the total oil production by 2050. Additionally, whether the behavior in the plastics demand continues, the global plastic waste volumes would grow 77% by 2030 in comparison with the 260 million tonnes per year in 2016. Moreover, the constant use of plastic is increasing the number of their pollutants in the environment, and today it's possible to find these in our food chain and even in our blood, placing them as a threat to human health (Moshood *et al.*, 2022).

On the other hand, in agriculture, plastic products are used in all aspects as the livestock production (feed and animal care), plant production, fisheries, and aquaculture. Plastic also are used in distribution and retail activities, with the goal to keep the agricultural products quality. Furthermore, some of the benefits from using these products in crops production are the reduction water demand, optimizing seed germination, increasing crop yields, crop protection, among others. However, most of the agricultural plastic products are single-use, and these can persist in the environment long after their intended use, threatening food security, food safety and potentially human health (FAO, 2021). In the face of this bleak outlook, bio-based plastics are already in the market as carbon neutral solutions. Notwithstanding, these renewable solutions have been mostly applied into packaging and agriculture activities in less of 2% of the total production plastics; this due the high demand of biomass to other uses, and the lower cost of fossil sources (Patrício-Silva, 2021). Hence, in this work is proposed the optimal planning of the supply chain for the revalorization of empty plastic pesticide and fertilizer containers (bottles) generated during the crops production. In this way, a mathematic model was proposed to represent all the steps involved in the supply chain, and codified in GAMS®. As a case of study, three states in Mexico were selected: Jalisco, Guanajuato and Colima, considering some of its municipalities with higher agricultural production. To obtain the supply chain optimal planning warehouses currently installed in each state were included, as well as the seasonality of crops, distances between the production sites, warehouses, and revalorization sites. Main results show that is possible to obtain 715 tonnes of pellets and flakes as products from pesticide and fertilizer containers. Moreover, it is possible to forecast an economic benefit of USD\$164,480 per year, and an annual reduction of 1,136 tonnes of $CO_2$, in comparison with the current situation in which these containers are left in the fields and burned. In this way, all the strategies with emissions reduction goals can be improved with the integration of optimization tools, even when part of the chain links already exist, or are installed. Additionally, all the information obtained from these optimal solutions represent a starting point for the promotion of public policies as well as a watershed for decision makers at all levels.

## 2. Problem statement

As a first approach to a regional analysis, 10 municipalities from Jalisco and Guanajuato states and eight from Colima state were taken into consideration as case study, due their highest respective amount of agricultural land. As strategy, it is proposed that in each selected municipality a primary storage center (CAP) will be installed, providing an easily identified by local farmers and does not need to be moved to another producing municipality. Subsequently, there are temporary storage centers (CAT) where more detailed handling of the packaging can be given (See figure 1). As installation sites for this kind of centers are considered in first stay existing, located in Tamazula de Gordiano (Jalisco), Juventino Rosas (Guanajuato), and Tecomán (Colima). In addition, it is possible, if it isn't enough with these three current CAT, to install some others in any of the municipalities identified as producers. For this, disjunctive equations are proposed that allow the existence decisions, which as a result will activate fixed and variable costs of each installed center. Finally, a specialized handling center (CAR) is proposed for all packaging with the capacity to generate value-added products, which has the possibility of being installed in any of the 28 selected municipalities.

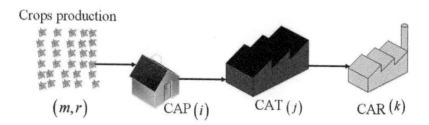

**Figure 1.** Proposed supply chain

## 3. Methodology

In the present work is proposed the optimal supply chain planning determination of empty agricultural containers, through the use of mathematical tools developed by the Operations Research area (Goldbeck et al., 2020). In this sense, as a case study, the current generation of residual containers of agricultural production of different selected crops in the states of Jalisco, Guanajuato and Colima was considered. As a starting point, a review was made of the current real situation, useful information for the choice of the 10 most representative crops, in each of the 28 selected municipalities.

**Table 1.** Selected crops.

| Jalisco | Corn, fodder corn, sugarcane, agave, sorghum, avocado, wheat, oats, bean and fodder sorghum |
|---|---|
| **Guanajuato** | Corn, sorghum, wheat, bean, barley, alfalfa, broccoli, oats, agave, onion. |
| **Colima** | Lemon, copra, sugarcane, corn, banana, mango, papaya, rice, coffee, onion. |

Subsequently, the formulation of a mathematical model was carried out, representing the matter and energy balances of the real problem. In this model were included all the activities involved in the supply chain, and described in detail in the section "Mathematical model". To feed the model it was necessary to collect real parameters of each selected municipality including crop kind, agricultural needs, land used for cultivation, distances, costs, $CO_2$ emissions (using the GREET software), among others. The model and other parameters were codified in the GAMS® platform, where it was resolved by integrating economic performance maximization and environmental emissions minimization. The solutions generated were classified into four main points, solution A (optimal economic performance), solution D (optimal emission reduction), and solutions B and C which are compromise solutions between both objectives.

### 3.1. Mathematical model

As was described before, the proposed approach takes into consideration all the steps involved to achieve the optimal planning of the supply chain for the revalorization of empty plastic pesticide and fertilizer containers (bottles), which are generated during the crops production. Equation 1 represents the balance to estimate the number of produced containers in each municipality per week ($FB_{j,i,t}$), which depends from the amount of area used to produce each kind of crop ($AUSE_{j,r,t}$) as well as the pack type factor linked to each crop ($FGEN_{r,i,t}$). Afterwards, the number of empty containers is transformed into mass flow ($FMB_{j,t}$), multiplying the particular weight of each container ($DB_i$) by the generated quantity from these ($FBC_{j,i,t}$), as equation 2 describes. Total containers mass flow ($FMB_{j,t}$) have two options the revalorization into pellets pathway ($FBE_{j,m,t}^{CAP}$) or to be sent it to a final disposition site, where normally are burned it ($FBEQUE_{j,t}$). Hence, in equation 3 is shown this mass balance. If the plastic flow take the revalorization pathway, hence, equation 4 represents the balance in each CAP, giving the total current flow ($Val_{m,t}^{RealCAP}$), from the subtraction of the flow that it sends to the CAT ($ED_{m,l,t}^{CAT}$) from the total received ($FBE_{j,m,t}^{CAP}$).

$$FBC_{j,i,t} = \sum_r AUSE_{j,r,t} \cdot FGEN_{r,i,t}, \quad \forall \; j \in J, i \in I, t \in T \qquad (1)$$

$$FMB_{j,t} = \sum_i FBC_{j,i,t} \cdot DB_i, \forall \, j \in J, t \in T \tag{2}$$

$$FMB_{j,t} = \sum_m FBE^{CAP}_{j,m,t} + FBEQUE_{j,t}, \forall \, j \in J, t \in T \tag{3}$$

$$Val^{RealCAP}_{m,t} = \sum_j FBE^{CAP}_{j,m,t} - \sum_l ED^{CAT}_{m,l,t}, \forall \, m \in M, t \in T \tag{4}$$

Afterwards, in equation 5 is shown the disjunction for the CAP installation, using the binary variable decision ($x^{CAP}_{m,c}$), constrained by the processing limits ($Limmi^{CAP}_{m,c}$ and $Limma^{CAP}_{m,c}$). Additionally, if the CAP is installed, then the fixed ($CF^{CAP}_{m,c}$) and variables cost ($CV^{CAP}_{m,c}$) are activated, giving the capital CAP installation cost ($Cost^{CAP}_{m,c}$). Similarly, the installation decisions of CAT's and CAR's were obtained in the same way that CAP. Profit ($Profit$) was obtained from the earnings by the pellets sale ($Gan^{Real}_l$), minus all the involved cost in the supply chain as equation 6 describes. Similarly, all the $CO_2$ emissions generated by each supply chain activity were calculated ($Emiss^{Re}$), resulting in emissions ($BE$) that can be avoided if the plastic container's takes the revalorization pathway instead of the final disposition site (see equation 7). Finally, the multi-objective function ($F.O$) was the profit maximization ($MaxProfit$) and the emissions reduction ($MinBE$) as equation 8 shown.

$$\bigvee_{m,c} \begin{bmatrix} x^{CAP}_{m,c} \\ Limmi^{CAP}_{m,c} \leq EN^{CAP}_{m,c} \leq Limma^{CAP}_{m,c} \\ Cost^{CAP}_{m,c} = CF^{CAP}_{m,c} + CV^{CAP}_{m,c} \cdot EN^{CAP}_{m,c} \end{bmatrix} \tag{5}$$

$$Profit = \sum_l Gan^{Real}_l - \begin{pmatrix} Cost^{Quema} + \sum_{m,c} Cost^{CAP}_{m,c} + Cost^{Tr-CAp} + \sum_l Cost^{CAt}_l \\ + Cost^{Tr-CAt} + \sum_p Cost^{CAr}_p + Cost^{Tr-CAr} \end{pmatrix} \tag{6}$$

$$BE = Emiss^{Que} - Emiss^{Re} \tag{7}$$
$$F.O = Max\,Profit;\, Min\,BE \tag{8}$$

## 4. Results

As was described in methodology section, the model and other parameters were codified in the GAMS® platform, where it was resolved by integrating economic performance maximization and environmental emissions minimization using the ε constrain method (Diwekar, 2010). The model is a Mixed Linear Integer model, since there are no equations with division of variable by variable, multiplication of these, or some other algebraic functions. The solutions were obtained using the CPLEX solver, with an analysis time of 0.844 seconds per test, calculating 141,231 variables, 14,680 equations, 142 binary variables and 451,389 elements. The CPU execution time per assay was 2.360 seconds. In order to obtain the solution for each scenario the CPLEX solver was used in an AMD® A10 processor running at 2.60 GHz with 8GB of RAM memory. Obtained solutions were classified in four different scenarios. The scenario A which represent the optimal economic performance, while the scenario D represents the optimal emission reduction. Scenarios B and C which show compromise solutions between both objectives, as is shown by Figure 2. It is possible to notice in Table 1 that solutions A and B are the only where the supply chain optimal planning is perceived to be profitable, due to the existence of earnings, while solution C and D show negative numbers. However, the results are given taken into consideration one year of operation; hence, all the installation cost are paid in the same year. Therefore, solutions C and D doesn't have any earnings, due that in these solutions all the CAT's installed are new; this means that the existent installation are not considered as strategic points for emission reduction. This could be avoided by considering the acquisition of a loan or sub-loan over a period of more than one year, perhaps considering a life period between 10 and 15 years.

**Table 1.** Main results obtained in each scenario.

| Scenario | A | B | C | D |
|---|---|---|---|---|
| **Earnings (USD$/y)** | 164,480 | 48,620 | -67,240 | -183,100 |
| **Emissions (Ton $CO_2$/y)** | 877 | -1,010 | -1,126 | -1,136 |

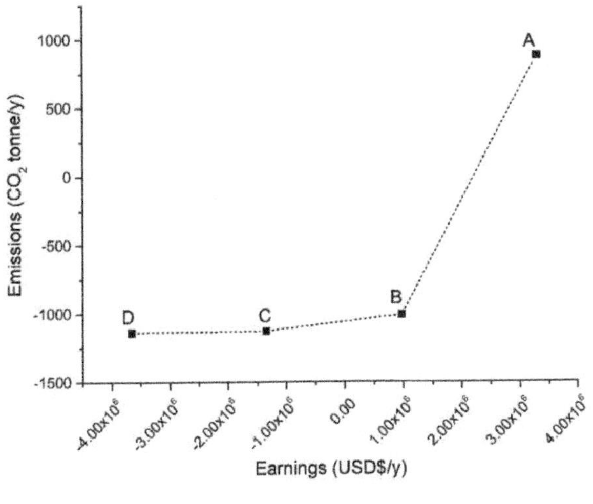

**Figure 2.** Pareto solution diagram

Results show for all the scenarios analyzed, the best solutions consider the existence of at least one CAP (Primary collection center) in each of the municipalities (28 overall). These have functions such as material storage as well as basic sorting, size reduction by crushing, as well as sending material to CAT (Revalorization center). The CAR's (Packaging and recycling center) installation are not taken into consideration, due the respective capacities; hence, in the installed CAT are carry out the rest of the revalorization activities. A final size reduction and pellets extrusion. For the CAT where considered 3 different capacities 0.76, 1.52, 2.3 tonnes/d; for all the solutions was selected by the model the lowest capacity. In scenario A, exchanges are allowed only between municipalities in the same state for savings in transport costs. While in scenario D only one municipality exchanges to three others, the rest to only two; this is due that transportation activities are constrained by emissions. In solution A, Romita and Dolores do not use CAT, their material is burned in filling, even when it was considered an economic penalty for carrying out this activity. Moreover, in scenario D burning is not allowed, due that in this scenario the emissions reduction tamed the model. Furthermore, in solution A all the existent installed CAT are taken into consideration as part of the supply chain, additionally to the installation of two new CAT's, having the capacity to process 665 tonnes of plastic containers per year. While in solution B are installed three new CAT's plus to the existing with a process capacity of 715 tonnes of plastic containers per year. In solution C only two of the existing CAT's are part of the supply chain planning, and four new are installed, with a total processing capacity of 715.5 tonnes/y. Lastly, as was described before in solution D any of the existing CAT's are including in the planning the six are new, with a total capacity to process 715.7 tonnes of empty plastic containers.

## 5. Conclusion

This kind of analysis presents an overview of the optimal configuration based on the data provided; however, considering any relevant change does not represent complexity for its study. Results shown that this kind of revalorization contributes with the emissions reduction and with an economic profit. Particularly, in scenarios with higher emissions reduction it is possible to obtain an economic benefit; however, this earning is reflected up to year two of operation, due that the investment required for new links in the supply chain is paid in first year. In this way, it was possible to notice that installation costs are the most relevant points in the economic performance; therefore, for the implementation of these kinds of strategies a network of decision makers is required, as well as the governmental and privet financing. Additionally, government incentives or subsidies in loan scheme, which can cushion the higher installation costs this in order to observe the behavior of the configuration. Current links installed (mainly storage sites) turn out to be unattractive optimal configurations since the environmental point of view, due that these are located so far from the main distribution ways. Hence, it is possible to conclude that each supply chain design and planning has to be analyzed using optimal configuration methods such as the proposed tool.

## 6. Acknowledgments.

Financial support provided by CONACYT, through grant 320583, is acknowledged.

## References

M. Pohjakallio, 2020, Secondary plastic products-examples and market trends, Plastic Waste and Recycling, 1, 467-479. 10.1016/B978-0-12-817880-5.00018-9

Patrício-Silva, A.L. Future proofing plastic waste management for a circular bioeconomy, Current Opinion in Enviromental Science & Health, 22,100263, 10.1016/j.coesh.2021.100263

T.D. Moshood, 2022, Sustainability of biodegradable plastics: New problem or solution to solve the global plastic pollution?, Current Research in Green and Sustainable Chemistry, 5, 100273, 10.1016/j.crgsc.2022.100273

"FAO" Food and Agriculture Organization of the United Nations, 2021, Assessment of agricultural plastics and their sustainability: a call for actions, available on: https://www.fao.org/policy-support/tools-and-publications/resources-details/es/c/1460015/

U. Diwekar, 2010, Introduction to Applied Optimization, Second ed, Springer, 10.1007/978-0-387-76635-5

GREET® "The Greenhouse gases, Regulated Emissions, and Energy use in Technologies Model", 2020, Agronne National Laboratory, Energy Systems, available: https://greet.es.anl.gov/

N. Goldbeck, P. Angeloudis, W. Ochieng, 2020, Optimal supply chain resilience with consideration of failure propagation and repair logistics, Transport Res E-Log, 133, 101830. 10.1016/j.tre.2019.101830

Antonis Kokossis, Michael C. Georgiadis, Efstratios N. Pistikopoulos (Eds.)
PROCEEDINGS OF THE 33rd European Symposium on Computer Aided Process Engineering
(ESCAPE33), June 18-21, 2023, Athens, Greece

# Developing a Comprehensive Decision Support Optimization Model for Biofuel Supply Chain

Brook Tesfamichael,[a] Ludovic Montastruc,[b,c] Stéphane Negny,[b,c]

[a]*Addis Ababa University, Addis Ababa Institute of Technology,  School of Chemical and Bio Engineering, Addis Ababa, Ethiopia*
[b]*Université de Toulouse, INP-ENSIACET, LGC (Laboratoire de Génie Chimique), 4, allée Emile Monso, F-31432 Toulouse Cedex 04, France*
[c]*CNRS, LGC (Laboratoire de Génie Chimique), F-31432 Toulouse Cedex 04, France*

## Abstract

Although several optimization-based decision support mathematical models are developed so far, they have limitations to be directly adapted and applied to real country-level cases. Therefore, the objective of this study is to develop a comprehensive and realistic mathematical optimization-based decision support model for the strategic design and tactical planning of a country's biofuel supply chain. First, a bi-objective economic objective optimization model, with objectives of profit maximization and investment cost minimization, is formulated. The model is devised to provide both the strategic and tactical decisions simultaneously. Then, the previous model is extended to a multi-objective optimization model by adding an environmental objective that aims to minimize the ecocost of the biofuel supply chain after conducting a comprehensive Life Cycle Assessment (LCA). The developed model in this study is applied to a case study in Ethiopia to support the policymakers and other stakeholders engaged in the country's biomass-to-biofuel projects.

**Keywords**: biofuel, supply chain, multi-objective optimization, economic-environment.

## 1. Introduction

Biofuel derived from biomass, on account of being renewable energy source and having high potential to substitute fossil fuels, have attracted considerable interest in both developed and developing countries. Despite there is a strong interest in biofuels, there are several challenges along the supply chain that hinder biofuel development and utilization progresses. The many challenges and uncertainties related to dynamic criteria need more quantitative research that supports policymakers to make evidence-based decisions along the biofuel supply chain.

Several mathematical models were developed to support decision-making in different supply chains. Among the mathematical models, optimization techniques have been employed in most of the studies to manage the biofuel supply chain from strategic, tactical and operational perspectives (Barbosa-Póvoa et al., 2018). The models coupled with an optimization method are effective when different parts of the supply chain (procurement, preprocessing, production, distribution, and transportation), different sustainability dimensions (economic, environmental, social, technological, and political) and different decision levels (strategic, tactical and operational) are integrated.

However, the previous studies have limitations to directly adapt and apply to real country-level cases.

Therefore, this research aims to develop a comprehensive and realistic mathematical optimization-based decision support model, for the strategic design and tactical planning of country's biofuel supply chain over a 20-year horizon. The economic-environment optimization model developed in this study broadens the preceding research endeavors by incorporating the following issues in the model simultaneously:

- A comprehensive biofuel supply chain, which includes all the principal supply chain components - upstream and downstream of the biorefinery along with a decentralized preprocessing unit is considered.
- A multi-product biofuel supply chain, with the intention of producing bioethanol and biodiesel along with the associated co-products, is considered in the model.
- The development of an integrated strategic-tactical level model is considered to prevent non-optimal and infeasible results, which may arise from hierarchical models.
- Several impact categories are considered to assess the impact of the biofuel supply chain on the environment. Moreover, a monetary-based environmental impact indicator is considered to compare with the economic objective clearly.
- A new approach that analyzes the compromise between objectives of large size model within a justifiable computational time and efficient optimization resolution is considered.
- Decisions associated with location, technology, and capacity is considered unlike to many researches, which consider either of these decisions exclusively or combination of two of them only, especially location and capacity.
- The investment decisions associated to location, technology, and capacity of the facilities are appeared on yearly basis contrarily to many studies that consider this decision only at the beginning of the planning period.

The model is applied to the real case of Ethiopia to support the policymakers and other stakeholders engaged in the country's biofuel projects.

## 2. Methodologies

### 2.1. General structure of the biofuel supply chain

This study considers all the principal biofuel supply chain components - upstream and downstream of the biorefinery, which includes biomass purchasing center, biomass preprocessing unit, biorefinery, biofuel distribution center, and demand zone. The superstructure representing the consecutive activities of the supply chain is illustrated in Figure 1 and the problem is described as follows. Various types of biomass feedstocks b, which are purchased from different supply sources h, are considered. For the sake of pretreatment, these biomasses are transported to a preprocessing unit at location i with capacity c and technology f. Then, the preprocessed biomasses d are conveyed to a biorefinery located at j with capacity e and technology g for the production of the respective biofuel u and co-product v. Then, the biofuel u goes to the final demand center m directly or it is shipped to a distribution center located at k with capacity a and then to a demand zone m. Meanwhile, the co-product v directly goes from the biorefinery j to the respective demand zone n.

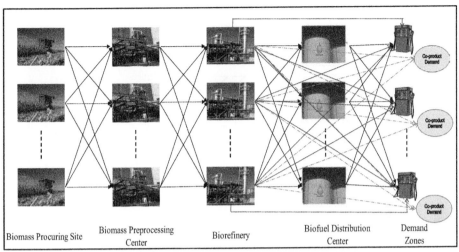

Figure 1: Biofuel supply chain structure

### 2.2. Model formulation

A deterministic model is selected since the solution of this model gives decision makers excellent insights for making excellent choices. To address the whole behavior of the supply chain, the problem is designed as a spatially explicit, multi-product, multi-feedstock, multi-period, and multi-echelon MILP modeling framework.

First, a strategic-level mono-objective optimization model, which intends NPV maximization of the biofuel supply, is developed. Here, the model considers a yearly time period. The objective function, as illustrated in Equation (1), comprises of revenue, total cost and initial investment.

$$NPV = \sum_{y \in Y} \left( \begin{bmatrix} \dfrac{1}{(1+ir)^y} \left( \mathrm{Re}\,venue_y - TotalCost_y \right) \end{bmatrix} - \begin{bmatrix} \dfrac{1}{(1+ir)^{y-1}} \left( InvestmentCost_y \right) \end{bmatrix} \right) \tag{1}$$

Where $y$ is the year and $ir$ is the discount rate

However, the supply chain design recommended by the strategic optimization model has resulted in infeasible solutions at tactical level, which makes this hierarchical approach not reliable to apply for long-term planning. Henceforth, second, an integrated strategic-tactical model is developed in order to prevent non-optimal and infeasible results, which arise from the conventional hierarchical approach. Nevertheless, no solution is acquired as the numerical solver-CPLEX was run out of memory. This is attributed to the sharp increment of the model size due to (a) requirement of vast data as it is a real and comprehensive national-level case study for a long-term planning of a sector and (b) existence of many binary variables due to numerous annual strategic choices related to the location, technology, and capacity of the supply chain components. Therefore, a new methodology is proposed to convert the mono-objective (NPV maximization) to bi-objective optimization model, which aims to maximize the profit and minimize the investment cost of the biofuel supply chain as illustrated in Equation (2).

$$Pr\,ofit = \sum_{y \in Y} \frac{1}{(1+ir)^y} \left[ Re\,venue_y - \begin{pmatrix} BiomassPurchase_y + Pr\,oductionCost_y \\ + InventoryCost_y + TransportCost_y \end{pmatrix} \right]$$

$$InvestmentCost = \sum_{y \in Y} \frac{1}{(1+ir)^{y-1}} \begin{bmatrix} \left( \sum_{i \in I} \sum_{f \in F} \sum_{c \in C} \left( Inv1_{f,c} * \left( S_{i,f,c,y} - S_{i,f,c,y-1} \right) \right) \right) + \\ \left( \sum_{j} \sum_{g} \sum_{e} \left( Inv2_{g,e} * \left( R_{j,g,e,y} - R_{j,g,e,y-1} \right) \right) \right) + \\ \left( \sum_{k \in K} \sum_{a \in A} \left( Inv3_a * \left( Q_{k,a,y} - Q_{k,a,y-1} \right) \right) \right) \end{bmatrix} \qquad (2)$$

Where Inv1f,c, Inv2g,e and Inv3a are capital investments to install the preprocessing facility with technology f and capacity c, the biorefinery with technology g and capacity e, and the distribution center with capacity a respectively. $S_{i,f,c,y}$, $R_{j,g,e,y}$ and $Q_{k,a,y}$ are binary variables with a value of 1 if preprocessing facility is installed in location i with technology f and capacity c at year y, if biorefinery is installed in location j with technology g and capacity e at year y and if distribution center is installed in location k with capacity a at year y respectively; otherwise 0.

Third, taking the previous bi-objective economic optimization model as the base model, an environmental objective function is added to it, which results a multi-objective MILP model. The environmental objective is to minimize total ecocost, which comprises the biomass processing, biofuel production and material transportation Ecocosts as indicated in Equation 3.

$$TotalEco\cos t = \sum_{y \in Y} \begin{pmatrix} Pr\,oces\sin gEco\cos t_y \\ + Pr\,oductionEco\cos t_y \\ + TransportationEco\cos t_y \end{pmatrix} \qquad (3)$$

Therefore, the mathematical model is comprised of two economic (profit maximization and investment cost minimization) and one environmental (ecocost minimization) objective functions. The design process is subjected to logical constraints and mass balances that must be satisfied at each supply chain nodes.

### 2.3. Case study economic, technical and environmental data

The developed model in this study will be applied to a case study in Ethiopia. The 58 zones in the country are considered as the candidate locations for the biomass pre-processing, biorefinery, and biofuel distribution centers. The prior feedstocks for biofuel development in Ethiopia are considered in this study; sugar cane molasses, bagasse and corn stover for bioethanol and jatropha and castor bean for biodiesel production. The annual production of the biomasses are estimated based on the current data obtained from different Ethiopian Ministry of Agriculture, Central Statistical Agency of Ethiopia, Ethiopian Sugar corporation, and biomass developers. The preprocessing mechanism considered for the two bioethanol feedstocks, i.e. bagasse and corn stover, is drying and size reduction. However, no preprocessing is considered for the molasses. On the other hand, technologies considered for biodiesel preprocessing are mechanical and solvent extraction. Biochemical and thermochemical conversion processes for bioethanol production and homogenous and heterogeneous catalysis transesterification for biodiesel production are considered as biorefinery technologies. Six potential capacity levels are selected for the preprocessing, biorefinery and distribution facilities. Due to the lack of real preprocessing and biorefinery investment and production costs data from commercial plant within Ethiopia, these costs are estimated with bibliographic data, assuming that the components follow the economy of scale, and then corrected with the available information and recent data. The biofuels' (bioethanol and biodiesel) demand are forecasted by considering the government plan. Based on the case study area features, only road transportation mode is assumed for transporting different materials within the supply chain (Tesfamichael et al., 2021).

LCA method is applied for evaluating the environmental impact. As indicated in Figure 1, the scope of this work encompasses the upstream stage (biomass feedstocks procurement, preprocessing, storage, and transportation), midstream stage (preprocessed biomasses conversion to biofuels and co-product), and downstream stage (biofuels distribution and transportation to final demand zones). The life cycle analysis of biomass feedstocks production and biofuels use are excluded because these activities are outside of the system boundary of this work. Furthermore, the life cycle analysis of material storage in all stages of the supply chain is excluded since there is insignificant emission and energy requirement associated with storage of materials. The LCA is carried out using primary data, information and data from prior studies, and LCA software - GREET LCA 2016 (a freely available tool from Argonne National Laboratory). The GREET software package is used to generate emission factors for the various biomass preprocessing and biofuel production (biorefinery) technologies by considering each type of biomass and preprocessed biomass. Moreover, the emission associated to transportation of materials is determined using prior vehicular emission study in Ethiopia. Finally, the Ecocost method is used to quantify the impacts of all the biofuel supply chain activities on the environment.

## 3. Result and Discussion

Since this planning problem relies on three objective functions, it requires a solution of multi-objective MILP. The three mono-objective optimization problems were considered independently before dealing with the multi-objective problem. The mono-objective optimization models are solved using CPLEX 12.8 algorithm embedded in IBM ILOG. Then, the intention was to make a payoff table and acquire balanced solution that helps to look for the best compromise among the three antagonistic issues. Nevertheless, the attempt to solve one of the objective functions (investment cost minimization) could not be successful as the numerical solver run out of memory due to the many binary variables associated with several strategic choices as well as vast data of national level. Therefore, a semi-heuristic approach was gradually developed through the following procedure. First, the two objective functions, namely profit maximization and ecocost minimization, were simulated with respect to different investment cost ranges. The results showed that there is a significant variation on the profit by varying the investment cost. Contrary, the ecocost variation is almost insignificant. Knowing that the profit is more sensitive parameter, second, the profit maximization was simulated with respect to different investment cost and ecocost ranges. Here, the profit maximization was run by taking four intervals for the ecocost and twenty-two intervals for the investment cost that generates a total of 88 feasible solutions that offers a good compromise between the three objectives. The model for this case had 1,348,772 constraints and 2,578,430 decision variables, of which 174,000 and 2,404,430 were binary and continuous variables respectively. The results were obtained in the ranges of 157.21 to 668.58 minutes with 0.01% optimality gap on an Intel 2.60-GHz processor. The simulation result is depicted in Figure 2.

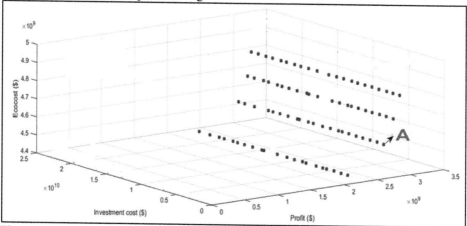

Figure 2:  Feasible solutions to the multi-objective problems

The most feasible solution that compromises the three objectives is indicated as point A in Figure 2. This solution has exclusively proposed the installation of biochemical and heterogeneous transesterification refineries for bioethanol and biodiesel production respectively throughout the planning period. Most of the refineries are located in areas proximate to the biomass supply locations rather than biofuel demand locations. Moreover, this solution favors the utilization of molasses in the first 10 planning years, which is then joined by both corn stover and bagasse to satisfy the bioethanol production in the next 11-20 years. Besides, it recommends the utilization of both jatropha and castor for biodiesel production in the planning period.

## 4. Conclusion

In this work, a comprehensive and realistic mathematical optimization-based decision/planning support model is developed by considering various issues simultaneously. The problem relies on three objective functions, namely, profit, investment cost and ecocost. A semi-heuristic strategy, which offers a feasible solution to the problem, is explored to analyze the compromise between the objectives. A first potential future expansion of this work is to broaden the supply chain boundary by incorporating biomass cultivation activity. A second extension could be to incorporate the social and political dimensions. A third expansion is to consolidate operational level planning in the integrated strategic-tactical level model developed here.

## References

Barbosa-Póvoa, A.P., da Silva, C., Carvalho, A., 2018. Opportunities and challenges in sustainable supply chain: An operations research perspective. Eur. J. Oper. Res. 268, 399–431. https://doi.org/10.1016/j.ejor.2017.10.036

Tesfamichael, B., Montastruc, L., Negny, S., Yimam, A., 2021. Designing and Planning of Ethiopia's Biomass-to-Biofuel Supply Chain through Integrated Strategic-Tactical Optimization Model considering Economic Dimension. Comput. Chem. Eng. https://doi.org/10.1016/j.compchemeng.2021.107425

Antonis Kokossis, Michael C. Georgiadis, Efstratios N. Pistikopoulos (Eds.)
PROCEEDINGS OF THE 33rd European Symposium on Computer Aided Process Engineering
(ESCAPE33), June 18-21, 2023, Athens, Greece

# Investigation of economic and environmental tradeoffs of spatially explicit biomass supply chains towards the production of net-negative biofuels

Eric G. O'Neill[a,b], Caleb H. Geissler[a,b], Christos T. Maravelias[a,b,c]

*aDeprartment of Chemical and Biological Engineering, Princeton University, Princeton, NJ 08544, USA*
*bDOE Great Lakes Bioenergy Research Center, USA*
*cAndlinger Center for Energy and the Environment, Princeton University, Princeton, NJ, 08544, USA*
*maravelias@princeton.edu*

## Abstract

Cellulosic biomass is an attractive source of renewable fuel because of its high greenhouse gas (GHG) mitigation potential. However, the optimal fuel conversion technology, amount of carbon capture and storage (CCS), and supply chain (SC) design depend on spatial features of the system which are essential to the systemwide GHG mitigation potential. We analyze the cost and GHG mitigation of a cellulosic biofuel SC with CCS using mixed-integer linear programming. While previous studies examine small high-resolution regions or large coarsely-represented regions, we consider a high-resolution SC for an 8-state region in the USA Midwest using, importantly, realistic biomass data. We show how the amount of biofuel produced and the level of carbon incentive contribute to substantial changes in the optimal SC configuration, biofuel conversion, and CCS technologies installed. While significant GHG mitigation is possible, sequestration credits may neglect to incentivize the further mitigation attainable by considering all sources of emissions.

**Keywords**: Supply chain, carbon capture and storage, biofuels

## 1. Introduction

For cellulosic biofuels to become economically and environmentally feasible, an efficient field-to-product supply chain (SC) is necessary. The field-to-product system consists of biomass growth and harvesting, the SC logistics network, and the biorefinery design and operation. Potential for biomass growth is highly distributed across the landscape, and careful selection of which fields to plant and the level of fertilization to apply to each field can significantly impact crop yields and the greenhouse gas (GHG) balance of the crop harvesting (Field et al. 2018). Within the SC, the facility location, transportation, and inventory management are highly dependent on the landscape design decisions, and spatial tradeoffs exist between the two problems. The final part of the value chain is producing biofuels at the biorefinery. Biomass can be converted into a variety of liquid fuels using different conversion technologies. The conversion technologies have different fuel yields, capital costs, and operating costs, which makes technology selection nontrivial. Additionally, carbon capture and storage (CCS) technologies can be installed at the biorefinery to improve the GHG mitigation potential of cellulosic biofuel, and, depending on the conversion technology, there is the potential to install CCS on a variety of process streams with varying $CO_2$ concentration and flow rates. Landscape, SC, and biorefinery design have largely been studied independently, which overlooks the interdependencies between these systems. By considering landscape, SC, and biorefinery design simultaneously at a high spatial resolution, optimization models can be used to study the tradeoffs between these systems to minimize cost and GHG emissions.

The fuel conversion and CCS technologies at the biorefinery are especially important for the design of the integrated system. The most technologically mature conversion routes for lignocellulosic biomass are fermentation, pyrolysis, and gasification. For a biorefinery using fermentation, $CO_2$ is emitted in three streams: from the fermentation process at >95 wt.%, in biogas from anaerobic digestion of wastewater at ~73 wt.%, and in flue gas from solid residue combustion at ~20 wt.% (Humbird et al., 2011). For pyrolysis, the biomass is thermochemically converted to a bio-oil that requires hydrogen to be upgraded into a mixture of gasoline and diesel. This hydrogen could be purchased from off-site (assumed to be from a natural gas source) or be produced on-site by converting some of the bio-oil into hydrogen to upgrade the remaining bio-oil fraction. For either source of hydrogen, the pyrolysis process emits $CO_2$ only in a flue gas stream at ~32 wt.% (Wright et al., 2010). Lastly, in gasification, the biomass is thermochemically converted to syngas. As a part of generating and cleaning the syngas, a >95 wt.% $CO_2$ stream is generated. The syngas can be converted into liquid fuels by Fischer-Tropsch synthesis, which results in an additional flue gas stream with ~15 wt.% $CO_2$ (Swanson et al., 2010). From a cost perspective, fermentation and pyrolysis with hydrogen purchase have relatively low capital investment, but high operating costs, while gasification and pyrolysis with hydrogen production have higher capital costs and lower operating costs.

The different conversion technologies have been compared at a biorefinery with CCS, but without the additional consideration of spatially explicit landscape and SC design (Geissler and Maravelias, 2022). Conversely, other studies that have considered SC and CCS simultaneously have only one conversion and CCS technology at the biorefinery (Lainez-Aguirre et al., 2017). Modeling the landscape, SC, and biorefinery design simultaneously at a high spatial resolution can identify tradeoffs between decisions at each stage of the value chain. This modeling improves the understanding of the complex system interactions but is not meant to be a full decision support tool. In section 2 we present a model for simultaneous optimization of landscape, SC, and biorefinery design. In section 3 we discuss the results of applying this model to an 8-state region in the USA Midwest. Finally, in section 4 we present conclusions and discuss further research avenues.

## 2. Supply chain and biorefinery model

The integrated modeling approach for simultaneous landscape, SC, and biorefinery optimization largely follows the work of O'Neill et al. (2022) with several key modifications and extensions to account for the additional spatially explicit aspects of the large-scale system and the inclusion of CCS (O'Neill et al., 2022). The data sources and processing strategies are described in section 2.1 and important model constraints are presented in section 2.2. Many of the model constraints are omitted in the interest of brevity.

### 2.1 Data

We consider an 8-state region in the USA Midwest, an area of interest to the US Department of Energy. The study area consists of roughly 400,000 fields identified as historically abandoned lands with the potential to establish biomass (Lark et al., 2020). The growth of native bioenergy grass was simulated over a 40-year time horizon at 0 kgN/ha and 50 kgN/ha of fertilization (Martinez-Feria and Basso, 2020). The average value for biomass yield (Mg/ha) and the annualized soil organic carbon sequestration (Mg/ha/y) at each field are taken as inputs to the landscape design model. The 400,000 fields are aggregated according to the unique soil-type/weather combinations and landscape design decisions are made on the aggregated fields to reduce the model size while maintaining landscape design accuracy.

The large study area motivates the consideration of additional spatially explicit features. The price and $CO_2$ impact of electricity available at the biorefinery depend on the location of the installed biorefinery. Furthermore, the transportation and injection cost of captured $CO_2$ depends on the location of both the injection sites and the installed biorefineries. Figure 1(a) shows the study area including 30 potential biorefineries, 800 potential depots and the high-level distribution of biomass yield. Figure 1(b) shows the different fuel conversion and CCS technologies considered at the biorefinery.

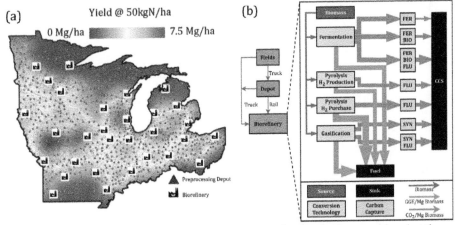

Figure 1. (a) Map of the study area and (b) summary of technologies considered at the biorefinery. The thickness of the gallons of gasoline equivalent (GGE) and $CO_2$ arrows is proportional to the relative mass/energy flows.

### 2.2 Selected model constraints

The objective of the integrated optimization model (equation 1) is to minimize the total annualized cost of the full field-to-product system consisting of capital cost $C^{CAP}$, feedstock cost including the annualized cost of crop establishment, harvesting, and handling $C^{LND}$, operational costs $C^{PRD}$, inventory costs $C^{INV}$, transportation costs $C^{TRA}$, and the cost (or credit) of electricity purchased (sold) at the biorefinery $C^{ELC}$.

$$OBJ = C^{CAP} + C^{LND} + C^{PRD} + C^{INV} + C^{TRA} + C^{CCS} + C^{ENV} + C^{ELC} \tag{1}$$

There are two terms in the objective function that account for the GHG emissions of the system. The credit for $CO_2$ captured at the biorefinery, $C^{CCS}$, is defined in equations 2-4.

$$C^{CCS} = \pi^{CCS} \sum_{i \in \{CO_2\}, l, t} L_{i,l,t} \tag{2}$$

$$P^{C-CB}_{i',l,m,t} = \sum_{i \in I^F} \eta_{i,i',m} G^{F-CB}_{i,l,m,t} + \sum_{i \in I^{ID}} \eta_{i,i',m} G^{ID-CB}_{i,l,m,t} \quad \forall i \in \{CO_2\}, l, m, t \tag{3}$$

$$L_{i,l,t} \leq P^{C-CB}_{i,l,m,t} \quad \forall i \in \{CO_2\}, l, m, t \tag{4}$$

where $\pi^{CCS}$ is the carbon sequestration credit, $L_{i,l,t}$ is the amount of species $i$ ($CO_2$) sequestered at refinery $l$ during time $t$, and $P^{C-CB}_{i',l,m,t}$ is the amount of $CO_2$ that is produced by technology $m$ that is available for capture. We assume the balance of the $CO_2$ in equation 4 is vented as biogenic $CO_2$ and does not contribute to the net emissions of the system. $\eta_{i,i',m}$ is the conversion coefficient of biomass to $CO_2$ able to be captured. $G_{i,l,m,t}^{F-CB}$ and $G_{i,l,m,t}^{ID-CB}$ are the consumption of raw and densified feedstock. The set $m \in \mathbf{M}$ includes the 11 possible combinations of conversion and CCS technology installations (Figure 1).

The GHG emissions from SC activities are described by equation 5 and include direct and indirect emissions from all sources other than the $CO_2$ captured at the biorefinery.

$$C^{ENV} = \pi^{SCC}(GHG^{TRA} + GHG^{LND} + GHG^{PRD} + GHG^{ELC}) \qquad (5)$$

where $\pi^{SCC}$ is the social cost of carbon, the monetary value placed on SC emissions (Nordhaus 2017). Emission sources include transportation, landscape (including annualized soil carbon sequestration), production, and the indirect contribution from grid electricity. Due to the large study area, the location of biorefineries and preprocessing depots determines the price and $CO_2$ impact of the available electricity and the parameters are considered in a spatially explicit manner in equations 6-8.

$$P_{i',l,m,t}^{E-CB} = \sum_{i \in I^F} \eta_{i,i',m} G_{i,l,m,t}^{F-CB} + \sum_{i \in I^{ID}} \eta_{i,i',m} G_{i,l,m,t}^{ID-CB} \quad \forall i \in \{ELC\}, l, m, t \qquad (6)$$

$$P_{i',l,m,t}^{E-PD} = \sum_{i \in I^F} \eta_{i,i',m} G_{i,k,m,t}^{F-PD} \quad \forall i \in \{ELC\}, k, m, t \qquad (7)$$

$$GHG^{ELC} = \sum_{i,l,m,t} \Gamma_l P_{i,l,m,t}^{E-CB} + \sum_{i,k,m,t} \Gamma_k P_{i,k,m,t}^{E-PD} \qquad (8)$$

where $\Gamma_l$ and $\Gamma_k$ are the $CO_2$ impact at each biorefinery $l$ and depot $k$ from the local grid. Note that the production of electricity at the biorefinery $P_{i',l,m,t}^{E-CB}$ is allowed to be negative which represents a technology configuration that produces excess electricity that is sold back to the grid and offsets grid emissions.

## 3. Results

Model instances are implemented in GAMS and solved using Gurobi 9.5.1. We consider two design cases to analyze the spatial interactions involved in the system. First, we consider the 'status-quo' case which corresponds to the current incentive structure in the USA where a credit is only applied to $CO_2$ captured using CCS (case A: $\pi^{SCC} = 0, \pi^{CCS} > 0$). Case A neglects to account for GHG emissions from SC activities and indirect emissions from other sources. The second case (case B: $\pi^{CCS} = \pi^{SCC}$) considers all $CO_2$ emissions equally. Case B treats avoided emissions in the SC the same as $CO_2$ captured with CCS. That is, the net emissions in $CO_2$ equivalents, including both $CO_2$ from CCS and from the SC receive the same economic credit or penalty in the objective function. By considering the net emissions of the entire system, the emissions at the landscape and SC level contribute to spatial tradeoffs that affect the optimal design, operation, and biorefinery technology portfolio.

Figure 2 shows a breakdown of the cost and GHG emissions for a representative sample of biofuel demands and sequestration credits for the two cases discussed above. In case A, the cost contributions remain relatively constant from each source. Transportation costs increase slightly at higher demands as biomass must be transported farther. The sequestration credits of 85 \$/Mg and 125 \$/Mg incentivize CCS and, as a tradeoff, there are higher contributions from the electricity and capital cost needed to perform CCS and receive the credit. In case A, pyrolysis with hydrogen purchase with ($P^H+$) and without ($P^H$) CCS is incentivized due to its high fuel yield. When CCS is incentivized, the biorefinery requires electricity, which is purchased from the grid.

In case B, $P^H$ and $P^H+$ are incentivized at lower credits, and gasification with syngas CCS (G+) and gasification with both syngas and flue gas CCS (G++) are incentivized at high credits. Fermentation results in two relatively concentrated $CO_2$ streams that are easy to capture, and pyrolysis with $H_2$ production does not have the indirect emissions from the purchase of $H_2$; however, because of the relatively high costs and low yields of fermentation and pyrolysis with $H_2$ production, they are never the optimal technology for any combination of demand and sequestration credit.

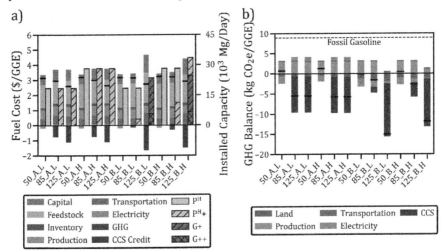

Figure 2. (a) Breakdown of costs and installed capacity of each technology and (b) GHG emissions for representative scenarios. The three indicators in the scenario names are the sequestration credit, case designation (A or B), and demand (L or H for a demand of 500MM of 850MM GGE/y, respectively). The horizontal black lines on the stacked bar show the overall cost and GHG balance.

When all GHG emissions are valued equally, CCS is no longer incentivized at every biorefinery at 85 $/MgCO$_2$. Instead, the spatial features of the system dictate where CCS is incentivized. Interestingly, at 85 $/MgCO$_2$ the net emissions for the cost-optimal system are higher when all emissions are considered equally. This is because in most locations, the sequestration credit is not sufficient to incentive CCS due to the economic penalty of GHG emissions from electricity. The sequestration credit does not offset the capital and operating cost of the additional CCS technology when also considering the indirect emissions of electricity except in areas where electricity is very cheap and clean.

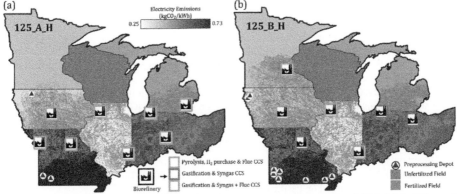

Figure 3. The supply chain configuration for a sequestration credit of 125 $/MgCO$_2$ and a demand of 850MM GGE/y for case A and B.

Figure 3. shows the spatial changes at a high sequestration credit (125 \$/MgCO$_2$). In case B, there is a dramatic shift in both the net emissions and the optimal technology portfolio. Gasification is preferred because it avoids indirect emissions from H$_2$ needed for pyrolysis with H$_2$ purchase and is essentially energetically self-sufficient. The high demand incentivizes constructing biorefineries with high yielding P$^H$+ to meet demand without having to plant poor fields. Refineries are strategically positioned so that P$^H$+ is installed in states with low electricity emissions and G+/G++ are installed in states with higher electricity emissions. Gasification has a lower fuel yield than pyrolysis which increases the amount of biomass that is planted leading to higher transportation and handling costs, but results in an additional opportunity for soil carbon sequestration. This increase in the amount of required biomass is somewhat offset by careful landscape design in which fields with high soil carbon sequestration are prioritized.

## 4. Conclusions

In this paper we used mixed-integer linear programming methods to analyze the spatially explicit tradeoffs for a full field-to-product biofuel production system under two incentive structures. We showed that for the USA Midwest, the current sequestration credit incentive may neglect to account for emissions related to the system's spatial interactions such as soil carbon sequestration, the local price and CO$_2$ emission rate of electricity, and biomass availability. When valuing all CO$_2$ equivalents equally from an economic perspective, the cost-optimal SC and technology portfolio requires higher credits to fully incentivize CCS. Additionally, the optimal technology shifts from pyrolysis to gasification because of the lower indirect emissions and the resulting landscape design plants additional biomass to compensate for the lower fuel yield. We also demonstrated the importance of large-scale modeling that considers the interactions of the full field-to-product system, particularly at a high resolution. The high-resolution modeling captures the system wide effects of CO$_2$ mitigation incentive structures and highlights the sensitivity of cellulosic biofuel landscapes and SCs to those incentives.

## References

J.L. Field, S.G. Evans, E. Marx, M. Easter, P.R. Adler, T. Dinh, B. Wilson, K. Paustian, 2018, High-Resolution Techno–Ecological Modelling of a Bioenergy Landscape to Identify Climate Mitigation Opportunities in Cellulosic Ethanol Production, Nat. Energy, 3, 211-19

C.H. Geissler, C.T. Maravelias, 2022, Analysis of alternative bioenergy with carbon capture strategies: present and future, Energy Environ. Sci, 15, 2679–2689.

D. Humbird, R. Davis, L. Tao, C. Kinchin, D. Hsu, A. Aden, 2011, Process design and economics for biochemical conversion of lignocellulosic biomass to ethanol: dilute acid pretreatment and enzymatic hydrolysis of corn stover, NREL/TP-5100-47764.

J.M. Lainez-Aguirre, M. Pérez-Fortes, L. Puigjaner, 2017, Economic evaluation of bio-based supply chains with CO2 capture and utilisation, Comput. Chem. Eng., 102, 213–225.

T.J. Lark, S.A. Spawn, M. Bougie, H.K. Gibbs, 2020, Cropland expansion in the United States produces marginal yields at high costs to wildlife, Nat. Commun., 11, 1, 1-11

R.A. Martinez-Feria, B. Basso, 2020, Predicting soil carbon changes in switchgrass grown on marginal lands under climate change and adaptation strategies, GCB Bioen., 12, 9, 742-755

W.D. Nordhaus, 2017, Revisiting the social cost of carbon, PNAS, 114, 7, 1518-1523

E.G. O'Neill, R.A. Martinez-Feria, B. Basso, C.T. Maravelias, 2022, Integrated Spatially Explicit Landscape and Cellulosic Biofuel Supply Chain Optimization Under Biomass Yield Uncertainty, Comput. Chem. Eng., 160, 107724.

R.M. Swanson, J.A. Satrio, R.C. Brown, A. Platon, D.D. Hsu, 2010, Techno-economic analysis of biofuels production based on gasification, NREL/TP-6A20-46587.

M.M. Wright, J.A. Satrio, R.C. Brown, D.E. Daugaard, D.D. Hsu, 2010, Techno-economic analysis of biomass fast pyrolysis to transportation fuels, NREL/TP-6A20-46586.

Antonis Kokossis, Michael C. Georgiadis, Efstratios N. Pistikopoulos (Eds.)
PROCEEDINGS OF THE 33rd European Symposium on Computer Aided Process Engineering
(ESCAPE33), June 18-21, 2023, Athens, Greece

# A MILP-based approach to manage logistics in large industrial gas supply chains

Sergio G. Bonino, [a] Luis J. Zeballos, [a] Akash Moolya,[c] Jose Lainez,[c] Jose M. Pinto,[c] Ignacio E. Grossmann,[b] Carlos A. Méndez[a]

[a]Intec (UNL-CONICET), Güemes 3430, Santa Fe 3000, Argentina
[b] Carnegie Mellon University, 5000 Forbes, Pittsburgh 15213, United States
[c]Praxair, Inc., a Linde company, Connecticut 06810, United States
cmendez@intec.unl.edu.ar

## Abstract

The high competitiveness between companies dedicated to the production and distribution of industrial gases make necessary to optimize their activities in order to improve their profitability. This paper addresses the production routing problem (PRP) of an industrial gas supply chain (SC). The work proposes a MILP-based approach to deal with this problem. The framework seeks to improve the company's profit by optimizing production and distribution activities. For the distribution part, a set of feasible routes are previously generated and selected. Then, considering only the selected routes, the model chooses the best combination of them to satisfy all the constraints. It is important to note that the model takes into account the effect of lead time on production and distribution decisions. Finally, a real case study is presented and solved. The results obtained demonstrate the effectiveness of the proposed approach in reasonable CPU times.

**Keywords**: Supply chain management, Production routing problem, Mathematical modelling.

## 1. Introduction

Recently, Vendor-managed inventory (VMI) policy has begun to be widely used in various industrial sectors. The gas industry has been one of them, and inventory is now controlled by the companies for most of its customers. This policy consists of the company constantly monitoring its customers' inventory to make decisions on when and how much product to deliver to its customers to ensure the proper performance of its daily tasks. Under this policy, customers should no longer issue replenishment orders to the companies (Dong et al., 2017). Due to this paradigm shift, companies are focusing their efforts on improving the SC performance in order to remain competitive in an increasingly aggressive market. One of the most important changes so far to try to optimize the logistics of companies is to simultaneously solve the problems of production and distribution of the products (Zhang et al., 2017). In a conventional approach, the production problem would be solved first, followed by distribution decisions. This sequential method may generate suboptimal solutions or in the worst case infeasible. By solving the integrated problem, lower-cost solutions can be found than those obtained with the sequential approach (Lee et al., 2022).

This paper addresses the problem in an integrated manner, considering explicitly the lead times in a VMI policy.

## 2. Problem Statement

This work addresses an industrial gas SC's production routing problem (PRP). The objective is to optimize the operation of the SC, seeking to minimize the total cost of production and distribution activities. The particularity of this SC is that the company that supplies industrial gases is in charge of controlling and managing the customers' inventory. This practice is known as vendor-managed inventory (VMI). For this reason, knowing the monthly demands of customers and their maximum and minimum inventory capacities, the company must generate optimal production and distribution strategies that allow it to visit customers on time to meet their demands. The products considered in this case are liquid oxygen and nitrogen. To meet daily demands, the company has production plants and inventory storage tanks. Each plant has a maximum production rate of product per day. Regarding distribution, each plant has a fleet of trucks for each type of product. A relevant characteristic of the problem considered here is that trucks can make several short trips per day or a single trip of several days. The trip duration depends on the distance to the clients considered in the trip, the order in which customers are visited, and the loading and unloading times of the products. Since the trips made can last several days, this problem explicitly considers the effect that the lead time has on the following:

- The time at which the product is released from the plant.
- The time at which the product arrives at the customer.
- The amount of time the trucks are not available for other trips.

## 3. Solution strategy and main assumptions

For this problem, an efficient discrete-time MILP approach to simultaneously minimize the production and distribution costs of the PRP is proposed. To address the mentioned problem characteristics, the model is based on the idea of the explicit generation/representation of the trips, thus when a trip is selected all the information about it is available and considered in the approach. The central decision variables of the model are a) the amount of each product manufactured in each plant per day, b) the customers visited per day, c) the customers visited on the same trip, d) the order in which customers are visited, e) the trips that trucks make each day, f) the amount of product loaded in the trucks per trip, g) the amount of product delivered to each customer included on the trips. The main assumptions under which the model was developed are as follows:

- Trucks can only be used 12 hours per day. More time implies a multiday trip.
- Routes of up to 48 hours (4 days) are considered.
- Routes of up to 3 customers are considered. The features of this problem makes this assumption valid.
- Lead time is taken into account when scheduling a customer visit.
- Trucks making trips longer than twelve hours are not available for use until their return to plant.
- Each customer's ending inventory is allowed to be below a certain percentage of the beginning inventory.
- The total ending inventory must be greater than or equal to the total beginning inventory.
- A truck can make 2 trips in one day only if the total time of both trips is less than or equal to 12 hours.
- A customer can be visited at most twice in the same day.

### 3.1. Route generation procedure

This section introduces a summary of the route generation procedure. The structure of this procedure is shown in Figure 1.

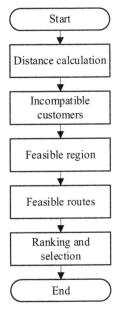

- The algorithm starts with the calculation of the distance and travel times between nodes, (i.e., customer-customer and plant-customer distance).
- Once the travel times between nodes are known, customer combinations that may lead to infeasible routes are discarded. This is because the total travel time of the route exceeds the maximum allowed or the customer demands are not compatible to be realized in the same trip.
- Step 3 defines a feasible region of visit for each customer starting from a given plant. This idea was initially presented by Dong et al. (2017) and consists of determining a region through a cone. Subsequently, each customer will be able to share routes with customers located within its region.
- In step 4, all possible feasible routes are generated, taking into account the regions determined in the previous step and the constraints between customers that cannot be on the same route.
- Finally, for each customer, a ranking of the routes is made taking into account the total time of the route and the arrival time to the customer. The ranking is done for each plant and each type of route (i.e., direct shipment, 2-customer route, 3-customer route). Subsequently, for each customer, the best 'x' routes per plant and per type are selected. This selection is made to reduce the number of possible alternatives to visit a client and reduce the combinatorial complexity of the problem to be solved.

**Figure 1**. Structure of Route Generation Procedure

The feasible routes generated with the procedure described above, provide the following information a) travel time of the route, b) clients visited, c) arrival time at each client, d) plant from where the route departs.

### 3.2. Model formulation

The MILP model developed aims to minimize the costs of production and distribution operations. In the subsections, due to the lack of space only the main equations of the model are presented. The definition of sets, parameters and variables of the models are defined as follows:

**Sets**

| | |
|---|---|
| $T$ | time periods |
| $I$ | products |
| $C$ | customers |
| $P$ | plants |
| $S$ | routes |
| $SI$ | routes s transporting product i |
| $SP$ | routes s departing from plant p |
| $SC$ | routes s visiting the customer c |
| $IC$ | customer c consuming product i |
| $IP$ | plants p producing product i |

**Parameters**

| | |
|---|---|
| $day_{c,s}$ | day of arrival at customer c with route s |
| $dayRoute_s$ | duration in days of route s |

**Continuous Variables**

| | |
|---|---|
| $LD_{i,p,t}$ | Product i transported from plant p during period t |
| $\overline{DL}_{i,p,s,t}$ | Product i transported from plant p in period t using route s |
| $\widehat{DL}_{i,p,s,c,t}$ | Product i transported to customer c from plant p in period t using route s |
| $DL_{i,c,t}$ | Product i received by customer c in period t |
| $TU_{i,p,t}$ | Trucks not available at plant p for period t |
| $CPP_{i,p,t}$ | Production cost of plant p in period t |
| $CTP_{i,p,t}$ | Transportation cost of plant p in period t |
| $PCC_t$ | Purchase cost for period t |
| $TC$ | Objective function (total cost) |

**Binary variable**

| | |
|---|---|
| $A_{i,p,s,t}$ | 1 if route s is used in period t |

### 3.2.1. Inventory update

This set of constraints is intended to update customer and plant inventories. In a given period, the inventory in the plants will be modified by the production made and the amount of product used to satisfy customer demand. The inventory of customers is updated taking into account their daily demand and the amount of product received through shipments or purchases.

Generally, in the literature, updating customer inventory takes into account the current period (t) and the previous period (t-1). In the proposed formulation, this idea is extended so that the quantity received by shipments ($DL_{i,c,t}$) takes into account products that left the plant up to t-3 periods ago.

### 3.2.2. Production and Distribution

All decisions related to the daily quantity to be produced at each plant are considered here, as well as determining which customers will be visited, and defining the assigned route and the quantity to be transported.

In this section, new restrictions appear for the treatment of lead time in deliveries. Equations 1 to 3 show how lead time is treated concerning product distribution.

$$LD_{i,p,t} = \sum_{s \in (SP \land SI)} \overline{DL}_{i,p,s,t}, \quad \forall p, i \in (IP_{p,i}) \tag{1}$$

$$\overline{DL}_{i,p,s,t} = \sum_{c \in (IC_{c,i} \land SC)} \widehat{DL}_{i,p,s,c,t}, \quad \forall p, i \in (IP_{P,i} \land SI \land SP) \tag{2}$$

$$DL_{i,c,t} = \sum_{(p,s) \in (IP \land SC \land SI \land SP \land (tt=t-day_{c,s}+1))} \widehat{DL}_{i,p,s,c,tt}, \quad \forall c, i, t \in (IC_{c,i}) \tag{3}$$

Equation 1 calculates the quantity of product that is transported from a given plant in a given period. Equation 2 indicates how much product is delivered to each customer when they are visited with route 's'. Finally, in equation 3, it is calculated when the customer receives the delivery taking into account the lead time, this is considered with the condition $tt = t - day_{c,s} + 1$.

### 3.2.3. Truck availability

The set of equations belonging to this subsection limits the number of available trucks per period and avoids the use of trucks that are traveling for more than 12 hours. These trucks become available again once the trip has been completed.

Constraint 4 shows how to calculate the number of unavailable trucks in period t for a given plant ($TU_{i,p,t}$). This is done only for trucks performing trips longer than 12 hours.

$$TU_{i,p,t} = \sum_{(s,tt) \in (SP \land SI \land (t-dayRoute_s+1 \leq tt \leq t-1) \land (dayRoute_s>1))} A_{i,p,s,tt} \tag{4}$$

$$\forall p, i, t \in (IP_{p,i} \land (t > 1))$$

### 3.2.4. Cost estimation and Objective Function

The objective function considered seeks to minimize the total operating cost, which is made up of the cost of production, transportation and purchasing. It is shown in equation 5.

$$minimize\ TC = \sum_{(p,i,t) \in (IP_{p,i})} CPP_{i,p,t} + CTP_{i,p,t} + \sum_t PCC_t \tag{5}$$

## 4. Case study and computational results

The real case study involves an industrial gases SC with 5 production plants, 2 products (liquid oxygen and nitrogen), approximately 500 monthly deliveries to 114 customers, 13 vehicles and a 30-day time horizon. Due to the large size of the addressed instance, several heuristics strategies and fit constraints were introduced to reduce the combinatorial explosion issue. Heuristics strategies are mainly dedicated to efficiently maintaining limited the number of trips considered. On the other hand, fit constraints are aimed at limiting the search for solutions to promote better truck-loading capacity utilization.

Due to space limitations, only the results obtained for the case of liquid oxygen (LO2) will be presented. It should be noted that the model can be used for both products. The LO2 problem have 5 production plants, 47 customers and 7 trucks for shipments. The location of customers and plants is shown in Figure 2. Plants 4 and 5 (P4 and P5) have the highest production rate and lowest costs, but shipping from there involves several days.

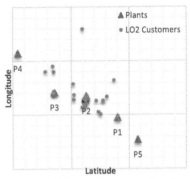

**Figure 2**. Plant and customer location

Three different scenarios were run for this case. In the first scenario, only direct shipment routes were considered. In scenario 2, all feasible routes generated with the algorithm were used. Finally, in the third scenario, the best route per plant and per type was selected for each customer. All scenarios were implemented in GAMS 32.0 and solved with GUROBI 10.0.0 on a desktop computer with 2.80GHz Intel(R) Core(TM) i9-10900F processor and 16 GB RAM on Windows 10. The maximum run time for each scenario was set to 3600 seconds.

Table 1 shows the results obtained for the different scenarios. In all 3 solutions, the model was able to satisfy all demand through shipments, thus avoiding purchases from external suppliers. As can be seen, when the model is given the possibility of combining customers on the same route, trips are better utilized and, consequently, the total cost is reduced (Scenario 1 vs. Scenarios 2 and 3).

**Table 1**. Results of the proposed scenarios

| Scenario | Model Size | | Number of Routes | Total Cost [$] | GAP [%] |
|---|---|---|---|---|---|
| | Continuous Variables | Discrete Variables | | | |
| 1 | 12,421 | 3,780 | 121 | 203,490.99 | 2.54 |
| 2 | 756,181 | 194,340 | 6,473 | 190,216.49 | 1.83 |
| 3 | 30,481 | 9,000 | 295 | 190,155.24 | 0.63 |

By comparison of scenarios 2 and 3, it can be observed that the route selection criteria considered for solving the model has an important impact on the complexity of the problem and the quality of the solutions that can be obtained in the same processing time. Another positive aspect to highlight of scenario 3 is that it was able to reach a solution with a 1.8% GAP in 100 seconds, while scenario 2 reached it in 3600 seconds of CPU time.

Figures 3 and 4 show examples of how lead time influences decisions. Figure 3 presents the inventory profile of customer 110, who receives shipments of product on days 3, 7, 13, 17, 22 and 27. These shipments leave plant 5 on days 2, 5, 12, 16, 21 and 26. The graph clearly shows the difference between the day the truck leaves the plant and the day it arrives at the customer. Figure 4 shows available trucks per day in plant 5, taking into account when trucks leave and return to the plant. Plant 5 has a fleet of 3 trucks.

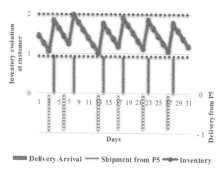

**Figure 3**. Inventory profile for customer 110

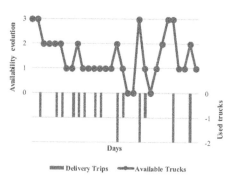

**Figure 4**. Truck availability at plant 5

## 5. Conclusion

The proposed MILP-based approach was found helpful to optimize decisions concerning daily production and customer deliveries. Lead time considerations were implemented, resulting in more accurate solutions. The computational results demonstrate the effectiveness of the proposed approach, obtaining efficient solutions in reasonable CPU times.

## References

Dong, Y., Maravelias, C. T., Pinto, J. M., & Sundaramoorthy, A. (2017). Solution methods for vehicle-based inventory routing problems. *Computers and Chemical Engineering, 101*, 259–278.

Lee, Y., Charitopoulos, V. M., Thyagarajan, K., Morris, I., Pinto, J. M., & Papageorgiou, L. G. (2022). Integrated production and inventory routing planning of oxygen supply chains. *Chemical Engineering Research and Design, 186*, 97–111.

Zhang, Q., Sundaramoorthy, A., Grossmann, I. E., & Pinto, J. M. (2017). Multiscale production routing in multicommodity supply chains with complex production facilities. *Computers and Operations Research, 79*(April 2016), 207–222

Antonis Kokossis, Michael C. Georgiadis, Efstratios N. Pistikopoulos (Eds.)
PROCEEDINGS OF THE 33rd European Symposium on Computer Aided Process Engineering
(ESCAPE33), June 18-21, 2023, Athens, Greece
© 2023 Elsevier B.V. All rights reserved.  http://dx.doi.org/10.1016/B978-0-443-15274-0.50530-8

# Modelling of reverse supply chains in the context of circular economy

Christiana M. Papapostolou, Emilia M. Kondili

*Optimisation of Production Systems Laboratory*
*Dept. of Mechanical Engineering, University of West Attica, Ancient Olive Grove*
*Campus, P. Ralli & Thivon Street, 12244, Egaleo, Greece*

## Abstract

The circular economy model has created a shift paradigm in materials and products utilisation throughout and at the end of their life cycle, by improving the economic, social and environmental performance of the respective supply chains both in terms of operation as well as in terms of interaction with the entire ecosystem. On that note, reverse supply chains offer an opportunity for manufacturing companies and practitioners to improve the supply chain performance too. By gaining the customers insights, the entire supply chain may be redesigned to fit the repurposing of improved services, eco-friendliness (also in line with Green Supply Chain Management) whilst at the same time meeting as well the cost minimisation goal. Reverse supply chains coupled with circular economy model principles can provide an optimised, modern model of supply chains operation, as waste-to-products resources and flows can be redesigned so as to maximise their use in the improved SC network.

The aim of this paper is to introduce via indicative case-studies, from the field of manufacturing, a modelling approach of reverse supply chains in the context of circular economy and provide valuable knowledge, alternatives and possibly organisation insights to make supply chains more sustainable. The developed modeling framework is based on the Resource-Task-Network leading to a novel approach for reverse supply chain optimisation.

**Keywords**: sustainability, optimisation, reverse supply chains, RTN

## 1. Introduction

Over the last decades the scope and definition of Supply Chains (SCs) and the relative Management (SCM) was widen to include aspects dealing with the sustainability at all SC stages. SCM, which is as an integrated network of business units, producers, traders, retailers and consumers, with the relative information and materials flow from the supplier, to the producer of the final product up to the final consumer, requires as minimum operational conditions: "A systems approach to viewing the supply chain as a whole, and to managing the total flow of goods inventory from the supplier to the ultimate customer; a strategic orientation toward cooperative efforts to synchronize and converge intrafirm and interfirm operational and strategic capabilities into a unified whole; a customer focus to create unique and individualized sources of customer value, leading to customer satisfaction" (Mentzer et al., 2001).

Owing that to a nexus of reasons (increased consumer awareness, legally imposed environmental constraints), the final SC stage which delivers the end product to customer, has grown in importance, necessitating the need for safe product returns as well as more environmentally friendly products and by-products, such as recyclable packaging materials. Reverse Supply Chain (RSC) which is the SC that starts from the end consumer and goes up to the step of materials acquisition, also entails the collaborative responsibility of suppliers, producers and consumers to reduce the waste by recycling.

Transforming the current, linear economic model towards a resource-efficient Circular Economy (CE) model requires a uniform understanding of the interactions amongst the various decision factors. Integrating the CE perspective implies that emphasis will be given on product transformation, reverse loops of materials and energy, circularity of resources in general, also enabling waste elimination and environmental pollution decrease. Hence, it is very critical to study the incorporation of the CE aspect in RSCs and which is the appropriate evaluation framework.

## 2. Reverse Supply Chains and Circular Economy

At the moment the classic, linear SC now called forward SC is at a transformative phase aiming at including responsible management of end-of-life (EoL) products and also sustainable manufacturing. Under that pressure, firms are considering designing their SC network to take control of the reverse flow of products as well. Reverse supply chain management (RSCM) focuses on materials recovery and inventory management issues with typical operational decisions including design, planning, coordination of inventory management, outsourcing/ 3rd party logistics selection, vehicle routing problems, recovery, recycling and return of materials. Transforming forward into reverse SCs (RSCs) aims at ensuring waste minimisation while reducing the excessive usage of raw materials and at the same time protecting the environment.

CE approach "focuses on the circularity of energy and material resources which provides economic, environmental and social benefits for manufacturing organisations" (Yadav et al., 2020). CE adoption concept supports the vision for transforming the linear Take-Make-Dispose to Take-Make-Use of material and energy flows to a model that entails reusability and recyclability along with environmental, economic and social benefits.

Energy and materials reuse and recycle are common industrial practices. However, the CE approach recently embraced, has put emphasis on: a) processes dealing with repairing and remanufacturing and b) the potential utilisation of renewable energy sources (RES) throughout the product value chain. As Korhonen et al., (2018) states, "CE promotes high value material cycles alongside more traditional recycling and develops systems approaches to the cooperation of producers, consumers and other societal actors in sustainable development work". As an evidence to that, lately, the coupling of industry 4.0 (I4.0) and CE is also widely examined by researchers (Dev et al., 2020, Stylianopoulou et al., 2022), recognising the synergies at SC level.

The CE business model reorients efficient, waste / secondary material utilisation and also creates multidimensional values; economic value (profit maximisation, cost reduction), customer value (satisfaction, awareness), environmental (sustainability, etc) (Pal et al. 2019). Effective management of reverse logistics provides the possibility of value maximisation across the entire SC by choosing the most appropriate recovery alternative that can generate additional profitability and reduce the utilisation of resources. Communication of information across different levels, concerning the volume and type of returned products, the customers' attitudes, the customers' preferences regarding the environmental impact of products, the changes in the consumer model (i.e. e-commerce), are pushing the firms for improved customer services, new business strategies, changes in products' materials and their respective life cycle.

The CE model employed in each RSC it's a nexus of decisions based on the type of business and inventory model and to the required network and logistics design. Therefore, in the following section three representative case studies are listed from the field of manufacturing, highlighting the benefits of coupling CE model principles in RSC remodelling.

## 3. Case studies from the field of Manufacturing

Selected cases studies from different field of manufacturing will be presented in this section; cases of reverse supply chain modelling coupled with CE approach and related decision, highlighting the importance of CE and RSCs "engagement".

*Field: pharmaceutical waste* **CE Decisions in RSCs:** *coordination of inventory management, third party logistics operation, recycling and return of materials*

Nami and Hosseini-Motlagh (2022) developed a non-linear programming model that also includes a flexible transfer price agreement, and the Nash-bargaining game model   to coordinate all parties of pharmaceutical RSC (i.e., pharma-manufacturer (DP Company), 3PL company, and customers), considering the initial number of unwanted medications as a source of uncertainty. Two reverse SC types are examined: a) the medications with an expiry date of more than six months from the collection date can be legally resold by DP in secondary markets and b) the medications with an expiry date of less than six months from the collection date, are safely discarded in disposal sites by DP under a fixed disposing cost. **Objective function:** profit maximisation of 3PL. **Model added value:** Improved responsiveness of the SC to revenue fluctuations, improved profitability of the entire production system, in the sustainability pillar / social helpful when the customers are reluctant to return their items.

*Field: car sharing waste components* **CE Decisions in RSCs:** *remanufactruning, recycling*

Rentizelas and Trivyza (2022) propose an optimised design of a RSC for reusable parts in sharing vehicles (type of vehicles of high mileage and short service life). They focus in the reusability and re-manufacturability of carbon fibre reinforced polymer car frame, which has a long-life span and light weight properties. The network design was optimised using a MILP model for three scenarios of car reusability at the end of the car life, for the case study of the UK. **Objective function:** minimisation of RSC annual cost. **Model added value:** Improved percentage of remanufactured frames / impact of economies of scale in cost reduction demonstrated.

*Field: membrane fuel cell used in hydrogen vehicles* **CE Decisions:** *network design, remanufacturing, recycling*

Alkahtani and Ziout, (2019) developed a multi-objective mixed integer linear model in in order to design the reverse logistic, recovery supply chain network  for remanufacturing the proton-exchange membrane fuel cell used in hydrogen vehicles of General Motors. **Objective function:** minimisation of the RSC network costs, including environmental factors ($CO_2$ emission) and social aspects (number of job openings), and to maximisation of social benefits. **Model added value:** Improved collection network design (economically, socially and environmentally) for collecting used products and locating to the remanufacturing plant.

***Field:*** *food SC – case study: coffee SC* **CE Decisions in RSCs:** *altenative process pathways, minimisation of waste losses*

(Baratsas *et al.*, 2021) developed a novel CE system engineering framework and decision-making tool for the modeling and optimisation of food supply chains. The MILP developed model is tested for a coffee SC under different goals and objectives. Five scenarios for the supply of coffee cherries and the demand of final coffee products are investigated for each of the single or multi-objective optimisation problem. **Objective functions:** Minimisation of generated waste, Maximisation of recycling, Minimisation of consumed raw materials and natural resources, Maximisation of total energy and/or renewable energy output, Minimisation of GHG emissions, Maximisation of product, equipment and packaging durability. **Model added value:** More efficient process pathways, improved design and operation of the SC.

## 4. The Reverse Supply Chain framework features

As evidenced from the cases listed above, typically in RSCs the decisions deal with: a) the design of the SC (i.e. improvement additional manufacturing-oriented methods for product design) b) the logistics/ supply networks, c) the inventory/ capacity of the warehouses d) the inventory management methods are of critical decisions to be made within the scope of the redesigned SC, e) the product recovery, while maximising the benefit along the entire SC.

While the CE aspect inclusion in the design and operation of the optimised RSCs can provide insight to the following:

- For which selling price of secondary raw materials is the RSC-CE economically viable?

- To which kind of remanufacturing and repairing operation should we focus?

- To which operation should we invest? i.e. raw material production or secondary raw materials?

- Which is the market demand for secondary raw materials? What is the required purity for the secondary raw materials?

- Which is the environmental footprint of the "downstream" operations such as the recycling and waste treatment?

The proposed RSC-CE framework seeks to appropriately model the interdependencies among the supply chain "parts" by providing key focus both on the forward and the reverse operations according to the scope of the optimisation problem. It entails the construction of Resource-Task-Network (RTN) representation and a generic model formulation linking interactions between tasks and resources. Resources, typically may include any type of material and/or energy in different states represented as a circle and tasks, represented as a rectangle, include processes (i.e. production, recycling, repairing, sorting, energy recovery etc) (Figure 2). Resources modelling also enables inventory management decisions (i.e. flows of materials supplier to consumers, selection of the supply network etc).

The benefit of the present modelling framework, which is meant to be formulated as a MILP model to include binary variables (0,1) for all type of decisions points, is that allows based on the focus aspect either of the CE or of the RSC to formulate the relevant optimisation criterion. Some indicatives examples are illustrated in Table1, whilst the key components of the model are listed in Table 2.

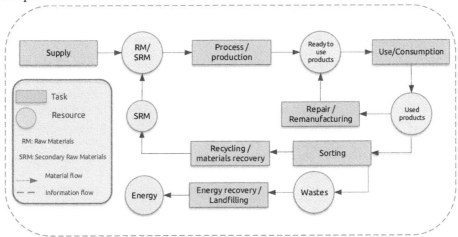

Figure 2: The remodelled RSC under the CE and the RTN concept

Table 1: Optimisation criterion and RSC and CE focus points.

| RSC focus | Optimisation Criterion | CE - Focus |
|---|---|---|
| On RMs supply in the production stage (decrease) | Minimisation of RMs supply | Increase of SRMs production |
| On wastes generated (decrease) | Maximisation of SRMs production | Invest/ select RMs with longer life span |
| On wastes generated (decrease) | Maximisation of recycling rate | Recovered materials to meet the market needs |
| SC environmental footprint (decrease) | Minimise $CO_2eq$ through the entire SC | More efficient processes, maximisation of RES utilisation |

Table 2: Modelling

| Sets |
|---|
| Resources (raw materials, secondary raw materials, ready-to-use products, used products, wastes, energy) |
| Time interval for which the problem is considered (hour, day, week, month, year) |
| Processes (production, consumption, sorting, repairing, recycling, landfilling) |
| **Variables** |
| *Decision variables (Based on the selected optimisation criterion):* Quantities of resources /year (produced, recycled, returned, reused) |
| *Binary variables* - For selecting the appropriate process pathway |

| Economic parameters |
|---|
| Prices of resources (€/item, €/kg…) |
| Process - based costs (€/processed item) |
| Transportation costs (€/processed item) |
| Process-conversion coefficients |
| **Demand – Balance Constraints** |
| Demand for raw materials (kg/year) |
| Demand for new products (items/year) |
| Demand for secondary raw materials (kg/year) |
| **Variables (cont.)** |
| Demand for ready-to-use products (new and refurbished (items/year) |

| Capacities of the processes (items or kg or m³/year) | Wastes constraints over the planning horizon (kg, m³/year) |
|---|---|
| **Environmental – CE** | Energy recovered over the planning horizon (% of total input) |
| Environmental footprint of the processes (tn $CO_2$ /per item recovered) | Circular material use rate |
| Emissions constraints over the planning horizon (tn $CO_2$ /year) | End-of-life recycling input rates |
| **Demand – Balance Constraints (cont.)** | |

## 5. Conclusions

In this work the basic structure and principles of an optimisation framework aiming at modelling RCSs in the context of CE is presented. The existing experience evidences that CE can strongly relate to RSCs remodeling and optimisation as it highlights the practical pathways towards that transition. Moreover, the literature review revealed that companies are interested in becoming more efficient and sustainable along the different SC manufacturing stages and are making real efforts towards that direction. A very interesting aspect, that will be investigated in a later work is the coupling of closed – loops SCs with the CE and RSCs in a holistic way.

## *Acknowledgments*

*The publication /registration fees were totally covered by the University of West Attica.*

## References

M. Alkahtani, A. Ziout, 2019, Design of a sustainable reverse supply chain in a remanufacturing environment: A case study of proton-exchange membrane fuel cell battery in Riyadh, Advances in Mechanical Engineering, 11, 4, 1–14

S.G. Baratsas, E.N. Pistikopoulos, S. Avraamidou, 2021, A systems engineering framework for the optimization of food supply chains under circular economy considerations, Science of the Total Environment, Elsevier B.V., 794, -, 148726

N.K. Dev, R. Shankar, F.H. Qaiser, 2020, Industry 4.0 and circular economy: Operational excellence for sustainable reverse supply chain performance, Resources, Conservation and Recycling, Elsevier, 153, -,104583

J. Korhonen, C. Nuur, A. Feldmann, S. Eshetu, 2018, Circular economy as an essentially contested concept, 175,-, 544-552

J.T. Mentzer, J.S. Keebler, N.W. Nix, C.D. Smith, and Z.G. Zacharia, 2001, Journal Of Business Logistics, 22, 2, 1–25

N. Nami, S.M. Hosseini-Motlagh, 2022, Central robust decision-making structure for reverse supply chain: a real pharmaceutical case, Comp. and Ind. Eng., Elsevier Ltd, 173,-, 108726

R. Pal, E. Sandberg, M.K. Paras, 2019, Multidimensional value creation through different reverse supply chain relationships in used clothing sector, Supply chain management, 24,6, 729-747.

A. Rentizelas, N.L. Trivyza, 2022, Enhancing circularity in the car sharing industry: Reverse supply chain network design optimisation for reusable car frames, Sustainable Production and Consumption, 32,-, 863–879

K.G. Stylianopoulou, E.M. Kondili, J.K. Kaldellis, 2022, Process Systems Engineering prospects in Circular Economy implementation in industry, in Montastruc, L. and Negny, S. (Eds.), 32nd European Symposium on Computer Aided Process Engineering, 51,-, 1309–1314

G. Yadav, S.K. Mangla, A. Bhattacharya, S. Luthra, 2020, Exploring indicators of circular economy adoption framework through a hybrid decision support approach, Journal of Cleaner Production, 277,-, 24186

R. Pal, E. Sandberg, M.K. Paras, 2019, Multidimensional value creation through different reverse supply chain relationships in used clothing sector, Supply chain management, 24,6, 729-747.

Antonis Kokossis, Michael C. Georgiadis, Efstratios N. Pistikopoulos (Eds.)
PROCEEDINGS OF THE 33rd European Symposium on Computer Aided Process Engineering
(ESCAPE33), June 18-21, 2023, Athens, Greece

# Modular vs centralized manufacturing supply chain: identifying the best solution under uncertainty

Alessandro Di Pretoro[a], Stéphane Negny[a], Ludovic Montastruc[a*]

[a]*Laboratoire de Génie Chimique, Université de Toulouse, CNRS/INP, Toulouse, France*
*alessandro.dipretoro@ensiacet.fr*

## Abstract

Although the economy of scale has been the production systems golden standard for investment costs minimization during the last century, the modular manufacturing supply has recently seen a renewed interest during the last decades. This approach allows to considerably reduce transportation and operating expenses based on small capacity units that can be installed on site and that, after their usage, can be transferred to a new customer. Moreover, when uncertain variables are involved, the optimal choice is not that trivial anymore and a quantitative approach is required to have a clear and conscious view of the best supply chain design solution for the specific application. For this purpose, a dedicated case study concerning production and supply of a multicomponent resin was set up. In the centralized scenario the entire production process is carried out in the factory and the final product is delivered to the customers while, in the distributed one, the raw materials are provided to the final user and the production process takes place in the customers' site. Transportation costs and optimal centralized factory location are then calculated by means of an adaptation of the methodology proposed by Di Pretoro et al. (2022). Customers position and demand are randomly generated within the expected range of variable fluctuation. The uncertainty is addressed by means of a stochastic methodology and the obtained results show that it is possible to generate mono- and multivariate probability distributions to describe the optimal centralized factory location as well as capital and operating expenses. This study proves that proposed methodology achieves its goal to identify the best solution between modular and centralized supply layout. Furthermore, it allows to quantify the expected costs for given sets of known and aleatory parameters. The study is then surely worth a deeper investigation for more complex and detailed case studies to further improve the quality of the outlined procedure.

Keywords: modular manufacturing, centralized manufacturing, supply chain, uncertainty, stochastic optimization.

## 1. Introduction

The transition process towards sustainable raw materials and renewable energy sources as well as the fast market dynamics and the volatility of goods price imply the spreading of uncertainty over all the sectors of the industrial domain. In particular, from a logistic perspective, customers are more and more frequently changing suppliers according to their particular needs. This trend results in non-negligible difficulties during the supply chain design in terms of uncertain demand and customers location. Moreover, the optimization related to the less expensive delivery layout and the optimal travel paths to meet the European standards (EEA, 2022) in terms of minimal emissions is compromised in terms of optimal solution accuracy whether the uncertainty is not taken into account since the early design phases. Therefore, the need for more flexible solution resulted in a renewed interest towards the modular unit approach (Baldea et al., 2017). With respect to the conventional centralized approach, that exploits the economy of scale to minimize investments, the modular approach is based on units (skid) with a limited capacity but that can be used to perform a part or the entire process on the customer site. Moreover, these units can be transferred to another customer when the contract with the previous one expires.

In this research work we address the comparison between centralized and modular approaches under uncertain customers location and demand. The selected stochastic method for this study is the Sample Average Approximation. This method allows to decouple the uncertainty from the system model at the expenses of the computational costs, that is a negligible drawback given the size of the system under analysis. Further details about the case study are provided in the following section.

## 2. Case study

The case study presented in this work is based on a supply chain case study for a chemical product that is made up of two components, namely A and B, and water. The geographic domain of interest is given by a rectangle whose sizes are 1500 X 2000 km respectively. A set of 20 customers with a demand of either 1 or 2 kton/y with random location are generated for each simulation. They are modeled as "new" customers, each of those appears every year and stays until the end of the simulation duration.

Two scenarios for the logistics approach are then analyzed. The first one is based on a centralized distribution strategy for which the optimal location of the centralized factory is obtained by minimizing the Total Annualized Cost function (TAC) described in detail in the next section. An illustrative example is shown in Figure 1.

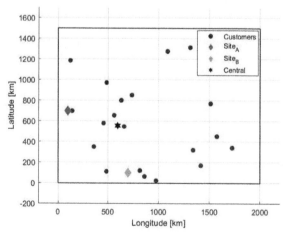

Figure 1 – Raw materials sites, centralized factory location and aleatory customers distribution

The second scenario is based on a modular approach. In this case water does not need to be delivered to the customers since water available on-site is used. As a consequence the delivery truck has a higher content of raw materials and the amount of required travels is way lower. Investment costs are given by the sum of the 1 or 2 kton skid units required to fulfill each customer demand according to the correlations of section 3.2.

Product composition, raw material supply centers location and other operating variables are listed in Table 1.

| System parameters | Value | Unit | Abbreviation |
|---|---|---|---|
| Site A location | 100 x 700 | km x km | $x_a$ x $y_a$ |
| Site B location | 700 x 100 | km x km | $x_a$ x $y_a$ |
| Truck capacity | 20 | ton | $Cap_T$ |
| **Composition** | | | |
| A fraction | 0.3 | kg/kg | $w_A$ |
| B fraction | 0.4 | kg/kg | $w_B$ |
| Water fraction | 0.3 | kg/kg | $w_W$ |

Table 1 – System operating parameters

Next section discusses in detail the methodology concerning optimization criteria and costs calculation previously introduced.

## 3. Methodology

The approach developed in this research work is a bi-level optimization based on a combination between Sample Average Approximation for the upper level and deterministic optimization for the lower one. The first method one is used to model aleatory customers, appearing and leaving during time in different geographical sites with different demand. The second one is used to find the optimal solution for a given scenario in terms of delivery paths and centralized factory location.

### 3.1. Objective function

The lower level optimization loop has the purpose to define the shortest travel path and the corresponding transport costs. is based on the cost function minimization. The objective function to minimize is defined as:

$$F_{obj}[\$/y] = d[km/y] \cdot \hat{C}_{tr}[€/km] \qquad (1)$$

where the considered specific transportation costs $\hat{C}_{tr}$ are equal to 1.2 €/km price and the travel distance is given, for the centralized scenario, by the sum of the terms:

$$d[km/y] = n_{A,C} \cdot dist_{A,C} + n_{B,C} \cdot dist_{B,C} + \sum_{i=1}^{n_{cust}} n_{C,i} \cdot dist_{C,i} \qquad (2)$$

The number of amount of travels $n_{ji}$ from the A, B and centralized site respectively are based on the ratio between demand composition and truck capacity as follows:

$$n_{A,C}[1/y] = \frac{w_A[kg/kg] \cdot dem_{tot}[kg/y]}{cap_{truck}[kg]} \qquad (3)$$

where $dem_{tot}$ is the total yearly demand. Differently from the first scenario, for the distributed approach the two terms related to raw material sites should be expressed as the sum weighted with respect to their distance from each customers and the third term is not taken into account since there is no centralized distribution center.

### 3.2. Costs calculation

Once the lower level optimization is completed, operating expenses (OPEX) can be calculated and combined to capital expenses (CAPEX) in order to quantify the Total Annualized Costs according to the equation:

$$TAC[\$/y] = OPEX[\$/y] + CRF[1/y] \cdot CAPEX[\$] \tag{4}$$

The Capital Recovery Factor (CRF) is defined as:

$$CRF[1/y] = \frac{i \cdot (i+1)^n}{(i+1)^n - 1} \tag{5}$$

where the discount rate $i$ and the plant lifetime $n$ for this case study are respectively equal to and 20. For CAPEX evaluation the Cobb-Douglas correlation is used as follows to resize the process unit cost according to its capacity:

$$Cost_{Centr} = C_{skid2} \cdot \left(\frac{Cap_{Centr} + 8000}{2000}\right)^{0.8} \tag{6}$$

$$Cost_{Centr} = C_{skid2} \cdot \left(\frac{1000}{2000}\right)^{0.8} \tag{7}$$

where the cost of a 2 kton skid is 300 k€ and the centralized factory is oversized by 8 kton. Finally, the production costs, i.e. raw materials and duties, are neglected during the comparison since they are the same for both scenarios.

## 4. Results

The case study simulation was run 5000 times. This value allows to have a results that can be represented by sufficiently significative and smooth Probability Distribution Functions (hereafter PDF).

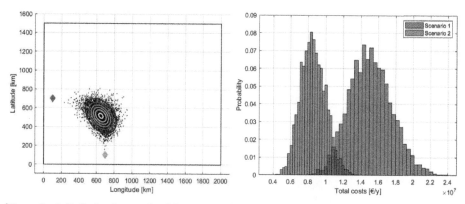

Figure 2 – left) Optimal centralized factory location and TAC distributions

As a first result, the 5000 positions for the optimal centralized factory location are outlined as shown in Figure 2. Based on the outcome, it is possible to regress the obtained data by means of a bi-variate probability distribution. This function could be then exploited to have a quantitative idea of the best places to locate the centralized distribution factory according to geographical (e.g. mountains, rivers etc.) and operational (e.g. electricity grid, duties or water sources availability etc.) constraints.

The second relevant result given by the TAC probability distribution. At a first glance, we can notice that, although the two distributions overlap over a small range, the modular scenario exhibits lower TAC with respect to the centralized one. Moreover, we can identify an average TAC value (without accounting for operating and raw materials cost for this example) equal about to 8.2 and 15.3 M€ per year respectively. The same analysis can be carried out concerning the standard deviation. Furthermore, if needed, the cumulative function could be derived in order to associate a given value of costs to the percentage of cases that fall outside the affordability threshold.

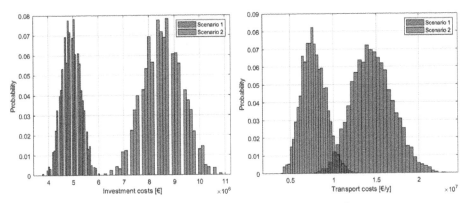

Figure 3 – left) Investment and right) operating costs distribution comparison

In order to analyze in deep the economic aspects, the TAC function could be decomposed into its parts. Figure 3 shows the outcome of this analysis for CAPEX (left) and transport costs (right).

As concern investment costs we can notice that they do not show a continuous trend. This is due to the fact that the customers demand could be either 1 or 2 kton per year resulting in a discretized distribution. In fact, it can be observed that, in terms of distribution shape, scenario 1 and 2 have the same trend. However, the modular approach results slightly less than twice as expensive as the centralized one as expected. On the other hand, in the transport costs plot the two distributions exhibit a different shape due to the fact that the travel paths are different in case of raw materials instead of final product distribution. Moreover, as it can be suddenly noticed as well, the magnitude of transport costs per year is comparable with the investments costs over the entire 20 years life of the plant with an average value of about 8.05 and 14.9 M€/y respectively.

For the sake of completeness, given that the truck travels are always performed at its full charge, the transport costs are proportional to the travel distance, i.e. with a scale factor represented by the ratio between specific fuel costs and specific fuel emissions, the equivalent $CO_2$ value (i.e. the GWP indicator) has the same trend as the plot in Figure 3 – right.

The obtained results and graphs allow then to conclude that, for this specific case study, due to the considerable impact of transport costs on the TAC, the modular solution results to be much more convenient than the conventional centralized one.

A more complete summary of the outcome of this research work is nevertheless provided in the next section.

## 5. Conclusions

The presented research work discusses a stochastic approach to optimize a supply chain system under uncertainty. The outcome of this study can be resumed in three main relevant points.

First, the proposed stochastic methodology based on Sample Average Approximation, although rather simple, allows to define a probability domain where the optimal centralized factory location should lie. Second, costs and emissions can be quantified both in terms of average value and standard deviation so that they can be compared for different scenarios in term of residual values associated to a given cost-emissions threshold and compromise. Finally, besides the results that are specifically related to the proposed case study, the comparison between a centralized and a modular industrial system configurations is viable. This aspect allows the decision maker to draw conscious conclusions based on thorough analysis and make the most suitable choice according to its specific needs.

As concerns further perspectives, the study could be extended to more complex systems in order to face the computational issue related to the fast growth of the amount of calculations with respect to the increase of the system parameters (e.g. number of customers, number of raw materials sites etc.). This aspect makes the research worth a deeper analysis in the future.

## References

M. Baldea, T.F. Edgar, B.L. Stanley, A. Kiss, 2017, Modular Manufacturing Processes: Status, Challenges, and Opportunities. AIChE Journal, 63 (10), 4262–4272. https://doi.org/10.1002/aic.15872.

A. Bhosekar, M. Ierapetritou, 2021, A Framework for Supply Chain Optimization for Modular Manufacturing with Production Feasibility Analysis. Computers & Chemical Engineering, 145, 107175. https://doi.org/10.1016/j.compchemeng.2020.107175.

C.W. Cobb, P.H. Douglas, 1928, A Theory of Production. American Economic Review. 18 (Supplement): 139–165. JSTOR 1811556

A. Di Pretoro, S. Negny, L. Montastruc, 2022, The Traveling Deliveryman Problem under Uncertainty: Fundamentals for Flexible Supply Chains. Computers & Chemical Engineering, 160, 107730. https://doi.org/10.1016/j.compchemeng.2022.107730.

European Environment Agency, Greenhouse gas emissions from transport. Retrieved at https://www.eea.europa.eu/ims/greenhouse-gas-emissions-from-transport. Accessed on 27/11/2022.

E. Alarcon-Gerbier, U. Buscher, 2022, Modular and mobile facility location problems: A systematic review. Computers & Industrial Engineering 173, 108734. https://doi.org/10.1016/j.cie.2022.108734

Antonis Kokossis, Michael C. Georgiadis, Efstratios N. Pistikopoulos (Eds.)
PROCEEDINGS OF THE 33rd European Symposium on Computer Aided Process Engineering
(ESCAPE33), June 18-21, 2023, Athens, Greece

# Stochastic Optimization of Agrochemical Supply Chains with Risk Management

Saba Ghasemi Naraghi,[a] Zheyu Jiang[a]*

[a]Oklahoma Sate University, 420 Engineering North, Stillwater, Oklahoma, USA 74078
*Corresponding author: zheyu.jiang@okstate.edu

## Abstract

The global agrochemical market is highly consolidated, with large multinational companies accounting for a major share of the market. Thus, even for a single agrochemical product, its supply chain typically involves many possible paths connecting the raw material sources of active ingredients to final customers. In addition to structural complexity, agrochemical supply chains are also subject to seasonality and various unique uncertainties, thereby demanding high system resilience and implementation of risk management strategies in the face of these uncertainties and disruptions. In this study, we formulate and optimize the supply chain of an agrochemical active ingredient by formulating a stochastic mixed-integer nonlinear programming (MINLP) model. This MINLP formulation is scenario-based with demand uncertainty addressed by Value-at-Risk (VaR) and Conditional Value-at-Risk (CVaR). For the first time, we propose to reformulate these nonlinear CVaR constraints using perspective reformulation techniques. We show that these perspective cuts give a tight approximation of the original MINLP model. Through an illustrative case study, we compare the results and performance of the original MINLP and the reformulated MILP.

Keywords: Agrochemical supply chain, Value-at-Risk (VaR), Conditional Value-at-Risk (CVaR), perspective cuts, mixed-integer nonlinear programming.

## 1. Introduction

In 2050, the global population is expected to increase by 2 billion people to 9.7 billion, which puts unprecedented stress on food, energy, and water resources as the global food production must increase by at least 70% (Searchinger et al., 2018). Therefore, the manufacturing and supply chain of agrochemicals, including pesticides, herbicides, fungicides, and insecticides, are critical to ensuring food production and security. The global agrochemical market is highly consolidated, with 60-70% of the global market share dominated by four agrochemical companies alone (IEPS-Food, 2017). Each of these leading companies has a diversified product line, and its supply chains are multistage networks involving many possible paths connecting the raw material sources to active ingredients to final products. In addition, agrochemical supply chains are further complicated by seasonality and various uncertainties due to climate change, more frequent black swan events (e.g., COVID-19 pandemic), and increasingly complex geopolitical landscape (e.g., the Russia-Ukraine war). In particular, seasonal demand is a unique characteristic for agrochemical supply chains. To design cost-effective, resilient, and well-managed agrochemical supply chains, in this work, we develop an optimization framework to effectively model the risks associated with these seasonality and uncertainties and propose a reformulation strategy to solve the optimization problem.

Among numerous recent works on supply chain optimization (Garcia and You, 2015), Bassett and Gardner (2009) presented one of the first mixed-integer linear programming (MILP) formulations for global agrochemical supply chain optimization considering seasonality and uncertainties in customer demand. Liu and Papageorgiou (2012) extended the agrochemical supply chain optimization framework by modeling and comparing different plant expansion strategies. To further ensure continuous use and inactivity of warehouses for continuous periods of time, Brunaud et al. (2017) developed dynamic contract policy constraints for warehouses and incorporated them to the agrochemical supply chain model. In terms of quantifying uncertainties and risks, You et al. (2009) proposed a scenario-based two-stage stochastic linear programming framework and decomposition strategies for mid-term planning of multi-product supply chain under demand and freight rate uncertainties. Later, Carneiro et al. (2010) focused on the oil supply chain optimization problem, in which they incorporated Conditional Value-at-Risk (CVaR) as a risk assessment measure that quantifies the tail risk in their investment portfolio. In this work, we develop a scenario-based two-stage mixed-integer nonlinear programming (MINLP) model for global agrochemical supply chain optimization and adopt the concepts of Value-at-Risk (VaR) and CVaR to quantify and control the risks associated with demand unfulfillment. Note that these risk measures are highly nonlinear. Therefore, we introduce perspective cuts to linearize the CVaR constraint and reformulate the MINLP model. Perspective cuts were first introduced by Frangioni and Gentile (2006), who showed that the convex envelope of the objective function containing semicontinuous variables in a general mixed-integer program (MIP) is the perspective function of MIP's continuous part. More recently, Bestuzheva et al. (2021) extended perspective cuts to nonlinear constraints in MINLPs. Consider a MINLP with a linear objective function $f$: $\min f(x, y, z)$ subject to nonlinear constraints $g(x) \leq 0$, in which $y \in \Omega, z \in \{0,1\}^n$, and $x \in \mathbb{R}^n$ are semi-continuous variables (for every $i = 1, \cdots, n$, $x_i = 0$ when $z_i = 0$ and $x_i \in [l, u]$ when $z_i = 1$). The perspective cuts for linearizing nonlinear constraints $g(x) \leq 0$ are given by:

$$\langle \nabla g(\bar{x}), x \rangle + [g(\bar{x}) - \langle \nabla g(\bar{x}), \bar{x} \rangle] z \leq 0 \tag{1}$$

where $\bar{x} \in [l, u]$ is an arbitrary parameter. After replacing $g(x) \leq 0$ with these perspective cuts, the MINLP is reformulated to a MILP, which can be solved iteratively. Specifically, starting from the second iteration, $\bar{x}$ is chosen to be the solution of the MILP from the previous iteration. Bestuzheva et al. (2021) also conducted a detailed computational study of perspective reformulation for MINLPs with convex and nonconvex nonlinear constraints. They showed that the perspective reformulation of convex MINLPs provides much tighter approximation of the original problems compared to conventional branch-and-cut approaches, thereby leading to significant computational time reduction. Nevertheless, they also reported that adding perspective cuts for nonconvex MINLPs had less impact on computational time, although it reduces the size of branch-and-cut trees and strengthens the root node relaxation.

## 2. Problem Statement and Model Formulation

In this illustrative case study, we consider the three-echelon supply chain of one active ingredient (AI) produced in an agrochemical company involving five AI production plants, four warehouses/distribution centers, and three market regions. We are interested in midterm planning (1 year) divided into 52 periods (i.e., 1 week per period). AI production plants and warehouses are connected by one or more transportation links, and so are warehouses and market regions. We allow different types of transportation modes for each transportation link. AI production plants can either be active or inactive during each time period. The manufacturing capacity of an AI production plant can be expanded at most once in a year. During the expansion period, AI production must be inactive. The AI produced can either be transported to warehouses or stored as inventory. The inventory level must be larger than or equal to the safety stock. As shown in Figure 1, the yearly demand of an agrochemical product typically follows a bimodal distribution (Bassett, 2018). For this case study, we consider three scenarios in customer demand. Also, we consider the risk of demand loss or unsatisfaction due to uncertainties related to production planning and warehouse capacity limitations. We are given the safety stock of an inventory, initial inventory, as well as unit costs associated with inventory holding, AI manufacturing and expansion, material transportation, warehouse storage and expansion, and demand loss or unsatisfaction (see Table 1). The objective function is to minimize the total cost of the supply chain. Due to space limitations, we only highlight some of the key points in our MINLP model:

1.  Following You et al. (2009), decision variables of the first time period (Week 1) are first-stage variables and are independent of scenarios. Second-stage variables and scenario-based stochasticity begins at the second time period (Week 2).

2.  We adopt the dynamic contract policy formulation from Brunaud et al. (2018) and extend it to AI production plants – Each AI production plant must remain in production for at least $U$ time periods, after which it might undergo cleanup for $F$ time periods, during which no production activities would take place:

$$-\alpha_i + \alpha_i^{start} \geq 0, \qquad \forall i \in I$$
$$\alpha_{i,t-1}^s - \alpha_{i,t}^s + \alpha_{i,t}^{s,start} \geq 0, \qquad \forall i \in I, s \in S, t \in T(t>1)$$
$$\alpha_i + \sum_{\tau=2}^{R} \alpha_{i,\tau}^s \geq U\alpha_i^{start}, \qquad \forall i \in I, \ s \in S$$
$$\sum_{\tau=t}^{t+R-1} \alpha_{i,\tau}^s \geq U\alpha_{i,t}^{s,start}, \qquad \forall i \in I, \ s \in S, \ t \in T(t>1, t+R-1 \leq |T|) \tag{2}$$
$$\alpha_{i,t+1}^s - \alpha_{i,t}^s + \alpha_{i,t}^{s,final} \geq 0, \qquad \forall i \in I, \ s \in S, \ t \in T$$
$$\sum_{\tau=t+1}^{t+F} \alpha_{i,\tau}^s + F\alpha_{i,t}^{s,final} \leq F, \qquad \forall i \in I, \ s \in S, \ t \in T(t+F \leq |T|)$$

where $\alpha_i$, $\alpha_i^{start}$, $\alpha_{i,t}^s$, $\alpha_{i,t}^{s,start}$, $\alpha_{i,t}^{s,final}$ are binary variables indicating whether the AI production plant $i \in I$ is in production (1) or not (0) at time period 1, starting at time period 1, at time period $t$ under scenario $s$, starting at time $t$ under scenario $s$, and ending at time $t$ under scenario $s$ respectively. $|T|$ is the total number of time periods.

3.  The total demand loss $\chi_t^s$ for time period $t$ under scenario $s$ is the sum of demand loss from all market regions. To quantify the risks due to demand loss, we introduce the CVaR constraint in the model. We assume that the demand loss follows a normal distribution, which enables us to express VaR in terms of $\chi_t^s$: $VaR^s = \frac{\sigma^s z_\beta}{\sqrt{|T|}}$, where $z_\beta$

is z-score at confidence interval $\beta$, $|T|$ is the total number of time periods (i.e., 52),

and $\sigma^s = \sqrt{\frac{1}{|T|-1}\left(\sum_{t\in T}\chi_t^{s2} - \frac{(\sum_{t\in T}\chi_t^s)^2}{|T|}\right)}$ is the standard deviation of the total

demand loss as for scenario $s$. From VaR, we calculate CVaR as $\frac{1}{1-\beta}\sum_{s\in S}p_s\text{VaR}^s$

following Carneiro et al. (2010), where $p_s$ is the probability of scenario $s$. By specifying a lower bound $P$ on CVaR (e.g., 30 mass units), we obtain the following CVaR constraint and add it into the formulation:

$$\text{CVaR} = \frac{z_\beta}{(1-\beta)\sqrt{|T|(|T|-1)}}\sum_{s\in S}p_s\sqrt{\left(\sum_{t\in T}\chi_t^{s2} - \frac{(\sum_{t\in T}\chi_t^s)^2}{|T|}\right)} \geq P \quad \forall s \in S, \qquad (2)$$

4.   Since Equation (2) is nonconvex and nonlinear, we introduce perspective cuts and reformulate the original MINLP into a MILP by substituting Equation (2) to Equation (1):

$$\left(P - R\sum_{s\in S}p_sQ_s - R\sum_{s\in S}p_s\frac{\bar\chi_t^s(\bar\chi_t^s - \frac{\sum_{t\in T}\bar\chi_t^s}{|T|})}{Q_s}\right)z_t - R\sum_{s\in S}p_s\frac{\chi_t^s\left(\bar\chi_t^s - \frac{\sum_{t\in T}\bar\chi_t^s}{|T|}\right)}{Q_s} \qquad (3)$$
$$\leq 0 \quad \forall t \in T,$$

where $R := \frac{z_\beta}{(1-\beta)\sqrt{|T|(|T|-1)}}$, $Q_s := \sqrt{\left(\sum_{t\in T}(\bar\chi_t^s)^2 - \frac{(\sum_{t\in T}\bar\chi_t^s)^2}{|T|}\right)}$, $z_t \in \{0,1\}$, and $\bar\chi_t^s$ is the

optimal demand loss from the previous iteration of introducing perspective cuts.

5.   We point out that this is the first linearization of CVaR constraint reported in the literature. Both problems are solved using SCIP v8.0 in GAMS 40.2.0 in a Dell Precision 7920 workstation with Intel Xeon Gold 6226R CPU @ 2.90 GHz and 96 GB of RAM, and the results are compared.

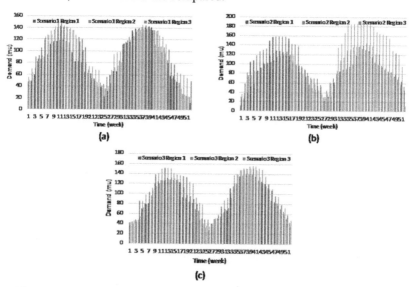

Figure 1. Bimodal demand curve for each market region under different scenarios.

Table 1. List of model parameters used in the illustrative case study.

| Model parameters | Values |
|---|---|
| Initial capacity in each of the 5 AI production plants (mu) | 100, 115, 100, 120, 110 |
| Safety stock in each AI production plant (mu) | 5, 5, 10, 10 ,5 |
| Initial inventory level in each AI production plant (mu) | 5, 5, 15, 0, 15 |
| Transportation capacity from AI production plant to warehouse (mu) | 400 for mode 1<br>350 for mode 2 |
| Transportation capacity from warehouse to market region (mu) | 100 for mode 3<br>200 for mode 4 |
| Storage capacity in each of the 4 warehouses (mu) | 550, 650, 500, 450 |
| Initial inventory level in each warehouse (mu) | 25, 20, 30, 10 |
| Probability of the three possible scenarios | 0.25, 0.45, 0.30 |
| Fixed cost in each of the 5 AI production plants ($\times 10^3$ \$) | 75, 100, 150, 100, 75 |
| Variable cost in each of the 5 AI production plants (\$) | 10, 15, 10, 5, 20 |
| Expansion cost in each of the 5 AI production plants ($\times 10^3$ \$) | 10, 50, 25, 35, 15 |
| Fixed transportation cost from AI production plant to warehouse (\$) | 25 for mode 1<br>30 for mode 2 |
| Fixed transportation cost from warehouse to market region (\$) | 15 for mode 3<br>30 for mode 4 |
| Variable transportation cost from AI production plant to warehouse (\$/mu) | 2 for mode 1<br>2.5 for mode 2 |
| Variable transportation cost from warehouse to market region (\$/mu) | 1.5 for mode 3<br>2.5 for mode 4 |
| Maximum total demand loss in each time period (mu) | 15 |
| Variable cost on demand loss (\$/mu) for each of the 3 market regions | 50, 55, 70 |

## 3. Discussion

The original MINLP model, which contains 9255 continuous variables and 1874 binary variables, has 14499 linear constraints and 2 nonlinear constraints of Equation (2) (one equality constraint and one inequality constraint). After the first iteration of adding perspective cuts, the reformulated MILP contains 14551 linear constraints (14499 linear constraints and 52 perspective cuts, each corresponding to one time period), 1874 binary variables, and 9254 continuous variables. We specify a solving time of 150 seconds, at which the original MINLP model has an objective function value of $\$1.509 \times 10^6$ and a gap of 2.39%, whereas the reformulated model shows an objective function value of $\$1.498 \times 10^6$ and a closer gap of 1.64%. We emphasize that the reformulated model always yields a feasible solution in the original formulation, suggesting that it provides a better optimal solution. This is due to the fact that the reformulated model is able to identify a solution with less overall demand loss $\sum_{s \in S} \sum_{t \in T} \chi_t^s$ compared to the solution obtained from the original MINLP. This suggests that the reformulated model produces a more efficient supply chain compared to the original model.

In a separate numerical study, we analyze the impact of problem size on the computational benefits of introducing perspective cuts. When we consider only 13 time periods (monthly) in the model, no significant computational speed improvement is observed in the reformulated model compared to the original MINLP. However, when considering 26 time periods (biweekly) in the model, the reformulated model solves to 1% gap in 29 seconds, whereas the original MINLP solves to the same objective function value as well as the same 1% gap in 41 seconds. This observation is consistent with that made by Bestuzheva et al. (2021), in the sense that the computational benefits of perspective cuts depend on the size of the problem. Perspective cuts should be accompanied by other reformulation strategies and bound-tightening constraints to maximize their benefits.

## 4. Conclusion

In this work, we optimize the supply chain of an agrochemical active ingredient by formulating and solving a scenario-based stochastic MINLP problem. The nonlinearity of the model comes from the CVaR constraint used to quantify risks associated with unforeseen demand loss. For the first time, we propose to reformulate the CVaR constraints using perspective reformulation techniques. The reformulated model, which is a MILP, always gives a feasible solution to the original MINLP model. Using a simple case study, we demonstrate the effectiveness of perspective cuts in fostering convergence and reducing computation time. In particular, we show that the reformulated model typically produces optimal solutions with less overall demand loss compared to the solution obtained from the original MINLP. Thus, adopting perspective reformulation could help identify a more efficient supply chain network and production/distribution plans with lower costs and carbon emissions. On the other hand, we point out that, depending on the problem size, adding perspective cuts for nonconvex MINLPs may not lead to significant computational time improvements. In this case, perspective cuts should be accompanied by other reformulation strategies and bound-tightening constraints to synergistically facilitate the solution of nonconvex MINLPs.

## References

M. Bassett, L. Gardner, 2009, Optimizing the design of global supply chains at Dow AgroSciences, *Computers & Chemical Engineering*, 34, 10, 254-265.

M. Bassett, 2018, Optimizing the design of new and existing supply chains at Dow AgroSciences, *Computers & Chemical Engineering*, 114, 18, 191-200.

K. Bestuzhev, A. Gleixner, S. Vigerske, 2021, A Computational Study of Perspective Cuts, preprint available at https://arxiv.org/abs/2103.09573

B. Brunaud, M.H. Bassett, A. Agarwal, J.M. Wassik I.E Grossmann, 2017, Efficient formulation for dynamic warehouse location under discrete transportation costs, *Computers & Chemical Engineering*, 111, 18, 311-323.

M.C. Carneiro, G.P Ribas, S. Hamacher, 2010, Risk management in supply chain: CVaR approach, *Industrial & Engineering Chemistry Research*, 49, 3286–3294.

A. Frangioni, C. Gentile, 2005, Perspective cuts for a class of convex 0–1 mixed integer programs, *Mathematical Programming*, 106, 225-236.

D.J. Garcia, F. You, 2015, Supply chain design and optimization: Challenges and opportunities, *Computers & Chemical Engineering*, 81, 15, 153-170.

IEPS-Food, 2017, Too big to feed: Exploring the impacts of mega-mergers, concentration, concentration of power in the agri-food sector, accessed via http://www.ipes-food.org/images/Reports/Concentration_FullReport.pdf

S. Lui, L.G. Papageorgiou, 2012, Multiobjective optimization of production, distribution and capacity planning of global supply chains in the process industry, *Omega*, 41,13, 369-382.

T. Searchinger, R. Waite, J. Ranganathan, P. Dumas, E. Matthews, 2018, World Resources Report: Creating a Sustainable Food Future, World Resources Institute.

F. You, J.M Wassik, I.E Grossmann, 2009, Risk management for a global supply chainplanning under uncertainty: Models and algorithms, *AIChE Journal*, 55, 4, 931-946.

Antonis Kokossis, Michael C. Georgiadis, Efstratios N. Pistikopoulos (Eds.)
PROCEEDINGS OF THE 33rd European Symposium on Computer Aided Process Engineering
(ESCAPE33), June 18-21, 2023, Athens, Greece

# Supply Chain Optimization Considering Disruption Demand Uncertainty

Oluwadare Badejo [a], Marianthi Ierapetritou [a]

[a] Department of Chemical and Biomolecular Engineering,
University of Delaware, Newark, 19711, USA,

## Abstract

In this paper, a mathematical framework was developed to optimize supply chains under disruption and demand uncertainty. A four-tier supply chain network is used as a directed graph with nodes representing supply chain entities and arcs representing the transportation system. The model was a two-stage stochastic optimization, aimed at minimizing costs while considering alternative sourcing, inventory levels, capacity flexibility, and demand uncertainty. The stochastic model was compared with a deterministic model using metrics such as total cost, service level, and cost of production. The results showed that the stochastic model made better decisions, achieved higher service levels, and reduced total costs in the long run. The model was also used in a rolling horizon framework, and the recommended actions for certain demand periods reduced costs and increased service levels. Future directions include exploring ways to model policies that incorporate risk averseness.

**Keywords**: Supply chain disruption, stochastic programming, rolling horizon

## 1. Introduction and Literature Review

The global supply chain network has experienced unprecedented challenges in recent times, such as the COVID-19 pandemic, geopolitical tensions, and economic uncertainties, leading to substantial disruptions. The ramifications of these disruptions on supply chain operations are widespread, affecting various industries and economies, with a majority of Fortune 1000 companies reporting significant supply chain disruptions (Supply Chain Disruption & How to Respond | Accenture, 2022). These disruptions not only result in revenue loss, but also a tarnished reputation, potentially causing customer loss to competitors (Ivanov et al., 2017; Shekarian and Mellat Parast, 2021). Enterprises are struggling with the management of these disruptions while also preparing for future recovery.

Supply chain disruptions and operational uncertainty present significant obstacles in enterprises' operations. These disruptions stem from unplanned, unexpected events such as man-made or natural disasters, disrupting the existing supply chain network topology (Badejo and Ierapetritou, 2022; Dolgui and Ivanov, 2021). Operational uncertainty is characterized by unpredictability in demand, supply, and other operational variables, hindering organizations' ability to make accurate forecasts and leading to inefficiencies. The operational uncertainty is well addressed in the literature (Bhosekar et al., 2021; Charitopoulos et al., 2018; Guillén-Gosálbez and Grossmann, 2009). The coexistence of supply chain disruptions and operational uncertainty presents a challenging situation for enterprises in managing their supply chains effectively. While previous studies have explored these uncertainties independently, the interaction between them has not been well studied. To address these challenges, this paper proposes a stochastic optimization framework for supply chain management, aiming at simultaneously mitigating the impact of disruptions and reducing the effects of operational uncertainty.

## 2. Methodology

### 2.1. Problem Description and Assumptions

The following assumptions were made regarding the disruptions and operational uncertainties. Known distributions were assumed for operational parameters, with a normal distribution for demand uncertainty and a uniform distribution for the cost parameters. Supply chain entities have two states: normal and disrupted, with normal entities functional and disrupted ones not.

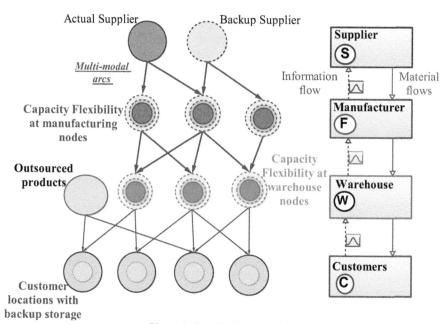

Figure 1: Supply chain topology

The problem considers a multi-products customer-driven supply chain network. This network produces a variety of products to meet the needs of different customer zones. The supply chain network consists of four echelons: supplier nodes $s$, manufacturing facilities $f$, warehouses $w$, and customer zones $c$ as shown in Figure *1*. A discrete time representation of the time horizon is considered. Raw material ordering, product manufacturing, storage, and shipping are executed to fulfill customer demand with unsatisfied demand resulting in lost sales and backorder penalty cost. The supply chain entities are vulnerable to disruptions, but buffer mechanisms are employed to mitigate their impact. The optimization problem aims to balance customer service level and minimize operating cost in a tactical supply chain problem under demand uncertainty and disruptions.

### 2.2. Mathematical Formulation

The objective of the problem is to minimize the total cost associated with the supply chain operations through optimization of raw materials and product flows across the network, subject to constraints on the capacities of the nodes and arcs, continuity balance and demand satisfactions. This is shown in equation (1), where the cost associated with the operations at each node includes the cost of normal operations, as well as recovery costs in case of disruptions. The cost of flow across the arcs is captured by the multi-modal transportation options, each incurring a different cost.

$$\min\{\, \mathbb{E}(nodeCost(\theta) + arcCost(\theta))\,\} \tag{1}$$

The constraints are augmented by incorporating integer variables to account for supplier selection, facility capacity utilization during disruptions, as expressed in equations (2a) to (2e).

$$y_{n,t}^l - y_{n',t}^l \geq 0 \quad \forall\, n \in \{S_a^n, W_a^n\}\,;\, n' \in S_{\hat{b}} \tag{2a}$$

$$y_{n,t}^l - y_{n,t}^{l'} \geq 0 \quad \forall\, l < l',\, n \in \{w, f\},\, t \in T \tag{2b}$$

$$y_{nt}^{l=1} := \begin{cases} 1 & \forall\, n \in (w, f)\,|\, n \in N_a^n,\, t \in T \\ 0 & \forall\, n \in (w, f)\,|\, n \in N_a^d,\, t \in T,\, t < t_R \end{cases} \tag{2c}$$

$$\sum_{\substack{i\in\{r,p\}\\ n',m}} Q_{i,n,n',m,t}(\theta) \leq \sum_l y_{n,t}^l \times cap_{n^l}$$

$$\forall\, n \in (s, f);\, t \in T\,;\, (n, n') \in \{(s, f), (f, w)\} \tag{2d}$$

$$\sum_{i\in\{r,p\}} Q_{i,n,n',m,t}(\theta) \leq x_{m,t}^{n,n'} \times tCap_m^{n,n'}$$

$$\forall\, (n, n') \in \{(s, f), (f, w), (w, c)\} \tag{2e}$$

The precedence constraints are established by Equations (2a) to (2c) where the binary variables $y_{n,t}^l$ indicate the operation of capacity level $l$ at node $n$ in time period $t$. Equation (2a) determines the priority of regular nodes $n$ over backup nodes $n'$, and equation (2b) and (2c) outlines the ordered selection of capacity levels. Once the capacity level is determined, equation (2d) assigns the corresponding activity level. Additionally, $Q_{(i,n,n',m,t)}(\theta)$ which represents the flow of commodity $i$ from through arc connecting nodes $n$ and $n'$ is bounded to the capacity constraints of the transportation modes, as expressed in Equation (2e).

At the warehouse nodes, constraints (3a) – (3b) for inventory management are used. Equation (3a) shows that the minimum inventory level is proportional to the standard deviation of the products and replenishment lead time, while equation (3b) limits the lower bound of the inventory to the safety stock. This equation assumes independent and identically distributed product demand (Brunaud et al., 2019). The cumulative normal distribution coefficient, $z$, is used to determine the required service level. In this study, a service level of 95% was assumed with a value of 1.65 for $z$.

$$I_{i,n,t}^{ss} = z \times \sqrt{L \times \sigma_p} \qquad \forall\, i \in p\,;\, n \in w \in W_{\{a\}}^n\,;\, t \in T \tag{3a}$$

$$I_{i,n,t}(\theta) \geq I_{i,n,t}^{ss} \qquad \forall\, i \in p\,;\, n \in w \in W_{\{a\}}^n\,;\, t \in T \tag{3b}$$

The proposed model adopts a multi-period mixed integer linear programming (MILP) formulation. The product demands are characterized by a temporal discretization, with a segment of certain demands and a segment forecasted from a distribution described by parameter θ. A two-stage stochastic model is adopted, as shown in equation (4): the first stage decisions $x$, represents the decisions at the time where information is certain and include the node configuration, the flow between the nodes to satisfy the product demands, and the inventory level at the warehouse to hedge against future demand variability, while in the second stage decisions $y(\theta)$ are adjusted with respect to the uncertainty realized. These decisions include the flow across adjacent nodes for all possible scenarios of the uncertain period, and the inventory policies to be adopted for all scenarios.

$$\min\left\{c^T x + \mathbb{E}[d^T y(\theta)] \left| \begin{array}{c} \mathbb{C}_i\big(x, y(\theta), p(\theta)\big) \leq 0 \\ x, y(\theta) \in \mathbb{X} \\ x \in \{\mathbb{R}_+ \times \mathbb{Z}\}, y(\theta) \in \mathbb{R} \end{array}\right.\right\} \tag{4}$$

To compare with a deterministic model, the expected value of the uncertain demands is used as value for the uncertain period. Thus, the deterministic formulation is shown in Equation (5). In this case we have decisions across time periods but implement only the decisions in the certain time segment.

$$\min\left\{c^T x \left| \begin{array}{c} \mathbb{C}_i(x, \mathbb{E}[p(\theta)]) \leq 0 \\ x \in \mathbb{X} \\ x \in \{\mathbb{R}_+ \times \mathbb{Z}\} \end{array}\right.\right\} \tag{5}$$

To address the dynamic and uncertain nature of supply chain operations, it employs a rolling horizon optimization approach. This approach involves solving the problem iteratively over multiple periods, with only the first stage being implemented. The model leverages the current state of the supply chain, including inventory levels and capacity utilization, as an initial condition for updating the solution in response to new information.

## 3. Results and Discussion

In this section a four-echelon supply chain with three products manufactured using two raw materials and six available suppliers (four actual and two backup) is studied. The enterprise operates four manufacturing facilities, two warehouses and supplies to five customer zones. Additionally, there is capacity for product storage at the customer locations. A monthly demand forecast with known demand for one month and forecasting for the next four is made to hedge against uncertainty. The goal is to minimize the total supply chain operation cost for a given period, including optimal tactical decisions during disruptions. In this case the disruptions considered are the breakdown of some arcs and the disrupted manufacturing facility. Decisions made include flow of materials between nodes, production amount, inventory, product delivery, outsourcing, and unmet demand.

Table 1: Metrics to compare the deterministic and stochastic solution.

| Metrics | Deterministic | Stochastic |
|---|---|---|
| Total Cost [$] | 200,498 | 235,659 |
| Implemented Cost [$] | 34,696.1 | 31,215.4 |
| Service Level | 80% | 98.7% |
| Cost Per Period [$/unit] | 65.60 | 47.84 |
| SC Efficiency | 71% | 89.65% |

The proposed model was evaluated on a PC with Intel Core i7-10510U, 2.30 GHz, and 16GB of RAM. The results of the two-stage model, which considers the disruptions and operational uncertainty, were compared to the deterministic model. 20 demand scenarios were sampled for each product over 5 time periods, with the first period being certain. The deterministic model utilized the expected values of the scenarios, while the two-stage model considered all scenarios. Both models were solved in GAMS/CPLEX (v 38.2.1).

The deterministic model had 6851 constraints, 8809 continuous variables, and 2262 binary variables, while the two-stage model had 63,781 constraints, 67,139 continuous variables, and 2262 discrete variables. The deterministic model was solved in 25s, and the two-stage model took 260s.

Comparative analysis between the two-stage stochastic model and deterministic model is presented in Table 1, where the total cost and implemented cost for the two-stage model are higher. This results in a higher service level and supply chain efficiency due to integer decisions for node and arc selection and utilization as shown in Figure 2 and Figure 3, respectively.

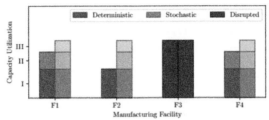

Figure 2: Manufacturing site capacity selections.

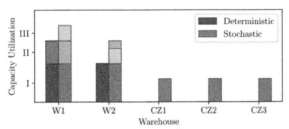

Figure 3: Warehouse capacity selections.

Table 2 provides the breakdown of implemented cost. The results from the stochastic model indicate a preference for higher utilization of manufacturing sites and warehouses, compared to the deterministic model, in order to minimize costs associated with node operations and uncertainty mitigation. This is evident from the higher values for service level and supply chain efficiency in the stochastic model. Conversely, the deterministic model optimizes only for certain demands and the average of all scenarios, resulting in increased backorder costs.

*Table 2: Breakdown of implemented cost for the deterministic and two-stage stochastic model.*

|  | Implemented Cost [$] | | |
|---|---|---|---|
|  | *Deterministic* | *Stochastic* | *Difference* |
| **Supplier Cost** | 1,763.49 | 2,664.03 | 900.54 |
| **Facility** | 10,989.70 | 16,287.30 | 5,297.60 |
| **Outsourcing** | 3,222.08 | 3,222.08 | 0 |
| **Inventory** | 228.44 | 1,044.47 | 816.03 |
| **Transportation** | 4,612.30 | 7,079.21 | 2466.91 |
| **Backorder cost** | 13,880.10 | 918.37 | -12,961.73 |

## 4. Conclusions

In this study, a resilient supply chain network model is presented that considers both supply chain disruptions and operational uncertainty. The objective is to minimize the total cost of the supply chain while ensuring demand fulfillment. A deterministic multi-period model and a two-stage stochastic model are compared, and the results indicate that the stochastic model performs better in terms of service level and decision-making for uncertainty. The rolling horizon approach is used to evaluate the spatial-temporal decisions made by both models and the results show that the stochastic model has better performance. However, incorporating risk measures into the stochastic model can provide risk-averse decisions and this will be explored in future work.

## 5. Acknowledgements

The authors are grateful for the financial support provided by the National Science Foundation through awards 2134471, OIA-2119754, and 2217472. These grants have greatly contributed to the successful completion of the research project.

## References

Badejo O, Ierapetritou M. Mathematical Programming Approach to Optimize Tactical and Operational Supply Chain Decisions under Disruptions. Ind Eng Chem Res 2022. https://doi.org/10.1021/acs.iecr.2c01641.

Bhosekar A, Badejo O, Ierapetritou M. Modular supply chain optimization considering demand uncertainty to manage risk. AIChE Journal 2021;n/a:e17367. https://doi.org/10.1002/aic.17367.

Brunaud B, Laínez-Aguirre JM, Pinto JM, Grossmann IE. Inventory policies and safety stock optimization for supply chain planning. AIChE Journal 2019;65:99–112. https://doi.org/10.1002/aic.16421.

Charitopoulos VM, Aguirre AM, Papageorgiou LG, Dua V. Uncertainty aware integration of planning, scheduling and multi-parametric control. In: Eden MR, Ierapetritou MG, Towler GP, editors. Computer Aided Chemical Engineering, vol. 44, Elsevier; 2018, p. 1171–6. https://doi.org/10.1016/B978-0-444-64241-7.50190-7.

Dolgui A, Ivanov D. Ripple effect and supply chain disruption management: new trends and research directions. International Journal of Production Research 2021;59:102–9. https://doi.org/10.1080/00207543.2021.1840148.

Guillén-Gosálbez G, Grossmann IE. Optimal design and planning of sustainable chemical supply chains under uncertainty. AIChE Journal 2009;55:99–121. https://doi.org/10.1002/aic.11662.

Ivanov D, Dolgui A, Sokolov B, Ivanova M. Literature review on disruption recovery in the supply chain. International Journal of Production Research 2017;55:6158–74. https://doi.org/10.1080/00207543.2017.1330572.

Shekarian M, Mellat Parast M. An Integrative approach to supply chain disruption risk and resilience management: a literature review. International Journal of Logistics Research and Applications 2021;24:427–55. https://doi.org/10.1080/13675567.2020.1763935.

Supply Chain Disruption & How to Respond | Accenture. 2022. https://www.accenture.com/us-en/insights/consulting/coronavirus-supply-chain-disruption (accessed February 6, 2023).

Antonis Kokossis, Michael C. Georgiadis, Efstratios N. Pistikopoulos (Eds.)
PROCEEDINGS OF THE 33rd European Symposium on Computer Aided Process Engineering
(ESCAPE33), June 18-21, 2023, Athens, Greece

# Integrating economic, environmental, and social concerns into the design and planning of supply chains using monetization strategies

Cátia da Silva[a*], Ana Paula Barbosa-Póvoa[a], Ana Carvalho[a]

[a]*CEG-IST, Instituto Superior Técnico, University of Lisbon, Av. Rovisco Pais, 1049-001 Lisboa, Portugal*

*catia.silva@tecnico.ulisboa.pt*

## Abstract

The growing concerns with sustainable aspects have influenced supply chain decision-makers to incorporate them into their efficient management. Thus, the decision-making process, which is traditionally based on economic profit, today also aims to take into account the environmental and social impacts of the supply chain so that decision-making is completer and more efficient, although complex. This work contributes to help decision-makers to take an informed decision and develops a decision support tool based on a mixed integer linear programming (MILP) model for the design and planning of supply chain that accounts for economic, environmental, and social performances in the same monetary unit. Environmental performance is considered in monetary units using the life cycle assessment methodology by applying the Environmental Priorities Strategies (EPS) as the life cycle assessment method. Social performance is measured through a social monetization approach based on job creation indicator (translated into a monetary units). In addition, this paper accounts for uncertainty in products' demand. Conclusions are drawn on how monetization can be a useful tool to support decision-making process and support supply chain's sustainable performances. A real-based case study is solved showing the applicability of the tool.

**Keywords:** sustainable supply chain, sustainability, monetization, uncertainty

## 1. Introduction

Sustainability is a relevant topic in today's world, having gradually grown in recent years. For this reason, supply chain management has also started to consider sustainability as a relevant aspect and a reason that allows supply chains to be competitive in the market. In this way, the supply chain previous focus on economic performance was expanded to include environmental and social performances. In fact, the importance of the overall supply chain performance reflects all three pillars of sustainability, namely the economic, environmental, and social pillars. Moreover, scientific papers and academic research increasingly highlight the need to answer to both environmental and social challenges combined with an improvement in the economic performance (Barbosa-Póvoa, da Silva, and Carvalho 2018). However, efficient supply chain management is not an easy task as supply chains are complex systems, and its complexity increases when the three performances are taken into account. Additionally, the evaluation of these performances can be challenging, particularly when considering both environmental and social pillars. Economic performance is known for years as several authors intend to quantify it using optimization models to reduce costs and improve financial profits. However, the quantification of environmental and social performances is yet difficult, as there are different valuation methods to assess them, and they are usually expressed in abstract units that are hard to understand by decision-makers. Thus, it can be important to realize how environmental and social supply chains' performances can be assessed and they can be translated in monetary units easily understood by decision-makers (Beske-Janssen, Johnson, and Schaltegger 2015).

## 2. Environmental and social monetization methodologies

Regarding environmental performance, life cycle assessment (LCA) has been considered the best methodology to assess environmental impacts related to a specific product or process (European Commission, 2013). This methodology includes four main steps: goal and scope definition, inventory analysis, life cycle impact assessment (LCIA), and life cycle interpretation. The most critical phase is LCIA, where decision-makers can assign weighting factors for objectives, which leads to subjectivity in results. In addition, there are several different LCIA methods that can be chosen to assess environmental impacts, particularly monetary and non-monetary methods. Monetary methods are the ones that can translate environmental impacts into monetary units, while others convert impacts into abstract or dimensionless units. In this work, Environmental Priorities Strategies (EPS) is the LCIA method chosen to convert impacts into monetary units.

There are several social indicators within the literature (Popovic et al., 2018), which are usually represented in non-monetary units (dimensionless units). Considering the need to better understand social impacts, this work intends to convert job creation indicator in monetary units so as decision-makers can really understand the real value of supply chains' social performance. To convert social indicators into monetary units, a correlation between economic indicators and supply chain variables is developed.

## 3. Problem description and model characterization

This study considers the design and planning of a sustainable supply chain, which is generically represented in Figure 1. The main flows are as follows: i) raw materials flow from suppliers to factories; ii) final products go from factories to warehouses or directly to markets; iii) end-of-life products can be recovered from the markets and sent to warehouses or directly to factories to be reprocessed. All these flows are guaranteed by road, air, or sea transport. Given: i) a possible set of entity locations; ii) production and remanufacturing technologies; iii) possible transport modes between entities; and iv) SC's products. The objective is to obtain: i) the structure of the SC network; ii) supply and purchase levels; iii) the capacities of the entities; iv) the transport network; v) production, remanufacturing, and storage levels; and vi) supply flows and the recovery levels of the materials. In order to: maximize profit, maximize social impact and minimize environmental impacts while guaranteeing the establish minimum market requirements.

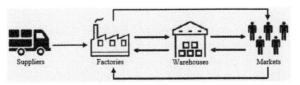

Figure 1. Scheme of SC network

To solve the problem on hands it is used a MILP model based on da Silva et al. (2020). The model was extended to consider the impact of supply chain social performance. The economic, social, and environmental performances are considered independently and simultaneously in the objective function. The economic objective is obtained through Eq. (1) that maximizes the Net Present Value (NPV), which considers the discounted cash flows (CF) in each period at a given interest rate. For the last time period, it is also considered the salvage values of the SC ($FCI\gamma$). The environmental impact is obtained using the EPS method. LCA is performed on the transportation activities and on entities installed in the SC boundaries. The Life Cycle Inventory is retrieved from the Ecoinvent database (assessed through SimaPro 9.4.0 software). From these results, it is determined the environmental impact of transportation and entities installation. The result values for transportation are used as input data in the first term of Eq. (2), while the values for entities installation are used in the second term. Moreover, considering that the focus of European Commission is to bet on promoting job creation and regional development, the social performance based on that is represented by Eq. (3). The monetarized social impact of job creation is obtained through the relationship between a macroeconomic indicator (i.e., GDP per capita) and the microeconomic variable (i.e., number of employees). The promotion of jobs in regions with higher unemployment rate, $\lambda_n$ is also taken into account. Finally, Eq. (4) reflects the objective function that is obtained through maximization of the equilibrium between economic (NPV), environmental (EnvImpact) and social (SocImpact) impacts.

$$max\,N\,PV = \sum_{t\in T}\frac{CF_t}{(1+ir)^t} - \sum_{\gamma} FCI_{\gamma} \tag{1}$$

$$min\,EnvImpact = \sum_{\substack{t\in T \\ (a,m,i,j)\in NetP}} ei_{ac}pw_m d_{ij}X_{maijt} + \sum_{i\in I_f\cup I_w} ei_{ic}YC_i \tag{2}$$

$$max\,SocImpact = \sum_{\substack{t\in T \\ n\in N \\ m\in M}} \frac{GDP_n^{pc}.NEmployees_{nmct}.\,\lambda_n}{(1+intr)^t} \tag{3}$$

$$maxNPV - EnvImpact + SocImpact \tag{4}$$

## 4. Case study

The model is applied to a chemical components' company located in Lyon, France (Silva et.al., 2020). The main suppliers are also placed in Lyon. The company supplies three markets that are located in different countries: Portugal, France, and Germany. France is the market that owns the highest percentage of company's sales, followed by Germany, and finally Portugal. Considering the willingness of the company's decision makers that want to expand its supply chain to three new markets (Ireland, Spain, and Canada), the company wants to know what changes could result from this expansion in financial terms. Currently, transportation is only performed by road mode. However, with the expansion there is the need of combining road transportation with air and sea transportation. Regarding company's portfolio, it sells three different types of chemical products (fp1, fp2, fp3) that can be sold within the chemical industry and to other industries. In the current production, three technologies (pr1, pr2, pr3) are used that produce respectively products fp1, fp2, and fp3. Furthermore, end-of-life products can be recovered and remanufactured into final products. This work accounts for product's demand uncertainty through a scenario tree approach.

## 5. Results

In this work first the objective functions were studied individually, that is, the different performances of the supply chain are studied separately. Then, the three performances are studied in the same objective function in order to perceive the different trade-offs between the three pillars of sustainability. Thus, the cases analysed are: i) Case A - represents the optimal economic performance; ii) Case B - represents the optimal social performance; iii) Case C - represents the optimal environmental performance; iv) Case D - represents the optimal equity between social, environmental, and economic performances. From the analysis of these cases, the obtained values are stated in Table 1.

Table 1 Outcomes for the economic, social, and environmental impacts.

| | Case A | Case B | Case C | Case D |
|---|---|---|---|---|
| Obj. Function | Max eNPV | Max eSocImpact | Min eEnvImpact | Max (eNPV+eSocImpact-eEnvImpact) |
| eNPV | $1.563 \times 10^9$ € | $1.486 \times 10^9$ € | $1.199 \times 10^9$ € | $1.512 \times 10^9$ € |
| eSocImpact | $0.571 \times 10^8$ € | $1.415 \times 10^8$ € | $0.710 \times 10^8$ € | $0.856 \times 10^8$ € |
| eEnvImpact | $1.024 \times 10^9$ € | $1.132 \times 10^9$ € | $9.446 \times 10^8$ € | $9.798 \times 10^8$ € |

Analyzing the obtained results, it is possible to verify that case A denotes the highest value of eNPV ($1.56 \times 10^9$ €) since its objective function is maximized. On the other hand, case B returns the highest value of eSocImpact ($1.42 \times 10^8$ €) because in this case the social component is maximized. Case C that considers the minimization of the environmental impact has the lowest value of eEnvImpact which corresponds to $9.45 \times 10^8$ €. Finally, in case D, where the three performances are considered in the same objective function a trade-off between the three goals was obtained. The network obtained in this case results from the trade-off between i) transport, production, and installation costs; ii) environmental impact of the transport and installation of entities; and iii) social impact of job creation. On the economic approach the global profit decrease of 5 million euros is observed when comparing to case A. On the environmental impact this has also decreased by around 45 million euros. For the social performance the value achieved between the values of cases A and B. Finally, it is possible to verify that the overall profit improved by more than 310 million euros between cases C and D, while the impact of the environment is worse at nearly 35 million. The resulting supply chain network structure for case D is described in Table 2. It can be seen that a new factory is needed in addition to the existing factory. In addition, there is a need to open new warehouses in order to increase the overall existing capacity. It is also possible to observe that all factories are supplied by all suppliers, which results from the balance between economic and environmental costs. In terms of intermodal transport, air transport is not used, only sea transport is used.

Table 2 Supply chain network structure for case D

| Allocation of suppliers | | All suppliers supply all factories |
|---|---|---|
| Factories | | Existing one plus Galway |
| Warehouses | | Existing one plus Galway and Bremen |
| Production | | Most production of fp1 is in the existing factory |
| | | Most production of fp2 is shared between factories |
| | | Most production of fp3 is in the new factories |
| Remanufacture | | Most of rp1 is in the existing facility |
| | | rp2 is only performed in the existing facility |
| | | Most of rp3 is in the existing facility |
| Recovered products | | Minimum possible |
| Technologies | | Alternative technologies are preferred in the new factories |
| Inventory | fp1 | Divided between all warehouses |
| | fp2 | 60% in Lyon, 25% in Galway, and 15% in Bremen |
| | fp3 | 25% in Lyon, 55% in Galway, and 20% in Bremen |
| Transportation | Road | 12 trucks |
| | Air | Not adopted |
| | Sea | Adopted |

## 6. Conclusions

This paper allows us to understand the importance of monetization in helping to understand the overall performances of the supply chain. Considering that this work includes the three pillars of sustainability, the process of monetization allows to convert both environmental and social performances into monetary units, which can be particularly useful for decision-makers that are used to deal with money when managing their supply chain. Such option permits to obtain in an easier form solution where a trade-off between the three sustainability goals is obtained.

Further research should be done on this topic to develop monetization methods to be a trustworthy alternative for multi-objective optimization approaches. Also, an extension of this work should account for other uncertainty sources.

## 7. Acknowledgements

This work is financed by national funds through the FCT-Foundation for Science and Technology, I.P., under the project UIDB/00097/2020.

## References

A. Barbosa-Póvoa, C. da Silva, and A. Carvalho. 2018. "Opportunities and Challenges in Sustainable Supply Chain: An Operations Research Perspective." *European Journal of Operational Research* 268 (2): 399–431. https://doi.org/10.1016/J.EJOR.2017.10.036.

C. da Silva, Ana Barbosa-Póvoa, and Ana Carvalho. 2020. "Environmental Monetization and Risk Assessment in Supply Chain Design and Planning." Journal of Cleaner Production 270 (October): 121552.

P. Beske-Janssen, Matthew Phillip Johnson, and Stefan Schaltegger. 2015. "20 Years of Performance Measurement in Sustainable Supply Chain Management – What Has Been Achieved?" *Supply Chain Management: An International Journal* 20 (6): 664–80. https://doi.org/10.1108/SCM-06-2015-0216.

European Commission. 2013. "Commission Recommendation of 9 April 2013 on the Use of Common Methods to Measure and Communicate the Life Cycle Environmental Performance of Products and Organisations."

T. Popovic, Ana P. Barbosa-Póvoa, Andrzej Kraslawski, and Ana Carvalho. 2018. "Quantitative Indicators for Social Sustainability Assessment of Supply Chains." Journal of Cleaner Production 180 (April): 748–68. https://doi.org/10.1016/j.jclepro.2018.01.142.

Antonis Kokossis, Michael C. Georgiadis, Efstratios N. Pistikopoulos (Eds.)
PROCEEDINGS OF THE 33rd European Symposium on Computer Aided Process Engineering
(ESCAPE33), June 18-21, 2023, Athens, Greece

# Strategic low-carbon hydrogen supply chain planning under market price uncertainty

Tushar Rathi[a], Jose M. Pinto[b], Qi Zhang*[a]

*a*Department of Chemical Engineering and Materials Science, University of Minnesota, Minneapolis, MN 55455, USA
*b*Linde Digital Americas, Linde plc, Danbury, CT 06810, USA
*qizh@umn.edu

## Abstract

With the increased emphasis on decarbonization in recent years, there is a growing interest in the development of sustainable industrial supply chains. With its widespread applications, clean hydrogen holds immense potential to push forward the goal of a net-zero economy. For this reason, we develop mathematical models to optimize the design and planning of low-carbon hydrogen supply chains, specifically when the potential markets are willing to pay certain premiums for hydrogen of different levels of carbon intensity. We introduce the concept of a hydrogen supply chain with virtual distribution of carbon intensities, which allows more cost-effective supply chain operations compared with the conventional model in which different carbon intensities associated with a product can only be achieved through physical blending. Additionally, owing to the difficulty in predicting future hydrogen prices, we propose a multistage stochastic programming framework to account for uncertainty in market prices. The proposed model is applied to a network of hydrogen production plants and potential markets, highlighting differences in decisions across different scenarios.

**Keywords**: hydrogen-based economy, virtual supply chain, mixed-integer nonlinear programming, nonconvex optimization, multistage stochastic programming

## 1. Introduction

Clean hydrogen is expected to play an important role in the decarbonization of multiple sectors, including energy, transportation, chemicals, and agriculture. This presents a major opportunity for hydrogen producers; however, hydrogen supply chain planning (Li et al., 2019; Zhang and Pinto, 2022) is a challenging problem as future demands and prices are difficult to predict. Also, with growing awareness of global environmental issues, we see an increasing number of organizations pledging to invest in decarbonization initiatives and meet sustainability goals. Over the next few years, we expect hydrogen markets to follow suit with a greater appetite for low-carbon hydrogen. However, the prices offered in different markets may vary substantially depending on the consumers' budgets, demands, and preferences. Additionally, we assume the price offered in each market to be a function of the "grade" of the low-carbon hydrogen requested, which corresponds to the carbon intensity of the hydrogen in the supplied batch. For example, 60%-grade hydrogen is equivalent to hydrogen that is composed of 60% hydrogen produced with zero carbon emissions and 40% conventionally produced hydrogen. To achieve a certain hydrogen grade, one may have to blend the hydrogen from different production facilities that exhibit different carbon intensities. Alternatively, since the chemical properties of the final product, namely hydrogen, do not depend on its grade (per our definition), one could also assign the grades virtually based on a global accounting of the carbon emissions, which may significantly reduce the need of physically transporting and blending the hydrogen. In this work, we explore the potential benefits of the latter approach over the former in the planning of a future low-carbon hydrogen supply chain over multiple years.

The proposed notion of a "virtual" hydrogen supply chain is inspired by the concept of renewable energy credits (RECs), which are certificates that represent proof that a given amount of electricity was generated from a renewable energy source (Berry, 2002). RECs can be traded and used by the buyers to offset their carbon emissions. As such, RECs allow renewable energy generated at one location to be counted toward the reduction in carbon intensity at a different location. This is analogous to the clean hydrogen produced at one location but virtually assigned to another location in our approach.

The prices offered in different markets will depend on, among other factors, the willingness of the consumers to pay a premium for clean hydrogen, which is not only highly uncertain but will likely change over time. Hence, we also extend the model to a multistage stochastic programming formulation (Ruszczyński and Shapiro, 2003) that effectively accounts for uncertainty in future market prices. We analyze the resulting investment strategies and draw initial insights via a case study involving a small network of hydrogen production plants and potential markets.

## 2. Mathematical formulation

We consider a network consisting of a set of hydrogen production plants $I$ and a set of potential buyers (markets) $J$. A hydrogen plant $i$ has initial production capacity $\overline{C}_{io}$ and can produce hydrogen of a fixed grade, $\lambda_i$, which can vary from 0% (gray hydrogen) to 100% (green hydrogen). Additionally, a plant $i$ has $|\mathcal{K}_i|$ permissible expansion points, with the difference between two consecutive expansion points $k$ and $k-1$ defined by the parameter $\overline{\Delta}_{ik}$. We consider a planning horizon $\mathcal{T}$, and a potential market $j$ is assumed to have a maximum demand $d_{jt}^{\max}$ in time period $t \in \mathcal{T}$. Importantly, a market $j$ offers different prices for different grades of hydrogen, which is captured by function $f_{jt}(c_{jt})$, where $c_{jt}$ is the grade of hydrogen promised to (requested by) market $j$ in time period $t$. The goal is then to determine the optimal capacity expansion and supply chain decisions to maximize the overall profit during the planning horizon. In the subsequent subsections, we discuss hydrogen supply chain optimization models with different characteristics.

### 2.1. Basic supply chain model

We first present a basic supply chain (BSC) model formulated as the following nonconvex mixed-integer nonlinear program (MINLP):

$$\underset{x,d,c,F,C,\Delta}{\text{maximize}} \sum_{t \in \mathcal{T}} \alpha_t \Big[ \sum_{i \in I} \sum_{j \in J} f_{jt}(c_{jt}) F_{ijt} - \sum_{i \in I} \sum_{k \in \mathcal{K}_i} q_{ikt} \overline{\Delta}_{ik} x_{ikt} -$$

$$\sum_{i \in I} \sum_{j \in J} r_{ij} F_{ijt} - \sum_{i \in I} b_{it} \sum_{j \in J} F_{ijt} \Big]$$

$$\text{subject to } C_{i0} = \overline{C}_{i0} \quad \forall\, i \in I \tag{1}$$

$$C_{it} = C_{i,t-1} + \Delta_{it} \quad \forall\, i \in I, t \in \mathcal{T} \tag{2}$$

$$\Delta_{it} = \sum_{k \in \mathcal{K}_i} x_{ikt} \overline{\Delta}_{ik} \quad \forall\, i \in I, t \in \mathcal{T} \tag{3}$$

$$x_{ikt} \le \sum_{\tau=1}^{t} x_{i,k-1,\tau} \quad \forall\, i \in I, k \in \mathcal{K}_i \backslash \{1\}, t \in \mathcal{T} \tag{4}$$

$$\sum_{\tau=1}^{t} x_{ik\tau} \le 1 \quad \forall\, i \in I, k \in \mathcal{K}_i, t \in \mathcal{T} \tag{5}$$

$$\sum_{j \in J} F_{ijt} \le C_{it} \quad \forall\, i \in I, t \in \mathcal{T} \tag{6}$$

$$\sum_{i \in I} F_{ijt} = d_{jt} \quad \forall j \in \mathcal{J}, t \in \mathcal{T} \tag{7}$$

$$\sum_{i \in I} \lambda_i F_{ijt} = c_{jt} d_{jt} \quad \forall j \in \mathcal{J}, t \in \mathcal{T} \tag{8}$$

$$0 \leq d_{jt} \leq d_{jt}^{\max} \quad \forall j \in \mathcal{J}, t \in \mathcal{T} \tag{9}$$

$$0 \leq c_{jt} \leq 1 \quad \forall j \in \mathcal{J}, t \in \mathcal{T} \tag{10}$$

$$F_{ijt} \geq 0 \quad \forall i \in I, j \in \mathcal{J}, t \in \mathcal{T} \tag{11}$$

$$C_{it}, \Delta_{it} \geq 0 \quad \forall i \in I, t \in \mathcal{T} \tag{12}$$

$$x_{ikt} \in \{0,1\} \quad \forall i \in \mathcal{J}, k \in \mathcal{K}_i, t \in \mathcal{T}, \tag{13}$$

where the binary variable $x_{ikt}$ equals 1 if the capacity of plant $i$ is increased to at least point $k$ in time period $t$. The capacity increase and the total capacity of plant $i$ in time period $t$ are denoted by $\Delta_{it}$ and $C_{it}$, respectively. The amount of hydrogen transported from plant $i$ to market $j$ in time period $t$ is denoted by $F_{ijt}$, whereas the net demand satisfied at market $j$ in time period $t$ is captured by variable $d_{jt}$. The grade of hydrogen for which a market $j$ eventually makes the payment in time period $t$ is denoted by $c_{jt}$. The cost coefficient $q_{ikt}$ is associated with the unit expansion for plant $i$ from point $k - 1$ to $k$ in time period $t$, $r_{ij}$ is the unit transportation cost between plant $i$ and market $j$, and the unit production cost for plant $i$ in time period $t$ is represented by coefficient $b_{it}$. The capacity constraints are adopted from our previous work (Rathi and Zhang, 2022), where constraints (1)-(3) represent the capacity balance. Constraints (4) ensure that to increase the capacity to point $k$, we must have already increased the capacity to $k - 1$ in the current or one of the preceding time periods. Constraints (5) state that the capacity cannot be increased to point $k$ more than once in any time period $t$. Constraints (6) ensure that production must not exceed the capacity, and constraints (7) enforce the usual demand satisfaction condition for each market. Equations (8) are the blending constraints. Lastly, constraints (9)-(13) enforce bounds on the decision variables. With $\alpha_t$ as the discount factor in time period $t$, the objective is to maximize the overall profit resulting from a difference of revenue generated from supplying hydrogen and costs incurred from capacity expansion, transportation, and production.

## 2.2. Virtual supply chain model

We now present the model that allows virtual distribution of carbon intensities and hence indirect satisfaction of hydrogen grade, which we refer to as the virtual supply chain (VSC) model. Compared to the BSC model, it requires the following modifications:

$$\overline{F}_{it} = \sum_{j \in \mathcal{J}} F_{ijt} \quad \forall i \in I, t \in \mathcal{T} \tag{14}$$

$$\sum_{i \in I} \lambda_i \overline{F}_{it} = \sum_{j \in \mathcal{J}} c_{jt} d_{jt} \quad \forall t \in \mathcal{T} \tag{15}$$

$$\overline{F}_{it} \geq 0 \quad \forall i \in I, t \in \mathcal{T}, \tag{16}$$

where we introduce $\overline{F}_{it}$ to denote the net hydrogen production at plant $i$ in time period $t$. Constraints (14) represent flow distribution from plants to markets. Unlike in the BSC model, where we have a blending constraint for each market in each time period, here we only consider an overall blending constraint per time period represented by constraints (15). Hence, the VSC model is a variant of the BSC model with the same objective function, new decision variable $\overline{F}_{it}$, additional constraints (14) and (16), and constraints (8) replaced by (15).

## 2.3. Stochastic virtual supply chain model

To account for market price uncertainty in the VSC model, we first define a set of possible realizations for the price profile of market $j$ in time period $t$, $\Xi_{jt} := \{f_{jt}^m(c_{jt}): m =$

$1, 2, \ldots, M_{jt}\}$, where $m$ and $M_{jt}$ denote the index of a specific realization and the number of possible realizations, respectively. Then the set of all possible scenarios is $S = \times_{t \in \mathcal{T}} (\times_{j \in \mathcal{J}} \Xi_{jt})$. The following is a compact representation of the corresponding multistage stochastic virtual supply chain (SVSC) model:

$$\text{maximize } \mathbb{E}[Z^{\text{VSC}}]$$
$$\text{subject to } w_s \in \mathcal{W}_s^{\text{VSC}} \quad \forall s \in S$$
$$\text{NACs},$$

where $Z^{\text{VSC}}$, $w_s$, and $\mathcal{W}_s^{\text{VSC}}$ denote the objective function, the set of variables for scenario $s$, and the feasible set for scenario $s$, respectively. NACs represent the nonanticipativity constraints on binary variables $x$, ensuring that the same capacity expansion decisions are made for indistinguishable scenarios at different time points during the planning horizon.

## 3. Case study

We consider a network with three hydrogen plants with gray (0%-grade), blue (50%-grade), and green (100%-grade) hydrogen production capacities, respectively. Each plant has an initial installed capacity of 10 units. Further, the network has five hydrogen markets, with linear price profiles positively correlated with the hydrogen grade, i.e., $f_{jt}(c_{jt})$ is linear in $c_{jt}$ with a nonnegative slope. The assumption of linear price profiles transforms the model into a nonconvex mixed-integer quadratically-constrained quadratic program (MIQCQP). We consider a planning horizon with three time periods and a discount factor of 3%. All models were implemented using JuMP v1.4.0 in Julia v1.8.2 and were solved using Gurobi v9.5.2.

For the deterministic cases (BSC and VSC), the variation in premium offered for 100%-grade hydrogen by different markets across the planning horizon is shown in Figure 1. Note that we assume the price offered by all markets for 0%-grade hydrogen is the same across all time periods. Figure 1 further summarizes the solutions for the deterministic cases. The plants and markets are represented using square and circular nodes, respectively. The color coding used is as follows: (i) For plants, gray, blue, and green nodes indicate 0%-, 50%-, and 100%-grade hydrogen production, respectively. The size of a plant node corresponds to its current installed capacity. For clarity, we also mention the additional capacity installed for each plant in each time period next to each plant node, e.g., "+5" implies a 5-unit capacity increase. (ii) For markets, the node color indicates the grade of hydrogen requested, and the color shade indicates the relative proportion of clean hydrogen in the requested batch. For example, 20-45%-grade hydrogen has a lighter shade of gray compared to a darker shade for <20%-grade hydrogen. The regular blue and green shades represent 45-60%- and >85%-grade hydrogen, respectively.

One can observe the following key differences in the expansion and supply chain decisions between the BSC and VSC models: (i) In the BSC case, the grade of hydrogen requested and the grade of hydrogen supplied (which may require blending) match exactly, whereas in the VSC case, this is often not the case. Since the chemical properties of hydrogen are the same regardless of its grade, we do not need to exactly match the requested hydrogen grade at each market and only need to ensure that the net production of a particular grade matches its overall demand within the network. For example, because Market 1 pays the highest premium for 100%-grade hydrogen, we simply supply it the same from Plant 3 in the BSC case, whereas in the VSC case, we supply it gray hydrogen from Plant 1 instead, which is more cost-effective due to lower transportation cost, yet it pays for clean hydrogen. (ii) In the BSC case, the price offered by Market 5 for any grade of hydrogen is not sufficient to offset the production and transportation cost, resulting in no hydrogen supply at all times, whereas in the VSC case, the liberty to supply a different grade of hydrogen than the one requested (due to having the same chemical properties) allow us to supply hydrogen to Market 5. (iii) Unlike in the BSC case, we see more localized transportation in the VSC case, owing to the VSC model's emphasis on cost savings through lower transportation costs while maximizing profits through higher premiums offered by markets for low-carbon hydrogen. In particular, the net profit earned increased from \$504,926 in the BSC case to \$725,903 in the VSC case, a significant 43.8% increase. (iv) Finally, in the VSC case, we see greater investment in the capacity expansion of the gray hydrogen Plant 1 because Market 1, which pays the highest premium, is located in its proximity. Since the objective is to maximize profit, it may or may not support the expansion of clean hydrogen plants. Instead, determining whether VSC promotes or stifles the expansion of clean hydrogen plants necessitates a careful examination of relative plant and market locations, as well as the various logistics costs.

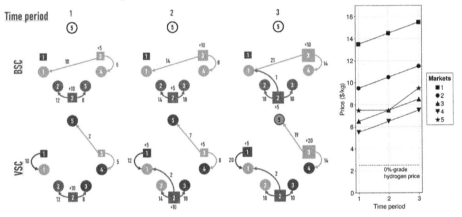

Figure 1: Illustrating differences in hydrogen supply chain decisions obtained via the BSC and VSC models. Plants and markets are represented by square and circular nodes, respectively. The color of the nodes represents the grade of hydrogen produced/requested at a plant/customer location. The numbers on the edges represent the flows; the size of a plant node represents its current production capacity. The number in red font next to a plant node represents the additional capacity installed. The plot on the right depicts the premiums offered by each market for 100%-grade hydrogen.

In the SVSC case, we consider eight equally probable scenarios with varying market prices across the planning horizon. To emphasize the importance of accounting for uncertainty in market price, we discuss differences in the decisions for two particular scenarios. The premium offered by different markets for 100%-grade hydrogen under the two scenarios and the corresponding solutions are shown in Figure 2. Scenarios 1 and 2 have very different price profiles, which significantly impact the grade of hydrogen requested by each market in each scenario. For example, in the first time period, Market 1 offers to pay the highest and lowest premium for 100%-grade hydrogen in Scenarios 1 and 2, respectively, which is reflected in the eventual decision of the grade requested in these scenarios. Similarly, in Scenario 2, Market 2 offers a significantly higher price for 100%-grade hydrogen than Scenario 1, making it more profitable to make it pay for green hydrogen. In addition to the transportation and production costs, different price profiles across scenarios affect the amount of hydrogen supplied by each plant, resulting in different capacity expansion decisions that satisfy the nonanticipativity conditions. For example, at the start of the planning horizon, both scenarios are indistinguishable; thus, the capacity expansion decisions made in each are identical, as illustrated in Figure 2.

Finally, we discover that a market's proximity to a hydrogen plant does not guarantee that its hydrogen demand will be met. For example, in the second time period of Scenario 1, Plant 3 has enough capacity to meet Market 4's maximum demand; however, the low price offered by Market 4 is insufficient to offset the transportation and high production costs. In the first time period, on the other hand, we see that Plant 3 does supply some hydrogen to Market 4, which was made possible by the high price offered for 100%-grade hydrogen by Markets 1 and 5, which helps offset the production and transportation costs.

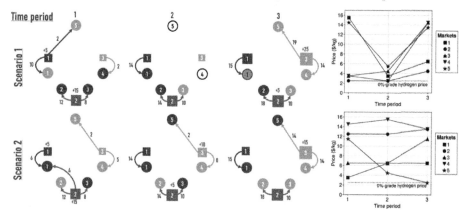

Figure 2: Illustrating differences in decisions between two particular scenarios, obtained by solving the SVSC model. The plots on the right depict the premiums offered by each market for 100%-grade hydrogen in the two scenarios.

## 4. Conclusions

In this work, we developed a multiperiod supply chain planning model for low-carbon hydrogen distribution, where each potential market offers a different price for different grades of hydrogen; here, a higher grade corresponds to hydrogen with a lower carbon intensity. The invariability in chemical properties of hydrogen with the mode of production relaxes the need to satisfy the exact hydrogen grade requests as long as the hydrogen production satisfies certain global production constraints within the network. As shown in our case study, this can lead to significant cost savings primarily from avoiding unnecessary transportation costs and relying more on the local distribution of hydrogen. Furthermore, accounting for market price uncertainty using the proposed stochastic programming framework allows for the generation of investment strategies tailored to each specific scenario while minimizing the overall expected cost.

## References

D. Berry, 2002. The market for tradable renewable energy credits. *Ecological Economics*, 42(3), 369-379.

L. Li, H. Manier, and M.A. Manier, 2019. Hydrogen supply chain network design: An optimization-oriented review. *Renewable and Sustainable Energy Reviews*, 103, pp. 342-360.

T. Rathi and Q. Zhang, 2022. Capacity planning with uncertain endogenous technology learning. *Computers & Chemical Engineering*, 164, 107868.

A. Ruszczyński and A. Shapiro, 2003. Stochastic programming models. *Handbooks in Operations Research and Management Science*, 10, pp. 1-64.

Q. Zhang and J.M. Pinto, 2022. Energy-aware enterprise-wide optimization and clean energy in the industrial gas industry. *Computers & Chemical Engineering*, 165, 107927.

Antonis Kokossis, Michael C. Georgiadis, Efstratios N. Pistikopoulos (Eds.)
PROCEEDINGS OF THE 33rd European Symposium on Computer Aided Process Engineering
(ESCAPE33), June 18-21, 2023, Athens, Greece

# Ontology Modelling for Valorisation of Sugarcane Bagasse

Maureen Chiebonam Okibe,[a] Michael Short,[a] Franjo Cecelja,[a] Madeleine Bussemaker,[a*]

*aDepartment of Chemical and Process Engineering, University of Surrey, Guildford, Surrey GU2 7XH, United Kingdom.*
m.bussemaker@surrey.ac.uk

## Abstract

Sugarcane bagasse (SCB) is an agro-industrial residue extracted during sugar processing. Sugar mills use basic process technologies for bagasse valorisation. Residues are often disposed improperly or burned inefficiently by thermal boilers causing environmental pollution. Biorefining bagasse as substrate for bio-based chemical production is superior to biomass disposal by incineration, burning and landfill. The conversion of bagasse for value-added applications may be economical with less environmental impact on humans and the ecosystem. Computer aided tools such as ontologies for knowledge modelling represent available information for bagasse feedstocks.  This paper presents a reference model referred to as the SCB Ontology which is limited to a framework for the modelling of knowledge on the current utilisation of SCB feedstocks from principal sugarcane-cultivating countries. The SCB Ontology identifies opportunities for efficient bagasse valorisation by principal sugarcane producers. Potential application of the SCB Ontology for bagasse valorisation which is a circular bioeconomy initiative was also discussed.

Keywords: Sugarcane Bagasse, Biorefining, Knowledge Modelling, Ontology

## 1. Introduction

Sugarcane is cultivated in over 100 countries around the world, mainly from tropical and sub-tropical regions. The global annual production of sugarcane is ~2 billion tonnes. For every tonne of sugarcane processed in sugar mills, ~30% of sugarcane bagasse (SCB) is generated (Narisetty et al., 2022). SCB are fibrous residues derived during sugar processing which are dense in polymeric substances.  Consequently, SCB feedstocks are considered the world's biggest second-generation lignocellulose biomass (LCB) (Konde et al., 2021). These complex polymers are the energy carriers found in the SCB biomass. SCB polymers require processing or valorisation using a range of process technologies prior its utilization (Konde et al., 2020). Commercial biorefining of SCB feedstocks has opened new horizons towards achieving circular bioeconomy initiatives by reusing second generation biomass for value-added products (Narisetty et al., 2022). However, the economic and environmental benefits of SCB valorisation are currently unmaximized.

Ontologies are tools for knowledge representation and modelling (Liyana et al., 2019). Scientific and engineering researchers use ontologies for modelling knowledge and data representation in an organised and structured manner. The level of organisation involved in Web Ontology Language (OWL) makes it possible for new knowledge to be inferred (Liyana et al., 2019). Computer aided tools can accelerate strategic decision-making for simpler and sustainable feedstock supply chains using knowledge modelling ontologies (Trokanas et al., 2018). OWL semantic infrastructure was promising for knowledge representation in lignocellulose biorefinery domain, where biorefining of various agricultural residues was modelled (Bussemaker et al., 2018; Trokanas et al., 2018). Ontologies were demonstrated to improve search and retrieval of biomass information, facilitate data integration, and enhance decision-making for biomass component utilization (Trokanas et al., 2018). Classifications of LCB with respect to biomass composition and potential use have also been discussed (Bussemaker et al., 2018). However, agro-industrial residues such as SCB were not considered in previous OWL studies.

The objective here, is to demonstrate a systematic approach to knowledge modelling for SCB availability and current use toward a proposed ontology framework. The framework was developed using semantic knowledge from SCB feedstocks and is interpretable by both computers and humans. The SCB Ontology aims to formalise knowledge representation toward decision support for future valorisation of SCB.

## 2. The SCB Ontology

Previous studies have shown that knowledge represented in OWL can be superior to data stored in traditional relational database management systems (RDBMS). To model complex highly connected data, an underlying graph model used by OWL is often both more intuitive and more efficient than RDBMS model, which can require several complex joins to link data (Ferrer et al., 2021). OWL framework provides directly accessible graph model i.e., knowledge graphs. In addition, OWL provides a semantic layer that is more abstract and closer to business and chemical process engineering models than relational models. OWL satisfies a World Wide Web Consortium (W3C) standard so it can facilitate interoperability (Dutta & DeBellis, 2020).

The SCB Ontology (Figure 1) is designed using the OWL with the Protégé 5.5.0 ontology editor from Stanford University (McGuinness, 2001). Designing the SCB Ontology follows an iterative process using a semantic framework. This Ontology is made up of classes, subclasses, properties, individuals, and rules. The axioms and data were gathered from literature sources. The semantics of OWL are defined by Description Logic which is a decidable subset of First Order Logic (FOL). Each subclass represents one aspect of SCB as gathered from literature sources on sugarcane bagasse.

Agwa et al. (2022) reported that major sugar-producing countries (Brazil, India, China, and Thailand) produce over 100 MT (Million Tonne) of sugarcane per year. These SCB nations were represented in the classes: SCB_Producer which is EquivalentTo Sugarcane_Producer (Figure 2a). Principal_Producer is a subclass of: SCB_Producer and is an example of a defined class. A defined class is represented in Protégé using a yellow circle with three small white lines (Figure 1). A defined class has both the necessary and sufficient conditions required for an Individual to be classified as an instance of that class completely defined. Thus, the OWL reasoner can automatically infer when an individual is an instance of a defined class based on the property values for that individual and the axioms defining the class (Figure 2a).

Classifications of producing nations were defined following classifications in literature (Gikonyo, 2021; Karp et al., 2022) into Top_Producer, Medium_Producer and

Low_Producer. An additional class (Principal_Producer) was created to encompass the four largest SCB producers, responsible for 70% of global SCB production. These defined subclasses possess data properties modelled on Sugarcane_Tonnage (Figure 2a). Each Principal_Producer produces >100 MT sugarcane (Figure 2a). The Top_Producer generates 8-100 MT of sugarcane. The Medium_Producer produces 1-8 MT. The Low_ Producer nations produce <1 MT. (Figure 2a).

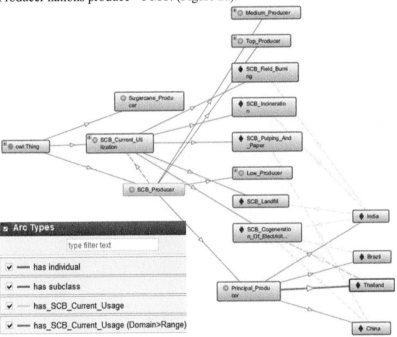

Figure 1: SCB Ontology with SCB_Producers and SCB_Current_Utilization Domains

The SCB_Producer class has a text descriptor known as the 'rdfs comment' (Figure 2a), providing descriptions which is characterised by the human readable property. This holds additional information that can be read by humans. Brazil, India, China, and Thailand were modelled in the SCB Ontology under Principal_Producer as individual instances illustrated using the purple diamonds. In the SCB Ontology, the object property holds property for SCB usage as 'has_SCB_Current_Usage'. Principal_Producer was modelled set against SCB_Current_Usage (Figure 1) which is an object property that has SCB_Current_Utilization as its domain (Figure 1). The class, SCB_Current_Utilization (Figure 1) was used to represent uses of SCB. Gikonyo (2021) reported on the uses of SCB by sugar processing mills in different countries. Principal_Producer models the producing nations against utilization of SCB (Figure 1). For example, Vandenberghe et al. (2022) reported that Brazil utilizes SCB for cogeneration of electricity and that usage was represented linking Brazil, a Principal_Producer (subclass of SCB_Producer EquivalentTo Sugarcane_Producer) to the individual: Cogeneration_Of_Electricity which is an instance of the class SCB_Current_Utilization (Figure 1).

Figure 2a: Schematic representation of User Interface showing Search on SCB_Producer

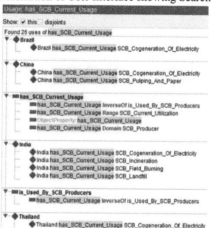

Figure 2b: Information Retrieval on Current Usage of Principal_Producer Countries

## 3. Potential Applications of the SCB Ontology

The SCB Ontology (Figures 2a and 2b) demonstrates some of the reasoning capabilities of OWL. Principal_Producer (i.e., China, Thailand, Brazil, and India) is a defined subclass of SCB_Producer. This means that the axioms used to define it provide both necessary and sufficient conditions for an individual to be an instance of that class. In the case of Principal_Producer the important axiom is that the producer creates more than 100 MT of sugarcane per year. The Ontology also records how the SCB is utilized, e.g., for fuels by burning in thermal boilers for cogeneration of electricity in sugar producing mills (Vandenberghe et al., 2022).

Utilizing bagasse for cogeneration of electricity is astronomical in Brazil as a current practice to curb the overdependency on fossil fuel energy and associated emissions preventing the climatic impact of global warming (Vandenberghe et al., 2022). However, Gil et al. (2013) reported that bagasse fuel generates emissions with significant impact on humans and the ecosystem. SCB feedstocks may be considered for more meaningful use with lower impacts on the environment and humans. For example, numerous organic acids and polyols which are platform chemicals may be explored by understanding the lifecycle stages during their production (Gil et al., 2013).

India, one of the Principal_Producer of SCB still disposes bagasse (~1500 metric tonne per day) in landfills and burns bagasse in incinerators and open fields (Konde et al., 2021). Data modelled from the SCB Ontology suggest that SCB_Producer may have newer opportunities from the diversification of SCB residues derived from sugar-processing mills, especially in India since SCB is still sent to landfills, burned in fields, and incinerated as disposal measures. This supports the circular bioeconomy initiative for the upcycle of SCB feedstocks (Narisetty et al., 2022).

The presented Ontology shows a framework for development of an ontology around SCB feedstocks and use. In this study, other subclasses of the SCB_Producer class were defined. For example, the SCB_Current_Utilization class defines the various ways (e.g., Cogeneration) that SCB can be utilized. The OWL reasoner automatically tracks the connections between the two domains: 21 and 26 uses of SCB_Producer and has_SCB_Current_Usage respectively (Figures: 2a and 2b).

Once all available SCB production knowledge is modelled and incorporated into the SCB Ontology, searches could infer new knowledge on domains, classifications and relationships. Through modelling environmental and economic knowledge on existing valorisation processes, new knowledge for cost-benefit analysis and life cycle assessment (LCA) can be inferred (Liang, 2021). Consequently, inferred data generated from new searches may inform decision-making and strategic initiatives for development of new, sustainable products with lower carbon footprints and environmental impact. Ontologies facilitate improved use of knowledge and will deliver more strategic decision which can mitigate scientific guesses by researchers. This type of semantic data representation meets the 'FAIR' requirements (Findable, Accessible, Interoperable and Reusable) of information during searches and information retrieval (Dutta & DeBellis, 2020). This can benefit LCB commercial players and researchers when making and justifying decisions.

## 4.  Conclusions and Future Work

An overview of the SCB Ontology framework, development of its structure and potential applications have been presented. This study discusses the background and usefulness of using the OWL framework to share data and represent SCB knowledge. Ontologies are useful for enhancing decision-making processes and supporting dynamic opportunities which can create rapid industrial change within the LCB biorefineries (Liyana et al., 2019). SCB Ontology benefits from the semantic interoperability of multiple subclasses and domains which would assist in driving optimal solutions for more strategic decisions. In future work, modelling the environmental and economic sustainability of SCB valorisation will be explored through semantics around carbon or greenhouse gas emissions and cost data (Liang, 2021). OWL will therefore be used to create a knowledge repository to support LCA and technoeconomic assessment (TEA) studies.

## Acknowledgements
The team would like to offer their gratitude to EPSRC Doctoral Training Programme for the PhD funding through the University of Surrey Doctoral College. Special thanks to Michael DeBellis for his continuous support on OWL Tutorial throughout this research.

# References

Agwa, I., Zeyad, A. M., Tayeh, B. A., Adesina, A., de Azevedo, A. R. G., Amin, M., & Hadzima-Nyarko, M. (2022). A comprehensive review on the use of sugarcane bagasse ash as a supplementary cementitious material to produce eco-friendly concretes. *Materials Today: Proceedings*

Bussemaker, M., Trokanas, N., Koo, L., & Cecelja, F. (2018). Ontology Modelling for Lignocellulosic Biomass: Composition and Conversion. In *Computer Aided Chemical Engineering* (Vol. 43, pp. 1565–1570). Elsevier B.V.

Dutta, B., & DeBellis, M. (2020). *CODO: An Ontology for Collection and Analysis of Covid-19 Data.*

Ferrer, B., Mohammed, W. M., Ahmad, M., Iarovyi, S., Zhang, J., Harrison, R., & Martinez Lastra, J. L. (2021). Comparing ontologies and databases: a critical review of lifecycle engineering models in manufacturing. *Knowledge and Information Systems, 63*(6), 1271–1304.

Gikonyo, B. (2021). *Sugarcane as biofuel feedstock : advances toward a sustainable energy solution.*

Karp, S. G., Schmitt, C. C., Moreira, R., de Oliveira Penha, R., de Mello, A. F. M., Herrmann, L. W., & Soccol, C. R. (2022). Sugarcane Biorefineries: Status and Perspectives in Bioeconomy. In *Bioenergy Research*. Springer.

Konde, K. S., Nagarajan, S., Kumar, V., Patil, S. v., & Ranade, V. v. (2021). Sugarcane bagasse based biorefineries in India: Potential and challenges. *Sustainable Energy and Fuels, 5*(1), 52–78.

Liang, J. S. (2021). A knowledge with ontology representation for product life cycle to support eco-design activities. *Journal of Engineering, Design and Technology.*

Liyana, N., Mohd, L., Law, F., Mahmoud, M. A., Tang, A. Y. C., Lim, F.-C., Kasim, H., Othman, M., & Yong, C. (2019a). A Review of Ontology Development Aspects. In *IJACSA) International Journal of Advanced Computer Science and Applications* (Vol. 10, Issue 7).

McGuinness, D. L. (2001). *Ontology Development 101: A Guide to Creating Your First Ontology.*

Narisetty, V., Okibe, M. C., Amulya, K., Jokodola, E. O., Coulon, F., Tyagi, V. K., Lens, P. N. L., Parameswaran, B., & Kumar, V. (2022). Technological advancements in valorization of second generation (2G) feedstocks for bio-based succinic acid production. *Bioresource Technology, 360*, 127513.

Gil, M., Contreras Moya, A. M., & Rosa Domínguez, E. (2013). Life cycle assessment of the cogeneration processes in the Cuban sugar industry. *Journal of Cleaner Production, 41*, 222–231.

Trokanas, N., Koo, L., & Cecelja, F. (2018). Towards a Methodology for Reusable Ontology Engineering: Application to the Process Engineering Domain. In *Computer Aided Chemical Engineering* (Vol. 43, pp. 471–476). Elsevier B.V.

Vandenberghe, L. P. S., Valladares-Diestra, K. K., Bittencourt, G. A., Zevallos Torres, L. A., Vieira, S., Karp, S. G., Sydney, E. B., de Carvalho, J. C., Thomaz Soccol, V., & Soccol, C. R. (2022). Beyond sugar and ethanol: The future of sugarcane biorefineries in Brazil. *Renewable and Sustainable Energy Reviews,*

Antonis Kokossis, Michael C. Georgiadis, Efstratios N. Pistikopoulos (Eds.)
PROCEEDINGS OF THE 33rd European Symposium on Computer Aided Process Engineering
(ESCAPE33), June 18-21, 2023, Athens, Greece
© 2023 Elsevier B.V. All rights reserved.  http://dx.doi.org/10.1016/B978-0-443-15274-0.50537-0

# Modelling availability and affordability concerns in the design and planning of pharmaceutical supply chains

Inês Duarte[a]; Bruna Mota[a]; Tânia Pinto-Varela[a]; Ana Amaro[b]; Ana Paula Barbosa-Povoa[a]

[a] *Centre for Management Studies of IST (CEG-IST), University of Lisbon.*
*Av Rovisco Pais, 1, 1049-001 Lisbon, Portugal*
[b] *Coimbra Business School-ISCAC/ IPC, Quinta Agrícola, 3045-601 Coimbra, Portugal*
ines.r.duarte@tecnico.ulisboa.pt

## Abstract

Although sustainability principles have been gaining attention when managing supply chains, integrating social objectives remains an essential concern to be explored. In particular, social impact concerns related to equity in access to pharmaceutical products are crucial to be considered. This work addresses this goal and proposes a decision-support tool based on a multi-objective MILP model that integrates strategic-tactical decisions while considering sustainability principles. The social pillar is modelled using two approaches: the location of facilities to maximize access to medicines where the incidence of disease is higher; and a second approach where a metric based on the economic concept of demand-to-price elasticity is used so as to measure how sensitive markets are to medicines' prices allowing producers to manage the trade-off between prices' portfolio and markets, enhancing social equity criteria, without profit losing. The economic pillar is addressed through the Net Present Value, and the environmental pillar follows a Life Cycle Analysis methodology. The model is applied to a representative case study and different scenarios are analysed where it is shown how strategic and tactical decisions impact these performance indicators.

**Keywords**: Pharmaceutical Supply Chains; Sustainability; Equity; Demand-to-price elasticity; Optimization

## 1. Introduction

Nowadays, pharmaceutical supply chain operations and their management face numerous challenges triggered by the fast-changing and competitive market, scientific and technological breakthroughs, as well as increased pressures from society. Sustainability has been recognized as one of the driving forces impacting supply chains. However, integrating sustainability aspects considerably increases the complexity of the supply chain design and planning decisions. The United Nation's 2030 agenda for sustainable development set 17 developing goals dedicated to helping build a path to a more sustainable and resilient world, that benefits current and future generations, as well as the planet. In particular, the third and tenth United Nations' sustainable developing goals underline the need to guarantee healthy lives and enhance universal coverage of well-being, reduce inequalities within and among countries, and ensure responsible consumption and production patterns, respectively (United Nations, 2015). Besides the undoubtedly economic and environmental impact, the pharmaceutical sector significantly impacts society, making it crucial to improve the supply chain network and promote global access to medicines. However, assessing the social sustainability dimension still remains a research (Duarte et al., 2022). Some authors evaluated social performance at an operational level while others assessed social concerns at the strategical level accounting for the number of jobs created.

In the context of the pharmaceutical sector, other social objectives reveal to be crucial. According to the Access to Medicine Index (AtMI), pharmaceutical products must be equitably accessible in all countries, and their accessibility should lean on two main pillars: availability and affordability (Menou et al., 2021). More precisely, according to this index, medicines are to be made, not only, available, but also affordable in countries with a higher burden of disease and less capacity to acquire these products, to improve equity in access among countries (Duarte et al., 2022). Based on this need, this work aims to contribute towards this end and so its main contributions are listed as follows:

- Proposing a pharmaceutical supply chain network design model that includes strategical and tactical decisions;
- Introducing a novel social approach regarding equity in access to pharmaceuticals, where availability and affordability objectives are explored;
- Considering economic, environmental, and social concerns as objective functions and analysing trade-offs between these three sustainability pillars;
- Applying the proposed model to a representative case study of a vaccine supply chain.

## 2. Problem Definition and Mathematical Formulation

The mathematical model, thoroughly described in Duarte et al. (2022), includes **decisions** at the strategical level, such as the number, location, and capacities of factories and warehouses, the selection of technologies for production and storage, as well as transportation modes for the distribution between entities; at the tactical level, decisions on defining supply, production, inventory and distribution planning are included. The problem was subjected to **material balance constraints** at factories, warehouses and hub terminals (Cross-docking at airports and seaports), **entity location and capacity constraints**, **transportation constraints** such as transhipment constraints at the airports and seaports, contracted capacity constraints with road, air and sea carriers, and quantification of the necessary number of trips between entities; Moreover, **technology constraints** regarding production and storage operations such as capacity, production and storage levels, as well as allocation of technologies are included. Finally, **demand constraints** are included to guarantee demand satisfaction of each market.

The sustainability objectives are integrated in the model through three objective functions: the economic performance of the supply chain; the environmental impact assessment; and the social performance. Moreover, an additional social approach is added and integrated to, together with the social objective function, fulfil two strong pillars of equity in access to pharmaceutical products: availability and affordability.

### 2.1. Social Assessment

The first social approach is introduced and explored in Duarte et al., (2022), through the objective function defined in Eq.1). The aim of this objective function is to improve the availability of pharmaceutical products by prioritizing the location of supply chain entities in geographical areas with higher burden of disease. The metric Disability-Adjusted Life Years (DALYs) reflects the burden of disease and is used as a rate per 100,000 population. In Eq. 1) the parameter $p_i^{DALY}$ is used together with the decision variable $Y_i$ (equals 1 if entity $i$ is installed) to prioritize the location of entity $i$ in geographical areas with higher DALY value.

$$\max PharmaAccess = \left( \sum_{i \in (I_f \cup I_w)} p_i^{DALY} \cdot Y_i \right) \tag{1}$$

The second social aspect reflects affordability and is based on the economic concept of demand-to-price elasticity. This relation was firstly introduced in the context of pharmaceutical supply chain design in the work of Amaro & Barbosa-póvoa (2009). The elasticity coefficient ($\epsilon_{mi}$) translates the relation between demand and price and is defined by the absolute value of the logarithmic derivative of demand to price. Hence, demand can be considered elastic if its relative change is greater than or equal to the corresponding relative price variation ($|\epsilon_{mi}| \geq 1$), and inelastic otherwise ($|\epsilon_{mi}| < 1$). The elasticity parameter ($\epsilon_{mi}$) is dependent from the product type ($m$) and the market ($i \epsilon I_c$) where the products are distributed and sold. This is because different geographical areas may have different affordability levels, leading to different sensibilities to price variations. Therefore, the main goal of this approach is to explore how the demand-to-price elasticity can be related to the quantity and the price that a company can apply, and to what extent the population is able to pay that price, defined in Eq. 2). The demand variable ($D_{mit}$) is obtained through polynomial relation with the corresponding price ($ps_{mit}$), and $B_{mit}$ defines the lower bound of demand for the minimum feasible price (Eq.3).

$$Dm_{mit} = \beta_{mit} \left(pm_{mit}\right)^{\epsilon_{mi}} \quad (2) \quad \leftrightarrow \quad \ln\left(Dm_{mit}\right) = \ln\left(\beta_{mit}\right) + \epsilon_{mi} \ln\left(pm_{mit}\right)$$

And a linear relation is achieved $\xrightarrow[\substack{D_{mit}=\ln(Dm_{mit}); \\ B_{mit}=\ln(\beta_{mit}) \\ ps_{mit}=\ln(pm_{mit})}]{} D_{mit} = B_{mit} + \epsilon_{mi} \, ps_{mit} \quad (3)$

## 2.2. Economic and Environmental assessment

The economic assessment is made through the maximization of the Net Present Value (NPV), which corresponds to the sum of the discounted cash flows of each time-period, at an interest rate. In turn, these cash flows are obtained through the net earnings ($NE_t$), which are given by the difference between incomes and overall costs, where the former corresponds to the amount of products sold ($X_{maijt}$) at a certain price ($ps_{mit}$), and the latter by the following costs. As seen in Eq. 4), these supply chain costs include raw material costs (first term), production operating costs (second term), storage costs (third term), transportation costs (fourth term), hub handling costs (fifth term), airline/freighter contracted costs (sixth term), inventory costs (seventh term), fixed and variable labour costs (eighth and ninth terms), and finally the labour costs for technologies' use (tenth term).

$$
\begin{aligned}
NE_t = (1-tr) \Bigg[ &\sum_{\substack{(m,i,j)\in F_{INCFP} \\ (a,m,i,j)\in NetP}} ps_{mi}X_{maijt} - \Bigg( \sum_{\substack{(m,i,j)\in F_{OUTSUPRM} \\ (a,m,i,j)\in NetP}} rmc_{mi}X_{maijt} + \sum_{\substack{(m,g)\in H_{prod} \\ i\in I_f}} opc_g P_{mgit} \\
&+ \sum_{\substack{(m,g)\in H_{stor} \\ i\in(I_f\cup I_w)}} opc_g S_{mgit} + \sum_{\substack{(a,m,i,j)\in NetP \\ a\in(A_{plane}\cup A_{boat}\cup A_{trucks})}} tc_a. pw_m. d_{ij}. X_{maijt} + \sum_{\substack{(a,m,i,j)\in NetP \\ (j\in I_{plane/boat} \wedge i \notin I_{plane/boat})}} hhc_j. X_{maijt} \\
&+ \sum_{i\in(I_{plane}\cup I_{boat})} cfp_i. Y_i + \sum_{\substack{(m,g)\in H_{stor} \\ (m,i)\in V}} sc_m S_{mgit} + \sum_{i\in(I_f\cup I_w)} w_i. lc_i. wwh. wpt. Y_i \\
&+ \sum_{i\in(I_f\cup I_w)} wpsq. lc_i. wwh. wpt. YC_i + \sum_{\substack{(m,g)\in H \\ i\in I_f}} w_g. lc_i. wwh. wpt. Z_{gmi} \Bigg) + tr. DP_t \Bigg] \quad (4)
\end{aligned}
$$

The environmental objective function is defined using the Life Cycle Analysis (LCA) methodology, where the minimization of the environmental impact of production, storage, transportation, and entity installation is calculated for each midpoint category c, summed, and normalized as represented in Eq. 5).

$$\min EnvImpact = \sum_c \eta_c \left( \sum_{\substack{t \in T \\ (m,g) \in H}} ei_{mgc} pw_m P_{mglt} + \sum_{\substack{t \in T \\ (m,g) \in H}} ei_{mgc} vpu_m S_{mglt} \right.$$
$$\left. + \sum_{\substack{t \in T \\ (a,m,i,j) \in H}} ei_{ac} pw_m d_{ij} X_{maijt} + \sum_{\substack{t \in T \\ (a,m,i,j) \in H}} ei_{ic} YC_i \right) \quad (5)$$

## 3. Case-Study

The analysed case-study refers to the production and distribution of a meningitis conjugate vaccine by a specific pharmaceutical company. The vaccine in study is characterized by significant use outside of routine immunization. Low- and middle-income countries do not purchase this vaccine due to its price. Moreover, countries in Africa and Eastern Mediterranean Region indicated an interest in introducing this vaccine into routine immunization programs but have struggled to access these vaccines due to the high price and limited availability (WHO, 2019). This pharmaceutical company's supply chain is currently composed of suppliers and factories, located in Europe and U.S., warehouses located in Europe, U.S and Australia, airports, seaports, and five markets, which are Europe, U.S., Australia, Africa and Middle East. A possible location for a new factory in Africa is included in the study to evaluate the possibility of increasing accessibility for this vaccine in this market. The Global Burden of Disease Results Tool is used to obtain the DALY Rate per 100.000 population for meningitis disease in each geographical area of the corresponding markets. Moreover, these markets have different demand and prices for this vaccine. Through the database MI4A/VP3 (Market Information for Access to Vaccines/Vaccine Product, Price and Procurement) published by WHO in 2022, information on demand and prices for the vaccine in study can be obtained. Based on the available data, demand to price elasticity coefficients for each market were estimated. As previously explained, demand is a decision of the model and its obtained value can depend on price variations, introduced by the demand to price elasticity coefficient. In the developed case-study the elasticity coefficient for the vaccine being distributed and sold are -5.81,-4.94, -3.45, -0.69, -0.05 for Europe, U.S., Australia, Middle East, and Africa, respectively. The first three markets are characterized by a more elastic demand-price elasticity, while Middle East and Africa are inelastic.

In the developed model, apart from demand, other decisions are made on facility location (suppliers, factories, warehouses and hub terminals), production and storage levels as well as transportation network established. Additionally, demand values for each market are also a decision of the model, whose values are influenced by price variations.

## 4. Results and Discussion

The results focus on three cases studies (A, B and C) over two scenarios (1 and 2) where a lexicographic optimization was used. Case A corresponds to the optimum economic performance. Case B corresponds to the optimum social performance and Case C to the optimum environmental performance. In both scenarios, Cases A, B and C were studied to explore the trade-off between each sustainability pillar. In the first scenario 1) no price variations are introduced, while the second scenario 2) considers an increase of 2% in the vaccine's price in U.S., Australia, and Europe markets, whereas a 15% decrease is applied to markets in Middle East and Africa. These price variations are introduced in the third year of a planning period of 10 years.

The obtained supply chain decision for each case and scenario are shown in Table 1, from where it is possible to observe that the same supply chain structure was obtained for all cases and scenarios. However, depending on the case and scenario, different decisions are taken, resulting in different performances for each sustainability objective. Table 1 summarizes the major results regarding the decisions taken on facility location and transportation network.

Table 1. Supply chain topology and performance indicators' results comparison

| | | Case A | Case B | Case C |
|---|---|---|---|---|
| **Scenarios 1 and 2** | **Suppliers and factories location** | U.S., Africa | U.S., Africa, Europe | U.S., Africa, Europe |
| | **Transports Network** | Trucks of big capacity, Intercontinental connections by boat (4 seaports) | Trucks of big capacity, Intercontinental connections by boat (3 seaports) | Trucks of big capacity, Intercontinental connections by boat (4 seaports) |
| **Scenario 1** | NPV (€) | 1.832E+09 | 1.810E+09 | 1.807E+09 |
| | PharmAccess | 3.740E+03 | 3.798E+03 | 3.798E+03 |
| | EnvImpact | 3.274E+06 | 3.274E+06 | 3.271E+06 |
| **Scenario 2** | NPV (€) | 1.723E+09 | 1.711E+09 | 1.707E+09 |
| | PharmAccess | 3.740E+03 | 3.798E+03 | 3.798E+03 |
| | EnvImpact | 3.268E+06 | 3.274E+06 | 3.264E+06 |

Case A corresponds to the most profitable solution but worst social and environmental performance. In Cases B and C, a small profit decrease of 1% and 2% is observed, but the best social and environmental performance, respectively are obtained. The small variation between cases is justified by the high amount of demand being allocated to only two markets: 54% of the total demand corresponds to U.S market, 45% to Middle East with the remaining percentage of demand corresponding to the other three markets. Moreover, African market has less than 1% of the total demand, possibly because the price of the meningitis vaccine considered is not affordable for the market, leading to very low demand. The performance of the social indicator is directly related to the decision of entities' locations. From Case A (best economic performance) to Cases B and C, the three factories located in Europe, Africa, and U.S are used for production, whereas in Case A only the factory in U.S. and Africa are used. This is explained by the more social beneficial solution being considered in Case B where the best performance of this indicator is achieved by deciding to allow all the three factories to open and contribute to the total value of the social factor $p_i^{DALY}$. In case C, since the environmental indicator has the highest priority a 12% decrease in the environmental impact is achieved by opening all facilities in order to reduce transportation between entities.

Table 2. Comparison between Scenario 1 and Scenario 2

| Market | Elasticity coefficient $\epsilon_{mi}$ | Price variations | Scenario 1 Contracted Demand (SKU*) | Scenario 2 Price variations Demand (SKU*) |
|---|---|---|---|---|
| Europe | -5.81 | ↑ 2% | 2000 | $t \le 2 : 2000$ ; $t > 2 : 3740$ |
| U.S. | -4.94 | ↑ 2% | 992965 | $t \le 2 : 992965$ ; $t > 2 : 899771$ |
| Australia | -3.45 | ↑ 2% | 3616 | $t \le 2 : 3616$ ; $t > 2 : 3356$ |
| Middle East | -0.69 | ↓15% | 831400 | $t \le 2 : 831400$ ; $t > 2 : 918697$ |
| Africa | -0.05 | ↓15% | 1200 | $t \le 2 : 1200$ ; $t > 2 : 1210$ |

*Each product stock keeping unit (SKU) contains 5 single-doses of meningitis vaccines

In Scenario 2, where price variations are introduced in the third year of the planning period, different demand responses depending on the market are obtained, as depicted in Table 2. In the markets where a price increase of 2% was introduced, a demand reduction of 11.8% in Europe, 9.4% U.S., 7.2% in Australia is obtained. On the other hand, a demand increase of 10.5 % in Middle East and 0.75% in Africa is obtained caused by a price reduction of 15%. Even though the effect of the same variation results in a consistent behaviour among markets, the magnitude of these responses is different. This is due to the different demand-price elasticities considered among markets. Europe, U.S., and Australia have elastic demand-price elasticities, resulting in great sensibilities to price variations. This can be explained by the existence of substitute vaccines produced by other companies in these three markets. Middle East and Africa do not experience the same, meaning that in these two markets there is no other company producing and distributing a substitute product for this vaccine, which results in a more inelastic relation between demand and price. The markets' response to price variations results in a 6% decrease in the NPV for the company. Therefore, it is important to explore trade-offs, not only between sustainability pillars, but also between the amount of products and price that a company can practice, and the amount of products that each market needs, at a price that is affordable for them.

## 5. Conclusions and Future work

This work presents an optimal approach for the design and planning of sustainable pharmaceutical supply chains, where the social component is the focus. Through the application of the model, it is possible to understand the existence of trade-offs between each sustainability pillar, and opportunities can be explored envisioning the improvement of availability and affordability of medicines. The concepts of demand-price elasticity are modelled to analyse the affordability of pharmaceutical products as in countries where the need is the highest this can be improved by analysing each market's response to price variation. Despite the promising results achieved in the present work, further research is required. In particular, it is crucial to study the possibility of including lower- and middle-income countries with significant lower prices when compared to the prices practiced in the HIC and UMIC studied in the present work.

## Acknowledgements

The authors acknowledge the support provided by FCT under the project PTDC/EME-SIS/6019/2020 and UIDB/00097/2020, and PhD Grant 2022.11365.BD.

## References

Amaro, A. C. S., & Barbosa-póvoa, A. P. F. D. (2009). *The effect of uncertainty on the optimal closed-loop supply chain planning under different partnerships structure. 33,* 2144–2158. https://doi.org/10.1016/j.compchemeng.2009.06.003

Duarte, I., Mota, B., Pinto-Varela, T., & Barbosa-Póvoa, A. P. (2022). Pharmaceutical industry supply chains: How to sustainably improve access to vaccines? *Chemical Engineering Research and Design, 182,* 324–341. https://doi.org/10.1016/j.cherd.2022.04.001

Menou, V., Hornstein, A., & Lipton-McCombie, E. (2021). *Access to Medicine Index 2021. 1–72.* http://www.accesstomedicineindex.org/sites/www.accesstomedicineindex.org/files/publication/2008_Index_Report.pdf

United Nations. (2015). *UN General Assembly, Transforming our world: the 2030 Agenda for Sustainable Development, 21 October 2015, A/RES/70/1, available at: https://www.refworld.org/docid/57b6e3e44.html [accessed 28 November 2019]. 16301*(October), 1–35.

Antonis Kokossis, Michael C. Georgiadis, Efstratios N. Pistikopoulos (Eds.)
PROCEEDINGS OF THE 33rd European Symposium on Computer Aided Process Engineering
(ESCAPE33), June 18-21, 2023, Athens, Greece

# Optimization of Decentralized Pine Needle-to-Electricity Supply Chain for Almora District of Uttarakhand, India

Gayatri Gawande,[a] Ankush Halba,[b] Pratham Arora,[b,]*

[a]*Department of Mechanical Engineering, National Institute of Technology Tiruchirappalli, Tiruchirappalli-620015, India*
[b]*Hydro and Renewable Energy Department, Indian Institute of Technology Roorkee, Roorkee-247667, India*
*pratham.arora@hre.iitr.ac.in@Indian Institute of Technology Roorkee, Roorkee, India.*
*+91-1332284921*

## Abstract

Approximately $3.4 \times 10^4$ km$^2$ of forest land in Uttarakhand is susceptible to wildfires, with an economic loss of around 1200 USD per hectare due to dry and flammable Pine needles. The Chir Pine occupies 26% of the state's forest, producing $1.67 \times 10^6$ tonnes of Pine needles annually. These Pine needles could be utilized in a gasifier system to provide electricity and solid cooking fuel to people residing in remote and rural areas of Uttarakhand. However, the short window for collection (100 days), inefficient supply chain, and high transportation costs pose significant challenges for implementing any gasifier-based project. The current study involves finding locations for these gasifier-based plants and optimizing the supply chain to reduce cost, distance, and CO$_2$ emissions. Economic analysis for ten different plant capacities ranging from 25 to 250 kW showed that the estimated cost ranged from $33 \times 10^3$ to $146 \times 10^3$ USD.

**Keywords**: Supply chain, Optimization, Gasification, Economic analysis, Electricity.

## 1. Introduction

The Uttarakhand state of India has an abundant Pine Forest, which is responsible for forest fires during the summer season because the leaves of Pine (Pine needles) are susceptible to catching fire due to high temperatures and low humidity levels in summer. Bisht and Thakur (2022) have suggested the utilization of Pine needles in a decentralized gasifier to produce electricity, which could provide electrification in the rural and remote regions of Uttarakhand state. They also looked at the roadblocks to the Pine needle-based gasifier project, discovering that an inefficient supply chain is the most significant obstacle. An efficient biomass supply chain is required to improve the utilization and conversion of biomass into bioenergy. The three most common components of the biomass supply chain are harvesting, transportation, and storage. Razak et al. (2021) optimized the supply chain for bioethanol production from Palm oil via integrated GIS-AHP for Malaysia. However, they have only considered the minimum travel distance parameter to minimize the logistic cost and GHG emissions. Fan and Klemeš (2020) used the Pinch Analysis based on the months to optimize the biomass supply chain for different types and amounts of biomass. They observed that each biomass has a different harvesting period, making the biomass supply chain complex. Durmaz and Bilgen (2020) have used multi-objective optimization for sustainable biomass supply chain design to produce biogas from poultry farms. They proposed a three-stage sequential solution to maximize profit and minimize the distance between the biogas facility and poultry farms. However, the long payback period and the high operational cost is the main hindrance to the biogas-based project.

To the best of the authors' knowledge, no significant research on Pine needle-based supply chain optimization for a gasification plant in India has been carried out, including the biomass pretreatment scenario such as shredding, pelletizing, and briquetting. In light of this, the present study aims to optimize the supply chain to reduce cost, distance, and $CO_2$ emissions for various densification and non-densification scenarios in the Indian context.

## 2. Methodology

The Pine needle to electricity supply chain optimization was performed to reduce the transportation distance, costs, and $CO_2$ emissions by considering various densification scenarios.. Shredding, pelletizing, and briquetting are considered to densify Pine needles. The flow chart of densification routes is presented in Figure 1. Baling, bundling, module construction, boxing, silo-bagging, packing, pelletizing, and briquetting or cubing are all examples of biomass densification (Ibitoye et al., 2021). Local merchants provided the prices for raw Pine needles and densified Pine needles. The average amount of Rupees 1 equals 0.0134 USD based on the market currency exchange rate in 2021.

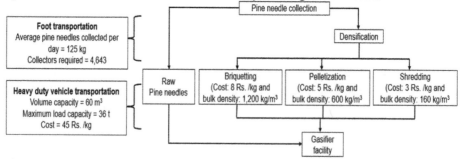

Figure 1: Densification routes

Data regarding the Pine needle availability for the forest blocks in the 13 districts of Uttarakhand is taken from the Forest department of the Uttarakhand Government (Forest Department in Uttarakhand, 2021). The data gives information about a total of 8,922 points yielding $1.67 \times 10^6$ t of Pine needles per annum from the forest compartments having a geographical area of $1.03 \times 10^4$ km$^2$. The flow chart of the Pine needle-based gasifier project for the Almora district of Uttrakhand is presented in Figure 2.

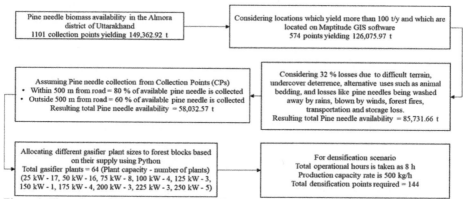

Figure 2: Flow chart of Pine needle-based gasifier project

## 3. Results and Discussion

Maptitude Geographical Interface System software was used to determine locations for densification centers and gasifier facilities based on the collection point candidates set. The facility allocation system employs Greenfield Analysis (GFA or "center of gravity analysis") to identify the locations for densification centers and the gasifier facilities. The results of Maptitude GIS software are presented in Figure 3.

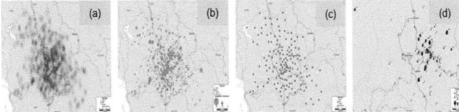

Figure 3: Results of Maptitude software for (a) Pine needle density map; (b) Pine needle collection points; (c) densification points; (d) gasifier facility points for Almora district

Using the Routing and Direction Tool of Maptiude GIS Software, straight-line distances are calculated considering Collection points as the origin/supply nodes and densification points as the destination/demand nodes, as shown in Figure 4.

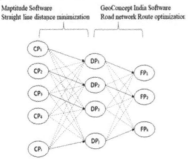

Figure 4: Transportation network flow

Foot transportation is done by Pine needle collectors from CPs to DPs in the hilly forest area of Uttarakhand, where there is a lack of a proper road network, and straight-line distances are considered. A matrix $[_iX_j]$ is generated for straight-line distances that the Pine needle collector has to travel from each collection point to each densification point. The average distances a Pine needle collector travels for the first 5, 10, 15, 20, 25, and 30 closest points from the supply nodes, $CP_i$ to the demand nodes $DP_j$ are calculated to be 2.9 km, 4.2 km, 5.3 km, 6.2 km, 7 km, 7.7 km. The relationship between the nth closest point and the average distance is derived using linear regression fit as y (km) = (0.207166 x + 1.91276) (km) with the R squared value of 0.9733, where y denotes the average distance and x denotes the $n^{th}$ closest distance. The route optimization results from GeoConcept India for the average distance a truck travels in the case of a Pine needle gasifier plant of 10 different capacities are depicted in Figure 5. On average, 125 kg of Pine needles per day is collected by a collector, so approximately 4,643 collectors would be required. Heavy-duty vehicle/ truck with a volume capacity of 60 m³, maximum load capacity of 36 tonnes, and cost of 45 Rs./km is considered for transportation from the DP to FP. Figure 6 depicts the transportation costs for the ten different gasifier facilities in the case of different densification scenarios based on the number of trips the truck has to make to transport the required Pine needle biomass in the 100-day window.

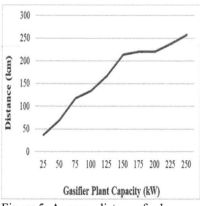

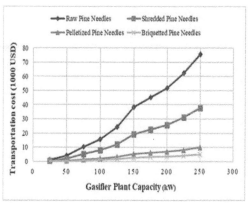

Figure 5: Average distance for heavy-duty vehicle/truck transportation

Figure 6: Transportation costs for densification scenarios

The Pine needle consumption is 1.5 kg/kWh, and the auxiliary power consumption is taken as 5%. The electricity sent out after auxiliary consumption is assumed to be sold at 8 Rs./kWh, and the charcoal produced (10% of Pine needle consumed) as a by-product from gasification is assumed to be sold at 20 Rs./kg as a cooking fuel (Renewable Energy Government of Uttarakhand, 2018). The procurement cost for raw Pine needles is considered as 1.5 Rs./kg, shredded Pine needles as 3 Rs./kg, pelletized Pine needles as 5 Rs./kg, and briquette Pine needles as 8 Rs./kg. Local sellers provided the prices for raw Pine needles and densified Pine needles. The cost model, including revenue, procurement, capital, and operational and maintenance costs, is considered for the gasifier plant, as presented in Figure 7.

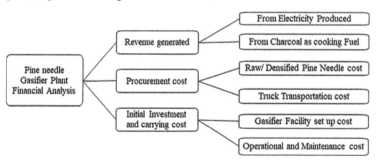

Figure 7: Cost model of Pine needle-based Gasifier plant

The cost of 25 to 250 kW was calculated using Eq. (1), ranging from 33 x $10^3$ to 146 x $10^3$ USD. The annual capacity factor was calculated to be 0.64, considering actual annual energy generation of 140,160 kWh and for a 25 kW Pine needle gasifier plant, which is operational for 16 hours. The annual profit/loss and return on investment (ROI) for raw, shredded, pelletized, and briquette Pine needles are presented in Figure 8.

$$\frac{C_2}{C_1} = \left(\frac{Q_2}{Q_1}\right)^x \tag{1}$$

Where, C = Facility cost, Q = Plant capacity, and x = Annual capacity factor.

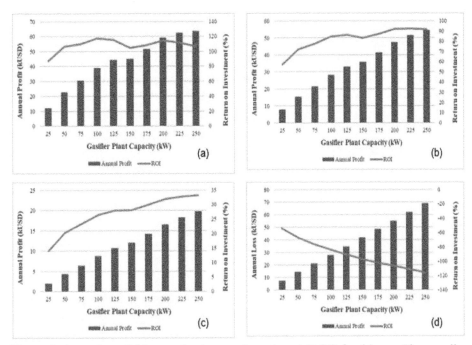

Figure 8: Annual profit/ loss and return on Investment (ROI) for (a) raw Pine needles scenario; (b) shredded Pine needles scenario; (c) pelletized Pine needles scenario; (d) briquette Pine needles scenario

The Almora district comes under the Northern Indian electricity grid, where the GHG emissions are estimated as 1.24 kg $CO_2$ eq/kWh. In contrast, GHG emissions from electricity generation through Pine needle gasification are 0.132 kg $CO_2$ eq/kWh (Briones-Hidrovo et al., 2021). The total GHG emissions from the conventional Northern Indian grid and Pine needles gasification are estimated as 41,537.82 tonnes of $CO_2$ eq and 4,421.77 tonnes of $CO_2$ eq for the 33.5 x $10^6$ kWh of electricity generation in the Almora district. The $CO_2$ emissions for the raw, shredded, pelletized, and briquette Pine needles scenario are calculated to be 419.9, 209.9, 55.9, and 27.9 tonnes based on the emission factor of 0.7375 kg $CO_2$/km for HDV in India as per the recommendation of India GHG Program 2015.

## 4. Conclusions

The $CO_2$ emissions from truck transportation are based on the number of vehicles and trips needed to supply the biomass to the gasifier facility in 100 days time window. A total of 64 Gasifier facilities comprising different capacities can be located in Almora based on the Pine needle biomass supply from different forest blocks. The total electricity produced by the 64 gasifier plants would be 33.5 × $10^6$ kWh, and the total capital cost would be 44 × $10^6$ USD. Among all the costs, procurement of raw/densified Pine needles accounts for 80% of the total costs, transportation accounts for 15%, and O&M accounts for 5% of the total costs. All scenarios except briquetting are profitable due to the high procurement cost of Pine needle briquettes at 0.104 USD/kg. The payback period for the raw Pine needles scenario ranged from 0.85-1.14 years, 1.08-1.76 years for the shredding scenario, and 3-7 years for the pelletizing scenario. The potential annual reduction in $CO_2$

emissions in Almora by generating electricity from a Pine needle biomass-based gasifier compared to the conventional grid is 37,116 tonnes of $CO_2$ eq.

## References

A. S. Bisht, N. S. Thakur, 2021, Identification & Prioritisation of Barriers in the Growth of Pine Needle Biomass Gasification Plants (<250 kW) for Electricity Generation in the Western Himalayan Region: Uttarakhand, India, Process Integration and Optimization for Sustainability, 6, 37-60. https://doi.org/10.1007/s41660-021-00199-y.

A. Briones-Hidrovo, J. Copa, L. A. Tarelho, C. Gonçalves, T. P. da Costa, A. C. Dias, 2021, Environmental and energy performance of residual forest biomass for electricity generation: Gasification vs. combustion, Journal of Cleaner Production, 289, 125680. https://doi.org/10.1016/j.jclepro.2020.125680.

Y. G. Durmaz, B. Bilgen, 2020, Multi-objective optimization of sustainable biomass supply chain network design, Applied Energy, 272, 115259. https://doi.org/10.1016/j.apenergy.2020.115259.

V. Y. Fan, J. J. Klemeš, 2020, Biomass supply and inventory management for energy conversion, Chemical Engineering Transactions, 78, 421-426. https://doi.org/10.3303/CET2078071.

Forest Department in Uttarakhand, 2021, Pine Needle Abundance Area in Uttarakhand <www.forest.uk.gov.in/pirul-abundance-areas>, accessed on 30.10.2022.

S. E. Ibitoye, T. C. Jen, R. M. Mahamood, E. T. Akinlabi, 2021, Densification of agro-residues for sustainable energy generation: an overview, Bioresources and Bioprocessing, 8, 75. https://doi.org/10.1186/s40643-021-00427-w.

ISFR, 2021, State of Forest Report 2021, Forest Survey of India <www.fsi.nic.in/forest-report-2021>, accessed on 1.04.2022.

M. Kumar, A. Kumar, R. Kumar, B. Konsam, N. A. Pala, J. A. Bhat, 2021, Carbon stock potential in Pinus roxburghii forests of Indian Himalayan regions, Environment, Development and Sustainability, 23, 12463-12478. https://doi.org/10.1007/s10668-020-01178-y.

MoEFCC, 2018, National Action Plan on Forest Fire <www.forests.tn.gov.in/app/webroot/img/NAPFF-Final%20Draft%2023.04.2018.pdf>, accessed on 19.10.2022.

N. H. Razak, H. Hashim, N. A. Yunus, J. J. Klemeš, 2021, Integrated GIS-AHP optimization for bioethanol from oil palm biomass supply chain network design. Chemical Engineering Transactions, 83, 571-576. https://doi.org/10.3303/CET2183096.

Renewable Energy Government of Uttarakhand, 2018, Pine Needle Power Generation, Uttarakhand <https://ureda.uk.gov.in/department2/library_file/file-17-07-2021-10-54-40.pdf>, accessed on 08.10.2022.

C. Venkataraman, G. Habib, D. Kadamba, M. Shrivastava, J. F. Leon, B. Crouzille, O. Boucher, D. G. Streets, 2006, Emissions from open biomass burning in India: Integrating the inventory approach with high-resolution Moderate Resolution Imaging Spectroradiometer (MODIS) active-fire and land cover data, Global biogeochemical cycles, 20(2). DOI: 10.1029/2005GB002547.

Antonis Kokossis, Michael C. Georgiadis, Efstratios N. Pistikopoulos (Eds.)
PROCEEDINGS OF THE 33rd European Symposium on Computer Aided Process Engineering
(ESCAPE33), June 18-21, 2023, Athens, Greece

# Life Cycle Assessment of Two Liquid Organic Hydrogen Carriers

Camille Bontron,[a] Diogo Rodrigues,[b] Catarina G. Braz,[b] Henrique A. Matos[b]

*aINP-ENSIACET, 4 All. Emile Monso, CS 44362, 31030 Toulouse Cedex 4, France*
*bCentro de Recursos Naturais e Ambiente, Instituto Superior Técnico, Universidade de Lisboa, Av. Rovisco Pais 1, 1049-001 Lisboa, Portugal*
*dfmr@tecnico.ulisboa.pt*

## Abstract

Liquid organic hydrogen carriers (LOHCs) can store $H_2$ through hydrogenation and dehydrogenation processes. Two systems are based on Toluene-methylcyclohexane (MCH) and dibenzyltoluene-perhydro-dibenzyltoluene (DBT-PHDBT). In this study, the life cycle assessment (LCA) methodology is applied to the two systems. The goal is to determine which molecule is the most suitable one. The general system comprises hydrogenation in Sines (Portugal), transport, and dehydrogenation in Rotterdam (Netherlands). The $H_2$ released during dehydrogenation is the functional unit. The amounts of waste, makeup, cooling water, electricity, heat, and transported quantity are calculated. SimaPro is used as the LCA tool, considering three impact assessment methods, IMPACT 2002+, ILCD MidPoint 2011, and ReCiPe MidPoint (H). The system based on DBT-PHDBT is found to have a smaller impact for all methods. In particular, the process based on Toluene-MCH emits more than twice as much $CO_2$ eq/kg of $H_2$. Energy efficiency improvements and renewable energy sources should be considered.

**Keywords**: Liquid organic hydrogen carriers, Hydrogenation, Dehydrogenation, Life cycle assessment.

## 1. Introduction

Liquid organic hydrogen carriers (LOHCs) can be used for long-term storage and long-distance transport of hydrogen. Hydrogen is stored in the organic molecule through a hydrogenation process and then unloaded via the reverse process of dehydrogenation. These organic molecules allow hydrogen to be handled at ambient conditions and transported using the existing crude oil-based global supply chain. In a previous study by Carvalho (2020), suitable organic molecules were reviewed, and two carrier systems based on Toluene-methylcyclohexane (MCH) and dibenzyltoluene-perhydro-dibenzyltoluene (DBT-PHDBT) were chosen. Toluene-MCH was selected as it is well studied and DBT-PHDBT is convenient for handling and safe. For both molecules, a techno-economic analysis was performed, which is the basis for this study. In this study, the life cycle assessment (LCA) methodology is applied to the two LOHC systems to evaluate and compare the corresponding processes. SimaPro is used as the LCA tool to determine the processes' impact on the resources, environment, and human health factors.

## 2. Context

The goal of this study is to compare the processes based on Toluene-MCH and on DBT-PHDBT and to determine which molecule is most suitable to be used as a LOHC. The

Ecoinvent 3.6 database is used for the background data assuming the Portuguese context for the hydrogenation process, and the Netherlands for the dehydrogenation process.
First, the boundaries of the system must be determined. The boundaries are gate to gate, meaning only hydrogen, LOHC makeup and purge will be used as material flows in this study. The general system used for both molecules is represented in Figure 1. The functional unit in this system is the release of 1 kg of hydrogen during dehydrogenation.

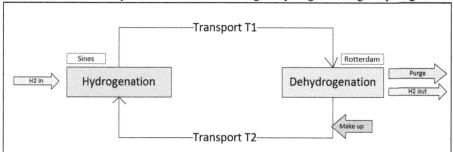

Figure 1 – General system for LCA study.

The general system comprises the hydrogenation process, located in Sines (Portugal), transport, and dehydrogenation in Rotterdam (Netherlands). The system used to transport the hydrogen is a two-way carrier. The dehydrogenated molecule is transported back to the hydrogenation process with the added makeup of toluene or DBT.
The first LOHC molecule studied is Toluene-MCH. It can transport 3 molecules of hydrogen. The other LOHC molecule studied and compared to Toluene-MCH is DBT-PHDBT. It can transport 9 hydrogen molecules.
The dehydrogenation processes release waste via a purge flow. The "Cut off" approach is used, meaning that the creator of pollution is the one responsible for it. Indeed, the pollutant molecules in the purge flow will be accounted for in the LCA.
The reactions need energy to be carried out. Electricity and heat exchangers are used for both the hydrogenation and dehydrogenation processes, and the amount needed comes from Carvalho (2020). For the Toluene-MCH and DBT-PHDBT systems, both the hydrogenation process and the dehydrogenation process may need fired heat, low-pressure steam (LPS), and high-pressure steam (HPS). Cooling water is also needed for both hydrogenation and dehydrogenation processes.
The LOHCs need to be transported from Sines (Portugal) where the hydrogenation takes place to Rotterdam (Netherlands) for dehydrogenation. Transport by ship is used as transport by rail or by road consumes more energy and produces more pollution. The maritime route is extracted from Godinho (2021).

## 3. LCA Inventory

To be used in SimaPro, DBT synthesis data had to be entered, as it was not initially in the database. To create this molecule, the RREM method is used (Huber et al., 2022), which consists of four steps: general research on the chemical process, setting up the reaction equation, researching the required thermal energy, and modeling of the dataset.
First, DBT has a molar mass of 272.38 g/mol. The reaction between toluene and benzyl chloride creates DBT and hydrogen chloride. We suppose the only side products are reactants that did not react. These reactants are recycled.
The production of DBT is 660 g, which represents 2.423 mol. The catalyst used is iron chloride. For catalyst and solvent, a 50% recycling rate is assumed. For 660 g of products,

50 g of catalyst is needed. With that information, and knowing there is a 70% yield, the toluene makeup and benzyl chloride makeup streams can be calculated. The hydrogen chloride waste is also calculated. As the energy for this reaction was not found in the literature, it is assumed that 1 kg of product needs 1.8 MJ to be created (Huber et al., 2022). Therefore, for 660 g of DBT produced, 1.188 MJ is needed.

The transport used is by ship, selected as "Transport, freight, sea, tanker for liquid goods other than petroleum and liquefied natural gas {GLO} | Cut-off, S". The impact of transport considers the quantity transported in both ways and the distance between Sines and Rotterdam by boat, which is 2537.24 km according to Godinho (2021).

As mentioned, both processes need electricity. Toluene hydrogenation also consumes HPS and MCH dehydrogenation consumes fired heat and LPS. PHDBT dehydrogenation also consumes fired heat. In SimaPro, those parameters are represented with heat from steam (called "heat, from steam, in chemical industry (RER)") or from natural gas (called "heat, district or industrial, natural gas (RER)). The data are taken from Carvalho (2020). On the other hand, DBT hydrogenation consumes fired heat and generates high-pressure steam (HPS). HPS is an avoided product as it is not directly used by the DBT/PHDBT process but can be used for other applications.

Cooling water is used during both hydrogenation and dehydrogenation processes. The used water can be recycled, but a makeup flow is needed to compensate the losses. In Carvalho (2020), the energy needed for cooling water is calculated. With that information, the makeup mass flow rate, which represents 2% of the cooling water mass flow rate, can be calculated (Vengateson, 2017). The water selected for the SimaPro simulation is "Water, cooling, unspecified natural origin, PT/NL" in the natural resources' entry.

Regarding the different out flows, waste, purge, and gases out, several compounds are released from the process. In the Toluene-MCH process, xylene, methane, benzene, carbon dioxide, and nitrogen dioxide are released. The DBT synthesis creates a hydrogen chloride release and the DBT-PHDBT process releases benzene, benzyltoluene, toluene, cyclohexane and MCH. By adding the different output flows, it is possible to calculate the emissions for each molecule.

In the inputs, the makeup needs to be entered. For the Toluene-MCH process, the makeup represents the quantity of toluene that must be added so that the recycled toluene plus makeup is equal to the quantity of toluene input needed. The toluene makeup needed is 915.4 kg. For DBT/PHDBT, the makeup needed is DBT. In the same way, DBT makeup is calculated from the DBT output and DBT input and equals 134.1 kg. The quantity of hydrogen needed in the input comes from the mass balance and equals 6312.5 kg for the Toluene-MCH process and 6509.1 kg for the DBT-PHDBT process.

## 4. Methodologies

LCA relies on different methods using several impact categories. The main issues treated are human health impact, environmental impact, and resources impact. The goal of the study is to determine which LOHCs create fewer effects for the three main impact categories, based on three methodologies. The three methods are ReCiPe MidPoint (H), IMPACT 2002+ and ILCD MidPoint 2011, which are international reference life cycle data systems in the European Union. Those methods have different minor categories to classify and focus on different pollution sources. They were chosen as they are the most universal and complete methodologies. They are all based on long-term data.

## 5. Results and analysis

The data are calculated for 1 kg of products created. The goal of this part is to analyze and compare the results for the DBT/PHDBT and Toluene/MCH processes, so one can choose which one impacts the least the environment, human health, and resources. To this purpose, the total for each category of impact is calculated.

### 5.1. ReCiPe MidPoint (H)

The ReCiPe methodology considers environmental, human health and resource issues with the same importance. The main impacts created by both processes, shown in Figure 2, are on global warming, terrestrial ecotoxicity, human non carcinogens effects, and fossil resource scarcity. Regarding impact on resources, the Toluene/MCH process has a clearly higher impact than DBT/PHDBT. Indeed, the total value of fossil resource scarcity is 5.63 kg oil eq for the Toluene/MCH process and only 3.98 kg oil eq for the DBT/PHDBT system. Regarding human health impact, more precisely human non carcinogens category, the DBT/PHDBT process has a smaller impact than the Toluene/MCH process. Indeed, the impact for Toluene/MCH is approximately twice as much as the one for DBT/PHDBT. Finally, regarding environmental impacts, terrestrial ecotoxicity and global warming are both at least two times smaller for the DBT/PHDBT process compared to the Toluene/MCH process. Moreover, Toluene/MCH releases 8.39 kg $CO_2$ eq and DBT/PHDBT releases 3.42 kg $CO_2$ eq.

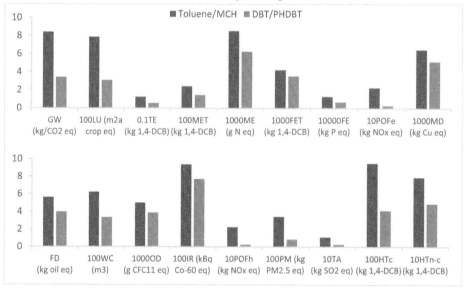

Figure 2 – Comparison of the impacts of the DBT/PHDBT and Toluene/MCH systems using the ReCiPe method. GW: global warming; LU: land use; TE: terrestrial ecotoxicity; MET: marine ecotoxicity; ME: marine eutrophication; FET: freshwater ecotoxicity; FE: freshwater eutrophication; POFe: photochemical ozone formation ecosystems; MD: mineral depletion; FD: fossil depletion; WC: water consumption; OD: ozone depletion; IR: ionizing radiation; POFh: photochemical ozone formation human health; PM: fine particulate matter formation; TA: terrestrial acidification; HTc: human carcinogenic toxicity; HTn-c: human non-carcinogenic toxicity.

## 5.2. Impact 2002+

With the IMPACT 2002+ method, one can observe in Figure 3 that the impact on human health is not significantly generated by the DBT/PHDBT process, in contrast to the Toluene/MCH process. Both processes have a significant impact on the environment and resources. One can compare the impact of each process on the different impact categories. DBT/PHDBT process mainly affects nonrenewable energy, respiratory inorganics, global warming, non-carcinogens effects and terrestrial ecotoxicity. Also, Toluene/MCH affects the same categories as well as terrestrial acid/nutrients. Regarding human health factors, the Toluene/MCH process has a significantly bigger impact on non-carcinogens effects and respiratory inorganics. For resource impacts, it is also the Toluene/MCH process which makes the largest impact as the total for nonrenewable energy is higher than with the DBT/PHDBT process. Finally, for environmental impact, one can see that the values for global warming, terrestrial ecotoxicity and terrestrial acid/nutrients are lower if the DBT/PHDBT process is used. Moreover, if one looks at the value of $CO_2$ equivalent for a kg of hydrogen, one can observe that, with the IMPACT 2002+ method, the Toluene/MCH process releases 7.92 kg $CO_2/H_2$, and the DBT/PHDBT process releases 3.21 kg $CO_2/H_2$.

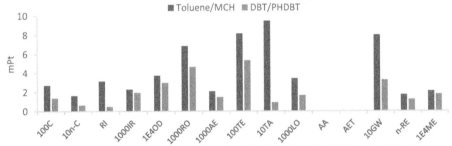

Figure 3 – Comparison of the impacts of the DBT/PHDBT and Toluene/MCH systems using the Impact 2002+ method. C: Carcinogens; n-C: Non-carcinogens; RI: Respiratory Inorganics; IR: Ionizing radiation; OD: Ozone layer depletion; RO: Respiratory organics; AE: Aquatic ecotoxicity; TE: Terrestrial ecotoxicity; TA: Terrestrial acidification/nutrification; LO: Land occupation; AA: Aquatic acidification; AET: Aquatic eutrophication; GW: Global warming; n-RE: Non-renewable energy; ME: Mineral Extraction.

## 5.3. ILCD MidPoint 2011

The results in Figure 4 show that this method does not focus on resources impact, for both processes. One can compare the impact of each process on the different categories, bearing in mind that the scale of Figure 4 is from 0 to 1 mPt, while the scale of Figures 2 and 3 is from 0 to 10 mPt. The resource impact is lower than the others. However, the impact on resources made by the Toluene/MCH process is always slightly higher than for DBT/PHDBT. Regarding human health factors, human toxic carcinogens impact is lower for DBT/PHDBT process than it is for Toluene/MCH, as well as human non carcinogens effects, particulate matter, and ionizing radiation HH. Hence, with the ILCD method, it appears that the DBT/PHDBT process is less harmful for human health than the one for Toluene/MCH. Finally, for the environmental impact, one can see that, once again, the Toluene/MCH process indicators are all higher than the ones for the other process. The sum of all impact categories is equal to 2.4 mPt for the Toluene/MCH process, and 0.59 mPt for the DBT/PHDBT process. Consequently, one can say that the DBT/PHDBT process has a lower impact than the one based on Toluene/MCH. Moreover, one can observe that the Toluene/MCH process releases 8.21 kg of $CO_2$/kg of hydrogen while the one for DBT/PHDBT only releases 3.33 kg of $CO_2$.

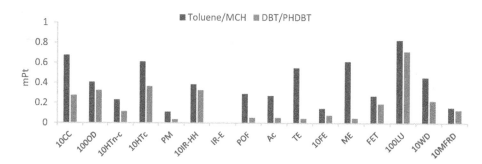

Figure 4 – Comparison of the impacts of the DBT/PHDBT and Toluene/MCH systems using the ILCD MidPoint 2011 method. CC: Climate change; OD: Ozone depletion; HTn-c: Human toxicity, non-cancer effects; HTc: Human toxicity, cancer effects; PM: Particulate matter; IR-HH: Ionizing radiation HH; IR-E: Ionizing radiation E (interim); POF: Photochemical ozone formation; Ac: Acidification; TE: Terrestrial eutrophication; FE: Freshwater eutrophication; ME: Marine eutrophication; FET: Freshwater ecotoxicity; LU: Land use; WD: Water resource depletion; MFRD: Mineral, fossil & ren resource depletion.

## 6. Discussion and conclusions

This study evaluates the impact of two systems for hydrogen storage and transport using two LOHCs, Toluene-MCH and DBT-PHDBT, on the resources, environment, and human health thanks to a LCA with the software SimaPro. For this study, the methods ReCiPe MidPoint (H), IMPACT 2002+ and ILCD MidPoint 2011 were considered. They were chosen as they are the most universal and complete methodologies.

Once the impacts are calculated by SimaPro for Impact 2002+ and ILCD MidPoint 2011 methods, a normalization is applied. After comparing the data, one can conclude that, for all methods, the DBT/PHDBT process appears to have a smaller impact on resources, environment, and human health factors than the Toluene/MCH process. In particular, the process based on Toluene-MCH emits more than twice as much $CO_2$ eq/kg of $H_2$ as the process based on DBT-PHDBT.

To conclude, some improvements could be made regarding data selection. Indeed, SimaPro does not allow the use of green hydrogen in the process. However, it is an important aspect since green hydrogen avoids using fossil energy or other non-renewable energies, which constitute a significant pollution source. The energy used for DBT synthesis could also be improved, as the value used is an approximation but could be more exact. Finally, to improve the impact of both processes, energy efficiency improvements and renewable energy sources should be considered, as both processes are energetically intensive. One could work on the heat exchanger and electricity values, as those units are the most consuming ones.

## References

M. Carvalho, 2020, Liquid Organic Hydrogen Carriers (LOHCs): A review and techno-economic analysis, MSc Thesis

J. Godinho, 2021, A greenhouse gas footprint and economic assessment of importing renewable H2 from Portugal to the Netherlands, using liquid organic hydrogen carriers, MSc Thesis

E. Huber, V. Bach, P. Holzapfel, D. Blizniukova, M. Finkbeiner, 2022, An Approach to Determine Missing Life Cycle Inventory Data for Chemicals (RREM), Sustainability, 14, 3161

U. Vengateson, 2017, Cooling Towers: Evaporation Loss and Makeup Water, https://www.chemengonline.com/cooling-towers-estimate-evaporation-loss-and-makeup-water-requirements/ (accessed Dec. 09, 2022)

Antonis Kokossis, Michael C. Georgiadis, Efstratios N. Pistikopoulos (Eds.)
PROCEEDINGS OF THE 33rd European Symposium on Computer Aided Process Engineering
(ESCAPE33), June 18-21, 2023, Athens, Greece

# Distribution planning of medical oxygen supply chains under uncertainty

Georgios L. Bounitsis, [a] Yena Lee, [a] Karthik Thyagarajan, [b] Jose M. Pinto, [b] Lazaros G. Papageorgiou, [a] Vassilis M. Charitopoulos [a]

[a] *The Sargent Centre for Process Systems Engineering, Department of Chemical Engineering, University College London, Torrington Place, London WC1E 7JE, UK*
[b] *Linde Digital Americas, Linde PLC, 10 Riverview Drive, Danbury CT, 06810, US*
*v.charitopoulos@ucl.ac.uk*

## Abstract

Recently, supply chain operations of medical products were put to test over the extreme uncertainties that COVID-19 pandemic induced. For instance, medical oxygen distribution to hospitals involves complex decision making due to volatility, which concern both industrial gas manufacturers and healthcare managers. In this work, we address the production and inventory routing problem (PIRP) of medical oxygen under demand uncertainty. A two-stage stochastic programming (TSSP) formulation is proposed where inventory decisions are set as the here-and-now variables. Uncertainty is captured via a novel framework, which exploits demand's forecasts and is coupled with data-driven scenario generation approaches. The methodology is examined on a case-study of medical oxygen distribution to hospitals in the UK during COVID-19 pandemic.

**Keywords**: Healthcare supply chain; Distribution Planning; Inventory Routing Problem; Optimisation under uncertainty; Stochastic Programming.

## 1. Motivation

During COVID-19 pandemic, medical oxygen demand at hospitals sporadically rocketed. Hence, efficient oxygen supply chain's optimal planning emerged as a very challenging problem as it requires simultaneous decisions on production, inventory, and distribution under extreme volatile circumstances. Oxygen supplier's objective is to minimise the cost while guaranteeing quality of service to hospitals and honouring related safety guidelines. In this work, we aim to extend the proposed Mixed-Integer Linear Programming (MILP) model of Lee et al. (2022) to account for uncertainty on oxygen supply chains. Thus, we propose a reformulation using scenario-based two-stage stochastic programming (TSSP), which accounts for uncertainties on COVID-19 cases and consequently oxygen demand at hospitals. Eventually, demand's scenario paths are generated from a novel framework which exploits both data from COVID-19 cases forecast models (COVID-19 Scenario Analysis Tool, 2022) and data-driven scenario generation methods (Bounitsis et al., 2022). As far as the modelling of the PIRP problem, the proposed TSSP remains MILP while decisions regarding inventory are the here-and-now decisions of the problem. Moreover, modelling includes the additional capability of emergency deliveries to the hospitals, in order to keep intact the security inventory levels of the hospitals for extreme scenarios with high demands of oxygen. Finally, a regional case study for hospitals in the UK is investigated to demonstrate the applicability of the proposed approach.

The remainder of the article is organised as follows: in Section 2 a brief literature review is conducted while the scenario generation framework and modelling advances are presented Section 3. In Section 4, we study a regional case study of medical oxygen distribution to hospitals in the UK. Finally, conclusions are summarised in Section 5.

## 2. Literature review

### 2.1. Production and Inventory Routing Problem

Integrated supply chain optimisation techniques have been studied in the literature aiming to make optimal production, inventory and distribution decisions simultaneously (Papageorgiou, 2009; Fahimnia et al., 2013). Production and Inventory Routing problem (PIRP) constitutes such an integrated problem, whose solution on chemical process industries can lead to significant benefits (Barbosa-Povoa & Pinto, 2020). In this context, You et al. (2011a) proposed an MILP model and solution techniques for the Inventory Routing problem (IRP) on industrial gas supply chains. Recently, Lee et al. (2022) developed an optimisation model for the PIRP of oxygen supply chains, using a two-level hybrid solution technique, which has been tested on a real-world supply chain planning problem in the UK during the COVID-19 pandemic. Although COVID-19 has brought uncertainties and risk on the planning problem, the latter work proposed a deterministic approach to confront the PIRP. IRP of industrial gases under uncertainty was examined by You et al. (2011b), where MINLP stochastic formulations were investigated. Focusing on stochastic IRP for medical applications, Nikzad et al. (2019) proposed TSSP model, chance constraint models and solution methods for a medical drug distribution problem under demand uncertainty.

### 2.2. Stochastic Programming & Scenario generation

Stochastic Programming (SP) is a risk-neutral mathematical approach for optimisation problems under uncertainty, in which the uncertainty is modelled via a known probability distribution. In cases of known discrete realisations, also called *scenarios*, optimisation problems are easily reformulated as scenario-based stochastic programs (so-called *deterministic equivalent problems*), which seek to optimise the expected value of the problem over the uncertain set. Stochastic programming problems are characterised as two-stage (TSSP) or multi-stage (MSSP) if uncertainty is revealed at a single or multiple steps respectively (Li & Grossmann, 2021). Scenario Generation (SG) methods are useful techniques to create a small set of scenarios, which is representative of the original uncertain set or the continuous stochastic process. Ultimately, scenario generation or reduction methods assist to efficiently solve computationally demanding SP problems.

Focusing on stochastic process, $F_1, ..., F_T$, discretisation through a scenario tree is the most popular approach. A scenario tree (visualized in Fig. 1a) comprises of stages $t \in T$, which establish the time representation, and nodes $n \in N$, which include information regarding the possible realisations for the uncertain parameters and their probabilities of occurrence. So, in a multi-stage setting, a scenario path $s \in S$ captures the full history of realisations from the root node till the leaf node (Li & Grossmann, 2021). However, when a Markovian data process is considered (i.e., the value of a parameter depends only on its precedent value), the less complex scenario lattice approach can be exploited to discretise the stochastic process (visualised in Fig. 1b).

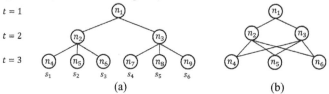

***Figure 1:*** *Three-stage scenario paths using (a) scenario tree & (b) scenario lattice.*

A scenario lattice is also organised by finite stages $t \in T$, but, in contrast to a scenario tree, a node of a lattice at stage $t$ succeeds all the nodes of the previous stage $t-1$. Hence, if $\bar{N}_t$ denotes the number of nodes at stage $t$, the total number of scenario paths is equal to $\prod_{t \in T} \bar{N}_t$. Finally, probability weights correspond to the outgoing arcs of a node, and their sum is equal to one (Löhndorf & Wozabal, 2021).

## 3. Methodology and mathematical developments

### 3.1. Proposed scenario generation methodology

Our ultimate goal is to generate scenario paths for oxygen demand at hospitals. This directly depends on the COVID-19 cases for each of the 3 countries of Great Britain (England, Scotland, Wales). Thus, towards the generation of future uncertain profiles of oxygen demand the input data include: (i) historical data for COVID-19 hospitalisations reported by the UK government (UK Health Security Agency, 2022), and (ii) predicted profiles of COVID-19 cases for the countries provided by advanced forecasting tools (COVID-19 Scenario Analysis Tool, 2022). These data are converted to medical oxygen demand and consequently the generated scenario paths refer directly to oxygen demand. The SG framework extends the work by Bounitsis et al. (2022) in a multi-stage setting, by assuming the data process as Markovian and employing the scenario lattice approach. Considering discrete time stages $t \in T$, the SG framework is outlined in Table 1.

***Table 1:*** *Steps of the proposed multi-stage scenario generation framework.*

| | |
|---|---|
| ***Step 1a*** | Historical data are used as input to identify a copula function with goal to capture the correlations between oxygen demands of the 3 countries |
| ***Step 1b*** | Normal distributions are simulated for each country and each $t \in T$ using forecasting values as mean and an increasing variance as time progresses |
| ***Step 2*** | Copula-based sampling of scenarios is performed as in Bounitsis et al. (2022) |
| ***Step 3*** | MILP Distribution Matching Problem (DMP) integrating clustering by Bounitsis et al. (2022) is executed for each $t \in T$ separately, generating $\bar{N}_t$ nodes per stage $t$ with corresponding values and probabilities |
| ***Step 4*** | Scenario lattice is constructed using the nodes resulting to $\prod_t \bar{N}_t$ scenario paths |
| ***Step 5*** | OSCAR (Li & Floudas, 2014) MILP probabilistic distance minimisation model for scenario reduction is extended to estimate the multi-stage distance by Pflug & Pichler (2012) towards the further reduction of scenario paths |

For instance, implementing the proposed SG framework, a final set of 10 scenario paths for the uncertain demand can be generated. These paths are visualised in Fig. 2.

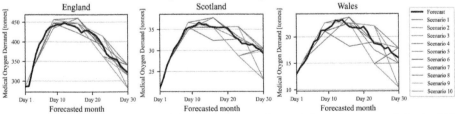

***Figure 2:*** *Scenario paths of total hospital oxygen demand for a future month in the UK.*

The small number of scenario paths for this example is selected because of the computational limitations of the case study problem. An exemplary SG process to generate 10 scenario paths is described as follows. In particular, the SG framework provides scenario paths with certain probabilities and values of oxygen demand for the 3 countries at each day. However, the time horizon of 30 days can be further discretised in stages $t \in T$. For instance, considering 5 time stages $t$ (which correspond to future days 2, 9, 16, 23, 30, i.e., weekly steps to cover the whole horizon) and a branching vector (4,4,4,4,4), demand scenarios for each $t$ are obtained by solving DMP. Then, a scenario lattice with 1024 scenario paths can be constructed. The demands on the in-between days can be determined by linear interpolation between the values of the nodes of the scenario paths. Finally, employing Step 5 of the SG framework, the set can sequentially be reduced to the 10 final scenario paths of Fig. 2, whose probabilities are also determined.

### 3.2. PIRP of medical oxygen under uncertainty

The proposed MILP is an extension of the upper-level problem for the PIRP of oxygen by Lee et al. (2022). This is reformulated as TSSP to account for demand's uncertainty, as it is captured by scenario paths. For the TSSP the decisions are classified into the "here-and-now" and the "wait-and-see" decisions. The proposed model sets the security inventory levels at the hospitals as here-and-now variables, which are determined before the realisation of the uncertainty and are common for every scenario in the imminent step. The rest wait-and-see variables are dependent on each scenario and assist to alleviate infeasibilities for extreme scenario paths while inducing corrective impact. To this end, additional assumptions to the problem statement are beneficial such as the allowable violations of the prespecified minimum inventory levels at hospitals (but obeying security guidelines), which should be satisfied via emergency deliveries. Thus, modifications on the upper-level model by Lee et al. (2022) are presented and we refer the interested readers to the original work for notation and complete model formulation. The scenario-based formulation is developed using index $s \in S$ for demand's scenario paths, $D_{kts}$, with corresponding probabilities $p_s$. Indices $i \in I, k \in K, t \in T$ refer to plants, customers, and days, respectively. Objective function aims at minimisation of expected cost:

$$minimise \sum_{s \in S} p_s \cdot (TP_s + TT_s + TI_s + TED_s + TOP_s) \tag{1}$$

where $TP_s$, $TT_s$ denote the production and transportation costs while $TI_s$, $TED_s$ and $TOP_s$ are new terms regarding plants' inventory cost, emergency delivery cost, and hospitals' inventory opportunity cost respectively. All emergency deliveries are conducted exclusively by vehicles from the plants $i \in I$. Terms regarding the costs are given below:

$$TI_s = \sum_{i \in I} \sum_{t \in T} f^{inv} C^{elec} USP I_{its} \quad \forall s \in S \tag{2}$$

$$TED_s = f^{tr} \sum_{i \in I} \sum_{k \in K_{iv}} \sum_{v \in V_i} \sum_{t \in T} C_v^{veh} L_{ik} A_{ikvts}^{ed} \quad \forall s \in S \tag{3}$$

$$TOP_s = f^{oc} \sum_{k \in K} \sum_{t \in T} (I_{kts} - ID_k) \quad \forall s \in S \tag{4}$$

Parameters $f^{inv}, f^{out}, f^{tr}$ are factors for the estimation of costs. Then, $TI_s$ and $TOP_s$ are estimated using corresponding unit costs, i.e., $f^{inv} C^{elec} USP$, and $f^{oc}$, which is the constant of opportunity cost $[£/kg - day]$. These are multiplied by the stored amounts $I_{its}$ and $(I_{kts} - ID_k)$ respectively. In this work, $ID_k$ denotes the here-and-now decisions on the optimal hospitals inventory levels, while prespecified (agreed-upon) lower bounds by the hospitals are denoted as $IH_k$. When such a lower bound is violated, hospital is on emergency and emergency deliveries are conducted, denoted as $A_{ikvts}^{ed}$. In particular, variables $Q_{kts}^{d,minus}$, which capture negative deviation from $IH_k$, are combined with binary variables, $E_{kts}$, in Eq. (5) to indicate if a hospital is on an emergency:

$$Q_{kts}^{d,minus} = \left(IH_k - I_k^{min}\right)E_{kts} \quad \forall k \in K, t \in T, s \in S \tag{5}$$

Parameter $I_k^{min}$ denotes the hard security bound for the normal operation of the hospitals, which must not be violated. Hence, Eq. (5) provides an upper bound for the allowable violated levels which varies for hospitals. For the sake of brevity, revised balances for hospitals inventory, $I_{kts}$, are provided in Eq. (6), including emergency loads ($Q_{ikvts}^{ed}$). Rest of the constraints are reformulated accordingly based on the model by Lee et al. (2022).

$$I_{kts} = I_k^{ini}\big|_{t=1} + I_{k,t-1,s}\big|_{t>1} + \sum_{i:k \in K_{iv}} \sum_{v \in V_i} \left(Q_{ikvts} + Q_{ikvts}^{ed}\right) - D_{kts} \quad \forall k \in K, t \in T, s \in S \tag{6}$$

## 4. Case study

This synthetic case study examines the PIRP problem of medical oxygen distribution in a certain geographical region in the UK and was developed in collaboration with our industrial partners. The regional case comprises of one plant, which supplies 56 hospitals using 6 vehicles over a time horizon of 30 days. As the presented modification of the model in Section 3.2 can easily be modified for various assumptions, we assume that emergency deliveries can be conducted by all available vehicles of the plant. Moreover, emergency deliveries are forced to be conducted to a customer $k$ the next day of its $IH_k$ level's violation. The latter is set by appropriate manipulation of binary variables $E_{kts}$. Model statistics are presented in Table 2 and costs are on monetary units [RMU] for confidentiality reasons. The deterministic model (DET) considers only one scenario path, i.e., the forecasted values of Fig. 2. Stochastic model (STOC) employs the 10 generated scenario paths, which are also visualised in Fig. 2. The executions are performed in a Dell workstation with Intel® Core™ i9-10900K CPU @ 3.70 GHz and 32.00 GB RAM using solver GUROBI 9.5 in GAMS 41.3 modelling and optimisation system. An optimality gap of 5% or 3,600s of execution time are set as stopping criteria.

**Table 2:** *Model statistics on the proposed case study.*

| Model | Solution [RMU] | Opt. gap [%] | CPU [s] | Total Equations | Total Variables | Discrete Variables |
|---|---|---|---|---|---|---|
| **DET** | 100.00 | 4.88 | 41 | 38,378 | 41,942 | 18,360 |
| **STOC** | 101.21 | 5.72 | 3,600 | 383,771 | 418,907 | 183,600 |

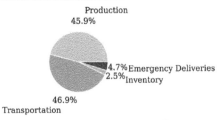

**Figure 3:** TSSP expected cost breakdown.

Statistics from Table 2 demonstrate that the problem is computationally demanding, and the number of discrete variables exaggerates with the number of scenarios. Despite the large number on model statistics near optimal solutions are computed within reasonable execution times. Towards the analysis of results, the breakdown of the expected costs for the stochastic formulations is visualised in Fig. 3. Emergency deliveries cost constitutes 4.7%. In the same context, revised minimum levels have been proposed for 16 of 56 of the examined hospitals. However, the maximum revision does not exceed 8% of the maximum capacity of a hospital. Besides, the adopted strategy for next day satisfaction of the violated levels do not allow wide and lasting violations and the stochastic problem remains feasible. Exemplary inventory profiles of hospitals at a certain scenario path are presented in Fig. 4.

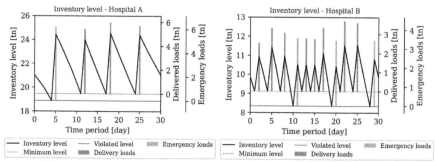

***Figure 4:*** *Inventory profiles for hospitals in a certain scenario path.*

## 5. Conclusions

The contribution of this problem is twofold: (i) to extend the PIRP planning of oxygen distribution to a stochastic context using stochastic programming, (ii) to propose a SG framework based on scenario lattice approach to discretise the demand stochastic process. As investigated problem remains computationally complex, future work within our research group focuses on the development of tailor-made solution techniques.

**Acknowledgements:** The authors would like to acknowledge financial support from the UK Engineering & Physical Sciences Research Council (under project EP/V050168/1).

## References

A.P. Barbosa-Povoa, J.M. Pinto, 2020. Process supply chains: Perspectives from academia and industry. Comput. Chem. Eng. 132, 106606.

G.L. Bounitsis, L.G. Papageorgiou, V.M. Charitopoulos, 2022. Data-driven scenario generation for two-stage stochastic programming. Chem. Eng. Res. Des. 187, 206-224.

COVID-19 Scenario Analysis Tool, 2022. MRC Centre for Global Infectious Disease Analysis, Imperial College London. www.covidsim.org

B. Fahimnia, R.Z. Farahani, R. Marian, L. Luong, 2013. A review and critique on integrated production–distribution planning models and techniques. J. Manuf. Syst. 32, 1–19.

Y. Lee, V.M. Charitopoulos, K. Thyagarajan, I. Morris, J.M. Pinto, L.G. Papageorgiou, 2022. Integrated production and inventory routing planning of oxygen supply chains. Chem. Eng. Res. Des. 186, 97–111.

C. Li, I.E. Grossmann, 2021. A Review of Stochastic Programming Methods for Optimization of Process Systems Under Uncertainty. Front. Chem. Eng. 2, 622241.

Z. Li, C.A. Floudas, 2014. Optimal scenario reduction framework based on distance of uncertainty distribution and output performance: I. Single reduction via mixed integer linear optimization. Comput. Chem. Eng. 70, 50–66.

N. Löhndorf, D. Wozabal, 2021. Gas storage valuation in incomplete markets. Eur. J. Oper. Res. 288, 318–330.

E. Nikzad, M. Bashiri, F. Oliveira, 2019. Two-stage stochastic programming approach for the medical drug inventory routing problem under uncertainty. Comput. Ind. Eng. 128, 358–370.

L.G. Papageorgiou, 2009. Supply chain optimisation for the process industries: Advances and opportunities. Comput. Chem. Eng., 33, 1931-1938.

G.C. Pflug, A. Pichler, 2012. A Distance For Multistage Stochastic Optimization Models. SIAM J. Optim. 22, 1–23.

UK Health Security Agency, 2022. Healthcare in UK. https://coronavirus.data.gov.uk

F. You, J.M. Pinto, E. Capón, I.E. Grossmann, N. Arora, L. Megan, 2011a, Optimal distribution-inventory planning of industrial gases. I. Fast computational strategies for large-scale problems. Ind. Eng. Chem. Res. 50, 2910–2927.

F. You, J.M. Pinto, I.E. Grossmann, L. Megan, 2011b, Optimal distribution-inventory planning of industrial gases. II. MINLP models and algorithms for stochastic cases. Ind. Eng. Chem. Res. 50, 2928–2945.

Antonis Kokossis, Michael C. Georgiadis, Efstratios N. Pistikopoulos (Eds.)
PROCEEDINGS OF THE 33rd European Symposium on Computer Aided Process Engineering
(ESCAPE33), June 18-21, 2023, Athens, Greece
© 2023 Elsevier B.V. All rights reserved.  http://dx.doi.org/10.1016/B978-0-443-15274-0.50541-2

# Life-cycle assessment of marine biofuels from thermochemical liquefaction of different olive residues in Spain

Sivaramakrishnan Chandrasekaran,[a] Puck Wammes,[a] John A. Posada,[a]

[a]*Delft University of Technology, Mekelweg 5, Delft and 2628 CD, the Netherlands*

## Abstract

Advanced biofuels from thermochemical liquefaction, such as pyrolysis (PY) and Hydrothermal liquefaction (HTL), of olive residues in the Andalusian region of Spain (specifically in the province of Jaen) can potentially play a crucial role in the reduction of greenhouse gas (GHG) emissions in the maritime sector. In this study, an attributional life-cycle assessment (ALCA) was performed to estimate and compare the GHG emissions for producing marine biofuels via pyrolysis and HTL from olive pomace (COP) and pruning biomass (OTPB), to provide 1 megajoule (MJ) of marine biofuel, as a functional unit. For convenience, the different technology-feedstock combination scenarios are represented as scenario 1 (PY_COP), scenario 2 (PY_OTPB), scenario 3 (HTL_COP), and scenario 4 (HTL_OTPB). The life-cycle GHG emissions of the biofuels were 42.0, 44.1, 22.1, and 32.1 g $CO_2$-eq/MJ for PY_COP, PY_OTPB, HTL_COP and HTL_OTPB scenarios, respectively, corresponding to 47–73% GHG emissions reduction compared with petroleum fuels. The scenarios were also evaluated based on other impact categories such as Sulphur dioxide in the air, Nitrogen oxides in the air, Particulates in the air, and Non-methane volatile organic compounds (NMVOCs) in the air. The scenarios reduced the $SO_2$ emissions, Nitrogen emissions, NVMOCs, and particulates in the air by at least 50%, 90%, 20%, and 25% respectively in comparison to fossil fuels. A contribution analysis revealed that olive cultivation and upgrading as hot spots for emission in pyrolysis-based systems. Likewise, HTL conversion and upgrading steps were emitting more emissions for an HTL-based system. Therefore, marine biofuel obtained through the thermochemical conversion of olive residues has better environmental performance on a life cycle basis, with a preference for HTL based system over pyrolysis.

**Keywords**: Marine biofuels, hydrothermal liquefaction, Pyrolysis, Life-cycle assessment, Greenhouse gas emissions.

## 1. Introduction

Ships play a central role in the global supply chain of any commodity. About 80% of the world's products are transported by the marine sector. This makes it one of the largest consumers of fossil-based fuels. The total consumption is estimated to be around 330 million metric tons of heavy fuel annually (Hsieh & Felby, 2017). In 2019, Spain consumed approximately 5 million tons of in terms of international maritime bunkering (Eurostat, 2022). Even though maritime transportation emits fewer pollutants per ton kilometer, it contributes to 15% of global carbon emissions. If left unregulated, the emissions from this sector are expected to grow by between 250% in 2050 (Rutherford & Comer, 2018). Decreasing these emissions can therefore greatly contribute to the current world's environmental challenges. Lignocellulosic biomass-based marine biofuels are seen as a must in reaching these goals because the $CO_2$ emitted during combustion is in balance with the $CO_2$ absorbed during the cultivation of biomass. Also, the lower Sulphur and nitrogen content in this type of biomass make them suitable to attain IMO regulations. The residues from the olive sector are one such potential candidate for producing biofuel for the maritime sector. In terms of availability, Spain devotes 2.5 million hectares with more than 180 million trees to this industry. In the province of Jaen, over 91% of the land is occupied by olive trees, making it one of the highest occupants in the entire EU. With accounting for 80% production capacity of olive oil in Spain, the Andalusian region is one of the largest agricultural sectors in the olive- and olive oil industry (UNESCO, 2017). Consequently, the sector produces a large amount of lignocellulosic biomass waste such as olive tree pruning biomass (OTPB), olive pits, leaves, and crude olive pomace (COP). For example, pruning biomass alone has an estimated waste of between 1.5 and 3 tons per hectare in a year (Ruiz et al., 2017). Thereby valorizing these residues will provide an opportunity for developing a bio-economy.

Thermochemical liquefaction, such as pyrolysis, hydrothermal liquefaction (HTL) and gasification, of biomass to bio-crude along with sequential upgrading to biofuel is one of the potential conversion routes for marine biofuel production. Although various studies have been conducted to investigate the thermochemical conversion of olive residues, very few studies have been conducted for biofuel production via HTL based on residues from the olive sector (De Filippis et al., 2016; Evcil et al., 2021). Based on this literature the thermochemical liquefaction of olive residues to produce biofuel is quite promising. With the amount of residues available in the region of Jaen, almost 10% of Spain's national HFO demand can be satisfied. Therefore, apart from techno-economical assessment, analysis based on the environmental aspect is necessary to evaluate the potential of these novel alternatives. Some of the literature also go further beyond the experimental work to evaluate the environmental performance of these methods (Hani & Hailat, 2016; Parascanu et al., 2018). As result indicating better performance in terms of the potential for carbon emission reduction along their life cycle. However, a comparative attributional life cycle analysis is needed to understand and select a suitable conversion pathway for marine biofuel production.

This study's objective is to provide a deeper understanding of the environmental impacts of utilizing olive industry residues, such as COP and OTPB, to biofuels for the maritime sector. To evaluate the environmental performance by quantification of the GHG emissions of these designs by identifying key performance indicators and performing life cycle analysis (LCA). Lastly, this work will serve as a basis for future studies by providing recommendations on improving GHG emission performance. To reach the objective, this thesis is structured to answer the following question: "What are the environmental life cycle impacts of utilizing lignocellulosic residues of the olive sector in Spain to produce marine biofuels via HTL or Pyrolysis?"

## 2. Methodology

This life cycle analysis (LCA) aims to evaluate the environmental impacts and hotspots of the thermochemical conversion of olive industry residues to produce marine biofuels in Spain. In this LCA, the entire proposed supply chain from cradle to grave is considered, from olive cultivation to the combustion of marine biofuel in ships. In this study, an Attributional LCA (ALCA) is performed. The ALCA is to find information on the global burdens that can be associated with a product life cycle, it uses cut-off rules and allocation to isolate the production system from the larger system to assess solely the route to marine biofuel. As for geographical coverage, the LCA is focused on the Jaen in the Andalusian region of Spain. The entire chain will be modeled in Spain or Europe. If necessary, global data was used. Figure 1 shows the overall system boundary encompassing all the scenarios. The system includes olive cultivation, primary Virgin olive oil (VOO) extraction, secondary extraction, thermochemical conversions, biofuel upgrading using hydrogen, and final combustion of marine biofuels.

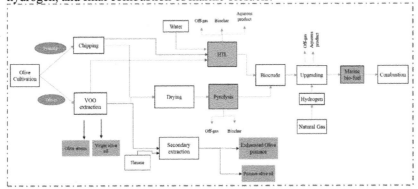

Figure 1: System boundary of scenarios to produce marine biofuels from olive residues in Spain. The green box indicates the products and co-products of the systems, and the blue-grey box indicates the thermochemical pathways. Dotted lines indicate the waste streams.

The analysis follows ISO 14040, the international standard for LCA, and the functional unit is set to be 1 megajoule (MJ) of biofuel produced. All emissions from each process and its associated upstream supply chain were accounted for in this study. But, the emission originating due to the construction of infrastructure, manufacture of equipment, wastewater treatment, biochar, and off-gas utilization were not included within the scope. Data quality and specificity are widely considered key criteria for any LCA studies. Local-specific data such as environmental uniqueness and spatial variation are one of the concerns that require special attention. Hence, the data consistency and accuracy are enhanced by utilizing local data of olive residues obtained from a field visit, e.g., the feedstock availability, the locations of biofuel supply chain nodes, the transportation, and the electricity mix. For the processes modeling and development, e.g., biofuel production and delivery including catalysts, hydro treating and hydrogen production, and nitrogen fertilizer, the GREET 2015 (Greenhouse gases, regulated emissions, and energy use in transportation) or Activity browser coupled with Eco invent v3.7 database was used to model the process emissions with modifications. When the data could not be found in the software database described above, they are collected from peer-reviewed journal articles or reports issued by the government and widely recognized scientific organizations (e.g., IPCC) or laboratories (e.g., PNNL and NREL).

The emissions from each process are obtained based on the physical allocation method. Specifically, mass and energy balances were initially calculated for each process through the Aspen Plus v12 process simulator and then multiplied by the corresponding emission factors. The aspen process model developed includes biomass pretreatment, hydrothermal reactor system, product separation and purification, and byproduct valorization. The off-gas and aqueous stream were recycled within the system. The collected raw data from the various sources described above were first compiled in Microsoft Excel to build the lifecycle inventory of marine biofuels, and then, IPCC 2007 Global warming potential factors were used to convert $CO_2$, $CH_4$, and $N_2O$ into $CO_2$- eq for a time horizon of 100 years.

## 3. Results

### 3.1. GHG emissions from product allocation

The GHG emissions obtained as a result of producing marine biofuel to reach the reference flow of 1 MJ is presented in Figure 2 as g $CO_2$-eq physically allocated to the fuel production system. Scenarios 1 and 2 emit 42.0 and 44.1 g $CO_2$-eq/MJ, respectively compared to 83.6 g $CO_2$-eq/MJ for HFO as calculated for 1 MJ by using the Eco invent database. This is approximately a 50% decrease in emissions. Likewise, Scenarios 3 and 4 even decreased the GHG emissions to approximately 25% of that of HFO with 22.1 and 32.1 g $CO_2$-eq/MJ. A similar reduction can be observed in terms of kg $CO_2$-eq/kg fuel where scenarios 1-4releases 1.6, 1.2, 0.,7, and 0.8 kg $CO_2$-eq/kg fuel compared against 3.42 kg $CO_2$-eq/kg fuel for HFO. These values are in the range of data reported in the literature (Capaz et al., 2020, 2021; Nie & Bi, 2018; Parascanu et al., 2018; Santos et al., 2018; Tanzer et al., 2019),

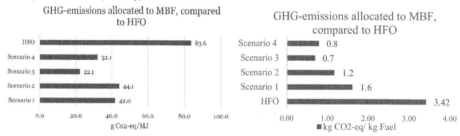

Figure 2: The physically allocated g $CO_2$-eq/MJ fuel (left) and kg $CO_2$-eq/kg fuel (right) per scenario compared to HFO from ecoinvent.

### 3.2. Other impact categories

The environmental performance of the four scenarios considering the other environmental impact criteria is discussed in this section. Figure 3, shows the LCI results for emissions $SO_2$, $NO_X$, NMVOC, and particulates <2.5 am, in centigrams per megajoule. This is

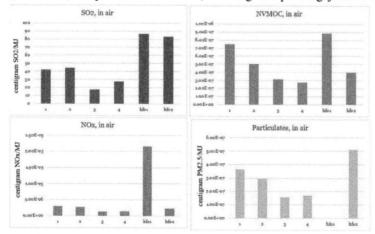

Figure 3: LCI results for emissions to air, compared to HFO from Eco invent and HFO from (Andersson et al., 2016) based on physical allocation

compared to HFO LCA results from the Eco invent database (hfo1) and the LCA results from literature (hfo2) (Andersson et al., 2016). The scenarios reduced the $SO_2$ emissions, Nitrogen emissions, NVMOCs, and particulates in the air by at least 50%, 90%, 20%, and 25% respectively in comparison to fossil fuels.

### 3.3. Contribution analysis

To determine the hotspots in the biofuel product systems, a contribution analysis is run through activity-browser, on the allocated model. The figure shows the life-cycle stage-wise GHG emissions of the four biofuel production scenarios. The contribution from main unit processes: Olive cultivation, virgin olive oil extraction, drying and crushing of biomass, HTL or pyrolysis conversion and upgrading, are analyzed.

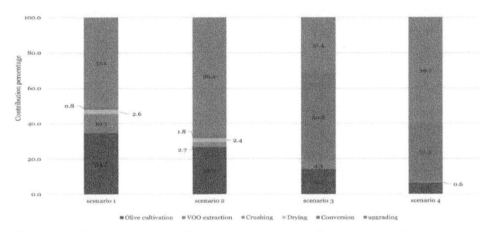

Figure 4: Contribution percentage of the unit processes that contribute to the scenarios

The most dominant contributor of Pyrolysis systems to GHG emissions is bio-crude upgrading, which makes up around 50-60% followed by olive cultivation. The most dominant for HTL_OP is the biomass conversion process, which counts for almost 50%, followed by upgrading with 31.5%. However, an opposite trend was observed for HTL_OTPB with upgrading causing 60% emission followed by conversion. This is might be due to the assumption of similar fuel characteristics of pyrolysis OTPB biofuel and HTL_OTPB biofuel which was made due to data unavailability.

## 4. Conclusion

This study shows that the product system towards marine biofuel (MBF) compared to HFO has lower allocated GHG emissions. The final GHG emissions from scenarios 1-4 are modeled to be: 42, 44.1, 22.1, and 32.1 g $CO_2$-eq/MJ, respectively. Which is all a decrease compared to 84 g $CO_2$-eq/MJ from HFO. Also, the use of MBF reduced the amount of $SO_2$, particulates, and PMVOC emissions into the air, specifically from 83 g $SO_2$/MJ (HFO) to 20-40g $SO_2$/MJ. Therefore, implementing the proposed systems could reduce two of the major environmental impacts of using HFO in marine shipping. Based on the analysis of bio-crude obtained from the thermochemical conversion pathways the nitrogen content was negligible hence corresponding NOx emissions while combusting the MBF are expected to be meager. Finally, the contribution analysis indicated that the conversion pathways were the hotspots for GHG emission in the scenarios. Thereby optimizing the process will lead to a further reduction in emissions to the environment.

However, sensitivity analysis and system expansion studies are recommended to effectively understand the impact of the scenarios.

# References

Andersson, K., Brynolf, S., Lindgren, J. F., & Wilewska-Bien, M. (2016). Shipping and the Environment: Improving Environmental Performance in Marine Transportation. *Shipping and the Environment: Improving Environmental Performance in Marine Transportation*, 1–426. https://doi.org/10.1007/978-3-662-49045-7

Capaz, R. S., de Medeiros, E. M., Falco, D. G., Seabra, J. E. A., Osseweijer, P., & Posada, J. A. (2020). Environmental trade-offs of renewable jet fuels in Brazil: Beyond the carbon footprint. *Science of the Total Environment*, *714*, 136696. https://doi.org/10.1016/j.scitotenv.2020.136696

Capaz, R. S., Guida, E., Seabra, J. E. A., Osseweijer, P., & Posada, J. A. (2021). Mitigating carbon emissions through sustainable aviation fuels: costs and potential. *Biofuels, Bioproducts and Biorefining*, *15*(2), 502–524. https://doi.org/10.1002/bbb.2168

De Filippis, P., De Caprariis, B., Scarsella, M., Petrullo, A., & Verdone, N. (2016). Biocrude production by hydrothermal liquefaction of olive residue. *International Journal of Sustainable Development and Planning*, *11*(5), 700–707. https://doi.org/10.2495/SDP-V11-N5-700-707

Eurostat. (2022). *Supply, transformation and consumption of oil and petroleum products*. https://ec.europa.eu/eurostat/databrowser/view/NRG_CB_OIL__custom_1359468/bookmark/bar?lang=en&bookmarkId=57d36982-0e9a-4226-9634-3ee6ead50431

Evcil, T., Tekin, K., Ucar, S., & Karagoz, S. (2021). Hydrothermal liquefaction of olive oil residues. *Sustainable Chemistry and Pharmacy*, *22*(June), 100476. https://doi.org/10.1016/j.scp.2021.100476

Hani, F. F. B., & Hailat, M. M. (2016). Production of Bio-Oil from Pyrolysis of Olive Biomass with/without Catalyst. *Advances in Chemical Engineering and Science*, *06*(04), 488–499. https://doi.org/10.4236/aces.2016.64043

Hsieh, C.-W. C., & Felby, C. (2017). *Biofuels for the marine shipping sector*. 86. http://task39.sites.olt.ubc.ca/files/2013/05/Marine-biofuel-report-final-Oct-2017.pdf%0Ahttps://www.ieabioenergy.com/wp-content/uploads/2018/02/Marine-biofuel-report-final-Oct-2017.pdf

Nie, Y., & Bi, X. (2018). Life-cycle assessment of transportation biofuels from hydrothermal liquefaction of forest residues in British Columbia. *Biotechnology for Biofuels*, *11*(1), 1–14. https://doi.org/10.1186/s13068-018-1019-x

Parascanu, M. M., Puig Gamero, M., Sánchez, P., Soreanu, G., Valverde, J. L., & Sanchez-Silva, L. (2018). Life cycle assessment of olive pomace valorisation through pyrolysis. *Renewable Energy*, *122*, 589–601. https://doi.org/10.1016/j.renene.2018.02.027

Ruiz, E., Romero-García, J. M., Romero, I., Manzanares, P., Negro, M. J., & Castro, E. (2017). Olive-derived biomass as a source of energy and chemicals. *Biofuels, Bioproducts and Biorefining*, *11*, 1077–1094. https://doi.org/10.1002/bbb.1812

Rutherford, D., & Comer, B. (2018). *THE INTERNATIONAL MARITIME ORGANIZATION'S INITIAL GREENHOUSE GAS STRATEGY*. https://theicct.org/sites/default/files/publications/IMO_GHG_StrategyFInalPolicyUpdate042318.pdf

Santos, C. I., Silva, C. C., Mussatto, S. I., Osseweijer, P., van der Wielen, L. A. M., & Posada, J. A. (2018). Integrated 1st and 2nd generation sugarcane bio-refinery for jet fuel production in Brazil: Techno-economic and greenhouse gas emissions assessment. *Renewable Energy*, *129*, 733–747. https://doi.org/10.1016/j.renene.2017.05.011

Tanzer, S. E., Posada, J., Geraedts, S., & Ramírez, A. (2019). Lignocellulosic marine biofuel: Technoeconomic and environmental assessment for production in Brazil and Sweden. *Journal of Cleaner Production*, *239*, 117845. https://doi.org/10.1016/j.jclepro.2019.117845

UNESCO. (2017). *The Olive Grove Landscapes of Andalusia*. https://whc.unesco.org/en/tentativelists/6169/

Antonis Kokossis, Michael C. Georgiadis, Efstratios N. Pistikopoulos (Eds.)
PROCEEDINGS OF THE 33rd European Symposium on Computer Aided Process Engineering
(ESCAPE33), June 18-21, 2023, Athens, Greece

# An optimisation approach for the design of distributed solar farms with shared energy storage in Pakistan

Obaid Khan[a], Ishanki De Mel[a], Robert A. Steven[a], Michael Short[a*]

[a]*Department of Chemical and Process Engineering, University of Surrey, Guildford, Surrey GU2 7XH, United Kingdom.*
*m.short@surrey.ac.uk*

## Abstract

In many developing nations, the carbon intensity of the grid is high while capacity is also constrained. Local distributed energy resources are expensive to deploy and own by private households. This work presents an optimisation-based approach to optimally locate renewable technologies at both local prosumer's dwellings and at community-level locations, incorporating the addition of distribution lines in a distributed energy system (DES) model to implement a solar photovoltaic (PV) energy farm with energy storage at the community level in densely populated urban areas. A case study of three scenarios in Karachi, Pakistan is selected to test the model. Scenario 1 presents a decentralised approach where every node has the possibility to install batteries locally. Scenario 2 considers a more centralised approach where only 2 central battery nodes are connected to different residential nodes. Lastly, the scalability of the model is tested with Scenario 3 which considers a model with 4 times as many nodes. The optimisation model indicates the profitability of different centralised/decentralised approaches with the highest level of decentralisation showing both the lowest cost and highest profit made, demonstrating the trade-off between battery sizing and line costs for privatised local energy storage.

Keywords: Distributed energy systems, renewable energy, energy systems.

## 1. Introduction

A long-term sustainable and renewable solution to increasing emissions resulting from fossil fuel consumption may be achieved through high penetration of renewable energy technologies such as solar PV, wind turbines, battery technologies, etc. which will be essential to meet rising energy demands while reducing greenhouse gas emissions. Solar energy systems require large space requirements to install, particularly in large cities, and in many countries there are political, financial, and institutional barriers that may make large-scale, grid-integrated solutions difficult to achieve. Battery storage can help to alleviate the intermittency associated with renewable generation and mismatches between generation and load but the cost of investment and operations makes it difficult to readily employ at scale and developing countries which may already have an energy shortfall cannot implement these technologies at current costs.

Pimm et al. (2018) studied local distribution networks and how privately-owned energy storage can save on peak tariff rates by storing and reducing peak load. Cedillos Alvarado et al. (2016) presented a technology and selection optimisation model in which the author optimised the real-time renewable energy resources with energy demand. This model is purely data-driven and encompasses whole life costing, carbon emissions and energy pricing. Most DES problems are formulated as mixed-integer linear programs (MILPs), which is a popular and effective strategy for solving large and complicated processes such as microgrid energy demand-supply planning (Silvente et al., 2015), albeit without integrating detailed power flow concerns (de Mel et al., 2022). While several studies have looked at optimal neighbourhood electrical storage, the area that this should service, along with whether electrical networks may need to be expanded, has not been studied in depth. This paper presents a DES model which seeks to find the optimal design of a distributed solar farm with energy storage, including the addition of distribution lines (Zakeri et al., 2021). In this case, both solar PV and battery storage are included and the resultant model is tested in a case study involving a neighbourhood in Karachi, Pakistan, where Khan & Arsalan (2016) determined that by utilising a neighbourhood's complete rooftop area, it is possible to create 10 times more electricity than it consumes by installing PVs.

## 2. Model formulation

The model formulation in this paper develops a DES MILP optimisation model which introduces additional distribution lines to connect the solar PV installed by end-users to battery storage distributed throughout a neighbourhood. The model for DES is based on the work of de Mel et al. (2021) and Mehleri et al. (2012). The geographical boundary of the neighbourhood is defined and the enclosed area is divided into several nodes, as shown in Figure 1, where each node contains both houses with and without solar PV installed and each house may be connected to battery storage units by a distribution line. The battery storage (in this case Li-ion batteries) is either sited at a point within each node or in separate centralised storage nodes.

Figure 1: Sample topology with red lines indicating neighbourhood boundaries, blue lines node boundaries, red circles indicating battery storage and yellow arrow indicating distribution lines.

The model itself is formulated as an MILP problem, where the objective function (1) minimises the system total annualised cost ($TAC$). This contains distribution line costs ($DLC$), electricity purchased from the grid ($C_s^{grid}$), distributed energy resource installation ($AC^{INV,DER}$) and operational costs ($C_s^{OM,DER}$) and seasonal selling costs of generated electricity ($I_S$).

$$TAC = DLC + \sum_{DER} AC^{INV,DER} + \sum_{s \in S} \left( C_s^{grid} + \left( \sum_{DER} C_s^{OM,DER} \right) - I_S \right) \qquad (1)$$

Here, the overall distribution line costs ($DLC_{i,k}$) are defined as:

$$DLC_{i,k} = \left( (BDC) * (CC) * (ReC) * \frac{Node\ Distance * CRF}{4} \right) * N_{houses} \qquad (2)$$

This contains the base distribution cost ($BDC$), conductor cost ($CC$), the re-conductor coefficient ($ReC$), capital recovery factor ($CRF$), the distance from each house to the central node (each house is only connected to a single node) and the total number of houses attached to the node. The summation subscript $s \in S$ is used to denote a seasonal formulation whereby both the irradiance and load profile datasets contain separate values for each of the four seasons.

The model constraints include power flow between the centralised battery storage and houses, considering both charging and discharging cycles, PV generation capacity, electricity export to the grid and battery capacities, omitted in this paper for brevity. Further constraints contain capital costs, seasonal formulations, ensuring energy is not bought and sold at the same time, operational and maintenance costs and the cost of both buying and selling electricity to the grid.

Here, the total solar PV power generated is:

$$E_{i,t}^{PV,used} + E_{i,t}^{PV,sold} + \sum_{c,k} E_{i,k,t,c}^{PV,charge} \leq N_i^{Panel} * A^{Panel} * Irr_t * \eta^{Panel} \qquad (3)$$

Where the power consumed ($E_{i,t}^{PV,used}$), generated ($E_{i,t}^{PV,sold}$) and used to charge the battery storage ($E_{i,k,t,c}^{PV,charge}$) is less than or equal to the product of the number of panels installed ($N_i^{Panel}$), the area of the panels ($A^{Panel}$), the irradiance received per panel ($Irr_t$) and the efficiency of the panel ($\eta^{Panel}$). The number of panels that can be installed is limited by the maximum roof area available, $N_i^{Panel} * A^{Panel} \leq A_i^{roof}$.

Battery parameters are also included, with battery energy balance equations are given as:

$$\mathcal{E}_{k,t,c}^{stored} = \left( E_{k,t,c}^{ch} * \eta^{ch} * \Delta t \right) - \frac{\sum_i E_{i,k,t,c}^{disch} * \Delta t}{\eta^{disch}}, t = 1 \qquad (4)$$

$$\mathcal{E}_{k,t,c}^{stored} = \mathcal{E}_{k,t-1,c}^{stored} + \left( E_{k,t,c}^{ch} * \eta^{ch} * \Delta t \right) - \frac{\sum_i E_{i,k,t,c}^{disch} * \Delta t}{\eta^{disch}}, t \geq 2 \qquad (5)$$

Containing the charging ($E_{k,t,c}^{ch}$) and discharging ($E_{k,t,c}^{disch}$) battery powers, with their corresponding efficiencies ($\eta^{ch}$, $\eta^{disch}$).

Table 1: Model Parameters

| Description | Values | Units |
|---|---|---|
| Electricity price in £ per kWh | 0.090651 | £/kWh |
| Capital cost of PV in £ per panel | 110 | £/panel |
| Fixed operational cost of PV | 12.5 | £/kWh-yr |
| Variable operational cost of PV | 0.005 | £/kWh |
| Tariff for exporting in £ per kWh | 0.0465 | £/kWh |
| Surface area per panel | 2.1 | m² |
| Base transmission cost | 5 | £/m |
| Conductor Cost | 2.5 | £/m |
| Re-conductor Cost | 1.7 | £/m |

## 3. Case study

A local neighbourhood in the city of Karachi was selected due to its wide-open spaces and large unutilised rooftop areas as well as its sizeable electricity demand.

For this case study, both real-world irradiance and load profile datasets were obtained, with the load data anonymised from a subset of residents and used to generate average load profiles. Other parameters such as PV cost, battery cost and the electricity tariff were set according to the local market rates. GAMS CPLEX 20.1.10.1 (IBM, 2021) was used to solve the MILP. A subset of the model parameters are given in Table 1.

### 3.1. Scenario 1

In the first scenario, five nodes with 12 houses per node are considered with one battery potentially installed at each node. The optimal system initially purchases energy from the grid during the night but this drops to near zero during the day as energy from solar panels is able to meet demand, with excess generation used to charge the batteries. Demand from the grid is also reduced in the evening hours as the battery storage is discharged.

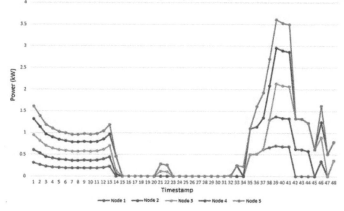

Figure 2 Scenario 1 external power purchased by nodes in representative autumn day

### 3.2. Scenario 2

In the second scenario, the same five nodes are considered but now battery storage is present at two separate, more centralised, battery storage nodes. Here, decision variables in the model determine which distribution lines should be installed, alongside whether house nodes should be powered from the battery storage or from the grid. The model determined that four of the five nodes should be connected to battery storage but that for node 2 it was more viable to draw power from the grid. Here, the model behaves in a similar way to Scenario 1, with power drawn from the grid at night, especially during the evening when there is a surge in demand. From timestamp 39 onwards the model determined that it was more suitable to fulfil the demand from the centralised batteries.

### 3.3. Scenario 3

Scenario 3 tests the validity of the model on a larger scale system, where the number of nodes is increased from 5 to 20 (now 3 houses per node), with 5 central battery storage nodes distributed across the neighbourhood. Unlike the previous results, here the model determined that the solar energy from the PV panels should be used solely to charge the battery storage, which is then used to provide power from timestamp 39 onwards. This is due to the higher cost of purchasing electricity from the grid after this point.

### 3.4. Cost Analysis

The cost components of the TAC objective function are shown in Table 2 and highlight the advantages and disadvantages of the various levels of decentralization within the community-level distributed PV farm with battery storage.

## 4. Discussion

The results of Scenarios 1 and 2 demonstrate the effectiveness of the model, with the power drawn from the grid dropping to nearly 0 kW during the day and the grid dependence being reduced in the evening due to the contribution from the stored battery power. The cost analysis shows the favourable values that can be obtained by placing batteries at each node (Scenario 1), shared among 12 households, in terms of all component metrics. Reduced distribution line costs come from lower distances between the individual houses and the battery storage nodes. Whilst power is still purchased from the grid, in Scenario 1 this cost is completely offset by the income made from selling power back to the grid. Scenario 3 shows the potential limits of the model, with comparatively large battery storage costs due to high fixed costs and low PV penetration. The results indicate that energy is mainly purchased from the grid during the day whilst the PV are used to charge the battery storage, subverting the original aim of the model. The high costs of purchasing this power from the grid greatly increases the TAC, making it an economically unattractive option. Note that in different locations with different price structures and regulatory conditions, the model results are likely to alter significantly. By examining the changes in the different components that make up the TAC, these results can be used to study the tradeoffs between centralisation/decentralisation of the DES, especially in terms of the relative storage and distribution line costs.

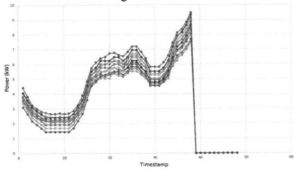

Figure 3 Scenario 3 Power Drawn from Grid

Table 2: TAC Components

| Variables | Scenario 1 | Scenario 2 | Scenario 3 |
|---|---|---|---|
| Annual grid cost | £734.89 | £10,842.97 | £340,677.40 |
| Annual investment cost of PVs | £11,595.10 | £47,895.23 | £2,986.81 |
| Annual operational cost of PVs | £7,441.30 | £9,786.59 | £1,170.78 |
| Annual investment cost of battery | £284.36 | £1,754.78 | £8,625.82 |
| Annual operational cost of battery | £240.40 | £1,156.23 | £5,556.47 |
| Export income from selling electricity | £932.76 | £9,776.87 | £570.45 |
| Distribution line cost | £4,124.33 | £10,596.89 | £26,589.87 |
| Total annual cost | £23,487.62 | £72,255.82 | £385,036.70 |
| Total annual cost per household | £391.46 | £1,204.26 | £6,417.28 |

## 5. Conclusion

In this study, an MILP-based optimisation model is proposed to minimize the total annual cost of a DES at the community level, with three different scenarios to demonstrate its applicability in a neighbourhood of Karachi, Pakistan. The suggested model uses solar PV as the DER, combined with battery storage. It also provides cost-based feasibility analysis and can determine design parameters such as the number of solar PVs required, the placement of distribution lines and the size and number of batteries to be installed. Whilst the given scenarios are for a local neighbourhood, the design parameters of a different environment can be calculated by providing the ground parameters and constraints of the specific area. The output of the model provides both investment and operational costs for the system as well as providing a tool to assess the correct scale of centralisation/decentralisation for community energy in a given neighbourhood. The three scenarios presented in this research validate the ability of the model to select the optimum energy sources based on cost efficiency and by examining the different components of the TAC, the relative benefits to prosumers and the larger community can be seen.

## References

D. C. Alvarado, S. Acha, N. Shah & C. N. Markides, 2016, A Technology Selection and Operation (TSO) optimisation model for distributed energy systems: Mathematical formulation and case study, Applied Energy, 180, 491–503

I. A. de Mel, O. V. Klymenko & M. Short, 2021, Levels of Approximation for the Optimal Design of Distributed Energy Systems, Computer Aided Chemical Engineering, 50, 1403–1408

I. de Mel, O. V. Klymenko & M. Short, 2022, Balancing accuracy and complexity in optimisation models of distributed energy systems and microgrids with optimal power flow: A review, Sustainable Energy Technologies and Assessments, 52

A. González-Briones, J. Prieto, F. De La Prieta, E. Herrera-Viedma & J. M. Corchado, 2018, Energy optimization using a case-based reasoning strategy, Sensors (Basel), 18, 3, 865-892

IBM, 2021, User's Manual for CPLEX 20.1.0,
https://www.ibm.com/docs/en/icos/20.1.0?topic=cplex-users-manual

I. Kantor, J-L. Robineau, H. Bütün & F. Maréchal, 2020, A Mixed-Integer Linear Programming Formulation for Optimizing Multi-Scale Material and Energy Integration, Frontiers in Energy Research, 8

J. Khan & M. H. Arsalan, 2016, Estimation of rooftop solar photovoltaic potential using geo-spatial techniques: A perspective from planned neighborhood of Karachi – Pakistan, Renewable Energy, 90, 188–203

J. F. Marquant, R. Evins, L. A. Bollinger & J. Carmeliet, 2017, A holarchic approach for multi-scale distributed energy system optimisation, Applied Energy, 208, 935–953.

E. D. Mehleri, H. Sarimveis, N. C. Markatos & L. G. Papageorgiou, 2012, A mathematical programming approach for optimal design of distributed energy systems at the neighbourhood level, Energy, 44, 1, 96–104

A. J. Pimm, T. T. Cockerill & P. G. Taylor, 2018, The potential for peak shaving on low voltage distribution networks using electricity storage, Journal of Energy Storage, 16, 231–242

J. Silvente, G. M. Kopanos, E. N. Pistikopoulos & A. Espuña, 2015, A rolling horizon optimization framework for the simultaneous energy supply and demand planning in microgrids, Applied Energy, 155, 485–501

B. Zakeri, G. C. Gissey, P. E. Dodds & D. Subkhankulova, 2021, Centralized vs. distributed energy storage – Benefits for residential users, Energy, 236

Antonis Kokossis, Michael C. Georgiadis, Efstratios N. Pistikopoulos (Eds.)
PROCEEDINGS OF THE 33rd European Symposium on Computer Aided Process Engineering
(ESCAPE33), June 18-21, 2023, Athens, Greece
© 2023 Elsevier B.V. All rights reserved.  http://dx.doi.org/10.1016/B978-0-443-15274-0.50543-6

# Integrating environmental sustainability in next-generation biopharmaceutical supply chains

Miriam Sarkis[a], Jesslyn Fung[a], Ming Hei Lee[a], Andrea Bernardi[a], Nilay Shah[a],
Maria M. Papathanasiou[a],*

[a]Sargent Centre for Process Systems Engineering, Department of Chemical
Engineering, Imperial College London, South Kensington Campus, London SW7 2AZ,
United Kingdom
*maria.papathanasiou11@imperial.ac.uk

## Abstract

Maximizing product availability to the public and minimizing costs are primary objectives in the biopharmaceutical sector. Nevertheless, awareness of the environmental sustainability of supply chain operations is becoming increasingly relevant in recent years. To assist decision-makers in balancing financial and environmental sustainability we present an optimization framework which determines candidate supply chain structures network designs and operational plans. Supply chain structures are assessed with respect to total cost and environmental score, with the latter integrating environmental impacts related to climate change, water usage and energy consumption. A Pareto set of candidate solutions is found which provides insights in complex trade-offs between impact categories and cost: centralized manufacturing is selected to lower unit production cost and better use water resources, whilst decentralized manufacturing improves energy usage. Emissions from $CO_2$ are lowered through cost minimization.

**Keywords**: mathematical programming, supply chain optimization, pharmaceutical manufacturing, environmental sustainability.

## 1. Introduction

The biopharmaceutical industry is uniquely placed to create value for the society, with novel therapeutics enabling the cure of an increasing number of life-threatening diseases. The significant societal impact of the life science sector drives manufacturers to orchestrate and expand resources to maximize product availability to patients from clinical to commercial stages. Minimizing capital and operating costs translate in higher returns on upfront R&D and capacity investments. Recent innovation is brought by Advanced Therapy Medicinal Products (ATMPs), which demonstrate promising results in the cure of life-threatening diseases, including cancer and neurodegenerative diseases. Gene therapies are ATMPs that utilize vectors to deliver extra-chromosomal material into target cells. The sector is expected to grow significantly with the FDA forecasting approvals for 50-60 cell and gene therapy products by 2025 (FDA, 2019). Viral vectors are at the forefront of gene therapy manufacturing and delivery and represent a case where supply chains are transitioning from clinical to commercial stages. Therefore, increasing pressure from governmental agencies to improve sustainability of the industrial operations is expected (HM Government, 2021; EFPIA, 2022; NHS 2022). In biopharmaceutical manufacturing, process steps are often water and energy intensive, while pollutants are emitted during distribution.

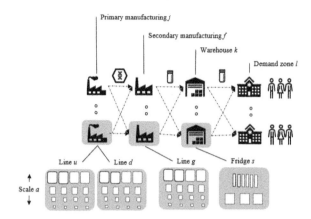

Figure 1: Schematic of supply chain superstructure

In this space, computer-aided decision-making can help assess trade-offs between financial and environmental sustainability. Integrating sustainability in supply chain planning has been explored in PSE operations research with multi-objective optimization approaches (Guillén-Gosálbez & Grossman, 2009; You *et al.* 2012; Barbosa-Póvoa *et al.*, 2018). A focus on the life science sector is presented in Duarte *et al.* (2022), where a large-scale vaccine multi-objective supply chain planning problem is integrated with life cycle analysis (LCA). In this work, we focus on a case study from viral vector-based therapeutics and consider a set of additional model decisions relevant to industrial scenarios, including selection of production scale and storage. A multi-objective optimization problem is presented, which compares minimization of cost and LCA-based supply chain environmental footprint.

## 2. Methodology

This study is based on a previously developed mixed-integer linear programming model presented in Sarkis *et al.* (2022), which consists in a multi-site capacity and distribution optimization for viral vector supply chains, where total costs are minimized and manufacturing is represented in terms of upstream (USP), downstream (DSP) and fill and finish (F&F) processes (Fig.1). Candidate locations are selected for primary manufacturing *j* comprising USP *u* and DSP *d* lines and available at a range of scales a, secondary manufacturing process *f* comprising g parallel filling lines and available in scales *a*, storage nodes *k* and demand zones *l*. Allowed node connections are *j-f, f-k, k-l, f-k* and are generalized as *n* and *n'* (Table 1). Viral vector-based product *i* is considered.

*2.1. Data collection*

Information regarding a generalized viral vector processes was obtained from the literature. A techno-economic model for primary and secondary manufacturing platform for lentivirus-based vectors was developed in SuperPro Designer (Intelligen) to calculate batch sizes $x_{a,i}$, process times $\alpha_u$, $\alpha_d$, $\alpha_g$, and cycle times $r_u$, $r_d$, $r_g$, costs, resources $w$ consumed (water, energy) or emissions ($CO_2$) $EF_{a,w}^u$, $EF_{a,w}^d$, $EF_{a,w}^g$ by the process at different scales a of primary manufacturing, namely 50, 200, 1000 L and 2000 L bioreactor working volumes and secondary manufacturing, namely 50, 100, 400 vials min⁻¹ filling rates. Viral vectors must be stored at low temperatures, therefore information regarding commercially available ultra-low storage freezers was collected (Martínez-Molina *et al.*, 2020). Specifically, costs $c_{k,s}^{CAP}$ and capacity $V_{box}$ for MATOS PLUS Cloud 300 UF (Cloud) and MATOS PLUS Eco 300 UF (Eco) freezers are used. Finally, information regarding packaging $m_{box}$ and shipping was obtained, including distances between nodes, costs, and emissions.

## 2.2. Supply chain network model

Given the inputs presented in Section 2.1, the optimization framework determines (i) supply chain structure, (ii) investment in new capacity at scale $a$, (iii) production levels in terms of batches at scale $a$ of product $i$ $B_{j,u,a,i}$, $B_{j,d,a,i}$, $B_{f,g,a,i}$ processed by $u$, $d$ and $g$ respectively (iv) transport flows $Q_{n,n',a,i}$ between nodes $n$ and $n'$, (v) emissions from supply chain activities. Production is planned in campaigns, with number of batches and allocated times calculated as a function of process times for $\alpha_u$, $\alpha_d$ and $\alpha_g$ and cycle times for $r_u$, $r_d$ and $r_g$. In this work, a more detailed description of storage and transport is presented compared to Sarkis *et al.* (2022). The number of freezers of type $s$ at the warehouse $k$, $N_{k,s}$, is found as a function of inbound flows of product $i$ and freezer capacity (Eq.1). Capital cost of storage is estimated based on type of freezers installed and their cost $C_{k,s}^{CAP}$ (Eq.2), whereas operating costs are calculated in terms of handling cost (Eq.3). Transport costs include contributions from the cost of freight $TC^{freight}$ and dry ice requirements $TC^{DI}$ for cold-chain shipping (Eq.4-5); which are a function of distances between nodes ($D_{n,n'}$) and dry ice requirements per dose ($C^{DI}$), respectively.

Table 1: Model equations to augment framework presented in Sarkis *et al.* (2022)

| N. Description | Equation | | N. |
|---|---|---|---|
| Number of freezers | $N_{k,s} = \frac{CAP_s}{DP_{vial}} \sum_{f,a,i} Q_{f,k,a,i} x_{a,i}$ | $\forall k,s$ | 1 |
| Capital cost of storage | $TC_k^{CAP} = \sum_k C_{k,s}^{CAP} N_{k,s}$ | | 2 |
| Operating cost of storage | $TC_k^{OP} = \sum_{t,l} C^{OPki} Q_{t,k,l,a,i} x_{a,i}$ | | 3 |
| Cost of transport (freight) | $TC^{freight} = t_c \sum_{n,n',a,i} D_{n,n'} x_{a,i} (Q_{n,n',a,i})$ | | 4 |
| Cost of transport (dry ice) | $TC^{DI} = m^{DI} C^{DI} \sum_{n,n',a,i} x_{a,i} (Q_{n,n',a,i})$ | | 5 |
| Storage emissions | $E^k = \sum_{k,s} N_{k,s} \varphi_s$ | | 6 |
| Emission from DI production | $E^{DI} = m^{DI} \sigma^{DI} \sum_{n,n',a,i} x_{a,i} (Q_{n,n',a,i})$ | | 7 |
| Load from transport $n$ to $n'$ | $L_{n,n'} = \sum_{a,i} Q_{n,n',a,i} x_{a,i} (m^{DI} + m_{box})$ | $\forall n,n'$ | 8-11 |
| Emission from transport $n$ to $n'$ | $E^{n,n'} = \sigma^{trans} (\sum_{n,n'} D_{n,n'} L_{n,n'})$ | $\forall n,n'$ | 12-14 |
| Total emissions from transport | $E^t = E^{DI} + \sum_{n,n'} E^{n,n'}$ | | 16 |
| Emission from manufacturing | $E_w^j = \sum_{j,u,d,a,i} EF_{a,w}^u B_{t,v,a,u,i} + EF_{a,w}^d B_{t,j,a,d,i} + \sum_{f,g,a,i} EF_{a,w}^g B_{t,f,a,g,i}$ | $\forall w$ | 17 |
| Impact factor for manufacturing | $I_w^j = \frac{E_w^j}{NF_w}$ | $\forall w$ | 18 |
| Impact factor for storage | $I^k = \frac{E^k}{NF_{energy}}$ | | 19 |
| Impact factor for transport | $I^t = \frac{E^t}{NF_{CO2}}$ | | 20 |
| Environmental score | $ES = \sum_w WF_w I_w^j + WF_{CO_2} I^t + WF_{Energy} I^k + WF_{CO_2} I_{penalty}$ | | 21 |
| Total cost | $TC = TC_j^{CAP} + TC_j^{OP} + TC_k^{CAP} + TC_k^{OP} + TC^{freight} + TC^{DI}$ | | 22 |

Table 2: Summary of normalization (NF) and weighting (WF) factors for each environmental impact considered in this work. NF has been scaled down by a factor of $10^8$ (Sala *et al.*, 2018).

| Impact category | Units | $NF_w$ | $WF_w$ |
|---|---|---|---|
| Climate change | kg $CO_2$-eq | $5.74 \times 10^5$ | 56% |
| Water usage | kg $H_2O$-eq | $7.86 \times 10^8$ | 22% |
| Energy consumption | kWh | $1.24 \times 10^6$ | 22% |

*2.3. Environmental constraints*

A set of environmental constraints is formulated to quantify an environmental score (ES) of each candidate optimization solution, with higher ES corresponding to larger environmental footprint. Emissions from manufacturing nodes $E_w^j$ account for the resource requirements of water and electricity per batch for each process section via $EF_{a,w}^u$, $EF_{a,w}^d$, $EF_{a,w}^g$ (Eq.17). $CO_2$ emissions result from manufacturing and transport, due to $CO_2$ emitted per kg of DI produced $E_{DI}^t$ and emitted $CO_2$ during shipping $E^{n,n'}$. These are respectively calculated as a function of dry ice requirements $m^{DI}$, emissions $\sigma^{DI}$, $\sigma^{trans}$ and the loads for each transport link $L_{n,n'}$ (Eq 7-16). Storage emissions $E^k$ result from electricity usage $\varphi_s$ for each storage type $s$ (Eq. 6). The normalised impact for each of these emissions can be obtained, namely $I_w^j$, $I^k$ and $I^t$ (Eq 18-20). The environmental score is calculated as weighted sum of the normalized impacts (Crenna *et al.*, 2019) (Eq. 21), implementing weights $WF_w$ obtained from Sala *et al.* (2018) (Table 2).

*2.4. Multi-objective Optimization*

Multi-objective optimization provides means of considering multiple objectives and analyze trade-offs. In this study, we compare the weighted-sum method (WSM) and the ε-constrained method, both of which enable the multi-objective problem to be reformulated as a single-objective one. The WSM assigns weights α and (1- α) to each objective respectively, ES and TC, and systematically optimizes the sum of objective functions obtained for realizations of α. TC and ES are normalized using the min-max method and limited between 0 and 1, preventing one attribute with large initial values from dominating. The ε-constrained method optimizes one objective function at the time, with an upper-level constraint placed on the other objective. The ε-constraint method is used to investigate potential non-convexity along the Pareto curve.

# 3. Results & Discussion

*3.1. Single-objective optimization*

Single-objective optimization was performed to investigate its decisions under two scenarios: (i) minimizing total cost (*min*-TC) and (ii) minimizing environmental score (*min*-ES). *min*-TC yielded the minimum TC and maximum ES, whereas min-ES produced the maximum TC and minimum ES. Alternative capacities of sites and network structures were selected in each scenario to meet equivalent demands across *l* (Figure 1). *min*-TC favors a centralized manufacturing as opposed to a more distributed configuration in *min*-ES. The selection of a single 2000 L scale bioreactor is justified by economies of scale, as unit production cost lowered at higher scales. Instead, a 2000 L is 2.3 times more energy intensive than a 1000 L, which means energy consumed per unit product is lower at lower scales. Hence in *min*-ES the optimal configuration involves 2 1000L sized USP and DSP lines. Although a larger scale would result in better usage of water per unit produced, the weighting by *NFs* and *w* in *ES* is lower than that of energy intensity. Therefore, the model prioritizes minimizing of energy usage, followed by $CO_2$ and water usage. With respect to secondary manufacturing the 50 vials min⁻¹ fill-finish plant is sufficient to process the incoming flows from the DSP process. Therefore, a higher number of batches of smaller scale are produced. In *min*-ES, only 4 batches were produced at small scale 50 vials min⁻¹ F&F size, with the rest processed by a single 100 vials min⁻¹ F&F. This is because larger scale improves water-efficiency in F&F. *min*-ES also results in the selection of Cloud as storage, as more energy-efficient; on the other hand *min*-TC favors Eco for its lower costs. With a total demand of 22500 doses, the capacity of a single freezer is sufficient.

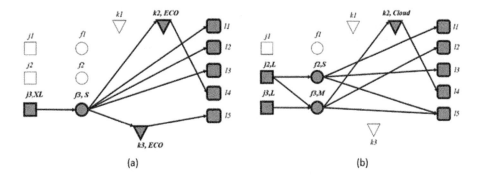

Figure 2: (a) single-objective optimisation network structures for (a) *min*-TC and (b) *min*-ES single-objective optimisation solutions. J: primary manufacturing, F: secondary manufacturing, K: storage, L: demand zones. Different scales are S (50 L), M (200 L), L(1000 L), XL(2000 L).

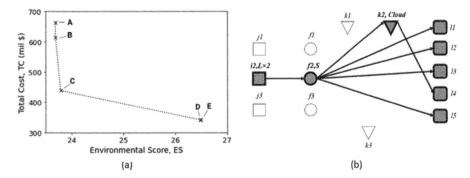

Figure 3: (a) multi-objective optimisation solutions on TC-ES Pareto frontier. Solutions correspond to different values of α: A (α=0) or *min*-ES, B (0<α<0.05), C (0.05< α<0.75), D (0.75< α<1), E (α=1) or *min*-TC. (b) Network structure for C.

*min*-TC suggests installing *k3* as the shipping cost reduction over this route outweighs the cost of installing a fridge in the location. In *min*-ES, demand in *l5* was served directly by *f2* and *f3*, removing storage node *k3* with associated energy consumption.

### 3.2. Multi-objective optimization

The Pareto front constructed via WSM provides solutions which achieve a compromise between *min*-ES and *min*-TC extrema (Solution A & E, Figure 3a). At α=0, solution E corresponds to the centralized SC of *min*-TC. As α increases, the relative importance of ES on TC increases. The network scales-out favoring two lines of 1000 L scale at the same location (Solution C, Figure 3a & b) as opposed to one at 2000 L (Solution A). At α=1, solution A is obtained, with two 1000 L lines 1 at different locations *j2* and *j3*. The methodology resulted in 5 identical solutions of that of WSM, confirming the lack of additional solutions and highlights the convexity of the Pareto front. Solution C presents lower costs to B, with lower capital and operating costs due to the absence of a second *f1* site and transport costs with shorter travel distances. Water-efficiency is improved with C implementing lower scales; however, this is outweighed by higher energy usage hence ES increases. By comparing C and D, solution C select two 1000 L USP lines and one DSP line. D instead opts for single USP, DSP and F&F lines at 2000 L scale.

This results in lower capital and operating costs per dose. D results 28% lower in TC and 10% higher ES and this is due again to higher net energy intensity of USP and DSP lines. C is found to be an example solution of a balanced compromise between TC and ES and covers a wide range of α. Capacity allocations switch due to the relative importance of cost, water-efficiency, improved at higher scales and energy-efficiency improved at lower scale. ES benefits from lower $CO_2$ emissions for solutions where transport cost is lowered.

## 4. Conclusion

This study presents an optimization framework to support decision-makers in biopharmaceutical sector in finding good compromises between environmental and financial sustainability. The problem of minimizing supply chain costs is integrated with life cycle analysis (LCA). Impacts brought by $CO_2$, energy and water usage are combined in a dimensionless indicator for environmental impact. Results from minimizing total supply chain costs show how centralized manufacturing at larger scale also minimizes of transport distances and $CO_2$ emissions and selects cheaper storage options. This translates in higher emissions from storage, however better utilization of water resources. By contrast, minimizing environmental impact favors smaller scales of manufacturing as smaller batches are more energy-efficient, with a removed benefit from economies of scale. As the identified solutions are likely sensitive to the assumed weights assigned to each impact category, on-going work is assessing the impact of such inputs on optimization outputs and considering additional impact categories. These may include emissions from the selection of using plastics-based single-use versus stainless steel equipment and extending the analysis to a wider range of resources used in manufacturing and distribution of viral vector-based advanced therapeutics.

## References

A.P. Barbosa-Póvoa, C. da Silva, A. Carvalho, 2018, Opportunities and challenges in sustainable supply chain: an operations research perspective, European Journal of Operations Research, 268, 399-431.

E. Crenna, M. Secchi, L. Benini, S. Sala, 2019, Global environemntal impacts: data sources and methodological choices for calculating normalization factors in LCA, International Journal of Life Cycle Assessment, 24.

I. Duarte, B. Mota, T. Pinto-Varela, A.P. Barbosa-Póvoa, 2022, Pharmaceutical industry supply chains: how to sustainably improve access to vaccines, Chemical Engineering Resarch and Design, 182, 324-341.

G. Guillén-Gosálbez & I. Grossman, 2009, Optimal design and planning of sustainable chemical supply chains under uncertainty, AIChE Journal, 55(1), 99-121.

EFPIA. 2022, Environment, Health, Safety and Sustainability.

E. Martínez-Molina, C. Chocarro-Wrona, D. Martinez-Moreno, J.A. Marchal, H. Boulaiz, 2020, Large-scale production of lentiviral vectors: current perspectives and challenges, Pharmaceutics, 12, 1051.

HM Government, 2021, Life Sciences Vision.

S. Sala, A.K. Cerutti, R. Pant, 2018, Development of a weighting approach for the environmental footprint. Publications Office of the European Union: Luxembourg.

M. Sarkis, K. Tak, B. Chachuat, N. Shah, M.M. Papathanasiou, 2021, Towards resilience in next-generation vaccines and therapeutics supply chains, Computer Aided Chemical Engineering, 51, 931-936.

NHS England. 2022, Delivering a 'Net Zero' National Health Service

F. You, L. Tao, D.J. Graziano, S.W. Snyder, 2012, Optimal design of sustainable cellulosic biofuel supply chains: multi-objective optimization coupled with life cycle assessment and input-output analysis, AIChE Journal, 58(4), 1157-1180.

U.S. Food & Drug Administration, 2019, Statement from FDA Commissioner

Antonis Kokossis, Michael C. Georgiadis, Efstratios N. Pistikopoulos (Eds.)
PROCEEDINGS OF THE 33rd European Symposium on Computer Aided Process Engineering
(ESCAPE33), June 18-21, 2023, Athens, Greece

# Techno-economic assessment of sustainable energy planning on renewable electricity demand-supply networks: A deep learning approach

Byeongmin Ha [a], Taehyun Kim [a], Jou-Hyeon Ahn [a], Soonho Hwangbo [a,*]

*[a] Department of Chemical Engineering, Gyeongsang National University, Jinjudae-ro 501, Jinju-si, Gyeongsangnam-do, 52828 Korea*
*s.hwangbo@gnu.ac.kr*

## Abstract

Most renewable energy networks rely on wind and solar energy, known as variable renewable energy (VRE), and its generation process is heavily dependent on weather conditions, leading to fluctuations in the supply side. As a result, this study aims to: 1) develop an optimal forecasting model to predict the supply-demand balance, 2) provide different thresholds to generate potential scenarios, and 3) compare the scenarios using a techno-economic assessment. The optimal model in this study is a GRU, which has an $R^2$ score of 0.994. The levelized cost of electricity (LCOE) ranges from 0.03 USD/kWh to 0.07 USD/kWh. The key conclusions of the study are as follows: 1) conversion factors are used to show that the processed data can be converted to match the feasible pattern of the target year's VRE data; 2) the sampling method accounts for uncertainties in future data and those caused by limited time-series data; 3) the optimal model can be identified by comparing various models using sample data as input; 4) the feasibility of scenarios consisting of a techno-economic component is validated by IRENA; and 5) the probability of LCOE can inform expected budget for energy policy.

**Keywords**: Variable renewable electricity, Forecasting model, Variational auto-encoder, Techno-economic assessment, National energy strategy

## 1. Introduction

The world is facing threats such as climate change and climate refugees caused by global warming. Since the signing of the 2015 Paris Agreement, many nations have been working to reduce carbon emissions and achieve a carbon-neutral economy. Solar and wind power generation, also known as variable renewable energy (VRE), are highly dependent on weather conditions. Despite this uncertainty, VRE accounts for a significant portion of renewable energy (RE) mix. Power generation is difficult to predict due to fluctuations and the costs of projects can vary greatly based on technological advancements and spatial and temporal regions. However, national policy-based energy sector projects must be evaluated to reach the goal of a carbon-neutral economy. To our knowledge, few studies have used deep learning models to perform techno-economic assessments based on national policy. The following steps are taken to achieve this goal: 1) Determine the generation/demand conversion factor using projected growth in RE sources and factors affecting generation and demand, 2) Use a DL-based sampling method to account for future uncertainties, 3) Calculate insufficient generation based on the scenario using a DL-based supply/demand prediction model, 4) Perform techno-economic assessment and find the optimal scenario. These steps allow for the consideration of future uncertainties and the validation of the feasibility of national policy.

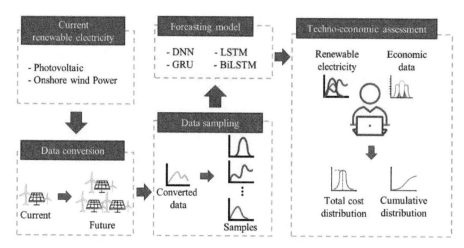

Fig. 1. Major steps in the techno-economic assessment.

## 2. Method

### 2.1. Gated recurrent unit

The GRU, a model based on recurrent neural networks (RNNs), has attractive performance in time-series data (Nam et al., 2020). The GRU revised from LSTM has only two gates and the hidden state, the GRU presents better performance for long-term forecasting compared to the LSTM. The primary mathematical equations of the GRU are as follows:

$$r_t = \sigma(W_{xr}^T \cdot x_t + W_{hr}^T \cdot h_{t-1} + b_r) \tag{1}$$

$$z_t = \sigma(W_{xz}^T \cdot x_t + W_{hz}^T \cdot h_{t-1} + b_z) \tag{2}$$

$$g_t = \tanh(W_{xg}^T \cdot x_t + W_{hg}^T \cdot (r_t \circ h_{t-1}) + b_g) \tag{3}$$

$$h_t = (1 - z_t) \circ h_{t-1} + z_t \circ g_t \tag{4}$$

where tanh and $\sigma$ are the hyperbolic tangent and the sigmoid function, respectively. $W$, $x$, and $b$ in Eq. (1) to (3) represent weights, the input data, and biases, respectively. The hidden state of the previous time (t-1) and the input of the present time are used to calculate the reset gate ($r_t$) and update gate ($z_t$), which have a value between 0 and 1 by sigmoid (Eqs. (1) and (2)). Reset gate decides how much past hidden state should be forgotten (Eqs. (3) and (4)). Update gate determines information composition composed previous information and current information (Eq. (4)).

### 2.2. Variational auto-encoder

Variational auto-encoder (VAE) has a similar structure to auto-encoder, but it performs a different role. VAE, deep learning-based generative model, consists of the reconstruction term and regularization term and minimizes argument of these two terms (Qi et al., 2020). The reconstruction term explains how this model can accurately reconstruct the input data from a sampling function, using the negative loglikelihood function (Eq. (5)). Regularization term manipulates the samples to make samples rely on the prior assumption distribution (Eq. (6)).

$$\sum_i -\mathbb{E}_{q_\emptyset(z|x_i)}\left[log\left(p(x_i|g_\theta(z))\right)\right]$$ (5)

$$KL(q_\emptyset(z|x_i)\|p(z))$$ (6)

$$arg\min_{\theta,\emptyset}\sum_i -\mathbb{E}_{q_\emptyset(z|x_i)}\left[log\left(p(x_i|g_\theta(z))\right)\right] + KL(q_\emptyset(z|x_i)\|p(z))$$ (7)

## 3. A case study

With the 3020 Implementation Plan, Korea plans to have 20% of its energy mix from renewable sources by 2030. To meet 3020 implement plan, Korea already meets target capacity of wind power, but solar power has to be supplemented (MOTIE, 2017).

Capital expenditure (CapEx), operating expenditure (OpEx), life span, and shortage of electricity supply are considered for components related to TEA. CapEx and OpEx estimations of PV based on IRENA are utilized for TEA-related to target year. CapEx and OpEx estimations of FPV are decreased by 5% and equal value compared to PV, respectively. Life span of PV is 20 years, and FPV ranges from 25 to 30. Since shortage of electricity related to target year is considered, supply/demand data are passed through 3 steps as follows: 1) converting the raw data to reference data based on national policy, 2) generating samples considering uncertainties, and 3) forecasting VRE supply/demand data using various models. The conversion factor consists of data that comes from the Korea Power Exchange (KPX), and generates 2030 reference data of supply/demand. Sampling method considers uncertainties of conversion and develops various scenarios. Techno-economic assessment evaluated scenarios and this operation was validated by LCOE.

## 4. Results and discussion

According to Korea's RE strategy, the conversion factor was calculated using the current capacity, OpEx, CapEx, and the capacity factor for 2030. Since components of conversion factors for solar power generations and demand do not change over period (e.g., capacity factors of solar power generations were assumed as constant), the conversion factor for each scenario was constant in the case of demand and solar power generations. However, wind power generation's capacity factor increases over period. The conversion factor of onshore ranged from 0.89 to 1.63, and offshore ranged from 276.53 to 506.97. Required capacity derived from shortage of electricity were considered for two types (i.e., PV 100% or FPV 100% additional projects). The conversion factor for offshore had a high value compared to other generation types since offshore generation plans to build lots of additional capacity.

Sample data, which was generated from reference data, had a large gap with reference data in the case of wind power generation (Fig. 2). The difference between solar power and wind power represents characteristic (i.e., solar power can function only during the day. Wind power is affected by many weather conditions.).

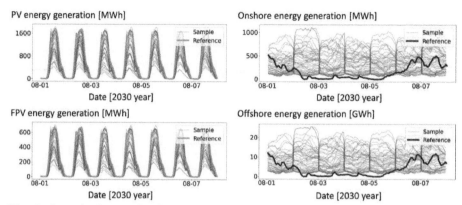

Fig. 2. Sample data and reference data of RE sources.

The $R^2$ score of the GRU was 0.994, which was comparable to the average $R^2$ score of 0.996 for other RNNs-based models, and the GRU had AIC/BIC values of 30,776 and 53,180, which are 6.5% and 15% lower than the LSTM for PV test data (Table. 1). The GRU was selected as the forecasting model in this study since it had comparable performances and lower values of AIC/BIC.

Table 1. A comparison of performance metrics and information criteria considering several forecasting models based on the PV test data; B, L, G, D, and A means BiLSTM, LSTM, GRU, DNN, and ARIMA.

|   | $R^2$ | RMSE | MAE | WAPE [%] | AIC [x10³] | BIC [x10³] |
|---|-------|------|-----|----------|-----------|-----------|
| B | 0.997 | 28 | 17 | 3.7 | 81 | 284 |
| L | 0.994 | 40 | 25 | 5.6 | 32.9 | 62.7 |
| G | 0.994 | 40 | 26 | 5.7 | 30.8 | 53.1 |
| D | 0.987 | 60 | 44 | 9.6 | - | - |
| A | 0.948 | 120 | 74 | 16.1 | - | - |

After calculating the maximum and minimum RE demand/supply using the generated sample and GRU, the scenario was assumed as follows:

Best scenario: maximum supply, minimum demand

Worst scenario: maximum demand, minimum supply
Considering Korea's 2030 target of RE generation, RE generation was insufficient by 15,239,418 MWh/year and 71,035,093 MWh/year in the best scenario and the worst scenario, respectively. The high proportion of offshore wind farms with large fluctuations appears to be the main factor in the difference in RE generation between scenarios. Required capacity and the related costs were presented in Table. 2. The total annual cost of PV ranged from 460.9 to 4,911 million USD/year, and FPV ranged from 330.9 to 3,740 million USD/year.

Table 2. Costs according to scenarios.

| | Best scenario | | Worst scenario | |
|---|---|---|---|---|
| | PV 100% | FPV 100% | PV 100% | FPV 100% |
| Required Capacity [MW] | 12,363 | 10,670 | 57,151 | 49,322 |
| CapEx [million USD/year] | 337.3 | 224.2 | 3,825 | 2,803 |
| OpEx [million USD/year] | 123.6 | 106.7 | 1,086 | 937 |
| Total cost [million USD/year] | 460.9 | 330.9 | 4,911 | 3,740 |

Since several FPV expansions were already anticipated for Korea, PV-based validation was conducted using IRENA LCOE based on the 2030 global average. The theoretical LCOE, which ranged from 0.02 to 0.08, was revised from 0.03 to 0.07 to consider Korea's technical level of RE. In Table. 3, the theoretical total cost was calculated by multiplying the theoretical LCOE and supply shortage, and the measured total cost presented the overall cost of this study. The results of validation show 0.8-1.2 absolute error, which means the feasibility of Korea's net-zero carbon.

Table 3. Cost verification by scenario.

| | Best scenario | Worst scenario |
|---|---|---|
| LCOE [USD/kWh] | 0.03 | 0.07 |
| Theoretical total cost [million USD/year] | 457.2 | 4,972 |
| Measured total cost [million USD/year] | 460.9 | 4,911 |
| Absolute error [%] | 0.8 | 1.2 |

Fig. 3 shows the cumulative density function of 1,000 total cost scenarios using key variables (i.e., CapEx, OpEx, and capacity). The result of this study (blue solid line) has a similar shape to the normal distribution (green solid line), and is most likely to form a price range of around 2,000 million USD. About 490 million USD will be allocated to RE in Korea in 2022, and it appears that this budget will need to be gradually increased in order to meet the country's 2030 RE objective.

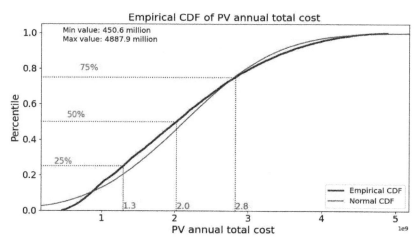

Fig. 3. Empirical cumulative density function of PV annual total cost.

## 5. Conclusions

This study carried out a techno-economic assessment based on national policy for a target year. A case study in Korea was used to calculate the LCOE for RE networks under different scenarios. The following steps were taken to perform the techno-economic assessment of the scenarios: 1) Consider the conversion factor estimated by the installed capacity and capacity factor over time, 2) Use a deep generative model-based sampling method to account for uncertainties, 3) Forecast 2030 supply and demand data using machine learning models. In this study, the GRU-based forecasting model was found to be the optimal model with the best performance and the lowest information scores. Using 2030 supply and demand data and technical data, a techno-economic assessment was carried out for a carbon-neutral economy based on national policy. The results showed that FPV are up to 28% more cost-effective compared to PV. The validity of the results was confirmed by the LCOE of each scenario, which showed an absolute error range of 0.8-1.2 compared to the theoretical total cost, indicating that a carbon-neutral economy in Korea is feasible. Further research will be conducted to consider various factors and extend the study to a global model.

## References

MOTIE, 2017, Renewable energy 3020 implementation plan, Seoul, Korea., The Government of the Republic of Korea.

K. J. Nam, S. Hwangbo, C. K. Yoo, 2020, A deep learning-based forecasting model for renewable energy scenarios to guide sustainable energy policy: A case study of Korea, Renewable and Sustainable Energy Reviews, 122(March 2019); 109725.

Y. Qi, W. Hu, Y. Dong, Y. Fan, L. Dong, M. Xiao, 2020, Optimal configuration of concentrating solar power in multienergy power systems with an improved variational autoencoder, Applied Energy, 274(June); 115124.

G. R. Timilsina, 2021, Are renewable energy technologies cost competitive for electricity generation?, Renewable Energy, 180; 658–672.

H. Wang, Z. Lei, X. Zhang, B. Zhou, J. Peng, 2019, A review of deep learning for renewable energy forecasting, Energy Conversion and Management, 198(April); 111799.

Antonis Kokossis, Michael C. Georgiadis, Efstratios N. Pistikopoulos (Eds.)
PROCEEDINGS OF THE 33rd European Symposium on Computer Aided Process Engineering
(ESCAPE33), June 18-21, 2023, Athens, Greece

# Evaluation of centralized/decentralized configuration schemes of CO2 electrochemical reduction-based supply chains

Thijmen Wiltink[a], Stijn Yska[a], Andrea Ramirez[a], Mar Pérez-Fortes[a]

[a] *Department of Engineering, Systems, and Services, Faculty of Technology, Policy, and Management, Delft University of Technology, Jaffalaan 5, 2628 BX Delft*
*T.J.Wiltink@TUDelft.nl*

## Abstract

Electrochemical reduction of $CO_2$ ($CO_2ER$) is an emerging technology with the potential to limit the use of fossil-based feedstocks in the petrochemical industry by converting $CO_2$ and renewable electricity into useful products such as syngas. Its successful deployment will depend not only on the technology's performance but also on its integration into the supply chain. In this work, a facility location model is used to gain insights regarding the capacity of $CO_2ER$ plants that produce syngas and the implications for the central/decentral placement of these $CO_2$-based syngas plants. Different optimal configurations are examined in the model by changing the syngas transport costs. In this exploratory case, the results indicate that centralization is only an option when the syngas and $CO_2$ transport costs are similar. When syngas transport is more expensive, decentralizing $CO_2$-based syngas plants in the supply chain appears more feasible.

**Keywords**: $CO_2$ electrochemical reduction; $CO_2$ utilization, supply chain modeling, optimization, supply chain configurations

## 1. Introduction

The European Green Deal includes the 2030 Climate Target Plan targeting a greenhouse gas (GHG) emission reduction of at least 55% in 2030 compared to 1990 levels and a net-zero GHG emissions target by 2050 (European Commission, 2019). This requires a drastic change in the petrochemical industry, which is challenging due to the industry's dependence on fossil fuels as its carbon feedstock. Currently, processes using $CO_2$ as an alternative feedstock are being developed. In the electrochemical reduction of $CO_2$ ($CO_2ER$), $CO_2$, water, and electricity are converted into a range of intermediates and final products that can be used for further chemical and fuel synthesis in multiple sectors. $CO_2ER$ is not yet a mature technology, and ultimately it will be integrated into already existing supply chains (SCs), which affects the SC configurations in terms of implementation scale and (de)centralization of the technology. In order to study the impact of the $CO_2ER$ technology in connection with its SC, a facility location optimization model was developed in the current work to understand the potential trade-offs of decentralized/centralized configurations when replacing fossil-based syngas with $CO_2$-based syngas from a $CO_2ER$ process. Centralized/decentralized business cases for $CO_2ER$ are explored from an SC perspective in the European petrochemical context using a hypothetical case study. Syngas is chosen as the product of interest, as it is a large-scale fossil-based industrial product, commercialized as a versatile commodity that can be used as a precursor for a wide range of processes in the petrochemical industry (Choe et al., 2022; Ebbehøj, 2015). Syngas is a mixture of hydrogen and carbon monoxide (CO). The CO molecule in syngas makes the mixture toxic, which adds safety requirements to the transportation and handling of this feedstock. Alternative feedstocks for syngas production are described in SC literature; the primary focus has so far been on the upstream part of the SC (e.g., (Ahmadvand and Sowlati, 2022; Marufuzzaman et al., 2016)). In these studies, the current business model is employed where syngas is produced on-site (i.e., without storage and transport). Transporting syngas to establish a centralized market is not considered. This work investigates how an industrial scale $CO_2$-based syngas SC could look like for different syngas transportation costs in relation to $CO_2$ transport costs. The facility location model selects the optimal locations, the number of $CO_2$-based syngas plants, the plant capacities, and connections between echelons in a three-stage SC, see Figure 1A.

## 2. Mathematical model formulation of CO2-based syngas supply chain

A fixed charge facility location problem (FLP) is formulated as a mixed integer linear program (MILP). This model is an uncapacitated multiple allocation FLP; the maximum size of the $CO_2$-based syngas plant is not constrained, and individual echelons can connect to multiple other echelons. The problem is formulated as a p-median problem, the foundations of which are laid by Hakimi (1964). The model is based on the SiLCaRD (simultaneous location of central and regional distribution facilities) model formulated in the work of Götzinger (2013).

Mass balance constraints ensure that the amount of $CO_2$ captured in the system is in equilibrium with the amount of syngas at the demand locations and that mass conservation is guaranteed. Location constraints specify where to establish and open the $CO_2$-based syngas plants, while allocation constraints select and connect the different echelons in the system. The piecewise linear transport constraints allow for dealing with non-linearities in transport. The mathematical is elaborated below and the decision variables are emphasized in bold font:

| | |
|---|---|
| $H$ | set of $CO_2$ source locations, indexed by $h$ |
| $J$ | set of potential $CO_2$-based syngas plant locations, indexed by $j$ |
| $K$ | set of syngas demand locations, indexed by $k$ |
| $Q$ | set of transport segments of the piecewise linear cost function, indexed by $q$ |
| $A_q$ | slope [€$_{2020}$/kilometer/Mtonne transported] of segment $q$ in the piecewise linear transport cost function |
| $B_q$ | intercept [€$_{2020}$] of segment $q$ in the piecewise linear transport cost function |
| $C_{hj}$ | distance [kilometers] from $CO_2$ source $h$ to $CO_2$-based syngas plant $j$ |
| $C_{jk}$ | distance [kilometers] from $CO_2$-based syngas plant $j$ to syngas consumer $k$ |
| $CC_h$ | average carbon capture cost [€$_{2020}$/Mtonne] at the $CO_2$ source (at cluster level) |
| $CF_{st}$ | cost factor of syngas transport [€$_{2020}$ syngas transported /€$_{2020}$ $CO_2$ transported] |
| $SG_{Conf}$ | $CO_2$-to-syngas conversion factor [Mtonne syngas/Mtonne $CO_2$] |
| $\mathbf{yq}_{hj}$ | 1 if the $CO_2$-based syngas plant $j$ is assigned to $CO_2$ source $h$ in segment $q$ of the piecewise linear transport function, 0 if not |
| $\mathbf{yq}_{jk}$ | 1 if the syngas consumer $k$ is assigned to the $CO_2$-based syngas plant $j$ in segment $q$ of the piecewise linear transport function, 0 if not |
| $\mathbf{z}_{hjq}$ | size [in Mtonne of $CO_2$ transported] from $CO_2$ source $h$ to $CO_2$-based syngas plant $j$ in segment $q$ of a piecewise linear function |
| $\mathbf{z}_{jkq}$ | size [in Mtonne syngas] transported from $CO_2$-based syngas plant $j$ to syngas consumer $k$ in segment $q$ of a piecewise linear function |

The objective function aims to minimize the yearly capture costs at the industrial cluster (1a), the yearly pipeline transport cost of $CO_2$ from $CO_2$ sources to $CO_2$-based syngas plants (1b), and the yearly (hypothetical) pipeline transport cost of syngas from $CO_2$-based syngas plants to syngas consumers (1c). The amount of $CO_2$ captured ($z_{hjq}$) and the size of the electrolyzer ($z_{jkq}$) is determined as a result of the minimization of the objective function to fulfill the syngas demand in the SC. A piecewise linear transport cost function is applied to all the transport links between the echelons in the model. The amount of $CO_2$ (from source to $CO_2$-based syngas plant) is multiplied with a $CO_2$-to-syngas conversion factor to calculate the plant's syngas production; see equation (2). Objective function - minimize:

$$(1a) \qquad\qquad (1b) \qquad\qquad\qquad (1c)$$

$$\sum_{h \in H}\sum_{j \in J}\sum_{q \in Q} z_{hjq} * CC_h \quad + \sum_{h \in H}\sum_{j \in J}\sum_{q \in Q} A_q * z_{hjq} \quad + \sum_{j \in J}\sum_{k \in K}\sum_{q \in Q}(A_q * z_{jkq} * C_{jk} + B_q * yq_{jk})$$

$$* C_{hj} + B_q * yq_{hj} \qquad\qquad * CF_{st}$$

$$SG_{Conf} * \sum_{h \in H}\sum_{q \in Q} z_{hjq} = \sum_{j \in J}\sum_{q \in Q} z_{jkq} \qquad\qquad \forall j \in J \quad (2)$$

## 3. Case study – CO₂-based syngas supply chains

A 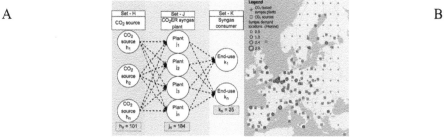 B

Figure 1 - A – Representation of the three-echelon supply chain model described in this case study. B – Industrial CO₂ sources in Europe, potential CO₂ -based syngas plant locations, and syngas demand locations with sizes.

The model uses geographical data from industrial clusters in Europe (EU-27+UK). It uses a discrete grid of potential $CO_2$-based syngas plant locations. A 100 x 100 grid was placed to create potential location sites for CO₂ER plants from the borders of Portugal to Finland. For the purpose of this study, plant locations over the sea were disregarded, and the industrial cluster locations were added as potential location sites, resulting in 185 potential electrolyzer locations, see Figure 1B. The current case study contains CO₂ emission data from 101 industrial clusters (with 944 individual plants within these clusters from 9 types of industries: ammonia, cement, lime, iron & steel, refining, petrochemical, oil & gas, power generation, and aluminum). Industry-specific CO₂ impurities were not considered, and it was assumed that CO₂ is in the same conditions irrespective of its source. The dataset is available via ArcGIS online (Boston Consulting Group, 2021) and is based on the European Pollutant Release and Transfer Register (European Environment Agency, 2020). The following considerations were taken into account:

• The worldwide syngas market was 150 Mtonne in 2018 (Jouny et al., 2018), with a CAGR of 9.5% it is estimated to reach 180 Mtonne in reference year 2020 (Inkwood Research, 2017). Europe uses approximately 22% of global syngas, with 51% in the petrochemical industry (IMARC, 2021). The estimated syngas demand in Europe's petrochemical industry used in this work was 20.3 Mtonne/year. In the model, the demand needs to be assigned to specific locations. In order to assign different syngas demands to different (hypothetical) sites, a syngas plant size of 0.482 Mtonne/year was assumed based on the syngas demand of a standard methanol plant size of 0.4 Mtonne/year (Ebbehøj, 2015). To fulfill the syngas demand using this standardized size, 42 $CO_2$-based syngas plants would be necessary. 42 of the 84 petrochemical plants in the European dataset were randomly selected to serve as syngas demand locations. The demand was summed when the selected plants were part of the same cluster.

• The costs of $CO_2$ transport were based on (hypothetical) existing onshore pipelines (i.e., only operating costs are considered). A piecewise linearization is used based on the values by d'Amore (2021).

• This work assumes an existing syngas transportation infrastructure (i.e., only operating costs are considered). Currently, there is limited data available on the transportation of syngas. Direct use of syngas is the dominant business case causing the lack of existence of commercial-scale syngas transportation networks. The costs of syngas transport are therefore highly uncertain and likely more expensive than $CO_2$ transport due to additional safety requirements. For the latter, Knoope (2015) has shown how $CO_2$ transport costs increase with additional safety measures. In this study, the costs of syngas transport are based on the transport costs of $CO_2$ but were multiplied with different cost factors to investigate its effect on the centralized/decentralized deployment and the SC configuration.

• The capture costs of $CO_2$ were averaged at the cluster level based on the mass of $CO_2$ emissions of individual plants in that cluster and the capture costs per industry. These capture costs [in $€_{2020}$] were based on the capture cost from Global CCS Institute (2021) and $CO_2$ compression costs from IEA (2020). The $CO_2$ coming from the petrochemical, oil, and gas industries was assumed to have the same capture and compression cost as from the oil refining industry.

## 4. Case study results

The problem formulation was formulated in GAMS (41.1) and optimized using the CPLEX 22.1.0.0 MIP solver. The system ran with an Intel®Core™ i7-1185G7 CPU 3GHz processor and 32GB RAM. The problem comprised 228,893 variables, of which 93,526 were binary and 350,303 equations. The model was solved for five different transport cost factors (CF) values (1-3) and took 11 minutes.

The SC configurations with varying cost factors for syngas transport are presented in Figure 2, while the different SC characteristics are presented in Table 1. For all the CFs, the same 25 syngas demand locations were selected. Plants were co-located when the $CO_2$ source, the $CO_2$-based syngas plant, and the syngas consumer were within the same industrial cluster. Co-locating reduces transport dependency; however, in some cases, $CO_2$/syngas transport was still needed to fulfill the syngas demand or desired to optimize costs. Remote $CO_2$ capture and transport can be cheaper to (partly) fulfill the demand compared to on-site capture due to capture cost differences between clusters. When the transport of syngas was more expensive than $CO_2$ co-locating the $CO_2$ source with the $CO_2$-based syngas plant became more viable. In CF2.5, there remains a need for $CO_2$ transport to 5 clusters to fulfill syngas demand. The cost factors affect the capacity of the

Table 1 Supply chains characteristics for different syngas transport cost factors

| Cost factor | Capacity CO₂-based syngas plants | | | CO₂ sources | CO₂-based syngas plants | Co-located plants |
|---|---|---|---|---|---|---|
| [-] | [Mtonne syngas] | | | [#] | [#] | [#] |
| | Min | Max | Avg. | | | |
| 1 | 0.24 | 3.5 | 0.99 | 21 | 21 | 15 |
| 1.5 | 0.24 | 3.5 | 0.87 | 24 | 24 | 18 |
| 2 | 0.24 | 3.5 | 0.87 | 25 | 24 | 20 |
| 2.5 | 0.50 | 3.0 | 0.83 | 26 | 25 | 21 |
| 3 | 0.50 | 3.0 | 0.83 | 26 | 25 | 21 |

individual plants, as the average capacity is higher at a lower cost factor. In other words, lower transport cost increase plant capacity leading to a more centralized SC.

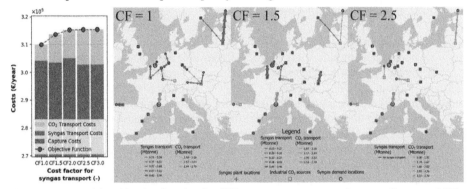

Figure 2 - Parts of the objective function for different syngas transportation costs factors and CO₂-based syngas supply chains with different syngas cost factors.

The total SC cost in the objective function is hardly affected by an increase in syngas transportation cost, see Figure 2. The CF1 SC can benefit from the cheapest CO₂ capture sources. When syngas transport becomes more expensive, the model chooses to pay more for capturing CO₂ at less favorable locations to avoid transportation. At a CF of 2.5, syngas transport is eliminated.

## 5. Conclusion and future work

A simplified CO₂-based syngas supply chain facility location model was developed in this work. The objective minimized the CO₂ capture, transportation, and syngas transport costs. In this case, when syngas transportation has the same price as CO₂ transport, there are options for centralization in the CO₂-based syngas SC. At higher syngas transportation costs, decentral SCs are preferred. When syngas transport is as expensive as CO₂ transport, syngas transport is favored due to its lower transport volume and potential to capitalize on clusters with lower capture costs. CO₂ transport is occasionally necessary for clusters with insufficient CO₂ to fulfill their syngas demand after CO2ER conversion.

In the next iteration of the model, a sensitivity analysis will be performed by exploring different syngas demand locations and sizes, which will help generalize the findings of this specific case. The current model is a starting point for developing a more exhaustive CO₂-to-syngas-based SC model, focusing on enhancing transportation details and refining the objective function. With this exploratory case, the first insights were gained regarding the scale of CO₂-based syngas plants and the preference for a centralized/decentralized configuration of the SC.

## Acknowledgments

This research receives funding from the project "Addressing the multiscale challenge of $CO_2$ electrochemical reduction", NWO ECCM tenure track grant (project number ECCM.TT.009), and "Sustainable design of multiscale $CO_2$ electrochemical conversion", MVI grant (ECCM.TT.MVITU.006).

## 6. References

Ahmadvand, S., Sowlati, T., 2022, A robust optimization model for tactical planning of the forest-based biomass supply chain for syngas production, Computers and Chemical Engineering, 159, 107693.

Boston Consulting Group, 2021, Hubs and Industry layer, Retrieved November 18, 2022, from https://edu.nl/g3twa

Choe, C., Cheon, S., Gu, J., Lim, H., 2022, Critical aspect of renewable syngas production for power-to-fuel via solid oxide electrolysis: Integrative assessment for potential renewable energy source, Renewable and Sustainable Energy Reviews, 161, April, 112398.

d'Amore, F., Romano, M. C., Bezzo, F., 2021, Optimal design of European supply chains for carbon capture and storage from industrial emission sources including pipe and ship transport, International Journal of Greenhouse Gas Control, 109.

Ebbehøj, S. L., 2015, Integration of CO2 air capture and solid oxide electrolysis for methane production, Department of Energy Conversion and Storage, Technical University of Denmark.

European Commission, 2019, The European Green Deal, European Commission, 53, 9.

European Environment Agency, 2020, The European Pollutant Release and Transfer Register (E-PRTR).

Global CCS Institute, 2021, Technology Readiness and Costs of CCS. Global CCS Insitute, March, 50.

Götzinger, M. J. W., 2013, Facility Location Planning for Distribution Networks and Infrastructure Locations, University of Freiburg, 160.

Hakimi, S. L., 1964, Optimum Locations of Switching Centers and the Absolute Centers and Medians of a Graph, Operations Research, 12, 3, 450–459.

IEA, 2020, Energy Technology Perspectives 2020 - Special Report on Carbon Capture Utilisation and Storage.

IMARC, 2021, Syngas Market: Global Industry Trends, Share, Size, Growth, Opportunity and Forecast 2022-2027, Retrieved November 7, 2022, from https://www.imarcgroup.com/syngas-market

Inkwood Research, 2017, Syngas Market - Global Trends, Size Share, Analysis Report 2017-2026, Retrieved November 9, 2022, from https://edu.nl/77qea

Jouny, M., Luc, W., Jiao, F, 2018, General Techno-Economic Analysis of CO2 Electrolysis Systems, Industrial and Engineering Chemistry Research, 57 ,6, 2165–2177.

Knoope, M. M. J., 2015, Costs, safety and uncertainties of CO2 infrastructure development, 359.

Marufuzzaman, M., Li, X., Yu, F., Zhou, F., 2016, Supply Chain Design and Management for Syngas Production, ACS Sustainable Chemistry and Engineering, 4, 3, 890–900.

Antonis Kokossis, Michael C. Georgiadis, Efstratios N. Pistikopoulos (Eds.)
PROCEEDINGS OF THE 33rd European Symposium on Computer Aided Process Engineering
(ESCAPE33), June 18-21, 2023, Athens, Greece
© 2023 Elsevier B.V. All rights reserved.  http://dx.doi.org/10.1016/B978-0-443-15274-0.50546-1

# Optimization of large-scale energy systems to achieve carbon emissions neutrality

Sanja Potrč,[a] Andreja Nemet,[a] Lidija Čuček,[a] Petar Varbanov,[b] Zdravko Kravanja,[a]

[a]*Faculty of Chemistry and Chemical Engineering, University of Maribor, Smetanova ulica 17, 2000 Maribor, Slovenia*
[b]*Sustainable Process Integration Laboratory – SPIL, NETME Centre, Faculty of Mechanical Engineering, Brno University of Technology – VUT Brno, Technicka 2896/2, 616 69 Brno, Czech Republic*

## Abstract

This contribution presents a synthesis of sustainable renewable energy supply networks to achieve a carbon emission neutral energy system in the EU by 2050, considering the generation and supply of heat and electricity from renewable and nuclear sources, second- and third-generation liquid biofuels, hydrogen and by-products from different sources using different conversion and storage technologies. A multi-period, mixed-integer linear programming (MILP) model is developed that aims to maximize the Sustainability Net Present Value of the EU's future energy system, emphasizing the role of energy storage technologies in achieving carbon emissions neutrality while taking into account the Earth's great potential for self-regeneration. The results show that in 2050, 502 TWh/y of electricity demand could be covered by electricity stored in batteries, followed by 213 TWh/y covered by pumped hydro storage, while applied thermal energy storage technologies are expected to meet 389 TWh/y of heat demand. The integration of the studied electricity and thermal storage technologies will also make an important contribution to achieving a carbon-neutral energy system in the EU with a 7.6 % reduction in $CO_2$ emissions in 2050 for the identified energy mix compared to the system without energy storages.

**Keywords**: supply network optimization, energy storage, renewable energy, energy transition, carbon emissions neutrality.

## 1. Introduction

In order to accomplish the EU's climate and energy goals, a rapid transformation of the energy system and further developments toward more efficient energy generation, supply and use are required. The integration of energy storage technologies plays an important role in the transition towards carbon emissions neutrality and provides a concrete means to improve the energy efficiency of the future energy system based on renewable energy sources, while increasing energy security in the EU (European Commission, 2020).
Several studies have examined the impact of integrating storage technologies in the transition to carbon emissions neutrality at different spatial and temporal scales. Child et al. (2018) examined the role of storage technologies in the gradual transition to a 100 % renewable power sector in Europe by 2050 and concluded that up to 15 % of electricity demand could be covered by battery storage, highlighting its important supporting role. In addition, the deployment of flexible renewable energy generation and energy storage could significantly reduce the levelized cost of electricity, especially when optimization

is performed at larger geographic scale (Child et al. 2019). The results of the study by Dowling et al. (2020) suggest that the introduction of long duration energy storage, such as pumped hydro storage and compressed air energy storage, could significantly reduce the cost of a future electricity system that relies on intermittent energy sources, and to a much greater extent that could be achieved by equivalent reductions in battery costs. Most of the transition pathways towards the renewable energy system have been simulated using the LUT energy system transition model or the EnergyPLAN hourly simulation model.

This study presents the optimization of renewable energy supply networks for the gradual transition to a renewable energy system in the EU to achieve carbon emission neutrality by 2050. A multi-period mixed-integer linear programming (MILP) model was developed that simultaneously considers all three aspects of sustainability, economic, environmental and social. Electricity, heat, second and third generation biofuels, and hydrogen generation and supply are taken into account to satisfy the demand in end-use sectors. Our previous work (Potrč et al., 2022) was extended to include energy storage technologies to show their potential in the EU's future energy system with a high share of renewables and their impact on achieving carbon emissions neutrality, while also considering the Earth's large potential for natural carbon sequestration.

## 2. Methodology for the synthesis of a large-scale renewable energy supply networks

The synthesis of large-scale supply networks involves a large number of highly complex interactions and by addressing these interactions simultaneously with effective solution procedures, many of the synergistic effects of the subsystems can be exploited. The simultaneous solving of these subsystems, which also guarantees the optimality of the results for a given set of conditions, is only possible with a mathematical programming approach. It is also important that the optimization criteria are sustainable, covering economic, environmental and social aspects of sustainability. For this purpose, a maximization of the composite criterion Sustainability Net Present Value (Zore et al., 2018) was used as an objective, Eq. (1).

$$\max NPV^{\text{Sustainability}} = NPV^{\text{Economic}} + NPV^{\text{Eco}} + NPV^{\text{Social}} \tag{1}$$

$NPV^{\text{Sustainability}}$ is defined as the sum of economic, environmental and social $NPVs$, with economic $NPV$ calculated as the sum of cash flows over the years, where each annual cash flow is discounted to the present. For the environmental $NPV$, burdening and unburdening effects of energy sources, pretreatment, conversion technologies, products, transportation and land-use were considered, while for the social NPV, the creation of additional jobs was the main contributor.

A gradual transition to a renewable energy system to achieve carbon emissions neutrality by 2050 was conducted with 10-year time steps, taking into account dynamic changes through the supply network using monthly, daily, and hourly time periods. Electricity and heat generation, demand and storage, as well as availability of variable sources, were modelled on an hourly basis, while monthly time periods were used for biofuels. Future price trends and potential improvements in the efficiency of existing and emerging technologies, as well as the EU projection for the nuclear energy use, were also considered.

The mathematical model accounts for several model size reduction techniques to keep the model solvable: (i) patterns in intermittent sources availability and electricity and heat generation, demand, and storage were applied to reduce computation time, where time periods were reduced to two periods per week and four periods per day; (ii) connectivity in a renewable energy supply network was reduced by specifying the maximum allowable distances between supply, pretreatment, storage, production, and demand sites; (iii) unnecessary variables and constraints with zero-flows were eliminated (Lam et al., 2011); (iv) the number of zones was reduced from 132 zones in the original formulation (Potrč et al., 2020) to 47 zones, emphasizing the regional characteristics in each country using geographically specific data. In addition, the nonlinear investment terms were linearized using a piecewise linear approximation, transforming the MINLP model to a MILP model. The model takes into account the generation and supply of electricity and heat, liquid biofuels (second and third generation), hydrogen, and other byproducts from various renewable and clean energy sources and biowaste, using different conversion and storage technologies. All integration options are shown in Figure 1.

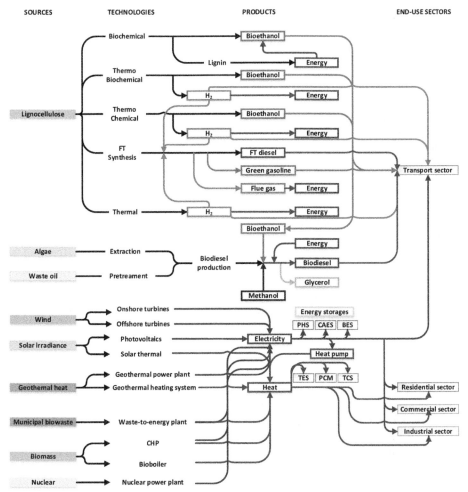

Figure 1. Integration possibilities in renewable energy supply network (modified after Potrč et al., 2022).

In addition, the possibility of converting thermal power plants currently in operation into biomass cogeneration plants is also being considered. The storage technologies considered are pumped hydro storage (PHS), utility-scale battery storage systems (BES), compressed air energy storage (CAES), thermal energy storage (TES), storage in phase change materials (PCM), and thermo-chemical energy storage (TCS). The TES technologies investigated in this study are hot water tanks for domestic hot water storage, large water tanks (seasonal), underground thermal energy storage, and molten salt storage. Data on the performance and costs of the storage technologies were taken from (IEA-ETSAP and IRENA, 2013; IRENA, 2019).

The model includes production and conversion constraints, constraints on plant capacities, pretreatment, investment, operating, storage and transportation costs, economic, environmental and social constraints, and also the area that could be used for energy generation in each zone is limited to preserve biodiversity. To predict the future concentration of $CO_2$ in the atmosphere, the Earth's $CO_2$ self-sequestration capability was considered, and the prediction model was developed based on historical data (Potrč at al., 2022). The overall synthesis model was formulated in the modeling system GAMS, and the solutions were obtained in about a week using the solver CPLEX on the HPC server DL580 G9 CTO (4 processors, 32-core, Intel® Xeon® CPU E5-4627 v2 @ 3.30 GHz, 768 GB RAM).

## 3. Results

The following gradual transition to highly renewable energy system in the EU by 2050 was studied to achieve carbon emission neutrality: (i) at least 50 % share of RES in electricity and heat supply in all end-use sectors, and 30 % share of RES in road transportation by 2030, (ii) at least 75 % share of electricity and heat from RES and at least 60 % share of RES in road transport by 2040, and (iii) in 2050, electricity supply in all sectors should be met by renewables or nuclear energy and the highest possible share of RES in heat supply and road transport should be achieved to reach the goal of a carbon neutral EU.

Figure 2 shows the proposed electricity and heat generation, and energy storage output of the various technologies over the years. The optimization results indicate that in the first years of the energy transition (until 2030), most of the electricity from RES will be generated by wind farms, 798 TWh/y, followed by 497 TWh/y from biomass cogeneration plants, 352 TWh/y from hydropower plants and 301 TWh/y from solar PV. The possibility of converting thermal power plants currently in operation into biomass cogeneration plant is also proposed in most of the Member States, as the investment costs of reconstruction are lower compared to the construction of new CHP plants. After 2030, faster spreading of electricity generation from wind turbines and solar PV is proposed, while the construction of additional CHP plants is not proposed after 2030. Electricity demand in the EU is expected to increase to about 5,400 TWh/y by 2050. 13.4 % of electricity generation would be covered by nuclear power plants, 38.2 % by wind turbines (onshore and offshore), 26.7 % by solar PV, while other technologies considered will contribute another 21.7 %. In terms of heat generation and supply, air-source heat pumps are expected to meet 37.5 % of heat demand, biomass cogeneration plants (newly constructed and converted from thermal power plants) 26.2 %, and solar thermal 16.1%, while smaller shares are expected from geothermal energy, biomass boilers, and WtE using biowaste fraction of municipal solid waste as a source.

As can be seen in Figure 2, the energy output from storage technologies correlates with energy production, especially that from intermittent sources. Pumped hydro storage, which currently accounts for 97 % of all electricity storage in the EU, is expected to meet 160 TWh/y of electricity demand by 2030. Utility-scale battery storage system is expected to cover 92 TWh in 2030, while by 2040 BES output is proposed to exceed PHS with 218 TWh/y of energy output to provide balances in shorter time periods due to the higher share of electricity generated from intermittent sources. CAES will enable an additional 115 TWh/y of electricity storage. BES is preferred over CAES due to its higher round-trip efficiency. In 2050, 1,254 TWh/y of electricity and heat demand is proposed to be met by applied storage technologies, of which 502 TWh/y corresponds to batteries, 324 TWh/y to sensible thermal energy storage, and 213 TWh/y to pumped hydro storage, while CAES, storage in PCM, and thermochemical energy storage are expected to meet 150 TWh/y, 29 TWh/y, and 36 TWh/y, respectively. Applied electricity storage technologies are expected to cover 865 TWh/y or 16 % of electricity demand across all end-use sectors and applied thermal energy storage technologies 389 TWh/y or 9 % of heat demand by 2050.

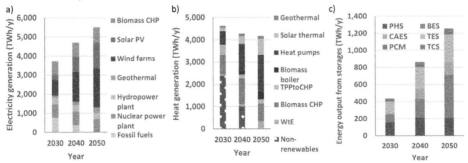

Figure 2. Production of a) electricity and b) heat, and c) energy output from storages in EU by 2050.

In the road transport sector, electricity is proposed to cover more than 55 % of the energy demand, while biodiesel and FT-diesel will account for 28 %, bioethanol and 'green' gasoline for 11 %, and hydrogen for 6 %. The Sustainability NPV of the proposed transition to a carbon-neutral energy system amounts to 5,865,975 M€, with the environmental NPV being the largest contributor.

It is interesting to note that the integration of storage technologies will also significantly reduce $CO_2$ emissions from generation and supply of energy. In our previous work (Potrč et al., 2022) the Earth's great potential for self-regeneration has been assessed, indicating that more than a half of the annual anthropogenic $CO_2$ emissions are removed through natural sequestration. The results show that anthropogenic $CO_2$ emissions would have to decrease by 69 % from 1990 levels to achieve emissions neutrality, with about 1.2 Gt/y of $CO_2$ released into the atmosphere and the same amount removed from the atmosphere by the Earth. Electricity storage is expected to account for 4.4 % and thermal energy storage for 3.2 % of the reduction in $CO_2$ emissions in 2050 at the energy mix identified for that year. Compared to the current energy mix, the reduction in $CO_2$ emissions will be even higher, accounting for 15.3 % of the emissions reduction.

## Conclusions

A high share of renewables, integration of energy storage technologies, and cross-sectoral energy integration will play a very important role in achieving carbon emissions neutrality by 2050. It is also important that the Earth's large $CO_2$ self-regeneration potential is considered when planning a transition pathway to achieve carbon emissions neutrality, as more than half of annual anthropogenic $CO_2$ emissions are removed from the atmosphere through natural carbon sequestration. The synthesis of such large systems involves a large number of highly complex interactions. For this purpose, various model linearization, convexification and model size reduction techniques have been applied, e.g., i) piecewise linear approximation of nonlinear nonconvex terms, reducing the MINLP model to a MILP model, ii) use of surrogate models for different production plants after the detailed synthesis of their individual flowsheets, iii) reduction of the number of zones, etc. The optimization of renewable and clean energy supply networks for the gradual transition to a highly renewable energy system in the EU to achieve carbon emissions neutrality was based on a multi-period MILP model that considers the production and supply of heat and electricity from renewable and nuclear sources, second- and third-generation liquid biofuels, hydrogen, and by-products from various sources using different conversion and storage technologies to meet the demand in all end-use sectors. The results show that pumped hydro storage is expected to dominate in the first year of the transition, while grid-scale battery storage systems are expected to increase after 2030 due to the larger share of intermittent sources. By 2050, 1,254 TWh/y of energy demand is expected to be met by applied storage technologies, with batteries accounting for 40 %, thermal energy storage technologies for 26 %, and pumped hydro storage for 17%, while the shares of compressed air energy storage, thermochemical energy storage and storage in phase change materials are expected to reach 12 %, 3 % and 2 %, respectively. The integration of the studied electricity and thermal storage technologies will also contribute significantly for achieving carbon emission neutrality with a 7.6 % reduction in $CO_2$ emissions in 2050 for the identified energy mix.

## References

M. Child, D. Bogdanov, C. Breyer, 2018, The role of storage technologies for the transition to a 100% renewable energy system in Europe, Energy Procedia, 155, 44-60.

M. Child, C. Kemfert, D. Bogdanov, C. Breyer, 2019, Flexible electricity generation, grid exchange and storage for the transition to a 100% renewable energy system in Europe, 139, 80-101.

J.A. Dowling, K.Z. Rinaldi, T.H. Ruggles, S.J. Davis, M. Yuan, F. Tong, N.S. Lewis, K. Caldeira, 2020, Role of Long-Duration Energy Storage in Variable Renewable Electricity Systems, Joule, 4, 9, 1907-1928.

European Commission, 2020, Study on energy storage - Contribution to the security of the electricity supply in Europe, Publications Office, https://data.europa.eu/doi/10.2833/077257, accessed on 29th November 2022.

IEA-ETSAP and IRENA, 2013, Technology Briefs, https://www.irena.org/publications/2013/jan/irena-iea-etsap-technology-briefs, accessed on 11th November 2022.

IRENA, 2019, Utility-Scale Batteries Innovation Landscape Brief, https://www.irena.org/-/media/Files/IRENA/Agency/Publication/2019/Sep/IRENA_Utility-scale-batteries_2019.pdf, accessed on 12th November 2022.

H. L. Lam, J.J. Klemeš, Z.Kravanja, 2011, Model-size reduction techniques for large-scale biomass production and supply networks, Energy, 36, 8, 4599-4608.

S. Potrč, L. Čuček, M. Martin, Z. Kravanja, 2020, Synthesis of European Union Biorefinery Supply Networks Considering Sustainability Objectives, Processes, 8, 12 1588.

S. Potrč, A. Nemet, L. Čuček, P. Varbanov, Z. Kravanja, 2022, Synthesis of a regenerative energy system – beyond carbon emissions neutrality, Renewable and sustainable energy reviews, 169, 112924.

Ž. Zore, L. Čuček, D. Širovnik, Z. Novak Pintarič, Z. Kravanja, 2018, Maximizing the sustainability net present value of renewable energy supply networks, Chemical Engineering Research and Design, 131, 245-265.

Antonis Kokossis, Michael C. Georgiadis, Efstratios N. Pistikopoulos (Eds.)
PROCEEDINGS OF THE 33rd European Symposium on Computer Aided Process Engineering
(ESCAPE33), June 18-21, 2023, Athens, Greece
© 2023 Elsevier B.V. All rights reserved.  http://dx.doi.org/10.1016/B978-0-443-15274-0.50547-3

# Multi-objective sustainable supply chain design under uncertainty in energy price

F.L. Garcia-Castro,[a] R. Ruiz-Femenia,[a]  R. Salcedo-Diaz,[a] J. A. Caballero[a]

[a]*Institute of Chemical Process Engineering, University of Alicante, Aparatado de Correos 99, Alicante 03080, Spain*

## Abstract

In our society, sustainability and global responsibility concepts have been gaining in importance over the years. For the manufacturing companies and supply chains there is a direct impact on their benefits, not only through an increasing demand of sustainable products, but also trough the regulations that aim to reduce the total emissions over the years. Moreover, due to the current political situation, the prices of energy could jeopardize many companies, whose production is no longer profitable.

For all these reasons, it is more important than ever to apply a holistic view in the design of supply chains and ensure a model that considers risk management.

Our case-study is a petrochemical three echelon supply chain in Europe, where we incorporate the cap-and-trade model from the European Union emissions Trading System, to directly link the emissions associated to consumption of raw material, energy consumption and transportation to the total benefit of the supply chain.

We present an optimal design of a supply chain facing uncertainty in energy prices, which is modelled by fitting historical data in an ARIMA model. It involves the solution of a multi-objective multi-period mixed integer linear program that was implemented in Python using Pyomo and solved using IBMs CPLEX solver.

**Keywords**: Energy price, carbon price, multi-objective optimization, risk management.

## 1. Introduction

Regarding the design of a supply chain, a vast amount of information and metrics need to be considered during the process of decision-making. One important aspect to consider are uncertainties of the underlying parameters, such as demand, carbon prices, energy prices, etc., leading to stochastic numerical models. Solving a stochastic model yields a supply chain design that is more robust against changes in the uncertain parameters, and will have a superior expected performance over designs resulting from deterministic models. The consideration of uncertainty has been widely addressed in the literature mainly for cost and demand, c.f. Yang. et al. 2015, Robles et al. 2020. In this work, we consider uncertainty of energy prices, a topic that has recently become very important in the euro zone, c.f. the article on energy prices and security of supply (2022). In order to generate possible pricing scenarios, we identify the best-suited parameters of an ARIMA model and fit it to the historical price data. We then use this model to forecast energy prices for the next 10 years.

Another important concept in the design of supply chains is evolving carbon regulations, which governments are implementing to control the available amount of carbon emissions for the industry. These regulations have been changing fast over the last years. In our model, we considered a cap-and-trade system based on the European Union Emissions Trading System. Each company is assigned a fraction of a total quantity of emissions that is reduced over time. The companies may then produce their goods and / or trade with their assigned emissions.

When it comes to making design decisions, it is not only important to assure robustness against possible future parameter changes, but also to consider the impact of decisions and the risk associated to them. Hence, instead of only maximizing the profit, we considered a multi-objective model that also aims to minimizes the downside risk (DR). The conjoint study of uncertainty in energy prices, risk management and carbon regulations will provide important information when taking design-decisions for supply chains. To the best of our knowledge, a similar study has never been performed.

## 2. Methodology

### 2.1. Problem statement

In this manuscript, we consider a three-echelon supply chain superstructure that consists of 6 plants, located in Hungary (Kazincbarcika), Germany (Leuna), Italy (Montova), Czech Republic (Neratovice), Spain (Tarragona) and Poland (Wloclaweck). All plants can produce acetone, acetaldehyde, cumene, acrylonitrile, isopropanol and phenol using one of six available technologies involving up to 18 different chemicals. For each plant, there is an associated warehouse having an initial inventory of zero tons. All plants and warehouses have a yearly expansion limit between 10 to 400 kt. The products can be sold on four different European markets, being Germany (Leuna), Czech Republic (Neratovice), Portugal (Sines) and Spain (Tarragona). For more details on the superstructure see Guillen-Gosalbez et al. (2009).

To obtain a more realistic model, no negligible quantities may be transported between plants and warehouses, respectively between warehouse and markets. A penalty term is introduced into the calculation of the net present value (NPV), that penalizes any insatisfaction of demand by 30% of the product price on each market. The initial cap for carbon dioxide emissions is set to $2 \cdot 10^8$ kg with a yearly reduction rate of 2.2%, see the EU ETS handbook for details (2015).

### 2.2. Supply chain model

The model proposed has the objectives of maximizing the profit and minimizing the downside risk, while satisfying equations related to mass balance, capacity constraints, environmental impact assessment and carbon regulations. The last one directly links the environmental to the economic performance. In this section, we will refer refer the reader to the articles of Garcia-Castro (2022) and Guillen-Gosalbez (2009) for details regarding the equations, variables and parameters of the model. Here, we will only focus on the equations that introduce uncertainty into the model.

The cost of transportation between a plant $p$ and a warehouse $w$ at timestep $t$ in pricing scenario $s$, $COSTTRA(p, w, t, s)$, depends on the quantity $TRA(p, w, t, s)$ transported, the distance $DISTA(p, w)$, and the price of diesel / energy, $PRICE_{ENERGY}(t, s)$,

$$COSTTRA(p, w, t, s) = TRA(p, w, t, s) \cdot DISTA(p, w) \cdot PRICE_{ENERGY}(t, s) \cdot 0.014.$$

Similarly, the cost of transportation between a warehouse $w$ and a market $k$ at timestep $t$ in pricing scenario $s$, $COSTTRB(w, k, t, s)$, depends on the transported quantity $TRB(w, k, t, s)$, the distance $DISTB(w, k)$, and the price of diesel / energy,

$$COSTTRB(w, k, t, s) = TRB(w, k, t, s) \cdot DISTB(w, k) \cdot PRICE_{ENERGY}(t, s) \cdot 0.014.$$

According to the Spanish Ministry of Public Works and Transportation, an articulated vehicle with a payload of 25t that travels around 120000 km annually, will have a fuel expenditure of more than 40700 liters of diesel, c.f. the report by the Spanish Ministry of Public Works and Transport (2019). This is equivalent to approx. 0.014 liters of diesel required to transport one ton of goods over a distance of one kilometer. The distances *DISTA* and *DISTB* are given in kilometers. Since the most common type of transportation of goods in Europe is via truck, we assumed for simplicity that all transportation is done in this way.

*2.3. Environmental impact assessment and carbon regulation*

In the model, we account for emissions related to raw material consumption, energy consumption, as well as emissions due to transportation between plants, warehouses and markets. We use Life Cycle Impact Assessment (LCIA) data obtained from the ECOINVENT Database to calculate the emissions in terms of global warming potential for a timespan of 100 years (GWP100a), c.f. Frischknecht et al., 2005 for details.

The cap-and-trade system incorporated by the European Union Emissions Trading System aims to help the EU become climate-neutral through the reduction of the maximum amount of emissions allowed over time. An initial emissions cap is introduced, together with a yearly reduction rate. The plants are assigned a fraction of the total emissions and they are allowed to also trade their emissions with other players.

*2.4. Uncertainty in energy prices*

In a supply chain, there are many parameters with possible uncertainties. Driven by the current political and social situation in Europe, we will in this work focus on uncertain future changes of the energy prices. To account for uncertainty in our model, various future pricing scenarios will be generated. This is done by fitting a suited autoregressive integrated moving average (ARIMA) model to the historical diesel prices of the last 25 years. ARIMA models are defined by three parameters, being the non-seasonal polynomial degree, the number of moving average terms, as well as the order of differentiation applied to the data in order to remove seasonal trends. To find the parameters that best fit the historical data, we employed the Akaike and Bayesian information criteria. It turns out, that the ARIMA(2,1,3) model is best suited to forecast future pricing scenarios. For details on time-series forecasting, see Brockwell et al. (2016).

*2.5. Risk management*

Uncertainty of parameters and increasing complexity of supply chains require risk analysis to take well-informed decisions. Different approaches for quantitative supply chain risk management are known and should be employed to predict performance. Some examples of risk metrics are the downside risk (DR), the value at risk (VaR), or the conditional value at risk (CVaR). These metrics are not redundant and all provide valuable information for the decision-makers. For details on a variety of risk metrics and their usage, see Heckmann 2014.

In this work, we will optimize the economic performance of the supply chain together with the expected downside risk, that is the expected unfavorable deviation of the profit from a target value $\Omega$,

$$DR(s, \Omega) = \mathbf{E}[\delta_\Omega(s)] = \int_{-\infty}^{\infty} \delta_\Omega(s) P(s, \xi) \, d\xi.$$

Here, $P$ is the probability distribution function, and

$$\delta_\Omega(s) = \begin{cases} \Omega - \text{Profit}(s), & \textit{if } \text{Profit}(s) < \Omega \\ 0, & \textit{if } Profit(s) \geq \Omega. \end{cases}$$

### 2.6. Multi-objective simulation

To solve the stochastic model, we generate 100 possible energy pricing scenarios and reduce them using the BIRCH (balanced iterative reducing and clustering using hierarchies) data mining algorithm. We use the S_dbw index, to measure the quality of the clustering for different numbers of scenarios. For an application of the clustering, each scenario is identified as a two-dimensional point consisting of its net present value and downside risk.

In the real world, the decision-makers have more than one objective when it comes to supply chain design, such as maximization of profit, minimization of risk, emissions, cost, etc. Therefore, we implement a multi-objective approach using the $\varepsilon$-constraint method. This approach requires more computational effort, but it provides a set of possible solutions, from which the decision-makers obtain a better overview of the dynamics of the supply chain.

First, we optimize the stochastic problem including all of the reduced scenarios by maximizing the profit. The corresponding downside risk is denoted $DR_{maxProfit}$. Then, we re-solve the model by minimizing the downside risk, obtaining $DR_{minDR}$. The obtained solutions represent the two extreme points of the pareto set of solutions. Afterwards, we add a new constraint to the model that sets a limit $\varepsilon$ for the expected downside risk and re-solve the model maximizing the profit. This bound is modified for each pareto point $i_{pp}$ considered,

$$\varepsilon = DR_{minDR} + \frac{DR_{maxProfit} - DR_{minDR}}{number\ pareto\ points} \cdot i_{pp}.$$

## 3. Results and discussion

The stochastic model was implemented and solved in Python using Pyomo and IBMs CPLEX algorithm. The simulations were conducted on a MacBook Pro model 2020 with 16 GB Ram and running macOS 11.2.1.

In figure 1, the left plot shows the original 100 scenarios that were grouped into 14 clusters and the "x" indicates the centroid of each cluster. In the right subplot from figure 1, the S_dbw index is represented for a changing number of clusters. It can be seen that the error measured in the S_dbw index is less than 10% for numbers of clusters larger than 13. The value of this indicator drops sharply for small numbers of clusters, before showing asymptotic behavior. The S_dbw index measures the mean dispersion of datapoints inside the clusters, as well as a between-cluster density, to compute a scoring for a given clustering (c.f. Desgraupes, 2017). Its values are positive and will be relatively small for a clustering that splits a highly connected point cloud approximately evenly. The foregoing explanation motivates our choice of 14 reduced clusters whose centers will be used as reduced set of scenarios.

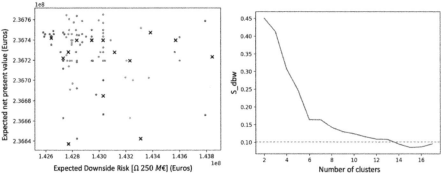

Figure 1: (Left) Economic performance and downside risk of the 100 deterministic scenarios. Each scenario is represented by a two-dimensional point, and all the points that form a cluster have the same color. The centroid of each cluster is indicated with "x". (Right) S_dbw index for different number of clusters.

In order to obtain a pareto curve, several steps have to be performed. First, the problems that provide the upper and lower limit for the epsilon are solved. Afterwards, the value of epsilon is varied in this interval to obtain the different pareto solutions. Figure 2 shows the cumulative distribution function for the solution maximizing the expected net present value. The obtained supply chain design was exposed to 100 possible energy pricing scenarios and the values of different risk metrics were calculated. The numerical results show, that the NPV of the worst-case scenario deviates from the expected NPV by less than 5%.

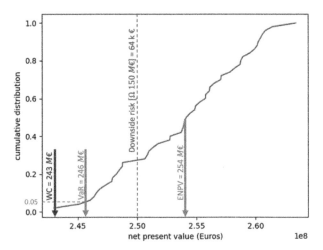

Figure 2: Cumulative distribution function for the obtained supply chain design. The expected net present value, downside risk for a target value of 250 million euros, VaR and worst-case scenario are represented.

## 4. Outlook and further work

So far, we only considered the influence of energy prices in the cost of transportation. However, since the model under study is a petrochemical supply chain, the cost of energy also influences the cost of raw materials and the cost of production.

Once we incorporated these influences into the model, we will then move on to computing the pareto curve of possible solutions using the $\varepsilon$-constraint method. The results will give us a better understanding of the influence of energy prices in the overall SC design.

As stated before, different risk indices provide valuable information and so far, we only implemented the downside risk. In upcoming work, we will introduce other of these risk indices as objectives into the model.

## Acknowledgements

The authors gratefully acknowledge financial support to the Conselleria de Innovacion, Universidades, Ciencia y Sociedad Digital of the Generalitat Valenciana, Spain under project PROMETEO/2020/064 and project PID2021-124139NB-C21.

## References

Spanish Ministry of Public Works and Transport, October 2019, Observatorio de Costes del Transporte de Mercancías por Carretera

Frischknecht et al., 2005, The ecoinvent Database: Overview and Methodological Framework, The International Journal of Life Cycle Assessment

Brockwell, P., Davis, R., 2016, Introduction to time series and forecasting, Springer Switzerland

Heckmann, I., Comes, T., Nickel, S., 2014, A Critical Review on Supply Chain Risk – Definition, Measure and Modeling

European Council, November 2022, Energy prices and security of supply, https://www.consilium.europa.eu/en/policies/energy-prices-and-security-of-supply/

Guillen-Gosalbez, G., Grossmann, I. E., 2009, Optimal Design and Planning of Sustainable Chemical Supply Chains Under Uncertainty, AIChE Journal, 55, pp. 99 – 121

European Union, 2015, EU ETS handbook, https://www.sallan.org/pdf-docs/ets_handbook_en.pdf

Desgraupes, B., 2017, Clustering indices, https://cran.r-project.org/web/packages/clusterCrit/vignettes/clusterCrit.pdf

Yang, G., Liu, Y., Yang, K., 2015, Multi-objective biogeography-based optimization for supply chain network design under uncertainty, Computers & Industrial Engineering, 85, pp.145-156

Robles, J.O., Azzaro-Pantel, C., Aguilar-Lasserre, A., 2020, Optimization of a hydrogen supply chain network design under demand uncertainty by multi-objective genetic algorithms, Computers & Chemical Engineering, 140

Antonis Kokossis, Michael C. Georgiadis, Efstratios N. Pistikopoulos (Eds.)
PROCEEDINGS OF THE 33rd European Symposium on Computer Aided Process Engineering
(ESCAPE33), June 18-21, 2023, Athens, Greece

# An Ecologically Safe and Socially Just Supply Chain Design for Li-battery

Ying Xue[a], Yazeed M. Aleissa[a], Bhavik R. Bakshi[a]

[a] *William G Lowrie Department of Chemical and Biomolecular Engineering, The Ohio State University, Columbus OH 43210, USA*

## Abstract

Global goals like "Net-zero", "Nature-positive", and "Socially Just" require human activities to reduce emissions, restore nature, and be socially equitable.  This work proposes an approach that includes ecological capacity and social justice requirements to guide engineering decisions and designs. We utilize the supply and demand of ecosystem services to identify the safe and just operating space[1,2].  The ecologically safe space is determined by the multiscale framework of Techno-Ecological Synergy (TES). The degree of overshoot quantifies the absolute environmental sustainability (AES) at the relevant spatial scale[3,4]. For the socially just space, we calculate a minimum threshold of necessary goods and services to meet basic food, energy, and water[5] needs. We demonstrate this approach by a multiobjective supply chain design of Li-battery which minimizes the ecological and social overshoot simultaneously.

**Keywords**: Safe and Just Space, Absolute Environmental Sustainability, Nature-Based Solution, Supply Chain Design, Multiobjective Optimization

## 1. Introduction

In the past several years, the COVID-19 pandemic, wildfires, unprecedented heat waves and other extreme natural events reinforced the fact that economic and social structures are untenable without resilient nature. Meanwhile, global goals such as "Nature-positive by 2030", "Net-zero by 2050", have been proposed and widely accepted as guidelines for future development. However, achieving these goals must not exacerbate social issues such as poverty, food insecurity, and equity. Hence, the concept of the "Safe and Just Space"[1,2] was introduced, which identifies an operating space for human activities to be within the ecological capacity of the planet and the social threshold where everyone has access to natural resources to meet their basic needs. This requires industry to develop and apply methods for achieving global goals. Due to the concerns of energy and sustainability, the demand for electric vehicles (EV) is growing fast. Li-battery is widely used in EV and its impact is important to the sustainable EV development. This study focuses on designing an ecologically safe and socially just supply chain for Li-battery.

Current sustainability assessment methods such as life cycle assessment (LCA) are useful for quantifying relative sustainability which encourages the reduction of environmental impacts[4]. Environmental sustainability requires human impact to not exceed nature's carrying capacity[6] but most methods ignore the capacity of nature. Reducing negative impact alone is not enough to get the full recovery of nature by 2050, as envisioned by the "Nature-positive" goal[7]. The idea of absolute environmental sustainability (AES) includes nature's carrying capacity in sustainability metrics as a reference value. Xue and Bakshi developed a multiscale approach for absolute environmental sustainability assessment (AESA) which encourages "Nature-positive" decisions[4]. Through biophysical models, this techno-ecological synergy (TES) based AES metric quantifies ecosystem services at different spatial scales to identify the ecological threshold with high geographical resolution. Furthermore, Aleissa and Bakshi[3] proposed a quantitative social threshold that aligns with the ecological threshold by using the flow of ecosystem goods and services. The social foundation represents the minimum human demand to meet their basic food, energy, and water needs from that ecosystem service.

This work brings in the concept of AES and social threshold into Li-battery supply chain design under the global goals of "Nature-positive" and "Socially Just". Four main sectors are considered along the supply chain: mining, processing production and packaging. Ecological and social thresholds are quantified at country level for each process using the methods mentioned in the previous paragraph. The ecological and social transgression levels for Li-battery supply chain are minimized simultaneously as design objectives rather than merely constraints. The transgression level is expressed as the ratio of human impact and ecological/social threshold, making it a linear fractional optimization problem. It is first transformed into a linear program through the Charnes-Cooper method and then solved by ε-constraint method. We also show how this framework can contribute to identifying hotspots and future improvement opportunities towards global goals. The major novelties of this work are: 1) A multiscale approach of ecological threshold quantification in supply chain design. 2) Quantifying and incorporating aspects of social justice in supply chain design. 3) Application to global safe and just supply chain design for Li-battery.

## 2. Methodology

### 2.1. The Ecological Ceiling

One popular approach for AESA is based on the Planetary boundary (PB) framework. PB framework identifies nine important earth system processes and defines the safe operating space (SOS) for human development[8]. This method downscales the SOS to specific processes/systems based on a sharing principle such as population which provides holistic perspectives but ignores spatial heterogeneity of ecosystems and has high subjectiveness. These shortcomings may be overcome by a multiscale TES approach.

The TES framework is built upon the concept of ecosystem services (ESs). It has been integrated with LCA (TES-LCA) for assessment and process design[9]. Instead of directly downscaling SOSs, the multiscale TES approach quantifies the capacity of ecosystems with biophysical models from different spatial scales, which is illustrated in Figure 1a. Public and private ownerships are considered for ecological threshold partitioning. Private ownership implies that only landowners own the ecosystem services, while for public ownership, ESs belong to every activity inside the region. Figure 1b illustrates a two-scale system (e.g. county and state). Considering a $n$-scale TES, the generalized mathematical expression of the system's ecological threshold can be expressed as:

$$S_i^{tot} = S_{i,1}^{pvt} + \sum_{j=2}^{J} S_{i,j}^{pub} \prod_{m=1}^{m=j} P_{m+1,m} \qquad (1.)$$

Here $i$ represents process $i$, $j$ represents the $j$-th scale, $m$ is a dummy variable. $S$ is the ecological threshold, $P$ denotes the sharing principle. In this study Equation (1) will be used to estimate the ecological safe space for each process in the supply chain. For process $i$ the absolute environmental sustainability metric – ecological overshoot ($EO_i$) is defined in Equation 2 and $D_i$ represents environmental impacts.

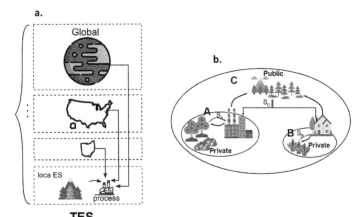

**TES**

Figure 1. (a) A four level TES example (local, state, country and global). (b) Illustration of public and private ownership of ecosystem supply.

$$EO_i = \frac{D_i}{S_i} \qquad (2.)$$

### 2.2. The Social Foundation

Aleissa and Bakshi[3] define the social threshold as the population's minimum demand ($D^{min}$) to meet their basic food, energy, and water needs from ecosystem services. This aligns with the UN sustainable development goals of zero hunger, clean water, and energy for everyone, which specify global standards that define the required amount of water, caloric intake, and electricity to sustain human lives[10]. Then, the social threshold can be formulated as the required emissions from food production and electricity generation to meet the energy and caloric intake thresholds for the entire population. The metric of social shortfall (SS) from the social threshold is expressed as:

$$SS_i = \frac{D_i^{min}}{D_i} \qquad (3.)$$

After identifying the safe and just space through the ecological and social thresholds, we can use the current level of demand to assess the operating conditions relative to the thresholds. Figure 2 shows the scenarios that arise with the relative demand levels and the other thresholds.

## 3. Development of Ecologically Safe and Socially just Supply Chains

### 3.1. General Problem Statement

The approaches described in the previous section will be integrated with LCA, multi-objective optimization for designing a safe and just supply chain. Life cycle environmental impact of each process, from cradle to gate, will be estimated. There are two objectives: the ecological objective is to minimize the ecological overshoot and the social objective is to minimize the social shortfall. Both objectives focus on carbon emissions. The major decision variables are selection of suppliers, location of warehouses, and transportation modes. The provided parameters are a set of suppliers and locations for each process in the supply chain, a set of transportation modes, production capacity, demand for the final product, etc. To simplify this problem, this study mainly focuses on selecting suppliers, in another word finding the most suitable country to produce a specific product from "Nature-positive" perspective.

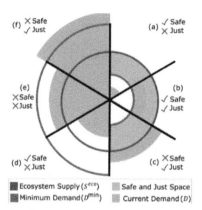

Figure 2. Possible scenarios for the SJS are determined by the current level of demand and the ecological and social thresholds.

### 3.2. Lithium-battery Supply Chain

Environmental impacts of EVs are mainly from the use phase and battery production. There are different supply chains for battery manufacturing based on the final product and the design application. However, many of these supply chains share similar stages: procurement of raw materials, processing these raw materials into valuable chemicals, production of battery components, and fabrication and packing of the battery cell. Each of these stages has its complex supply chains across the world currently. In this problem, we assume it is a linear supply chain, also products and processes has a one-to-one corresponding relation.

### 3.3. Supplier Selection

We want to find the optimal set of suppliers that minimize the ecological overshoot and the social shortfall (Equation 2, 3) along the supply chain from the perspective of $CO_2$ emission. Using these metrics as objectives results in a mixed-integer linear fractional programming (MILFP) problem that can be optimized to minimize a single objective locally at each stage of the supply chain, or to minimize the metrics in terms of the aggregate supply and demands for the entire supply chain. The set of countries ($I$) and main processes ($J$) are given. $S_i$ denotes the ES supply (ecological threshold) and $D_i^{min}$ represents the minimum impact to meet human needs in country $i$ ($i \in I$). $x_{i,j}$ and $c_{i,j}$ are both binary variables. $x_{i,j} = 1$ if process $j$ is to be established in country $i$; 0 otherwise. $c_{i,j} = 1$ when country $i$ can have process $j$; 0 otherwise. $D_i$ is the demand of ecosystem services (environmental impact). The general form of total emission can be expressed in Equation 4 where $g_j$ is life cycle emission factor (EF) for product $j$, $e_{j,k}$ is EF for product $j$ in transportation mode $k$. $Q_{j,k,i,i'}$ and $l_{i,i',k}$ are flow rate and distance from $i$ to $i'$.

$$D_i = \sum_i \sum_{i'} \sum_j \sum_k g_j Q_{j,k,i,i'} + e_{j,k} Q_{j,k,i,i'} l_{i,i',k} \tag{4.}$$

The model formulation for the entire supply chain in this study is shown as below.

$$\min EO = \frac{\sum_i D_i}{\sum_i S_i} \tag{5.}$$

$$\min SS = \frac{\sum_i D_i^{min}}{\sum_i S_i} \tag{6.}$$

$$s.t. \quad x_{i,j} \in \{0,1\} \quad \forall i \in I, j \in J \tag{7.}$$

$$\sum_{i \in I} x_{i,j} = 1 \quad \forall j \in J \tag{8.}$$

$$x_{i,j} \leq c_{i,j} \quad \forall i \in I, j \in J \tag{9.}$$

$$c_{i,j} \in \{0,1\} \quad \forall i \in I, j \in J \tag{10.}$$

The constraint in equation (8) ensures that each process included in Li-battery supply chain is assigned to only one country. Equation (9) makes sure that process $j$ is assigned to country $i$ only when country $i$ can produce that product. Figure 3 shows the results for the optimal supply chains that minimize the ecological overshoot and social shortfall, for both local and aggregate approaches.

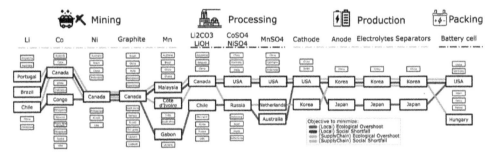

Figure 3. Supply chain results for optimal suppliers' network for the different objectives. For example, minimizing the ecological overshoot at each stage of the supply chain result gives a solution of (Chile, Congo, Canada, Canada, Gabon, Chile, Russia, Australia, South Korea, Japan, Japan, Japan, USA), More details are available in the work of Aleissa[11].

These results represent the best combinations of suppliers in the current market. However, political relations and economic deals, in addition to logistic and transportation constraints, can limit the selection of supplier networks. In addition, single-objective optimization does not reveal information about the interaction with other objectives. Hence, we performed multi-objective analysis and optimization to find the best set of solutions that define the trade-offs between the objectives. We also compare the optimal global supply chains to the current supply chains of Tesla using their limited supplier network[12], as shown in Figure 4.

These results can be used to identify hotspots along the supply chains that affect the performance of the social and ecological objectives. For example, the suppliers for lithium for Tesla performed worse than other suppliers in the market in terms of ecological overshoot. Tesla's recent investment in manganese mines in the United States improved their supply chain social performance but greatly downgraded the ecological performance compared to suppliers from Gabon or Ghana.

## 4. Conclusions

In this work we demonstrate the necessity of including absolute environmental sustainability and social justice into sustainability assessment and design to achieve the 'Nature-positive' and 'Socially-Just' goals. We propose a method for sustainable supply network design which accounts for nature's capacity and social needs. This method can be tailored to activities at different scales and has been applied to a battery supply chain design. LCA coupled with multiobjective optimization guides the selection of suppliers from ecological and social aspects, and the Pareto curve is obtained showing the trade-off between these two aspects.

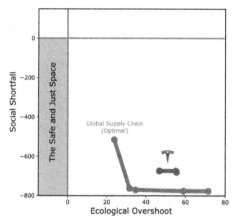

Figure 4. Comparison between Tesla's supply chains and the global optimal supply chains for Li-ion batteries.

**Acknowledgements:** King Abdulaziz University, Jeddah, Saudi Arabia for support of Yazeed Aleissa and the National Science Foundation (SBE-1739909; CBET 1804943).

## References

1. J. Rockström, et al., 2009, A safe operating space for humanity, Nature, 461.7263, 472-475.
2. K. Raworth, 2012. A safe and just space for humanity: can we live within the doughnut. Oxfam.
3. Y. M. Aleissa, and B. R. Bakshi, 2022, Meeting National Food-Energy-Water Needs in an Environmentally Safe and Socially Just Manner, Submitted.
4. Y. Xue, and B. R. Bakshi, 2022, Metrics for a nature-positive world: A multiscale approach for absolute environmental sustainability assessment. Science of The Total Environment, 846, 157373.
5. B. R. Bakshi (editor), Engineering and Ecosystems: Seeking Synergies for a Nature-Positive World. in preparation. Springer, 2022.
6. Fiksel, Joseph. "Sustainability and resilience: toward a systems approach." Sustainability: Science, Practice and Policy 2.2 (2006): 14-21.
7. Locke, Harvey, et al. "A nature-positive world: the global goal for nature." (2021).
8. Steffen, Will, et al. "Planetary boundaries: Guiding human development on a changing planet." science 347.6223 (2015): 1259855.
9. Liu, Xinyu, and Bhavik R. Bakshi. "Ecosystem services in life cycle assessment while encouraging techno - ecological synergies." Journal of Industrial Ecology 23.2 (2019): 347-360.
10. United Nations, 2015, Transforming our world: The 2030 agenda for sustainable development. A/RES/70/1.
11. Y. M. Aleissa, 2022, Sustainable Process Design to Meet Ecological and Social Goals Through Novel Simulation Tools and Optimization, Doctoral dissertation, The Ohio State University.
12. Tesla, 2022, Tesla impact report (2021).

Antonis Kokossis, Michael C. Georgiadis, Efstratios N. Pistikopoulos (Eds.)
PROCEEDINGS OF THE 33rd European Symposium on Computer Aided Process Engineering
(ESCAPE33), June 18-21, 2023, Athens, Greece

# Leveraging Semantics and Machine Learning to Automate Circular Economy Operations for the Scrap Metals Industry

Manolis Vasileiadis[a], Konstantinos Mexis[a], Nikolaos Trokanas[a], Theodoros Dalamagas[b,d], Thomas Papageorgiou[c], and Antonis Kokossis[a]*

[a]*School of Chemical Engineering, National Technical University of Athens, Athens, Greece;* [b]*Symbiolabs, SYMBIOLABS, Circular Intelligence, Artemidos 6 & Epidavrou, Marousi 6, 15125, Athens, Greece;* [c]*ANAMET S.A.,160 NATO Av.,19300, Aspropyrgos, Greece;* [d] *IMIS ATHENA Research Center, Athens, Greece*
*Corresponding author akokossis@mail.ntua.gr*

## Abstract

Circular Economy operations and supply chains are becoming increasingly intricate. From raw material extraction, manufacturers and retailers to consumers and recyclers, the benefits stemming from an organized and transparent circular economy network are numerous. Scrap materials have the potential to contribute significantly to the reduction of energy consumption and resource consumption. One is challenged to combine data from scrap metal collection and management, shredding and separation stages, data related to the suppliers and customers as well as background data as they are available from reference sources and classifications available by the metal industry. Integration of data from dispersed and heterogenous sources with in-house ERP systems, alongside a need to automate and extract knowledge and support, call upon a semantically enabled approach as the one demonstrated in the paper. The work combines knowledge from a sizeable actual plant (ANAMET), data technologies (Symbiolabs) and modelling expertise (NTUA). The approach proposes the means to enhance circular economy operations for scrap metal materials with the use of semantic technologies and machine learning techniques presenting examples and cases as they have been used in real-life.

**Keywords**: circular economy, scrap, ontology, machine learning

## 1. Introduction

Circular Economy operations for many types of materials, including metals, are characterized by high complexity. From raw material extraction, manufacturers and retailers to consumers and recyclers, the benefits stemming from an organized and transparent circular economy network are numerous. The use of semantic web technologies, and ontologies in specific, offers many benefits towards efforts to automate low-end knowledge work, automate processes and extract insights for Circular Economy operations. The collection, processing and valorization of secondary materials (waste and/or by-products), have a key role to play in the realization and successful operation of circular economy. Scrap metals (e.g. ferrous and non-ferrous, such as copper, aluminium and iron), in particular, have the potential to contribute significantly in the reduction of energy consumption and resource consumption. Scrap metals are commonly by-products and waste of the manufacturing and consumption of vehicles, electrical and electronic devices, machinery, wiring, tubes and many other products. This makes their valorization (recycling or otherwise) an attractive proposition for businesses and environmentalists alike. The collection, processing and valorization of by-products or waste materials are key components of a successful circular economy. More specifically, the identification/classification and valorization of scrap metals can play a key role in reducing energy consumption, as well as the waste ending up in landfills. Scrap metals are usually a by-product of manufacturing operations characterized by variability in composition and in their defining characteristics. This variability makes identifying, classifying and standardizing scrap metal burdensome and time-consuming. Circular Economy operations for scrap metals rely on tacit knowledge, embedded on the humans involved in the process. However, the lack of a systemic and standardized approach makes it difficult to leverage this knowledge. In this paper, we attempt to bridge that gap with the use of semantic technologies and machine learning techniques. Ontologies and knowledge graphs (KG) are used to formalize the knowledge in the domain of scrap (and non-scrap) materials and waste, as well as the processing technologies that participate in the valorization paths of scrap metals. Machine learning (ML) techniques are employed to build on the formalized knowledge of the ontology and facilitate further inferences that can help automate the process of identifying and classifying scrap materials, with a view to improve circular economy operations.

## 2. Semantics & Machine Learning for Scrap Metal

### 2.1. Ontologies & Knowledge Graphs

Ontologies and knowledge graphs are knowledge modelling tools that have been extensively used in Process Systems Engineering (PSE), addressing a wide range of knowledge-intensive tasks in a wide range of sectors, with applications ranging from R&D linked data facilitating data sharing, different facets of product development including smart production and data interoperability for manufacturing and product development (Hailemariam and Venkatasubramanian, 2010) as well as decision making for specific processing steps (Akkisetty et al., 2009). Ontologies have also been widely used in applications related to supply chains across a range of sectors. In process industries, ontologies have been used for data integration (Chang and Terpenny, 2009), improved product traceability, information sharing (Munoz et al., 2012), knowledge representation and decision-making (Trokanas et al., 2016). In discrete industries, ontologies have been used for decision-making tasks, such as supply chain negotiations (Wang et al., 2013), knowledge and data integration (Huang and Diao, 2008) among others.

In this work, we developed an ontology to represent the knowledge of the domain. The ontology model is simple,

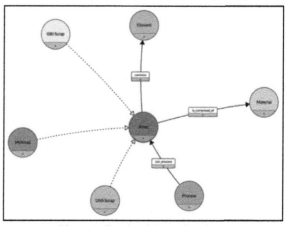

Figure 1. Top-level Scrap Ontology

aiming to facilitate ML tasks. To that end, Scrap is modelled as follows (Figure 1). Scrap materials can be classified in three distinct ways, allowing the end-user to extract as much information as possible when classifying a scrap metal. ISRI Scrap (ISRI, 2018), The Scrap Specifications Circular is a set of guidelines for scrap trading. UNS Scrap, Unified Numbering System is a composition-based system of commercial materials, and MyScrap: the reference company classification (name to indicate the generic approach to the problem).    Each type of scrap classification is populated from the relevant documentation and relationships to other relevant entities (i.e. Elements, Materials) are defined.

Materials class represents mostly metal materials that are needed to properly define scrap metals. They form a taxonomy of metals, the top-level structure of which is depicted in (simplified) Figure 2. The ontology is populated with indicative data provided by the partner company, to create the application-level knowledge graph. This KG will be used as input for the ML models and

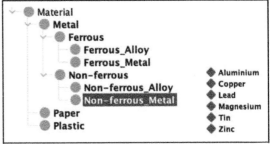

Figure 2. Materials ontology branch and sample instances

facilitate inference of new knowledge about our data. The use of an ontology provides the means to break existing information 'silos' and integrate data from different sources. The amalgamation of different sources allows the inference of additional knowledge about different types of scrap and offers a flexibility in describing scrap materials based on three different approaches. All the different scrap metals populate the ontology to form the ScrapKG, a knowledge graph that contains data about scrap materials, their composition, their potential to be processed by certain processing technologies as well as chemical and physical characteristics. ScrapKG is 'fed' into the machine learning models (described in the section below), enabling a number of circular economy applications.

## 2.2. Machine Learning

Machine Learning is a branch of Artificial Intelligence (AI) that focuses on the study of algorithms and statistical models that computer systems use to perform a specific task without being explicitly programmed. With the abundance of datasets available, the demand for machine learning is on the rise. In general, ML algorithms have been widely used in waste management, and Artificial Neural Networks (ANN) was the most commonly used method. Several studies have applied ML algorithms to predict the fill levels of waste bins and improve the transportation costs (Pereira Ramos et al., 2018). Finally, various computer vision methods have been implemented for waste classification for effective waste disposal (Ping et al., 2020). Through classification, useful materials are recycled and utilized, which is crucial for a circular economy. Most of the existing literature works use a computer vision approach to the waste management problem, using various waste related images as inputs for the machine learning algorithms. In our work, we attempt to enhance circular economy operations for scrap metal materials with the use of semantic technologies and machine learning techniques. Knowledge graphs and ontologies could formalise (codify) the existing knowledge in the waste management problem, while the use of ML techniques will assist to facilitate further inferences that can help automate the process of identifying and classifying scrap materials, with a view to improve circular economy operations. In this work, we leverage ML techniques to achieve 2 main objectives, namely to:

(i) identify the main (missing) material of scrap by identifying missing links in the knowledge graph. This builds on processing data provided by our partners and identifying links between scrap materials and metals. The nature of knowledge graphs allows us to use these inferences to expand our KG and facilitate other ML tasks.

(ii) develop an ML model that classifies scrap metal materials, based on the ISRI standard and the proprietary company scrap classifications of the ontology, allowing users to make inferences about the type of scrap they are dealing with.

## 3. Use Cases/Applications

### 3.1. Identifying missing links

For this task, we leverage the structure of the graph and the data it contains to develop supervised classification models to identify additional relationships between graph entities. In the case of ScrapKG, we used classification ML methods to identify the composition of different scrap metals. The aim of this task is to improve the completeness of the data for new scrap metals when they arrive at the processing/recycling location, enabling better decision making, by predicting the 'hasMaterial' relationship, between scrap metals and materials. To achieve that, several supervised classification methods were trained on the description provided on the ISRI Scrap dataset to predict the material composing the referred scrap. The input of the model contained the text provided in the scrap's description, whereas the answer set contained the material composing each scrap. Different types of scrap are represented as nodes in the graph and converted into vectors. The models were initially fitted on the training set and then the fitted models were used to predict the responses for the observations in the validation set. The validation set provides an unbiased evaluation of a model's fit on the training set. The accuracy of all the fitted models on the validation set is presented in Table 1.

Table 1. ML model accuracy

| Model | Accuracy on *Validation set* |
|---|---|
| **Support Vector Machines** | 85.18% |
| **Random Forest Classifier** | 85.19% |
| **Gaussian Process** | 92.25% |
| **K-Nearest Neighbors Classifier** | 81.88% |

To test the validity of the model, we created a new and external test set, consisting of scrap metal descriptions (defined by the seller) from an online marketplace. The input is the description of the scrap materials. Each ML model predicts a material and these results participate in a voting mechanism, to identify the

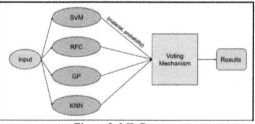

Figure 3. ML Process

top composition material(s) (Figure 3). Some examples are presented in Table 2 (predicted material). The predicted results are correct, and the accuracy of the test set is 85%.

### 3.2. Classification of scrap

For this task, we leverage the structure of the knowledge graph and the data it contains to develop unsupervised learning models that allow us to classify any given scrap. Classification is based on two distinct ontology branches and entities (scrap) are classified and compared to ISRI classification and the proprietary company classification, allowing users to evaluate the scrap by juxtaposing new types of scrap into existing scrap types.

For this task, both ISRI Scrap dataset and the proprietary company scrap dataset were combined to develop unsupervised clustering models to identify clusters of similar scrap metals. The aim of this task is to allow users to make inferences about the type of scrap they are dealing with. To achieve that, we implemented the KMeans clustering algorithm, an unsupervised learning algorithm that partitions $n$ observations into $k$ clusters, where each observation belongs to the cluster with the nearest mean serving as a prototype of the cluster. The KMeans algorithm was trained on the description provided on both the ISRI and the proprietary company datasets. Similar to the previous task, graph nodes were converted into vectors. When a new, unknown scrap is provided, the KMeans algorithm will predict the closest cluster it belongs to. Finally, the most similar ISRI or proprietary company scrap will be defined based on the cosine similarity of the nodes of the two scraps. The selected number of clusters was $k = 4$. Using principal component analysis to transform the data in two-dimensional space we are able to visualise the clustering (Figure 4). The *black dots* in Figure 4 represent the new and external test data described on the previous task. defined by the seller in an online marketplace.

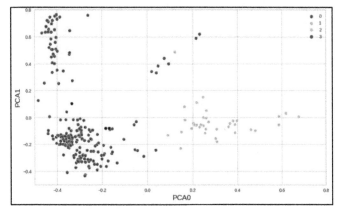

All of them were classified at cluster 0. The most similar, in terms of cosine similarity, ISRI scrap types are presented in Table 2. From that we can compare the new scrap types to existing categories, to inform decision making.

Table 2 Sample results for composition prediction based on scrap classification

| Scrap Description | Closest Category | Predicted Material |
|---|---|---|
| **Open Extinguisher with no heads \| 6061 grade** | ISRI_85 | Aluminium |
| **Regulary purchase of galvalume dross, capacity 300-500mt/month** | ISRI_99 | Zinc |
| **With no cable, plate or grit. CuSN in cable, plate or grit, separately. Not mixed. In the case of small packaged (30x30 cm) and palletized cable, ball and shot in BIG BAGS** | ISRI_61 | Copper, Aluminium |

## 4. Discussion & Conclusions

We have presented a method that combines semantic technologies such as ontologies and knowledge graphs and machine learning approaches, to design a framework aiming to automate and assist with circular economy operations for scrap metal materials. We have organized the knowledge of this domain into an ontology and a knowledge graph and used these structured data to identify the key material of a scrap and subsequently classify it based on existing and known classifications of scrap metals. The 'new' scrap is then represented as a graph and is compared and clustered along with already known categories, aiming to identify a cluster and the most similar categories in our graph, allowing users to understand what they have and allow them to make informed decisions regarding the next steps of the scrap material in question.

In future work, the knowledge graph will be extended to include more types of scrap, hence reducing the bias and allowing the implementation of more advanced machine learning models, such as Artificial Neural Networks, aiming to learn and make predictions with minimal data. Additionally, processing technologies will be modelled and populated in the graph, allowing us to predict the best valorization for each scrap metal at the point of receipt.

## Acknowledgments

This research has been co-financed by the European Regional Development Fund of the European Union and Greek national funds through the Operational Program Competitiveness, Entrepreneurship and Innovation, under the call RESEARCH – CREATE – INNOVATE (project code:T1EDK-03010)

## References

ISRI (2018) Scrap specifications circular: guidelines for nonferrous scrap, ferrous scrap, glass cullet, paper stock, plastic scrap, electronics scrap, and tire scrap. Washington

Akkisetty, G.V. Reklaitis and V. Venkatasubramanian, 2009. Ontological informatics based decision support system for pharmaceutical product development: Milling as a case study. Computer Aided Chemical Engineering, 26, pp.159-164.

Chang, and J. Terpenny, 2009. Ontology-based data integration and decision support for product e-Design. Robotics and Computer-Integrated Manufacturing, 25(6), pp.863-870.

Hailemariam & V. Venkatasubramanian. J Pharm Innov (2010) 5: 88. doi:10.1007/s12247-010-9081-3.

Huang, and S. Diao, 2008. Ontology-based enterprise knowledge integration. Robotics and Computer-Integrated Manufacturing, 24(4), pp.562-571.

Trokanas, M. Bussemaker, and F. Cecelja, 2016. Utilising Semantics for Improved Decision Making in Bio-refinery Value Chains. Computer-Aided Chemical Engineering, 38, pp.2097-2102.

Wang, T.N. Wong, and X. Wang, 2013. An ontology based approach to organize multi-agent assisted supply chain negotiations. Computers & Industrial Engineering, 65(1), pp.2-15.

Xia, W., Jiang, Y., Chen, X., & Zhao, R. (2021). Application of machine learning algorithms in municipal solid waste management: A mini review. Waste Management &Amp; Research: The Journal for a Sustainable Circular Economy, 40(6), 609–624.

Abbasi M, El Hanandeh A. (2016) Forecasting municipal solid waste generation using artificial intelligence modelling approaches. Waste Management 56: 13–22.

Pereira Ramos TR, de Morais CS, Barbosa-Povoa AP. (2018) The smart waste collection routing problem: Alternative operational management approaches. Expert Systems with Applications 103: 146–158.

Ping P, Xu G, Kumala E, et al. (2020) Smart street litter detection and classification based on faster R-CNN and edge computing. International Journal of Software Engineering and Knowledge Engineering 30: 537–553.

Antonis Kokossis, Michael C. Georgiadis, Efstratios N. Pistikopoulos (Eds.)
PROCEEDINGS OF THE 33rd European Symposium on Computer Aided Process Engineering
(ESCAPE33), June 18-21, 2023, Athens, Greece

# System identification of scrap metal shredders under minimal process and feedstock information

Manolis Vasileiadis[a] Thomas Papageorgiou[b] Kyriakos Syrmakezis[b] Antonis Kokossis[a,*]

[a] National Technical University of Athens, 9 Heroon Polytechniou Str., 15780, Athens, Greece
[b] ANAMET S.A., 160 NATO Av., 19300, Aspropyrgos, Greece
* Corresponding author: akokossis@mail.ntua.gr

## Abstract

Shredders are essential processes in the metal scrap industry. Their efficiency is critical to sustainable recycling as shredders account for the largest energy consumers and the most expensive units to operate in the plant. While such processes are based on relatively simple principles and in operation for a long time, their feedstock (scrap) is difficult to characterize and relate to standard control schemes; operation is carried out empirically with an apparent scope for energy savings once the system is better understood. The paper presents a mathematical modelling approach, specifically aiming at the identification of a conventional shredder with minimum information about its input and output flows. A set of hypotheses, together with a mathematical optimization approach, are combined to estimate energy consumption and the breakdown of feedstock into the major metals involved. The model can be exploited to minimize energy and to connect with available model-based control technology in applications that are not addressed in this paper.

Keywords: Scrap metal shredder, mathematical optimization, model identification, energy efficiency

## 1. Introduction

Metal recycling is imperative for environmental and sustainable development. Recycling technologies have attracted significant attention, getting increasingly mature (Reuter et al. 2013) and expected to assume a fundamental role in the transition towards circular economy (George et al. 2015). Rather than based on a fixed composition of virgin materials, scrap metals account for a wide range of by-products (waste) and industrial activities (also referred as end-of-life products) such as end-of-life vehicles (ELVs), waste electric and electronic equipment (WEEE), used beverage cans (UBCs), etc. The importance of metal recycling is undisputed (Hageluken, 2016) with numerous companies already in place to recycle metal scrap. Trading and treatment companies receive scrap from collector companies, recover the metal by physical processes such as dismantling, shredding, etc., and then sell it to metal refining industries. A systems approach to analyze the energy use in the shredders is still missing in the literature, due to a general lack of information and data about the process.

Metal shredders are core processes in trading and treatment companies. Process efficiency is critical to sustainable recycling as shredders account for the largest energy consumers and the most expensive units to operate on-site. While process optimization could deliver significant savings in operating costs, process feedstocks (scrap) are difficult to characterize or systematically relate to the energy input required by the process; the shredder is eventually operated empirically. To that purpose, the paper introduces a systems approach for the estimation of input to a metal shredder using minimal information largely based on metals composition in the output. The approach fills in for missing information using material properties (especially those related to energies) while its model parameters are prepared for tuning and data embedding using online measurements. The development and validation of the methodology have been coordinated with real-life metal shredders from ANAMET S.A., the largest trading and treatment recycling company in Greece.

## 2. Shredding process: introduction and background

Shredding is a process ultimately aiming in the separation of various metals found in end of life (EOL) products. Shredding generally may be performed in various ways, including metal shredders and aims in the fragmentation of EOL products at a sufficiently fine granularity. Subsequently separation units separate the various materials composing the feedstock that has been shredded. The underlying assumption is that fragments of the original EOL products are sufficiently small so that each one consists of a single material. Energy use relates to the use of hammers (in our case 16 hammers) that break metals into fragments (shredded products) that are usually separated with magnetic separators followed by eddy-current separators. Handpicking is also used at various stages of the process. Products may vary and are typically classified as (1) "Shredded", (2) Zorba, (3) CuFe, (4) Inox and a by-product (5) Fluff. Feeds, however, include a much wider range of materials and EOL products that include whole cars, car engines, water heaters etc. In our case, they are organized in 21 different scrap categories (ISRI Scrap Specifications Circular, 2022).

Several batch processes, $N_d$, are repeated throughout a working day, $d$. Each day, $d$, a prespecified subset, $S_d \in \mathcal{P}(\{1,2,\dots,21\})$, of the 21 different scrap types is fed to the shredder. In each batch, $t \in \{1,2,\dots,N_d\}$, a mass, $m_t$ of one of the 21 different scrap types, $s_t \in S_d$, is fed to the shredder. Once the shredder drum is empty a new batch is introduced. While products $M_d^i \ \ i = 1,2\dots,5$, are weighted every day and they are known, the actual process input is not known precisely. Namely, every day, $d$, the subset $S_d$ is known but the total mass $m_d^k$ of scrap type $k \in S_d$ that is fed on day $d$ is unknown. A model is subsequently required to provide estimates $m_d^k$ for each different day $d$. Reliable measurements and data mostly relate to the product produced and separated on each different day. They include mass flowrates (kg/d), the energy consumption of the metal shredder (kWh), operating hours (each day), and the downtimes (each day). Operational data were made available for 6 consecutive years (2015-2021) and accounted for almost 1200 production days. Measurements of feedstocks are limited and are used as empirical and grossly uncertain estimates.

## 3. Energy consumption at the shredder $\widetilde{E_d}$

The energy consumption of the metal shredder depends largely on the feedstock, $(m_t, s_t), \quad t = 1, \dots, N_t$. We assume that (i) the sequence that the various batches are processed is not significant, and (ii) the mechanical properties of the scrap metals are the ones mostly contributing to the energy dissipation in the process. The mechanical properties are strong functions of the composition of each type of scrap, but we can ignore other affecting reasons (such as the scrap shape, heterogeneity etc.). Instead, we are in search for an analytical expression, $f$, in the form

$$\widetilde{E_d} \approx f(m_d^1 \cdot x^{1,1}, \dots m_d^{21} \cdot x^{5,21}) \approx \sum_{i=1}^{5} \sum_{k=1}^{21} e^i \cdot m_d^k \cdot x^{i,k} + c \tag{1}$$

The function $f$ is unknown and, as simplification, it was assumed that it is linear. Then, $e^i$ are parameters to be determined via regression analysis of available data. Simple algebraic manipulation of equation (1) results in:

$$\left(\widetilde{\frac{E_d}{M_d}}\right) \approx \sum_{i=1}^{4} e^i \cdot \frac{M_d^{j_i}}{M_d} + c \tag{2}$$

where $j_i \in \{1,2,3,4,5\}$ $\forall i = 1,2,3,4$. $M_d$ is the total production on day $d$ and $M_d^{j_i}$ is the mass of product $j_i$ on day $d$. In Equation (2) the choice of index to be excluded from $j_i$ is arbitrary and aims to achieve better results. Here we allow $j_i = 1,2,3,4$. Equation (2) is fitted to available measured data of energy consumption and mass of products for one month. To simplify this process and ensure that $e^i > 0$, $\forall i = 1, \dots ,4$ we assumed that there are correlations between parameters $e^i$ when fitting our available data. These correlations are assumed to be of the form:

$$e^1 = a^{\kappa_1} \cdot e^2; \ e^3 = a^{\kappa_2} \cdot e^2; e^4 = a^{\kappa_3} \cdot e^2 \tag{3}$$

where the $\kappa_i$ constant parameters measure the average strength of each type of scrap; $a$ is a parameter determined by the solution of the constrained regression:

$$\min_a \sum_{d=1}^{20} \frac{100}{20} \cdot \left( \frac{(\widetilde{E_d/M_d}) - (E_d/M_d)\left(\widetilde{M}_d^i; c(a), e^2(a)\right)}{(\overline{E/M})_d} \right) \tag{4}$$

$$s.t \quad c(a), e^2(a) > 0$$

The objective spans 20 working days of November 2011 to which Equations (2) and (3) are fitted; $\kappa_i$ are estimated using values of the tensile strength (Calister, 2017) of the major material comprising each product.

## 4. Estimation of feedstock

The feedstock is estimated to minimize real and expected production. This is formally expressed in Equation (5), where $\widetilde{M}_d^i$ is the estimation of the mass of product, $i$, based on the assumed feedstock and B.O.M. $M_d^i$ is the measured mass of product and $i$, $x^{i,k}$ represent the bills of material (B.O.M.) that express fractional compositions of the scrap type, $k \in \{1, 2, \dots, 21\}$ on product $i$. The first set of linear constraints express the mass balances for each product. These expressions are easily derived considering $x_t^i = x^{i,k}$ $\forall t \in \{t': s_{t'} = k\}$. Both values refer to date, $d$; $\widehat{m}_d^k$ is the empirical estimate of the scrap feedstock $k$ on each day. Finally, $D$, is a parameter (essentially a degree of freedom) that defines the number of days, that together with a specific day, $d_1'$, specify a date range within which the optimization problem is solved.

$$\min_{\{m_d^k: k=1,2,\dots,21\}} \sum_{d=d_1'}^{d_1'+D} \sum_{i=1}^{5} \left(\widetilde{M}_d^i - M_d^i\right)^2$$

$$s.t. \begin{cases} \widetilde{M}_d^i = \sum_{k=1}^{21} m_d^k \cdot x^{i,k} & \forall\, i = 1,2,3,4,5 \\[2ex] M_d = \sum_{i=1}^{5} \widetilde{M}_d^i & d = d_1, d_1 + 1, \dots, d_1 + D \\[2ex] \sum_{d=d_1}^{d_1+D} m_d^k = \sum_{d=d_1}^{d_1+D} \widehat{m}_d^k & \forall\, k = 1,2,\dots,21 \\[2ex] 0 \le m_d^k \le m^{k,U} & \forall\, k = 1,2,\dots,19 \end{cases} \qquad (5)$$

The optimization minimizes deviations between the estimated production and the production as measured within a specific date range. The second set of constraints enforces that, besides daily deviations between estimates and real measurements, the total production, $M_d$, should be equal. Similarly, the last set of equality constraints enforces that, besides deviations in empirical estimates, $\widehat{m}_d^k$, and model estimates, $m_d^k$, the total flowrates should be equal within the specified date range, $\{d_1', \dots, d_1' + D\}$. The constraints essentially guarantee that the new estimation $m_d^k$ across a prespecified date range add up to the total scrap quantity of type, $k$, that the company received within the date range. This constraint could change as the practice to monitor the overall process changes.

## 5. Results

### 5.1. Energy Estimation

The optimization problem of equation (4) is solved by the enumeration of the objective function on 41 evenly distributed points in the interval $a \in [1,3]$; $a$ is selected to match the lower objective while simultaneously satisfying the constraints of equation (4). Figure 1 shows the objective function of the optimization problem of equation (4) as a function of parameter $a$. Given these results the parameter $a$ is selected to the value 2. The average error in the estimation of energy consumption increases with the use of Equation (2) (e.g. by imposing physical constraints and positive coefficients on $e^i$) but the latter constraint is important to maintain a physically interpretable solution. The estimated parameters are $e^2 = 0.7485\text{kWh/kg}$ and $c = 29.1857$ kWh.

### 5.2. Feedstock Estimation

The methodology for the feedstock estimates, as presented in Section 4, has been applied starting from a reference day $d_1$ (set to 1/4/2019) towards the end of the horizon ($D = 20$). The problem is solved in subsequent iterations whereby $D$ is set to 18, 16, …, 2 etc., essentially as many times as necessary to cover the largest subset of periods from day $d_1$.

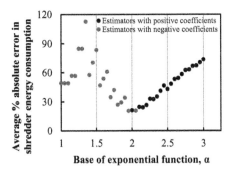

Figure 1. Average error in the estimation of energy consumption as function of $a$ in equation (4).

The approach always produced feasible solutions with the characteristics described in the previous section. A measure of accuracy was based on an average error:

$$\Delta = \langle \frac{1}{5} \sum_{i=1}^{5} |M_d^i - \widetilde{M}_d^i| \rangle \tag{6}$$

Brackets $\langle \ \rangle$ in Eq. (6) denote the average error over 20 dates of $d_1$. Figure 2 compares $\Delta$ with empirical measurements with an apparent improvement in the overall estimation as $\Delta$ decreases as function of $D$ reaching an eventual plateau.

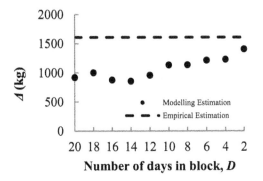

Figure 2 Average error of estimated production over a twenty-day working period starting from 1st of April 2019

Figure 3 illustrates the average production error of the proposed methodology on day $d_1$; the error is consistently lower in comparison with empirical estimates for values in $D$. The average production error on $d_2$ appears instead fluctuating, as a consequence of the optimization problem (5) whereby production errors are simultaneously minimized for more days.

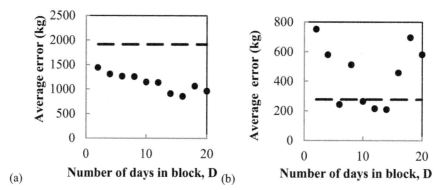

(a)  **Number of days in block, D** (b)    **Number of days in block, D**

Figure 3 Average error in days 1&2Conclusion

A mathematical modelling approach is presented to identify the composition of unknown feedstocks in scrap metal industries, a problem challenged by incomplete information and process complexity that prevents proper monitoring of the operation. Available data include production flows and energy consumption; feedstock information is available by means of empirical classes of scrap types sorted at the gate. Even with the limited information available, a mathematical modelling approach is validated to deliver reliable input-output relationships with assumptions that include a linear function for energy consumption and five independent parameters assigned for the different product types. Constraints include mass balances, property constraints, classification constraints (feedstocks, products) alongside the postulation of a linear energy function with plenty of room for improvements in considering additional properties for the scrap. The approach is tested on real-life shredders against existing empirical approaches and demonstrating significant improvements for the entire time window tested. Deviations and errors remain significant (e.g. 20%) but this is acceptable given the nature of the problem and the uncertainties that characterize scrap. The work further prepares shredders for control applications by providing reliable estimates for feedstock manipulation (e.g. scrap mixtures) while most expressions in the classification constraints and the energy function are natural entries for data embedding and machine learning. Future research will certainly consider these challenges.

## Acknowledgments

This research has been co-financed by the European Regional Development Fund of the European Union and Greek national funds through the Operational Program Competitiveness, Entrepreneurship and Innovation, under the call RESEARCH – CREATE – INNOVATE (project code:T1EDK-03010)

## References

M. Reuter et al., 2013, Metal recycling. Opportunities, Limits, Infrastruture, United Nations Environment Programme, Editor: International Resource Panel, Working Group on the Global Metal Flows

D.A.R. George, B. C-A Lin, Y. Chen, 2015, A Circular economy model of economic growth, Environmental, Modelling & Software, 73, 60-63

C. Hageluken et al., 2016 The EU circular economy and its relevance to metal recycling, Recycling 1, 242-253

Institute of Scrap Recycling Industries, 2022, ISRI Specs: ISRI Scrap Specificaitons Circular.

W.D. Callister, D.G. Rethwisch, 2015, Fundamentals of materials science and engineering. An integrated approach,

Antonis Kokossis, Michael C. Georgiadis, Efstratios N. Pistikopoulos (Eds.)
PROCEEDINGS OF THE 33rd European Symposium on Computer Aided Process Engineering
(ESCAPE33), June 18-21, 2023, Athens, Greece
© 2023 Elsevier B.V. All rights reserved.  http://dx.doi.org/10.1016/B978-0-443-15274-0.50551-5

# Development of a user-friendly platform for binary interaction parameter estimation

Oscar D. Lara-Montaño, [a] Fernando I. Gómez-Castro, [a*] Emilio Alba-Robles, [a]

Brayan Alejandro González-Abundis, [a] Sergio Yovani Rodríguez-Rojo, [a]

Cristian Geovanni Gutiérrez-Cano, [a] Patricia Isela de la Cruz-Morales, [b] Luis

Fernando Corado-Castañeda [c]

*[a]Departamento de Ingeniería Química, División de Ciencias Naturales y Exactas,
Campus Guanajuato, Universidad de Guanajuato, Noria Alta S/N, Guanajuato,
Guanajuato 36050, Mexico*
*[b]División de Ingeniería Química, Campus Centla, Tecnológico Nacional de México, C.
Ejido S/N, Col. Siglo XXI, Centro, Frontera, Tabasco, 86751, México*
*[b]Escuela de Ingeniería Química, Facultad de Ingeniería, Campus Central, Universidad
de San Carlos de Guatemala, 11 Avenida Zona 12, Ciudad de Guatemala,
Departamento de Guatemala, 01012, Guatemala*
*fgomez@ugto.mx*

## Abstract

Thermodynamic modeling and phase equilibrium calculations are among the core aspects
of the formation of chemical engineers. In this work, a platform has been developed to
estimate binary interaction parameters for the best fitting of the NRTL and the Wilson
models from data provided by the user. Moreover, the user can choose which optimization
algorithm will be used. The options currently available are Differential Evolution, Grey
Wolf Optimizer, and Jaya Algorithm. To test the platform, the binary mixture composed
of allyl alcohol–ethylene is employed. Although the four optimization algorithms can
converge to the best solution with enough iterations, the most efficient algorithm for both
optimization problems is Differential Evolution. This algorithm produces the smallest
deviation from experimental data.

**Keywords**: phase equilibria, binary interaction parameter, user-friendly platform.

## 1. Introduction

Many different chemical engineering processes rely on accurate phase equilibrium
calculations. Cubic equations of state, such as Peng-Robinson, Redlich-Kwong, and
Soave-Redlich-Kwong, are commonly used to predict the vapor-liquid equilibrium
(VLE). However, these equations cannot accurately describe the behavior that occurs in
the liquid phase for non-ideal mixtures (Tosun, 2021). To overcome this issue, binary
activity coefficient models are employed to predict the interactions occurring in the liquid
phase. Some examples of these liquid-phase predicting models are the Wilson equation
and the Non-Random Two-Liquid (NRTL) model. Both representations require binary
interaction parameters obtained from fitting with experimental data. Once the value of

the binary interaction parameters is obtained, they can be used and introduced into simulation environments to predict the thermodynamic behavior of complex systems.

To identify the value of the binary interaction parameters of the Wilson and NRTL models, it is necessary to have experimental data as the vapor and liquid fractions of the components when phase equilibrium occurs. An optimization procedure can be employed to find the best values of the binary interaction parameters. The objective is the minimization of the deviation between the experimental and the calculated values (Tosun, 2021).

Metaheuristic optimization algorithms are powerful techniques for global optimization. Different authors have employed various metaheuristic techniques to search interaction parameters for activity coefficient models due to the nonlinearity of the equations involved in such optimization problems. Khansary and Sani (2014) used particle swarm optimization (PSO) and genetic algorithms (GAs) to calculate the binary interaction parameters for four quaternary systems for the Wilson, NRTL, and UNIQUAC models. They conclude that the NRTL and UNIQUAC models can better predict the liquid-liquid equilibria (LLE); moreover, the PSO algorithms perform better than GAs. Vakili-Nezhaad et al. (2013) employed GAs to identify the values of binary interaction and non-randomness parameters for the NRTL model and two variants considering 20 ternary aromatic extraction systems containing 16 different ionic liquids at different temperatures. The calculated values produced a satisfactory prediction of the LLE. Jaime-Leal et al. (2015) identified the binary interaction parameters for two case studies using the cuckoo search (CS) algorithm and the e-NRTL model. They report that the CS has a success rate of approximately 90%; also, it is mentioned that the optimization algorithm may fail, especially when evaluating a local optimum solution comparable with the global optimum solution.

This study presents a user-friendly platform developed in Python to determine the binary interaction parameters for the Wilson and NRTL models. The platform is compatible with the three main operative systems (Windows, macOS, and Linux). It can be easily used for teaching purposes to help the student to understand the importance of counting with accurate binary interaction parameters. The user can select among three different metaheuristic algorithms widely used to solve engineering optimization problems; these are differential evolution (DE), grey wolf optimizer (GWO), and Jaya algorithm (JA). Thus, it allows to understand the importance on selecting an adequate optimization algorithm, and on its proper tuning. Also, the user can select among two different objective functions.

## 2. Optimization algorithms

The platform presented in this work allow selecting among three metaheuristic algorithms. The three optimization algorithms are population-based. Each algorithm is briefly described below.

### 2.1. Differential Evolution

The Differential Evolution (DE) algorithm is an evolution-based algorithm proposed by Storn, (1996). This algorithm implements mutation, crossover, and selection as operators in its structure. Different versions of DE are available. In this work, the version DE/x/y/z is employed, where DE refers to Differential Evolution, $x$ indicates a string denoting the base vector that is being perturbed, $y$ refers to the number of different vectors used in the perturbation of $x$, and $z$ involves the type of crossover. In mutation, a candidate solution, $V_i^t$, is generated with the equation 1, where $x_{r1}^t$, $x_{r2}^t$, and $x_{r3}^t$ are three different random solutions, and $t$ refers to the current iteration. $F$ is a scaling factor that for the selected version is equal to 0.5.

$$V_i^t = x_{r_1}^t + F(X_{r_2}^t - X_{r_3}^t) \tag{1}$$

The crossover operator is applied to the mutant vector $V_i^t$ to produce a new vector $U^t{}_i = u_{i,2}, u_{i,2}, \cdots, u_{i,dim}$, where $dim$ refers to the number of dimensions. The candidate solution $X_i^t$ and the vector $V_i^t$ are considered in the crossover process that uses a probability criterium $c_r$ as shown in equation 2. $rand(0,1)$ is a random number between 0 and 1. In the selection process, the new solution vector $U_i^t$ passes to the new iteration only if it is fitter that the candidate solution $X_i^t$.

$$u_{i,j} = \begin{cases} v_{i,j}^t & if \ rand(0,1) \leq c_r \\ x_{i,j}^t & otherwise \end{cases} \tag{2}$$

## 2.2. Grey Wolf Optimizer

The Grey Wolf Optimizer (GWO) was proposed by Mirjalili et al. (2014). It emulates the hunting behavior of grey wolves in nature, which expose a highly hierarchized society. Three main stages are identified in the hunting process: track and chase the prey, pursue, and encircle the prey, and attack the prey.

In this algorithm, the best three solutions of each iteration are identified as α, β, and δ; these candidate solutions lead the search process. The first phase of the algorithm (encircling the prey) is modeled according to equations 3 and 4. $A_i$ and $C_i$ are vectors of coefficients calculated as $A_i = 2a \cdot r_1 - \alpha$ and $C_i = 2r_2$, where $r_1$ and $r_2$ are random numbers between 0 and 1. $A$ is a parameter that linearly decreases from 2 to 0 in the iterative process.

$$\vec{D} = \left| \vec{C_i} \cdot \overrightarrow{X_p^t} - \overrightarrow{X_i^t} \right| \tag{3}$$

$$\overrightarrow{X_i^{t+1}} = \overrightarrow{X_p^t} - \vec{A} \cdot \vec{D} \tag{4}$$

According to the inspiration of this algorithm, the optimal global solution is the prey; nerveless, in most optimization problems, the solution is unknown. The best three candidate solutions in the current iteration are used to estimate the position in the $dim$-dimensional space, as shown in equation 5. $X_1$, $X_2$ and $X_3$ are the best, second-best, and third-best candidate solutions, respectively.

$$\overrightarrow{X_p^t} = \frac{\overrightarrow{X_1} + \overrightarrow{X_2} + \overrightarrow{X_3}}{3} \tag{5}$$

As the value of the parameter $a$ decrease, the transition from exploration to exploitation occurs.

## 2.3. Jaya Algorithm

The Jaya algorithm (JA) presented by Rao (2016) is a simple parameter-free metaheuristic optimization algorithm based on the idea that the newly generated candidate solutions must be created towards the best current solution, avoiding the space close to the worst current solution. Equation 6 is employed to update the candidate solutions, $X$ is the matrix of candidate solutions, $j$ indicates the decision variable, $k$ is the candidate solution, and $i$ the current iteration. The subscript *best* and *worst* refers to the best and worst current candidate solutions, respectively. $X'_{j,k,i}$ is only accepted if its evaluation in the objective function is lower than the evaluation of $X_{j,k,i}$, for a minimization problem. The parameters $r\_1$ and $r\_2$ are random numbers between 0 and 1.

$$X'_{j,k,i} = X_{j,k,i} + r_{1,j,i}(X_{j,best,i} - |X_{j,k,i}|) - + r_{2,j,i}(X_{i,worst,k} - |X_{j,k,i}|) \tag{6}$$

## 3. Optimization problem

The purpose of the presented platform is to find parameters for the Wilson and NRTL models, to represent the phase equilibrium from binary experimental data. For a binary system, to calculate the activity coefficients through the Wilson approach, equations 7 and 8 are employed, where $x_1$ and $x_2$ are the mole fractions of the liquid phase for components 1 and 2. $\Lambda_{12}$ and $\Lambda_{21}$ are the parameters whose value must be determined through the optimization procedure. Equations 9 and 10 are employed to calculate the activity coefficient using the NRTL model, where $\tau_{21}$ and $\tau_{12}$ are temperature-dependent parameters. $G_{12}$ and $G_{21}$ are calculated as $G_{12} = exp(-\alpha\tau_{12})$ and $G_{21} = exp(-\alpha\tau_{21})$ and $\alpha$ is the nonrandomness parameter.

$$ln\,\gamma_1 = -ln(x_1 + \Lambda_{12}x_2) + x_2 \left( \frac{\Lambda_{12}}{x_1 + \Lambda_{12}x_2} - \frac{\Lambda_{21}}{x_2 + \Lambda_{21}x_1} \right) \tag{7}$$

$$ln\,\gamma_2 = -ln(x_2 + \Lambda_{21}x_1) + x_1 \left( \frac{\Lambda_{12}}{x_2 + \Lambda_{12}x_1} - \frac{\Lambda_{12}}{x_1 + \Lambda_{12}x_2} \right) \tag{8}$$

$$ln\,\gamma_1 = x_2^2 \left[ \tau_{21} \left( \frac{G_{21}}{x_1 + G_{21}x_1} \right)^2 + \frac{\tau_{12}G_{12}}{(x_2 + G_{12}x_1)^2} \right] \tag{9}$$

$$ln\,\gamma_2 = x_1^2 \left[ \tau_{12} \left( \frac{G_{12}}{x_2 + G_{12}x_1} \right)^2 + \frac{\tau_{21}G_{12}}{(x_1 + G_{21}x_2)^2} \right] \tag{10}$$

The platform allows the user to select between two objective functions. The first is shown in equation 11; this minimizes the squared error between the experimental and the calculated activity coefficients. The second, shown in equation 12, minimizes the squared error between the experimental and calculated mole fractions on the liquid phase. $N$ is the number of experimental values (Tosun, 2021).

$$F = \sum_{i=1}^{N} \left[ \left( \gamma_{1,exp} - \gamma_{1,calc} \right)_i^2 + \left( \gamma_{2,exp} - \gamma_{2,calc} \right)_i^2 \right] \tag{11}$$

$$F = \sum_{i=1}^{N} \sum_{k=1}^{2} \left[ \left( x_{i,k}^{I,exp} - x_{i,k}^{I,calc} \right)^2 + \left( x_{i,k}^{II,exp} - x_{i,k}^{II,calc} \right)^2 \right] \tag{12}$$

The decision variables involved in the optimization problem where the Wilson model is present are $\Lambda_{12}$ and $\Lambda_{21}$. Lower and upper limits are given for decision variables, for both these are 0 and 10, respectively. In the optimization problem where the NRTL model is employed, the decision variables are $\tau_{12}$ and $\tau_{21}$, with -5 and 5 as lower and upper boundaries. $\alpha$ is also a decision variable, the lower boundary is 0.2 and the upper boundary is 0.5.

## 4. Results

The platform to find the binary interaction parameters is developed in Python. The interface is presented in Figure 1. To introduce the experimental data, the user must click on the button "*VLE Data*". This opens a window, where it is necessary to select a .xlsx or a .csv file that contains the experimental values. If the user requires to save the obtained values of the parameters it is necessary to click on *Select record*, then the user can choose where to save the results for the optimization problem. After, the user can proceed to introduce the names of the substances that conforms the binary mixture and the pressure of the system. Also, the objective function must be chosen, and the general parameters of the optimization algorithms such as population and number of individuals must be given.

As a results, the user obtains the *x-y* and *T-xy* diagrams, and the best values found for the binary interaction parameters.

To test the platform, the system allyl alcohol–ethylene glycol is employed. Experimental equilibrium data has been taken from Dong et al. (2018). Table 1 shows the results obtained for both models using the three optimization algorithms. The calculated squared error (SE) is also included. A population size of 50 individuals and 100 iterations are employed. The results obtained in the Wilson model produce very small variations between experimental and calculated activity coefficients. The values obtained for the parameters required in the NRTL model produce a slightly larger SE, but it still correctly predicting the phase equilibrium. DE calculates the lowest SE for both activity coefficient models.

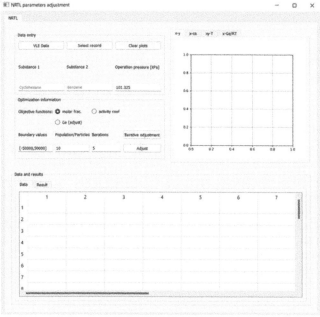

Figure 1. User interface of the platform.

Table 1. Optimal binary interaction parameters.

| Optimization algorithm | Wilson model | | | NRTL model | | | |
|---|---|---|---|---|---|---|---|
| | $\Lambda_{12}$ | $\Lambda_{21}$ | SE | $\tau_{12}$ | $\tau_{21}$ | $\alpha$ | SE |
| DE | 0.5932 | 0.3480 | 0.0054 | 1.0355 | 0.5524 | 0.5 | 0.0117 |
| GWO | 0.5923 | 0.3486 | 0.0055 | 1.0363 | 0.5517 | 0.4735 | 0.0117 |
| JA | 0.5932 | 0.3480 | 0.0054 | 1.0372 | 0.5402 | 0.4851 | 0.0143 |

Figure 2 shows the plot for the experimental and calculated activity coefficient for allyl alcohol using the parameters generated by the DE algorithm for the Wilson model. It can be appreciated that all the points lie on the 45° line. On the other hand, Figure 3 presents the experimental and calculated activity coefficient using the best value found for the parameters of the NRTL model with the DE algorithm. Although almost all the points are very close to the 45° line, the data points of the center slightly deviate. This could be due to the higher complexity of the NRTL model. However, the deviation is small. In general terms, it is observed that the three algorithms generate low values for the deviation, producing reliable values for the interaction parameters.

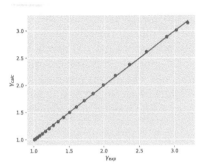
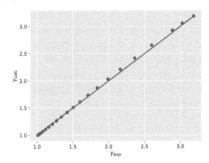

Figure 2. Experimental and calculated activity coefficient for allyl-alcohol using the Wilson model with $\Lambda_{12} = 0.5932$ and $\Lambda_{21} = 0.3480$.

Figure 3. Experimental and calculated activity coefficient for allyl-alcohol using the NRTL model with $\tau_{12} = 1.0355$, $\tau_{21} = 0.5524$ and $\alpha = 0.5$.

## 5. Conclusions

The presented platform is designed to be used with educational purposes to obtain the optimal interaction parameters for binary mixtures represented by the Wilson and NRTL models. The obtained parameters allow the lowest deviation between experimental and calculated composition and activity coefficient values. The platform has a user-friendly interface that allows introducing own experimental data from .csv or .xlsx files. Three optimization algorithms are employed independently either to find the best values for the parameters, or to compare the performance of the algorithms for this application. The quality of the solution depends on the size of the population and the number of iterations. The interface deploys different plots to compare the experimental and the calculated data.

## References

Y. Dong, R. Zhu, Y. Guo, Z. Lei, 2018, A united chemical thermodynamic model: COSMO-UNIFAC, Industrial & Engineering Chemistry Research, 57, 46, 15954–15958.

J.E. Jaime-Leal, A. Bonilla-Petriciolet, V. Bhargava, S.E.K. Fateen, 2015, Nonlinear parameter estimation of e-NRTL model for quaternary ammonium ionic liquids using Cuckoo Search, Chemical Engineering Research and Design, 93, 464–472.

M.A. Khansary, A.H. Sani, 2014, Using genetic algorithm (GA) and particle swarm optimization (PSO) methods for determination of interaction parameters in multicomponent systems of liquid–liquid equilibria, Fluid Phase Equilibria, 365, 141–145.

S. Mirjalili, S.M. Mirjalili, A. Lewis, 2014, Grey Wolf Optimizer, Advances in Engineering Software, 69, 46–61.

R.V. Rao, 2016, Jaya: A simple and new optimization algorithm for solving constrained and unconstrained optimization problems. International Journal of Industrial Engineering Computations, 7, 19–34.

R. Storn, 1996, On the usage of differential evolution for function optimization, Proceedings of North American Fuzzy Information Processing, 519–523.

I. Tosun, 2021, The Thermodynamics of Phase and Reaction Equilibria, Elsevier Science Publishing Co Inc.

G. Vakili-Nezhaad, M. Vatani, M. Asghari, 2013, Calculation of the binary interaction and nonrandomness parameters of NRTL, NRTL1 and NRTL2 models using genetic algorithm for ternary ionic liquid systems, Chemical Engineering Communications, 200, 8, 1102–1120.

Antonis Kokossis, Michael C. Georgiadis, Efstratios N. Pistikopoulos (Eds.)
PROCEEDINGS OF THE 33rd European Symposium on Computer Aided Process Engineering
(ESCAPE33), June 18-21, 2023, Athens, Greece

# Liquid-Liquid Equilibrium Data Correlation: Predicting a robust and consistent set of initial NRTL parameters

Juan A. Labarta*, José A. Caballero, Antonio F. Marcilla

*Department of Chemical Engineering & Institute of Chemical Process Engineering, University of Alicante, PO 99, Alicante E-03080, Spain.*

## Abstract

In the present work, the NRTL model has been analyzed to obtain a good representation of the different ternary liquid-liquid equilibria that this thermodynamic model can reproduce satisfactorily. To do that, the main characteristics of different possible binary subsystems, ternary binodal curves (location in the composition diagram, size, tie-lines orientation, and plait point location), and LLLE tie triangles have been evaluated. With more than two hundred systems studied, the different behaviors have been parametrized to create, as the main objective of the present work, a database and a graphical user interface associated. This resource (publicly available for teaching and research uses) allows, given a set of ternary experimental LLE data to obtain by comparison with the elements of the database, a consistent set of initial NRTL parameters ($\tau_{i,j}$, $\alpha_{i,j}$) to start the corresponding correlation data procedure with enough guarantees.

**Keywords**: NRTL model, phase equilibria, experimental data correlation, LLE, initial parameters.

## 1. Introduction

The correlation of liquid-liquid equilibrium data is still currently a challenging problem not fully resolved, especially for complex systems such as those involving for instance ionic liquids (Zhang et al. 2020), biodiesel (Bazooyar et al. 2021), etc. where the high nonlinearity and non-convexity of the equations involved produce convergence problems, with a strong dependence on the initialization values used of the obtained solution (Labarta et al. 2022a, Klerk and Schwarz, 2023). At this point, it is also important to remark that parameters of thermodynamic models (such as NRTL and UNIQUAC) that are inconsistent with the experimental behavior that is intended to be correlated can be found in the literature as it has been pointed out previously (Marcilla et al. 2017, Glass et al. 2017).

At present, different tools have been developed to help researchers, professionals, and students that have to deal with phase equilibrium correlation to avoid the intrinsic convergence difficulties of these calculations, reduce the search space, and/or confirm the consistency of the obtained results (interaction parameters) in the whole range of composition. For instance, the Graphical User Interface (GUI) Boundaries_LL_NRTL allows the visualization of the different LL and LV equilibrium regions that are possible to observe in the NRTL binary interaction parameters space. The modeling as constraints of these boundaries helps to reduce significantly the search space of the unknown parameters in the correlation process (Labarta et al. 2022b). Other GUIs such as GMcal_TieLinesLL or GMcal_TieLinesLV (Figure 2) allow checking the consistency of the parameter obtained in the correlation of binary and ternary LLE or (isobaric or isothermal) LVE experimental data, respectively, by analyzing the topology of the corresponding Gibbs Energy of mixing functions (calculated with NRTL, UNIQUAC or any other alternative model) and its consistency with the equilibrium of the system under study (Labarta et al. 2022c-d). These tools include also, in the case of the LLE, the analysis of the Hessian matrix, Spinodal curve, and critical point location, and in the case of the LVE, additionally the analysis of the necessity of an additional dependence with the temperature or pressure of the binary interaction parameters, and also the possible existence of distillation boundaries.

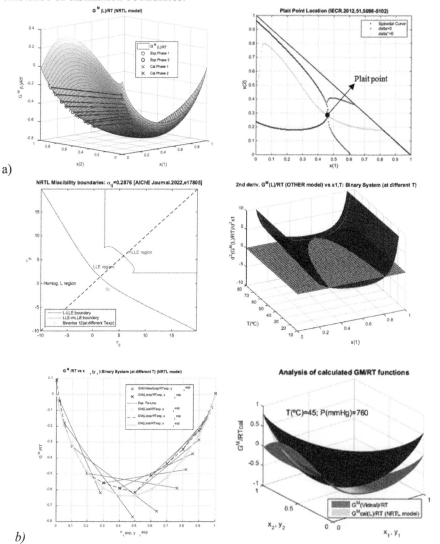

*Figure 1. GUIs for the Topological Analysis of Binary and Ternary LLE or LVE Correlation Data Results. Examples of calculations: a) GMcal_TieLinesLL. b) GMcal_TieLinesVL*

## 2. Methodology and results

In the present work, the NRTL model has been analyzed through more than 200 LLE ternary systems (including type I, II, III, and 0 or island, following the Treybal classification) to obtain a good representation of the different possible LLE (i.e. binodal curves, tie triangles, etc.) that this model can reproduce satisfactorily, in a wide enough interval of values of the different parameters ($\tau_{i,j}$, $\alpha_{i,j}$). Figure 2 shows different examples of the results obtained in this scanning of the NRTL model, where it is possible to observe several systems with differences in the number of binary subsystems partially miscible, in the size of the LLE region, and even presenting different possibilities of LLLE tie-tringles.

The equilibrium region of all these systems has been parametrized regarding the main characteristics of the corresponding LLE depending on the classification of the system:

- Systems type 1 (with only one binary subsystem partially miscible). In this case, the location and extension of the equilibrium LL regions have been characterized by 5 parameters:
  - Size and average composition of the binary partially miscible (2 parameters)
  - Composition of the plait point (2 parameters)
  - Average slope of the experimental ternary tie lines (1 parameter)
- Systems type 2 (with two binary subsystems partially miscible). 6+4 parameters:
  - Size and average composition of the two partially miscible binaries (4 parameters)
  - Maximum size and average slope of the experimental ternary tie lines (2 parameters)
  - Composition of the two plait points, if exit (4 additional parameters)
- Systems type 3 (with three binary subsystems partially miscible). 12 parameters:
  - Size and average composition of the three partially miscible binaries (6 parameters)
  - Composition of the three points that configure the tie triangle, or the composition of the different plait points, if exit (6 parameters)
- Systems type 0 (with no binary subsystems partially miscible). 8 parameters:
  - Average composition of all the tie lines (2 parameters)
  - Average and maximum size of the tie lines (2 parameters)
  - Composition of the two plait points (4 parameters)

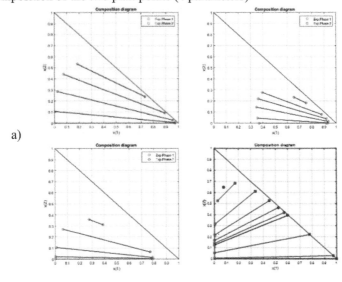

a)

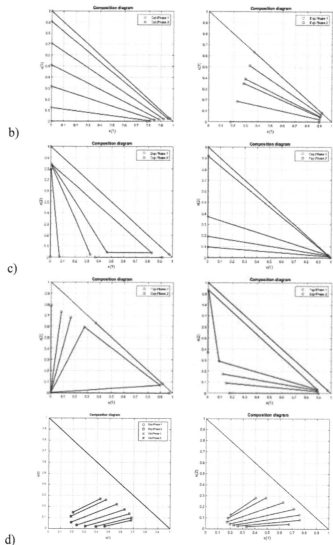

b)

c)

d)

*Figure 2. Examples of different LLE behaviors: a) Type I with only one binary partially miscible,
b) Type II with two binaries partially miscible, c) Type III with three binaries partially miscible
and a tie-triangle, d) Type 0 without binaries partially miscible but with an internal region of two
liquids partially miscible.*

With this parametrization, we have created a database and a new graphical user interface ParamIni_LL_NRTL (Labarta et al. 2022e) that allows loading a set of liquid-liquid experimental data, to obtain by comparison with the different elements of the database, a consistent set of initial NRTL parameters that predicts the parametrized LLE nearest the experimental one (Figure 3). The topology of the Gibbs Energy of mixing function regarding the behavior of the experimental data studied can be also checked, in order to evaluate the goodness of the binary interaction parameters suggested as an initial point in the corresponding correlation data algorithm.

Finally, the suggested set of the binary interaction parameters can be used now in any correlation data algorithm (using the corresponding equilibrium condition: isoactivity, minimum of the global Gibbs energy of mixing, or the Gibbs energy of mixing minor common tangent plane) to obtain the final rigorous solution (Marcilla et al. 2011, Díaz et al. 2019).

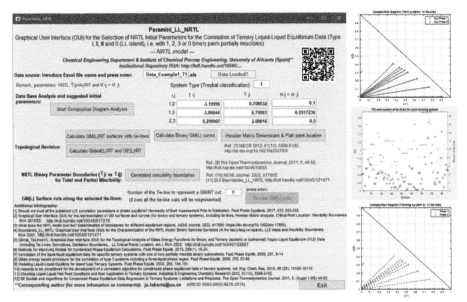

*Figure 3. ParamIni_LL_NRTL: Graphical User Interface (GUI) for the Selection of NRTL Initial Parameters for the Correlation of Ternary Liquid-Liquid Equilibrium Data (Type I, II, III and 0 (LL island), i.e. with 1, 2, 3 or 0 binary pairs partially miscible).*

## 3. Conclusions

We believe that the present work with the analysis and tool developed can help in the task of correlating experimental liquid-liquid equilibrium data, in the sense that allows obtaining a <u>consistent</u> set of <u>initial</u> NRTL parameters, regarding the main characteristics of the experimental data in comparison with the elements of the database, in order to start the corresponding correlation data process. Obviously, the intention is to periodically update the database with more systems, and also to include the UNIQUAC model, which together with the NRTL model is still currently one of the most used models to calculate fluid phase equilibria, taking into account that the correct calculation of the phase equilibrium is a key point in the optimal (efficient and sustainable) design of the corresponding processes and equipment.

## Acknowledgments

The authors gratefully acknowledge the financial support by the Ministry of Science and Innovation from Spain, under the project PID2021-124139NB-C21: SUS4Energy, 2022/00666/001 (AEI).

## References

B. Bazooyar, F. Shaahmadi, M.A. Anbaz, A. Jomekian, 2021, Intelligent modelling and analysis of biodiesel/alcohol/glycerol liquid-liquid equilibria, Journal of Molecular Liquids, 322, 114972.

A. Bazyleva, J. Abildskov, A. Anderko, O. Baudouin, Y. Chernyak, J. Hemptinne, V. Diky, R. Dohrn, J. Elliott, J. Jacquemin, J. Jaubert, K. Joback, U. Kattner, G. Kontogeorgis, H. Loria, P. Mathias, J. O'Connell, W. Schröer, G. Smith, A. Soto, S. Wang, R. Weir, 2021, Good reporting practice for thermophysical and thermochemical property measurements (IUPAC Technical Report). Pure and Applied Chemistry93(2): 253-272.

I. Díaz, M- Rodríguez, E.J. González, M. González-Miquel, 2019, A simple and reliable procedure to accurately estimate NRTL interaction parameters from liquid-liquid equilibrium data. Chem. Eng. Sci., 193: 370-378.

M. Glass, M. Aigner, J. Viell, A. Jupke, A. Mitsos, 2017, Liquid-liquid equilibrium of 2-methyltetrahydrofuran/water over wide temperature range: Measurements and rigorous regression. Fluid Phase Equilib., 433, 212-225.

D.L. de Klerk. C.E. Schwarz, 2023, Simplified Approach to the Parameterization of the NRTL Model for Partially Miscible Binary Systems: Tττ LLE Methodology, Industrial & Engineering Chemistry Research, 62, 4, 2021-2035.

J.A. Labarta, J.A. Caballero, 2022e, ParamIni_LL_NRTL: Graphical User Interface (GUI) for the Selection of NRTL Initial Parameters for the Correlation of Ternary Liquid-Liquid Equilibrium Data (Type I, II, III and 0 (LL island), i.e. with 1, 2, 3 or 0 binary pairs partially miscible), Institutional Repository of the University of Alicante, publicly available at: http://hdl.handle.net/10045/130017.

J.A. Labarta, M.M. Olaya, A. Marcilla, 2022a, What does the NRTL model look like? Determination of boundaries for different fluid phase equilibrium regions, AIChE Journal, e17805.

J.A. Labarta, M.M. Olaya, A. Marcilla, 2022b, Boundaries_LL_NRTL: Graphical User Interface (GUI) for the characterization of the NRTL model: Binary Spinodal Surfaces (in the τi,j-τj,i-xi space), LLE maps and Miscibility Boundaries, Institutional Repository of the University of Alicante, publicly available at: http://hdl.handle.net/10045/121471.

J.A. Labarta, M.M. Olaya, A. Marcilla, 2022c, GMcal_TieLinesLL: Graphical User Interface (GUI) for the representation of GM surfaces and curves (for binary and ternary systems), including tie-lines, Hessian Matrix analysis, Critical Point Location, Miscibility Boundaries, etc. Institutional Repository of the University of Alicante, http://hdl.handle.net/10045/51725.

J.A. Labarta, M.M. Olaya, A. Marcilla, 2022d, GMcal_TieLinesVL: Graphical User Interface (GUI) for the Topological Analysis of Experimental and Calculated GM Functions for Binary and Ternary (isobaric or isothermal) Vapor-Liquid Equilibrium (VLE) data (including Tie-Lines, Derivatives, Distillation Boundaries, LL Critical Points Location, etc.), Institutional Repository of the University of Alicante, http://hdl.handle.net/10045/122857.

A. Marcilla, J.A. Labarta, M.M Olaya, 2017, Should we trust all the published LLE correlation parameters in phase equilibria? Necessity of their Assessment Prior to Publication, Fluid Phase Equilibria. 433, 243-252.

A. Marcilla, J.A. Labarta, M.D. Serrano, M.M. Olaya, 2011, GE Models and Algorithms for Condensed Phase Equilibrium Data Regression in Ternary Systems: Limitations and Proposals. The Open Thermodynamics Journal, 5 (Suppl 1-M5), 48-62.

L. Zhang, X. Bing, Z. Cui, J.A. Labarta, D. Xu, J. Gao, S. Zhou, Y. Wang, 2021, Multiscale Exploration and Experimental Insights into Separating Neutral Heterocyclic Nitrogen Compounds Using [emim][NO3] as an Extractant, ACS Sustainable Chem. Eng. 2020, 8, 14, 5662-5673.

Antonis Kokossis, Michael C. Georgiadis, Efstratios N. Pistikopoulos (Eds.)
PROCEEDINGS OF THE 33rd European Symposium on Computer Aided Process Engineering
(ESCAPE33), June 18-21, 2023, Athens, Greece

# Practical learning activities to increase the interest of university applicants in STEM careers in the era of Industry 4.0

Monica Tirapelle*, Dian Ning Chia, Fanyi Duanmu, Konstantinos Katsoulas, Alberto Marchetto and Eva Sorensen

*aDepartment of Chemical Engineering, University College London, Torrington Place, London WC1E 7JE, UK*

*m.tirapelle@ucl.ac.uk

## Abstract

Inspiring young students, especially young girls, about STEM disciplines is crucial to address the current shortage of engineers. Since the engineering skills that are required by graduates are evolving in line with technological progress, there is now an even stronger need for graduates with strong Process Systems Engineering skills. In this work, we describe an effective way to promote the chemical engineering curriculum, with particular emphasis on computational tools, to a group of Year 12 high school students during a one-week course in our department. The course was designed to engage students in active learning through interactive sessions and practical hands-on activities. Through the course, the students gained a better understanding of the importance of STEM subjects and, in particular, of the challenges and opportunities that engineers encounter in the era of Industry 4.0 with ever-increasing use of digitalization in process design and operation.

**Keywords**: Engineering Education, Hands-on activities, Active learning, Orientation to university, PSE computational tools

## 1. Introduction

The world is currently facing unprecedented challenges in our efforts to achieve the UN's sustainability goals, of which many are closely related to the work of chemical engineers. To achieve these goals, we need a workforce that is suitably equipped to handle the complexities of these challenges, and key to this is science, technology, engineering and maths (STEM) skills (Perkins, 2013). The recruitment into STEM subjects is, at least in the UK, still limited, particularly with respect to gender. In 2019, female students in the UK accounted for only 39% of pre-university, or A-level, examination entries in mathematics, 22% in physics, and 13% in computing. Importantly, relatively few girls opted for two or more STEM subjects at A-Level, which is a requirement to access many university STEM degrees (Department for Education, 2020). To increase the interest of secondary school students towards STEM disciplines and to encourage the enrolment in engineering courses, universities offer outreach activities. Several authors have looked at the impact of these activities and found that, generally, the participants gain a better understanding of STEM fields and enhance their STEM skills (Little and León de la Barra, 2009; Gumaelius et al., 2016). Process Systems Engineering (PSE) involves the use of not only fundamental STEM skills but also of computational tools, and these are not generally considered in schools when teaching science and maths. As a result, potential applicants to chemical engineering degrees may not be aware of the career opportunities that PSE may offer, or of the new challenges that the profession is facing in the Industry 4.0 era.

In this work, we describe an effective way to promote PSE to Year 12 students, in particular to female students, which is considered at UCL. The students spent one week in the department with the aim of increasing their motivation toward STEM disciplines, and of making them aware of challenges and opportunities that engineers will encounter in the era of Industry 4.0. The course is taking place in the summer before the final year of their final pre-university education (between Year 12 and Year 13). The course was designed to engage students in active and practical learning (Biggs and Tang, 2011; Lucas and Hanson, 2021). To deliver basic key concepts, traditional teaching techniques were replaced with brief interactive sessions. To consolidate learning and to apply knowledge in practice, the students were assigned hands-on activities that involved the use of typical PSE tools, e.g., Excel, Python, MATLAB, and Aspen Plus. The topics covered included basic principles of fluid separations, optimisation, and machine learning. As a final task, the students were asked to present their work to peers and other teaching staff.

The following sections will present the various hands-on activities that were used, as well as the practical requirements for a department to deliver such a course. We also discuss our students' perceptions of STEM before and after attending the course. We found that their attitudes towards STEM, and their interest in pursuing STEM-related careers, increased. More interestingly, their attitudes towards the PSE-related aspects of engineering increased considerably.

## 2. Teaching methods

The aim of the one-week course is to encourage high-school students, particularly female students, to pursue studies within STEM disciplines and to introduce them to the current challenges and opportunities of Industry 4.0 and the associated use of PSE tools. The week was therefore designed based on topics related to these areas that are not usually covered in the high school curriculum (details can be found in Section 3). To deliver these topics, which can be far from trivial to understand for a high school student, we employed a student-centred teaching approach (Catalano and Catalano, 1999) by providing ad-hoc hands-on activities to enable active learning and by creating an informal learning environment.

Wisniewski et al. (2019) introduced the easy-to-hard effect, which states that a person is more likely to learn a difficult topic if the learning process is progressed from easy to difficult levels. Therefore, the activities in the course were sorted by complexity. In the first couple of days, the students were introduced to the basic concepts and operating principles of mainstream separation processes (see Sections 3.1 to 3.3) by using either Excel spreadsheets or commercially available process simulators. The students were then introduced to the more concept- and code-based topics of optimisation and machine learning (see Sections 3.4 and 3.5). Each topic was kick-started with a simple introduction followed by everyday life examples. This approach elicited the students' curiosity and made them realise how most of the concepts within STEM are inspired by nature and are closely related to their lives.

To deliver the topics, an active learning and inquiry-based approach was adopted. The students were actively engaged in the learning process by allowing them time to ask questions, participate in peer group discussions and hands-on activities to encourage critical thinking (Felder and Brent, 2009). For the hands-on activities, students were split into pairs to work in a team (see Section 3 for more details). To consolidate their learning and to enhance their communication skills, the students were also given time to record the different topics and their achievements by gradually preparing a PowerPoint presentation that they refined and improved throughout the week and then presented to their peers and teaching staff during the last day of the course. The overall teaching method, with details on the primary goals, is summarized in Figure 1.

Last but not least, we focused the programme development and delivery also on diversity and equality, which we believe to be key concepts underpinning teaching and learning. The teaching team consisted of two female and three male researchers coming from different cultural backgrounds, and during each session, at least one female and one male researcher were present. Such a multicultural teaching team allowed for a free and wide-reaching exchange of ideas and gave the students a taste of university student life, especially in a global university like UCL, which has had strong commitments to diversity and inclusion from its foundation almost 200 years ago. Moreover, by providing female role models, we tried to break the stereotype that engineering is mainly for males and to inspire the female students to apply for STEM university degrees.

Figure 1. Pedagogical framework

## 3. Case studies

In the following, we will discuss the five main topics covered in the course. The topics cover traditional fluid separation processes such as chromatography and distillation, as well as various methods commonly employed in PSE that are of importance for attaining the UN's sustainability goals. Note that all of these topics are embedded within the chemical engineering undergraduate curriculum at UCL.

### 3.1. Topic 1 - Liquid Chromatography

On the first day of the course, we introduced the students to the basic principles of liquid chromatography, focusing on the influence of key design and operating parameters on the degree of separation. To get the students interested, we started by showing clips of movies where chromatography is employed by forensic scientists. We proceeded with a brief overview of the topic followed by several short educational videos covering the main terms and definitions of chromatography as well as the basic principles involved. The students were then given an assignment, working in pairs, to find a combination of operational conditions to achieve the separation of an analyte whilst satisfying certain constraints such as maximum time of analysis and minimum peak resolution. To this end, students were provided with an Excel spreadsheet developed by Guillarme and Veuthey (Guillarme and Veuthey, 2016; Veuthey and Guillarme, 2016). The students could explore by themselves the impact of some of the main design parameters on the degree of separation, such as column length, temperature, flow rate, and solvent strength. Furthermore, they learned that trial-and-error approaches are time-consuming, may lead to non-optimal results and, in a real industrial setting, may lead to an increase in operating costs and wastage. With this experience and awareness, the students were ready to be introduced to optimisation techniques later on in the course (see Section 3.4).

*3.2. Topic 2 - Adsorption*

The first session of day two involved an introduction to adsorption, a physicochemical phenomenon involved in various processes studied in Chemical Engineering (i.e., chromatography, catalytic reactions and fluid separation). The students first watched YouTube videos that explained the basic principles of adsorption, and briefly covered the derivation of very simple mass balances and isotherms. We then focused on the significance of isotherm equations, while pointing out that an isotherm includes parameters that are often unknown, and thus have to be estimated, normally from fitting an isotherm equation to experimental data. The next activity involved a hands-on session where the students fitted the Langmuir isotherm to experimental data provided to them by using non-linear regression methods in Excel. The students were able to estimate the isotherm parameters by minimising the mean squared error between the experimental and calculated values of solid phase concentration. This activity allowed the students to handle some experimental data and to experience parameter estimation.

*3.3. Topic 3 - Distillation*

The students were then introduced to distillation. This topic started with the fundamental concepts of distillation, including vaporisation, condensation, and vapour-liquid equilibrium. Then, two different types of distillation processes, batch and continuous distillation, were briefly presented. A group discussion followed about the relative benefits, drawbacks, and applications of each mode of operation, not only to encourage the students' critical thinking but also to examine their understanding. Next, a commonly used process simulator, Aspen Plus (Aspen Technology Inc., 2017), was introduced with step-by-step guidance on how to set up a proper distillation simulation. Next, a hands-on activity of separating a binary mixture in a continuous distillation column was considered, followed by a discussion of the effects of the key design variables on the separation performance using sensitivity analysis. This topic ended with a discussion about distillation column sequencing for the separation of multi-component mixtures (without considering azeotropes) and of energy efficiency. By the end of the day, the students had a better understanding of how highly energy-demanding processes, such as distillation, may become more energy-efficient, smarter, and safer when digital tools are used in their process design and optimisation.

*3.4. Topic 4 - Optimisation techniques*

The third day was focused on the concept of optimisation as one of the main steps for designing a sustainable chemical process. The students were first introduced to the basic elements of optimisation, such as objective function and problem constraints, and then to the following optimisation methods: Linear Programming (LP), Genetic Algorithm (GA) and Particle Swarm Optimisation (PSO).

LP is one of the simplest methods with which to perform deterministic optimisation of linear problems. We first demonstrated how an LP problem could be formulated through equations, that is, by specifying the objective function and the constraints, and then demonstrated the solution using the graphical method. When the students became more familiar with the equation formulation, we demonstrated the solution to the same problem using the Excel optimiser. For the hands-on session, the students had to formulate the equations for four different problems and find the optimal solution using Excel. After the hands-on problems, the students were confident in their ability to express an LP problem using linear equations and in finding the optimum using Excel spreadsheets.

Unlike LP, GA and PSO are heuristic-based stochastic optimisation methods designed to solve more complex problems. We started this topic by showing the students a video on how humans have evolved following the concept of "survival of the fittest", which are the key features of GA (parent selection, crossover, and mutation). Then, a hands-on activity based on the famous travelling salesman problem, built-in in MATLAB, was used to help the students understand the power of GA optimisation and how to tune the GA parameters. Next, a similar teaching procedure was used for PSO. The students were tasked with obtaining the global optimum by changing the key PSO settings, such as the number of swarms, cognitive parameter, and social parameter. This activity also made the students realise that the results from the optimisation may not be 100% reliable, and that it is necessary to double-check the results using different approaches (e.g., different optimisation methods combined with sound engineering judgement).

### 3.5. Topic 5 - Machine learning

On the final day, the students were introduced to data-driven modelling and cheminformatics related activities. In particular, they were shown how to apply regression techniques for molecular aqueous solubility prediction starting from selected molecular descriptors as input (Todeschini and Consonni, 2008). Data used to build the machine-learning models were taken from the literature (Huuskonen, 2000). A fully interactive approach for this topic would be quite difficult due to its high complexity. Nevertheless, the students were actively involved when they were asked to calculate some molecular descriptors of interest from the Simplified Molecular Input Line Entry System (SMILES) representation of ten selected molecules among those available in the data set. AlvaDesc (Mauri, 2020), a commercial cheminformatics software, was adopted for this purpose. The students were also shown common preliminary data analysis and data curation techniques, used prior to data-driven model development. Modelling-wise, the students were shown how to perform a linear regression with regularisation techniques to penalise model complexity, as well as how to present results through parity and box plots.

## 4. Results and discussion

The hands-on activities were designed to give the students the opportunity to consolidate their learning and to put their new knowledge to work. Even if the student background on the topics covered was either very limited or null, the students' performance was outstanding. They were able to complete each task in the time allocated and to attain reliable results. This implies that adopting teaching methods that enable active learning is advantageous and has a positive impact on student learning. To ascertain the students' perspective on the course, we asked the students to fill out the same survey both before and at the end of the course. We designed the survey to target both the students' motivation of pursuing STEM careers (i.e., commitment, perceived value, and awareness), as well as their knowledge and understanding of the topics covered during the week. Questions were Likert-type questions based on a 5-points scale ranging from strongly disagree to strongly agree. Due to the small number of students involved, we cannot do meaningful statistical analysis on the survey results, however, looking at the average scores and comparing the answers given before and after the placement, we can conclude that the course had not actually impacted much on their interest in STEM careers, as this was already high. The students have probably already been exposed to STEM disciplines and were already conscious that a strong STEM workforce is needed, today more than ever, to achieve a sustainable process industry. It appeared, however, that the students felt much more confident about the topics they had considered, and their interest in computational tools had increased. This reflects the fact that the two-ways teaching methods, the teaching environments and the hands-on activities have been adequately applied and had achieved our goal of introducing them to the wonderful world of PSE. At the end of the course, we also asked the student to fill a questionnaire about their general satisfaction. All students would recommend the placement to a friend.

## 5. Conclusions

In this work, we have presented an engaging way to promote the chemical engineering curriculum to high school students during a one-week course by utilizing an interactive teaching method that involves brief interactive sessions followed by hands-on activities. Through the course, we have enhanced student awareness about the role of chemical engineers in the era of Industry 4.0, and we have promoted the role of females in STEM disciplines. From pre- and post- surveys, we were able to gather some student feedback. Even if we did not significantly impact their interest in pursuing a STEM career, we were able to improve their knowledge of the basic concepts of fluid separation, but more importantly, to increase their curiosity towards the use of computational tools commonly employed by process system engineers. This evidences that the implemented pedagogical method and the informal learning environment, as well as the contents covered in the course, represent effective tools towards getting students engaged and enthused about the subject. We believe that this course can help students in their career choices and, hopefully, get them started on a career journey within Process Systems Engineering. To improve even further the effectiveness of this course, we suggest including an informal meeting with a few engineering employers.

## References

Aspen Technology Inc., 2017. Aspen Plus V10.
　　URL https://www.aspentech.com/en/products/engineering/aspen-plus
J. Biggs, C. Tang, 2011. Teaching for quality learning at university. McGraw-hill education (UK).
G. D. Catalano, K. Catalano, 1999. Transformation: From teacher-centered to student-centered engineering education. Journal of Engineering Education 88 (1), 59–64.
Department for Education, 2020. Applying behavioural insights to increase female students' uptake of stem subjects at a level.
R. M. Felder, R. Brent, 2009. Active learning: An introduction. ASQ higher education brief 2 (4).
D. Guillarme, J. L. Veuthey, 2016. HPLC teaching assistant: a new tool for learning and teaching liquid chromatography, part i. LCGC North America 34 (10), 804–811.
L. Gumaelius, M. Almqvist, A. Árnadóttir, A. Axelsson, J. A. Conejero, J. P. García-Sabater, ... & M. Voss, 2016. Outreach initiatives operated by universities for increasing interest in science and technology. European Journal of Engineering Education, 41 (6), 589-622.
J. Huuskonen, 2000. Estimation of aqueous solubility for a diverse set of organic compounds based on molecular topology. Journal of Chemical Information and Computer Sciences 40 (3), 773–777.
A. J. Little, B. A. León de la Barra, 2009. Attracting girls to science, engineering and technology: An Australian perspective. European Journal of Engineering Education, 34 (5), 439-445.
B. Lucas, J. Hanson, 2021. Reimagining practical learning in secondary schools: A review of the evidence.
A. Mauri, 2020. alvaDesc: A tool to calculate and analyze molecular descriptors and fingerprints. Humana Press Inc.
J. Perkins, 2013. Professor John Perkins' review of engineering skills. London, Department for Business Innovation and Skills.
R. Todeschini, V. Consonni, 2008. Handbook of molecular descriptors. John Wiley & Sons.
J. L. Veuthey, D. Guillarme, 2016. HPLC teaching assistant: A new tool for learning and teaching liquid chromatography, part ii. LCGC North America 34 (12), 906–915.
M. G. Wisniewski, B. A. Church, E. Mercado, M. L. Radell, A. C. Zakrzewski, 2019. Easy-to-hard effects in perceptual learning depend upon the degree to which initial trials are "easy". Psychonomic Bulletin and Review 26 (6), 1889–1895.

Antonis Kokossis, Michael C. Georgiadis, Efstratios N. Pistikopoulos (Eds.)
PROCEEDINGS OF THE 33rd European Symposium on Computer Aided Process Engineering
(ESCAPE33), June 18-21, 2023, Athens, Greece

# Integrating Python in the (bio)chemical engineering curriculum: challenges and opportunities

Fiammetta Caccavale [a], Carina L. Gargalo [a], Krist V. Gernaey [a], Ulrich Krühne[a]

*[a]PROSYS, Dept. of Chemical and Biochemical Engineering, Technical University of Denmark, Søltofts Plads, Building 228 A, 2800 Kgs. Lyngby, Denmark.*
*ulkr@kt.dtu.dk*

## Abstract

In times when developments in digital transformation and online education are accelerating due to the push of the Fourth Industrial Revolution and the Covid-19 pandemic, Education and Digitalization are becoming increasingly intertwined. These recent events have proved the necessity for engineers to adapt by acquiring new technical skills. To facilitate the shift to digital technologies, as well as to enhance students' engagement, this study investigates the introduction of Python as a tool to solve chemical engineering problems, aiming to improve students' learning experience by providing stimulating material and gamification. The Python material, covering topics such as stoichiometry, design of chemical reactors, and mass and energy balances, was embedded into the curriculum of a BEng. Course in Chemical Reaction Engineering at the Technical University of Denmark. Preliminary results seem to confirm that digital tools generate higher engagement and participation among students, leading to better understanding and higher performance.

Keywords: Python, digital education, programming in engineering curriculum

## 1. Introduction

In these times of educational disruption, drastic changes have been accelerated, resulting in significant advances in adopting digitalization strategies (Gargalo *et al.*, 2020). In this transformation climate, engineers should be adequately educated to face the challenges and acquire the new skills imposed by Industry 4.0 (dos Santos *et al.*, 2018; Narayanan *et al.*, 2020), coupled with the new learnings from the Covid-19 pandemic.

Previous studies (C. de Las Heras *et al.*, 2021) highlight a clear urgency expressed by students to acquire programming skills in (bio)chemical engineering education, and shed light on the insufficient presence of programming in the curriculum and students' preference to use only one programming language (Python favored over MATLAB).

Python is considered a favorable choice for students and engineers that want to adapt to this digital transformation due to its widespread usage, straightforward syntax, readability, available libraries, broad documentation, support, and suitability for data science applications. Moreover, contrary to tools like MATLAB, it is open-source. Because of all these reasons, Python is attracting the interest of both students and professionals in the chemical engineering community.

Although some tailored courses to learn Python, both broadly and specifically for chemical engineers, are currently available (PyCRE, 2022; AIChE, 2022), they are often not open access, while the few open-source courses available do not seem to have thorough explanations of either the theory or coding guidelines.

This work aims to evaluate the introduction of a hands-on Python programming course in the (bio)chemical engineering curriculum to (i) address the need to prepare engineers for Industry 4.0; (ii) increase students' engagement and participation in the courses; and, (iii) answer their request for more programming. The course chosen to test the introduction of Python is the BEng Chemical Reaction Engineering course (https://kurser.dtu.dk/course/28342) at the Technical University of Denmark (DTU). This course was considered a suitable candidate since educators observed that students generally perform significantly better in group assignments than in the final exam, attributing this to the low active participation in class, especially in the practical exercise sessions.

The main contributions of this work are the following:

(i)     We implement and release a Python course on Chemical Reaction Engineering on GitHub;

(ii)    We embed this course in the educational curriculum and assess it through both quantitative metrics and qualitative evaluations;

(iii)   We discuss the learned challenges and opportunities in embedding programming in the chemical engineering curriculum and summarize our suggestions in a structured framework.

## 2. Methods

### 2.1 Course framework

The *Chemical Reaction Engineering in Python* course was developed at DTU and it seeks to teach Python by providing real use cases and applicable tools. It covers topics such as stoichiometry, design of chemical reactors, and mass and energy balances. The course was created based upon three pillars: (i) relevance and usefulness, with a focus on chemical reaction engineering exercises; (ii) informativeness, aiming to provide thorough explanations, background, fun facts, links to bonus material; and, (iii) entertainment through stimulant exercises and gamification, with embedded reward through three difficulty levels. Practically, the material for each week is divided into two sections: (i) a theory folder, including Jupyter Notebook tutorials, explanations, and coding examples; and, (ii) a practice folder, where students are given exercises.

This material was introduced in the Chemical Reaction Engineering course at DTU (fall 2022). The programming material was designed to run in parallel to the conventional chemical reaction engineering lectures. The general course consisted of four hours per week (plus 5 hours of self-study), where two hours were allocated for lectures and two for exercises. In the last two hours of the class, the Python tutorials were explained and students could work on the exercises and get help from the teachers. The exercises generally followed the theory explained in class, however, some more advanced exercises covered examples solved manually by the students the previous week. This was designed to grant students the time to understand the theory and group exercises explained in class and, once they were confident about these, then they only needed to code the solution in Python. In this manner, the students also had the opportunity to revise the topics from the previous week.

## 2.2 Metrics

To evaluate the success of the course, it was necessary to establish rigorous and concrete metrics. Since the focus of this work is on education, it is essential to measure the learnings. This was done by comparing students' performance in the first given assignment with the results of the same assignment given before the introduction of Python. Additionally, both students' and teachers' perspectives were taken into consideration. Two surveys were conducted to measure the students' opinions regarding learning Python, therefore both quantitative and qualitative analysis can be performed.

## 3. Results and Discussion

### 3.1 Students' perspective

The updated course description, to reflect the introduction of coding in the course, was made available to students before they had to register and start the course. However, the initial survey, conducted at the beginning of the course to quantify the students' interest in learning Python, highlights that only 11.5% of students (among the 26/40 who responded to the survey) were aware that Python would be used in the course. This could be considered as a conclusion by itself since it seems that students did not read the course description in detail and were perhaps not prepared to learn to program.

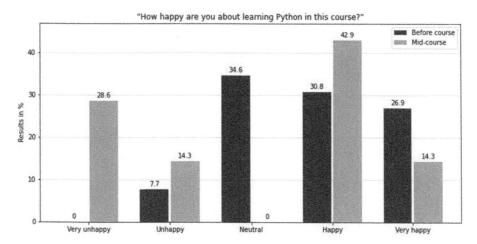

Figure 1: "How happy are you about learning Python in this course?" - Comparison between students' responses before the course started and midway through the course.

Among the various questions, students were asked how happy they were with learning Python. The results in Figure 1 show that 57.7% of the students were either happy or very happy to learn Python, the remaining being mostly neutral (34.6%). We administered another survey to evaluate the Python material in the middle of the course. In this second survey, 57.2% of the students were happy or very happy, while the rest were either unhappy (14.3%) or really unhappy (28.6%). The interesting trend shown is that all the students that had a neutral opinion regarding Python at the beginning, express more polarity in the second survey, turning mostly to unhappy.

In the first survey, when asked if they prefer another tool, 88.5% of students answered negatively. In the second survey, 71.4% of students said that they would rather not use another tool, but the remaining students suggested that the use of Maple and Excel would be enough for this course. This seems to highlight that only 17.4% of students changed their mind about Python as a tool itself, while the general discontent might be caused by other factors, such as the challenges introduced by adding additional material to an already challenging course or the short amount of time available to learn to program. In the mid-course evaluation survey, only 14.3% of the students found Python not useful, while the rest found it useful (57.2%) or remained neutral (28.6%). Unfortunately, only 7 students responded to the second survey, therefore the results should be considered only as an indication of a possible trend as they are not statistically significant.

Students' feedback on the course (16 comments collected in total) is summarized in the word cloud in Figure 2. Overall, students expressed that they found the course to be too difficult since they had to learn both chemical reactions and Python at the same time.

Figure 2: Word Cloud summarizing the mid-term evaluation of the course.

An insight that emerged from the mid-term evaluation is the disconnect between tools and programming languages used in courses in the Bachelor's Degree at DTU. In fact, students complained that multiple tools are used in different courses, such as Maple, MATLAB, Python, R, and others.

*3.2 Teachers' perspective*

During the practical exercise sections, teachers noted that the students were carefully reflecting on the assumptions to make while solving the Python exercises. In comparison to students enrolled in previous editions of the course, they noticed an increased attendance during the practical sessions and a substantially higher engagement during the activities, observing that both the number and the quality of the questions were higher. This might result from the fact that students had to make assumptions in order to make their code run successfully, while they could simply write down the general equations on paper previously. This seems to suggest that, although the introduction of Python in the course was challenging and overwhelming for many students, it pushed them to think critically and actively reflect in order to be able to code the exercises.

### *3.3 Performance in the assignments*

To help students learn additional skills and material, in the 2022 fall edition of the course it was decided to only administer two assignments instead of five. Python exercises, allowing students to practice their developing knowledge were however given every week, but these were not graded. The first assignment was submitted by 72.5% of the students (29/40) enrolled in the course, while in the fall 2021 edition, 72% of students (36/50) submitted an answer to the assignment released in the same period. The same assignment was given to students in the fall 2021 edition earlier in the semester, and 42/50 students submitted it. Worth mentioning is that some of the students registered do not actively participate in the course, but are only interested in the re-exam.

In 2021 students gained, on average, a score of 7.86/10, while the students taking the course in the fall of 2022 have an average score of 8.17/10. Although the difference is not significant, it could indicate that programming helps students to be more engaged. The course is still ongoing, therefore we do not know the performance of the students in the final exams; however, we expect them to perform better than in the last years, given that many students seemed to be engaged in the lectures and the exercise sessions, asking questions and actively participating.

## 4. Learnings and Educational Framework

Among the learnings from this experiment, is that students consider the amount of work required by the course to be too high since they also need to learn and understand the regular material designed for the specific course. However, it is also important to reflect upon and weigh students' opinions regarding the amount of material, since the course needs to be challenging and stimulate their critical thinking. Therefore, it is necessary to balance the amount of work required while making the course intellectually stimulating and educational. This could be solved in the future by dividing the material into mandatory and optional modules. This division would allow the students that do not feel too comfortable with programming to still learn the basic syntax and how to solve easier exercises, while the students that are more motivated to learn Python could challenge themselves with more advanced exercises.

An issue that students have pointed out is the variety of programming languages and tools required by different courses during their education. An effort should be made at institutional level to align on a common tool, or at least to give the students the option to choose among a few selected software/programming languages for each course. This would also reduce the added stress of having to learn to program during another course because it would be a skill that could be taught independently as a stand-alone course.

The course was designed to be self-sufficient, enabling students to go through the material and learn by themselves. However, as also suggested by the students in the survey, probably more guided and in-class programming would be helpful to students to better understand how to read, write and think in code.

Although the subject of the course (chemical reaction engineering) might seem very specific, the content covered (i.e., general syntax, data structures, data visualization, stoichiometry, solving differential equations and integrals) can be used in many more topics within the chemical engineering field. Its large applicability and relevance are the motivations behind the open-source nature of the course. The Python course is publicly available on GitHub at https://github.com/FiammettaC/Chemical-Reaction-Engineering-in-Python and in the near future, it will be integrated into BioVL (www.biovl.com), an online educational platform for (bio)chemical processes developed by the authors.

This project is part of a series of courses designed to teach Python to Chemical Engineers. In the future, we plan to compare the results of the course in two different settings: (i) embedded into the curriculum of a selected Bachelor's course at DTU, and (ii) open-source on GitHub, therefore available to whoever wants to take the course. The aim of this comparison is to investigate various approaches to teach chemical engineering students how to code in Python and share our learnings to improve the educational methods needed to prepare future engineers for Industry 4.0.

## 5. Conclusion

This work establishes and evaluates a pedagogical framework to teach chemical reaction engineering in Python. The course has been embedded in the educational system at DTU. It aims to educate future engineers for Industry 4.0 and improve the quality of education of (bio)chemical engineering processes and increase students' engagement.

Even though generating changes in the educational system and promoting digitalization initiatives is rather challenging, we evaluate the introduction of a new tool in the engineering curriculum and discuss the learnings from this experience. Among these, students considered having the Python material introduced in parallel to the normal course as time-consuming and quite difficult, since they had to develop two sets of skills at the same time. A better approach could be to have a stand-alone programming course at the beginning of their education, which the other courses build upon. This would also solve another challenge discovered in this work, that there is no institutional coherence in the tools chosen by every single course, resulting in students having to learn a variety of programs for different courses. Overall, students found the course to be useful. The course, which has large applicability and relevance across various chemical engineering areas, is publicly available on GitHub.

## References

de Las Heras, S.C., Gargalo, C.L., Gernaey, K.V. and Krühne, U., 2021. Programming skills across the (bio) engineering curriculum–a students' perspective. In Computer Aided Chemical Engineering (Vol. 50, pp. 2039-2044). Elsevier.

dos Santos, M.T., Vianna Jr, A.S. and Le Roux, G.A., 2018. Programming skills in the industry 4.0: are chemical engineering students able to face new problems?. Education for Chemical Engineers, 22, pp.69-76.

Gargalo, C.L., Heras, S.C.D.L., Jones, M.N., Udugama, I., Mansouri, S.S., Krühne, U. and Gernaey, K.V., 2020. Towards the development of digital twins for the bio-manufacturing industry. Digital Twins, pp.1-34.

Narayanan, H., Luna, M.F., von Stosch, M., Cruz Bournazou, M.N., Polotti, G., Morbidelli, M., Butté, A. and Sokolov, M., 2020. Bioprocessing in the digital age: the role of process models. Biotechnology journal, 15(1), p.1900172. S. C. de Las Heras, et al, 2021, Programming skills across the (bio) engineering curriculum–a students' perspective, in Computer Aided Chemical Engineering, vol. 50, pp. 2039–2044, Elsevier.

PyCRE 2022, Python for Chemical Reaction Engineering (PyCRE), 2022, Available at: https://www.lct.ugent.be/PyCRE (Accessed 30/11/2022).

AIChE 2022, Introduction to Python for Chemical Engineers, Available at: https://www.aiche.org/academy/courses/ela270/introduction-python-chemical-engineers (Accessed 30/11/2022).

Antonis Kokossis, Michael C. Georgiadis, Efstratios N. Pistikopoulos (Eds.)
PROCEEDINGS OF THE 33rd European Symposium on Computer Aided Process Engineering
(ESCAPE33), June 18-21, 2023, Athens, Greece

# An Online Course for Teaching Process Simulation

Daniel R. Lewin,[a] Assaf Simon,[a] Sapir Lifshiz Simon,[a] Asia Matatyaho Ya'akobi,[a] and Abigail Barzilai[b]

[a]Department of Chemical Engineering, Technion. I. I. T., Haifa 32000, Israel
[b]Centre for the Promotion of Learning and Teaching, Technion, Haifa 32000, Israel

Email for correspondance: dlewin@technion.ac.il

## Abstract

A course in process simulation prepares students to take on a capstone design project, in that it teaches them to use a commercial process flowsheet simulator effectively. This paper describes an online process simulation course with the following features: (a) Self-paced instruction using online multimedia modules; (b) Regular practice using UniSim® to ensure efficient and effective modeling capability; (c) Online examination of the students' mastery including programming assignments using UniSim. The paper shows that not only do the students accept the importance of acquiring practical capabilities in process simulation, but analysis also shows that the learning outcomes have improved since the move to online practical examination as part of the course.

**Keywords**: Process simulation, process design, online education, commercial simulators.

## 1. Introduction

Most undergraduate programs in chemical engineering incorporate a capstone design project completed in the last year of study, which usually requires the student participants to use a commercial process flowsheet simulator efficiently, intelligently, and critically. It is impractical to expect students to be able to tackle large-scale design projects at the same time that they are learning how to acquire adequate capabilities in process simulation. Belton (2016) advocates teaching students to use the simulator in the first year of studies. However, most chemical engineering programs teach the principal building-blocks of the curricula over time. In the first year, students would not have the background and engineering sophistication to use the simulator, with the danger that students would resolve problems technically, and without understanding the physical phenomena underlying each unit operation simulated. Alternatively, as suggested by Dahm et al. (2002), this training could be integrated throughout the curriculum, by introducing elements of simulation applications in all of the core courses (e.g., thermodynamics, heat transfer, separation processes, and reactor design). However, summative assessment of the skills acquired by students is more difficult for this alternative (Lewin et al., 2006). The solution that has been implemented at Technion since 2005 is to require students to take a course in process simulation one semester in advance of the capstone design course (Lewin and Barzilai, 2021). This is similar to the learning approach offered in the book "Learn Aspen Plus in 24 Hours," (Adams, 2022). The main advantage of these "just in time" solutions is that students receive training in the usage of a process simulator in parallel to their formal instruction in core subjects such as multi-component thermodynamics, reactor engineering, and multiple-stage separations, and are thus better equipped to integrate their formal knowledge of these subjects with their practical implementation.

Before the COVID-19 pandemic, the course was run as a two-hour/week lab, in which students worked at their own pace, guided by multimedia modules (Lewin et al., 2003). At Technion, we use UniSim® as the process simulator. To exhibit mastery, students were required to pass a closed-book exam comprising of largely theoretical, multiple-choice questions. It has become clear that successfully passing such an exam is not a guarantee that students have actually mastered the practical usage of UniSim, a fact that was observed in the average student's performance on the capstone design project in the semester following the course. The COVID-19 pandemic required the students to work 100% online, meaning that they had to install UniSim on their own PCs, and the weekly sessions were moved to Zoom Breakout Rooms. Furthermore, the exam was run online also, making it feasible to test the students' practical capabilities on typical design tasks using UniSim as part of the exam. This change was the most influential in significantly improving the students' capabilities. Since the pandemic, the 100% online format of the course and its exam has been retained, thus maintaining the level of mastery required from the students. This paper presents the course syllabus and its learning outcomes. We also compare course outcomes before and after the changes described above. Finally, we present salient conclusions from a poll conducted on the students in the class of 2022, the year after the COVID-19 pandemic largely abated, which was the third time that we ran the course 100% online.

## 2. Course Learning Objectives, Syllabus and Schedule

The course runs over 12 weeks, according to the schedule shown in Table 1. The main learning objective of the course is to instruct students to effectively use UniSim to model process flowsheets. Each week, students proceed at their own pace, guided by self-paced multimedia modules (Lewin et al, 2003). The multimedia modules covering UniSim are freely available at the link: https://www.seas.upenn.edu/~cbe400/hysys-unisim/.

Table 1. Simulation Laboratory Weekly Schedule.

| Week | Topic | Content |
|------|-------|---------|
| 1 | Getting started in UniSim | User interface, simulation basis, stream definition, and unit operations. Definition of degrees of freedom. |
| 2 | M&E balances and recycle | Recycle convergence. Dealing with multiple recycles. |
| 3 | Thermo-package selection | Package selection rules. Adjust and set operations. |
| 4 | Heat exchangers | Coolers, heaters, and heat exchanger operations. |
| 5 | Plantwide simulation | Modeling the reaction section in the Hydrodealkylation of toluene (HDA) process. |
| 6 | Reactors (Part 1) | Defining reactions: conversion, equilibrium and PFR operations. Simulation of a cold shot $NH_3$ converter. |
| 7 | Reactors (Part 2) | CSTR operation. Multiplicity. |
| 8 | Separations | Separator, splitter, shortcut column, and distillation column operations. |
| 9 | Distillation column workshop | Separation of a ternary mixture of hydrocarbons into three products of specified purity using two columns. |
| 10 | Optimization | Two examples using the UniSim optimizer. |
| 11 | Project | Developing a separation sequence to produce ethanol from beer (involving flash, distillation and absorbing columns). |
| 12 | Recap | Preparation for multiple-choice exam questions. |

Weekly quizzes and several extended programming assignments enable students to formatively gauge their acquired capabilities, with a final exam intended for summative assessment. The course grading is distributed as follows: Final exam – 75%, Three assignments – 13%, Seven weekly quizzes – 7%, Weekly attendance – 5%. Note that 25% of the course grade is awarded for attending and carrying out the in-course tasks, with the lion's share being awarded to successfully demonstrating mastery in the exam. Before the COVID-19 pandemic, the weekly meetings were held in our computer laboratory, in 2-hr sessions of 20 students in each session, with work carried out using UniSim installed on the lab's computers. The final exam involved theoretical multiple-choice questions, which did not adequately test practical abilities on UniSim. Since the annual enrolment in the course is usually in excess of 50 students, the computer lab's capacity of 20 stations effectively eliminated even having a portion of the exam to include practical testing of UniSim mastery.

The COVID-19 pandemic forced all teaching to move to 100% online, and this meant moving the simulation course to be run on Zoom, requiring all students to also transfer their UniSim licenses to their own laptops, which is permitted by the company. Consequently, the weekly exercise sessions were run in Zoom Breakout Rooms, enabling self-paced learning by the students as before, but in addition permitting staff to assist individual students on demand. In each session, sufficient breakout rooms were opened, allowing students to work alone or in teams of their choosing, and supporting peer instruction and teaching them to work in groups. The summative exams also had to be run on Zoom, with appropriate proctoring. In the first year of the pandemic, the previous exam format relying on theoretical multiple-choice questions was retained, but in the following year, the format was changed to include two extended UniSim assignments, intended to test the students' capabilities in detail. Typical UniSim questions would be:

- Given a fully defined feed stream consisting of three components, design a distillation train to produce three product streams of 99% purity, while ensuring reboiler duties do not exceed a specific amount, while maintaining the total number of trays used below a certain amount.
- Set up a refrigeration cycle using ammonia as the refrigerant so that the heat duty in the evaporator meets a given specification.

## 3. Outcomes Assessment

Table 2. Exam grades and fitted bimodal model parameters, 2017-2022.

| Year | $N$ | $N_{fail}$ | $\mu$ | $\sigma$ | $\mu_1$ | $\mu_2$ | $\sigma_1$ | $\sigma_2$ | $p$ |
|------|-----|-----------|-------|----------|---------|---------|-----------|-----------|-----|
| 2017 | 81 | 7 (9%) | 0.72 | 0.15 | 0.77 | 0.73 | 0.08 | 0.18 | 0.33 |
| 2018 | 61 | 17 (28%) | 0.68 | 0.18 | 0.80 | 0.42 | 0.10 | 0.07 | 0.78 |
| 2019 | 54 | 14 (26%) | 0.67 | 0.16 | 0.77 | 0.45 | 0.08 | 0.06 | 0.74 |
| 2020 | 40 | 5 (13%) | 0.68 | 0.15 | 0.75 | 0.70 | 0.04 | 0.18 | 0.34 |
| 2021 | 46 | 3 (7%) | 0.78 | 0.26 | 0.88 | 0.74 | 0.15 | 0.03 | 0.90 |
| 2022 | 58 | 13 (22%) | 0.73 | 0.22 | 0.94 | 0.38 | 0.29 | 0.08 | 0.91 |

Table 2 presents summative data from the last six years, that is, exam grade averages, standard deviations, and failure rates, as well as computed parameters for a bimodal distribution model fitted to the grade distributions. Figure 1(a) shows the evolution of course outcomes, as brought by the final exam grade distribution, as approximated following the approach of Lewin (2021); each exam grade distribution is approximated by a bimodal distribution model comprising a weighted sum of two normal distributions, yielding estimates for averages and standard deviations of high- and low-performing subpopulations ($\mu_1$, $\sigma_1$, $\mu_2$, and $\sigma_2$), as well as the fraction of high-performers ($p$). The fitted model for the grade distribution is therefore:

$$f(x) = \frac{p}{\sigma_1 \sqrt{2\pi}} e^{-\frac{1}{2}\left(\frac{x-\mu_1}{\sigma_1}\right)^2} + \frac{1-p}{\sigma_2 \sqrt{2\pi}} e^{-\frac{1}{2}\left(\frac{x-\mu_2}{\sigma_2}\right)^2}. \tag{1}$$

Figure 1(b) shows a typical fit, for the exceptionally good exam grade distribution of 2021, the first year that the final exam included practical assignments using UniSim.

In Figure 1(a), each year's result is represented by a disk centered on the average grade for the high- and low-performing students, $\mu_1$ and $\mu_2$, respectively, with a disk diameter proportional to $p$. Evidently, a good outcome is either characterized by high values of $\mu_1$ and $\mu_2$, in which case the magnitude of $p$ is not important, or high values of $\mu_1$ and $p$, in which case the magnitude of $\mu_2$ is less important. Thus, disks of arbitrary diameter positioned on the top right of the bubble plot, or disks of large diameter positioned anywhere on the right of the diagram constitute desirable outcomes. In Figure 1(a), the red bubble shows the outcome in 2020, when the course was taught online for the first time, using an exam format as in previous years. It is noted that the outcomes are in the range seen in previous years, when the course was taught face-to-face in the computer laboratory. From 2021, the online exam has included practical exercises involving the usage of UniSim, and it is noted that the outcomes have significantly improved: Both the blue disk, for 2021 and the green disk, for 2022, are to the right of the plot, indicating significantly improved outcomes over those achieved before the switch to requiring mastery in practical UniSim assignments. The exam format change did not affect its level of difficulty. The difficulty level of the multiple choice questions was the same as in previous years, as were the practical UniSim questions.

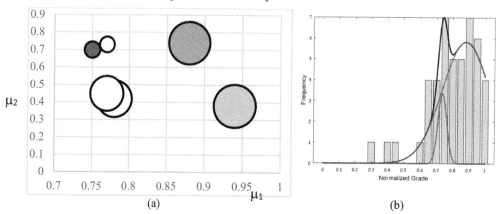

Figure 1. (a) Bubble plot showing the evolution of course outcomes from 2017-2022. The white disks indicate the outcomes for 2017-2019, when the course was taught face-to-face and examined on paper. From 2020, the course was taught and examined online, and from 2021, the online exam has included UniSim assignments. The 2020, 2021 and 2022 outcomes are shown in red, blue, and green, respectively. (b) A typical bimodal distribution fitted to the exceptionally good exam grades for 2021, where the normal distribution for the high- and low-performing students are shown in red-dotted lines, the combined bimodal distribution is shown in black, and the histogram of actual grades is shown in blue.

## 4. Feedback from Students

The students enrolled in the Simulations Lab in the Spring of 2022 were asked to respond to an online questionnaire, involving 11 questions, mostly requiring a response on a Likert scale from 1, indicating the lowest level of confidence or highest level of disagreement to a statement, through 3, indicating ambivalence, to 5, indicating the highest level of confidence or highest level of agreement to a statement. The number of responses (out of a total of 65 enrolled students), average scores and standard deviations for each question are presented in Table 3.

The first 10 questions all returned positive, non-ambivalent responses (scored averages greater than 3), indicating positive feedback overall. Q1 and Q4 scored the lowest, most likely because many students may have been uncertain about the meaning of "critical thinking" and "troubleshooting." Q6 – Q9 scored the highest: The highest score was returned on the exam as a motivator for learning to use UniSim, with a slightly lower score also on the subsequent semester's design project as a motivator, though the difference is not statistically significant. Most students agreed that the online format is the most suitable way of teaching software skills.

Table 3. 2022 Questionnaire and Responses

| Question | $n$ | $\mu$ | $\sigma$ |
|---|---|---|---|
| To what extent did working with the simulator help you acquire/improve the following skills: | | | |
| Q1. Critical thinking | 50 | 3.06 | 1.17 |
| Q2. Solving engineering problems | 51 | 3.67 | 0.91 |
| Q3. Solving complex engineering problems | 50 | 3.54 | 0.95 |
| Q4. Troubleshooting | 50 | 3.34 | 1.12 |
| Q5. Application of knowledge from previous courses | 51 | 3.71 | 1.10 |
| Q6. Design skills | 49 | 3.82 | 0.86 |
| Q7. To what extent do you recommend learning software in a format similar to the one studied in the current course? | 50 | 3.94 | 1.08 |
| Q8. To what extent did the knowledge that you would be required to solve problems with the simulator during the exam affect your motivation to learn to work with the simulator during the course? | 50 | 4.02 | 1.08 |
| Q9. To what extent did the knowledge that you would be required to solve problems with the simulator in next semester's design project affect your motivation to learn the simulator during the course? | 51 | 3.84 | 1.16 |
| Q10.To what extent do you recommend continuing with this type of exam format? | 49 | 3.65 | 1.01 |
| Q11.Any other comments? | See typical responses below | | |

The last question prompted verbal responses from many students, and we report here some example responses, indicating mostly a favorable impression of the course's pedagogical approach:

- The format of the course is very efficient in terms of independent work and the presence of the teaching assistants when needed.
- I really like learning in this style. It was a perfect course and excellent practitioners!!
- In this course, distance learning works very well because there is only self-learning. And when the moment of practice comes, working online works very well because all the operations are only on the computer.

- All in all, I enjoyed learning to apply the knowledge acquired in the degree with the help of UniSim.

- Overall, the course was fine, sometimes some of the videos were not the most understandable and we got a little stuck.

- Sometimes watching the videos and doing what they do feels pointless.

- In my opinion, it was good that the course was via Zoom. I missed that we almost didn't see live demonstrations of you doing things and why.

- In my opinion, this course is the most fun and among the most useful in the degree. I would have preferred if had there been more time to learn the principles of the software and its capabilities in depth instead of focusing on the basics.

## 5. Conclusions

It is self-evident that students in the capstone design course would benefit from having acquired the necessary skills in operating a commercial process simulator in advance. The simulation lab offered at the Technion one semester ahead of the design course is one way of achieving this objective. This paper has described the current online format used in the course, its syllabus and schedule, and the online assessment methods used to verify mastery. The main conclusions are: (1) The level of support that can be tendered to students by course staff in an online setting using Zoom Breakout Rooms is at least as good if not better than that provided in regular face-to-face lab sessions; (2) Having students work on their own PCs with UniSim improved the level of individual student competence, as shown by the summative assessment evolution as well as the observed performance of the students in the subsequent capstone design course; (3) Online exams including practical usage of UniSim made a huge impact on the resulting competency of the average student: Students opinioned that the knowledge that their practical UniSim skills would be tested in the final exam and be required in the capstone design project were significant motivation for them to learn these skills during the semester; (4) We therefore recommend moving examinations online to allow for practical examination of competence in all courses that merit this feature (for example, in practical design of control systems using Matlab and Simulink for the course on process control).

## References

T. A. Adams III, 2022, "Learn Aspen Plus in 24 Hours," 2nd Edition, McGraw-Hill, New york.

D. J. Belton, 2016, "Teaching process simulation using video-enhanced and discovery/inquiry-based learning: Methodology and analysis within a theoretical framework for skill acquisition," *Education for Chemical Engineers*, 17, 54-64.

K. D. Dahm, R. P. Hesketh, and M. J. Savelski, 2002, "Is process simulation used effectively in ChE courses?" *Chem. Eng. Educ.*, 191-198.

D. R. Lewin, W. D. Seider, J. D. Seader, E. Dassau, J. Golbert, D. Goldberg, M. J. Fucci, E. Filiba, and R. B. Nathanson, 2003, "Using Process Simulators in the Chemical Engineering Curriculum – A Multimedia Guide for the Core Curriculum," Version 2.3, Multimedia CD-ROM, John Wiley, New York.

D. R. Lewin, E. Dassau, and A. Goldis, 2006, "Effective Process Design Instruction: From Simulation to Plant Design," *16th European Symposium on Computer Aided Process Engineering*, 719-724.

D. R. Lewin and A. Barzilai, 2021, "Teaching Process Design to Chemical Engineering Undergraduates – an Evolution," *Chem. Eng. Educ.*, 55(3), 157-172.

D. R. Lewin, 2021, "What Can We Learn from Exam Grade Distributions?" *International Journal for the Scholarship of Teaching and Learning*, 15(2), Article 7.

Antonis Kokossis, Michael C. Georgiadis, Efstratios N. Pistikopoulos (Eds.)
PROCEEDINGS OF THE 33rd European Symposium on Computer Aided Process Engineering
(ESCAPE33), June 18-21, 2023, Athens, Greece
© 2023 Elsevier B.V. All rights reserved.  http://dx.doi.org/10.1016/B978-0-443-15274-0.50556-4

# Designing an interactive environment to share educational materials and resources. Application to the Geomatics Hub at UniLaSalle Beauvais

Réjanne LE BIVIC[a] , Sébastien OTTAVI[a], Pierre SAULET[a], Pauline LOUIS[a], Arnaud COUTU[a]

[a]*Institut Polytechnique UniLaSalle, 19 rue Pierre Waguet, 60000 BEAUVAIS, France*
*arnaud.coutu@unilasalle.fr*

## Abstract

Teaching is a process requiring a logical and progressive frame, which is formalized in the pedagogic curriculum. Selecting, arranging, and framing the content is necessary to enhance the learning experience (Deng, 2011). The making of a curriculum implies the creation of materials that can be numerous. These pedagogic resources can be of different kinds: course materials, exercise instructions, or help tools. Using technology to provide easier access to these resources to students through an online platform is a great way to perpetuate these materials and ease the work of teachers (Nachmias et al., 2008). Furthermore, the development of such online media permits a valorization of the pedagogic resources and their innovations (Mahajan, 2010). It is a step towards an open science approach to teaching geomatics which goes further than actual textbooks (Bell et al. , 2018). The focus of this paper is on the online platform created by the Institut Polytechnique UniLaSalle Beauvais for Geographic Information System (GIS) courses, known as the Geomatics Hub. The general public has access to over 75% of the content on this platform for free, while the remaining content is only available to students. 54 answers were collected from a survey to collect the experience of students on this online tool. 87% declared that this platform allows better access to pedagogic resources while 89% indicated that its organization is clear and logical. The Geomatics hub is also a way to display the results of projects led by either teachers or students. The use of an innovative solution with digital open access has a reach that is not limited to the students. The display of the education tools produced by UniLaSalle Beauvais for GIS can be noticed by companies, potential partners, or former students.

Keywords: Innovation diffusion; open science; e-Learning; Educational innovation

## 1. Introduction: teaching geomatics at UniLaSalle – Campus of Beauvais

Geomatics is an umbrella term for all disciplines related to collecting, analyzing, and storing geographic data. It gathers Geographic Information Systems (GIS), Remote Sensing, and Photogrammetry. The sensors and platforms are extremely varied, from ground-based GNSS to imaging satellites, or airborne LiDAR systems. The full Data Life Cycle is included, from the acquisition to the processing and communication of the results (Levitin and Redman, 1993). At UniLaSalle, the topics studied are mostly centered around Earth Observation, and more precisely Agriculture and Geology.

UniLaSalle Beauvais is an engineering school, that teaches about 3000 students in 5 years.

Geomatics is an important part of the curriculum, with an average of 10 % of the time spent learning GIS, Remote Sensing, and Photogrammetry, with an emphasis on the former (REN, 2022). Since the students have different career ambitions in Earth and Life sciences, being able to offer a wide range of real-life examples, especially for lab sessions, is a major way to keep them interested and therefore more engaged. One goal is to bring the students to work autonomously on labs that they choose from the online repository. Taking ownership of their learning experience by choosing exercises could increase the efficiency of the course (Kolb and Kolb, 2005).

Teaching involves creating a significant amount of materials, and although some teachers opt to make them accessible on their professional or personal website, some of these resources can still be lost. Making all materials available for the teachers of an organization could provide more time for others to improve their curriculum, without having to reproduce materials that already exist. It is also in line with the Open Access movement claims, which is that everyone would gain from making materials public, by avoiding duplicate work (Hylén, 2021).

Creating interactive online course materials was selected as the way to evolve teaching Geomatics at UniLaSalle. The Geomatics Hub was invented as a platform to gather all those materials and bring them beyond the classroom, in the light of the new paradigm of Education 4.0 which emphasizes experimentation as a way to learn, especially by taking advantage of emerging technologies (Almeida and Simoes, 2019).

## 2. Development of the Geomatics Hub

### 2.1. The Geomatics Hub: a repository for course material

The Geomatics hub was developed in 2019. It is freely accessible online at https://hub-geomatique-unilasalle-fr.hub.arcgis.com/. The main strategy is to provide students, as future technicians and engineers, with real-world examples and problem-based exercises to work on.

The original idea is to give more autonomy to students by making them work on a workflow-based approach, where they were provided data, some context, a general workflow, and access to a user manual created by the teacher. This allows the teacher to focus on students with more difficulties. Students can work in complete autonomy, by choosing a library of labs with varying levels of difficulty, and also check their skills autonomously using lists of technical skills.

The three main disciplines are easily available: GIS, Remote Sensing, and Photogrammetry. For GIS, the main parts are the lecture slides, about different topics related to GIS, the exercises as lab Sessions, and online help on three software: ArcGIS Pro, ArcGIS Online, and qGIS. Online skills trees also guide students to different parts of the user manual depending on the skill they want to practice.

For the Photogrammetry part, lecture slides are available as well as online help on the software Agisoft Metashape (proprietary). There is a similar structure for Remote Sensing: lecture slides, labs, and online help on ENVI (proprietary). In terms of web hosting, the user manuals are written and hosted on Scenarii, the lecture slides are in Genially, and the labs are on ESRI's servers in the form of Story Maps.

### 2.2. The Hub as a pedagogic tool

The use of StoryMaps allows us to set levels for the lab sessions. For the GIS part, all lab sessions are taught as Problem-based-Learning, where a situation is described to the student, who then has to follow the steps of the processing tasks to complete the scenario. While in the first labs, the workflow is often given to the student, it is progressively less and less detailed, to let the student, improve and decide on their own which tools to use, with the end goal of writing and developing their workflows.

 In Photogrammetry, the students are provided with a generic workflow and a detailed user manual, developed by the teaching team. The student then has to apply the processing to given sets of data, which can be changed year after year depending on the current need, for example when we want to student to work on new data.

The display tools chosen as support (StoryMaps, ESRI hub, Scenari) are easy to edit if the leading teacher is not in charge of the Hub anymore, as has been the case in this study. As for now, the platform is in French only.

### 2.3. The Geomatics hub is a showcase platform to enhance relations between companies and education

The Geomatics Hub is in close relation with the GéoLab, an innovation center at UniLaSalle Beauvais that provide an access to students to work on innovative numeric tools for 3D modeling and 3D printing. This includes high-quality PCs, software licenses, technical support, and more. The Hub is a way to present current and past student projects. Beyond being a platform for students, it is also an opportunity to build bridges between the academic world and industry. By showcasing the researcher's and students' work, companies are more willing to offer internships or job offers or rent the services of the GéoLab for one-time projects, such as fossils and minerals 3D modeling, and bio-mimicry research work. By interacting both with students and professionals, the benefits are coming back to students because the teachers are on the front line and can estimate the needs of the companies, by being in direct communication with them (see Figure 1).

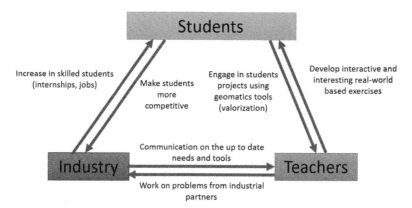

Figure 1 - Multi-parts benefits of Open Educational Resources with an emphasis on the communication between all three actors of learning: students, teachers, and the industry

## 3. Three years in evaluating the use of the platform

The main objectives of the Geomatics Hub are (1) to be an efficient tool for current students at UniLaSalle Beauvais, (2) to be useful for former students (3) to be used as a showcasing website for external users, whether they are individuals or companies. Two metrics are here studied to quantify the success of the platform. Firstly, we will evaluate the impact on a student through surveys. Secondly, a study of the hub engagement metrics will be used to quantify the impact of the website.

### 3.1. Students survey

A study was conducted in September 2022, and 66 students answered out of the 406 students surveyed. 48.5% of the students who replied are in their third year at UniLaSalle. The questions were divided into three sections: The Geomatics Hub in general, the chronology of the lab Sessions, and the skills tree.

To the first question ("To which occasions are you using the Geomatics Hub?"), and besides a use during the class, 67% say they use the Hub when studying for the exam, 17% say they use it to know more about geomatics in general, 56% say they use it for projects outside of the class, and 15% say they are using it when working for a company (either during an apprenticeship, internships, or in their new position for the recently graduated students). When asked which resources the students were looking at the most, the first place comes for the course materials (73%), then the chronology of Exercises in ArcGIS (59%), the user manuals (55%), the library of exercises/examples (41%). About the use of the Hub outside of the classroom, a third of the student said they were using it regularly (33%°), a third replied they were using it outside of the classroom but not regularly (35%) and another third replied that they were not using it outside of the classroom (31%). Three following questions are about the display and ease of use of the platform. A large majority, of students, find that the Hub is easy to use (90%), and would recommend it to someone who is a total beginner in GIS (94%). However, those results are put in perspective with some written comments by students who say that the interface is sometimes too busy and that there are too many steps to get to the course content.

The second part of the survey deals with the chronology of the exercises. Almost all the students say that the chronology is easy to understand and use (98%) and that it allows them to understand better the course in terms of skills to learn, by putting all the exercises in perspective (94%). The third part of the survey is about the skills list. While only half of the students had seen the skills list before (53%), a large majority of them think that it can be useful for them to learn GIS (85%) and that they would use it autonomously, without being expressively told to during a lecture (75%).

This first experience in surveying the students provided insights on the use of the platform but will also be used to improve the next surveys, especially in terms of focusing questions and getting the students more engaged.

*3.2. Website engagement overview*

In the past year (Nov.2021 to Nov. 2022), over 15,000 visits were recorded on the Hub website, with an average of 1,400 visits per month over the past three months. Those metrics are limited but give a good quantitative indicator of the website's relevance and use.

## 4. Conclusion

After three years of use of the platform, the feedback from students and teachers alike is in the majority positive. The students can work autonomously, during labs the teacher is in a support position. Students can follow their own pace and see the big picture of the skills expected from them at any time of their education. During the lifetime of the platform, teachers in Geomatics have partially changed. The existence of the platform made those changes easier and lessened the disruption for students. The school's industrial partners also gave positive feedback. ESRI France, the French branch of the leader in GIS and Remote Sensing software, broadcasted the Geomatics Hub in their magazine "SIGMag" in December 2020.

With the improvement in topics such as small objects photogrammetry, there is a need to update the tutorials. New topics related to Spatial Data Science should be included, like Machine Learning techniques, now broadly used in Spatial Data Science, including Geomatics. A part on data mining and data downloading should also be added, as well as reflecting on how to include the data acquisition part. A translation into English would also be a plus. Following the survey with students, it seems important to modify the architecture of the website to streamline access to the different parts of the materials. A focus should also be made on accessibility (option for contrast, image alternative text for example). One main risk taken with the architecture of the hub is that it relies heavily on external storage. The StoryMaps and main interface are hosted on ESRI's servers, the data is hosted internally on the school's platform, Claroline. The software manuals are hosted on Scenarii, and the slides are hosted on Genially and also archived on the teacher's computers. A way to bypass this would be to develop a server internal to the school, like an ESRI ArcGIS Enterprise solution.

In terms of pedagogy, more didactic tools should be tested, such as glossaries, quizzes, and serious games. The pandemic led to a chance for teachers to reexamine their teaching practices. A study from the University of Genoa showed that techniques such as Team-based learning, Problem-based learning, and tools such as Glossaries and quizzes are effective (Botto et al., 2022). Our lab uses Problem-based learning and plans to build on the study's positive results. The use of free open-source software was also beneficial, as it's more accessible and flexible (Quinn, 2021) . This is part of our future plans at the Geomatics Hub. While universities widely use Learning Management Systems, recent studies show a low use of the interactive tools (Al-Sharhan et al., 2020). The Geomatics Hub will aim to utilize these past findings to overcome limitations and offer students a more engaging environment.

## References

Almeida, F., Simoes, J., 2019. The role of serious games, gamification and industry 4.0 tools in the education 4.0 paradigm. Contemp. Educ. Technol. 10, 120–136.

Al-Sharhan, S., Al-Hunaiyyan, A., Alhajri, R., Al-Huwail, N., 2020. Utilization of Learning Management System (LMS) Among Instructors and Students, in: Zakaria, Z., Ahmad, R. (Eds.), Advances in Electronics Engineering, Lecture Notes in Electrical Engineering. Springer, Singapore, pp. 15–23. https://doi.org/10.1007/978-981-15-1289-6_2

Bell, S., Ross, H.M., Epp, J., Bates, K., 2018. Geomatics and Open Textbooks (No. 2516–2314). EasyChair.

Botto, M., Federici, B., Ferrando, I., Gagliolo, S., Sguerso, D., 2022. Innovations in geomatics teaching during the COVID-19 emergency. Appl. Geomat. 1–14.

Deng, Z., 2011. Deng, Zongyi," Revisiting Curriculum Potential," Curriculum Inquiry, 41 (December, 2011), 538-559.

Hylén, J., 2021. Open educational resources: Opportunities and challenges.

Kolb, A.Y., Kolb, D.A., 2005. Learning styles and learning spaces: Enhancing experiential learning in higher education. Acad. Manag. Learn. Educ. 4, 193–212.

Levitin, A.V., Redman, T.C., 1993. A model of the data (life) cycles with application to quality. Inf. Softw. Technol. 35, 217–223. https://doi.org/10.1016/0950-5849(93)90069-F

Mahajan, V., 2010. Innovation diffusion. Wiley Int. Encycl. Mark.

Nachmias, R., Mioduser, D., Forkosh-Baruch, A., 2008. Innovative pedagogical practices using technology: The curriculum perspective, in: International Handbook of Information Technology in Primary and Secondary Education. Springer, pp. 163–179.

Quinn, S., 2021. Using Free and Open Source Software to Teach University GIS Courses Online: Lessons Learned During a Pandemic. Int. Arch. Photogramm. Remote Sens. Spat. Inf. Sci.

REN, F., 2022. L'enseignement des Systèmes d'Informations Géographiques à UniLaSalle Beauvais. UniLaSalle Beauvais.

Antonis Kokossis, Michael C. Georgiadis, Efstratios N. Pistikopoulos (Eds.)
PROCEEDINGS OF THE 33rd European Symposium on Computer Aided Process Engineering
(ESCAPE33), June 18-21, 2023, Athens, Greece

# Immersive learning through simulation: implementing twin screw extrusion in Unity

Pedro Santos Bartolomé[a], Daniel Just[b], Ariana Bampouli[a], Simon Kemmerling[b], Aleksandra Buczko[b], Tom Van Gerven[a]

*[a]Process Engineering for Sustainable Systems (ProcESS), KU Leuven. Celestijnenlaan 200F, 3001, Leuven, Belgium*
*[b]Fraunhofer-Institut für Chemische Technologie ICT, Polymer Engineering. Joseph-von-Fraunhofer-Str. 7, 76327 Pfinztal, Germany*

## Abstract

The use of immersive environments for education is a topic that attracts growing interest, particularly within process engineering. The engines for the design of immersive environments are ill-suited for process simulation (as is the case with Unity), leading to one of three main options: either discarding the use of these tools, with the consequent discarding as well of the easy integration in many platforms and graphical and physics engines; setting an interconnection with external simulation engines, with the consequent limitations; or focusing on a simulation-free implementation altogether.

In this work, we demonstrate instead the implementation of a twin-screw extrusion simulation within Unity by benefitting from the available C# optimization library alglib and using complementarity constraints, in contrast with the previous literature. We study the computational time demanded and compare the results with simulations carried out with LUDOVIC, a state of the art simulator for twin-screw extrusion. The obtained results show that this alternative provides solid performance while simplifying the deployment of the final tool for its use by students.

**Keywords**: Unity, Twin Screw Extrusion, Educational Simulation, Complementarity Constraints.

## 1. Introduction

Twin screw extrusion is a popular process in the polymer, chemical and food industries, where an intermeshing extruder (see Fig.1) is used for mixing highly viscous materials, favored for its good mixing performance and short residence times, amongst other properties (Eitzlmayr et al., 2014). However, it is also a complex process: the operating conditions mean that most properties, such as the filling ratio or the pressure, have little identifiability in practice; the screw must be designed specifically in different sections, taking into account the geometry, length and rotating speed, a design which is meant to compensate for the complex physical phenomena of mass and heat transport, as well as the temperature rise due to viscous dissipation; all of these effects come into play in the operation of the process. Finally, it is also complex to formulate and solve, as the mass balance results in a constrained Ordinary Differential Equation (ODE).

In view of the complexity of the process, there is a clear incentive to develop training tools for both operators and engineers which would allow them to familiarize themselves with the different elements and mechanics of the process. There are many alternatives for this: the first is simulation-free environments, where the interaction of each element is hand-coded by the designer: this has the advantage of requiring little time for simple cases, but has the disadvantage of exponential complexity that arises as a new element added has to interact with all the other previously designed ones. Alternatives include connecting with available simulators, such as the authors previously discussed in (Santos Bartolome and Van Gerven, 2022), but this alternative was not available in the field of extrusion simulation. Finally it can be opted to develop the tool in a different software, not intended for environment design, such as a user interface in python: the caveat for our case is that this offers limited functionality and realism.

Instead, we have opted to implement a simulation of a twin extruder directly in Unity, by benefiting from available libraries in C#, particularly alglib (ALGLIB, 2022). This allows for great flexibility in the design of the environment, at a cost of rigidity in the simulation software itself. The prototype tool has been developed to demonstrate the feasibility of this approach, and in it we have developed the model presented in Figure 1, which consists of 49 compartments, and for which data has also been generated with a rigorous polymer extrusion software (Vergnes et al., 1998).

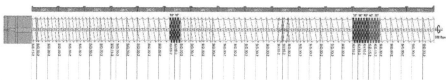

Figure 1 : Twin extruder design used in the simulation.

We will introduce the model in the follwing section, after which we expand on the technical implementation into Unity. Section 4 shows the results obtained, followed by conclusions and proposals of future work.

## 2. Twin screw extruder modelling

The twin screw extrusion system can be rigorously modeled with CFD simulation, however, this results in a great computational demand, which makes its use unadvisable for an educational tool (Solmaz and Van Gerven, 2022). Instead, we will use the 1D model developed by (Eitzlmayr et al., 2014), which provides an extensive study of the effects of each physical phenomenon, based on the properties of the geometry and the chosen polymer. This model subdivides the screw elements into sections which are considered perfectly mixed, with homogeneous properties.

Due to its complexity we will not extend on every term of the model here, and instead will focus on the main elements of the mass an energy balance. We take $f_m^{(i)}(u, x)$, to provide the derivative of the mass of the $i^{th}$ screw element, and $f_Q^{(i)}(u, x)$, to provide the derivative of its heat. Both are functions of $u$, the process inputs, and $x$, the internal states of the process, resulting in:

$$f_m^{(i)}(u, x) = \sum_{j=1}^{k} \dot{m}_{conv}^{(k \to i)} + \dot{m}_P^{(k \to i)}$$

Where k is the index of the last screw element, $\dot{m}_{conv}^{(k \to i)}$ is the flow by convection from the $k^{th}$ element to the $i^{th}$, and $\dot{m}_P^{(k \to i)}$ is the pressure flow from the same.
The heat balance is instead composed of:

$$f_Q^{(i)}(u, x) = \sum_{j=1}^{k} C_p^{(j)} T^{(j)} \left( \dot{m}_{conv}^{(k \to i)} + \dot{m}_P^{(k \to i)} \right) + \alpha^{(i)} A_b^{(i)} \left( T_b^{(i)} - T^{(i)} \right) + Q_{diss}^{(i)}$$

Where $C_p^{(i)}$ is the heat capacity at the $i^{th}$ element, $T^{(i)}$ it's temperature, $\alpha^{(i)}$ the heat transfer coefficient with the barrel, which is assumed to be constant, $A_b^{(i)}$ the surface area of the barrel segment, $T_b^{(i)}$ the temperature of the barrel, and $Q_{diss}^{(i)}$ the heat generated by viscous dissipation, which, due to the complexity of full viscous dissipation terms, we simplify significantly to:

$$Q_{diss}^{(i)} = \left( K_{diss}^{(i)} n \right)^2 \eta^{(i)}$$

Once the model has been chosen, we have designed an optimization problem to solve the mass balance, and a linear equation for the energy balance, which are solved sequentially to obtain the mass balance and energy balance. This sequential approach was chosen due to the already significant time required to solve the mass balance by the chosen solver, which we preferred to not prolong by increasing the number of variables. The balances are connected due to the changes in property values, but we consider this changes not significant on sufficiently small step sizes (when calculating steady state results, five iterations are done to arrive to convergence).

### 2.1. Mass (and Pressure) Balance with Complementarity Constraints

The greatest challenge when calculating the mass balance of the twin extruder is the condition that the pressure cannot rise higher than the atmospheric pressure as long as the compartment is not filled completely. This can be expressed as a constrained ODE in the form:

$$\frac{dm^{(i)}}{dt} = f_m^{(i)}(u, x) \ \forall i$$
$$0 \le m^{(i)} \le m_{max} \ \forall i \ ; P^{(i)} \ge P_{atm} \ \forall i$$
$$P^{(i)} = P_{atm} \ \forall i \in \{i | m^{(i)} \ne m_{max}\}$$

In the literature we have found approaches to find the solution to these balances by using iterative calculation (Vergnes et al., 1998), by iteratively classifying compartments as filled or not filled (Choulak et al., 2004), and by introducing an additional differential equation for the pressure (Cegla and Engell, 2021). Some of the limitations of these approaches are, respectively: not using the information available due to ignoring the gradients; required small time steps or use of more complex integration schemes; and need of tuning of an additional parameter.

Instead, in this work we propose to tackle this process based complementarity constraints, as described in (Biegler, 2010). These are paired constraints for which one of them must always be active, which is the case in our system. This turns the equations to:

$$\frac{dm^{(i)}}{dt} = f_m^{(i)}(u, x) \ \forall i$$
$$0 \le m^{(i)} \ \forall i$$
$$m^{(i)} \le m_{max} \perp P^{(i)} \ge P_{atm} \ \forall i$$

This equation can then be solved as an NLP with the approach listed in (Biegler, 2010) as RegComp:

$$\min_m \varepsilon$$
$$\frac{dm^{(i)}}{dt} = f_m^{(i)}(u, x) \ \forall i$$
$$0 \le m^{(i)} \le m_{max} \ \forall i$$
$$P^{(i)} \ge P_{atm} \ \forall i$$
$$\left(-m^{(i)} + m_{max}\right)\left(P^{(i)} - P_{atm}\right) \le \varepsilon \ \forall i$$

We can observe that both terms on the last constraint will be positive in the feasible region of the rest of the problem, and $\varepsilon$ reaches its minimum value of 0 when at least one of the constraints is active for all compartments, meaning that they are each either full or are at atmospheric pressure.

### 2.2. Heat Balance

Once the mass balance is solved, the heat balance is comparatively simpler, as there are no restrictions necessary and instead is solved only as an ODE:

$$\frac{dQ^{(i)}}{dt} = f_Q^{(i)}(u, x) \ \forall i$$

Where some of the states in x have been obtained in the previous step.

## 3. Implementation in Unity

After the design of the model we implement the simulation into the game engine Unity, which allows for the creation of an interactive educational environment. We give a summary in this section:

### 3.1. Optimization

The optimization is conducted with the SQL solver included in (ALGLIB, 2022) within their augmented Lagrangian (minnlc) C# package, which was found to be the best performant of all available algorithms. Restraints are added as boxed, linear or non-linear, in that order of preference. The heat balance is solved with the matrix solver rmatrixsolve. All derivatives are implemented with the backwards Euler method.

The library can be added directly in the assets folder of the project with no further modifications. Although multiple warnings are displayed in the editor regarding duplicated namespaces, we found no issues either in the editor nor when compiling or playing a compiled version.

### 3.2. Game elements

Each compartment is integrated as a game object, whose properties such as length $\Delta x$, diameter $D$ or barrel temperature $T_b$ can be changed directly, whereas the simulation is centralized into an empty object which contains a list of all active compartments, as well as all central variables such as the time step $\Delta t$ and the rotational speed $n$.

Plots are added to represent the evolution of the variables either with regards to the position in the extruder or with time. These are added from the Chart and Graph utility (Graph And Chart, 2022), and edited by the main simulation object upon each new result.

## 4. Results

We have collected both the computational time needed to solve the system and the accuracy of the steady-state results, compared with results obtained in the state of the art twin extrusion simulator Ludovic (Vergnes et al., 1998). Since the parameters dependent on screw geometry were not available, they have been fitted by comparing with the Ludovic results. All compartments not part of the extruder die have been considered to have the same geometry to avoid overfitting. Due to the results only needing to be generally correct for learning, the parameters were tuned by visual comparison instead of using more sophisticated methods such as data reconciliation (Pitarch et al., 2019).

All data are collected within the Unity 2021.3.4f1 editor in Windows 10 Enterprise, with a 11th Gen Intel(R) Core(TM) i7-11850H at 2.50 GHz and 16 GB of RAM.

*4.1. Computational time demanded*

We have observed that compartments where the pressure goes above atmospheric are the most computationally consuming, which led to the use as a comparison a series of mixing elements with a single forward conveying element in the first location. Figure 2 shows the evolution of the average computational time demanded with the number of elements, which shows that the time demand is prohibitive for real-time simulation of the extruder design proposed (which contains 49 compartments). However, it is still possible to use the system to show students the basic effects in smaller, less representative designs. Further work on the solver settings might lead to a significant improvement.

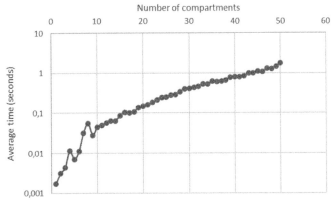

Figure 2. Average time consumed by solving the mass balance in Unity (logarithmic scale) against number of compartments.

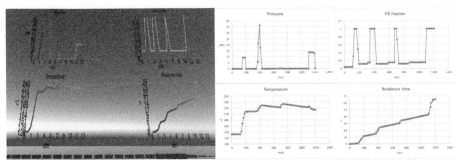

Figure 3. Comparison of results in Unity (left) and Ludovic (right). The game objects representing the extruder compartments can be seen in the bottom left as default black boxes.

*4.2. Comparison of results*
Figure 3 shows the comparison of the results obtained in Ludovic and in Unity for temperature, pressure, filled fraction and residence time. Although there are differences of magnitude, which we attribute to the limited ability to tune the parameters, it appears that the profiles are sufficiently similar for the students to learn the effects and interactions of different screw designs and process parameters.

## 5. Conclusions

The work has satisfactorily dealt with the simulation of a twin extruder in an educational environment designed in Unity, showing that the available tools are sufficient to consider direct development of the model in the engine as a valid alternative for design. Due to the computational load, the prototype designed is of limited use for dynamic simulation of systems with a large number of compartments, but is otherwise useful for steady state simulation, and for dynamic simulation of simpler systems, as the profiles obtained have been shown to be similar to those obtained by state of the art tools. We believe that these educational environments can be used as tools for the benefit of the learning of students and trainees of all kinds.

Besides this main goal, we have also introduced the formulation of the twin extruder as an ODE with complementarity constraints, as opposed to the previous approaches present in the literature. It remains necessary to study how this approach compares in practice with the already existing ones, both in stability and time demand, both for pure modelling and for other objectives such as control.

## Acknowledgements

This project has received funding from the European Union's EU Framework Programme for Research and Innovation Horizon 2020 under Grant Agreement 812716 (SIMPLIFY). Project website: www.spire2030.eu/simplify.

## References

ALGLIB, 2022. ALGLIB - C++/C# numerical analysis library. https://www.alglib.net
Biegler, L.T., 2010. Nonlinear Programming: Concepts, Algorithms, and Applications to Chemical Processes. Chapter 11.
Cegla, M., Engell, S., 2021. Application of Model Predictive Control to the reactive extrusion of e-Caprolactone in a twin-screw extruder. IFAC-Pap., 16th IFAC Symposium on Advanced Control of Chemical Processes 2021 54, 225–230.
Choulak, S. et al., 2004. Generic Dynamic Model for Simulation and Control of Reactive Extrusion. Ind. Eng. Chem. Res. 43,
Eitzlmayr et al., 2014. Mechanistic modeling of modular co-rotating twin-screw extruders. Int. J. Pharm. 474, 157–176.
Graph And Chart, 2022. Graph And Chart | GUI Tools https:assetstore.unity.com/packages/tools/gui/graph-and-chart-78488.
Pitarch, J.L., Sala, A., de Prada, C., 2019b. A Systematic Grey-Box Modeling Methodology via Data Reconciliation and SOS Constrained Regression. Processes 7, 170.
Santos, P., Van Gerven, T., 2020. Aspen Hysys – Unity Interconnection. An Approach for Rigorous Computer- Based Chemical Engineering Training, CACE, 30. pp. 2053–2058.
Solmaz, S., Van Gerven, T., 2022. Automated integration of extract-based CFD results with AR/VR in engineering education for practitioners. Multimed. Tools Appl. 81, 14869–14891.
Vergnes, B., Valle, G.D., Delamare, L., 1998. A global computer software for polymer flows in corotating twin screw extruders. Polym. Eng. Sci. 38, 1781–1792.

Antonis Kokossis, Michael C. Georgiadis, Efstratios N. Pistikopoulos (Eds.)
PROCEEDINGS OF THE 33rd European Symposium on Computer Aided Process Engineering
(ESCAPE33), June 18-21, 2023, Athens, Greece

# An Educational Workshop for Effective PSE Course Development

Daniel R. Lewin,[a] Edwin Zondervan,[b] Meik Franke,[b] Anton A. Kiss,[c] Stefan Krämer,[d] Mar Pérez-Fortes,[e] Artur M. Schweidtmann,[c] Petronella M. (Ellen) Slegers,[f] Ana Somoza-Tornos,[c] Pieter L.J. Swinkels,[e] and Bart Wentink[g]

[a] *Department of Chemical Engineering, Technion. I. I. T., Haifa 32000, Israel*
[b] *Department of Chemical Engineering, University of Twente, the Netherlands*
[c] *Department of Chemical Engineering, TU Delft, the Netherlands*
[d] *Bayer AG, Engineering & Technology, Leverkusen, Germany*
[e] *Engineering, Systems and Services, TU Delft, the Netherlands*
[f] *Operations Research and Logistics, Wageningen University & Research, the Netherlands*
[g] *BASF SE, Carporate Technology, Ludwigshafen, Germany*

*Email for correspondance: dlewin@technion.ac.il*

## Abstract

An educational workshop for developing Process Systems Engineering (PSE) courses will be held during ESCAPE-33, following the model workshop that was run during the CAPE Forum 2022 held at the University of Twente, in the Netherlands. This 3-hour workshop distributes the participants into four teams working together to develop the outline of a course on a novel application area in PSE motivated by a selected plenary or keynote talk at the conference, with each team led by authors of this contribution. This paper provides an overview of the approach used in the workshop for the effective development of a PSE course.

**Keywords**: PSE education, course development, learning objectives.

## 1. Introduction

From 14-16 September 2022 a workshop on developing Process Systems Engineering (PSE) courses was held at the CAPE Forum 2022 at the University of Twente in the Netherlands (www.pse-nl.com/index.php/cape-forum-2022). Working in teams, participants of the forum with different backgrounds developed education plans for a complete course on one of four selected subjects: Carbon-neutral PSE, Sustainable bio-based PSE, Energy efficient PSE, and Artificial Intelligence (AI) in PSE. These are representative novel application areas described by Lewin et al. (2022) as suitable emerging fields that offer new horizons to students from the basic areas of process design, process control and numerical methods, and, of course, rely heavily on them as foundations. These topics are also fully in line with the recently described PSE developments in industry and academia (Kiss and Grievink, 2020). The specific topics selected in CAPE Forum 2022 were inspired by the four keynote talks delivered at the meeting and the team leaders for the course development were the four keynote speakers from industry and academia (Bart Wentink, Ellen Slegers, Stefan Krämer, and Artur Schweidtmann).

The workshop was held in two sessions. In the first session, each team worked on developing learning objectives and a syllabus for the entire course. They also proposed more detailed learning objectives and content for at least one week of activity of the course. In the second session, each team developed suitable activities for students for each of the weeks of activity specified in the first session. Each of the courses developed relied on the *flipped classroom* paradigm (Lewin and Barzilai, 2022; Lewin, 2022), in which every week of class activity is divided into three sequential phases: (1) *preparation*, in which students prepare for the week's activities by completing online lessons consisting of a series of short video clips and associated quiz questions that test comprehension; (2) *class meeting*, in which students improve their understanding, comprehension, and capabilities by tackling open-ended exercises and discussion mentored by the teacher, and (3) *active tutorial*, in which students solve exercises on their own or in small groups with their peers, mentored by the course staff. For more details, the reader is referred to the referenced papers, and the YouTube video clips mentioned in Section 3.

## 2. Course Development Steps

A systematic framework for course development follows the following top-down approach:

**Step 1:** At the highest level, one needs to answer the question: *"What do I want my students to learn and why?"* In other words, to specify what skills and attributes students need be able to demonstrate on successfully completing the proposed course. These are best defined in terms of learning objectives. For example, for a typical 13-week course on *Process Dynamics and Control* (equivalent to 5 ECTS), the course learning objectives would be divided into those concerning dynamic modelling and those concerning control design, defining what a student needs to exhibit on successfully completing the course:

Process modelling (Weeks 1-6):

L01: Capability to model dynamic response of processing systems using material and energy balances

L02: Ability to linearize models and generate transfer function approximations

L03: Ability to generate overall transfer functions from block diagrams

L04: Ability to analyse the transient response of linear systems

Process control synthesis (Weeks 7-13):

L05: Frequency domain analysis capabilities, enabling transition between Laplace, frequency, and time domains

L06: Stability analysis capability

L07: Knowing how to tune PID controllers effectively

L08: Capability to synthesize feedback control systems to meet closed-loop performance specifications

L09: Capability to design effective cascade and feedforward control systems

**Step 2:** Identify the best teaching approaches for the type of learning you want. For efficient learning, we recommend active learning strategies. This implies freeing some or all of the contact student-staff time to allow students to get involved in staff-assisted problem-solving. An established way to do this is by *flipping the classroom* (Lewin, 2022), which moves some or all of the lecture material to student online self-study activities. An alternative approach would be to reduce the volume of lecture material, and indeed, any approach that frees some student-staff contact time for practice is appropriate.

**Step 3:** Select the course content, organized as a weekly schedule, in which each week is driven by its learning objectives. For example, for the process control course, the weekly schedule could be as shown in Figure 1. Therein, specific learning objectives are defined for each week. For example, in Week 10, the learning objectives would concern the Root Locus method:

On completing week 10 of the process control course, the student should be able to:

- Sketch the root locus, given transfer functions for a process and its controller,

- Sketch the output response of a controlled process, given locations of closed-loop poles on the root locus, and

- Use the root locus to design a controller, given the transfer function of the process to be controlled, to meet the desired closed-loop response specifications (e.g., overshoot and settling time).

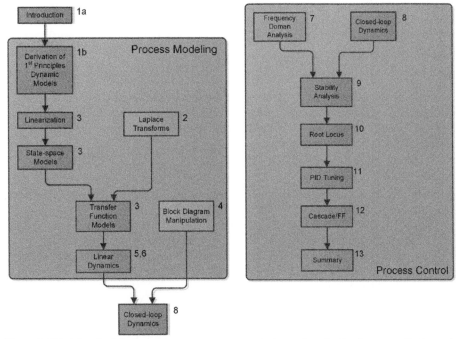

Figure 1. Weekly schedule for a course on process control; numbers in the diagram refer to weeks in the course.

**Step 4:** For each week, develop student assignments, projects, and class activities so that all the learning objectives are practiced by the students, with repeats as necessary. This is by far the most important content of the course, as it defines the mechanisms by which students will "learn by doing." Some of the activities should be designed to be guided activities (e.g., open-ended problem solving in class meetings, guided by the instructor), which other activities are designed to be for students working alone or in groups. An example exercise for Week 10 of the process control course that tests accomplishment of all three learning objectives would be the following:

Given the open loop transfer function: $PC(s) = \dfrac{K_C(s+2)(s+4)}{s(s+1)(s+5)(s+10)}$

(a)   Draw the root locus for $PC$(s).

(b)   Determine the value of $K_C$ that will give the fastest possible closed-loop response with no oscillations.

(c)   Sketch (qualitatively – there is no need to compute the response) the closed-loop response to a unit step change in the setpoint, with the value of $K_C$ as determined in part (b).

**Step 5:** No work on course development is ever final. One should always make an effort to improve the course plan with class experience and feedback.

## 3. Outline and outcomes of the CAPE Forum 2022 Workshop

*3.1. Workshop activity*

In the spirit of "flipping" the course, the Forum participants were invited to review the short videos describing how the flipped class is used to teach PSE subjects before attending the CAPE Forum:

Webinar talk (14 min):  www.youtube.com/watch?v=O3hoSlYaGo4

ESCAPE-31 Keynote (28 min): www.youtube.com/watch?v=b6w6mqSPxp0

The workshop was organized with three points of contact during CAPE Forum 2022. Splitting the workshop into three points of contact gave the opportunity for group members to get together informally and discuss course content during the entire forum. The three points of contact were:

1.   15th September 2022, morning – Participants were distributed into one of the four topics by a suitable color code on their badges. A 5-min announcement introduced the workshop. Each of the four teams was asked to prepare an outline for a new course in the following subjects:
     Topic 1: Carbon-neutral PSE, led by Bart Wentink and Leyla Özkan
     Topic 2: Sustainable biobased PSE, led by Ellen Slegers and Meik Franke
     Topic 3: Energy efficient PSE, led by Stefan Krämer and Pieter Swinkels
     Topic 4: Artificial intelligence (AI) for PSE, led by Artur Schweidtmann and Ana Somoza-Tornos

2.   15th September 2022, afternoon – First 90-minute session. The workshop presenter introduced the activity and initiated a hands-on session in which the four groups worked on developing each of the courses (**Steps 1** and **3**), led by one of the keynote speakers. This session was positioned after the last of the four keynotes.

3.   16th September 2022, afternoon – Second 90-minute session. The workshop presenter introduced a hands-on session in which the four groups worked on **Step 4**, developing activities for students appropriate for at least one of the detailed weeks planned in **Step 3** for the first hour, each group being led by one of the keynote speakers. In the last 30 minutes, the groups presented their course

plan outlines to all participants and received immediate feedback from the instructor and the group.

## 3.2. Example course layout

As an example of the outcomes that can be expected from the course development workshop, we present here in detail the course outline for Topic 4, on "AI in PSE," as completed by a team of eight participants, headed by the keynote speaker, Artur Schweidtmann. Similar outcomes were achieved by the other three teams. This section details the course learning objective, and syllabus and expands on the planned activities for Week 2 of the course.

### 3.2.1. Topic 4: Course learning outcomes and schedule

The team working on Topic 4 developed the outline for a master's level elective course of 4-5 ECTS on "AI for PSE." Students of the course need to have chemical engineering basics, matrix algebra, calculus, and an introductory course in statistics as prerequisites. It would be advantageous to also have programming experience in Python and have taken an introductory course in optimization. At the end of the course, the student will be able to:

- LO1: Explain the concepts of AI and data analysis
- LO2: Discuss the potential and limitations of different AI methods/tools for given chemical engineering applications
- LO3: Design an AI system to solve a given chemical engineering problem
- LO4: Implement a given or designed AI system using Python
- LO5: Validate an AI model based on data
- LO6: Comprehend state-of-the-art AI research

The course schedule as devised by the team was divided into two approximately equal parts, the first covering the foundations and the second covering applications and project work:

- Week 1: Introduction to Python
- Weeks 2-6: AI foundations
  - Week 2: Data analysis
  - Weeks 3-4: Regression
  - Weeks 5-6: Classification
- Weeks 7-13: Applications of AI in PSE
  - Week 7: Molecular property prediction
  - Week 8: Hybrid modelling
  - Week 9: Demand forecasting
  - ...
  - Week 13: Project presentations and assessment

### 3.2.2. Topic 4: Course plan for Week 2

Team 4 also produced a detailed plan for Week 2, covering data analysis methods. The week's activity is driven by four learning objectives that indicate that after successfully completing week 2, the student will be able to:

- LO1: Select an appropriate regression method for a given problem
- LO2: Train a regression model on data using common packages
- LO3: Validate a regression model based on data

- LO4: Discuss advantages and disadvantages of common regression tools for a given application

These LOs are achieved by a combination of two phases of self-learning supported by online videos and quiz questions, each followed by in-person sessions involving online quizzes, class discussions, and programming activities in the lab. As shown in Figure 2, the activities have multiple connections to all four learning objectives.

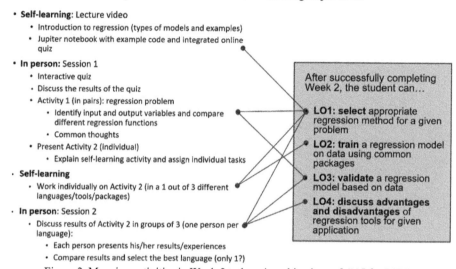

- **Self-learning**: Lecture video
  - Introduction to regression (types of models and examples)
  - Jupiter notebook with example code and integrated online quiz
- **In person**: Session 1
  - Interactive quiz
  - Discuss the results of the quiz
  - Activity 1 (in pairs): regression problem
    - Identify input and output variables and compare different regression functions
    - Common thoughts
  - Present Activity 2 (individual)
    - Explain self-learning activity and assign individual tasks
- **Self-learning**
  - Work individually on Activity 2 (in a 1 out of 3 different languages/tools/packages)
- **In person**: Session 2
  - Discuss results of Activity 2 in groups of 3 (one person per language):
    - Each person presents his/her results/experiences
    - Compare results and select the best language (only 1?)

After successfully completing Week 2, the student can…

**LO1: select** appropriate regression method for a given problem

**LO2: train** a regression model on data using common packages

**LO3: validate** a regression model based on data

**LO4: discuss advantages and disadvantages** of regression tools for given application

Figure 2. Mapping activities in Week 2 to learning objectives of "AI for PSE".

## 4. Conclusions

The outcomes of the CAPE Forum 2022 workshop were four master plans, one for each of the topics discussed in the keynote talks (i.e. Carbon-neutral PSE, Sustainable biobased PSE, Energy efficient PSE, and AI for PSE). Each master plan was characterized by a syllabus and a week-by-week schedule, of which most were linked to the learning objectives. In addition, the teams devised exercises, assignments, and projects to be carried out by students of the courses, which address the same learning objectives. The workshop gave a useful course development experience to junior faculty, PhD and EngD students. Following these successful outcomes, a similar educational workshop will be offered as part of the ESCAPE-33 conference program.

## References

A. A. Kiss, J. Grievink, 2020, "Process Systems Engineering developments in Europe from an industrial and academic perspective", *Computers & Chemical Engineering*, 138, 106823.

D. R. Lewin and A. Barzilai, 2022, "The Flip Side of Teaching Process Design and Process Control to Chemical Engineering Undergraduates – and Completely Online to Boot," *Education for Chemical Engineers*, 39, 44-57.

D. R. Lewin, 2022, "Teaching PSE Mastery During, and After, the COVID-19 Pandemic," *Comput. Chem. Eng.*, 160, 107741.

D. R. Lewin, E. M. Kondili, I. T. Cameron, G. Léonard, S. Soheil Mansouri, F. G. Martins, L. Ricardez-Sandoval, H. Sugiyama, and E. Zondervan, 2022, "Agile Process Systems Engineering Education: What to teach, and how to teach it," submitted to *Computers and Chemical Engineering*.

Antonis Kokossis, Michael C. Georgiadis, Efstratios N. Pistikopoulos (Eds.)
PROCEEDINGS OF THE 33rd European Symposium on Computer Aided Process Engineering
(ESCAPE33), June 18-21, 2023, Athens, Greece

# Teaching strategies for the effective use of computational tools within the Chemical Engineering curriculum

A. Tsatse, E. Sorensen

*Department of Chemical Engineering, University College London, Torrington Place, WC1E 7JE London, UK*

## Abstract

This work discusses the rationale behind, and strategies followed, when delivering chemical engineering modules which have a significant requirement of computational work, and how to coordinate this delivery across an entire curriculum. It will be shown how the complicated aspects of PSE-related subjects can be considered and introduced to students through several modules spread across UCL Chemical Engineering Year 2 programme, and how student learning is supported, whilst providing them with the best opportunity for applying their new computational knowledge and skills and for innovation. It will also be discussed how this procedure prepares students for their capstone design project in Year 3, indicating that this approach has several benefits, including but not limited to, students' understanding of PSE tools and the development of their critical engineering thinking.

**Keywords**: Chemical Engineering, Process Systems Engineering, problem-based learning, computational tools

## 1. Introduction

UCL Engineering's Integrated Engineering Programme (IEP) was introduced in 2014/15 and is based on innovative teaching practices which include the use of scenario- and problem-based learning (Graham, 2018) across Years 1 and 2 of the programme. Within the Department of Chemical Engineering, several IEP teaching activities have strong computational elements (Tsatse and Sorensen, 2021). Most of the computational tools are introduced in the Year 2 curriculum, which is the focus of this work, as this year includes various modules that make use of computational tools (see Figure 1). The Department employs a wide range of techniques to ensure that the Year 2 students know how to use a wide range of computational tools; that they have the required knowledge of how to select the most suitable software based on the given problem; and for them to reflect on their work before proceeding to the capstone design project in Year 3 of the programme. In addition, teaching staff needs to regularly evaluate the material delivered, to ensure that the concepts and topics discussed align with current research directions and the constantly evolving industrial needs (e.g. integration of multiple computational tools).

In all modules that will be discussed below, assessed projects and team reports evaluate whether the learning outcomes are met, whilst tutorials for the relevant computational tool(s) take place before the release of the material for which the software is required (e.g. project, coursework etc.). In addition, computational help desk sessions are scheduled before the respective assessment deadline so that support by staff is provided to students who may be facing difficulties with the specific software used. As this work focuses on Year 2 modules, it is useful to note that, in Year 1, students are made familiar with the fundamentals of GAMS (GAMS, 2022) and gPROMS (Siemens Process Systems Engineering, 2022), and are thus able to solve simple computational problems such as how to solve a mass balance around a buffer tank and calculate the respective liquid height. Year 1 does not include any teaching material on AspenPlus (Aspentech 2022), so this is an entirely new computational tool for the students when starting Year 2.

During their studies, students have continuous access to online learning material for all the computational tools used across the entire curriculum (i.e. AspenPlus, gPROMS, GAMS and MATLAB). The material for each of the tools includes how-to videos and step-by-step presentations that explain various concepts and processes, and how these can be implemented and solved using the respective tool. The material is updated regularly to make sure it aligns with the theory taught, or any new elements added, as well as updated versions of the software. For instance, material on how to consider distributed models in gPROMS, and relevant examples thereof, is available for students to download, study and apply in their own time. Relevant material is available online also for aspects that are not formally considered or assessed as part of any of the taught modules, such as solids processing, so that students can refer to this if they need to consider these aspects as part of an open-end project, for instance in a Scenario (Sorensen, 2016). This supporting material provides additional resources which students appreciate, especially when they proceed to more challenging projects in their 3rd or 4th year, when they need to consider processes not previously covered in individual taught modules.

Each of the following sections discusses the rationale and teaching strategy for the use of computational tools within our programme. The case studies discussed are presented in order of increasing difficulty for the students, and the discussion includes the strategy for how the students learn how theory and experimental data can be combined, as well as how a proposed process synthesis can be verified using computational tools. In addition, the strategy for how to include computational work in open-ended problem-based learning in the form of a week-long IEP project (i.e. Scenarios) is also presented, along with a discussion of how students are prepared for their 3rd Year capstone design project through all these teaching activities. A diagram of the PSE-related modules in Year 2 and their associated, increasing, difficulty is presented in Figure 1.

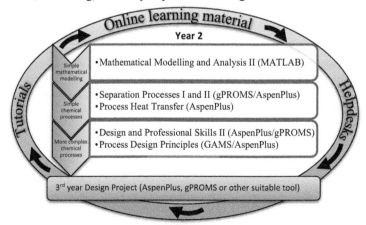

Figure 1: Distribution of PSE related modules and available support over the Year 2 curriculum

## 2. Computational tools for mathematical modelling and analysis

One of the core modules in Year 2 is Mathematical Modelling and Analysis II (the first part of the topic is taught in Year 1) (UCL Module Catalogue, 2022). For each of the topics considered (e.g. Taylor and Fourier series, Transforms, Partial Differential Equations etc.), students participate in a tutorial where they have the opportunity to solve real-life examples, relevant to their engineering discipline, for which the specific mathematical concept is required. They mainly use MATLAB (Mathworks, 2022) in order to solve these problems.

As an example, students are asked to find the tangential velocity of a space capsule when it re-enters Earth's atmosphere, using Euler's method. Students first provide their answer symbolically using the relevant theory taught, and then proceed to solve the problem and find the exact solution using MATLAB. This exercise helps students to familiarise themselves with MATLAB and to learn, in general, how to use a suitable computational tool to solve challenging mathematical problems that are difficult, if not impossible, to solve by hand or analytically. Furthermore, part of the aim is for the students to realise that they can use MATLAB to solve similar problems later in their studies.

## 3. Combination of computational and experimental work

A particular aspect of our programme is the combination of computational and experimental work within most modules, which is taught in an integrated manner alongside the theoretical concepts. This is to ensure that the students not only understand the fundamentals, but also know how to solve relevant problems using computational tools, as well as understand how the various unit operations function practically through lab experiments and how experimental input may be required when modelling these units.

### 3.1 Separation Processes I and II

Within the Separation Processes I module, students have two pieces of coursework worth 20% each to the overall mark, each of them focusing on a different computational tool. For the first piece of coursework, when students have been made familiar with the concepts of flash separations and binary and multi-component distillation and their relevant equation sets, students are asked to model a dynamic equilibrium stage within gPROMS and observe its performance under different conditions (e.g. varying relative volatility and stage holdup). As mentioned above, gPROMS is also taught in Year 1 so students are expected to be familiar with how this software works, however, this is the first time they are given a more complex problem involving multiple components.

For the second piece of coursework, students are asked to simulate heat transfer and various separation processes (heat exchangers followed by distillation, absorption and/or liquid-liquid extraction) in AspenPlus with data that they themselves have obtained in the laboratory during a relevant experiment within the Engineering Experimentation module, and to discuss and justify any differences observed between the experimental and computational results. This coursework is due after the completion of the module to ensure that all students have obtained the relevant experimental data as the experiments are conducted throughout several weeks due to the large cohort size. The aim of this exercise is to encourage students to familiarise themselves with core industrial processes;

to understand how these work from both a practical and theoretical perspective; to think about the validity of any assumptions made when modelling each unit operation; as well as to reflect on the underlying assumptions and equations and their implications which are often 'hidden' within the computational tool.

As an example, in a distillation experiment students calculate the stage efficiency of the small-scale column they have operated. Then, they are asked to simulate the corresponding distillation process in AspenPlus using a rigorous column model such as RADFRAC, and to compare the cases when stages are ideal (i.e. stage efficiency is considered 100%) and when stages have the efficiency they found in the experiment. Discussion of the impact of stage efficiency on process performance is required, to encourage students to think about the importance of this parameter when designing a distillation unit. An additional aspect of this coursework includes the selection of the thermo-physical property method to be used in AspenPlus and for students to properly justify their choice, which usually requires them to look into literature to find experimental data that confirm the suitability of the specific method chosen. Other examples include students modelling a packed column with data obtained in the lab to observe and understand how column hydraulics work, as well as to simulate a continuous liquid-liquid-extraction process and discuss how the findings differ from the equivalent batch process they considered in the lab. Both of these exercises are also making use of AspenPlus.

For the Separation Processes II module, students are asked to simulate a crystallisation process using data from the relevant experiment. gPROMS is most suitable for this and therefore used in this case, and students are able to simulate the process, analyse, plot and discuss the generated results.

### 3.2 Process Heat Transfer

Within the Process Heat Transfer module, students are asked to use their data, obtained in the relevant experiment, to model a shell and tube heat exchanger in AspenPlus as part of their 20% coursework, after having made a number of theoretical calculations. Students are asked to design the heat exchanger using a relevant heat exchanger model, state any assumptions made and provide their results such as the overall heat transfer coefficient and stream outlets.

The learning outcome for the students, in addition to learning how to model heat exchanger units using a higher level of detail, is to understand and critically discuss the underlying equations and assumptions when modelling such units, their design characteristics (e.g. in terms of equipment geometry) as well as the results generated (e.g. temperature profiles). This knowledge is expected to help them later on in their studies, especially when they come across the concept of heat integration and how heat exchangers are among the units which can help achieve this.

## 4. Modelling and simulation of more complex PSE concepts

### 4.1 Process Design Principles

The Process Design Principles module focuses on using theoretical approaches for the synthesis and design of more complex processes (i.e. processes that include several units). It is crucial that students learn not only how to consider process synthesis but also how to consider their design using computational tools (GAMS and AspenPlus in this module).

In the first part of the module, GAMS is used to solve the synthesis model of interest. Students should be able to identify all the input based on the problem description (e.g. feed conditions and unit specifications), and structure the code properly so that they are able to generate the desired results, for instance product compositions.

Later in the term, students are given a project on a specific design problem (e.g. the production of formaldehyde etc.) and are initially asked to synthesise and design a suitable process using the Douglas approach. They are then asked to simulate the conceptual process using AspenPlus, which typically requires the steady-state design of core units including, but not limited to, heat exchangers, plug-flow or continuous-stirred reactors and separation units. Students are also asked to find the heating and cooling requirements based on the generated results, as the overall aim of the project is to evaluate whether the design is economically attractive or not, making use of the relevant Economics Evaluation tool in AspenPlus.

In this project, students typically struggle with the existence of one or more recycle streams and how to properly include them in the flowsheet, and must consider the addition of tear streams and the selection of suitable initialisation procedures and initial conditions so that the simulation converges. This module clearly builds upon the previously discussed modules in order to expand the students' knowledge and capabilities on how to use computational tools by introducing them to more complex flowsheets and demanding procedures such as the inclusion of recycle streams.

### 4.2 Design and Professional Skills II (Scenarios)

In addition to the traditional taught modules discussed above, the chemical engineering programme at UCL includes a number of problem-based activities typically running over a whole week each, whereby the students work in teams to solve real-world problems, the so-called Scenarios (Graham, 2018). The aim of these problem- and scenario-based activities is to produce independent and self-directed engineers (Sorensen, 2016). Scenarios 3 and 4 (out of a total 6 Scenarios taught over Year 1 and Year 2) are typically related to Process Systems Engineering. This is an excellent opportunity for students to apply their knowledge from the taught modules, including the link between computational and experimental work mentioned above, but also apply their own ideas for the Scenario deliverables.

For instance, one Scenario 4 problem focused on Process Intensification and Reactive Distillation, where students considered fundamental process modelling and alternative process improvements using relevant simulation tools (in this case AspenPlus). The deliverables included, but were not limited to, column internals consideration; critical discussion of temperature and composition profiles; evaluation of process economics and environmental impact; as well as process safety. For each aspect they were required to justify their decisions based on their simulation findings from a well-rounded perspective. This particular Scenario also aimed at reminding students of the relevant computational knowledge obtained within Process Heat Transfer, to train and encourage students to make connections between different modules and apply knowledge obtained in one module for the purposes, and within the context of, a different module. For Scenario 4, students were asked to consider various types of distillation column condensers and reboilers, their suitability based on the specific process considered, as well as report the heating and cooling demands of the process, along with the required utilities.

## 5. Transition to 3ʳᵈ year capstone design project

Once students have completed their Year 2 modules, they are familiar with the majority of the capabilities of the various computational tools and are therefore ready and well-equipped for the 3ʳᵈ year's Process Plant Design Project module. The design project requires the modelling of a complete chemical engineering process using several computational tools (most often gPROMS and Aspen Plus depending on the particular units on which they are focusing) and the consideration of various aspects of those designs. These aspects, which are all considered using these tools and the critical engineering thinking of the students, include the optimal design of the process with respect to product quality, control performance, economics, environmental impact and sustainability, as well as process safety. This project works in practice as evaluation and confirmation of whether the learning outcomes of the Y2 modules and strategies discussed were successfully met, and how students employed the knowledge previously acquired for their open-ended project in Y3.

## 6. Conclusions

UCL's chemical engineering programme offers a number of opportunities for students to familiarise themselves with various computational tools through taught modules and problem-based learning. Students gradually become regular and confident users of PSE-related computational tools, learn how each of these works, understand their underlying equations and assumptions, as well as appreciate where experimental data is required. At the end of Year 2, students start becoming digitally literate as they are capable of simulating a wide range of simple and more complex chemical processes, including more challenging concepts such as recycle streams and heat integration, and evaluate these processes from various perspectives such as economical, environmental etc. The most important learning outcome, however, is that they perform these tasks making at the same time use of their own critical engineering thinking, and therefore make full use of all the potential benefits that PSE has to offer chemical engineering graduates.

## References

Aspentech (2022). Aspen Plus USA, Aspen Technology. Inc., https://www.aspentech.com/en/products/engineering/aspen-plus [Accessed 27/10/2022]

GAMS (2022). https://www.gams.com [Accessed 27/10/2022]

Graham, R. H. (2018). The global state of the art in engineering education. Cambridge, MA: Massachusetts Institute of Technology.

Mathworks (2022). https://uk.mathworks.com/products/matlab.html [Accessed 27/10/2022]

Siemens Process Systems Engineering (2022). gPROMS, https://www.psenterprise.com/products/gproms/process, 1997-2022.

Sorensen, E. (2016). Changing the World. The Chemical Engineer, 27-30.

Tsatse, A. and Sorensen, E. (2021) Reflections on the development of scenario and problem-based chemical engineering projects. Computer Aided Chemical Engineering 50, 2033-2038.

UCL Module Catalogue, https://www.ucl.ac.uk/module-catalogue/ [Accessed 27/10/2022].

Antonis Kokossis, Michael C. Georgiadis, Efstratios N. Pistikopoulos (Eds.)
PROCEEDINGS OF THE 33rd European Symposium on Computer Aided Process Engineering
(ESCAPE33), June 18-21, 2023, Athens, Greece

# Teaching courses to STEM students – Lessons learned from the Pandemics

Nelson Chibeles-Martins,[a,b] Lourdes B. Afonso,[a,b]

[a]*Departamento de Matemática, FCT-NOVA , 2829-516 Caparica, Portugal*
[b]*NOVAMATH Centro de Matemática e Aplicações, FCT-NOVA , 2829-516 Caparica, Portugal*

## Abstract

The current pandemic has been having a huge effect in teaching at all levels. Particularly, in Portugal, for STEM (Science, Technology, Engineering and Mathematics) students attending Universities and taking high learning degrees, it was particularly harsh. Nevertheless, the teaching crisis triggered by the SARS-CoV-2 pandemic was fertile terrain for pedagogical experimenting, learning and growing. In a previous work (Chibeles-Martins and Afonso, 2022) the authors described their experience during three eventful semesters teaching Applied Mathematics courses to STEM students.

In this work the authors present several teaching practices that were firstly introduced during the aforementioned period as an emergency patch-up but revealed to be so curiously thought provoking that caused them rethink how courses were taught before the Pandemic versus how they should be effectively taught. The authors explore how these teaching practices had to be readapted to a face-to-face teaching situation with the Lockdowns' end and what were their effect on students' learning experiences in a post-pandemic environment. In class and home-work assignments; working and discussion groups; lectures by students; more dynamical MOODLE pages, filled with on-line asynchronous activities; and more diverse evaluation moments are some of the practices that will be described and explored though out this presentation.

**Keywords**: Teaching Practices, Pandemics, Active Learning, Peer Instruction.

## 1. Introduction

FCT NOVA (NOVA SST - School of Sciences and Technology) is one of the most renowned Sciences and Engineering schools in Portugal. It offers doctorate, master and bachelor's degrees in mathematics, Computer Sciences, Physics, Chemistry, Industrial Management, Geology, Environmental Sciences, Material Sciences, among others. All offered degree programs are accredited by the national agency for assessment and accreditation of higher education and all Engineering programs have the EUR-ACE certification. Around 8,000 students, 400 professors, 1,000 researchers and 200 staff (NOVA School of Sciences and Technology, 2022) study, work and live inside the campus.

The current CoViD19 pandemic had a tremendous impact in this community slowing down research and teaching activities, leading to students dropping out of their hard-earned higher learning opportunities. Teachers had to reinvent their pedagogical practices in order to keep their lectures, tutoring classes and laboratorial sessions interesting during the successive lockdowns. And amid the crisis opportunities bloomed.

## 2. Lessons Learned

During the Pandemics that has been affecting us since the end of 2019 Academia had to face terrible challenges like every institution. But by facing them teachers also had the opportunity to become more deeply aware of some issues that were mainly dormant. In the following the authors will address some of the situations they experienced and the lessons they learned from them.

### 2.1. Recorded Lectures

At NOVA SST the majority of professors would feel uncomfortable when confronted with the notion of having to record their lectures. This occurs due to several factors:

- Discomfort from potential over exposition;
- Fear of students skipping classes because they have the lecture's recording available;
- Apprehension from the technology needed to create a good quality recording.

The pandemic forced us to be creative on the ways to reach our students and a lot of teachers accepted the challenge of recording their lectures. A considerable number of students were missing remote synchronous lectures due to illness, technical issues or simply because all their families was disputing the only available computer at their homes.

And despite all the previous reservations we found that:

- Non expensive movie maker software is easily available online;
- The recordings' access can be monitored. It is impossible to ensure it will not end up on YouTube but you can have some control on who can initially view your movies;
- Students rather attend to lectures. They usually only resort to recorded lectures if they cannot attend to the real deal. Or when they do not remember a particular detail and want to review it.

On the other hand, keeping a collection of lecture recordings online updated can be particularly time consuming and the learning curve for the necessary software and equipment can be off putting.

Nevertheless, recorded lectures are a very useful pedagogical tools and teachers should not be afraid to use them.

### 2.2. e-learning platforms

During the 2000s, at NOVA SST, some members of the teaching staff became aware of the MOODLE[1] project and an e-learning office was created to help teachers who wanted

---

[1]  MOODLE is the acronym to Modular Object-Oriented Dynamic Learning Environment. It is a digital learning platform designed to provide an integrated, secure

to learn how to create and manage MOODLE pages. In spite of its usefulness the use of MOODLE pages was considerably limited to a small number of more gimmick inclined teachers.

During the harsher initial Lockdowns midterm tests, presential lectures and face-to-face tutoring sessions were cancelled. Suddenly, most teachers had to fall back to digital online tools to complement on-line lectures. And realized how the use of e-learning platforms, namely MOODLE pages, would help tremendously with organizing and providing studying material, creating on-line evaluations, informing students, monitoring students' interaction with the proposed tasks, ...

At NOVA SST the number of Courses being supported by MOODLE increased immensely overnight. And did not stop after the Pandemics lost steam. Currently the number of active MOODLE pages per semester is so high that the server where they are lodged is getting overworked with an alarming frequency and it is on the process of being replaced/upgraded.

It is undeniable that online support provided by e-learning tools greatly improves the dynamics of any academic course. It does not really matter the preferred environment. MOODLE pages, Virtual Classrooms, simple online home pages. Circumstances that would be hard to remedy, like students not attending classes due to illness, athletic competitions or because they accumulate their academic life with a full-time job, are easily solved with the support of an e-learning platform.

Still, e-learning platforms need to be lodged somewhere and the generalized use of these tools imply a considerable investment in stable servers and internet connections. That can be an obstacle for learning institutions with tighter budgets.

But, despite its technical demands, currently, there are no motives to keep lectures solely to the physical classrooms.

### 2.3. Diversified Evaluation

Midterm and final tests, and exams are one of the most common kind of evaluations available to teachers. And in spite of its more complicated and cumbersome organizational logistics it is a very comfortable way of individually and quantitatively assessing students' performance in a course. Nevertheless, during the Lockdowns tests and exams were heavily restricted and teachers had to opt between postponing them *sine die* or adopt an alternative way of evaluating their students.

Group assignments, on-line presentations, essays, short on-line quizzes, small workshops, individual reports, and exercises solved and submitted on a short period of time were different types of evaluations that were explored as alternatives to midterm and final tests. And that imposed diversity in evaluation brought to mind an issue that was usually ignored: a more diversified evaluation enables assessing skills, abilities, competences and

---

and highly flexible system for teachers, educators and students. (The Moodle Project, 2020). Often used by schools and universities as an e-learning platform.

knowledges that are harder to evaluate through a standard test. Additionally, they alleviate tests and exams' psychological load and their relative importance from students' minds.

It is also easier to schedule a single test to a convenient date if courses do not have their evaluation centered solely on midterm and final tests. There will be a lesser number of tests to schedule and therefore the overlapping risk is much lower.

Obviously, this diversity can generate an all-new batch or evaluation problems the teaching staff is not used to address. What is the adequate balance between traditional tests and oral presentation evaluations? How to minimize personal biases during the more personal and potentially more subjective evaluation moments like group assignment discussions or lectures done by students? Additionally, paradigm shifts like these often have unexpected consequences... What will be the characteristics of top grades students under a generalized evaluation focus shift?

In conclusion, the constraints imposed by the Pandemics revealed that it is possible to evaluate students more accurately, more effectively and with less burden on the students during the critical periods of midterm and semesters' end.

### 2.4. Videoconferencing

Not many years ago using videoconference systems was not exactly an everyday event for most academics. Nevertheless, the Pandemics forced teachers and researchers to resort to these communication platforms daily, sometimes *ad nauseam*. Currently with Life in Academia going back to some kind of normalcy one would expect to go back to those times when videoconferencing was seldom used.

Actually, nowadays it became part of our routine. As most companies already knew it is an incredibly useful tool for team meetings. Training courses for teachers can have both videoconference components and presential sessions, making them more accessible to non-local teachers. Tutoring times can be scheduled to more convenient hours for both students and tutors when held on a videoconference.

With the investment already made in videoconference technology, hybrid lectures are the new normal, allowing some students to follow the lecture remotely. Additionally, for public learning institutions it is currently more economically viable to invite guest professors for occasional seminars. Travelling is becoming more expensive and having an invited speaker lecturing by videoconference may be less appellative for the attendants, but it certainly is a lesser expense for the inviting school.

### 2.5. Versatility, adaptability and inclusion

Change is usually faced with some apprehension in the Academia. Teaching is more comfortable when grounded on known routines. When teachers know what to expect and everything go according to what was planned their time can be more efficiently managed and they can be more productive. Nevertheless, almost every other semester some particular circumstances may challenge those routines and submit the course's planning to a stress test. An unexpected foreigner student with visa problems is not able to attend the course presentially, a sudden change on the regular class format due to space constraints, a student that has special learning needs enrolls on the course... All these circumstances can be stressful and anxiety inducing to even a well-prepared teacher.

But the Pandemic brought the unexpected and the exceptional to our Academia in unprecedented wave after wave. Teachers had to adapt quickly and ruthlessly. Every week something worse was happening and demanding another adjustment. We had to invent, create, became more tolerant and versatile. Way beyond we ever thought we were able to do.

It was tremendously hard, stressful and time consuming. But we learned we could get more efficient, more effective, and abler to deal with accidental and unforeseen events and circumstances affecting our teaching activity.

In the aftermath of the hardest part of the current Pandemic we became aware that, by comparison, the previous stressful happenstances that came knocking at our classroom's doors were mere nuisances. And that teachers are much more versatile, adaptable and resilient they ever considered being before.

## 3. Conclusions

The pedagogical tools mentioned previously were already known but seldom used by a large number of Academia members. The current CoViD19 pandemics put us all to a hard and long stress test. Teachers had to become more inventive, creative and resourceful resorting to those already available tools and use them at their full potential in order to keep students motivated, involved and obtaining high performance levels.

After the end of the Lockdowns, we noticed we kept using this tools even when lectures were fully presential. And that their contribution for a better learning experience were still considerable. Actually, in certain circumstances their effect was even better during on site classes.

We believe we will not go back to a time when teaching and learning did not include these tools and mind frames. Some of them can be time consuming and expensive. But a considerable investment in equipment and training was made during the Pandemics. The social distancing forced the Academia to pay a terrible mental and emotional price that is yet to be fully understood. It would be a huge waste of resources and acquired knowledge if we do not exploit to their fullest all the hard lessons, we learned during this trouble times.

### Acknowledgments

This works was partially funded by national funds through the FCT – Fundação para a Ciência e a Tecnologia, I.P. (National Foundation for Science and Technology), under the scope of the project UIDB/00297/2020.

This work was partially funded by Magentakoncept, lda.

### References

N. Chibeles-Martins and L. B. Afonso, 2022, Teaching courses heavily dependent on computational resources to STEM students during Pandemics, Computer Aided Chemical Engineering, 51, 1687-1692

Nova School of Sciences and Technology, 2022, *Overview*. https://www.fct.unl.pt/en/about-fct/overview

The Moodle Project, 2020, *About Moodle*. https://docs.moodle.org/311/en/About_Moodle

Antonis Kokossis, Michael C. Georgiadis, Efstratios N. Pistikopoulos (Eds.)
PROCEEDINGS OF THE 33rd European Symposium on Computer Aided Process Engineering
(ESCAPE33), June 18-21, 2023, Athens, Greece

# Enhancing Human Machine Interface design using cognitive metrics of process operators

Mohammed Aatif Shahab,[a] Babji Srinivasan,[a,c] Rajagopalan Srinivasan[b,c]

[a]*Department of Applied Mechanics, Indian Institute of Technology Madras, Chennai, 600036, India*
[b]*Department of Chemical Engineering, Indian Institute of Technology Madras, Chennai, 600036, India*
[c]*American Express Lab for Data Analytics, Risk and Technology, Indian Institute of Technology Madras, Chennai, 600036, India*
*babji.srinivasan@iitm.ac.in, raj@iitm.ac.in*

## Abstract

In a typical process industry, Human Machine Interfaces (HMIs) are essential for all aspects of communication and interaction between operators and processes, vital for process safety, quality, and efficiency. Good interface design enables operators to accomplish their duties efficiently and effectively with minimal errors. Consequently, it is crucial to design HMIs in a way that facilitates collaboration between automation and operators. Current HMI design practices have a lot of subjectivity and often ignore operator's cognitive behavior. In this work, we propose a quantitative approach that uses cognitive metrics – association and salience metrics – obtained using eye-tracking to improve HMI design for process operators. The association metric helps in identifying information sources which are often used together while salience metric informs about information sources which are extensively used from the HMI. Based on insights from these cognitive metrics, we designed a new HMI. To evaluate the relative efficacy of each HMI, human subject studies were conducted. The results indicate that the new HMI developed with the use of cognitive metrics improved the operators' efficiency. Thus, the proposed approach can help enhance usability of industrial HMIs.

**Keywords**: Human Machine Interface, Cognitive Behavior, Eye-tracking, Correspondence Analysis, Safety

## 1. Introduction

The Human Machine Interfaces (HMIs) used in modern industries depict complex systems, massive amounts of data, high degrees of automation, and safety management systems. These developments place more cognitive workload on operators increasing their chances of errors. Good interface design enables operators to accomplish their duties efficiently and effectively with minimal errors. Poor design results in an increase in reaction times and likelihood of error in perception and understanding. A poor HMI information display reduces the likelihood of properly anticipating an abnormal event by five times (Krajewski, 2014). Studies reveal that human error accounts for 70% of industrial accidents (Mannan, 2013). Therefore, it is crucial to develop HMIs driven by operators' requirements to enhance how they utilize, manage, and retain the process information.

The development of industrial HMIs has traditionally been guided by standards issued by organizations such as the International Society of Automation (ISA). Common practices in this area include the use of P&ID images (Lee et al., 2017) as a display for Distributed Control Systems (DCS) and the depiction of real-time process data. Despite significant advancements in the display capabilities of DCS, a significant proportion of operator graphics still follow this paradigm, with only limited improvements in their practical effectiveness and capability. Information on HMIs is typically organized according to hierarchies, with data pertaining to the physical components that support key functions displayed together (Jamieson et al., 2007). To assess the usability of these HMIs, various measures have been proposed, including task-based measures, operator actions, and expert opinion. An expert-based approach to evaluate HMI usability involves using a well-defined process with specific evaluation items to pinpoint areas for improvement (Aranburu et al., 2019). This method has been tested in experiments and found to enable participants to identify numerous aspects of the evaluated interface that could be improved. In yet another study, task-based measures such as success rate, total time on task, response time and subjective rating scale were used to evaluate usability of a power plants HMI (Lee et al., 2017).

In summary, current HMI design practices rely heavily on the expertise of subject-matter experts and lack objective evaluations of the cognitive abilities of operators (Ikuma et al., 2014). These abilities, such as information processing, reasoning with process states, and decision-making processes, play a crucial role in reducing the likelihood of human error. To address this issue, this study proposes the use of eye tracking to develop cognitive metrics for enhancing usability of industrial HMIs. The validity of this approach is demonstrated through human subject studies conducted on an in-house chemical process simulator.

## 2. Literature Studies

With the digitalization in industries, HMI systems are becoming pivotal in interaction between the operator and the process. It is, therefore, necessary to keep track of operator cognitive behavior while designing HMI. An efficient HMI reduces operators' cognitive workload and assists them in accomplishing their duties with minimal errors. The performance of operators improves when they are provided with physical, functional, and task information in addition to the traditional physical and functional data on HMI (Jamieson et al., 2007).

In recent years, researchers have used eye-tracking to evaluate and improve HMIs in high-risk industries using the cognitive behavior of operators. An eye-tracking based methodology was developed to enhance the usability of a nuclear power plants HMI (Ha et al., 2018). Eye-tracking measures such as fixation-to-importance ratio (FIR) and selective attention effectiveness (SAE) were developed to identify the effective attention of operators on the HMI. The FIR indicates the usefulness of a single information source, whereas the SAE is a measure of the usefulness of all available information sources taken together. FIR and SAE values were found to be much lower on steam generator level suggesting less attention to the information source. The participants reported that they had a difficulty understanding the pattern of level change of the variable. Accordingly, the HMI design was enhanced.

The current studies to enhance HMI design using operator cognitive behavior are restricted in their ability to be generalizable to other industries and do not give an objective foundation to improve HMI design. Previously, we have used eye-tracking to get insights into operator's cognitive behavior in process industries (Shahab et al., 2021a; Iqbal et al., 2018). Shahab et al. (2022) developed Hidden Markov Model based methodology to capture operators' mental models using eye-tracking. The study of mental models is very relevant to HMI design as it reveals how operators perceive the information from the HMI. In this work, we propose a methodology that uses cognitive metrics to improve HMI design for process control applications.

## 3. Experimental Studies and Methodology

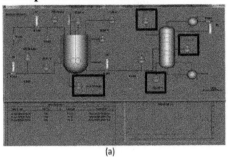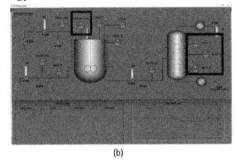

(a)                         (b)

Fig. 1 (a) Old HMI of the experimental testbed (b) New HMI of the experimental testbed

The experimental testbed consists of a simulated ethanol process plant. A typical distributed control system is used to control the process. The operators need to monitor the process and intervene during abnormalities. Ten participants interacted with the process through an HMI (Fig. 1 (a)). The study consisted of six different scenarios and each participant repeated all the scenarios multiple times, henceforth called as trials. This ensures that participants develop enough expertise in monitoring and dealing with process abnormalities. We recorded process, data, operator actions and eye gaze data during each trial.

The proposed methodology is based on the percept that the operators pay attention only to those information sources that they think have a relationship with the current abnormal situation. We used correspondence analysis (CA), a multivariate tool, to obtain an asymmetric plot showing operator's attention allocation on various information sources of HMI, henceforth called as Areas of Interest (AOIs), during the abnormal scenarios. CA shows the relationship between two categorical variables, in the current study, areas of interest (AOIs) on the HMI and various abnormalities relating to the disturbance in the plant. The operator's attention on various AOIs is crucial for determining their preferences during abnormal situations and can be exploited to place information sources on the HMI to help them achieve the task efficiently.

We develop two quantitative cognitive metrics – association and salience metric – based on the angle between a scenario and an AOI and the distance of an AOI from the origin on the asymmetric plot. The association metric captures the operator's attention to key variables that they believe to have a causal relation with the abnormal situation. Association metric reaches unity if a variable(s) has a causal relationship with an abnormal scenario. Therefore, such variables should be placed together on the HMI to increase its efficiency. The salience metric captures the prevalence of AOIs, which are extensively used on the HMI. Such AOIs should be easily accessible during abnormal situations. Interested readers are referred to Shahab et al. (2021b) for a detailed description of the calculation procedure. Using the insights from CA of eye gaze data, the HMI is redesigned. For the sake of simplicity, we will call the redesigned HMI as the new

HMI and the previous HMI as the old HMI. We conducted similar human subject studies to compare the performance of operators in both the HMIs (old HMI and new HMI).

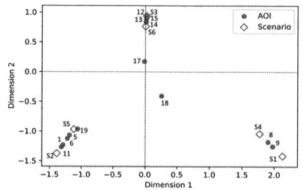

Fig. 2 Asymmetric plot obtained from correspondence analysis of eye gaze data from an expert operator

## 4. Results and discussion

In this section, we illustrate the application of the proposed methodology in enhancing the HMI design.

As discussed in the previous section, we obtained the asymmetric plot from the correspondence analysis of the operator's eye gaze data. Fig. 2 shows the asymmetric plot for a typical expert operator. The numbers 1-19 represent the areas of interest (AOIs) on the human-machine interface (HMI), while S1-S6 indicate six disturbance scenarios. The scenarios represent disturbances in one or more process variables, including low coolant flow rate and low reflux ratio. As shown in Fig. 2, AOIs 12-15 are closer to scenarios S3 and S6 (low reflux ratio disturbance), indicating that the operator primarily focuses their attention on AOIs 12 (temperature of the 8th tray of the distillation column), 13 (reflux flow control valve V401), 14 (temperature of the 4th tray), and 15 (temperature of the 3rd tray). The association metric between the scenarios and AOIs is approximately one.

The operator's focus on only a few information sources (AOIs) on the HMI indicates the significance of these variables in relation to the abnormal situation at hand. Hence, these variables should be kept together on the HMI. In the current HMI design, T104, T105, and T106 are in different places and separate from the control valve V401 (see Fig. 1(a)). Based on the insights from the asymmetric plot, these variables should be kept together. Therefore, the HMI was redesigned and these variables were kept together, as shown by rectangular boxes in Fig.1(b).

The proposed methodology also has the potential to identify incorrect information placement on the HMI. For example, as shown in Fig. 2, for scenarios S2 and S5, the operators' preferences are AOIs 1 (feed flow to the reactor tag), 5 (feed flow to distillation column control valve), 6 (feed flow to the reactor control valve), 1 (flow rate to distillation column tag), and 19 (concentration of ethanol in the reactor). These scenarios are related to a disturbance in the feed flow to the reactor, which triggers alarms at F101 (AOI 1), F105 (AOI 11) and C101 (AOI 19). The correct action is to manipulate valve V102 (AOI 6). Although the operator successfully completes the task using V102, Fig. 2 shows that AOI 5 is close to scenarios S2 and S5 indicating they have also thought about V201 which making decision to control the abnormality. This confusion is due to the proximity of

C101 and V201 on the HMI (Fig. 1(a)). To avoid such confusion, in the new HMI design (Fig. 1(b)), the location of C101 was changed to be near the feed flow to the reactor line, helping operators diagnose the root cause of alarm C101 as a disturbance in the feed flow to the reactor. Additionally, Fig. 2 shows that AOI 17 (trend panel) is close to the origin on the asymmetric plot (salience metric approximately equal to 0), indicating that the trend panel was extensively used during all subnormal scenarios and should be easily accessible during abnormalities. Therefore, the position of the trend panel was left unchanged. Next, we compare the operator's performance in both HMIs.

Table 1: Operator performance measures obtained from both the HMIs

| Operator performance measures | Old HMI | New HMI |
|---|---|---|
| Time taken to first correct control action (seconds) | 9.9 | 5.7 |
| Time to first fixation on correct action (seconds) | 7.5 | 3.7 |
| Scanpath length from first alarm to correct action (pixels) | 2056 | 1206 |
| Task completion time (seconds) | 38.7 | 38.2 |
| Fixation count | 35 | 20 |

### 4.1. Operator performance evaluation

As discussed previously, similar experiments were carried out using the new HMI. To evaluate the efficiency of HMIs, we used operator performance measures that describe the speed and accuracy of the task performed by the operator.

Consider two participants, operator A, and operator B, who deal with an abnormal situation involving a disturbance in feed flow to the reactor resulting in alarm F101, alarm F105, and alarm C101. Operator A interacted with the process using the old HMI, while operator B interacted using the new HMI. Both operators have a similar level of expertise. For the proposed methodology to be effective, it is expected that operator performance in the new HMI should be better. The performance measures of operators A and B are listed in Table 1. The time to the first fixation on correct control action and time taken to correct action in response to the abnormal situation is lower in the new HMI compared to the old HMI. The lesser time taken with the new HMI signifies that the new HMI design helps the operator for early identification of the corrective action in response to the abnormality.

Further, the scanpath length from alarm occurrence to the application of the first control action is lower in the new HMI (Table 1). Scanpath length is a productivity measure that can be used for defining optimal visual search (Goldberg and Kotval, 1999). The lower values of scanpath length signify that the new HMI aids the operator during visual searches, such as locating the correct control action. The task completion time shows no difference, probably because the operators have similar expertise. The number of fixations is related to the number of components the user must process. When searching for a target, a large number of fixations indicates the user explored many other information sources prior to selecting the target, as if distracted or hindered from isolating the target (Goldberg and Kotval, 1999). As reported in Table 1, the number of fixations after the occurrence of the alarm till the correct control action is lower using the new HMI, indicating an enhancement in operator performance. The critical measure of an HMI is how well it performs when the demands are greatest – in an abnormal situation. As such, the new HMI design based on developed cognitive metrics outperforms the old HMI in all aspects of performance. The results revealed that the new HMI aids the operator in dealing with process abnormality.

## 5. Conclusions

We put forward the idea of incorporating operator cognitive behavior into the design of industrial HMIs to improve their usability. Our approach is based on the percept that operators tend to attend only relevant information sources during abnormal situations. Therefore, such information sources should be placed together on the HMI to enhance its usability. We used correspondence analysis of operator eye gaze data to develop quantitative cognitive metrics - association and salience metrics - that identify the most relevant information sources during various abnormal scenarios. Based on these findings, we redesigned the HMI and kept the relevant information sources together, thereby reducing confusion and improving the operator's ability to diagnose and resolve disturbances efficiently. The efficacy of the new HMI was validated through human subject studies, which showed enhanced operator performance compared to the original HMI. In future studies, we plan to conduct statistical analysis with large scale human subject experiments. Additionally, we will utilize electroencephalography (EEG) to measure the cognitive workload of operators using both HMIs.

## References

Aranburu, E., Lasa, G., & Gerrikagoitia, J. K. (2019, June). HEMEI: new user experience evaluation tool for Human-Machine Interfaces. In Proceedings of the XX International Conference on Human Computer Interaction (pp. 1-2).

Goldberg, J. H., & Kotval, X. P. (1999). Computer interface evaluation using eye movements: methods and constructs. International journal of industrial ergonomics, 24(6), 631-645.

Ha, J. S., Byon, Y. J., Cho, C. S., & Seong, P. H. (2018). Eye-tracking studies based on attentional-resource effectiveness and insights into future research. Nuclear Technology, 202(2-3)

Ikuma, L. H., Harvey, C., Taylor, C. F., & Handal, C. (2014). A guide for assessing control room operator performance using speed and accuracy, perceived workload, situation awareness, and eye tracking. Journal of loss prevention in the process industries, 32, 454-465.

Iqbal, M. U., Srinivasan, B., & Srinivasan, R. (2018). Towards obviating human errors in real-time through eye tracking. In Computer Aided Chemical Engineering (Vol. 43, pp. 1189-1194). Elsevier.

Jamieson, G. A. (2007). Ecological interface design for petrochemical process control: An empirical assessment. IEEE Transactions on systems, man, and cybernetics-Part A: Systems and Humans, 37(6), 906-920.

Krajewski, J. (2014). Situational awareness–the next leap in industrial human machine interface design. White paper, Invensys Systems, Houston, USA.

Lee, S. T., Kim, S. Y., & Gilmore, D. (2017, October). Human-in-the-loop evaluation of human-machine interface for power plant operators. In 2017 IEEE International Conference on Systems, Man, and Cybernetics (SMC) (pp. 34-39). IEEE.

Mannan, S. (2013). Lees' Process Safety Essentials: Hazard Identification, Assessment and Control. Butterworth-Heinemann.

Shahab, M. A., Iqbal, M. U., Srinivasan, B., & Srinivasan, R. (2022). HMM-based models of control room operator's cognition during process abnormalities. 1. formalism and model identification. Journal of Loss Prevention in the Process Industries, 76, 104748.

Shahab, M. A., Iqbal, M. U., Srinivasan, B., & Srinivasan, R. (2021b). Metrics for objectively assessing operator training using eye gaze patterns. Process Safety and Environmental Protection, 156, 508-520.

Shahab, M. A., Srinivasan, B., & Srinivasan, R. (2021a). Evaluating control room operator training outcomes through eye gaze augmented multi-scale data. In Computer Aided Chemical Engineering (Vol. 50, pp. 1307-1312). Elsevier.

Antonis Kokossis, Michael C. Georgiadis, Efstratios N. Pistikopoulos (Eds.)
PROCEEDINGS OF THE 33rd European Symposium on Computer Aided Process Engineering
(ESCAPE33), June 18-21, 2023, Athens, Greece

# A Cloud-based Collaborative Interactive Platform for Education and Research in Dynamic Process Modelling

Vinay Gautam, Alberto Rodríguez-Fernández, and Heinz A. Preisig

*Department of Chemical Engineering, Norwegian University of Science and Technology, Trondheim, Norway, 7491, Norway.*
*heinz.preisig@ntnu.no*

## Abstract

Process modelling is used in many disciplines for various purposes like simulation, process design, optimisation and control. Although there is an increasing demand to build large, complex process models involving multiple disciplines, a systematic approach to developing such models is largely missing from engineering education and research. The ontology-based methodology and ProcessModeller (ProMo) tool suite developed over the years (Preisig, 2021, 2020; Elve and Preisig, 2018) help users to build multi-disciplinary and multi-scale models systematically. This paper presents a cloud-based platform ProMo-Remote that uses Simphony-Remote, a free and open-source web service. In this platform, the graphical user interfaces of the ProMo tool suite are accessible using a regular web browser, freeing the user from installing the desktop tool locally. Users can save, download/upload modelling data and use it in computational workflows utilising cloud-based interactive computing tools like Jupyter notebooks. The user can also collaborate with others by screen sharing in real time. The platform can easily be configured and deployed with additional applications to facilitate further education, training and research on the systematic development of complex process models.

**Keywords**: Process modelling; computer-aided modelling; Simphony-remote; Jupyterhub.

## 1. Introduction

Models play a central role in many engineering disciplines and process systems engineering is particularly driven by models. Model design moves into a more dominating position as a research and development domain since the processes involved with domain models are the key bottleneck. The formulation of the model and its effective handling all the way through the generation of the target code are just two of the numerous difficulties that must be overcome. The basic models are traditionally written by hand, which means that equations from published or developed models are converted into a target language and then made accessible as a module in a library. These library modules of unit operations or equivalent are then combined using interactive tools to create models.

The modelling methodology implemented in the ProMo tool (Preisig, 2021) captures multidisciplinary aspect in the model generation process by using reductionism, where model generation is based on identifying the smallest underlying basic entities in the context of the intended application. A network of these interacting basic entities then describes the behaviour of the modelled system.

Modern processes and materials modelling workflows are becoming increasingly dependent on cloud infrastructure, e.g. AiiDAlab (Yakutovich et al., 2021) and Materials Cloud (Talirz et al., 2020). The sheer volume of data generated by models and tools used in a workflow simulation would be hard to analyse without high-performance computing infrastructure. In the cloud, a task that could have taken days or weeks on a desktop computer might be finished in a matter of hours. This gap is frequently great enough to execute previously deemed impossible calculations.

We developed a cloud-based deployment of the ProMo tool to give remote access to users on the web. The platform uses Simphony-Remote (SR), a web service created as part of the Horizon2020 Simphony and MarketPlace projects and is free and open-source. The ProMo-Remote platform has the following highlighting features. First, ProMo is a modelling suite that consists of a set of modules built using Python. Several external dependencies are required and installing them is rather demanding for users without previous knowledge of Python. ProMo-Remote does not require users to install anything on their machine because the tool can be accessed using any regular browser. Second, the ProMo-Remote runs remotely in a container, making it easier to administer and configure the overall platform. Third, onboard apps can share a dataspace while running in their own Docker containers, making it simple to create and share computational workflows utilising cloud-based interactive computing tools like Jupyter notebooks.

## 2. The ProMo Workflow

Figure 1 shows the basic ProMo workflow used when designing a model. It all starts by building an ontology (Gruber, 1993) tailored to the application domain.

The ontology provides a common namespace and the fundamental structures for the behaviour description and represents the construction blueprint for complex models (Elve and Preisig, 2018). Next, all the equations necessary to describe the application processes are inserted. Following this, entities are constructed, and groups of equations representing particular behaviours are linked. Up to this point, a high level of expertise is required to ensure that all the information is included correctly.

The regular user will interact more with the modules to the rsight of the dashed line in Figure 1. In the Model Composer, the previously constructed entities can be used as basic blocks to graphically represent the application processes' physical topology. A high level of re-usability is promoted by allowing to save and reuse of parts of this topology. Finally, in the Task Generator module, the user may choose to generate the code necessary to perform different tasks using the model designed.

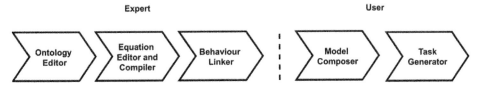

Figure 1: The ProMo workflow consists of several modules used in sequence. There is a clear division between modules based on the level of expertise required to use them.

## 3. Simphony-Remote Web Service

Simphony-Remote is an open-source project that resulted from the development efforts of several European projects, starting from the SimPhoNy project and the most recent the H2020 FORCE and Marketplace projects. The SR provides a JupyterHub[1] based web interface for running desktop and web applications in Docker containers. Figure 2 provides a graphical overview of the main components in the SR. It uses JupyterHub to configure and control the cloud

---

[1]          JupyterHub provides a multi-user Hub that spawns the Jupyter Notebook server per user. The Hub consists of a configurable proxy to serve requests from the client's browser and an authentication class to manage how users interact with the system. It provides several authentication options, e.g., Lightweight Directory Access Protocol (LDAP) and OAuth.

infrastructure. Three types of users can access the service: admin, the non-admin and remote viewer. The admin user has roles in building and configuring the platform and extends roles to authenticated non-admin users to access containerised onboard apps. The third type of users are remote users who can access the application via a shared link from the authenticated users and do not need to authenticate directly to get access.

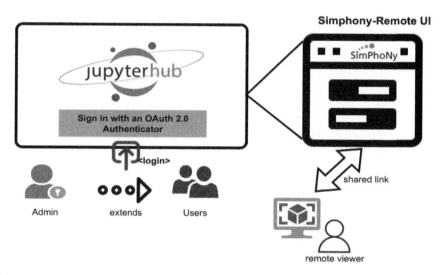

Figure 2: An overview of the Simphony-Remote web service.

## 4. The ProMo-Remote Platform

The ProMo-Remote platform is preconfigured with three applications: the ProMo app, a file manager app and a Jupyter notebooks app, as shown in Figure 3. These containerised apps are first built using the Docker build process and then deployed on cloud infrastructure, as discussed below. The Docker images encapsulate applications as stand-alone software entities that can be run independently as software processes while sharing a common dataspace among the apps.

### 4.1. Building application containers

Containerised apps are built in two steps. First, a base image of the host operating system with some add-ons, such as virtual network control (VNC) application, is built. Second, the application's Docker image is built on top of the base image.

### 4.2. Cloud Deployment

Cloud deployment of the ProMo-Remote platform involves two steps. First, an instance of SR is configured and launched as a web service that uses nginx and reverse proxy. Second, the prebuilt containerised images of the apps are uploaded to the SR web service from its user interface.

### 4.3. Running the Applications

The users can log in to the platform and will see a list of applications that they have access to, which is enabled by admin. As shown in Figure 3, the user *'vinay.gautam'* has access to all three currently deployed apps in the ProMo-Remote. The user can select an application and run it by simply clicking the target application's start icon, which opens the GUI of the application. The user can interact with it and switch between different apps. The user can also share an app's running session with other remote users for collaborating in real time. Running apps are affected neither by the web browser's accidental closing nor by temporal network connectivity loss. It should be noted that closing an app would erase all its data, and the app will reset to its initial state, except the data saved on the shared dataspace directory named `workspace'.

### 5. Conclusion

The ProMo-Remote provides a cloud-based platform to systematically design multidisciplinary process models using the ontology-based methodology and ProMo tool. The platform is easy to manage, configure and deploy on cloud infrastructure, and its web interface is accessible on any regular web browser. The platform has a shared dataspace, making it easy to create and share computational workflows, for example, by utilizing cloud-based interactive computing tools like Jupyter notebooks. The platform can be used for education, research and knowledge transfer in the dynamic processes modelling community by enabling higher collaboration between expert and non-expert users. We provide a set of model-building exercises to help users familiarise themselves with the ProMo tool's usage to create process models systematically. We aim to create more training and pedagogical content to assist others in using this infrastructure to educate and train modellers in systematically building multi-disciplinary, complex process model workflows.

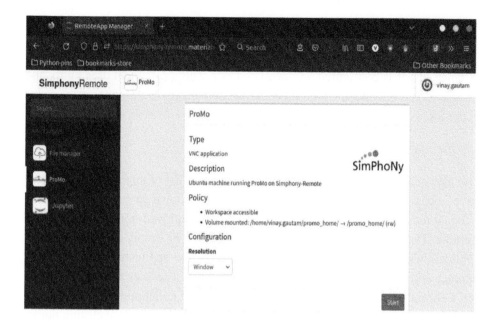

Figure 3: A snapshot of the ProMo-Remote platform running on a web browser.

## Acknowledgements

Bio4Fuels RCN: 257622, MarketPlace H2020-NMBP-25-2017:760173, VIPCOAT H2020-NMBP-TO-IND-2020:952903, NanoLodge NFR 299363.

## References

Elve, A. T., & Preisig, H. A., 2018. A framework for multi-network modelling. *Computer Aided Chemical Engineering, 44*, 2215–2220.

Gruber, T. R., 1993. A translation approach to portable ontology specifications. *Knowledge Acquisition, 5*(2), 199–220.

Preisig, H. A., 2020. Promo - a Multi-disciplinary Process Modelling Suite. *Computer Aided Chemical Engineering, 48*, 571–576.

Preisig, H. A., 2021. Ontology-Based Process Modelling-with Examples of Physical Topologies. *Processes 2021, Vol. 9, Page 592, 9*(4), 592.

Talirz et a., 2020 . Materials Cloud, a platform for open computational science. *Scientific Data 2020 7:1, 7*(1), 1–12.

Yakutovich et al., 2021. AiiDAlab – an ecosystem for developing, executing, and sharing scientific workflows. *Computational Materials Science, 188*, 110165.

# INDEX